Immunology for
of Medicin

J. H. HUMPHREY
M.D. B.Chir. F.R.S.
Head of Division of Immunology,
National Institute for Medical Research
Mill Hill, London

AND

R. G. WHITE
M.A. D.M. M.R.C.P. F.R.S. (Ed.)
Gardiner Professor of Bacteriology and Immunology
University of Glasgow

THIRD
EDITION

SECOND PRINTING

Blackwell Scientific Publications
Oxford and Edinburgh

SBN 632 02180 2

FIRST PUBLISHED 1963
SECOND EDITION 1964
REPRINTED 1965
THIRD EDITION 1970
REPRINTED 1971

SPANISH TRANSLATION 1964
ITALIAN TRANSLATION 1967
GERMAN TRANSLATION 1970

Text printed by
WESTERN PRINTING SERVICES LTD., BRISTOL
Plates printed by
MARTIN CADBURY PRINTING GROUP, CHELTENHAM
Bound by
KEMP-HALL BINDERY, OXFORD

Contents

	Preface	v
	Acknowledgements	ix
1	Introduction	1
2	Non-specific Mechanisms of Immunity—Innate Immunity	35
3	The Specific Immunological Response	84
4	Immunoglobulins	148
5	Complement and other Auxiliary Factors	188
6	Antigens: Immunogens and Haptens	204
7	The Fate of Antigen and the Process of Antibody Production	238
8	Clinical Aspects of Immunoglobulin Metabolism: Aberrations of Immunoglobulin Production and Immunity	306
9	Serological Aspects of the Antigen–Antibody Reaction: the Detection and Measurement of Antigen and Antibody	348
10	The Protective Effects of Antibody	408
11	Hypersensitivity Mediated by Antibodies	428
12	Delayed-type Hypersensitivity Specific cell-mediated Hypersensitivity	493
13	Immunological Aspects of Tissue Transplantation	546

Contents

14 Immunological Aspects of Cancer 580

15 Auto-immunity (Auto-allergy) and its Relation to Human Disease 600

16 Prophylactic Immunization and Serotherapy 671

Glossary 711

Index 723

Preface to the First Edition

At a time when new scientific journals are being started at the rate of 700–800 a year, and the shelves of those medical libraries which can afford to buy them, and the memories of their readers, groan under the weight of the published proceedings of specialized symposia, colloquia, reviews and monographs of various aspects of medical science, the production of another textbook requires some justification. This is even more so since the years after the Second World War have seen the appearance of a number of reference books containing excellent sections dealing with immunology and of textbooks devoted to the subject. Our reason for adding another to their number is that we have been impressed with the need for a book whose specific aim is to give students of medicine an understanding of the basic principles and of current problems in immunology with a view to their application in medical practice rather than in bacteriology, immunochemistry, systematics, etc. Catalysed by immunological hypotheses, clinicians and pathologists in recent years have made observations, such as those in the field of autoimmune disease and the reticuloses, which have provided unique information sought but never clearly obtained by purely laboratory investigators. Our hope is that an immunological approach to the prophylaxis, treatment and pathogenesis of disease states will provide an insight which will serve both to improve understanding of these processes and to stimulate further observations and research into them. A consideration which has been uppermost in our minds has been to provide a book which would not frighten either because of its length or its price. In achieving this the publishers have co-operated nobly, but at the same time the writers have been forced to become rather more eclectic and more dogmatic than is the laboratory worker's wont. There is a danger that to the reader who likes to have his facts and theories cut and dried the presentation will appear too vague, while to others, who are aware of the limits of most generalizations, it will appear too definite. Should this prove to be the case we must plead with the first that immunology is so rapidly growing a subject that dogmatism is still impossible, and urge the second to follow up some of the suggestions for further reading appended to each chapter.

J. H. HUMPHREY
R. G. WHITE

Preface to the Third Edition

In preparing a third edition we have taken the opportunity not only to try to bring up to date the subject matter of the previous edition, but to enlarge upon some aspects which previously seemed to us too uncertain to justify the somewhat dogmatic treatment inevitable in a book of broad scope but limited length. During the five years since the first edition was published, great conceptual advances have been made in understanding the detailed structure of immunoglobulins and the nature of their antibody activity, and in elucidating the life cycle of lymphocytes and their role as the source of immunologically competent cells. At the same time, there has grown up on the one hand, a clearer recognition of the different biological functions of different classes of antibody, and on the other, an appreciation of the importance of immunological reactions mediated by direct interaction between antigens and specifically sensitized cells. On the clinical side increasing attention has been paid to disorders of the immunological responses, to organ transplantation and to prevention of tumour growth. These have been helped by increased understanding of the mechanism of immunological tolerance and the development of improved immunosuppressive agents.

In order to incorporate the newer knowledge without discarding the old, we have rearranged and rewritten much of the book, and have included four new chapters (on the Specific Immune Response; Complement; The Mechanism of Immunoglobulins and Disorders of Immunoglobulin Production; The Immunology of Tumours). We hope nevertheless that the increase in length has been kept to a tolerable minimum. As in previous editions the text has been made more readable by exclusion from it of references and of personal attributions, except where a name is particularly closely associated with a phenomenon or test for historical reasons, or by common usage. These exclusions in no way diminish our admiration nor, we hope, that of the readers for our anonymous colleagues. The suggestions for further reading have been extended so as to provide more signposts for those who wish to explore the original literature.

Problems of nomenclature in this edition have been greatly eased by using wherever possible the nomenclature upon which agreement has been reached at meetings of international experts called together from time to time by the World Health Organization, and subsequently published in the Bulletin of the World Health Organization.

J. H. Humphrey
R. G. White

Acknowledgements

We are indebted to the following for provision of data, figures or photographs which have been individually acknowledged in their respective captions: Dr J. F. Ackroyd, Mrs H. R. Anderson, Dr Brigitte Askonas, K. F. Austen, Dr D. R. Bangham, Dr Mollie Barr, Dr K. J. Bloch, Professor F. W. R. Brambell, F.R.S., W. E. Brocklehurst, Sir Macfarlane Burnet, F.R.S., Professor C. A. Clarke, Professor S. Cohen, Dr R. C. Collins, Dr J. S. Comaish, Dr G. de Muralt, Dr F. J. Dixon, Dr Sheila Doak, Dr R. Dourmashkin, Dr D. C. Dumonde, Professor G. Edelman, Dr J. M. Estevez, Dr A. Feinstein, Dr J. D. Feldman, Dr T. Freeman, Dr V. French, A. T. Glenny, Professor R. A. Good, Dr A. H. Gordon, Dr J. Gordon, Dr G. Grant, Dr W. P. Harrington, Dr A. G. S. Hill, Dr J. R. Hobbs, Dr E. V. Holborow, Dr B. Hopkins, Dr A. Isaacs, Dr E. H. Kass, Dr H. U. Keller, Dr S. M. Kurtz, Professor E. Leduc, Dr J. McCormick, Dr A. H. E. Marshall, Dr J. Milne, Dr D. G. Miller, Dr Judith Mitchell, Dr H. Müller-Eberhard, Dr D. S. Nelson, Dr Janet Niven, Professor G. J. V. Nossal, Professor C. L. Oakley, F.R.S., Dr J. Oort, Dr S. Otani, Dr Delphine M. V. Parrott, Professor L. Pauling, Dr J. S. Porterfield, Dr F. W. Putnam, Professor M. Raynaud, Dr E. H. Relyveld, Professor D. Rowley, Dr R. M. E. Seal, Dr O. Smithies, Dr J. M. Stark, Dr G. Taylor, Dr J. W. Uhr, Dr E. R. Unanue, Dr R. C. Valentine, Dr R. M. Vetters, Professor B. H. Waksman, Dr W. O. Weigle, Dr J. O. L. Whitby, Dr C. A. Williams Jr., Dr H. H. Wortis.

We also wish to thank the editors and publishers of the following journals and books for their permission to use the figures ascribed to them in the individual captions: *Proceedings of the Royal Society of Medicine*, *Experimental Cell Research*, *Journal of Experimental Medicine*, *Journal of Laboratory and Clinical Medicine*, *Journal of Pathology and Bacteriology*, *Journal of Hygiene*, *Journal of Immunology*, *Lectures on the Scientific Basis of Medicine* (Athlone Press), *Lancet*, *Annals of the New York Academy of Science*, *New*

Scientist, *British Journal of Experimental Pathology*, *Journal of Infectious Diseases*, *Biochemical Journal*, *Scientific American*, *Allergic Encephalomyelitis* (Charles C. Thomas), *Essentials of Bacteriology* (Pitman Medical Publications), *American Journal of Ophthalmology*, *Journal of Physiology*, *Endeavour*, *Advances in Protein Chemistry* (Academic Press, New York), *Annales de l'Institut Pasteur*, *Archives of Pathology*, *Advances in Immunology* (Academic Press, New York), *Annals of Internal Medicine*, *Australian Journal of Experimental Biology and Medical Science*, *Journal of Clinical Pathology*, *La maturation de l'immunité humorale chez l'homme* (Schwabe, Basel), *Progress in Allergy*, *Hospital Medicine*.

CHAPTER ONE

Introduction

THE germ of immunology grew out of the common knowledge that those who survive an infectious disease seldom contract that disease again during their lifetime. Thucydides recorded that when the plague was raging in Athens, the sick and dying would have received no nursing at all had it not been for the devotion of those who had already had the plague and recovered from it, since it was known that no one ever caught it a second time.

In 1733 Voltaire, in his delightful volume of 'Letters', wrote appraisingly of the Chinese custom, practised since the fifteenth century, of prophylactic induction of smallpox infection by taking by the nose 'in the same manner as we take snuff', dried powders of smallpox crusts. In the same essay he records, 'that in the beginning of the Reign of King George the First, the Lady Wortley Montague, a woman of so fine a genius, and endued with as great a strength of mind, as any of her sex in the British Kingdoms, being with her husband who was Ambassador at the Port, made no scruple to communicate the smallpox to an infant of which she was delivered in Constantinople. The Chaplain represented to his Lady, but to no purpose, that this was an unchristian operation, and therefore that it could succeed with none but infidels. However, it had the most happy effect upon the son of the Lady Wortley Montague, who at her return to England communicated the experiment to the Princess of Wales (later Queen of George II).'

According to Voltaire, the Turks derived the custom of inoculation from the inhabitants of Circassia, of whom he says, 'They are poor, and their daughters are beautiful, and indeed 'tis in them they chiefly trade. They furnish with beauties the seraglios of the Turkish Sultan, of the Persian Sophy, and of all those who are wealthy enough to purchase and maintain such precious merchandise. These maidens are very honourably and virtuously instructed to fondle and caress men, are taught dances of a very mobile and effeminate kind; and how to heighten by the most voluptuous artifices, the pleasures of their disdainful masters for whom they are designed.' However, he adds 'frequently, when the smallpox became epidemical, trade was suspended for several years, which thinned very considerably the seraglios of Persia and Turkey'. 'In order therefore to preserve the life and beauty of their children, the thing remaining was, to give them the smallpox in their infant years. This they did, by inoculating in the body of a child, a pustule taken from the most regular, and at the same time the most favourable sort of smallpox that could be procured.'

The practice of prophylaxis by inoculation of human smallpox material is termed *variolation* (variola: smallpox) and must be accounted a desperate and hazardous undertaking. The risk of generalization with possibly fatal results could not with certainty be controlled. However, the fact that these risks were accepted is understandable when it is realized that in England at the time of Voltaire's writing, 'three score persons in every hundred have the smallpox. Of these three score, twenty die of it in the most favourable season of life, and as many more wear the disagreeable remains of it in their faces so long as they live.'* The first step to a safer procedure was to substitute material derived from the lesions of cowpox for the inoculation. The earliest recorded trial of this procedure was in the spring of 1774 when Benjamin Jesty, a Dorsetshire farmer, obtained his virus 'on the spot from the cows of farmer Elford of Chittenhall', near Yetminster, and inoculated his wife in the arm under the elbow with a needle.

The first physician to embark methodically on experiments to test the popular view of the prophylactic power of cowpox in preventing subsequent smallpox was Edward Jenner, born in Gloucestershire in 1749. As an assistant in practice, his advice was sought by a young countrywoman who, at the mention of the disease smallpox, observed that she could not have that disease, since she had already had cowpox. Many investigations were made by Jenner before he

* Variolation was practised widely, especially in country districts and the smaller towns, and its efficacy in preventing the deaths from smallpox of young children and of women at childbirth was probably the major cause of the great increase in the population which began during the first half of the eighteenth century.

embarked on the crucial experiment in which James Phipps was inoculated with cowpox material with a view to inducing an immunity to smallpox. In 1798 he published his first memoir, 'An enquiry into the causes and effects of the variolae vacciniae'. Although the evidence accumulated by Jenner seemed conclusive, the practice met with violent opposition. However, the eventual acceptance of his thesis was signified in a public declaration by upwards of seventy of the principal physicians and surgeons in London. The learned societies throughout Europe hastened to elect him to membership—with the notable exception of the College of Physicians, which required him to pass an examination in Classics.

The extension of this knowledge required the development of the germ theory of disease. Since the beginnings of bacteriology as an experimental science in the hands of Pasteur, one of the main tasks had been to study the question of immunity from every aspect.

Although interested in what bacteria were, Pasteur was even more concerned to prevent the diseases caused by them and as such he became the first great experimental immunologist. Pasteur was vitally concerned with the practical immunological applications of the developing knowledge concerning microbes. His lack of interest in bacteria as such is apparent from his retort to an expert microscopist, who had explained to him in cautious language that a certain organism which Pasteur had taken for a coccus was in reality a very small bacillus. Pasteur's reply after a powerful pause was, 'If you only knew how little difference that makes to me!'

Even though comparatively little was understood of the ways in which bacteria could cause harm in the body, Pasteur proceeded to develop valid methods for immunization. The first procedure was suggested by a laboratory accident. Chicken cholera is due to the chicken cholera bacillus and Pasteur possessed a culture which regularly induced fatal disease. After being left on the laboratory bench during a summer vacation, these organisms were found to have lost much of their ability to produce disease in the chicken. Moreover, fresh cultures also failed to infect those chickens which had received inoculation with this old culture, although they regularly produced disease in untreated birds. The *virulent* organisms had become *attenuated*, a change which Pasteur later reproduced in other cultures by prolonged culture under anaerobic conditions. The similarity between this situation and Jenner's method of *variolation* was at once apparent and, in honour of Jenner, Pasteur called his treatment *vaccination*, a term which has been used subsequently for injection with (or ingestion of) bacteria, viruses, their products, and even pollen materials, as a method of deriving future immunity against disease.

Within a matter of months, Pasteur had uncovered the same phenomenon in veterinary anthrax. By the similar device of maintaining the infective agent under adverse laboratory conditions—this time in shallow broth culture at 42°–43°C—he obtained the altered bacilli, which formed the vaccine used in the famous public experiment at Pouilly-le-Fort, when 24 sheep, 1 goat and 6 cattle were nearly all protected against a dose of virulent anthrax bacilli which killed most of the control animals.

Another method of attenuation was evolved by serial passage of the organism through rabbits. The rabbits become infected by the bacillus and die, but the organisms recovered are less virulent for the pig, although of increased virulence for the homologous species—the rabbit. Passage of the organism in the pigeon produces the opposite effect—an increase in virulence so far as the pig is concerned. Hence Pasteur's vaccination procedure consisted in a preliminary course of injections of rabbit-attenuated bacilli, followed by another course of pigeon-passaged organisms of increased virulence.

The most dramatic of all vaccination procedures was finally adopted by Pasteur for the human disease hydrophobia or rabies. Attenuation of the virus in this case was achieved by drying spinal cords taken from infected rabbits, in air. He was able to show that daily injections of the emulsion of such infected spinal cords, which were later changed to cords dried for a shorter period of time, not only protected dogs from fully virulent virus, but also from the disease induced by injection of rabid saliva ('street virus'). Moreover, in order to be of practical service, vaccination had to work even when started after the virulent virus was already present in the body. The disease fortunately has an unusually long incubation period of 1–3 months. The experiment of vaccinating a dog after it had had a rabid bite showed protection to be possible, if done early in the incubation period.

After these carefully planned preliminary experiments, the chance to test the procedure on a human patient arrived in July 1885 when a boy, Joseph Meister, was brought to Pasteur with severe and multiple bites from a dog which was certainly rabid. The first of the series of thirteen injections of spinal cord emulsions was given on the third day after the bites. The boy survived, later to become the gate-porter of the Pasteur Institute in Paris.

The risk that is involved in relying on an attenuated agent, which may spontaneously revert to an increased degree of virulence, means that while the use of such vaccines is permissible in veterinary practice, in man a safer method must usually be sought. Then in 1886 a notable advance was made by Salmon and Theobald Smith by the demonstration that heat-killed cultures of chicken cholera bacilli were also effective in protecting pigeons from infection. The importance of this observation was that it showed that the interaction of the living organisms with the cells of the body was not essential for the acquisition of immunity, but that this could result from the introduction of dead organic material.

Although Pasteur was so successful in the practical achievement of securing immunity, the mechanism whereby such protection arose remained to him quite obscure. Clearly some important change was brought about in the animal treated, but of the nature of this nothing was then known. Pasteur put forward in 1880 a vague and tentative hypothesis that immunity was brought about by the disappearance from the body of some necessary foodstuff which was used up during the first attack of the microbe. This so-called 'exhaustion hypothesis' was later forced to give way before the weight of data showing that immunity depends on a positive or active contribution by the host.

The course of immunology had now reached an important turning point—the discovery that antibody is formed during the process of immunization. The discovery by Roux and Yersin in 1888 (at the Pasteur Institute, Paris) that a bacterium-free filtrate of a culture of the diphtheria bacillus contained the exotoxin of this organism proved to be fundamental in this connection. It was readily shown that immunity can be developed against such a toxin, and that this is due to the development of a specific neutralizing substance or antitoxin in the blood of the immune animal, and that by means of such antitoxin immunity can be transferred to another animal, i.e. that immunity can be passively conferred. This result was first recorded in the case of tetanus antitoxin by von Behring and Kitasato in 1890 (at Koch's Institute in Berlin). It was shown also later for diphtheria antitoxin by von Behring. The body, it appeared, was capable of manufacturing specific antidotes (which were referred to generally as 'antibodies') if it was invaded by an injurious substance or microbe. It was soon shown, moreover, that antitoxins could be developed against toxins other than those of bacterial origin. Thus, as discovered by the German chemist

Ehrlich, after injections of ricin—a poisonous extract of castor oil—the blood serum quickly acquired the power to neutralize the haemolytic and lethal action of this substance.

The next step was the discovery of other properties attaching to 'antibody'. Another German, Richard Pfeiffer (1894), established the striking fact that in an animal immunized against the cholera vibrio there appear in the blood specific antibodies which lead to the death and dissolution of the organisms, and that by means of the serum of such an animal immunity can be transferred to a fresh animal. Soon afterwards two other phenomena brought about by an antibacterial serum came to be recognized: *agglutination* and *precipitation*.

In 1889 Charrin and Roger found that when the gut organism *Pseudomonas pyocyanea* was grown in the presence of serum of an animal injected with that organism, its growth took place in a lumpy manner instead of diffusely to give a milky fluid. The clinical application of this agglutination reaction to the diagnosis of enteric fever was made by Widal in 1896. In 1897 Kraus showed that a clear filtrate of a bacterial culture could often induce, after injection into a suitable animal, an antibody which formed a precipitate when added to the filtrate used for injection. Subsequently it was shown that the type of antibody (a so-called *precipitin*) could be developed regularly after the injection of a great variety of proteins and complex polysaccharides, an essential condition being, however, that they should be foreign to the animal into which they are injected.

On this theoretical basis the era of serotherapy dawned. Roux was able to announce in 1894 that the serum of an immunized horse, when injected into patients suffering from diphtheria, would cure this disease. Hope soared that other diseases could be similarly treated by preformed antibody. Unfortunately, in no case was serum ever found to act as dramatically as in diphtheria. The symptoms of tetanus, for example, are brought about by an exotoxin of the organism which works in a similar way to diphtheria toxin. The response to antitoxin is, however, much less impressive, mainly since most cases, by the time they are diagnosed, already have a dangerous amount of tetanus toxin fixed in their nervous tissue. Horse tetanus antitoxin has nevertheless achieved wide use for *prophylaxis*, i.e. for providing antibody so that it is present before the toxin is able to become attached at its site of action. The use of such tetanus antitoxin after wounding succeeded dramatically in reducing the incidence of tetanus after its introduction in November 1914 to the troops in Flanders.

The interest in serotherapy led to further knowledge of the immunological properties of serum. In 1893 Buchner described how serum, which when fresh was able to kill certain bacteria, lost this ability after heating at 56°C. The heat-labile constituent which either had, or aided, this bactericidal action was called *alexine*. A more modern synonym is *complement*. Serum factors, which were active in the serum of guinea-pigs, immunized by heat-killed organisms, had been shown by Pfeiffer in 1894 actually to accomplish the dissolution of cholera vibrios. The bactericidal factor in this case proved to be specific for these organisms. A year later Bordet showed that the bacteriolytic and -cidal activity of an immune serum against cholera vibrios depended on two distinct factors: one was thermolabile and also present in normal serum (i.e. it resembled *alexine*), and the other was thermostable and specific (antibody). The accumulating evidence for the presence of antitoxic and antimicrobial activity in serum was considered sufficient to provide the basic explanation for the facts of immunity to infective disease. This view, however, was vigorously opposed by a protagonist for the role of cells rather than humoral factors in immunity. This was the rumbustious Russian Eli Metchnikoff, who was convinced that phagocytosis by leucocytes constituted the important factor in immunity.

Metchnikoff was born in 1845 in the province of Kharkoff in Russia.

His studies at the Universities of Kharkoff and Petersburg were in the fields of zoology and embryology. He subsequently pursued a rather erratic career in biology. In 1882 he resigned from his professorship at Messina and, jobless, proceeded to relax on the shores of the Mediterranean. In his own words, 'I was resting from the shock of the events which provoked my resignation from the University and indulging enthusiastically in researches in the splendid setting of the Straits of Messina.

'One day when the family had gone to a circus to see some extraordinary performing apes, I remained alone at my microscope, observing the life in the mobile cells of a transparent starfish larva, when a new thought suddenly flashed across my brain. It struck me that similar cells might serve in the defence of the organism against intruders. Feeling that there was in this something of surpassing interest, I felt so excited that I began striding up and down the room and even went to the seashore in order to collect my thoughts.

'I said to myself that, if my supposition was true, a splinter introduced into the body of a starfish larva, devoid of blood vessels or of a nervous sytem, should soon be surrounded by mobile cells as is to be observed in a man who runs a splinter into his finger. This was no sooner said than done.

'There was a small garden to our dwelling, in which we had a few days previously organized a "Christmas tree" for the children on a little tangerine tree; I fetched from it a few rose thorns and introduced them at once under the skin of some beautiful starfish larvae as transparent as water.

'I was too excited to sleep that night in the expectation of the result of my experiment, and very early the next morning I ascertained that it had fully succeeded.

'That experiment formed the basis of the phagocyte theory, to the development of which I devoted the next twenty-five years of my life.'

Later Metchnikoff was received into Pasteur's new Institute in Paris. From here, he for many years engaged in violent controversy with the German workers over the relative importance of cellular and humoral factors in natural resistance. Metchnikoff, while willing to admit the function of serum components in acquired immunity, vigorously denied them any part in contributing to innate (or more exactly non-specific) immunity. In regard to the bactericidal effect of 'normal' serum Metchnikoff pointed out that such effects were the exception rather than the rule; the vast majority of bacteria, both virulent and avirulent, were not killed merely by exposure to serum. The situation became later complicated by the fact that certain serum factors (complement, natural antibodies) were shown to facilitate the phagocytic process. This, the work of Almroth Wright in this country, and Denys in Belgium, resulted in a compromise between the extreme views of humoral and cellular hypotheses of immunity.

The acceptance of the concept that phagocytes are of importance for resistance against infections was a gradual process. Such cellular uptake of microbes had previously been regarded as a nuisance, since the mobility of such cells risked the spread of disease. Today, it is widely accepted that the relative importance of phagocytes and humoral factors differs with the species of host and with the nature of the pathogen, but few would deny the wide biological importance of this defence mechanism. Metchnikoff from his studies in comparative physiology was able to indicate the basic importance of these processes throughout evolution from early forms of animal life. He was able to trace the continuity of phagocytic and digestive activity from the amoeba, in which nutrition and destruction or elimination of potentially harmful micro-organisms are inseparable functions within a single cell, through the colonial protozoa (primitive sponges) in which two cell layers can be distinguished, an outer provided with flagella and providing a means of locomotion, and an inner core of amoeboid cells with phagocytic activity. In more developed sponges two types of phagocytic cells are distinguishable. The inner food canal is lined by endodermal phagocytes which capture the food (including bacteria) and water flowing past them, and pass these on to mesodermal phagocytes, which either digest them or reject them to the exterior. With the development of the ability to secrete digestive enzymes, phagocytosis becomes no longer a necessary attribute of the canal-lining cells and these are no longer phagocytic in higher animals.

Most of the evidence for the role of the phagocytes in defence is admittedly circumstantial. Metchnikoff gave as a prototype for his ideas the interaction between the water flea *Daphnia* and the spores of a primitive type of fungus *Monospora bicuspidata*. The *Daphnia* is a crustacean, small enough and transparent enough to be directly observed in the living state under the microscope. Spores are narrow pointed bodies which can penetrate from the gut into the body cavity. A direct correlation was found to exist between resistance and successful phagocytosis. When phagocytosis failed, the fungus flourished and eventually its host, the water flea, died. The difficulties which prevent a sure assessment of the role of phagocytosis in defence in higher animals are discussed further in Chapter Two.

In this country, Almroth Wright effected his own theoretical reconciliation of the theories by proposing that the main action of the increased amounts of specific antibody after infection was to reinforce the destructive action of the phagocytes. He called this property acquired by the blood, *opsonic* from the Greek 'opsono'—'I prepare food for . . .', and the substance itself *opsonin*.

Almroth Wright also attempted the measurement of this property by use of an *in vitro* system of phagocytes and serum. This was advocated to be of great use in diagnosis and prognosis. The *opsonic index* (see Glossary) related the opsonic power of the blood at a certain time with that of a normal serum, and was proposed as a specific means of following the course of an infective process in a truly quantitative way.

Wright was an enthusiast who believed that in vaccination lay the means of not only preventing but also treating infective disease generally. His dictum, 'The doctor of the future will be an immunizator', led him into many therapeutic attempts 'to mobilize the immunological garrisons'. Such was the procedure of auto-immunization. In cases of local infection, the types of organism responsible were determined, cultured and killed by suitable means to yield 'auto-vaccines'. These were injected into the patient, who was followed by repeated estimation of the opsonic index of his serum. In the early years of the present century inoculation departments mushroomed in many hospitals and sophisticated non-medical opinion was drawn into the discussion by G. B. Shaw's play 'The Doctor's Dilemma', in which a thinly disguised Sir Almroth Wright is to be found in the character of Sir Colenso Ridgeon. Wright's message to the practitioners of medicine, as seen through Shaw's eyes, is exemplified by the following page from Act 1:

'*Sir Ralph Bloomfield Bonington.* Drugs can only repress symptoms: they cannot eradicate disease. The true remedy for all diseases is Nature's remedy. Nature and Science are at one, Sir Patrick, believe me; though you were taught differently. Nature has provided in the white corpuscles as you call them—in the phagocytes as we call them—a natural means of devouring and destroying all disease germs. There is at bottom only one genuinely scientific treatment of all diseases, and that is to stimulate the phagocytes. Stimulate the phagocytes. Drugs are a delusion. Find the germ of the disease; prepare from it a suitable antitoxin; inject it three times a day quarter of an hour before meals; and what is the result? The phagocytes are stimulated; they devour the disease; and the patient recovers—unless, of course, he's too far gone. That, I take it, is the essence of Ridgeon's discovery.'

In Wright's dogmatic view no one recovered from an acute or chronic bacterial disease unless assisted by the appropriate immune response. Therefore, he argued, the aim of surgery should be the avoidance of all things which could interfere with such natural defence mechanisms, especially the leucocytes. Wright was therefore the champion of the notion of the virtue of 'laudable pus'. He devised *in vitro* tests of the activity of such leucocytes against bacteria, and showed that, in general, any of the currently available ordinary chemical antiseptics in sufficient concentration to kill the bacteria would also kill the leucocytes. Hence, it became his vigorous contention that antiseptics in infected wounds usually did no good and might often do harm.

Up to this juncture we have followed the relation between the concept of immunity and resistance to infections. In the opening years of the century Bordet and others made it clear that antibody formation was an event which followed constantly the parenteral injection of bland proteins, as well as harmful microbes or their toxins. It was realized that this was a basic physiological reaction to proteins which had avoided the enzymes available for their catabolism in the digestive tract. Moreover, it followed that antibodies would often be produced in the course of bacterial disease which need bear no relation to the state of resistance against the invading microbe.

The outstanding characteristic of an antibody is its *specificity*. As immunologists became aware of the exquisite selectivity of such a tool, they were soon exploiting it for an analysis of the antigenic make-up of bacteria and other antigenic complexes.

In 1900 Landsteiner used natural antisera to recognize the different antigenic components—the A, B, and O blood groups—in the erythrocytes of various human beings. Also in 1900 Nuttall, Wassermann and Schütze reported that by means of the precipitin test they could distinguish human, cow's and goat's milk. Shortly afterwards (1900–1) Uhlenhuth published papers on the differentiation of the egg-whites of different species of birds by the precipitin method and so paved the way for the application of the reaction to forensic work in the recognition of the presence of human blood in blood stains.

There is a limit, however, to the high precision of serological specificity. When homologous proteins or carbohydrates of zoologically related species are used (such as the serum globulins of man and monkey injected into a rabbit) the antibodies for one antigen may react with another, although usually less strongly. These are called *cross-reactions*. The very extensive investigations of Nuttall of such cross-reactions provided data which proved of great help to zoologists in deciding the disputed questions of animal relationships even though the sera which he used as antigens contained a complex mixture of proteins. Thus, Nuttall showed a close tie between the blood of man and the anthropoid apes, but obtained considerably less cross-reaction with the blood of man and the lower apes. By injecting monkeys with human blood Uhlenhuth obtained serum which reacted with human but not with monkey serum proteins and, in this way, devised an approach to the differentiation of nearly-allied species.

In the early years of this century several investigators turned their interest to the fundamental aspects of the manner in which antibody interacted with its homologous antigen. At that time the means for the solution of this most complex problem were desperately scanty, for nothing was then known about the molecular weights of antigens and antibodies, or about the composition of the antigen–antibody precipitate. A great deal of the early discussions centred on the neutralization of toxin by antitoxin. The idea that the toxin was simply destroyed by the antitoxin was clearly shown to be false by the experiments of Hans Buchner (1893). He found that a tetanus toxin–antitoxin mixture which was neutral (i.e. non-toxic) for mice, was nevertheless lethal for the guinea-pig, and argued that the antitoxin could not have destroyed the toxin, otherwise the mixture should have been non-toxic both in mice and guinea-pigs. Similarly, Calmette had shown that by heating the neutral mixture of snake venom and antibody to 68° it became once more fully toxic.

The next important contribution to this problem was made by Paul Ehrlich, who may be regarded as the pioneer of immunochemistry since he was the first to introduce exact quantitative measurements as being the most likely approach to the solution of this problem. The facts that he early uncovered bolstered his belief that the process of combination was essentially a chemical reaction, being speeded by an increase in temperature and in the concentration of the reactants. However, he soon realized from his tests that antigen and antibody are not limited to a combination in equivalent proportions. This provoked him into a thoroughgoing analysis of the whole question of neutralization of toxin and antitoxin, and his results have since formed the basis of the methods of standardizing antitoxin for practical purposes. At the theoretical level, Ehrlich's conception that toxin and antitoxin became firmly united, as a strong acid with a strong base, led him to the complicated assumption that there must exist a whole range of distinct forms of toxoid differing from one another in their affinity for antitoxin. In this way he accounted for the varying proportions of antigen and antibody in combination.

A fundamental notion developed by Ehrlich was that the ability to combine with antitoxin and the lethal action represent two separate activities. This was explained by the assumption that the toxin molecule possessed two distinct reactive areas, one of which—the *haptophore*—brought about the union with antitoxin, and the other—the *toxophore*—bore the determinant of toxicity. The toxophore group was able to change to a non-toxic state, whereas the haptophore was relatively more stable. This change of toxin to toxoid was necessary to account for the fact that a given specimen of toxin required progressively less and less antitoxin for neutralization on standing at room temperature over the course of a few months.

Ehrlich (1897) in addition put forward a general theory of immunity which, under the name of the 'side chain' or 'receptor' theory, had a profound influence in stimulating fundamental work on the mechanism of antibody production.

A different view of the process of antigen–antibody union was introduced by Bordet in 1903, in which the possibility of combination in varying proportions was envisaged. In consequence, Bordet considered that serological reactions were akin to adsorptive phenomena. At the time, this implied the exclusion of the problem from the class of chemical interactions. Subsequent progress towards a solution of this problem now became dependent upon the growth of understanding of the nature of the forces responsible for attracting one macromolecule to another.

Further criticism of Ehrlich's theory was forthcoming. In 1902 Danysz discovered a phenomenon since known by his name. He found in connection with the interaction of ricin and antiricin that a mixture of both components was less toxic when they were mixed simultaneously than when half of the antigen was added to the antibody and the other half was added twenty-four hours later. This fact was brought forward as strong evidence against Ehrlich's view of a chemical union in fixed proportions. The chemists Arrhenius and Madsen (1902) also provided notable additions to this controversy, maintaining that the curve of neutralization of toxin and antitoxin is similar to that in which one weak acid is neutralized by one weak base. The fact that predictions made from this hypothesis were apparently borne out in practice has subsequently been found to be fortuitous.

The widely held teleological view that antibody production was designed specifically to protect the infected host received a blow from another direction with the observation that sometimes the access of antigen to the body results in severe symptoms and even death. This phenomenon, in which an immunological response leads to reactions damaging to the cells of the body, is referred to as *hypersensitivity*. The original data on which this idea is based were provided by Portier and Richet (1902) and the ensuing is a translation of their words.

'During a cruise on Prince Albert of Monaco's yacht, the Prince suggested* to Portier and myself a study of the toxin production of *Physalia* (the jelly-fish known as Portuguese Man-of-War) found in the South Seas. On board the Prince's yacht, experiments were carried out proving that an aqueous glycerine extract of the filaments of *Physalia* is extremely toxic to ducks and rabbits. On returning to France, I could not obtain *Physalia* and decided to study comparatively the tentacles of *Actinaria* (sea anemone). . . . While endeavouring to determine the toxic dose (of extracts), we soon discovered that some days must elapse before fixing it; for several dogs did not die until the fourth or fifth day after administration or even later. We kept those that had been given insufficient to kill, in order to carry out a second investigation upon these when they had recovered. At this point an unforeseen event occurred. The dogs which had recovered were intensely sensitive and died a few minutes after the administration of small doses. The most typical experiment, that in which the result was indisputable, was carried out on a particularly healthy dog. It was given at first 0·1 ml of the glycerin extract without becoming ill: twenty-two days later, as it was in perfect health, I gave it a second injection of the same amount. In a few seconds it was extremely ill; breathing became distressful and panting; it could scarcely drag itself along, lay on its side, was seized with diarrhoea, vomited blood and died in twenty-five minutes.'

The development of sensitivity to relatively harmless substances was termed by these authors *anaphylaxis*, in contract to *prophylaxis*. Local inflammatory reactions to reinjection of substances which

* Perhaps because his sea-bathing activities had been hampered by these creatures.

were completely harmless at their first administration were first described by Arthus (1903). He had injected daily doses of horse serum subcutaneously into rabbits. The first five or six doses were absorbed without any local reaction, but all succeeding doses produced foci of oedema with surrounding inflammation, and finally a condition was reached in which a dose of 2 ccm of horse serum under the skin produced an area of definite necrosis. Arthus regarded this as a form of anaphylaxis (which he later termed 'proteo-anaphylaxis' to indicate that it could be evoked by a wide variety of proteins), but maintained that it was also an aspect of immunity. This Arthus phenomenon, although usually elicited in the skin, might be produced also in other tissues such as the heart or brain, depending upon the site of the subsequent injection.

At this time—the first decade of the present century—horse serum, more or less fractionated, was in constant use for the treatment of diphtheria. In their classic monograph on serum sickness, published in 1905, von Pirquet and Schick showed that repeated use of serum in the same individual was not only attended by grave risk of anaphylactic reactions, but led to increasingly severe attacks of a delayed complex of symptoms known as serum sickness.

The problem of avoiding such reactions following treatment with foreign serum has indeed never been completely solved, but it has been greatly ameliorated in consequence of the observation made some thirty years later that mild enzymic digestion of antibody globulins could be accomplished in such a way that their protective activity was retained while their antigenicity, and consequent tendency to cause serum sickness, was largely lost.

Anaphylactic reactions and attempts to determine their mechanism attracted much interest before the First World War, and gave rise to explanations which bear quite a marked general resemblance to some which are presently the focus of attention. It was suggested, and experimental evidence was produced to support it, that when antigen and antibody reacted together in the plasma they activated a latent proteolytic enzyme which proceeded to split off highly toxic fragments from the antigen, and that these were responsible for the symptoms of anaphylaxis. A difficulty about the explanation lay in the fact that an animal which had been sensitized so as to undergo anaphylactic shock upon reinjection of the antigen could sometimes have no detectable antibody in its circulation, and the proponents of the idea that humoral events were responsible for anaphylaxis were opposed by others who claimed that only 'sessile' antibodies, fixed on cells, could be involved. The question appeared finally to have been settled when in 1910 Dale discovered the pharmacological properties of histamine and showed that histamine injections would mimic many, though not quite all, of the effects of anaphylaxis. Histamine was present in blood or tissue cells, but not in plasma, and the interaction of antigen with sessile antibody on the cells, so as to damage these cells, with resultant histamine release and perhaps other manifestations, seemed to provide a satisfactory explanation of the phenomenon; this was made the more secure when histamine was later proved unequivocally to be released during anaphylaxis. As happens not infrequently, and as will appear in Chapter Eleven, closer examination has shown that both the humoral and the cellular notions are valid in different contexts. Meanwhile, the search for histamine antagonists, developed originally as a by-product of research to prevent sea-sickness, has given rise to a complete branch of the pharmaceutical industry, and from these drugs in turn have arisen—like branches of a banyan tree—many of the tranquillizing drugs.

Anaphylaxis and serum sickness and the Arthus phenomenon were the first recognized examples of processes which are nowadays often grouped under the heading immunopathology, to various aspects of which three of the later chapters of this book are devoted. Having once recognized that the immunological response was not evoked only by toxins but also by many bland foreign substances, and that the reintroduction of the antigen could produce a harmful reaction in a sensitized animal, it was natural to seek an explanation for some diseases, where the role of infective agents was not obvious, in terms of the untoward consequences of responses which under other circumstances might be useful. For example, it had been recognized since Blackley's monograph on 'The Causes and Nature of Hay Fever' written in 1873, that pollen was closely associated with hay fever and asthma, but how this association came about was quite obscure. In 1911, Noon in America and Freeman in Britain, followed by Cooke who between 1916 and 1933 made an extensive study of skin sensitivity, clearly showed that these diseases were often associated with an anaphylactic type of sensitivity to pollen extracts. Following an early observation that sensitized animals could be made temporarily resistant to anaphylaxis by cautious administration of large doses of antigen by subcutaneous injection

Freeman began the practice of desensitization which was greatly extended by Cooke. Other workers, particularly among the German pathologists in the 1920's, were much impressed by the similarity between the histological appearance of lesions produced by reinjection of antigen into sensitized animals—which they recognized as a form of inflammatory response and named 'allergische hyperergische Entzündung'—and those seen in rheumatic fever. They were unable to reproduce a sufficiently exact counterpart to the human disease, however, and medical opinion as a whole remained unimpressed. When the Japanese pathologist Masugi in 1934 injected antiserum prepared in ducks against rabbit kidney tissue back into rabbits, and produced an acute glomerulonephritis which was the first even passable experimental imitation of the human disease, interest in a possible immunological aetiology was revived. Nevertheless, no one pretended that such experimental glomerulonephritis could be more than an imperfect model for human nephritis, and indeed it provided no explanation for the well-recognized clinical association between acute nephritis and streptococcal infection.

Another possibility which occurred to some of the early workers was that the body might make antibodies against constituents of its own tissues. Many investigations, some systematic and some purely exploratory, were conducted on the ability of various cells (mostly red blood cells) and tissues from different species to elicit antibodies, and tests were made of the extent to which cross-reactions occurred between the antibodies and extracts of these tissues obtained from the different species. Such tests were conducted by a process of absorbing the antisera successively with one tissue after another, and determining what reactivities remained after each absorption—in much the same way as the immunological classification of the bacterial species *Salmonella*, for example, was worked out painstakingly and brilliantly by Kauffmann and White. The outcome of this work, much of which was due to Witebsky, was to show that some tissues (e.g. the eye lens, the pancreas, the thyroid, the brain) contained antigenic materials specific to the tissue but which were, in part at least, common to many species. In the case of a few tissues, such as the eye lens, antibodies made against the foreign tissue would react *in vitro* with the corresponding tissue of the species in which the antibodies were made. Attempts to immunize animals against tissues obtained from the same species were, however, generally unsuccessful, except occasionally, as in the case of brain tissue, when injections were continued over many months—and immunization of animals with their own tissues apparently did not occur. In no cases was it possible to attribute pathological changes to auto-immunization, and the generalization, first enunciated by Ehrlich in the phrase 'horror autotoxicus', that the body would not react against its own constituents gained general credence. As far as most immunologists were concerned this was not shaken until Coombs, Mourant and Race introduced the antiglobulin test for incomplete Rh antibodies in 1945; in the following year Boorman, Loutit and Dodd used the test to show that certain patients with acquired haemolytic anaemia had antibodies against their own red cells, and soon afterwards it was found possible to produce experimental diseases, namely aspermatogenesis (first demonstrated in 1951 by Voisin, Delaunay and Barber) and encephalomyelitis (by Morgan in 1946) in animals injected respectively with testicular or brain tissue incorporated in the adjuvant mixture devised by Freund. The pathological significance of auto-immunity reactions has now become widely recognized and is discussed in Chapter Fifteen.

Interest in investigation of the pathology of immunological reactions in experimental animals waxed strong in the first two decades of this century and, as we have described, has now received a new impetus, but the main steady stimulus to the development of immunology has been the hope of developing more effective means of immunizing man and domestic animals against disease. Apart from vaccination against smallpox, and the Pasteurian treatment for rabies mentioned already (an heroic treatment appropriate to a desperate condition), the first applications to human disease were passive serum treatment first of diphtheria and later, during the First World War, of tetanus and gas gangrene. Active immunization against enteric disease was introduced for troops serving abroad in the early 1900's, but except for this, active immunization was virtually confined to animals, mainly because the immunizing agents used were crude, often not without risk, and very liable to cause severe reactions. Furthermore, several injections were usually required to produce the requisite degree of immunity.

A great step forward was made when in 1923 Glenny and Ramon independently discovered that careful formaldehyde treatment of several toxin preparations destroyed their toxic properties without diminishing their immunizing capacity—thus providing a safer and more effective alternative to the mixtures of toxin and horse antitoxin which had been used for immunizing before. Another discovery of practical importance made shortly afterwards by Glenny was that adsorption of antigens on to alum (or various other materials) often rendered them much more effective as immunizing agents, so that a more long-lasting response was obtained with fewer injections and by the use of less material. Prophylactic immunization against diphtheria on a mass scale became a practicable policy, and a fine example was set by the town of Hamilton, Ontario, which by 1933 succeeded in wiping out completely this disease from its population. A tetanus prophylactic (formaldehyde-treated toxin) was developed about the same time, but was not tested on a large scale until the Second World War when it was found to reduce the incidence of tetanus infection of wounds to an almost negligible proportion. Many other immunizing agents were tried out during the years between the two World Wars, in the form of killed bacteria and their products, killed virus-infected tissues or living attenuated strains. Some were very successful, such as the attenuated yellow fever vaccine developed around 1936, while others, such as those against streptococci and staphylococci, were for reasons which will be described below apparently useless.

With the advent of sulphonamides in 1936, and of penicillin in 1941, followed by a variety of antibiotics and other chemotherapeutic agents whose potency and range of action far surpassed even Ehrlich's most optimistic hopes for any 'magic bullet', it might at first glance have been supposed that the need for prophylactic immunization or for serum treatment had vanished. In respect of treatment this has proved largely to be the case, but the very success of chemotherapy in treatment of the major bacterial infections emphasized its deficiencies in combating viral diseases. Furthermore, such treatment must be available at the right moment, and it is expensive. Prevention still remains better than cure.

Improved methods for growing and purifying viruses, together with a better understanding of their epidemiology, have rendered active immunization against several virus diseases safe, easy and effective. Although Chapter Sixteen only describes vaccines for yellow fever, smallpox, rabies, typhus, poliomyelitis and influenza, it is likely that in the near future we shall see on the market vaccines for diseases such as measles, adenovirus infections and even for the common cold. At the same time, improved methods of culture and for preservation of the important antigenic components of bacteria, with a minimum of toxic factors, have led to the development of effective vaccines for pertussis and plague, although those against such scourges as cholera and against helminthic and protozoal diseases are still not satisfactory. Living bacterial vaccines, of which the first to be used on a wide scale in man was BCG (the attenuated strain of tubercle bacilli named Bacille Calmette-Guérin, after its originators), have also been developed. These now include attenuated strains of *Brucella abortus* and of *Br. tularense*, which are proving useful where the incidence of disease due to these organisms is high.

Prophylactic immunization usually fails when the number of antigenically distinct strains of the infective bacterium, virus or rickettsia at large in a community is so great that they cannot all be included in the prophylactic preparation, or when they do not all act by elaborating a single kind of exotoxin. Streptococcal infections in man provide an example of such a state of affairs. As shown by Griffith between 1926 and 1935, there are many types of pathogenic streptococci belonging to Lancefield's Group A, and therefore, although infection with any given type appears to confer long lasting immunity against clinical reinfection with the same type, the individual may nevertheless suffer repeated attacks from streptococci of other types. The same holds for pneumococci, of which more than sixty types are known. Nevertheless, because in the days before chemotherapy untreated pneumococcal pneumonia had a high mortality, and because the great majority of clinical infections were due to organisms belonging to only a relatively few types, an attempt at active immunization of service personnel against the five commoner types, by intracutaneous injection of purified capsular polysaccharide, was made by Heidelberger and his colleagues during the Second World War (see Chapter Ten). The attempt was successful, in so far as morbidity due to infections with pneumococci of these types was sharply diminished.

During the 1930's, treatment of pneumonia by administering type-specific antibody made in horses (or better in rabbits, because the antibody was of lower molecular weight and penetrated more readily into the tissue fluids) was widely practised, and this treatment—for all its disadvantages—greatly improved the prognosis. Large amounts of antibody were required, and it was therefore neither economical nor practical to give a polyvalent antiserum. Consequently, it was necessary to identify the type of the causative organisms as rapidly as possible, and this was often done directly by means of Neufeld's 'Quellung' (capsule swelling) phenomenon on pneumococci in the sputum, or by precipitin tests for specific capsular material which had been excreted by the kidneys and was present in the urine. In the U.S.A. most different States held 'banks' of type-specific antisera against the commoner types of pneumococci. The reason for mentioning in some detail these developments, which have now faded into history, is that the observations upon which they were based were of considerable importance in the development of the understanding of immunological specificity. Neufeld originally observed in 1902 that when pneumococci were mixed with antiserum against them their capsules became sharply outlined and the organisms were apparently swollen (Plate 10.1, following p. 404). He also observed a few years later that strains of pneumococci varied sharply according to whether or not any particular antiserum would protect mice against their lethal effects or would cause their capsules to swell. By studying antisera against a large number of strains isolated from cases of lobar pneumonia in man, Dochez and Avery between 1913 and 1917 were able to group the strains into three distinct main Types I–III and a group of heterogeneous strains which belonged to none of the three types and were somewhat misleadingly lumped together in a Group IV. Avery and Heidelberger then set out to study the pneumococcal antigens by chemical means and were able to isolate antigenically active capsular materials of Types I, II and III in a high degree of purity, and found that they were not proteins but complex polysaccharides made up largely from a few quite simple sugar residues. Although the analysis of their detailed structure could not be worked out with the existing techniques, and was not achieved until many years later, this observation had a twofold significance. In the first place it showed that antigenic properties were not confined, as had previously been believed, to proteins, and that some relatively simple carbohydrates could confer antigenic specificity; in the second place it gave a general significance to the work on the antigenic function of simple chemical groups artificially introduced into proteins which had been begun by Landsteiner in 1917.

Landsteiner, who had studied chemistry before he became a pathological anatomist in Vienna, was now well set upon the path which led him brilliantly to develop the ideas concerning the detailed nature of the interaction between antibodies and certain directive or 'haptenic' groups on the antigen molecule, which are the foundation of current ideas on antigenic specificity, some of which are discussed in Chapters Four and Six. It was not at first clear, however, whether his findings were peculiar to proteins containing artificially conjugated groups, or whether this approach had a general validity for all sorts of antigens and antibodies. After the demonstration that such well-recognized protective antibodies as those against pneumococci owed their specificity to ability to combine with a variety of carbohydrates whose common feature was the possession of certain simple chemical groups, all doubts on this point vanished. Perhaps the final vindication of this approach came when Goebel and Avery were able to evoke protective antibodies in rabbits against pneumococcus Type III by means of an artificial conjugate of horse serum proteins and a pure protein-free capsular polysaccharide, which by itself was not antigenic.

Thanks to the extreme sensitivity and specificity of the immunological response it is readily possible to distinguish antigenic differences between strains of micro-organisms, and by systematic testing with antisera absorbed with one strain after another to detect and analyse even several co-existing antigenic differences. Work along these lines requires patience and insight, but in the hands of Kauffmann and White, for example, it led to the extraordinarily detailed scheme for classification of *Salmonellae* which is associated with their name. With the progress of analytical chemical techniques and of methods for breaking the structure of bacteria by relatively mild means (e.g. by solvent extraction or by means of specific enzymes), the chemical nature of the antigenic determinants of Gram-negative bacilli, of strains of *Haemophilus*, of *Streptococcus* and of other bacteria is gradually being revealed, so that Roman numerals or letters in immunological classifications are now coming to stand for specific mono- or oligosaccharides—a few examples of which are mentioned in Chapter Six. The classifications based upon immunological techniques, and the methods evolved in the course of working them out, are the foundation upon which is based the structure of bacterial genetics and the information which has flowered from studies in this field. Furthermore, it appears that the susceptibility of an organism to a particular bacteriophage may depend upon its possession of the antigenically distinguishable structures whose chemical constitution is now being revealed by the powerful combination of chemical and immuno-chemical methods.

Bacteria have thus been shown to possess antigenic differences due to structural components at the surface. The same applies even more to metazoa and to our prime concern, man. The first demonstration of the main blood-group differences, A, B, AB and O, was by Landsteiner in 1901. His discoveries were not applied to the practice of blood transfusion as rapidly as might nowadays have been expected, probably because effective anticoagulants had not been discovered at the time (the use of sodium citrate was not introduced until 1915) and blood transfusion was very uncommon. After the First World War this situation was changed, but the widespread use of stored blood which transformed the procedure from one which was so elaborate as to be reserved for dire emergencies (when it was often too little and too late) to an everyday event came only with the Second World War. From Blood Transfusion Centres and special centres working on the racial distribution and genetics of blood groups there is flowing nowadays a steady stream of discovery of more and more heritable antigenic features on red cells, mostly revealed by the development of agglutinating antibodies in persons who have had multiple transfusions or following pregnancy—i.e. by *iso-antibodies*, developed within animals of the species which made the antigens. By comparison of their results on an international scale it was already possible by 1959 to distinguish fifty-nine separate blood-group antigens in man (see for example, *British Medical Bulletin*, Vol. 15, No. 2 (1959) on 'Blood Groups').

Much of the early work was due to Landsteiner and Levine, who made use of antibodies prepared by injecting human red cells into animals of some other species such as the rabbit. Such *hetero-antibodies* lack the power of fine discrimination provided by iso-antibodies, since they are directed against a multitude of foreign antigens in the red cells, most of which are common to all human red cells. Nevertheless by their means the M, N and P antigens were added to A_1, A_2 and B, and the existence was shown of an antigen common to the red cells of the Rhesus monkey and of most, but not all, of the white population of North America. This last antigen was the Rhesus antigen, which assumed great clinical importance when it was implicated in 1938 by Levine as the main relevant factor in haemolytic disease of the new-born. From following up the ramifications of this immunological disease has sprung much of our present-day knowledge of the human blood groups. One of these ramifications, namely the occurrence of Rh antibodies which would unite with the specific antigens on the red cell without, however, bringing about subsequent agglutination, led to the development by Coombs, Mourant and Race in 1945 of a technique for recognizing such antibodies. This was the antiglobulin sensitization test, in which antibody prepared in another species against human globulin was applied to the cells coated with non-agglutinating Rh antibody so as to cause them to agglutinate by a secondary process. This test, and variations of it, has proved of great importance in demonstrating the presence of antibodies against cells of various tissues in a number of diseases (including acquired haemolytic anaemia to which it was first applied) which are discussed in Chapter Fifteen.

The existence of several specific antigens has now been shown for other cells, such as the leucocytes and epithelial cells, and the antigenic individuality of animals, other than those belonging to highly inbred, so-called 'pure' lines, no longer requires emphasis. It has even been shown to apply to at least some of the plasma proteins. Thus the investigations of Cumley and Irwin in 1943 showed the existence of definite antigenic differences between plasma proteins of different varieties of pigeon, and in man inherited antigenic differences (allotypes) have been found in α- and β-globulins, as well as the γ-globulin groups which are discussed in Chapter Four.

The importance of such antigenic individuality has been underlined by studies on the transplantation of tumours and of normal tissues such as skin, or of whole organs. That very few tumours could be successfully grafted in ordinary stocks of outbred laboratory animals had been known since Rous's studies during the 1920's. Grafting of most tumours and of living normal tissues, other than the cornea, failed. Even with the greatest technical expertise such grafts never did better than to survive for a few days, after which they regressed—and second grafts never took at all. Such failures were certainly considered possibly to have an immunological explanation, but deficiencies of technique could not be excluded until the use of antibiotics virtually abolished the risks of infection, and until it was found that within inbred strains of mice tumours and tissue grafts would take readily. It is now accepted largely as the result of the extensive studies in rabbits by Medawar in 1944–5 that rejection of heterografts, made between individuals from different species, and of homografts between members of an outbred strain of the same species, is due to immunization of the recipient by the donor's tissue. Furthermore, it has also become evident that one of the factors which may determine whether growth or regression of tumours occurs, even of those arising spontaneously, is the degree to which the tumour cells are antigenically distinct from those of the host.

To a considerable extent the development of ideas about antigenic individuality and its biological importance has followed the paths already traced by the earlier workers on bacterial immunology, and has not depended upon knowledge of the structure of antigens and antibodies or of their interaction. Such knowledge, however, is essential to any understanding of how immunological processes work, and to a great many practical matters such as measurement of antibodies and their preparation and purification. Heidelberger and Marrack and their colleagues from 1930 onwards studied the interaction of antigen and antibody by exact and sensitive quantitative methods, which had not been available to earlier workers such as Ehrlich. From their studies was developed the 'Lattice' hypothesis, outlined briefly in Chapter Nine, which succeeded in explaining how interaction between two large molecules by means of specific and definite bonds could apparently lead to combination in variable proportions—a type of interaction which was at the time unfamiliar to classical chemists, although it is nowadays well known to those who study polymer formation. With the help of the theoretical understanding provided by the lattice hypothesis, and by use of quantitative micro-methods, it was possible to measure precipitating antibodies in serum accurately, and to predict how antigen- and antibody-interactions would behave in the test tube.

In practice, apart from a relatively few instances in which antisera prepared against highly purified antigens were studied, antigen–antibody systems *in vitro* mostly departed from the behaviour predicted for them. The reason was generally found to be that the antigens were impure, and that what was being examined was not a single system but a mixture of several antigen–antibody systems each reacting independently and so giving several zones of precipitation (see Chapter Nine). By the simple trick of allowing the antigens and the antibodies to diffuse towards one another through an agar gel instead of being mixed in a test tube, it could be contrived that the different precipitation zones in a mixed system formed at distinct sites in the gel. The idea of doing this was suggested in different ways by Elek, by Oudin and by Ouchterlony in 1946, and the techniques evolved have great resolving power for demonstrating mixtures of antigens, and are very simple to perform. Furthermore, such gel diffusion methods, as explained in Chapter Nine, can be used to demonstrate whether or not antigens in complex mixtures are identical, related or distinct, as well as something of their chemical nature. The information given is usually of a qualitative nature only, but it is won so cheaply—and would be so difficult to obtain in any other way—that immunological methods of this kind are rapidly becoming standard aids to analysis by workers in many disciplines (e.g. biochemistry or genetics) who until recently were largely uninterested in antibodies.

By first separating antigens according to their electrophoretic properties (migration in an electric field) in agar or some other medium, and then demonstrating their presence by means of precipitation zones with antibody, even more information can be obtained. This technique was first introduced by Grabar and Williams in 1953 and named by them immuno-electrophoresis. With its help the existence of protein components in a complex mixture such as serum, against which antibodies can be formed in another species, can be demonstrated, and by the use of antisera of known specificity, or by comparing their behaviour with that of known purified serum proteins, many of the components can be identified. Human serum has already been shown by such means to contain at least forty distinguishable proteins—and doubtless more will be added with time. It is indeed by means of immunoelectrophoresis that several serum protein abnormalities, such as the existence of split (double) albumin or the absence of γ- or of macroglobulins are most readily recognized. It may appear unusual to discourse upon a technical method in an introductory chapter, but especially when combined with electrophoretic methods with greater resolving power, such as migration in a starch gel, the technique can provide such a degree of discrimination that it has opened up important new possibilities for investigating and understanding the behaviour of plasma and other proteins.

The progress which we have touched upon in understanding the mechanism of antigen–antibody interaction, and in putting this to practical use, could have occurred irrespective of any detailed knowledge of the chemical nature of antibodies or of the cells in which they are made. It may come as a surprise to learn that antibodies were not known to be γ-globulins until Tiselius and Kabat showed them to be so in 1938. They were, of course, known to be 'globulins' but this term included a rather wide variety of proteins, and it was not until Tiselius in 1937 separated serum proteins on the basis of their migration in an electric field into albumin, α-, β- and γ-globulins that further progress became possible. We now know that antibodies are mainly γ-globulins, but, as Chapter Four discloses, they comprise a heterogeneous group of proteins sharing certain common properties, and this definition is no longer adequate. In fact a special term 'immunoglobulin' has recently been introduced to describe proteins belonging to this group. The discovery by R. R. Porter in 1959 that γ-globulins and antibodies could be split by papain into three pieces, two of which contained the antibody combining sites and a third which was later shown to possess some of the other biological properties of γ-globulin (such as selective transmission across the placenta or fixation of complement), opened up a new approach to their structure, which is now in principle known.

It is still a moot question whether the immunoglobulins of serum are all antibodies developed by the animal in response to bacteria, fungi, food dust and other antigens in the environment—even though we may by our tests be able to recognize but a fraction of them—or whether there is such a thing as 'normal' immunoglobulin, of which antibodies represent minor but highly specific modifications. It might be supposed that animals born by Caesarian section and reared in a bacteriologically sterile environment would provide an answer to this question, since they might be expected to be subject to no antigenic stimulation and, if all immunoglobulins were antibodies, they should have none. Experiments along these lines have been made with rats and chicks, but so far it has proved impossible to rear them successfully on a completely synthetic and defined diet. Animals so reared have less immunoglobulin than normals, and make it later after birth, but they still have some and they have been found to make antibodies against bacterial antigens in the autoclaved diet on which they are fed.

It is now well known that plasma proteins are continually being broken down and renewed. This important knowledge dates only from experiments reported in 1942 by Schoenheimer, Heidelberger and Rittenberg who administered intravenously to rabbits homologous plasma proteins marked by means of ^{15}N (the stable heavy isotope of nitrogen) and showed that the labelled proteins were lost at an exponential rate from the plasma, while the actual protein concentration remained steady. Antibodies provide a form of labelled protein which can be recognized and measured with much greater ease than can ^{15}N, and it had been shown by Glenny as early as 1923 that specific antibodies transfused to an unimmunized animal disappeared exponentially from the circulation (with, in fact, the same half lives as were later found for γ-globulins by the use of proteins labelled with radioactive isotopes). If antibodies had been regarded as normal plasma constituents, rather than as in a class apart, the revolutionary change of outlook which came from the discovery of the dynamic turnover of plasma proteins might have taken place nearly two decades earlier. It is sufficient to state here that we know that antibody levels are maintained by continuous production of new antibody, and that when production decreases the level falls.

Where are antibodies made? Already in 1898 Pfeiffer and Marx had deduced, by measuring antibody levels in different tissues at various time intervals after immunization, that antibodies must originate mostly in the spleen, bone marrow, lymph nodes and lung. However, cells which make antibodies were not finally identified until Fagraeus in 1948 showed that not only was antibody formation more closely correlated with the development of cells of the plasma cell series than with any other obvious cytological changes, but also that fragments of spleen red pulp rich in such cells made antibody when cultured *in vitro*. Shortly afterwards in 1955 unequivocal proof that such cells contain antibody was provided by the elegant fluorescent antibody technique (see Chapters Seven and Nine) developed by Coons and his colleagues, and since then several workers have shown that single isolated plasma cells from lymph nodes stimulated by antigen, maintained in tiny droplets of culture medium, secrete detectable amounts of antibody. The cytological basis of antibody formation and the question whether only such cells are involved is discussed at greater length in Chapter Seven.

Certain sorts of hyperreactivity to antigens, however, are not associated with detectable circulating antibody, nor with plasma cell development. These are the 'delayed-type' hypersensitivities to which is devoted Chapter Twelve, and of which the classical example is the reaction of a tuberculous patient to tuberculin but which include contact dermatitis and a number of conditions important in medicine. That the reintroduction into the body of bacteria (even of dead bacterial bodies) elicited a response which differed from that produced by simple protein antigens (anaphylaxis or the Arthus response) was stressed especially by Zinsser in the early years of this century. 'Bacterial allergy', as it was termed, differed by being slower in onset and was accompanied by a cellular infiltration in which mononuclear cells were much in evidence. If severe, it ended in local necrosis of tissue (usually the skin, since this was the most convenient injection site). The capacity to produce such a response was not transferred when serum from a sensitive animal was administered to a normal recipient, and the mechanism was—and to some extent remains—a mystery.

The importance of bacterial allergy in tuberculosis was recognized by Koch in the 1890's and later explored and emphasized by Rich. In 1928 Dienes showed that simple protein antigens could also elicit a rather similar response under certain conditions—e.g. if they were injected into a site of tuberculous infection, and the skin tests were made early, before circulating antibody had begun to appear. This observation was not extended at the time, but it is now accepted by most workers that the elicitation of delayed-type hypersensitivity is a general phenomenon which can be produced by most antigenic substances, although some are much more active in this respect than others. One effective way of eliciting delayed-type hypersensitivity is by application to the skin of chemicals which combine readily with proteins. The chemical specificity of such sensitizing agents interested Landsteiner greatly, and the phenomenon was studied extensively by him and Jacobs and Chase during the 1930's. In 1942 Chase succeeded in transferring such a state of sensitivity to normal guinea-pigs by means of spleen, lymph node or peritoneal exudate cells obtained from highly sensitized donors. Their observations, and those of others since, have indicated that the active cells are lymphocytes—though just which lymphocytes are involved, and how they differ from normal lymphocytes, constitutes, indeed, one of the most challenging questions in immunology at the present time.

It is now widely accepted that the most important immunological response involved in the rejection of tissue homografts is that which results in delayed type hypersensitivity. In fact the response may profitably be regarded as a cell-mediated immunity, by which the sensitized lymphocytes are in some unknown way able to destroy living foreign cells. A biological function for the response is then not far to seek. The foreign cells which matter from the point of view of survival value are not, of course, those introduced by surgical intervention but aberrant autochthonous cells (including potential tumour cells) which arise as a result of somatic mutation or virus infection or by the action of chemical mutagenic agents. Such a *surveillance* function presumably could provide a mechanism of broad biological significance for preserving the integrity of all higher organisms.

In retrospect it appears that during the exciting early years after bacteria were discovered and the formation of antibodies was recognized, the years of Ehrlich, Pasteur, Von Behring, Bordet and Metchnikoff, progress in immunology was very rapid. During this period the main phenomena were described, and the existence of the important auxiliary factor, complement, was established. The succeeding generation saw a slower progress, a process of consolidation and enlargement of knowledge and of practical application but of few dramatic advances. It was not until the late 1930's that the pace accelerated again, so that shortly after the end of the Second World War it might be claimed that there were well-founded concepts concerning the nature of antibodies and their interaction with antigens, the dynamics of antibody metabolism, and the nature of the cells involved in the immune response. The time had come when the study of immunology, quite apart from its practical importance, had accumulated a sufficiently large, ordered and consistent mass of facts to challenge chemists, biochemists, geneticists and others to carry their techniques into this field.

The time was also ripe for an attempt to assemble the facts into some general theoretical framework. Any hypothesis needed to explain not only how or why an immune response occurs following the introduction of foreign antigenic material, but also why there is no response to an animal's own bodily constituents, which would be effective antigens in another species.

Since Ehrlich's first attempted explanation in terms of 'toxophore' and 'haptophore' groups on cells, no serious alternative hypotheses were put forward until around 1932 when Haurowitz, Mudd and Alexander each proposed that the antigen must somehow be able to act as a 'template' at the site of globulin synthesis in the antibody-forming cell, and so alter the arrangement of the amino-acids in the globulin which was being made that part of the surface configuration was complementary to that of the antigen. It was impossible on the basis of current knowledge of protein synthesis or of cytoplasmic organization to push this hypothesis any deeper than a general proposition that the antigen directs the synthesis of antibody *de novo*, and the proposers had nothing to say on the question why 'self' proteins evoke no immune response. As explained briefly in Chapter Three, this and other 'directive' hypotheses have now been superseded by modifications of the 'clonal selection' theory (put forward by Burnet and Lederberg). In 1949 Burnet and Fenner wrote a monograph on 'The Production of Antibody', largely from a biological point of view, in which they proposed that certain mesenchymal cells in the body were concerned both in the disposal of effete body cells and of foreign organic material. The former function did not involve an antibody response, whereas the second did. In order to allow this differentiation of function, expendable body cells were postulated to carry 'self-marker' components which allowed recognition of their 'self' character. The nature of such components and the means by which they were recognized could not be explained in detail, but Burnet and Fenner predicted that any potential antigen which reaches the scavenging cell system before a certain critical point, around the time of birth or hatching, would be accepted as 'self' and its presence in subsequent life would not provoke antibody production. In 1953 Billingham, Brent and Medawar tested this hypothesis by inoculating mouse embryos from one genetically homogeneous pure line of mice *in utero* with cell suspensions from another inbred strain, and found that when the inoculated mice grew up they would accept skin grafts from mice of their own or of the second strain, but not from mice of other strains. In other words, the cells of the second strain were now accepted as 'self', as predicted, because of some modification of the host cells during the last stage of embryonic life. This is the phenomenon of specific acquired immunological tolerance, which is discussed in Chapter Three. It applies not only to cell antigens but to many others, such as soluble proteins. Although the mechanism is still obscure, and probably not as simple as Burnet and Fenner originally conceived it to be, the fulfilment of their prediction not only opened a new chapter of great potential importance in immunology, but it indicated that the biological phenomena of immunology could be fruitfully approached from a broad theoretical angle. This alone has provided a very powerful additional incentive to research on the fundamental nature of the immune response.

Nature herself has also assisted by inflicting certain immunological deficiencies or peculiarities upon rare individuals, whose disabilities have been put to good account by providing clues to the structure of antibodies and the control of their synthesis which would have been almost unattainable by other means. Perhaps the most important clues have come from the study of patients with multiple myeloma, a disease associated with the proliferation of single cell lines, or 'clones', producing in most cases a single kind of very homogeneous immunoglobulin, in sufficient quantity to allow it to be isolated in a reasonably pure state. Multiple myelomatosis was for long regarded as a bizarre form of tumour producing abnormal globulins termed 'paraproteins', but extensive examination of these proteins forced the conclusion that they differed from normal immunoglobulins in no significant way except for their homogeneity and for the fact that they had no recognizable antibody activity. Recognition of this not only encouraged fruitful immunochemical and genetic studies to be made with these myeloma proteins, but also emphasized the extreme heterogeneity of normal plasma immunoglobulins. Unlike most other plasma proteins the immunoglobulins are not physico-chemically homogeneous, but include a spectrum of molecules having generally similar chemical properties but varying widely in charge, possessing different sequences in the amino acids which make up their polypeptide chains, and even differing in their molecular weights. Since myeloma cells each make a constant immunoglobulin product it seemed likely that the enormous diversity of immunoglobulins in any individual must be based on an equal diversity—even if not morphologically obvious—in the cells which make them. All work aimed at checking this hypothesis had tended to verify it. F.M. Burnet and J. Lederberg in 1959 suggested for other reasons that the diversity of antibody specificities was also based on a diversity of cells each making a single, or possibly two, unique immunoglobulin products. When put to the test this also has been found usually to be the case. However the diversity of antibody specificities and the diversity of physicochemical properties of the immunoglobulins are, so far as we know, quite unrelated to one another. Furthermore the manifold cells which make these different yet related products are not constant features of the body's architecture, such as are the liver, or the gut or the integument. They wax and wane in response to antigenic stimuli, and are themselves probably derived from precursor cells numbered among the population of 'lymphocytes'. These rather featureless cells, most of which consist of a nucleus with just sufficient cytoplasm to keep them alive, are apparently the source of this extraordinary diversity. Thus one of the key problems in immunology has become to discover how such diversity is achieved.

During the past ten years almost 10 per cent of the scientific papers read at the annual meeting of the Federation of American Societies for Experimental Biology have been related to immunology or employed immunological methods. The pace of advance has become so rapid, and the volume of information so great, that the selection of topics for inclusion in a textbook presents a difficult task which can only be solved arbitrarily, according to the tastes of the authors and the supposed wishes of the readers. We have purposely not avoided aspects which are controversial or in which ideas are changing rapidly, and for this reason we must ask for indulgence if statements which appear now to be true, later prove false in the light of newer knowledge.

FURTHER READING*

AVERY O.T. (1877–1955) *Biographical Memoirs of Fellows of the Royal Society.* Vol. 2, p. 35 (1956)

BORDET J. (1920) *Traité de l'Immunité dans les maladies infectieuses.* Masson, Paris

BULLOCH W. (1938) *The History of Bacteriology.* Oxford University Press, London

CAMERON G.R. (1952) *Pathology of the Cell.* Oliver & Boyd, Edinburgh (See in particular The Role of Phagocytosis, pp. 164–212)

COLEBROOK L. (1954) *Almroth Wright.* Arnold, London

DALE H.H. (1953) *Adventures in physiology, with excursions into autopharmacology; a selection from the scientific publications of Sir Henry Hallett Dale.* Pergamon Press, London

DE KRUIF P.H. (1926) *The Microbe Hunters.* Pocket Books Inc., New York

* Suggestions for further reading are listed at the end of each chapter. They are in no way intended to be exhaustive, but rather to introduce the reader who wishes to delve more deeply into the literature on each subject. For this reason the suggestions consist of books and review articles rather than of original papers.

Dubos R.J. & Dubos J.P. (1952) *The White Plague; tuberculosis, man and society*. Little, Boston

Dubos R.J. (1950) *Louis Pasteur, free lance of science*. Little, Boston

Ehrlich P. (1900) On immunity with special reference to cell life (Croonian Lecture). *Proc. Roy. Soc., London*, **66,** 424–48

Landsteiner K. (1868–1943) *Obituary Notices of Fellows of the Royal Society*. Vol. 5, p. 295

Metchnikoff E. (1901) *L'Immunité dans les maladies infectieuses*. Masson, Paris

Richet C. (1913) *Anaphylaxis*, translated by J.M. Bligh. Liverpool University Press; Constable, London

Shaw G.B. (1908) *The Doctor's Dilemma*. Penguin Books, London, 1946

Smith, Theobald (1859–1934) *Obituary Notices of Fellows of the Royal Society*. Vol. 1, p. 515

Wilson G.S. & Miles A.A. (ed.) (1964) *Topley and Wilson's Principles of Bacteriology and Immunity*, 5th edition. Arnold, London

Zinsser H. (1935) *Rats, lice and history*. Routledge, London

CHAPTER TWO

Non-specific Mechanisms of Immunity: Innate Immunity

THE capacity of the normal animal to maintain itself free from infection by parasitic micro-organisms and to rid itself of these when they are implanted in its tissues can be referred to as *innate* or *natural immunity*. To be more explicit, innate immunity is envisaged as the resistance displayed by an animal *ab initio*, by an animal that has never experienced the particular pathogenic organism either as a pathogen or as a related non-pathogenic variant. With the vast majority of micro-organisms these mechanisms of resistance alone are sufficient to maintain the animal body at all times free from invasion. Many times in a gardening week-end we break the surface of our skin. In the majority of cases the subsequent inflammatory signs of an infected wound fail to develop. This happens in spite of the fact that the chemical components of these tissues would appear to have all the makings of a good bacteriological culture medium.

Nevertheless, these remarkable mechanisms are occasionally powerless to prevent the infection. If a normal child or adult has contact with the virus of measles then the well-known and characteristic symptoms of the disease almost always follow. The patient who recovers from this initial infection with measles virus is able, usually for the rest of his life, to resist a second onslaught from this particular virus. Such *acquired immunity* does not exist except as a result of previous exposure to the micro-organism. It is a state of resistance which applies only to this specific microbe and it depends upon the individual's active contribution. Hence, we could refer to it as *specific active acquired immunity*. As we shall see later, sometimes the same result can be produced without the active contribution of the subject as, for instance, when a mother transfers the resistance mechanisms temporarily to the foetus and new-born child. Also, artificial means of inducing the same state of resistance exist, which avoid the need for actually passing through the mill of the experience of the disease.

So a preliminary classification of the major divisions of resistance mechanisms is the following:

Non-specific Immunity
Specific Acquired Immunity
Active: Natural and artificial.
Passive: Natural and artificial.

The commonly-used term *innate immunity* includes *non-specific* resistance mechanisms as well as some degree of passively acquired specific immunity. The latter is an important contribution in the form of antibodies derived from the mother. Theoretically, if this were withheld, as in the case of a calf or piglet reared without colostrum, the new-born animal could start life with only the non-specific mechanisms.

DETERMINANTS OF NON-SPECIFIC IMMUNITY

In spite of its obvious importance to man in his day-to-day existence little is known about many of the fundamental processes of innate or non-specific immunity. Certainly, it can vary from a complete insusceptibility to a disease agent to no resistance, in which case invasion by the microbe results in rapid death.

GENETIC INFLUENCES

Non-specific resistance is sometimes referred to as *constitutional* or *genetic* immunity since it is regarded as something which is laid down in one's heredity. As would be expected from such a genetic endowment, it is sometimes possible to discern a more or less common behaviour in a given microbe throughout a single species. The rat as a species is strikingly resistant to diphtheria, whereas man and the guinea-pig are susceptible. Presumably all rats derive such innate resistance to diphtheria by a genetic mechanism. Differences in resistance depending upon a genetic mechanism can be observed also within a species. A classical example is the greater resistance to anthrax of Algerian sheep as compared with European sheep. Inasmuch as such differences are genetically controlled it should be possible to vary the degree of resistance experimentally by selective breeding. This has been accomplished for several types of infection and in several animal species. Lurie succeeded in breeding two strains of rabbits, one of higher and one of lower resistance than the average for this species in respect of tuberculous infection.

Recent evidence has suggested one way in which such a genetic difference is manifested. The peritoneal macrophages derived from the resistant rabbit strain have been shown to possess greater numbers of cytoplasmic lysosomes and increased activity of certain hydrolytic enzymes such as acid phosphatase, which are considered to be responsible for the intracellular destruction of bacteria. Chapter Eight includes descriptions of hereditary deficiencies of immunity mediated through defective polymorphonuclear leucocytes (granulomatous disease of childhood and Chediak-Higashi syndrome).

Racial Differences in Immunity in Man

The racial differences in susceptibility to various diseases are difficult to analyse, since environment may affect immunity in many ways. The habits or living conditions of a community may contribute to a wide spread of an infection at an early age, so that all adults of the group appear resistant (an example of acquired immunity). We must beware, therefore, of attributing such differences to genetic immunity. This acquired immunity sometimes leads to strikingly different manifestations of disease in the natives as opposed to the visitors or foreigners. Thus during the 1939–45 war it was tragically evident that severe cases of poliomyelitis could occur in epidemic form among the young adult naval and army recruits who visited the island of Malta, in spite of an almost complete lack of such cases among the native populace. The evidence that we have does not, however, support the idea of a genetically-determined difference in natural immunity between the Maltese and the Anglo-Saxon races. Rather, it is thought that owing to the free dispersion of virus among the Maltese population, probably by the alimentary route, infection and the state of immunity are acquired by a majority of the population at a very early age. Owing to a different social structure, and in particular the use of efficient water sanitary methods for disposal of faeces, a similar early acquisition of immunity does not occur to the same extent in the inhabitants of Great Britain.

In man, segregative and inbreeding experiments cannot be used, such as were used by Lurie in rabbits, but the role of genetic factors in susceptibility to tuberculosis can be illustrated from the study of homozygotic and heterozygotic twins. If one homozygotic twin has clinical tuberculosis, the other twin has three chances in four of being affected, whereas, if one heterozygotic twin has the disease, the other has only one chance in three of developing clinical tuberculosis.

The incidence and the type of this disease are different in the American Indian, the negro and the white races, the first two being apparently far more susceptible. But these differences are very difficult to evaluate because of the divergence in living conditions. In white races tuberculosis in the first infection is most often self-limited, being confined to the primary focus (usually at the periphery of the lungs) and to the group of lymph nodes which drain it. By contrast many studies have shown that negroes are much more likely to develop disseminated disease. Also, it is reported that negroes can develop successive primary-type infections. The secondary or reinfection type of disease, with its tendency to fibrosis, is regarded as depending upon some degree of immune response. According to this view, the white races owe their relative resistance to a process of natural selection consequent upon widespread infection with this organism over several thousands of years. The American negro with his higher infection rate and mortality is regarded as still in an early phase of this process. However, it must be admitted that all studies of racial groups are difficult to keep free from the prejudices arising from social and economic factors.

Recently, it has been described how a genetic factor determining a high degree of resistance to malaria is linked with the known hereditary trait of sickling. The sickle cell is an abnormal erythrocyte which rapidly assumes a sickle or spindle shape when the cells are maintained *in vitro* in the absence of oxygen. This is due to the presence of a variety of haemoglobin, differing from the normal by a single amino acid substitution in the polypeptide chain, which readily crystallizes in the reduced state. The sickle cells have a decreased life-span in the circulation, and anaemia may occur on this account. However, such cells are less readily parasitized by the *Plasmodia* of malaria. Apparently normal haemoglobin is an essential source of nutriment for the parasite, which is less able to utilize the alternative in the sickle cells.

DIFFERENCES DUE TO AGE

The susceptibility of animals to infectious agents is modified greatly by age, often for reasons which are ill understood. The medical student is taught by long tradition to observe the age as an important item of history-taking and this, as a piece of information, in no way loses its value in the infective diseases. Some microbes are able to colonize their hosts at all ages, others can do so only at specific periods in the life of the host. As a general rule, most infective diseases are more severe at the extremes of life than in adolescence or during adult life.

Several infections result in severe damage when they occur during foetal life. German measles virus (rubella) may produce permanent defects, such as cataract, deafness and heart lesions, when occurring in the foetus during the first three months of pregnancy (see Table 2.1). This is possibly because the interferon mechanism (see pp. 54–56) is not effective at this age. The protozoon *Toxoplasma gondii*, which can be acquired at any age, has a much higher chance of causing severe disease if it infects during foetal life. Experimentally it is often found that a given virus or other disease agent can be made to cause infection only in very young animals, and for this reason, chick embryos or new-born mice are frequently chosen for the isolation of human virus agents. The relative immunological unresponsiveness of the embryo may help to explain this (see Chapter Three).

Of practical importance is the realization that the young animal possesses much less reserve of dietary materials than does the adult. Below, the important experiments of Dubos on the relationship between starvation and infection will be discussed. Protein deficiency was shown by Dubos to lead to greatly increased susceptibility to bacterial infection in young mice. In adults, with their greater protein reserves, such a result was far more difficult to demonstrate.

The ability to localize infection is noticeably greater in the adult than in the child. Before the advent of sulphonamide drugs and penicillin, infections in the infant (below 6 years) with *Streptococcus pyogenes* often resulted in a long-continued, low-grade process of infection, with frequent suppurative complications, erysipelas or spreading cellulitis, and widespread dissemination of organisms to produce metastatic lesions such as osteomyelitis. Later in life, the pattern of disease changes and in the case of a 10-year-old child a sharp throat infection, lasting for about a week, would be typical, with the chance of getting such late sequelae as rheumatic fever or nephritis. Similarly, disseminated tuberculosis is also commoner in the young. However, in such instances the effects of specific immunization acquired following a contact in early life are difficult to evaluate. The interplay of subsequent immunity and delayed-type hypersensitivity (see Chapter Twelve) is thought to account for many aspects of the altered pattern of disease in later life.

TABLE 2.1

Incidence of congenital abnormalities due to rubella in relation to age of foetus

Month	No. of cases of congenital abnormality	Incidence per pregnancy (%)
1	89	17·9
2	149	30·6
3	105	21·3
4	44	8·3
5	7	<1
6	8	<1
7	7	<1
8	3	<1
9	1	<1

Data taken from Swan C. (1949) *J. Obstet. Gynaec. Brit. Emp.* **56**, 341, 591.

However, numerous physiological and environmental factors may also play a part. Increasing age does not necessarily mean an increase in resistance, even in early life. Thus, resistance to tuberculosis is high in the age group 5 to 15 years (the so-called 'golden years') and is low both before and immediately after this period.

In young animals the visible inflammatory response to various irritants and toxic stimuli is less developed than in the adult. A striking example of this is the common failure of young children to respond to a small dose of diphtheria toxin injected into the skin, as in the Schick test. This lack of response is not attributable to antibody.

Hormonal influences can sometimes explain the incidence of specific infections at certain characteristic periods of life. In the very young, vaginal as opposed to other types of infection with gonococci becomes relatively common. Here, due to low level of oestrogen, glycogen is lacking from the epithelial cells of the vagina, and the pH, which is normally acid due to the fermentative production of lactic acid by the lacto-bacilli, rises. Presumably hormonal effects are responsible for the severe infections often manifest during pregnancy. This applies to several virus infections, e.g. mumps, which is usually a mild infection, but often runs a severe course if contracted during pregnancy, when mumps mastitis is a frequent complication.

In the elderly, too, anatomical defects are often responsible for increased susceptibility. The impairment of the outflow of urine by an enlarged prostate will lead to just those local conditions which favour development of urinary infections (pyelitis and cystitis) at any age.

HORMONAL INFLUENCES

Already, during the discussion of the variation of resistance at different age periods, the influence of hormones has been noted. Since, in general, hormones appear to play an increasing role in the control of homeostatic mechanisms as the biological organization of the individual becomes increasingly complex during the evolutionary process, it would be expected that deprivation of many hormones would affect adversely the ability to withstand harmful infective and other agents.

The clinical data bearing on these issues is not as clear as it might be, but the following observations seem valid and require explanation:

(i) In diabetes mellitus there is an increased incidence of surface infections such as boils and carbuncles, of tuberculosis and of infections of the urinary tract.

(ii) Hypothyroidism tends to be associated with a somewhat diminished resistance to infection.

(iii) Both hypoadrenal (Addison's disease) and hyperadrenal states (Cushing's disease) are associated with increased susceptibility to infection.

Attempts to explain these findings are, in general, incomplete. The possible basis for the susceptibility of the tissues during the altered metabolism of diabetes is dealt with below (Dubos's hypothesis). With regard to (iii), the isolated glucocorticoid principles of the adrenal gland have shown striking ability to alter the course of many infections. During treatment with these drugs, cases of human tuberculosis have shown dramatic deterioration with extension of pulmonary lesions and vast increase in the numbers of bacteria in the tissues and expelled with the sputum. Also clinical observation has shown that the long-term administration of cortisone in a number of unrelated diseases, e.g. rheumatoid arthritis and Hodgkin's disease, has been followed by the occurrence of active tuberculosis. It is commonly believed and supported by post-mortem findings that the healing of the primary lesion in tuberculosis is associated with the continued residence within the affected tissue of *Mycobacterium tuberculosis* in an attenuated state of very slow multiplication. The administration of cortisone disturbs this *in vivo* equilibrium between resistance and bacillary multiplication, and the organisms again proliferate.

A similar result can be provoked in experimental animals. An apparently healthy strain of rats treated with cortisone will develop fatal infections with *Corynebacterium pseudotuberculosis*, an organism which resides latent in the tissues of 'healthy' rats.

Experimental attempts to explain the effect of cortico-steroids on resistance have shown several possible mechanisms at work:

(i) *Anti-inflammatory Effects*

It is clear that glucocorticoids (usually in large doses) reduce the inflammatory response by a mechanism which raises the threshold at which a damaging agent causes increased permeability of the small vessels, thereby reducing the exudation of fluid and phagocytic cells. A presumably related effect is the inhibition of granuloma formation.

(ii) *Anti-phagocytic Effects*

The uptake of some organisms, e.g. *Strep. pneumoniae*, from the blood into the cells of the reticulo-endothelial system is strikingly diminished under the effect of cortisone. Often there has been no demonstrable effect on the uptake of inert particles or other kinds of organisms, but it is shown that the rate at which the phagocytes can dispose of such ingested particles (bacteria and erythrocytes) is decreased. Cortisone may act within the cell by stabilizing unduly the lysosome membrane, so impeding the release of various hydrolytic enzymes from the lysosomes into the digestive vacuole.

(iii) *Antagonisms of Toxins*

Besides their effects on the physiological consequences of an infection, glucocorticoids protect against certain specific pharmacological effects of microbes. Thus the lethal effect of typhoid vaccine (due to the endotoxin in the large numbers of bacterial bodies) in animals can be overcome by simultaneous administration of glucocorticoids. It is possible that the final common pathway for the destructive action of a variety of toxins as widely different as endotoxins, streptolysins, silica and beryllium lies in the rupture of lysosomes with the consequent intracellular release of hydrolytic enzymes. This process is impeded by the stabilizing effect of glucocorticoids on the lysosomal membrane. The same endotoxins are powerful pyrogens in man and cortisone will also interfere with this effect. However, cortisone enhances the general Shwartzman reaction to endotoxin and this aspect of its activity is discussed further in Chapter Eleven.

(iv) *Effect on Antibody Production and the Cellular Immune Response* (see also Chapter Four)

The dose range of glucocorticosteroids producing significant effects on metabolism differs strikingly between animal species. Species such as rat, mouse and rabbit are characteristically sensitive to low doses of glucocorticoids whereas the guinea-pig, monkey and man are relatively insusceptible. It has been found that cortisone administration will markedly diminish the antibody response to a variety of antigens in the rat and the rabbit but has much less effect in guinea-pigs and primates. By contrast cortisone can diminish the manifestations of delayed type hypersensitivity (as seen in a skin test) over a wide range of species. This aspect is discussed further in Chapter Twelve.

It is apparent that the effect of a glucocorticoid drug on a particular infection may be hardly predictable owing to the complexity of the resulting effects. Moreover, resistance which may follow small doses may give way to susceptibility at larger doses. As shown in Fig. 2.1, adrenalectomy markedly increases the susceptibility of mice to pneumococcal infection (as demonstrated by the lower LD_{50} or number of organisms required to kill half the experimental group of animals), whereas cortisone in small doses restores resistance and in large doses again results in decreased resistance.

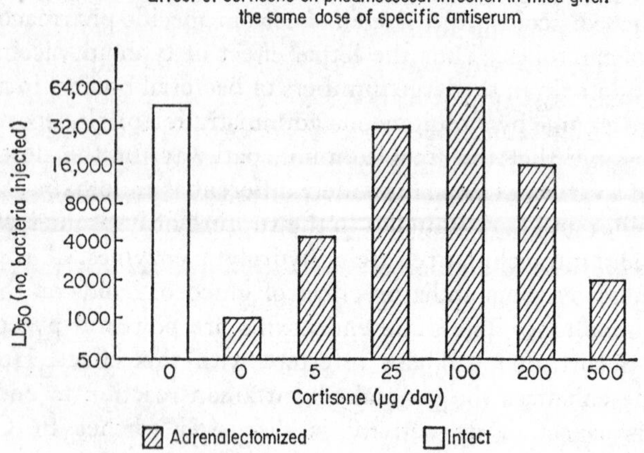

FIG. 2.1. Mice were given a dose of antibody sufficient to protect half of the *normal* mice against injection of 50,000 virulent organisms (LD_{50} = 50,000). When the LD_{50} for adrenalectomized mice was determined far fewer organisms were required. Treatment with moderate doses of cortisone partially restored the resistance of adrenalectomized mice, but large doses rendered them more susceptible again. [From Kass E. H. (1960) *Ann. N.Y. Acad. Sci.* **88,** [108.]

CELLULAR VERSUS HUMORAL IMMUNITY

The defences of the tissues are conveniently considered at two levels of activity: chemical or humoral agents and cellular mechanisms. It is not possible in all instances to separate the activity of the cells from that of the chemical components of tissues, for often the two are organized to act in concert. Frequently the action of a chemical factor appears to be to facilitate the defensive role of cells.

The measurement of the activity of the different defence mechanisms and evaluation of their relative importance in resistance to infection presents many difficulties, and these have been responsible for a long neglect of the subject of non-specific resistance mechanisms. In the past, prodigal amounts of verbal energy have been dissipated by controversies directed towards proving the importance of a humoral as opposed to a cellular mechanism, or *vice versa.* The ease with which specific antibody globulin can be measured and manipulated outside the bo[illegible] resulted in its receiving a somewhat disproportionate a[illegible]nt of attention. The congenital disease hypo-γ-globulinaemia can be regarded as an experiment of nature in which young human subjects are virtually deprived of circulating antibodies. We find in consequence that they become a prey to a wide variety of diseases due to common bacterial species such as staphylococci, streptococci and pneumococci. Undoubtedly in these instances specific antibody is of high importance in resistance. However, the resistance of these patients to tuberculosis and a wide variety of virus infections appears to be unimpaired. It is apparent that in many respects the body can dispense with the services of antibody. Also it would seem that the specific biosynthesis of antibody is too slow and ponderous a mechanism for many of the purposes of defence. Indeed, the recent investigations of Miles and his colleagues have stressed the critical importance of the rapidly occurring events at the local site of infection in the first hour, which occur with such speed as to defy any explanation either in terms of classical local inflammation or of a *de novo* specific antibody response.

HUMORAL MECHANISMS OF NON-SPECIFIC IMMUNITY

AT THE SURFACE OF THE BODY

The skin and mucous membranes, in addition to acting as physical barriers to penetration by would-be parasites, are provided with active mechanisms for killing bacteria and other organisms. This can be shown by the simple experiment of comparing the survival of an organism like *Salmonella typhi* on the skin surface and on a glass plate. A culture of such organisms smeared over the surface of the skin, and subcultured at intervals of a few minutes, will decrease to small numbers within 15–20 minutes, whereas that on the glass plate will continue to yield large numbers of viable bacteria. It is recorded that if this experiment is repeated on the skin of a human corpse the difference between survival on the glass and skin surface is much less. Lactic acid in the sweat and fatty acids in the sebaceous secretions are possibly responsible for this bactericidal activity.

A striking difference exists between the resistance of the skin to dermatophyte fungi (ringworm) before and after puberty. Scalp ringworm due to, say, *Microsporon audouini* may prove quite intractable to all forms of treatment throughout childhood, only to resolve spontaneously at puberty. A hypothesis to account for this change is that the post-pubertal sebaceous secretion contains higher amounts of saturated fatty acids from C_8 (caprylic acid) to C_{11} (undecylic acid) which are demonstrably fungicidal *in vitro*.

The sebum from the sebaceous glands, continuously replenished at the rate of 1–2 g daily, provides a continuous bactericidal surface layer. In the internal auditory meatus the sebum is modified to form *wax* (or cerumen) and over the glans penis to form *smegma*. Besides the saturated acids which are antagonistic to *M. audouini*, the sebum contains unsaturated fatty acids like *oleic acid* which are bactericidal.

The self-sterilizing power of the skin depends on the presence of these fatty acids. This mechanism will be impaired by undue moisture of the skin. The charwoman's sodden skin is a likely site for infection by yeasts and bacteria in the form of recurrent paronychia. A practical point to remember is that skin dressings which aim to preserve these mechanisms should be non-absorbent and permeable so as to allow evaporation from the skin surface.

The ability of the secretions of the sebaceous gland to inhibit and kill the fungi possibly also explains why the dermatophyte fungi, such as *Trichophyton* and *Epidermophyton* in cases of tinea pedis or 'athlete's foot', attack the interspaces between the toes, the plantar surfaces of the toes, the soles and sides of the feet, for these are areas devoid of hair follicles and sebaceous glands.

Similarly the mucus of the respiratory and genital mucosa and of the conjunctiva possesses bactericidal (see an example in lysozyme below) and viricidal properties. In 1942 Hirst found that influenza virus caused agglutination of chicken red blood cells. Investigation of this phenomenon revealed that the virus which adsorbed to the red cell surface could later spontaneously free itself. Excised lung tissue similarly shows adsorption of the virus and the mechanism is regarded as a basic step in virus invasion of susceptible tissues. The reaction is interpreted as due to a viral enzyme (neuraminidase) which unites with its substrate (an oligosaccharide) on the cell surface. Neuraminidase attacks the linkage between the terminal group of the oligosaccharide (N-acetyl muramic acid) and deeper components of the cell surface. It can be shown that a variety of mucoproteins from serum, urine and nasal mucus are potent inhibitors of haemagglutination by influenza virus. These apparently act as substrate for the virus enzyme and divert it from attaching to the receptors on susceptible cells.

The fluid of the respiratory mucosa is continuously in motion, being swept outwards by the cilia of the underlying cells. These devices operating with anatomical baffles like the nasal turbinates, effectively prevent all but a small percentage of dust particles in the inspired air from reaching the lung alveoli.

The gastro-intestinal tract provides, in the stomach, a medium of such high acidity that it is not surprising to find its contents are usually sterile. Few organisms, also, can be recovered from the duodenum and small intestine. This is illustrated by the observation that persons with even temporary achlorhydria are highly susceptible to intestinal pathogens ingested by the mouth, especially *Vibrio cholerae*. The large intestine is loaded with a profusion of various bacteriological types. Massive invasion of this stretch of its surface is, however, apparently uncommon for reasons ill understood, but may occur with disastrous consequences following X-irradiation and antibiotic therapy. The lowered resistance following irradiation is usually attributed to an effect on host cells and is discussed below (p. 80). The effect of antibiotics is usually attributed to disturbance of the normal flora of bacteria and yeasts. Thus in clinical practice staphylococcal enterocolitis or infection with the yeast *Monilia albicans* not uncommonly arises during long-term treatment with broad spectrum antibiotics. Germ-free animals show a similar increase in susceptibility to certain infectious agents. Bacillary dysentery cannot be produced in ordinary guinea-pigs even with large doses of virulent organisms; yet the same micro-organism will produce fatal enteritis in germ-free animals. Presumably many such effects result from interference by the established flora with a newcomer which would be competing for a limited supply of nutrient. An alternative explanation would involve production by the normal flora of antibiotics. Many bacteria produce bactericidal substances active upon other bacteria. These may be organized self-reproducing particles such as bacteriophage or non-reproducing agents, e.g. bacteriocines such as *colicines* which are specific inhibitory agents produced by one strain of *Escherichia coli* and active against another strain.

WITHIN THE TISSUES

The existence in the tissues of highly effective mechanisms of resistance to bacteria and fungi is manifestly obvious in the everyday experience that most wounds at the body's surface fail to lead to obvious infection. It is quite apparent that in order to account for this we must postulate the existence in normal tissues of a range of pre-existing defence mechanisms. We think that we can characterize some of these and the activities of a few can be expressed in simple chemical terms. However, before these are described it is necessary at the outset to recognize that the tissues of a 'normal' mammalian body are usually far from being completely devoid of micro-organisms or sterile. Most human beings, and indeed possibly all living things, carry within themselves a variety of microbial agents which are potentially pathogenic for them. Under most conditions, these pathogens do not manifest their presence by either symptoms or lesions and only when something occurs to upset the equilibrium of the host–parasite relationship does infection develop into *disease*. This subject, the analysis of which cannot be pursued in this context, is referred to as *latency* or subclinical infection. Suffice it now to add that latency can be demonstrated to occur with microbial agents of all classes—bacteria, viruses, rickettsiae, protozoa and fungi; to stress that the mechanisms of resistance may not always achieve a completely sterile environment in the tissues; and to accept that sometimes the best interests of the body appear to be served instead by a state of balanced symbiosis or parasitism, in which the continued presence of the organisms at the aurface of the body or even within the cells and tissues is more or less permanently tolerated.

Resistance Mechanisms of the Blood

Vast researches have been undertaken in the past to elucidate the ability of the *blood* to suppress putrefaction. The basis for these bactericidal activities resides in many different mechanisms, which act with varying success on different organisms. These are partly humoral and partly cellular. The latter are referred to on p. 59.

Later on, we shall discuss the role of specific antibodies, which are not generally thought to occur prior to the exposure of the body to stimulation by specific antigens. However, the blood of any normal animal will contain substances which closely resemble antibodies in their action on micro-organisms. These 'normal' antibodies, which occur in serum from early life, at first sight seem to have arisen without any prior antigenic stimulus.

Natural or Normal Antibody

We have to admit that, in many instances, these so-called 'normal antibodies' may have been brought into existence as a result of a true immune response to an unrecognized infection with a specific microbe. Indeed, much evidence has been assembled which plausibly explains the presence of diphtheria antitoxin, for example, in the blood of persons who have never suffered from clinical diphtheria, on the basis of unrecognized contact with *Corynebacterium diphtheriae*.

Thus, in a study of boys at the Royal Naval School, Greenwich, in 1923, it was noted that epidemics of diphtheria at the school were followed by a change from a Schick positive to a Schick negative state among many of those who had been casual contacts of the infection, but had not acquired the disease. The influence of contact was shown by the fact that the rate of Schick conversion among a group of day-boys was much slower than among the boarders.

Such *normal antibodies* are absent at birth except in so far as they have been transmitted from the mother and generally increase throughout the early years of life. This too suggests that their occurrence depends on or is increased by experience. But, can we really believe that in a few years of their early life animals can possibly come into contact with so wide a range of exotic microbes as *Salmonella paratyphi A*, *B* and *C*, *Vibrio cholerae*, *Salmonella enteriditis*? In fact we need not postulate such multiple past infections by specific organisms. The antigenic components of dead bacterial cells may sometimes pass from the intestines into the animal's tissues and act to stimulate antibody formation. Many bacteria in the intestinal tract contain antigens in common with apparently unrelated organisms. Thus, the sera of normal adult rabbits regularly contain agglutinins for *Shigella shigae*, the cause of human shiga dysentery. However, the *Shig. shigae* agglutinins are found to be identical with those of a normal inhabitant of the rabbit's intestines, an enterococcus, which has a chemically similar antigen in its constitution. The idea that such antibodies arise by heterologous rather than homologous stimulation is supported by the fact that their specificity is less than would be expected of antibodies resulting from an immune response. Thus although exposure of the serum to the organisms may absorb out these normal antibodies, the number of organisms required to do this is much greater than would be expected from the small amount of antibody present and, moreover, such absorption may remove 'normal antibodies' for other bacteria. This suggests a rather poor 'fit' between a 'normal antibody' and the antigen in question.

The bactericidal activity of the natural antibodies of the blood on bacteria varies according to the organism. The most susceptible are the Gram-negative species. Sometimes visible lysis of the micro-organisms occurs as well as killing. For this activity, besides the natural antibody (heat stable), another serum component, the heat labile *complement*, is necessary (for a further discussion of the origin of normal antibody and an explanation of the nature of complement the reader is referred to Chapter Five).

Properdin

After the 'natural antibodies' come a heterogeneous group of agents which under certain circumstances can be invoked in killing bacteria or viruses. An important role in protecting man against natural infection has been claimed for a normal serum protein of high molecular weight named properdin (*perdere*; L. to destroy). In the presence of complement and Mg ions, properdin will kill a number of Gram-negative bacteria as well as Gram-positive organisms such as *Bacillus subtilis* or *Streptococcus faecalis*, and will inactivate certain viruses. The reasons for regarding properdin as distinct from normal antibody are perhaps over-subtle. The matter is discussed further on p. 201.

HUMORAL MECHANISMS AVAILABLE WITHIN NORMAL TISSUES

Natural Inhibitors of Enzymes

Normal tissue fluids contain a variety of enzyme inhibitors. Although these are probably mainly concerned with regulation of the action of enzymes produced by the body's own tissues a number of them have been shown to inhibit bacterial enzymes also. For example, there is a potent inhibitor of hyaluronidase; an inhibitor of trypsin-like enzymes which also inhibits the proteolytic enzymes produced by a variety of Gram-positive spore-forming bacilli such as *B. subtilis* (but not the proteolytic enzymes of pathogenic clostridia); a lipoprotein inhibitor of streptolysin S. It may be because of the existence of such natural inhibitors that it has proved difficult to correlate the virulence of microorganisms with their production of most of the recognized exotoxins.

The Role of Common Intermediary Metabolites

Besides the antibodies present in blood and other body fluids, the normal tissues may derive immunity from simple metabolites or certain special antibacterial mechanisms.

The environment of the microbe in the tissues immediately after implantation is the physiologist's 'milieu intérieur'. But the physiological environment is rapidly changed by the phenomenon of inflammation, and becomes vastly different from that of the normal tissue. Inflammation is attended by an influx of cells, mainly polymorphs, with intense glycolytic activity, resulting in conversion of glucose to lactic acid and a marked drop in the pH. The acidity of the inflammatory zone in normal tissue is maintained mainly by lactic acid which can, at the concentrations attained (250 μg per 100 ml), kill many bacteria *in vitro*. The effectiveness of this mechanism is possibly shown by the clinical observation that the diabetic patient possesses a much increased tendency to necrotic infections particularly with staphylococci and tubercle bacilli. In diabetes the lowered pH of the inflammatory zone is maintained rather by α-ketoglutaric and β-hydroxybutyric acids than by lactic acid and Dubos has demonstrated *in vitro* that these are much inferior to lactic acid in bactericidal effect. Also the gaseous environment may have a direct effect on the fate of micro-organisms in tissues. Thus, the anaerobic spore-bearing bacilli (genus *Clostridia*) are unable to parasitize normal tissue, so that no disease follows the intravenous injection of numerous spores of these organisms in the healthy animal. In fact the spores of *Cl. tetani* or *Cl. welchii* can persist for years in the tissues without causing any disease symptoms or even multiplying. However, if a local tissue area becomes devitalized by injury so that the oxygen tension within it falls, or this effect is produced more directly by injection of the vasoconstrictor adrenaline, a local proliferation of these organisms is permitted and infection becomes established.

The tubercle bacillus provides a converse example. For growth *in vitro* this organism requires a liberal supply of oxygen, which may explain why secondary tuberculosis commonly selects the lung apices. These areas of the lungs receive a relatively poor supply of blood from the right heart, and hence less oxygen is withdrawn from the alveoli. The right apex is particularly prone to this effect since the right pulmonary artery is longer and has a more tortuous course than the left. An increase in pulmonary arterial pressure might make the apices less vulnerable and may explain why apical tuberculosis is less common in subjects with mitral stenosis, and more common in cases of pulmonary stenosis. Further, it can be seen why rest in complete recumbency is a logical method of treatment.

Specific Tissue Resistance Factors

Many tissue extracts can inactivate bacteria and even viruses and this activity has been attributed to their content of proteolytic enzymes. Nevertheless, it has been shown that bacteria can persist alive in high concentrations of many proteolytic enzymes *in vitro*. In fact, the only enzyme with undisputed bactericidal activity is *lysozyme*, first characterized by Fleming in 1922. Lysozyme is a basic protein which functions as a mucolytic enzyme, splitting the bond between N-acetyl glucosamine and N-acetyl muramic acid in the mucopeptide complexes of the bacterial cell wall. By this chemical action, in a few species actual lysis, a bursting of the walls with release of content, results (see Plate 2.1, facing p. 148); in addition, many more bacterial species exist which are killed by the enzyme, although not lysed. Lysozyme occurs in many types of animal tissues and body fluids. It would seem of particular significance that this enzyme is present in high concentration in the granules of polymorphs and in pulmonary macrophages, and can be readily released from these cells by injury. Also since lysozyme occurs in the conjunctival secretion, nasal and intestinal mucus, as well as the saliva, it presumably is of great use in preventing the wholesale multiplication of the saprophytic bacteria of the body surface. Furthermore lysozyme may cooperate with γA immunoglobulins (see Chapter Four) to cause lysis of otherwise resistant bacteria.

This discussion of specific tissue factors in resistance must perforce restrict itself to but a few examples of the numerous chemicals which have been isolated. Among such, it has been shown that several types of animal tissues can yield basic peptides which can inhibit the growth *in vitro* of many bacterial species. One, of high lysine content, was originally discovered by its activity against anthrax bacilli, but it may also kill *Staphylococcus aureus* and β-*haemolytic streptococci* as well as certain viruses. Another compound was unearthed by a follow-up of the observation that the development of miliary spread of tuberculosis in the guinea-pig is characterized by the development of the characteristic millet-like lesions in large numbers in almost all organs *with the singular exception* of the kidney. This phenomenon led to exploration of the activity of extracts of kidney tissue prepared with acid-ethanol. A crystalline tetra-amine (spermine) was later isolated from beef kidney which in low concentration completely inhibited the growth of mammalian mycobacteria *in vitro*. Further studies *in vitro* revealed that spermine exerts its effect on tubercle bacilli only in the presence of serum or extracts of tissues. The serum constituent was shown to be an α-globulin which acted as an amine oxidase specific for spermine (and a related compound spermidine). At present the role of the spermine-spermine oxidase system in the host resistance to tubercle bacilli is difficult to assess. In any given tissue many factors may determine the activity of this system—amount of spermine, presence of the enzyme, availability of substrate for enzyme and so on.

NATURAL DEFENCES AGAINST VIRUS INFECTIONS

So far this discussion has not paid attention to mechanisms specifically directed to resistance against viruses. Virus-neutralizing properties can be found in human plasma and interestingly enough in the nasal secretions. The mechanism of the latter is particularly relevant to viruses of the influenza type (myxoviruses) which appear to possess a special mechanism of attachment to, and specific pathogenicity for, cells of the ciliated epithelium of nasal cavity and bronchial epithelium. In 1942, Hirst found that influenza virus causes agglutination of chicken red blood cells. The virus is first adsorbed to the cells for a time and then, quite spontaneously, releases itself. The freed virus is infective but the red cell is modified so that it no longer agglutinates with virus. The same attachment and release can be obtained in isolated preparations of lungs by allowing contact of the virus suspensions with the bronchial lining cells. The mechanism of attachment is due to the combination of an enzyme (in this case a mucolytic enzyme: neuraminidase) with its substrate (a mucopolysaccharide receptor on the surface of red cells or bronchial epithelial cells which contains neuraminic acid). Attachment is only the start of the process of infection since virus particles can be altered by agencies such as ultra-violet radiation so that they can still agglutinate red cells but lack the ability to cause infection. Haemagglutination is inhibited by a component of normal serum (shown to be a mucoprotein) and by mucoproteins in mucus, urine, etc. These act by diverting the activity of the virus from susceptible cells to themselves as alternative substrate.

However, the exact conditions under which virus breaks through these normal inhibitory mechanisms is far from clear.

Interferon

A quite distinct and very important mechanism of resistance in virus infections is the production of *interferon*, first described in 1957. For many years it had been known, from experimental virus infections, that an animal or tissue infected with one virus was

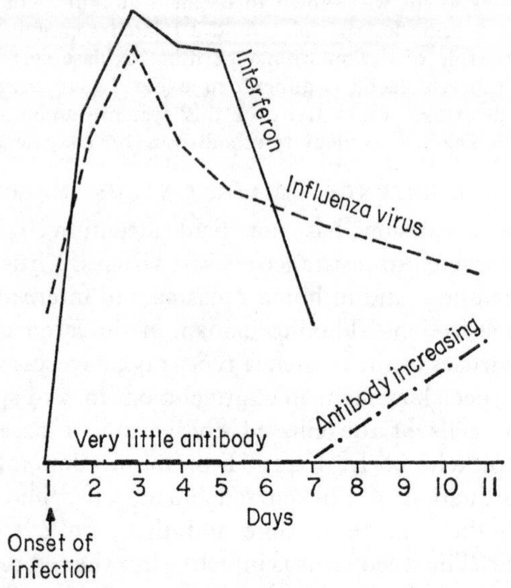

FIG. 2.2. The pattern of production of interferon and antibody in response to influenza virus infection in the lungs of mice. [From Isaacs (1961) *New Scientist* **11**, 81.]

liable to resist infection with a second (even quite unrelated) virus, and the phenomenon was known as viral interference. A remarkable aspect of this phenomenon is that the interfering virus need not be alive but can still produce its effect even when rendered non-infective by mild heat or by irradiation with ultra-violet light. Isaacs and Lindenmann, working with chick embryos which had been exposed to large amounts of inactivated influenza virus, found that an agent, named by them *interferon*, was released after a few hours into the fluids of the embryos; this agent had the property, when applied to pieces of fresh chorio-allantoic membrane, of preventing the growth of live virus applied subsequently. The evidence indicates that interferon is a protein which can be produced by many types of cell when these are stimulated by various kinds of inactivated viruses. It is a normal product of the cell, rather than of the virus which stimulates it, and it is remarkably stable to acid—a property which enables it to be separated from live virus when the two are present together. During the course of an infection with a live virus, such as influenza, a certain amount of inactive virus is made and some interferon is produced quite early on; when cells treated with interferon are exposed to live virus the latter not only does not grow but causes more interferon to be released; and consequently, if the animal or chick embryo survives long enough, the infection becomes self-limiting since the interferon brings its progress to a halt. There is strong evidence that such a mechanism operates during experimental infections in whole animals, and that interferon rather than specific antibody is responsible for recovery from (as opposed to prevention of) a virus infection. For example, in the case of pulmonary infection of mice with influenza virus the amount of virus in the lungs begins to decline at the time when the interferon concentration reaches its peak, and antibody only becomes detectable later (see Fig. 2.2). Furthermore, animals which have been irradiated with X-rays so as temporarily to block antibody formation can still recover from virus infections in the normal way.

The discovery of interferon has shed new light on the mode of action of a variety of agents which have apparently nonspecific effects on virus multiplication. It appears that there are two general ways in which an interferon response can be elicited. One, as described above, is a consequence of the entry of virus into cells; the molecular weight of the interferon which results is between 20,000 and 30,000; and studies with metabolic inhibitors, such as actinomycin and puromycin, have shown that these prevent such interferon production. This suggests that the interferon is synthesized *de novo* in response to the virus. The other response occurs in whole animals when these are treated with agents so widely different as bacterial endotoxin (q.v.), phytohaemagglutinin (q.v.), *Brucella abortus* or cyclohexamide, a compound which itself inhibits protein synthesis. In this second kind of response the interferon is released more rapidly than that in response to viral infection and apparently does not require to be formed *de novo*. Interferon produced in this way is generally also distinguishable by having a larger molecular weight (about 90,000). No major differences have been found between the effects of interferon elicited in either way so far as concerns its capacity to inhibit virus replication.

As regards the mode of action of interferon, most studies have been made with that elicited by viruses themselves. Interferon produced in response to one virus cannot be distinguished from that produced in response to another, and the same interferon protects against many different viruses. Although it was earlier thought that interferon produced in one species of animal was also active in other species, more recent work with highly purified interferon has indicated that there is a marked species specificity, at least between man, mouse and chick. The way in which it acts to inhibit virus multiplication is still obscure, but some of the ideas about this mentioned in earlier editions of this book have had to be changed. Purified interferon has little detectable effect upon the metabolism of uninfected cells. Furthermore it has no antiviral activity in cells treated with actinomycin, so as to prevent the action of DNA-primed RNA polymerase and consequently to inhibit the synthesis of new messenger RNA and of any novel cell protein. This suggests that interferon acts indirectly by stimulating the formation of some new (presumably protein) material. Certain RNA viruses, such as encephalomyocarditis virus, can multiply quite well in cells treated with actinomycin since the viral RNA can itself initiate synthesis of the proteins required for its own replication. By studying systems of this kind it has been possible to obtain evidence that the presumed active product of interferon interferes with the use of the cell's ribosomes for protein synthesis by the viral RNA, but not by ordinary messenger RNA. The way in which this is brought about, however, is at present unknown.

An interesting observation is that interferon does not prevent virus growth in the cells of chick embryos during the first third of embryonic life. If this is true also for mammalian embryos it may provide a clue to the mystery why rubella infections during pregnancy result in foetal damage only when they occur during the first three months of gestation.

CELLULAR MECHANISMS INVOLVED IN NATURAL RESISTANCE

The cellular defences are among the most plastic and adaptive of all mechanisms available to resist the invasion of the body by parasitic micro-organisms. For the purposes of this discussion we can regard them as organized on three levels: the local inflammatory response (the area of primary lodgement), the chain of lymph nodes (lymphatic lodgement), and the blood-stream lodgement.

It must not be assumed that infecting particles necessarily progress into the body by attacking these defences in order. Any wound at the body's surface must cut across both blood and lymph vessels, with both of which the superficial layers of the dermis are very liberally supplied. While the flow of blood from the cut blood vessels might prevent entry of microbes to these channels, which are also rapidly closed by contraction, the open lymphatics must provide an easy entrance for all kinds of infective particles. In striking contrast to the pressure in blood capillaries, the normal lymph pressure is nil. It can readily be shown that particulate dyes introduced into a fresh wound find their way rapidly into the draining lymphatics. Also, blood culture studies have shown that many simple manipulations like the passage of a urinary catheter or firm grinding together of the teeth cause showers of organisms to pass directly into the blood-stream.

Both blood and lymphatic streams are extremely well organized for defence against such infective particles. Thus, in the mouse, although a single virulent encapsulated pneumococcus may cause death on intraperitoneal injection, 100,000 of the same organisms introduced intravenously may fail to do so. In peripheral wounds, even if the bacteria are early able to escape beyond the front lines of defence they will promptly be dealt with centrally by mechanisms which are more organized and efficient than those at the periphery.

RELATION OF THE INFLAMMATORY RESPONSE TO DEFENCE

Even before microscopic observations revealed the intricate role of cells in this event, inflammation was regarded as a useful homeostatic mechanism, primarily involving vascular mechanisms. John Hunter in 1794 considered inflammation 'only as a disturbed state of the parts, which require a new but salutary mode of action to restore them to that state wherein a natural mode of action alone is necessary; for such a view of the subject therefore, inflammation is not considered a disease but as a salutary operation, consequent to some violence or disease'.

The direct observation of the blood vessels was achieved as early as 1757 by Albrecht von Haller who used the mesentery of a living frog which can be pinned out on a surface until it is so thin as to be observable by the high powers of a microscope. More recently the events of inflammation have been followed in mammalian tissue using a chamber which allows the blood vessels and surrounding tissue, enclosed between two parallel glass plates fixed in the rabbit's ear, to be directly observed under a microscope.

By the use of such a chamber we can readily determine the main components of the inflammatory response, as seen following an injury such as a small burn. (1) After their initial constriction, lasting for a few moments, the arterioles gradually relax so that the blood flow increases over the normal rate. (2) Later the flow slows down and leucocytes adhere to the walls of the blood vessels and emigrate through the walls into the tissues. (3) The emigrated leucocytes (microphages of Metchnikoff) can take up infective particles. They can accumulate to form large masses extra-vascularly and many die and disintegrate. Later, many mononuclear cells (the macrophages of Metchnikoff) accumulate and become the predominating cells during wound healing or in many forms of chronic inflammation. They show phagocytosis of the infective particles and also of dead and disintegrating polymorphs.

The cellular pattern of this response varies a good deal depending on the type of tissue affected and the kind of infecting organism. The variations may be thought of in terms of variations in the cell–parasite relationship. For instance, it would seem that the two bacteria *Staphylococcus pyogenes* and *Mycobacterium tuberculosis* both at first stimulate the exudation of microphages (polymorphonuclear leucocytes). But eventually they produce quite different inflammatory lesions. We can argue plausibly that *S. aureus* is able to multiply rapidly outside cells and to produce an exotoxin. This will continue the irritation of neighbouring blood vessels so that the polymorph emigration continues. Eventually the result is a typical pus-containing abscess. The story with *Mycobacterium tuberculosis* is different. The diapedesis of polymorphs comes to an end and an impressive accumulation of macrophages occurs, partly derived from the blood-stream and partly from a local multiplication of resting cells which were there in the tissue from the first. *Myco. tuberculosis* lacks a potent exotoxin, but having been taken up by phagocytes is able to grow slowly and inexorably within the cytoplasm of these cells. The microphages first take up such bacilli but are either rather readily killed by the latter or, in any case disintegrate, and are themselves ingested by the newly arrived macrophages, which continue to act as host to the bacilli.

We have, of course, to admit that this plausible reconstruction of the differing inflammatory responses to a predominantly extracellular microbe which produces an exotoxin and to a predominantly intracellular, relatively non-toxic microbe is too simple. Other factors are undoubtedly at work as we shall see later.

The Phagocytes

The ability to engulf and digest particles is an essential nutritional mechanism in the free-living as well as the parasitic protozoa. The amoeba presumably achieves two advantages in engulfing and digesting micro-organisms—it uses these as a source of food and it protects itself from a fatal infection. Eli Metchnikoff, a non-medical Russian biologist, first pointed out to the doctors of medicine that a specialized corps of phagocytic (eating) cells within the mesenchyme would be of great importance in providing a defence mechanism. He traced the essential continuity of the phagocytes during the evolutionary stages from protozoa, through the primitive metazoa and sponges to the mesenchymal phagocytic cell systems of higher animals. In the protospongia two types of cell could be distinguished: an outer layer of flagellated cells providing locomotion and an inner core of amoeba-like cells serving for digestion of food and for defence. The next step in the progress of differentiation is seen in the sponges which have a canalicular system lined by entodermal phagocytes and, as well, have phagocytes in the mesoderm. With the development of an entodermal layer which could secrete enzymes into the digestive canal, phagocytosis in these cells is no longer necessary. But the phagocytes of the mesoderm are retained in all higher forms and appear to keep all their primitive functions. They act as scavengers for short-lived cells such as the erythrocytes and polymorphonuclear leucocytes of the blood, which are taken up at the end of their life-span and digested, thus completing a normal cycle in which their chemical components are reintroduced into the body's economy.

They also act in defence against infections at each of the three levels of lodgement. The importance of the migrating polymorphs in the inflammatory cellular reactions of man is shown by what occurs in the disease *agranulocytosis* in which these cells are sparse or absent from the blood. In this condition infection with the pyogenic cocci (such as streptococci and staphylococci) results in spreading lesions instead of the more usual localized pustule or boil. Clinically a spreading cellulitis with extensive ulceration of the pharyngeal wall is commonly encountered. Agranulocytosis could, and often did, terminate fatally in absence of means for controlling such infections. Nowadays treatment depends on the administration of antibiotics which can restrain the infections until the bone marrow resumes a normal production of microphages. There also exist two congenitally determined conditions in which the phagocytes are abnormal and fail to kill ingested micro-organisms. These are chronic granulomatous disease of childhood and the Chediak-Higashi syndrome referred to in Chapter Eight. Both lead to repeated bacterial infections.

Another demonstration of the role of the local phagocytes in defence is provided by organisms such as the pneumococcus and influenza bacillus (*Haemophilus influenzae*) whose ability to resist the local defences, and to spread through the tissues, can be shown to depend on the possession of surface capsules which enable the microbe to resist phagocytosis. In the absence of such anti-phagocytic devices the same organisms are rapidly engulfed and digested, and strains lacking capsules are shown experimentally to be unable to produce a progressive infection.

Mechanism of Phagocytic Action

The concept of the micro- and macrophages as a defensive resistance movement or police force runs into all the dangers of over-enthusiastic teleology. However, some explanation is required of how these individual cells make contact with infective particles.

Direct observation of the tissues during inflammation shows that as the flow of blood slows in the dilated vessels, the leucocytes leave the axial stream and enter the peripheral plasmatic zone of fluid blood in contact with the endothelium ('pavementing'). They appear to stick to the vessel wall, and with adequate injury, some make their way through, apparently aided by their own active movements. The lymphocytes adhere less readily than the granulocytes, which migrate faster and in much greater numbers.

Since adhesion occurs on the vessel wall first on the side of the injury, the suggestion is that 'stickiness' results from local products of the site of injury which diffuse towards the vessels. This view is discussed below under *chemotaxis*.

It should not be overlooked that the walls of capillaries are composed of living cells which actively maintain the tone of the vessel. In inflammation these cells can be seen to swell and put out pseudopodial processes. Recent studies with the electron microscope indicate that pseudopodial processes of the endothelial cells can actually embrace and transport the phagocytic cells across their substance. However, appearances in other electron micrographs suggest that migrating cells usually dissect into and pass through the intercellular junctions of inflamed endothelium.

Chemotaxis and the Migration of Phagocytic Cells

A plausible explanation of the accumulation of leucocytes at certain inflammatory tissue sites is that they are attracted thither by chemicals (chemotaxis) and since they can be made to accumulate without the actual presence of microbes, some have thought that the tissues themselves must release a substance (phlogistine, leucotaxine) chemotactic for leucocytes. Recent findings indicate that activation of the complement system by antigen–antibody complexes can indeed lead to the formation of agents strongly chemotactic for polymorphs (see Chapter Five, p. 199). Furthermore, lysosomes extracted from or extruded by micro- and macrophages have been found to generate a similar activity on incubation with fresh serum and there is evidence that these cells also contain some other macromolecular material which is chemotactic in the absence of serum. Thus a reasonable case exists for invoking chemotactic agents as responsible for initiating leucocyte accumulation when antigen–antibody interactions are involved, and for maintaining the process, whatever its origin, so long as damage to the accumulated cells continues. In addition, it is easy to show *in vitro* that both micro- and macrophages will migrate towards a wide range of bacteria, and that some bacteria release unidentified chemotactic agents which are apparently different from those described above, and may attract one or the other type of cell selectively. The term '*cytotaxins*' has been proposed as a general term for any materials which are chemotactic *per se* when microbes have gained access to a tissue. Chemotaxis is probably not involved in the emigration of cells through the nearby vessel walls, but is likely to direct their movement towards the microbes once the cells are outside the vessels.

The vascular dilatation of inflammation is necessary for the collection of leucocytes in the tissues. Adrenaline injected two hours after an injection of staphylococci prevents the vascular dilatation and emigration of leucocytes, and greatly reduces the numbers of staphylococci (and other organisms such as *Cl. septicum* and *Streptococcus pyogenes*) necessary to establish an infection.

It has been shown that the most effective period for local disposal of micro-organisms is the first few hours after implantation of infection. Adrenaline and other procedures which can inhibit the exudation of fluid and cells were found to be without effect if applied after 2–5 hours. The main accumulation of leucocytes and exudation of fluid seems to occur after this 'critical early-killing' period. It appears that the local exudation of plasma bactericidins, by a rapid mechanism which increases capillary permeability, is highly effective in defence and may be the major event. The local extra-vascular accumulation of leucocytes may be an important factor also, but the main bulk of such migration occurs after the early period when the organisms are usually effectively killed, and may be a second line of defence to cover failure of the early mechanism.

The Immunological Role of Inflammation

It has become almost traditional to marshal arguments to support a beneficial localizing action for inflammation, which is regarded as a mechanism preventing the spread of infective particles and their toxins into the body. Often it is difficult to see clearly the value to the body of such devices as the copious exudation of fluid. It is argued that the toxins of the invading organisms are thereby diluted. This seems valid in the case of non-living toxins, but is questionable in defence against virulent bacteria, which could be swept by it through the surrounding tissue. It was claimed by Menkin that such spread of infective particles is impeded by a '*fibrin barrier*' which is envisaged as a kind of net which would trap the dispersing microbes. But the initial wave of fluid exudation would appear to be sufficient to accomplish a disastrous spread of organisms before the formation of such a fibrin barrier can possibly have become effective. Thirdly, the increased flow of lymph would appear to provide an escape route for bacteria. Menkin invoked the formation of fibrin thrombi as plugs which could suppress such a flow of bacteria-laden lymph. But actual measurement shows an increase rather than a decrease of flow of lymph from an inflamed area.

In other words, the arguments that the inflammation acts to restrain the spread of organisms seem questionable. Indeed, it might be argued that the early exudation of fluid actually benefits the body by early dispersal of organisms. Since the body is provided with an extremely rich plexus of lymphatic channels under the skin and mucous membranes, dispersal *via* such a network is an initial event with many wounds, and it might be expected that a defence mechanism would evolve towards conditions of dispersal rather than of attempted localization. In point of fact, the body is able to handle infection with a wide range of organisms, when they are dispersed *via* the intravenous route, with complete success, whereas the same organisms entering *via* the peritoneal route prove rapidly fatal. In confirmation of the idea that dispersal of bacteria may actually aid the defence mechanism may be cited experiments in which organisms have been inoculated into the skin together with the enzyme hyaluronidase. This enzyme depolymerizes the gel-like matrix in which the cells are embedded and so enables the bacteria to spread widely. With many kinds of bacteria the result is to decrease or even annul the local lesion.

It is nevertheless fairly certain that inflammation can benefit the body by effecting an increased local supply of bactericidal substances such as serum antibody and complement. This is clearly indicated by the enhancement in the local lesion which follows the injection of an antagonist for serum complement such as Liquoid (sodium polyethanol sulphonate), or when the arrival of complement is prevented by other means.

Factors Affecting Phagocytosis

Phagocytosis depends not only on contact being established between particle and cell surface but also upon the development of adhesion. A most important influence is exerted by components of blood plasma, known collectively as *opsonins*. It would appear that the main common denominator in opsonic action is the ability to coat the surface of the microbe so as to decrease the surface electrical potential and promote adhesion to other such particles (agglutination) and to the surface of the phagocyte.

In fluid media containing normal serum, most bacteria are readily phagocytosed after contact has been established. The striking exceptions to this rule are provided by *Streptococcus pneumoniae*, *Haemophilus influenzae*, *Klebsiella pneumoniae* (Friedländer's bacillus) and *Bacillus anthracis*. These organisms possess hydrated polysaccharide or polypeptide (*B. anthracis*) capsules, which surround the organism with a glairy or slimy layer of material. Variants of the above bacterial species, which lack capsules, are readily phagocytosed in normal serum.

The most active opsonins are the specific antibodies, occurring in the serum of immunized subjects, which combine with the antigenic chemical components (the polysaccharides or polypeptides) of the bacillary capsules.

Although these specific antibodies occur in high titre after specific immunization, as discussed previously small amounts of them exist in 'normal' serum. The activity of such 'normal' antibodies is greatly enhanced by the presence of complement. Indeed the antibody by itself is often present in such small amounts in 'normal' sera that it is too weak by itself to secure full opsonization.

An important point is that whereas for phagocytosis in liquid media a coating of antibody is necessary, when the phagocytes act on a suitable rough surface, they may be successful without specific antibody. Even capsulated pneumococci (of types other than the heavily encapsulated Type III) can be taken up readily by leucocytes on filter paper or membranes of fibrin. The walls of the pulmonary alveoli similarly appear to offer a surface which is appropriate for phagocytosis in the absence of opsonins. It is practically impossible to establish infection with pneumococci in the mouse by causing this animal to inhale bacterial suspensions, although one or two of such organisms when injected intraperitoneally will cause death. When, however, some initial pulmonary exudation has been induced by the inhalation of mustard gas, infection of the lungs by inhaled pneumococci is easily accomplished. Presumably such considerations are of crucial importance in the early spread of infection in lobar pneumonia. Here the advancing wave of microbial invasion is probably achieved by oedema fluid carrying pneumococci throughout the ramifications of the pulmonary lobar branches. After the development of 'red hepatization', which involves the laying down within the alveoli of a fibrin scaffolding, surface phagocytosis becomes possible and may be crucial to the eventual turning of the tide against the invader and the sudden onset of resolution in this disease.

CELLULAR IMMUNITY

The concept of the phagocytes as a corps of scavenger cells strategically disposed so as to be always ready to spring to the defence of the host originated with and was elaborated by Metchnikoff. But phagocytosis may or may not be a protective measure against infection. It may be so for many bacteria such as *Proteus* or the pneumococcus which die within a few minutes after having been engulfed. This can be shown by seeing the organisms disintegrate (see Plates 2.2, 2.3, following p. 150) rapidly within the phagocytes, or by observing the rapid decrease in the numbers which can be cultured from the tissues. However, there are numerous cases in which the ingested micro-organisms multiply within the phagocyte, quite apart from viruses and rickettsiae which are all obligate intracellular parasites. In infections by *Myco. tuberculosis* or by *Brucella* species the organisms are found to multiply within macrophages, as can be clearly shown by seeding virulent tubercle bacilli into a tissue culture of macrophages and preventing the extra-cellular multiplication by a well-judged concentration of streptomycin or other antibiotic. Indeed, the virulent mycobacteria can be distinguished from the avirulent by virtue of their ability to multiply within macrophages, which therefore appears to be an essential attribute for a successful parasite in these groups of bacteria. Similarly, staphylococci which are avirulent are killed inside polymorphs, but the coagulase-positive, disease-producing organisms grow into intracellular micro-colonies which eventually kill the cell and are released.

Indeed, it may be argued that not only do microbes multiply within phagocytic cells, but these actually protect them from the activities of antibody or chemotherapeutic drugs. By the tissue culture method it can be shown that the concentration of certain antibiotics, e.g. streptomycin, which are necessary to kill tubercle bacilli within macrophages, are 50 or 100 times more than those required when the organisms are free. In history, the belief that phagocytosis acts to spread infection in the body preceded the opposite or Metchnikovian view and appears to have been widespread among medical pathologists. Before Metchnikoff, the function of uptake of foreign particles by these cells was known, but it was generally held that such cells were simply scavengers. The cells merely picked up the foreign body and carried it to suitable disposal sites. It can be seen therefore that Metchnikoff was the pioneer in concepts of *cellular immunity*.

NON-SPECIFIC CELLULAR ACQUIRED IMMUNITY

For many years Metchnikoff was engaged in violent controversy, mainly with the German school of investigators, concerning the relative role of cellular and humoral factors in natural immunity to infection. Metchnikoff admitted the role of antibody in *acquired* immunity, although even here the final destruction of most microbes is secured by intracellular processes. The serum antibody acts to improve the phagocytosis or capture of the microbe by the cell. Many, including Metchnikoff, have believed that acquired immunity could also be associated with an increased digestive capacity of the phagocytic cells. Attempts to show this with polymorphonuclear neutrophils have generally failed. On the other hand there are numerous recent studies which show that macrophages from immunized animals are more capable than those from normal subjects in restraining the intracellular multiplication of tubercle bacilli, *Brucella* species and *Listeria* spp, under conditions in which the intervention of serum factors is excluded.

One way of doing this is to cause macrophages from normal and tuberculous animals to ingest tubercle bacilli *in vitro*, and then inject the cells into the anterior chambers of the eyes of normal rabbits. Cultures set up by Lurie of the anterior chamber fluid and cells showed that more bacilli had developed after two weeks in the eyes that had received normal cells than in those injected with tuberculous macrophages.

Other evidence has been derived from tissue cultures of peritoneal macrophages in which the intracellular growth of tubercle bacilli can be studied after using antibiotics to prevent extracellular division. A clear growth-inhibitory effect of macrophages derived from guinea-pigs which had been immunized with BCG vaccine was shown by Suter, but other investigators using different methods for induction of the macrophage exudates and generally heavier doses of infecting bacilli found no differences in macrophages from normal or BCG-vaccinated animals. That the phagocytes of tuberculous animals possess increased phagocytic activity of a non-specific kind is clearly shown by the demonstration of increased ability to clear carbon particles from the blood and an increased ability to become mobilized at a site of injection of an unrelated substance such as paraffin oil.

More recent experiments with *Brucella* organisms, with *Salmonella enteritidis* and with *Listeria monocytogenes* have provided clear-cut evidence that macrophages from immunized animals can possess greatly enhanced ability to inactivate intracellular micro-organisms. All these organisms are pathogens which are capable of prolonged association with their host. Moreover, these pathogens induce, during their intracellular residence, the state of delayed-type hypersensitivity in their host, and recent evidence suggests that this may be responsible for the heightened intracellular digestive properties of the macrophages. The macrophages of mice infected experimentally with moderate doses of *Listeria monocytogenes* develop rather suddenly at the fourth or fifth day after injection a state of enhanced resistance which lasts for several weeks. This correlates closely with the onset of delayed-type hypersensitivity to extracts of the microorganism. However, when the macrophages of the mice became resistant to *Listeria* they also became more resistant to *Brucella* and to *Mycobacteria*—organisms which are not considered to be related antigenically. Furthermore, such cross resistance can be evoked by any of the three bacterial species, under the same circumstances in which delayed-type hypersensitivity reactions develop against the specific sensitizing organisms. The inference is that where continual release of an antigen takes place in an animal exhibiting delayed-type hypersensitivity to that antigen, the macrophages become in some way generally activated. It also follows from the above that the degree of cellular immunity should vary in proportion to the severity of infection. Thus, mice which have been infected with *Salmonella typhimurium* show differences in their ability to kill a superinfecting inoculum of *Listeria monocytogenes*, the rate of inactivation being related to the number of Salmonella organisms present in the tissues at the time of challenge. This striking finding is opposite to that which would be expected if the resistance were dependent on anti-bacterial antibody.

Factors Involved in the Activation of Macrophages

As mentioned in a preceding section of this chapter, it is well established that non-specific increases or decreases in immunity can be induced in the whole animals by, for example, the injection of killed bacterial cells, their cell walls or their component somatic antigens (endotoxins of Gram-negative bacilli) as well as such chemicals as high molecular weight dextrans. It is far from clear, however, how much of these changes are due to cellular or to humoral factors.

The Stimulation of Non-specific Immunity

In the literature of 1920–40 there are recorded many procedures which induce increases of non-specific resistance in animals, e.g. the injection of vaccines of killed Gram-negative organisms, injection of nuclein, exposure to a mustard plaster or ultra-violet rays. In accord with the enthusiastic predictions of Sir Almroth Wright that 'the doctor of the future will be an immunizator' (p. 10) considerable effort was directed by himself and his colleagues to discover practical means for the enhancement of non-specific immunity.

Wright in his studies of typhoid vaccination, observed a 'negative phase of resistance' (or decreased immunity) which ensued within a few hours of the injections of killed enterobacteria organisms and which preceded the development of demonstrable immunity. More recent work was established that these effects can be reproduced by a wide variety of O-antigens of Gram-negative bacteria. These on injection into mice cause a sharp decrease, within a few hours, in the resistance to challenge by various Gram-negative bacteria, as well as by Gram-positive species such as *Staphylococcus* or *Myco. tuberculosis.* This is rapidly followed by a period of a few days in which resistance is increased to the same organisms. Part of this effect may involve fluctuation in the bactericidal activity of the serum, which can be shown by *in vitro* tests. It is claimed that such increases in *in vitro* bactericidal activity can be removed by exposure of the serum to individual Gram-negative organisms, which remove the increased bactericidal activity for themselves but not for other organisms. The increased bactericidal or opsonic activity of the serum would therefore seem to depend on the concerted increase of a range of individual antibodies. In addition to this, and possibly of far greater importance in the whole animal, endotoxin has been shown to cause a striking non-specific increase in the activity of the reticulo-endothelial system, as shown by increased clearance rates of injected particulate material such as carbon particles. (Cf. p. 74.)

THE STRATEGIC DISPOSITION OF PHAGOCYTIC CELLS

LYMPHATIC LODGEMENT

If one injects a suspension of dye particles into the skin, using a fine needle and avoiding entry into blood capillaries, the dye can be seen to diffuse rapidly into lymphatic channels, of which there is an extremely dense plexus in the superficial layers of the dermis.

As pointed out above, the pressure in the lymph channels is *nil.* If a cannula is introduced in a main lymph trunk there will be no detectable flow of lymph unless there is muscle activity in the limb or this is massaged. Carbon particles injected intraperitoneally rapidly appear in the circulating blood. This is due to passage by way of the diaphragmatic and mediastinal lymphatics. Because of the rise and fall of the diaphragm, the flow of fluid along the lymphatics in this instance is rapid, and within five minutes of injection the particles may be detected in the thoracic duct lymph.

The walls of lymphatic capillaries are made up of a single layer of thin endothelial cells only, and are bound to surrounding tissues by virtue of their arrangement on a reticulum of fibrils. This means that when the tissue swells by the local accumulation of fluid, the vessels become distended from without. Bacteria consequently will pass rapidly from the site of inoculation to the first draining lymph node. Furthermore, the chances are that they will easily pass beyond; for it has long been known that normal lymph nodes are relatively inefficient filters and that bacteria injected into normal animals may pass rapidly through them to reach the blood-stream. By taking blood cultures it is easy to demonstrate such an initial rush of organisms to the blood-stream, and it can also be shown that ligation of the thoracic duct will prevent it.

The first change which occurs in the lymph node is a dilatation of the sinuses. Dilatation of the nodal sinuses will slow the flow of lymph and act to retain organisms within the node. Next, an important inflammatory polymorph migration occurs, especially into the intermediary sinuses, where the organisms are most numerous. Cells carried by the lymph through the node tend to aggregate in the hilar sinuses before the outlet, 'simulating a log-jam at the narrow outlet of a mill pond' (W.B. Wood) and this cellular mass greatly enhances the normal filtration power of the node. Even the encapsulated pneumococcus was shown to be promptly taken up by such intra-nodal leucocytes—in less than 30 minutes after their inoculation at the periphery, so that it must be assumed that such prompt phagocytosis is too early to involve newly formed specific antibody and depends on 'intracellular' or 'surface' phagocytosis (see previous section: phagocytosis). Thus the ineffective filter rapidly becomes an effective one by the strategic accumulation of microphages which come from capillaries within the node itself rather than from the primary site of inflammation.

Investigation of variations in lymph flow during inflammation revealed that while there was no measurable pressure of lymph in the leg of an anaesthetized dog, the pressure rose to 120 cm of water during inflammation, and the lymph flow from the limb was greatly increased. As pointed out above this makes the hypothesis of localization of infective particles by 'lymphatic blockade' difficult to accept.

THE RETICULO-ENDOTHELIAL SYSTEM

The phagocytic cells which have been discussed so far are those which are present in the blood and gain access to a local inflammatory site after infection has occurred. Mention has been made of phagocytes normally existing *in situ* in the tissues, and most tissues have such resident *histiocytes*. The special needs of the lymphatic drainage system and the blood vascular system are, in addition, catered for by a strategically situated system of cells. Knowledge of the siting of phagocytic cells in the various tissues of the body followed the observations of Ribbert (1904) that lithium carmine, after injection, was taken up by certain cells. Colloidal dyes which behave in this way are referred to as *vital dyes*. The term *reticulo-endothelial system* was used by Aschoff to designate all the cells which are actively phagocytic, as demonstrated by uptake of significant quantities of vital dyes when these are injected into the bloodstream. The distribution of such cells in a lymph node is shown in Plate 2.4, between pp. 150 and 151.

The reticulo-endothelial system is primarily a physiological or functional concept, and the cells belonging to this 'system' were originally defined on the basis of their ability to take up dyes such as trypan blue or carbon particles such as indian ink when these are injected into the blood or lymph. Aschoff divided all cells with the ability to store vital dyes or particulate material into groups. The first consisted of the endothelial cells of the blood and lymph vessels (excluding sinuses) and the fibroblasts of connective tissue, but these cells showed such faint vital staining that Aschoff excluded them from the reticulo-endothelial system. The second was made up of certain stellate cells of the pulp strands of the spleen or the medullary cords of lymph nodes (reticulum cells or stellate macrophages). The third comprised the lining cells of lymph sinuses and the sinusoids of the liver and bone marrow, and similar cells in the suprarenal and pituitary glands. The term reticulo-endothelial system was derived from the fact that one main group, the stellate macrophages of spleen and lymph nodes, was thought to form a network or 'reticulum' and another lined the dilated blood or lymph sinuses. The histiocytes of the tissues generally and the monocytes of the blood were included. The system was one of phagocytic cells, but, rather arbitrarily, only the macrophages were included. The microphages (Metchnikoff's term for polymorphonuclear leucocytes) and the megakaryocytes were excluded, in spite of their both being obviously phagocytes.

Owing to the existence of the blood-brain barrier, injection of vital dyes into the blood still leaves the phagocytic cells of the brain unstained. If the surface of the brain is damaged locally, as by applying a cautery needle, the breakdown of the 'barrier' allows dye uptake by numerous local cells. Presumably such cells should be included in a functionally conceived reticulo-endothelial system. Using silver impregnation methods the Spanish neuropathologist Del Rio Hortega delineated among the neuroglia a cell with an affinity for silver carbonate possessing a compact rod-like body and numerous ramifying and branched cytoplasmic processes, which he called *microglia*. Hortega further showed that in foci of cerebral inflammation these cells changed to rounded amoeboid forms which were actively phagocytic—the so-called *compound granular corpuscles*. Hortega, de Asúa and others later used the same method to show that cells resembling the microglia existed in tissues outside the central nervous system, and that in many pathological processes a corresponding change of microglial form to amoeboid phagocyte took place. Thus a system of cells in fixed tissues can be delineated and referred to generally as *metalophil cells*, which include besides functionally active phagocytes their immediate precursors. The reticulo-endothelial system may then be regarded as a functional division of some of the *metalophil cells*.

The neat organization of the metalophil cells of the rabbit spleen is shown by reference to Plate 2.5, following p. 150, in which several morphological types are to be recognized:

(1) the free amoeboid macrophages of the sinuses;
(2) the sinus-lining cells;
(3) the stellate macrophages of the pulp strands;
(4) the microglial-like cells which are orientated around the periphery of the Malpighian bodies (lymphoid nodules).

The Sinuses

It is necessary to stress the specialized structure of blood and lymph sinuses. Sinuses are vessels within whose broad lumen the flow becomes relatively sluggish. The phagocytic cells which line the sinuses are elongated, flattened squamous cells under normal conditions, but they can thicken up after ingesting particles and project like polypi into the lumen, or even become detached to form free amoeboid cells.

The liver provides by far the greatest single collection of such cells in relation to the blood-stream, namely the Kupffer cells. Next in importance are the sinus-lining cells of the spleen and bone marrow. Sinuses, lined by similar phagocytic cells, are also present in the pituitary and adrenal glands.

The Histiocytes

The phagocytic cells which are scattered throughout the connective tissue of various organs are usually termed *histiocytes*. For many years the relationship between blood monocytes and tissue histiocytes (or macrophages) was a matter of controversy, but it is now established that monocytes are generated continuously from stem cells in the bone marrow and migrate into the tissues to become histiocytes. Local multiplication of histiocytes can also occur at sites of inflammation.

TABLE 2.2

Phagocytic cells of the body

Microphages	Macrophages (Collectively and in a functional sense making up the *reticulo-endothelial system*)				
Polymorphonuclear neutrophil leucocytes	connective tissue in organs generally	blood	central nervous system	spleen, liver, adrenals, bone marrow, anterior pituitary	lymphoreticular tissues, spleen, lymph nodes, bone marrow, thymus
Eosinophil leucocytes	histiocytes	monocytes	microglia	sinus lining cells	reticulum cells

At certain sites the histiocytes are vastly concentrated. This occurs in the whitish areas ('milk spots' or '*tâches laiteuses*') on the surface of the omentum, lying along the vessels. When microorganisms get into the peritoneal cavity the number of free macrophages in the fluid content increases and it seems highly likely that these are formed by emigration of histiocytes from the milk spots.

The lung is also particularly well supplied with histiocytes, which are present in the alveolar walls, as resting or precursor cells with a microglial morphology, but which can become activated and emerge into the alveolar spaces when dust particles or bacteria gain admission to the alveoli. Many of these cells pass with their load of dust particles, haemosiderin or bacteria up the bronchial tree to be swallowed or spat out of the mouth. The contribution made to such cells by the blood monocytes is debatable but is probably of major importance during inflammation. There is evidence for a clearance of particle-laden phagocytes from the blood-stream (mainly Kupffer cells) to the pulmonary capillaries and out *via* the bronchial tree.

RETICULO-ENDOTHELIAL BLOCKADE AND STIMULATION

The cells of the reticulo-endothelial system are largely responsible for removal from the blood-stream of many colloidal or finely particulate materials in addition to dyes or carbon particles. They remove, for example, partially denatured proteins, and have an extremely fine discrimination in detecting minor alterations in serum proteins which cause the molecules to aggregate somewhat, even though they may stay in solution (e.g. after minor degrees of denaturation or the formation of soluble antigen–antibody complexes). Advantage has been taken of this property to measure the overall function of the reticulo-endothelial system, by injecting intravenously a solution of partly denatured serum albumin, trace-labelled with radioactive iodine, and following its clearance from the blood-stream. The rapid removal which occurs in a normal animal is illustrated by curve A in Fig. 2.3.

By overloading the cells with relatively large amounts of a colloidal suspension, such as carbon in the form of indian ink, or thorium dioxide as 'thorotrast', it is possible temporarily to depress their phagocytic function towards other colloids. This is shown by curve B, which relates to animals whose reticulo-endothelial cells have been 'blockaded' in such a way. However, such depression lasts only for a few hours, or a day or two, because the cells have great power of proliferation and recovery. It has been suggested that persistent bacteraemia in some infections is due to overloading of the reticulo-endothelial system, or failure of its phagocytic capacity for some other reason (e.g. a toxin), but there is no real evidence that this occurs in the ordinary course of disease in an animal whose liver and spleen are intact and which has a normal circulation. As mentioned below, impairment of phagocytic function can occur in haemorrhagic shock, and it is quite possible that the clearance mechanism can fail terminally and so accelerate death.

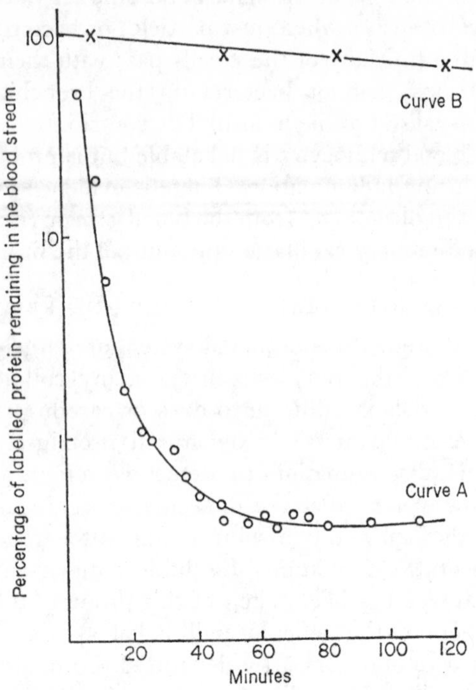

FIG. 2.3. Clearance of heat-aggregated protein from the blood-stream. The effect of blockade of the reticulo-endothelial system.

Human serum albumin, denatured by heating and labelled with radioactive iodine, was injected intravenously into normal rats and rats which had received 50 mg indian ink 6 hours previously.

O——O normal rats.
X——X rats treated with indian ink.

The indian ink temporarily blocks uptake by the reticulo-endothelial system. [From Freeman, Gordon and Humphrey (1958) *Brit. J. exp. Path.* **39,** 463.]

When followed under standard conditions the rate of clearance of radio-labelled denatured proteins from the blood-stream (or of finely divided carbon, which was used first in experimental animals) permits an accurate measurement of the phagocytic activity of the reticulo-endothelial system. By these means it has been possible to discover conditions in which this activity is markedly stimulated. Most of the experimental work has been done in rats and mice, and it is not certain how far the results may be generalized to include other species. Stimulation is evident after administration of oestrogens, of certain lipids (e.g. glycerol trioleate), and of cortisone in suitable doses, although in higher doses it depresses (see Fig. 2.1). A finding of considerable interest is that injection of living BCG (a strain of attenuated tubercle bacilli) causes a prolonged and considerable increase in the phagocytic capacity of the reticulo-endothelial system, which becomes evident about one week after injection and lasts for three weeks or more. It is possible, though not experimentally proved, that this stimulation is a consequence of the development of delayed-type hypersensitivity (see Chapter Ten) while the antigenic stimulus, namely the tubercle bacilli, is still present—so that, until the bacilli are finally eliminated, a chronic delayed-type reaction is going on in the animals.

REMOVAL OF BACTERIA FROM THE BLOOD

The body possesses remarkably efficient mechanisms for sterilizing the blood-stream. As has been previously stressed, most bacteria are less capable of causing disease when injected intravenously than when given by any other route. With most bacterial species, large numbers of living organisms can be swiftly cleared from the circulation.

When large numbers of living bacteria are injected into the veins of an experimental animal the count of organisms, as revealed by repeated quantitative blood cultures, in general follows the type of curve as shown in Fig. 2.4, curve A. In the first phase, clearance is extremely rapid and the count may fall from a billion to less than a hundred per millilitre in 10 minutes. This rapid initial fall in numbers occurs with most organisms, and is not dependent on prior experience with the invading micro-organism. Subsequent to this phase the course varies with the virulence characteristics of the organism. In general, although a few bacteria may persist for some time, all disappear completely within an hour or so. The main exceptions are provided by the encapsulated virulent strains of *Streptococcus pneumoniae* (the pneumococcus), *Klebsiella pneumoniae* (Friedländer's bacillus) and *Bacillus anthracis*. The pneumoncoccus may be taken as an example (Fig. 2.4). With an average 24-hour culture of a virulent type, the bulk of the organisms will have lost their capsules and consequently the initial drop of organisms may assume the usual rapid fall. This leaves a few encapsulated forms which persist, and their multiplication produces a climb which may eventually result in death in septicaemia with 10^9 organisms per ml of blood. With a young culture (8 hours) of a recently isolated virulent type, virtually all the organisms will possess capsules and also be in an actively dividing growth phase. In this case no measurable initial clearance may occur and the count of organisms in the blood will rise from the moment of injection until death eventually occurs (Fig. 2.4, curve C).

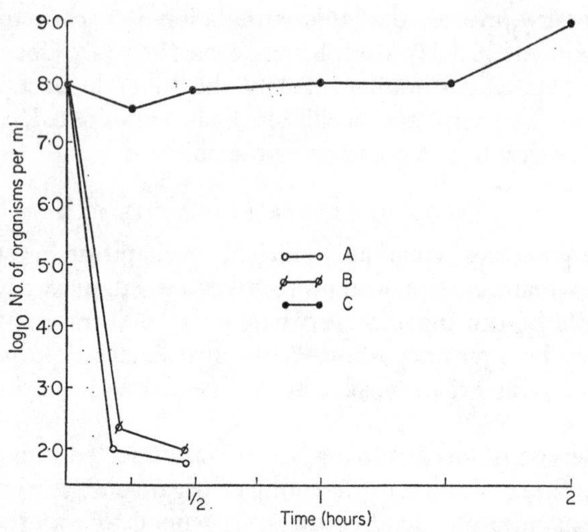

FIG. 2.4. Clearance of organisms from the blood-stream of the rabbit.

A course of bacteraemia after injection of avirulent, unencapsulated *Streptococcus pneumoniae* into a normal previously uninjected animal.

B course of bacteraemia after injection of an 8-hour culture of fully virulent, encapsulated organisms into a previously immunized animal.

C course of bacteraemia after injection of an 8-hour culture of fully virulent, encapsulated organisms into a normal previously uninjected animal. Death occurred at 48 hours.

In the case of such an encapsulated micro-organism as the pneumococcus, immune serum containing antibody specific for the type carbohydrate of the capsule can be shown to have a dramatic influence on the phagocytic process as shown in Fig. 2.4, curve B.

Experiments which utilize the perfused isolated liver show that encapsulated pneumococci can be passed repeatedly through such a preparation without removal when suspended in normal serum, but such organisms were promptly removed when suspended in immune serum. It is thus apparent that, as in the case of the polymorphonuclear leucocyte, serum factors such as antibody and complement are required to create an efficient trapping mechanism.

Studies with repeated large doses of living bacteria suggest that the trapping capacity of the reticulo-endothelial system is rarely, if ever, exceeded. Repeated intravenous injections of bacteria are each cleared with equal speed. This clearly indicates that in bacteraemias in normal hosts due to organisms other than the encapsulated species, the continued presence of the organisms in the circulation depends upon a continuous supply from an extravascular focus. The simplest examples result from the multiplication of bacteria in an area of the body bathed by the circulating blood such as is provided in bacterial endocarditis by bacteria-laden vegetations on the heart valves or in a patent ductus arteriosus. Another kind of focus may be a septic thrombophlebitis—as in the cavernous sinus in staphylococcal furunculosis of the face. In such cases the localized subcutaneous infection progresses to infection of the vein walls and so causes secondary thrombosis, colonization of the clot by bacteria and feeding of the latter into the blood-stream.

Organisms can spread from the blood to gain access to tissues with apparent ease. When pneumococci are injected intravenously into rabbits organisms appear in the thoracic duct lymph within one hour from injection. In this case the non-motile organism has rapidly achieved the crossing of both vascular and lymphatic endothelium without preliminary thrombosis.

Most of the bacteria removed from the blood after a single injection are found in the macrophages of the liver and spleen. Even in long-standing bacterial endocarditis in man the power of uptake of organisms by these tissues is maintained in spite of the persistent bacteraemia. By collecting arterial samples from the femoral artery and venous samples from several sites by an intravenous catheter, it has been found that the bacterial count of the arterial blood remains remarkably stable. There was no evidence of removal of bacteria from the blood circulating through the extremities, or the kidney, but as blood passed through the liver a dramatic reduction in bacterial count occurred.

Role of the Polymorphonuclear Leucocytes in Clearing the Blood-stream

The above account of the activities of the reticulo-endothelial system establishes beyond doubt the importance of the macrophage system. But although most of the bacteria removed from the circulation find their way to the liver and spleen, some organisms can be seen to enter the polymorphonuclear leucocytes, and clumps of cells laden with bacteria can be seen within the capillaries of various organs, especially the lungs. The probable destination of such cells is to the macrophages of the reticulo-endothelial system, which finally dispose of both microphages and bacteria.

However, in certain stages of the clearance process the lung may also play a role in the removal of circulating bacteria. The intravenous injection of staphylococci produces a profound leucopenia. Almost all circulating microphages disappear from the blood for about 20 minutes. Most lodge in the lung capillaries where they may still be capable of clearing bacteria from the blood. Rabbits which are rendered leucopenic by whole body X-ray treatment maintain high levels of organisms in the blood, following intravenous injection of *Bact. coli*, far longer than do normal animals. However, if such leucopenic animals are transfused with healthy rabbit leucocytes, subsequent injections of *Bact. coli* are cleared normally. This occurs despite the fact that the transfused leucocytes have disappeared from the blood. These facts suggest that polymorphonuclear leucocytes accumulating within the pulmonary capillary bed may create a progressively efficient supplementary filter.

With other organisms, there is evidence that the leucocytes can act to prevent the efficient destruction of intravenous bacteria under certain circumstances. Coagulase positive staphylococci and gonococci can persist within the microphages. When large numbers of staphylococci are injected intravenously in rabbits, they disappear rapidly from the blood but a mild bacteraemia persists for several hours. The suggestion is that many taken up by leucocytes can be released again and re-seed the blood. Rabbits rendered leucopenic can actually remove staphylococci from their circulation better than normal animals. This is a rather unique example of a defect in the clearance mechanism, but it stresses the fact that the disappearance of micro-organisms from the blood-stream is not equivalent to their final destruction.

Transient bacteraemia is a frequent occurrence in the lives of all of us. The sudden shower of organisms into the blood-stream is followed by rapid and complete clearing in most cases. Some extra-vascular infections are likely to shower organisms into the blood. This occurs in acute lobar pneumonia which often commences with a sudden sensation of chill and rigor, due presumably to the transient initial bacteraemia. However, about a quarter of such patients may show persistent bacteraemia, and before the advent of the antibiotics such cases carried a poor prognosis. Presumably the bacteraemia in this case was a direct indication of the spreading invasion of pulmonary tissue.

Several simple operative or manipulative procedures can result in transient bacteraemia: the passage of a catheter (catheter fever), the operation of tonsillectomy, uterine curettage or prostatectomy, normal labour, dental manipulations or simply hard chewing on defective teeth.

The significance of such transient bacteraemias is in relation to the pathogenesis of bacterial endocarditis in patients with anatomical or rheumatic cardiac defects. Tonsillectomy, dental procedures, normal labour and catheterization are well-known precipitating causes of endocarditis.

THE ALTERATION OF NON-SPECIFIC DEFENCE MECHANISMS IN VARIOUS PATHOLOGICAL CONDITIONS

Clinical experience indicates that most diseased patients may easily become 'secondarily' infected. Such a concept is extremely difficult to evaluate and analyse scientifically, but there are some particular structural and functional abnormalities which render affected subjects especially susceptible to infection.

The post-operative patient is one who is particularly liable to develop infection. Diverse influences may be at work including the effects of shock and anaesthetics.

Traumatic and Haemorrhagic Shock

In these cases the clinical observations can be upheld by animal experiments, which show a markedly lowered resistance generally to infections. Under conditions of haemorrhagic shock, it can be shown that bacteria are cleared less readily from the blood-stream of dogs, indicating a functional defect in the activity of the reticulo-endothelial system. The local inflammatory response is also impaired (compare the effect of cortisone) and shocked animals are found to lack the ability to mobilize the blood leucocytes at a site of injury. Also the normal bactericidal effect of serum is decreased in such animals. It has been claimed that the breakdown of such natural defence factors leads to invasion of the body by commensal intestinal organisms and that their contained endotoxin is the major cause of death after shock. This is probably not the whole story since in a germ-free rat haemorrhagic shock and death can be induced in the absence of viable bacteria in the gut. However, the fact that antibiotics substantially protect against the effects of shock is important evidence for the involvement of bacteria or their products in producing these effects.

Anaesthesia

Several possible mechanisms combine to produce a lowering of natural resistance following general anaesthesia. First, the activity of the cilia of the respiratory passages is severely depressed. The wave action of the cilia aids in the clearing of foreign particles and microbes from the respiratory tract. Also, the usual premedication results in a decreased amount of bronchial secretion which is of abnormally high viscosity. Secondly, ether anaesthesia at least may result in metabolic changes expressed in manifest ketosis, which has been shown previously to be a factor in decreased resistance to staphylococci and other organisms. Thirdly, as in shock, anaesthetized animals are found to lack the ability fully to mobilize the blood leucocytes at inflammatory sites. Lastly, the collapse of a lung segment is a frequent complication of major abdominal or thoracic surgery.

Irradiation Damage

At moderately large (close to lethal) doses of a whole-body irradiation by X-rays, the most frequent terminal event is a bacteraemia involving the intestinal organisms. In irradiated animals the administration of antibiotics results in considerable reduction in mortality. Presumably the bacteraemia represents a major cause of death at this level of X-ray dosage. In animals which receive higher (so-called supra-lethal) doses, antibiotics do not reduce mortality and other factors must be responsible for death.

Bacteraemia is usually observed during the second week after close-to-lethal doses of X-rays. Damage to the intestinal mucosa can be shown soon after irradiation and one view holds that the bacteraemia derives from this source. But according to recent work it seems clear that even in the normal animal the intestinal mucosa is not an effective barrier to the Gram-negative organisms of the gut. In other words, organisms are breaking through into the blood continuously and irradiation presumably must act by impairing the defence mechanism which normally deals with these. X-rays even in low doses induce severe leucopenia, but in the experimental animal it is difficult to correlate this effect with decreased resistance. Several other changes occur which may be related, including decreased levels of properdin in the blood, but possibly decreased function of the reticulo-endothelial cells provides a better explanation. Although carbon clearance studies and histological evidence show that these cells are radio-resistant, other findings indicate a loss of their normal ability to proliferate rapidly and to dispose of intracellular bacilli.

PYREXIA AS A MECHANISM OF RESISTANCE

Fever is so general a response of the body to microbial infection that it might seem likely to constitute a part of the body's normal defence. However, its role is only vaguely sensed. Indeed, anti-pyretic drugs are very widely used—spontaneously by patients and on the prescriptions of physicians—without apparently causing markedly obvious deterioration. Fever can possibly influence resistance to infection in several ways. The micro-organisms themselves may be sensitive to temperature or may fail to elaborate their toxins. Alternatively the various cellular and humoral mechanisms of the body's resistance may be enhanced by a rise of temperature.

There are several examples of microbes which are killed *in vitro* at the temperatures 40–42°C which are attainable by pyrexia in man. In two human infections the evidence for the efficacy of artificial fever therapy is excellent. This is the case in urethritis, arthritis and ophthalmitis due to the gonococcus, and in neurosyphilis due to *Treponema pallidum*. Gonorrhoeal urethritis and ophthalmia, and neurosyphilis are usually afebrile diseases. This might lead to the speculation that the diseases could not develop if a 'normal' febrile response had occurred. However, apparently in gonococcal endocarditis temperatures of 40°C (104°F) can be maintained for long periods without leading to spontaneous cure, although examples of the latter have been recorded.

The temperature sensitivity of certain organisms may account for the pattern of their localization in the body. Infection with two mycobacteria, *Myco. ulcerans* and *Myco. balnei*, result in rather similar ulceration of exposed skin surfaces. No tendency for the infection to spread systemically ever occurs. Both organisms show optimal growth *in vitro* in the temperature range 30–32°C. The results of injecting *Myco. balnei* into experimental animals follows exactly the expectations derived from a concept that tissues at 37°C and above are protected. In guinea-pigs the only lesions observed are in males and form ulcers of the scrotum. Chickens with their higher general body temperature are unaffected. Frogs and turtles develop generalized fatal disease.

Another mycobacterium, the leprosy bacillus, shows no selective localization in the human body, judging by the distribution of the acid-fast bacilli which are presumably viable organisms, although no method of artificial cultivation exists to prove this at present. However, its lesions are curiously localized to the skin, the superficial segments of peripheral nerves such as the posterior auricular, the ulnar behind the elbow, the superficial peroneal and radial, the conjunctiva, the nasal mucosa and, in males, the testes. These are areas of decreased temperature, and the suggestion is strong that in order to produce parenchymal destructive lesions the organism must operate under these particular conditions. Although the 'febrile crises' of leprosy are known to be followed by regression of lesions, the results of fever therapy are reported to be disappointing.

However, the above examples represent very special cases whereas fever is a rather uniform concomitant of infections, and it is far from evident that pyrexia has any *general* effect on resistance. Attempts have been made to show increased phagocytic powers for the leucocytes in fever, but the changes which are described again probably lack general application. Thus it is convincingly shown that the phagocytosis of staphylococci by human and guinea-pig leucocytes in normal serum is maximal at temperatures above the normal body temperature.

Many studies have been made in experimental animals of the pyrogenic action of bacterial endotoxins (see Chapter Six). As little as 0·01 μg per kg body weight will elicit a definite febrile reaction in the rabbit and in man. These endotoxins when administered into the blood-stream act mainly by causing the release from the recipient's own cells of an α-globulin with pyrogenic activity. One important source of this 'endogenous pyrogen' is the polymorphonuclear leucocyte, but other cells (perhaps macrophages) must also be involved since leucopaenic animals show little impairment of their pyrogenic reaction to endotoxin. Endogenous pyrogen appears to be released as a consequence of damage to or stimulation of the susceptible cells.

Although the pyrexia which follows administration of vaccines containing Gram-negative bacteria (e.g. enteric organisms) is mainly due to their endotoxin content, the sustained pyrexia which accompanies persisting infections with many different microbes has been shown not to be due to pyrogens released from them.

FURTHER READING

ALLISON A.C. (1961) Genetic factors in resistance to malaria. *Ann. N.Y. Acad. Sci.* **91,** 710

ALLISON A.C. (1967) Lysosomes and Disease. *Scientific American* **217,** No. 5, 62

BENACERRAF B. (1960) Influence of irradiation on resistance to infection. *Bacteriol. Rev.* **24,** 35.

DE REUCK A.V.S. & CAMERON, M.P. (ed.) (1963) *Lysosomes,* Ciba Foundation Symposium. Churchill, London

DUBOS R.J. (1954) *Biochemical Determinants of Microbial Diseases.* Harvard University Press, Cambridge, Mass.

ELBERG, S.S. (1960) Cellular immunity. *Bacteriol. Rev.* **24,** 67

FINTER N.B. *The Interferons.* Academic Press, New York. 1967

GOWEN J.W. (1960) Genetic effects in non-specific resistance to infectious disease. *Bacteriol. Rev.* **24,** 192.

HARRIS H. (1954) Role of chemotaxis in inflammation. *Physiol. Rev.* **34,** 529.

HARRIS H. (1960) Mobilization of defensive cells in inflammatory tissue. *Bacteriol. Rev.* **24,** 3

HIRSCH J.G. (1959) Immunity to infectious diseases: review of some concepts of Metchnikoff. *Bacteriol. Rev.* **23,** 48–60

HIRSCH J.G. (1960) Anti-microbial factors in tissues and phagocytic cells. *Bacteriol. Rev.* **24,** 133

INTERFERON. Ciba Foundation Symposium. [Ed. Wolstenholme G.E.W. and O'Connor M.]. Churchill, London, 1968

JENKIN C.R. (1963) Heterophil antigens and their significance in the host-parasite relationship. *Adv. Immunol.* **3,** 351

JENKIN C.R. & ROWLEY D. (1963) Basis for immunity to typhoid in mice and the question of 'cellular immunity'. *Bacteriol. Rev.* **27,** 391

KARNOVSKY M.L. (1962) Metabolic basis of phagocytic activity. *Physiol. Rev.* **42,** 143

KELLER H.U. & SORKIN E. (1968) Chemotaxis of leucocytes. *Experientia* **24,** 641

KEPPIE J. (1964) Host and tissue specificity. In *Microbial behaviour* 'in vitro' *and* 'in vivo', a Symposium of The Society for General Microbiology [Ed. Smith H. and Taylor J.]. Cambridge Univ. Press, Cambridge

MACKANESS G.B. (1964) The behaviour of microbial parasites in relation to phagocytic cells *in vitro* and *in vivo.* In *Microbial behaviour* 'in vitro' *and* 'in vivo', A Symposium of The Society for General Microbiology [Ed. Smith H. and Taylor J.]. Cambridge Univ. Press, Cambridge

MACKANESS G.B. & BLANDEN, R.V. (1967) Cellular Immunity. *Progr. Allergy* **11,** 89

METCHNIKOFF E. (1905) *Immunity in Infective Diseases,* translated from the French by Francis G. Binnie. Cambridge Univ. Press, Cambridge

NELSON D.S. (1968) *Macrophages and Immunity.* North Holland Publishing Co.

ROWLEY D. (1962) Phagocytosis. *Adv. Immunol.* **2,** 241

RUSTAD R.C. (1961) Pinocytosis. *Sci. Am.* (April 1961)

SALTON M.R.J. (1957) The properties of lysozyme and its action on micro-organisms. *Bacteriol. Rev.* **21,** 82.

SHILO M. (1959) Non-specific resistance to infections. *Ann Rev. Microbiol.* **13,** 255

SKARNES R.C. & WATSON D.W. (1957) Antimicrobial factors of normal tissues and fluids. *Bacteriol. Rev.* **21,** 272.

SUTER E. (1956) Interaction between phagocytes and pathogenic micro-organisms. *Bacteriol. Rev.* **20,** 94.

SUTER E. & RAMSEIER H. (1964) Cellular reactions in infection. *Adv. Immunol.* **4,** 117

THOMAS L. (1954) The physiological disturbances produced by endotoxins. *Ann Rev. Physiol.* **16,** 467

THORBECKE G.J. & BENACERRAF B. (1962) The reticulo-endothelial system and immunological phenomena. In *Progr. Allergy* **vi,** 559

WEDGWOOD R.G. (1964) Properdin. In *Immunological Methods* [Ed. Ackroyd J.F.] p. 25. Blackwell, Oxford

WILSON G.S. & MILES A.A. (ed.) (1964) *Topley and Wilson's Principles of Bacteriology and Immunity,* 5th edition. Arnold, London

WOOD W.B. (1960) Phagocytosis with particular reference to encapsulated bacteria. *Bacteriol. Rev.* **24,** 41

CHAPTER THREE

The Specific Immunological Response

THIS chapter will attempt to describe the sequence of cellular events which accompany a specific immunological response and to discuss in general terms how these are initiated and what controls them. In doing so it will be necessary both to anticipate and to take for granted some of the properties of the specific antibodies and the specifically sensitized cells which are the consequence of such responses, and of the antigens which cause them to come about. More detailed discussion of these will be found in later chapters, and it may be advisable for the reader after a first reading to return to this chapter in the light of what is written later.

A specific immunological response is the result of introducing into the body, by infection or by other means, materials which are recognized as foreign. Such materials are termed *antigens* or *immunogens*. The response is specific because, in addition to effects of a general nature (such as inflammation, phagocytosis) which may be caused by many substances, there result changes in reactivity of the organism towards the antigen which caused the response, confined to that antigen and to substances very closely resembling it. The changes are usually, but not always, a heightened reactivity or increased resistance. For example, after an immunological response to diphtheria toxin, the responding animal will be much less susceptible to the toxic action of that toxin, but may now react to injecting the chemically closely related, but harmless, diphtheria toxoid by a more vigorous inflammation. Despite these changes the animal's susceptibility to some unrelated substance, such as tetanus toxin, will be quite unaltered. As is explained in Chapter Six, the specific immunological response is evoked by and made against individual relatively small and well defined areas of the surface of the antigen molecule known as *antigenic determinant* or hapten groups, which differ from one antigen to another and of which any antigen molecule which is complex (as most are) possesses a number of distinct varieties. The capacity to make a specific immunological response against harmful substances or infectious micro-organisms confers an enormous advantage for survival, and is presumably the reason why this response has evolved in higher animals, but it must be stressed that in order to evoke such a response a substance need not be intrinsically harmful. It needs rather to possess antigenic determinants which are foreign to the animal into which it is introduced.

The specific immunological response includes four distinct elements. These are outlined below briefly, and will be elaborated in more detail later in this chapter.

1. *Antibody Production*

Antibodies, as explained more fully in Chapter Four, are immunoglobulins which have the property of interacting specifically with and binding on to the antigenic determinants in response to which they are made. For each molecule of the immunogen millions of specific antibody molecules may be formed and secreted into the body fluids. These antibody molecules are responsible not only for the enhanced capacity to neutralize toxic substances or to phagocytose and kill microbes etc. (see Chapter Ten) but also for several forms of heightened reactivity to antigens, collectively termed immediate type hypersensitivity, which are described in Chapter Eleven. It is necessary here to anticipate Chapter Four, and to add that all antibodies have a basically similar structure but that antibodies with closely similar capacities to react with a given antigen can be made which differ in respect of their structure of that part of the molecule which governs their biological properties. They may also differ in molecular size.

2. *The Development of Specific Cell-Mediated Immunity*

This somewhat cumbrous, though descriptively accurate term is used to describe the appearance of a heightened reactivity towards the antigen manifested by such phenomena as delayed type hypersensitivity and rejection of foreign tissue grafts, which are discussed more fully in Chapter Twelve. Heightened reactivity of this kind is also specific for the antigen which elicited it, but has not been shown to depend upon the formation of any antibodies detectable in the body fluids. It depends rather upon the presence of cells, primarily lymphocytes, which have the property of specifically interacting with the antigen so as to produce the complex biological phenomena by which cell-mediated immunity is recognized. Such cells are said to be specifically sensitized. For reasons which will become apparent later there exist at present no purely chemical means of recognizing sensitization of this kind.

3. *Immunological Memory, or the Phenomenon of the Secondary Response*

When an antigen with which an animal has never come into contact is administered as a single dose for the first time, and in amounts which are relatively small (from a fraction of a microgram to a few milligrams, depending upon the nature of the antigen and the size of the animal) but nevertheless sufficient to elicit a specific response of antibody production and/or cell-mediated specific immunity, there is first a latent period lasting several days during which no response is detectable. The more sensitive the method of detection, the shorter is the latent period, but it is rarely less than 3 or 4 days and sometimes as long as a fortnight. Following this period the amount of circulating antibody or the intensity of cell-mediated immunity reactions increases rapidly. In the case of circulating antibody, whose concentration can be measured accurately, the rate of increase is usually found to be exponential during the next 2–3 days or more to reach a peak level, after which there is a gradual decline. By the time that two months or more have elapsed since the first administration of antigen, the antibody levels commonly decline to a very low or an undetectable level. If now a similar amount of the same antigen is administered by the same route, the immunological response is very much more brisk. The latent period is shorter, the antibody level rises faster and higher (tenfold or more), and after reaching its peak it declines much more slowly. This phenomenon is illustrated by one of the early quantitative experiments on this subject shown in Fig. 3.1. The antibody elicited by a second stimulation also tends to have a greater avidity, or capacity to bind to the antigen (see p. 134).

Although similar quantitative data relating to cell-mediated specific immunity are not available, it has generally been observed that when this sort of response has once been established (e.g. by a tissue graft) a second graft of the same tissue also elicits a more brisk and intense response.

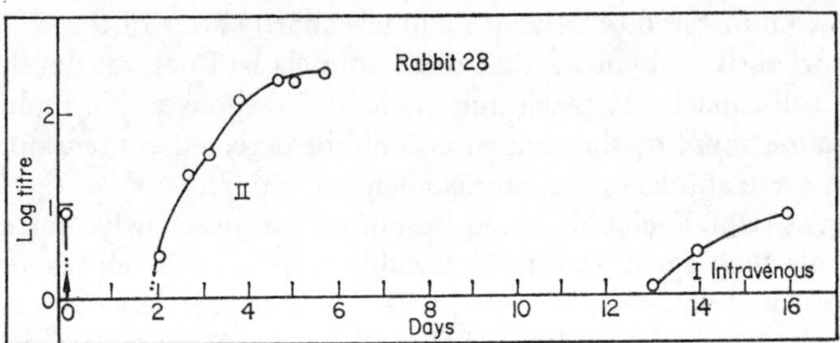

FIG. 3.1. Primary and secondary antibody responses following intravenous injection of staphylococcal toxoid in the rabbit.

The primary (I) shows a slow rise to a low level starting 13 days after injection; the secondary response (II) shows an initial drop in titre ('negative phase') followed after 2 days by a rapid rise to a much higher level. [Burnet F.M. and Freeman M. (1932) *J. Path. Bact.* **35**, 477.]

The observation that prior contact with an antigen conditions an animal to respond more vigorously to subsequent contact with the same antigen, giving what is called a *secondary response* (alternatively a 'booster' response), has given rise to the idea that the animal has acquired some sort of *immunological memory*. As will be explained below, this can be accounted for by the production, as a result of the primary stimulus, of a new (or a greatly enlarged) population of cells specifically able to respond to the antigen. Such cells are sometimes conveniently called 'memory' cells.

4. *Immunological Tolerance, Paralysis or Specific Immunological Unresponsiveness*

The above terms are used synonymously to describe the observation that the administration of certain antigens in certain circumstances, instead of causing an immunological response, leads to a complete absence or a great diminution of the expected subsequent immunological reactivity towards those antigens. Although this statement is hedged with qualifications, the phenomenon is probably applicable in principle (though not in practice) to all antigens. We shall return later to a fuller discussion of the circumstances in which immunological tolerance can be elicited, and mention here only those in which it was first produced on purpose experimentally. Rather large amounts of foreign antigen, in the form of soluble proteins or of living cells from a genetically different (*allogeneic*) strain of animal, were administered to newborn animals shortly after birth—i.e. at a time when it was known that these animals had not yet developed their full capacity to make immunological responses. No immunological response by the recipients could be detected at the time, and when these animals were later challenged with amounts of the same antigens which elicited good responses in previously untreated controls they again gave no detectable responses. They responded to unrelated antigens, however, with a vigour precisely comparable to the control animals. Their failure to respond was in fact specific for the antigen used to induce tolerance.

Underlying this experiment was an attempt to explain why animals do not respond immunologically to the constituents of their own tissues and body fluids, which have been shown again and again to evoke immunological responses when injected in animals of another species. In other words, how they distinguish 'self' from 'not self' constituents. A clue had been given by the observation that when cattle have binovular (i.e. genetically different) twin calves, which share a common placenta *in utero* and are consequently bathed in each other's blood before birth, they sometimes prove to be chimaeras (see p. 567)—i.e. they contain blood cells derived from the other twin. This condition of chimaerism may persist long after birth and the twin's cells elicit no immunological reaction, even though cells from a different calf administered later will do so in the expected fashion. It was reasoned that potential antigens, present at a time when the immunological apparatus was immature, might become tolerated and treated as 'self' rather than as 'not self'. This reasoning, as we shall see later, is only partly correct, since it has subsequently been found that specific immunological tolerance can be produced by some antigens in adult animals.

Tolerance is included as an essential element of the immunological response because any explanation of how such a response is elicited by a potential antigen must include an explanation of how it can also be specifically suppressed.

The immunologically competent cell

Many observations have shown that immunological responses are accompanied by differentiation and multiplication of cells in the specialized lymphoid tissues (notably spleen, lymph nodes, bone marrow) associated with the reticulo-endothelial system. Complementary experiments, mainly based on the results of passive transfer of pieces of tissue (or cell suspensions prepared from them) from animals making an immunological response to unstimulated recipients, have shown that these same specialized lymphoid tissues contain the bulk of the cells responsible both for antibody formation and cell mediated specific immunity. Because the tissues contain a mixture of cell types, and because it is uncertain to what extent one may differentiate into another, such experiments cannot, however, determine what particular kind of cell is responsible. The suggestion was put forward by P.B. Medawar that there are special cells, for which he suggested the term 'immunologically competent', which are able to respond to contact with any particular antigenic determinant by manifesting or developing a specific immunological capacity. Such responsiveness would include the formation of specific antibody or the capacity to initiate specific cell-mediated immunity reactions. Immunologically competent cells would include both cells which had not yet been stimulated by contact with antigen and others which, as a result of previous antigenic stimulation, were able to respond selectively to one particular antigen and were considered as possibly 'committed'. F.M. Burnet proposed that immunologically competent cells are mesenchymal cells, particularly lymphocytes (for which at the time no function was known). As will appear later in this chapter, his prediction appears to have been largely correct. Important clues relating to the origin and development of immunologically competent cells have been obtained from studies of the phylogenetic development of immunological responses, and this subject is discussed briefly in the following section.

PHYLOGENETIC DEVELOPMENT OF THE IMMUNOLOGICAL RESPONSE

In Chapters One and Two it is related how several of the early studies of immunological mechanisms made use of the lower poikilothermic vertebrates and invertebrates. In this way Metchnikoff, from his studies in comparative physiology, was able to indicate the basic importance throughout evolution of the processes of phagocytosis. He was able to trace the continuity of phagocytic and digestive activity from the amoeba, in which nutrition and digestion or elimination of potentially harmful micro-organisms are inseparable functions, through the sponges in which the digestive endodermal phagocytes are separated from the mesodermal phagocytes.

The phagocytes of the mesoderm are retained unchanged in appearance and function in all higher forms of life. Metchnikoff cited as a prototype of the role of the macrophage in defence the interaction between the water flea *Daphnia* and the spores of the primitive fungus *Monospora bicuspidata.* A direct correlation exists between resistance and the success of phagocytosis in this species; as Metchnikoff directly observed, when phagocytosis fails the fungus flourishes and its host, the water flea, dies.

Cellular immunity is, therefore, regarded as of crucial importance in invertebrates. In earthworms and caterpillars inflammatory reactions occur to injected foreign material and bacteria with resultant phagocytosis of these. On other occasions a proliferation of coelomic cells results in encapsulation of the foreign material into a cyst.

The role of humoral factors in serum and lymph is less certain. Invertebrate coelomic fluid and haemolymph can contain agglutinins to the erythrocytes of higher animals and bactericidal substances. These substances do not appear to be proteins resembling the immunoglobulins of mammals. None of the invertebrates possess proteins which migrate electrophoretically with the characteristics of γ-globulin in mammalian sera. Although some invertebrate species can produce bactericidal substances adaptively (i.e. in increased amounts) after injection of bacteria these substances are not usually specific for the bacteria used for immunization.

The invertebrates generally appear to be unable to distinguish between autografts and homografts. The evidence in this case extends to coelenterates, planarians, insects, earthworms and echinoderms.

When the representative species of reptiles, amphibians and birds have been investigated, it has been found that both humoral and cellular mechanisms are present. Animals of all these orders react to injection of a very wide range of different antigens by the formation of antibodies which migrate in electrophoresis with the slowest (or most electropositive) group of plasma proteins. All develop immunological memory, i.e. react much more vigorously and quickly to the *second* stimulus of the same antigen than to the first. All have the capacity to develop delayed-type hypersensitivity and to effect homograft and heterograft rejection.

In evaluating the presence or absence of a response in a given species due regard must be paid to the effect of temperature. In frogs the agglutinin response to injected bacteria occurs when the animals are maintained above 20° but fails at 12°. The difference has usually been found to be quantitative rather than qualitative and, providing that sufficient time is allowed, significant amounts of antibodies can be produced by reptiles and amphibians even if they are continuously maintained at a low temperature. In the case of the desert iguana, an animal adapted to high environmental temperatures, agglutinin formation to *Salmonella typhosa* occurs far better at 35° than 25°. Among the fishes, the higher forms (teleosts) are able to respond to a wide variety of antigenic stimuli by antibody synthesis and to reject homografts, some (the goldfish) even more rapidly than mammals. The phylogenetically lower fishes, e.g. the guitarfish, will produce antibody to a restricted range of those antigens which have been found to be potent immunogens in mammals, for example, bacteriophage and haemocyanin. Much of this antibody in both teleosts and elasmobranchs was found to sediment rapidly in the ultracentrifuge (19S) and was readily converted, after rupture of disulphide bonds by 2-mercaptoethanol, to inactive fragments similarly to mammalian immunoglobulin M (see Chapter Four).

The most primitive of the true vertebrates are the cyclostomes, which are divided into two main groups; the hagfishes (*Eptatretidae*) and lampreys (*Petromyzonidae*). Hagfishes are considered to be the more primitive on the basis of anatomical structure, biochemical studies of the haemoglobin and plasma ionic concentration, which resembles sea water more closely than that of any other vertebrate. The hagfish (*Eptatretus stoutii*) lives in the mud at the ocean bottom, and preys upon dead or dying fish, entering their mouths and eating the flesh from the inside. All attempts to induce antibody formation with a variety of antigens have failed in this species. Even when antigens were injected in Freund's adjuvant no antibody developed and, in contrast to higher fishes, a necrotizing inflammatory response did not develop at the injection site. Delayed-type hypersensitivity did not follow BCG vaccination. Transfer of homo- and autografts was technically very difficult; however when once the grafts healed successfully, homo- but not autografts were subsequently rejected.

The next step in vertebrate evolution is the higher cyclostome: the lamprey (*Petromyzon marinus*). This parasitic fish can form antibodies against certain antigens, although antibody production may fail even after prolonged stimulation by certain of the antigens which succeed in higher vertebrates. These animals accept autografts, but reject, albeit slowly, homografts of skin. They can develop delayed-type allergic responses to tuberculin. Thus the present evidence indicates that in a vertebrate which may be ancestral to the higher cyclostomes there occurred the evolutionary step which enabled the accomplishment of both humoral and cellular types of immunological responses.

The hagfishes, although lacking all forms of acquired specific immunological responses, do possess a primitive spleen and a primitive haemopoietic organ in the pronephros. These animals have no thymus, no lymph nodes and no foci of lympho-epithelial cells along the gastro-intestinal tract. Their tissues do not contain plasma cells. Their blood contains primitive granulocytes but no large, medium or small lymphocytes. At sites of injury granulocytes and 'mononuclear' cells (presumably macrophage derivatives) infiltrate the local site of inflammation. Recent studies have established that the lamprey possesses an epithelial type thymus, with scanty lymphoid cells, and its blood contains small, medium and large lymphocytes. Foci of lymphocytes are also present in the bone-marrow and spleen. The electrophoretic pattern of lamprey serum includes a single band corresponding in mobility with the fast γ-globulin of mammals (Plate 3.1, following p. 148). However, cells resembling plasma cells have not been found in the tissues.

In contrast to the cyclostomes, the elasmobranch and teleost fishes have thymuses which develop into circumscribed organs. The stained section has a well-marked differentiation into a cortex, which is densely packed with small lymphocytes and a less cellular medulla. A good correlation thus exists between the first phylogenetic manifestations of specific immunity and the development of the thymus and the families of circulating lymphocytes. Phylogenetic findings therefore support the theorem of Dr J. Beard (1900) that the thymus is the progenitor of the lymph nodes and circulating lymphocytes, and in consequence it would be anticipated that immunologically competent lymphocytes could not precede the evolutionary development of the thymus. The same close sequence of events also characterizes the ontogenetic development of the thymus, appearance of circulating lymphocytes and the development of peripheral lymphoid tissues; in the embryo immunological responses have not been shown to precede the development of a thymus.

The immunological mechanisms shown to be present in the lamprey appear to be less complete than those of the elasmobranch fishes, as judged by the number of different antigens which can call forth successful antibody production in the latter. Even so, the mechanisms available to the elasmobranchs are very primitive, and, unlike teleost fishes and mammals, their immunoglobulins appear to contain only a single class of heavy chain. Thus, although both heavy molecular weight (19S) and light (7S) immunoglobulins have been found in sharks, both molecular species had identical heavy chain structure.

Particular interest attaches to the development of immunological systems in the birds which are unique in possessing the lymphoid organ; the bursa of Fabricius, in addition to the thymus. The immunological functions which are embodied by the bursa have been defined by studies of neonatally bursectomized birds which in addition have been subjected to whole-body irradiation. These chickens fail to develop later in life the ability to synthesize circulating antibodies. They also fail to produce plasma cells in their tissues and to form germinal centres in their spleens. They do, however, develop normal numbers of circulating lymphocytes and become able to reject homografts of skin and to develop normal reactions of delayed hypersensitivity. This evidence indicates that the bursa of Fabricius may control the development of the germinal centres in the spleen, and the avian cellular mechanism of immunoglobulin synthesis by plasma cells. No organ analogous to the bursa has been found in mammals or amphibia, although speculation has centred on the possibility that some section of the gut-associated lymphoid tissue such as the Peyer's patches and appendix may play such a role.

Throughout phylogeny substantial evidence exists for a correlation of germinal centre formation and immunological memory, defined as ability to react to second antigenic stimuli by significantly faster and greater production of antibody. Both features are present in birds and mammals, including the primitive monotreme: the echidna. Both are absent from such amphibians as the toad *Bufo marinus*. However, the correlation may break down in the case of the lamprey and some of the higher fishes in which it is claimed that a form of immunological memory can occur in animals which lack any organization of their lymphoid tissue into germinal centres.

THE IMMUNOLOGICALLY COMPETENT CELL

The phylogenetic evidence outlined above suggests that the development of specific immunological competence coincides with the development of lymphocytes, and that these depend upon the presence of a thymus gland. In recent years much evidence, amounting to proof, has been accumulated that in mammals immunologically competent cells do indeed form part of the population of lymphocytes. However, the term *lymphocyte* is used to describe a variety of morphologically rather similar cells whose immediate origins and life cycles are undoubtedly different, and it is necessary to discuss briefly what is meant by this term. Lymphocytes are described as small, medium or large, based mainly upon their size when examined in stained smears of cell suspensions. Such a classification is bound to be arbitrary, especially since the cells are subjected to a variable degree of distortion during preparation of the smears, but, as will emerge below, it does in fact separate groups of cells whose functions and life cycles are distinct.

Small Lymphocytes

These rather featureless cells are 6–10 microns in diameter, and have a dense (pachychromatic) nucleus in which the chromatin occurs in condensed clumps. In conventionally stained preparations no nucleolus is detectable, though a small nucleolus is found in appropriately cut thin sections examined by electron microscopy. The cytoplasm is scanty and stains pale blue with Romanovsky stains. Electron microscopy (Plate 3.2, between pp. 148–9) reveals the presence of mitochondria, and a definite, small Golgi apparatus. Free ribosomes are present, either singly or in rosettes, but are fewer than in most other active cells. Endoplasmic reticulum is usually absent, though some lymphocytes contain a few short filaments or vesicles.

Small lymphocytes in fact have the general appearance of nuclei surrounded by just sufficient cytoplasm to keep them alive. Except in certain circumstances mentioned below there is no evidence that small lymphocytes are dividing cells and make new DNA (i.e. they do not incorporate radioactive DNA precursors such as ^{3}H-thymidine). However, they synthesize new RNA and protein quite extensively both *in vitro* and *in vivo*. Under tissue culture conditions they are seen to be actively mobile, and have a marked tendency to move around the surface of other cells, especially macrophages, and can sometimes be seen to leave a strand of cytoplasm behind when they move away. Small lymphocytes within lymphoid tissues contain at the most one or two small lysosomes, but in those free in the body fluids, these organelles tend to be more numerous and more prominent.

Cells with the morphological features described above have been estimated to form somewhat under 1 per cent of the total body weight. They are found in large numbers in the blood, in lymphatic vessels (especially in the thoracic duct), in the thymus, in lymph nodes and lymphatic tissue such as the appendix, in the spleen and in the bone marrow. There is much evidence to indicate that despite their similar morphology small lymphocytes form a heterogeneous population, whose composition varies in different tissues. For example, they can be separated by methods depending upon their density into four or more distinct fractions, although the physiological significance of such a separation is obscure. More important is the finding from experiments in which radioactive thymidine was administered continuously so that it was available for incorporation into the DNA of dividing cells, over a period of about three days, and the lymphocytes taken two hours later were examined by autoradiography. The nuclei of virtually all the lymphocytes in the bone marrow were labelled, whereas the proportion labelled in other tissues varied from about 70 per cent in the thymus, 50 per cent in the spleen, 20 per cent in the blood, 10 per cent in the mesenteric lymph nodes and 5 per cent in the thoracic duct. These observations indicated that in the bone marrow and thymus the great majority of small lymphocytes were newly derived from precursors which had divided during the period of infusion, whereas far fewer of those in the nodes and almost none in the thoracic duct were newly formed. They have been interpreted as meaning that there are at least two populations of small lymphocytes, a smaller which is short lived and continuously being regenerated, while the other larger population is much longer lived and regenerated very slowly. These experiments were carried out using rats. Other experiments in the same species, some of which are described below, have pointed to the same conclusion. It is beyond the scope of this book to consider all the evidence upon which current ideas concerning the life cycle of lymphocytes are based, and the reader who wishes to enquire more deeply is referred to the suggestions for further reading relating to this chapter. Some of the experimental methods by which the evidence has been derived are mentioned in Chapter Nine (p. 404). What follows is a brief and necessarily dogmatic outline in order to provide a background for further consideration of the relationship between lymphocytes and immunologically competent cells.

First let us consider the *long-lived small lymphocytes*. The cells from which all lymphocytes arise are undifferentiated *stem cells*, which originate both in the liver and bone marrow during foetal life but only in the bone marrow after birth. Both before and after birth, some stem cells travel via the blood stream to the thymus, where they differentiate to lymphocyte precursors. These divide continuously and rapidly in the thymus to give rise to small lymphocytes, which while resident in this organ are termed thymocytes. Most of the thymocytes appear to die without leaving the thymus, which explains why so large a proportion of these cells are found to be newly formed when their turnover is studied by administering radioactive thymidine. However, a proportion of the thymocytes leave (? via the efferent thymus lymphatics) and are disseminated through the blood to lymphoid tissues such as lymph nodes and spleen. This process begins around the time of birth, before which time lymphoid tissues contain few small lymphocytes. Having once been disseminated from the thymus the small lymphocytes become long-lived—that is they neither die nor divide, and may persist for many months in rodents (or even years in man). They are concentrated in specialized areas of lymphoid tissues, namely the *paracortical* or *marginal zones* of lymph nodes and a sheath surrounding the central artery of the *Malpighian bodies* of the spleen (see Chapter Seven). These are the 'thymus dependent' areas, and the lymphocytes which inhabit them are sometimes termed 'thymus-derived'. Such lymphocytes are not static but circulate continuously around the body. They leave via the efferent lymphatic vessels (and perhaps via the venous blood, having entered the medullary sinuses) and are largely collected in the main lymph stream travelling along the thoracic duct to the blood. From the blood they return to the lymphoid tissues via *postcapillary venules*, which have an unusual type of columnar epithelium through which the lymphocytes pass. In addition to the supply of long-lived lymphocytes derived continuously from the thymus the number of such cells is probably maintained by their replication in the lymphoid tissues themselves. This may depend upon antigenic stimulation, as will be discussed more fully below (p. 120).

A characteristic of the thymus-derived long-lived small lymphocytes is that in the presence of a variety of substances known as 'transforming agents' or 'mitogens' these cells are stimulated to differentiate and to divide, both *in vitro* and *in vivo*. The transforming agents include proteins extracted from plants (e.g. red kidney beans, pokeweed) which are associated but not identical with the lectins mentioned in Chapter Six; an agent associated with streptolysin S, derived from streptococci; and a factor present in filtrates from strains of staphylocci which produce α-toxin. These agents have similar actions on small lymphocytes of all species examined, ranging from the primitive larval lamprey to man. How they act is unknown, though there is some circumstantial evidence that they all cause mild damage to lysosomes, and that their action is prevented by agents such as hydrocortisone which increase lysosomal stability. The earliest effect described is to cause increased synthesis of RNA, then of proteins, and finally, after 36–48 hours, of DNA. The cells increase in size; the nucleus becomes larger and the chromatin mesh more open (leptochromatic) and one or two nucleoli become visible, and the cytoplasm is more extensive and more basophilic. After 72 hours in tissue culture most of the cells have the appearance of haemocytoblasts, and many undergo mitosis. The cytoplasm of the cells at this stage usually contains several vesicular bodies which correspond to lysosomes, and the cells have a considerable general resemblance to activated macrophages. It has been claimed that they may synthesize immunoglobulins, and that in the case of stimulation by pokeweed mitogen they come to resemble plasma cells precursors, but these claims are open to criticism for technical reasons. Under certain circumstances (p. 123) a similar transformation occurs when lymphocytes from animals with specific cell-mediated immunity to an antigen are incubated with the antigen, and there is evidence that such transformed cells may revert to what are morphologically typical lymphocytes.

The effect of kidney bean mitogen on human peripheral blood lymphocytes is often used as a convenient method for obtaining cells in mitosis suitable for analysis of their chromosomes. Cultures are carried out in the presence of low concentrations of colchicine, which arrests mitosis in the metaphase, when the chromosomes are separate and can be seen by staining by the periodic acid-Schiff technique. When lymphocytes were examined taken from subjects who had received large doses of X-irradiation (for therapeutic purposes) it was found that a proportion of the mitotic figures contained bizarre chromosomes, so abnormal that the daughter cells could not have survived and divided a second time. This was interpreted as implying that the chromosomal damage resulted from the earlier X-irradiation, and that the cells could not have undergone mitosis since the time when the damage was inflicted. Since the lymphocytes were nevertheless present in the circulation they must have survived in the body since that time. The interval between irradiation and the blood examination was in some instances as long as ten years and this observation provides striking confirmation of the existence of long-lived lymphocytes in man.

The origin and life cycle of *short-lived small lymphocytes* is uncertain, and probably complex. As has already been mentioned, the thymus contains many such cells within it, of which the great majority appear to die without leaving this organ, and their function is unknown. In a thymectomized animal, even when any existing stock of small lymphocytes in the thymus-dependent areas of lymphoid tissues is depleted (by, for example, X-irradiation) and the number of small lymphocytes in the thoracic duct lymph is very small, the number in the blood does not fall correspondingly. However, those in the blood are now largely of the short-lived variety. It is probable that many of them arise from the bone marrow, and include stem cells with small-lymphocyte morphology and perhaps also the precursors of free or wandering macrophages (such as those found in the peritoneal cavity), which are known to have their origin in the bone marrow. Another possible origin is from the 'blast' cells of the germinal centres of lymphoid tissues (see Chapter Seven, p. 273). These are not affected by removal of the thymus, and are known to divide frequently. It is uncertain what is their origin and to what sort of cells they give rise, but one possibility —at present subject to dispute—is that they are the progenitors of lymphocytes which are in turn the precursors of antibody-forming cells found in the medulla of lymph nodes and spleen. This problem will recur in considering the function of the bursa of Fabricius of birds, and the evidence that immunoglobulin production may be dissociated from specific cell mediated immunity (p. 105).

Medium and Large Lymphocytes of Tissue and Lymph

The terms 'medium' and 'large' lymphocytes are commonly used in different senses by haematologists in their examination of blood smears on the one hand, and immunologists examining lymphoid tissues or lymph on the other. The term medium lymphocyte is not really useful, since it tends to include the larger forms of small lymphocyte and the smaller forms of large lymphocyte, and we shall attempt to define large lymphocytes only.

Large Lymphocytes of the Haematologist

This cell is seen in blood smears stained by Romanovsky dyes as a cell 12–16 μm in diameter, with an ovoid nucleus which stains deeply and contains large chromatin masses separated by lighter fissure-like lines. A small indentation in one of its long sides is fairly common. Nucleoli are not seen and mitoses are rare. The fairly extensive cytoplasm is clear, transparent, stained a uniform pale greenish-blue and is empty except for a few azure granules. The nature and function of these cells is at present uncertain.

In certain conditions (e.g. infectious mononucleosis) large lymphocytes resembling those described below are also seen in the blood. They are commonly referred to as 'irritation' or 'Turk' cells.

Large Lymphocytes of Tissue and Lymph

The term large lymphocyte is applied to cells which are readily recognizable in thoracic duct lymph, or in suspensions of cells from lymphoid tissues. The diameter of such cells is greater than 8 μm. With Romanovsky stains the nucleus has a fine granular structure. Nucleoli are not obvious though they may be demonstrated by special methods. Mitotic figures are seen in a proportion of the cells. The cytoplasm is more basophilic than that of the small lymphocytes, and may be deeply basophilic. A characteristic feature of such cells is that they incorporate tritiated thymidine into their DNA when incubated for short periods *in vitro*, and they are presumably cells preparing for mitosis. In this respect and in their general morphology they resemble small lymphocytes in the early stages after stimulation by immunogens to undergo transformation.

The origin and fate of large lymphocytes has been studied less intensively than those of small lymphocytes. After transfusion of radioactively labelled large lymphocytes from the thoracic duct of rats into other syngeneic rats many became lodged in the stroma of the villi of the small intestine, where they came to resemble immature plasma cells, while others appeared to divide and give rise to new labelled small lymphocytes.

Small Lymphocytes as Immunologically Competent Cells

The first clear demonstration that immunologically competent cells were to be found in the population of lymphocytes came from experiments on rats which had indwelling cannulae in their thoracic ducts, such that the cells emerging via the thoracic duct lymph could be removed while the cell-free lymph could be returned via a vein. During the first 24 hours of thoracic duct drainage some 10^9 cells were collected, of which the great majority (about 95 per cent) were 'small' and the remainder were 'medium' or 'large' lymphocytes. As thoracic duct drainage was continued the number of small lymphocytes in the lymph gradually decreased, and simultaneously the blood and the lymph nodes and spleen became almost completely depleted of lymphocytes from the 'thymus dependent' areas (p. 274). The number of large lymphocytes in the lymph was not correspondingly diminished. After the thoracic duct fistula was closed the small lymphocyte population was slowly restored during the course of the next 4 to 5 weeks.

The small lymphocytes could be readily distinguished from medium and large lymphocytes by incubating the lymph with added ^3H-labelled thymidine, since the small lymphocytes failed to incorporate the label into their nuclei whereas almost all the other cells did so. Furthermore, when the thoracic duct cells were incubated at 37° for 24 hours with constant shaking the small lymphocytes survived intact whereas the others all died. This provided a means for preparing small lymphocytes in virtually pure suspension, and thereby for testing the effects of returning a pure population of small lymphocytes to the depleted rats. A population of cells relatively enriched in medium and large lymphocytes could be obtained from thoracic duct lymph taken after 4 or 5 days' drainage.

The rats which had been drained of lymphocytes in this way for 5 days or more proved to be unable during the next few weeks to make antibody (or made only very small amounts) in response to a *primary* injection of powerful immunogens, such as sheep erythrocytes or tetanus toxoid, which elicited a good antibody response in normal rats. However, their capacity to respond was immediately and completely restored by injection of 10^9 small lymphocytes from the thoracic duct lymph of a normal syngeneic rat. Injection of a corresponding number of large and medium lymphocytes, with a much smaller number of small lymphocytes, did not restore the capacity to make an antibody response. These experiments demonstrated that small lymphocytes were necessary for an antibody response to occur, but did not rule out the possibility that the function of such cells was secondary—e.g. that they performed some nonspecific nutritive function. However, when the small lymphocytes used for restoration of the depleted rat were taken from an animal which had been made immunologically tolerant to sheep erythrocytes (by repeated injections soon after birth) the capacity to respond to sheep erythrocytes was *not* restored, although that to tetanus toxoid was. There was thus no doubt that the immunologically competent cells for a primary antibody response must themselves be small lymphocytes. This conclusion is supported by many other observations that destruction or absence of small lymphocytes is accompanied by failure to make antibodies, and it may be regarded as firmly established although, as will appear below, it is not yet clear which cells among those classed as small lymphocytes are actually involved.

Small lymphocytes also include the immunologically competent cells responsible for the cell-mediated specific immunity reactions such as homograft rejection and delayed-type hypersensitivity discussed later in Chapters Twelve and Thirteen. Again one of the crucial experiments to prove this was done with thoracic duct small lymphocytes. It involved administering small lymphocytes from rats of a highly inbred strain (A) to other rats which were first generation (F_1) hybrids between strain A and a second inbred strain B which differed from A in respect of some of the transplantation antigens. The F_1 hybrid recipient rats, being genetically A/B, were foreign to the A strain donor cells in respect of the antigens derived from the B parent, but since both possessed the antigens characteristic of the A strain the donor cells would not be recognized as foreign by the A/B recipient. Thus a one-way graft *versus* host reaction (see Chapter Thirteen) would be expected, which, in the rat, results in death of the recipient within a few days. Quite small numbers (less than 2×10^5) of small lymphocytes were found to produce this reaction, whereas one hundred times as many large lymphocytes could not do so. Small lymphocytes which had been killed were totally ineffective. Many other experiments, mainly involving the passive transfer of cell-mediated specific immunity of various kinds from one animal to another, have confirmed that such immunity or reactivity is transferred by living cell populations which include small lymphocytes, and not when these are excluded. Furthermore, when certain categories of small lymphocytes—notably those associated with the thymus-dependent areas of lymphoid tissues are absent or destroyed—cell-mediated specific immunity does not develop.

'*Memory*' *cells*—that is the cells responsible for the enhanced response which follows a subsequent contact with the immunogen—must also be classed among the small lymphocytes. This was clearly shown by an experiment similar to that described above. Rats were immunized by a single *primary* injection of a bacteriophage of *E. coli* ØX, which elicited a sharp antibody response, followed by a gradual decline of the level of circulating antibody until it returned to that found in normal uninjected rats. About a year after the primary injection the rats were shown to respond to a second injection of ØX by rapidly forming large amounts of antibody, much larger than the response to a similar injection administered to normal rats of the same age. Some of the primed rats were subjected to thoracic duct drainage, and the small lymphocytes so obtained were transferred to previously uninjected syngeneic rats which had been irradiated shortly beforehand with a dose of X-rays (800 roentgens) sufficient to destroy their own lymphocytes and to render them incapable of responding at all to the immunogen on their own. These recipient rats responded to administration of ØX by making antibody as fast and almost as well as if they had been the donors themselves. In other experiments thoracic duct lymphocytes from rats primed with tetanus toxoid have been incubated briefly with the immunogen *in vitro*, washed, and then transferred to *mice* lethally irradiated but capable of surviving for a week or more. The spleens of the mice two or three days later were found to contain large numbers of plasma cells (at various stages of development) making specific antibody to tetanus toxoid, and these cells were shown to be of *rat* origin. Such experiments prove that 'memory' cells can be found among the small lymphocytes in the thoracic duct; that they can be stimulated to turn into antibody-forming cells even by contact with the antigen *in vitro*; and they also showed, incidentally, that the stimulated 'memory' cells settled in those areas of lymphoid tissue in which antibody-producing cells are normally found in an intact animal to which antigen has been administered.

These experiments did not show, however, that *all* memory cells are small lymphocytes which circulate via the thoracic duct. The primed donor mice subjected to thoracic duct drainage for five days, which would suffice to abolish or greatly diminish their capacity to give a primary response, were found to respond (after closing the fistula) to secondary stimulation by making antibody almost as well as did primed mice which had not been operated upon. This implies that a considerable proportion of the 'memory' cells remained in the donors, despite thoracic duct drainage. Whereabouts in the lymphoid tissues such cells reside, and what they look like, are at present not known.

Although immunologically competent cells can now be accepted as being numbered among the population of lymphocytes, a great many questions remain to be answered such as about their origin and life cycle, the mechanism whereby they interact with antigens, and the extraordinary diversity of specific responses which they can make. Some of these questions will be discussed later in this chapter.

One further observation needs to be mentioned at this stage. This is that some experimental observations have indicated that for an antibody response to foreign erythrocytes to be made in mice the presence (and presumably cooperation) of two different kinds of cells is required. One of these kinds of cell appears to be derived directly from the bone marrow, and the other directly or indirectly from the thymus. Both are present in lymphoid tissues such as the spleen. They have not been distinguished morphologically, but can be separated by methods depending upon fine differences in their density. These observations are very recent, and their significance is difficult to evaluate. At present they are interpreted as implying that the thymus derived cells are involved in the initial specific interaction with antigen but that the bone-marrow-derived cells synthesize the specific antibody. If this interpretation is correct, and similar observations are made with other immunogens, the current concept of what is an immunologically competent cell will clearly require revision.*

Wasting Disease Following Neonatal Thymectomy

Many workers have observed that mice, and some other rodents, subjected to thymectomy a few hours after birth not only lose their capacity to develop cell-mediated specific immunity and have a diminished capacity to make primary antibody responses, but develop within a few weeks or months a characteristic syndrome of 'wasting disease'. A similar syndrome follows neonatal administration of large doses of hydrocortisone, which damages lymphocytes in the thymus and elsewhere so severely as to amount effectively to

* See p. 146.

thymectomy lasting during the first weeks of life. This syndrome includes sudden cessation of normal growth followed by loss of weight, ruffled fur, hunched posture, oedema round the eyes, diarrhoea and death. The lymphoid tissues show the expected depletion of small lymphocytes, but there is proliferation of reticulum cells both in the cortex and the medulla and large numbers of plasma cells are present. The skin and the intestinal wall are paper thin, and the intestinal villi markedly atrophied. Many mice (but not all) when they die show evidence of viral hepatitis, of varying degrees of severity.

The incidence of wasting disease following neonatal thymectomy varies from strain to strain and from laboratory to laboratory. It is always prevented by transfusion of syngeneic spleen cells, but not by transfusion of pooled normal serum given as a source of antibodies against ambient microbes. In several ways the syndrome resembles the 'runt' disease produced by severe graft *versus* host reactions (see Chapter Thirteen) and there has been considerable speculation about its causation. Some light is thrown upon this by the observation that wasting can sometimes be prevented by continuous administration of broad spectrum antibiotics, and that it does not occur in neonatally thymectomized mice which are maintained under completely germ-free conditions. When such mice are later removed to a conventional environment, however, wasting disease ensues some weeks later. Thus the wasting must in some way be due to infection, and is probably associated with increased susceptibility to viruses rather than to bacteria.

It is an interesting observation that neonatally thymectomized mice maintained germ free showed notably *less* immunological impairment than did similar mice in a normal environment, as judged by their capacity to reject homografts or to make antibodies against non-infectious test antigens. This would appear to weaken the case for the key role of the thymus as the source of immunologically competent cells. It can be argued however that neonatally thymectomized mice possess a relatively small complement of such cells, which were seeded from the thymus before birth, and that, in the absence of antigenic stimulation from exogenous infective agents, a higher proportion will be available to respond to the test antigens.

The Role of the Bursa of Fabricius in Birds

It has already been mentioned that in the chicken extirpation of the bursa of Fabricius at the time of hatching results in a diminished germinal centre formation in the lymphoid tissues, fewer plasma cells and weaker antibody responses—even though the small lymphocyte population and the development of cell-mediated immunity are apparently unaffected. If young birds are first subjected to bursectomy and then irradiated with a large but not lethal dose of X-rays the effect of bursectomy is exaggerated, and some (but not all) investigators have found that after recovery from the effect of the X-irradiation birds so treated completely lacked germinal centres and plasma cells and were incapable of making immunoglobulins. Nevertheless the thymus and the thymus-dependent areas of the lymphoid tissues regained their normal appearance, with a full complement of small lymphocytes, and allograft rejection was unimpaired. If the thymus tissue (but not the bursa) was totally removed before X-irradiation was performed the situation was reversed. Those birds which recovered lacked small lymphocytes in the thymus-dependent areas of lymphoid tissues, but germinal centres and plasma cells were prominent and immunoglobulin production was undiminished. Despite this, such birds were found not to make the expected antibody responses to injection of various potential immunogens. Not all investigators have obtained such clear-cut results as those described above. Nevertheless there is a strong case for considering that the capacity of birds to make immunoglobulins is in some way dependent upon the presence of the bursa. This organ at hatching consists of numerous follicles. They have an epithelial lining derived from endodermal cells, which proliferate to form a medulla among which are numerous lymphocytes, the origin of which is uncertain. It has been proposed that they are actually derived from epithelial cells, but it is perhaps more probable —following the analogy of the thymus—that they are derived from mesenchymal stem cells which become lymphocytes under the influence of the epithelium. It is also possible that some are derived from cells which have migrated from the thymus. Outside the medulla is a cortex, containing large numbers of small lymphocytes which are thought to have migrated from the medulla, but it is not known at present what is their subsequent fate.

Immunoglobulin-producing cells have not been found in the

bursa itself. Furthermore the bursa involutes at the time of sexual maturity, which is actually before the capacity of fowls to make antibody responses has reached its peak. The organ cannot therefore be directly concerned with immunoglobulin production. Its function may be described (though not explained) in terms of 'conditioning' the cells which pass through or arise in it so that they form germinal centres and plasma cells, in a way somewhat similar to that in which the thymus 'conditions' lymphocytes which settle in and migrate through the thymus-dependent areas. In view of the evidence that in thymectomized and irradiated birds immunoglobulin production may be normal while specific antibody responses are defective, it seems that thymus-derived cells must be required for specific proliferation of antibody-producing cells to take place.

No exact counterpart to the avian bursa of Fabricius has been found in man or other mammals, although there are suggestions that perhaps the tonsils and the lymphoid tissues of the gut may play an analogous role. The justification for considering the subject at such length in this chapter is twofold. Firstly that in birds we have an example of apparent dissociation of cell-mediated immunity from specific antibody responses, associated with the function of two distinct organs. Secondly that clear-cut examples of a similar dissociation are found in certain human immunological deficiency diseases, such as hypogammaglobulinaemia and thymic agenesis discussed in Chapter Eight. An explanation for the findings in birds is likely to be relevant to those in man.

The Life Cycle of Immunologically Competent Cells

It is possible to formulate a hypothetical scheme which takes into account many of the observations mentioned in the preceding pages along the following lines:

The *stem cells* from which lymphocytes originally arise are in the bone marrow (and in the liver during foetal life). From the bone marrow some travel *via* the bloodstream to the thymus, where they give rise to thymus lymphocytes (thymocytes) as a result of intensive multiplication. The great majority of the thymocytes die within the thymus, but some leave *via* the efferent lymphatics and populate the 'thymus dependent' areas of lymphoid tissues. Residence within the thymus confers a special property upon the lymphocytes which is manifested not only by their tendency to migrate to these defined areas of lymphoid tissues, but also by their becoming capable of longevity and by their continuous circulation from lymphoid tissues *via* the efferent lymphatics to the thoracic duct and into the blood stream, whence they return (*via* postcapillary venules) to the same areas of lymphoid tissues. This property is likely to depend upon some special characteristic of the cell surface, though no such characteristic has been identified or proved. Such cells are immunologically competent, in the sense that they (or some of them) respond to stimulation following interaction with those antigens which elicit cell-mediated specific immunity by undergoing a process of differentiation and multiplication to form an increased population of 'specifically reactive' lymphocytes, as described later in this chapter. The same cell population may contain precursors of cells responsible for making circulating antibody against some antigens—possibly against all—but there is a strong indication that in birds antibody secretion requires the participation of other lymphocytes dependent upon the bursa of Fabricius. There are hints that a similar situation applies in mammals, although the role of the analogue to the avian bursa has not been ascribed to any one site in lymphoid tissues.

The entry of stem cells from the bone marrow into the thymus and of seeding of lymphocytes from the thymus to the lymphoid tissues normally continues, at a diminishing rate, throughout life. Nevertheless, lymphocytes which have once been seeded in this manner must be able to continue an independent existence, multiplying in the lymphoid tissues and retaining their special characteristics in the absence of a thymus. There is direct evidence, using chromosome markers, that this is so, but it must also follow from two well-attested observations. The first is that the immunological competence of a neonatally thymectomized mouse can be completely restored by a transfusion of spleen cells from a normal adult syngeneic mouse, and this restoration appears to persist indefinitely in most, but not all, mice; the second is that thymectomy of animals in adult life, or even a few weeks after birth, results in no obvious impairment of their immunological capacity, although if tested for carefully a slow and gradually increasing impairment can be demonstrated.

Although seeding of lymphocytes to the lymphoid tissues is probably the main way in which the thymus exerts its effects, it also appears to have a function, which might be described as hormonal, exercised by the thymus epithelial cells. The evidence comes from three kinds of observation. The first is that the lymphocyte levels and immunological capacity of neonatally thymectomized mice can be restored (to a variable extent) by implanting grafts of thymus tissue enclosed in cell-impermeable diffusion chambers. The second observation is that neonatally thymectomized mice which become pregnant and deliver a litter of babies also become restored immunologically. By the use of chromosomal markers the exchange of cells between the mother and foetus was excluded as accounting for this, as was the hormonal effect of pregnancy *per se*, and the most probable explanation is the transfer from the foetuses of a humoral thymic factor to the mother. Thirdly, thymus grafts can restore neonatally thymectomized mice even when the grafts are allogeneic and have been irradiated with a dose of X-rays sufficient to destroy their thymocytes but not their epithelial cells. These and other observations indicate that some humoral influence from the thymus epithelium (which has indeed been shown by histology to contain unique secretory granules of unknown function) enables stem cells to mature into immunologically competent small lymphocytes without necessarily passing through the thymus. It is a remarkable observation that this influence apparently need act only temporarily, since removal of the thymus graft after one or two weeks still leaves the mice at least partially restored immunologically. Much effort has been directed towards isolating a hormone from the thymus which could mimic the effects of thymus grafts. Although some materials have been obtained which are claimed to induce lymphocytosis and to stimulate cellular proliferation in lymph nodes, their chemical nature and therapeutic potentiality remains to be explored.

A theoretically important question is whether immunological capacity can be acquired or reacquired in the total absence of thymus tissue. Congenital total absence of the thymus in man can be accompanied by a condition in which the lymphoid tissues are depleted of small lymphocytes and there is a failure of cell-mediated specific immunity, but germinal centres and plasma cells are plentiful and the overall plasma immunoglobulin level is within normal limits ('thymic agenesis', Chapter Eight). Congenital absence of the thymus can occur as a recessive condition in mice, and such mice, though unusually prone to disease, have been found to possess at least some immunoglobulins. The few children with thymic agenesis studied while still reasonably well were able to make antibody, including secondary type responses, to a variety of antigens.

Mice thymectomized in adult life and then exposed to a *sub-lethal* dose of whole-body irradiation (sufficient to destroy the great majority of small lymphocytes but not to prevent later spontaneous recovery of haemopoiesis) immediately lost their capacity to make primary immunological responses, as did control animals subjected to sham thymectomy and irradiation. However, whereas the latter recovered their immunological capacity within three to four weeks, those which had no thymus required as many months to do so. Secondary responses were relatively little impaired in either group of animals. These experiments imply that regeneration of new immunologically competent cells could occur slowly in the absence of a thymus, but it could not be ruled out that the regeneration was due to a few pre-existing immunologically competent cells which survived irradiation. When similar experiments were carried out using potentially lethal levels of irradiation, and the mice were protected by transfusions of syngeneic bone marrow or foetal liver as a source of stem cells for haemopoiesis, the thymectomized group recovered their capacity to reject homografts and to make antibodies against sheep erythrocytes even more slowly or not at all. This was especially so when the lethal effect of irradiation was counteracted by transfusing foetal liver cells, possibly because this tissue lacks even the few thymus-derived immunologically competent cells which may be present in adult bone marrow. Such thymectomized mice which had received potentially lethal irradiation nevertheless had normal and sometimes even raised immunoglobulin levels. Similar findings have been reported in neonatally thymectomized mice. The capacity of such mice to make primary antibody responses has been found not to be wholly impaired, but rather to be impaired in respect of certain immunogens such as sheep erythrocytes while remaining relatively intact in respect of some others (e.g. haemocyanin). These observations support the view that immunologically competent lymphocytes capable of carrying out cell-mediated immunity responses and *some* antibody responses are only generated in the presence of a thymus. However, it also appears that the formation of germinal centres and development of cells making immunoglobulins (including some specific antibodies) can be independent of the presence of a thymus. Presumably the cells involved are also derived from stem cells in the marrow, but their maturation has occurred without the influence of a thymus hormone. It is an important but unsettled question at present to what extent specific antibody responses can be made in these circumstances, and whether the range and diversity of antibodies present in the immunoglobulin population is restricted.

It has been mentioned above that in birds the development of germinal centres and of plasma cells producing immunoglobulins depends upon the presence of the bursa of Fabricius. Chickens lacking a thymus, but with functioning bursal tissue and normal immunoglobulin levels, are nevertheless stated to be unable to give the expected antibody response following stimulation with certain immunogens. The participation of thymus-derived cells in directing specific antibody responses can therefore not be excluded, even in this species in which thymus and bursa functions are most readily separable experimentally.

Although it is hard to make any unequivocal statement at present, the evidence suggests that some degree of specific antibody production is possible in the absence of the thymus, although the variety and intensity of antibody responses is restricted. The role of the thymus would appear to be on the one hand to supply cells able to engage in specific cell-mediated immunity and on the other to increase the efficiency of antigenic stimulation of specific antibody production. Such an hypothesis would be in accord with the evidence mentioned above (p. 103) that thymus-derived cells are involved in the initial specific interaction with antigen but that bone marrow-derived cells actually synthesize specific antibody.*

THE INTERACTION OF ANTIGENS WITH IMMUNOLOGICALLY COMPETENT CELLS

The nature of antigens forms the subject matter of Chapter Six in which it is explained that the term antigen covers both substances which can evoke a specific immunological response (and are *immunogens* or *immunogenic*) and substances which can interact specifically with pre-existing antibodies but may not be able themselves to evoke a specific response and are properly termed *haptens* or *haptenic*. Immunogens have haptenic properties, but not *vice versa*. At this stage there are only three points which require emphasis. The first is that the feature of an immunogen which is recognized by immunologically competent cells and to which a specific response is made is a specific *surface configuration* or determinant. In the case of a complex immunogen composed of several distinct molecules such a configuration may even involve parts of adjacent molecules.

* See p. 146.

The importance of this lies in its implication that the immunogen when it interacts with the cell which responds to it, must be in an essentially undistorted and undegraded form. The second is that most natural immunogens possess a variety of different potentially haptenic surface configurations. The third, which follows from the first, is that for an immunogen to stimulate an immunologically competent cell its specific determinants must be *available*—i.e. not obscured by pre-existing circulating antibody, for example, which binds so strongly as to mask the determinants. As we shall see later there are circumstances in which the presence of pre-existing antibody can actually prevent or cut short the process of immunization.

Although for many years it was considered possible that immunologically competent cells might be stimulated indifferently by any immunogen—for example that the immunogen actually penetrates the responsive cell and alters its synthetic processes so as to cause it to synthesize new complementary antibody molecules of a kind which it could otherwise never have made—there are powerful arguments why this should not be what actually happens. Some of these arguments are discussed in a later section. It is nowadays considered that the cell responds by making many more molecules of a kind which it was already making (or able to make) by virtue of its genetic constitution. That is, the immunogen *selects* and stimulates only cells already capable of making a specific response to it, rather than instructs indifferent cells to respond. It is assumed that the population of immunologically competent cells contains a very wide variety of individual cells each of which is able to respond only to a limited number (possibly only to one) of specific determinants. The range of possible responses is accounted for by the range of specificities of the individual cells and the intensity of any given response depends upon the number of cells capable of stimulation by the immunogen. An important problem arises about whether any given immunologically competent cell can respond at a given time to more than one specific stimulus, but the discussion of this also will be deferred until later. We shall be concerned in this section with the question of what happens when immunogens and immunologically competent cells interact, and how the different consequences mentioned at the beginning of this chapter follow.

If the responsive cell is specifically selected by the immunogen there must be some means whereby the cell recognizes its presence (i.e. some specific receptor). An obvious possibility would be that the cell which is capable after stimulation of making detectable quantities of antibody against a given immunogen (or, more strictly, immunogenic determinant) normally makes trace amounts of such antibody. If the antibody were present at the cell surface (not necessarily secreted), it would provide a specific means of holding the immunogen in close contact with the cell surface. Although this would not explain how the subsequent events occur, it would at least explain how they might be initiated.

To demonstrate directly that some lymphocytes in a previously unstimulated animal have specific antibody on their surface is liable to be extremely difficult, both because specifically responsive cells may form only a very small proportion of the total population and because the amount of antibody may be minute. Some attempts have been made, using radioactive immunogens labelled at very high specific activities, which indicate that a small proportion of normal lymphocytes do in fact bind a given immunogen, but these findings cannot at present be regarded as proving that this is due to specific antibody. However, there is a considerable weight of evidence that most, if not all, small lymphocytes have traces of immunoglobulin at their surface and that at least some of this is not simply adsorbed from the blood or lymph in which they are bathed but must have been synthesized by them. This does not prove that the immunoglobulin is specific antibody, nor that interaction with an immunogen will stimulate the lymphocytes to make a specific response, but there are two additional observations which add support to the idea that this hypothesis may be true. These observations are as follows:

1. Lymphocytes from the peripheral blood or thoracic duct lymph of animals from several species, which have been immunized so as to manifest specific cell-mediated immunity, are stimulated by contact with the specific immunogen in tissue culture conditions to undergo a process of transformation akin to that induced by the mitogens described above (p. 97). The proportion of lymphocytes so stimulated may be from 5 to 25 per cent. The stimulation by immunogens is undoubtedly due to some specific interaction with the responsive cells. Similarly lymphocytes treated with specific antibody against immunoglobulin are also stimulated to transform—the proportion of cells which do so reaching about 80 per cent. In the latter instance the stimulus is presumably an antigen–antibody

reaction involving immunoglobulin at the lymphocyte surface, and it seems reasonable to infer that in the former the stimulus is similar.

2. When an animal makes an antibody response against an immunogen containing artificially attached determinant groups (such as dinitrophenol) and the avidity (see Chapter Four, p. 179) of the antibody which it makes is measured, it is found that the smaller the amount of immunogen used for immunization the greater is the average avidity of the antibody produced and *vice versa*. This implies that with small amounts of immunogen only those cells are stimulated to respond whose specific receptors are very avid for the immunogen (thereby capturing it in a low ambient concentration), and that the antibody which they go on to make is similarly avid. The detailed argument, and the evidence to support it lie outside the scope of this book, but the implication is clear that the properties of the specific receptor on the cell and of the antibody which it can make resemble one another.

It must be stressed that the thesis that the specific receptor for antigen in an immunologically competent cell is some form of antibody is not proved. Indeed it has difficulty in explaining various phenomena including that of 'carrier specificity' discussed below (p. 133). Nevertheless it has the virtue of simplicity and considerable predictive value, and it is convenient to adopt it for the purposes of the rest of this chapter. It now becomes necessary to consider what determines, and what occurs when interaction of the immunogen with immunologically competent cells results in specific tolerance, cell-mediated immunity, antibody production or memory. In many, or even most instances in the whole animal these different effects may occur simultaneously, affecting different members of the responsive cell population, and the outcome represents the balance between them.

Specific Immunological Tolerance or Paralysis

As has already been stated, the idea that the capacity of an animal to make an immunological response to an antigen might be nullified if the antigen came into contact with the immunological apparatus while this was still immature, was put forward (by F.M. Burnet) to explain why animals do not appear normally to respond to components of their own tissues, even though these are often excellent immunogens in other species. Paul Ehrlich recognized that it might be disastrous if an animal became immunized against itself and coined the term 'horror autotoxicus' to cover the general rule that this did not happen. This term was derived from his idea that antibodies represented cell receptors for nutritive or toxic substances, manufactured in excess and shed into the circulation, and contained the assumption that the body would not make substances toxic to itself and hence would not have cell receptors for such substances. As will appear in Chapter Fifteen, this rule, like other rules, has many exceptions. However, Burnet's prediction was found to be readily verifiable by numerous investigators, who demonstrated that injection of many immunogens into animals of many species at, or shortly after birth produced a state of specific immunological tolerance so that the animals made no immunological response on subsequent challenge with the same immunogen, while responding normally to other unrelated immunogens. This state of tolerance gradually wore off and responsiveness returned after months or years, but it could be prolonged indefinitely by repeated administration of the immunogen. The larger the initial dose of immunogen the longer the state of complete tolerance tended to persist in the absence of subsequent injections. This suggested that the maintenance of tolerance might depend upon the continued presence of the immunogen. However, in several instances evidence was produced that tolerance persisted long after all the immunogen had been cleared from the circulation.

Although the induction of immunological tolerance was originally thought of as a normal phenomenon—rather than as an unexplained exception to the process of immunization—in relation to foetal or newborn animals it soon became evident that it is a normal phenomenon at all ages. When very large amounts of a potential immunogen are administered to adult animals specific tolerance or paralysis may also result. Furthermore when the capacity of the adult animal to make an immunological response is temporarily greatly diminished, as it is in the foetus or the newborn animal, the amounts of antigen required to induce paralysis are—weight for weight—no greater than those which are effective when given at birth. Such a temporary diminution of general responsiveness can be achieved for example by thymectomy or by X-irradiation; also by a variety of antimetabolites or cortisone, as is explained in a later section (p. 116).

The induction of immunological paralysis as described so far involves the use of relatively large quantities of immunogen, substantially *greater* than those normally required to elicit a positive immunological response, and may be termed *'high zone' paralysis*. It stands in contrast to another mode of inducing immunological paralysis, which has only recently been clearly recognized but is of greater significance, namely *'low zone' paralysis*. By this is meant that repeated or continuous administration over a long time of amounts of an immunogen *smaller* than those which elicit a detectable response can also gradually produce specific paralysis. There appears to be a threshold level of immunogen below which no detectable effect results. However, for a number of immunogens in mice it has been found that 'low zone' paralysis results from repeated administration of amounts one to ten thousand times smaller than those required to produce 'high zone' paralysis. When immunogen is administered in amounts lying between these extremes immunization usually results.

In discussing the induction of tolerance or paralysis it is difficult to make general statements, because different immunogens show a wide range of behaviour. This probably depends, among other things, upon the size and complexity (including the number of determinant groups); the rapidity with which they are broken down and eliminated from the body; the extent to which they are taken up by macrophages. However, it is possible to divide antigenic materials broadly into weak and powerful immunogens. Weak immunogens tend to be soluble proteins, phylogenetically not too distant from the host (or other substances possessing relatively few kinds of determinant groups), which are available in the circulation over relatively long periods of time, and which are not rapidly taken up by macrophages. Weak immunogens can often be converted to powerful immunogens by combining them with adjuvants (see Chapter Seven), the effects of which usually include rendering the immunogen less soluble and increasing its uptake by macrophages. Weak immunogens readily cause paralysis, whereas powerful immunogens only do so when administered in enormous doses, often greater than can be achieved in practice.

In order to amplify and to provide a possible explanation of these observations it is necessary to consider whether immunological paralysis can be produced in an animal which has already been primarily immunized and possesses 'memory' cells as well as possibly cells actually secreting antibody. In such an animal it is found that even very small amounts of the immunogen will stimulate a vigorous secondary antibody response, and there is no evidence that 'low zone' paralysis can be produced. Administration of very large amounts of immunogen however can sometimes achieve a subsequent state of paralysis—i.e. it can overcome 'memory'—especially if the immunogen is a weak one, and especially if it is given under circumstances when the possibility of an immunological response is diminished by X-irradiation or immunosuppressive drugs. These findings suggest that 'low zone' paralysis is a phenomenon which involves immunologically competent cells which have not already been stimulated by antigen, and that 'high zone' paralysis involves both these and already primed 'memory' cells.

A partial explanation of these phenomena, which is supported by quite a body of indirect evidence, is as follows:—

When an immunogen interacts with the specific receptors on an immunologically competent cell 'low zone' paralysis is an alternative consequence to stimulation, and is due either to death of the cell or to permanent blocking of its capacity to respond. (It is difficult to devise a means of deciding between or verifying these alternatives, because only a minute proportion of the cells are likely to be involved and a persisting 'tolerant' cell would, by definition, not be detectable by its reactivity with antigen.) What determines that paralysis rather than stimulation should occur is unknown, but there is a suggestion that the availability of the immunogen in free solution, and avoidance of uptake by neighbouring macrophages, may be important. The observation that only antigens which are also immunogens can induce tolerance makes it likely that the cell receptors involved are identical. For all the cells in an animal competent to respond to any given immunogen to become paralysed in this way it seems to be necessary for the antigen to be available to interact with them over a considerable period of time and yet to *avoid causing concomitant immunization.* This is presumably why weak immunogens cause paralysis more readily than powerful immunogens, and also why the induction of paralysis is greatly facilitated when the possibility of concomitant immunization is diminished by immunosuppressive measures, or in circumstances, such as in the neonatal period, when the number of cells capable of responding is small.

In 'low zone' paralysis, then, the potentially reactive cells are thought to be effectively eliminated without ever becoming stimulated. Such an explanation cannot apply to 'high zone' paralysis, however, since the amounts of immunogen required exceed the level at which a specific response is known to result, and furthermore 'high zone' paralysis may be produced in animals which have already made a response to the immunogen and possess 'memory' cells. To explain this it is necessary to anticipate some of the discussion in the following sections, and to state that when immunologically competent cells are stimulated by an immunogen they differentiate and divide to produce on the one hand 'memory' cells and on the other antibody-secreting plasma cells. Further contact with the immunogen stimulates the 'memory' cells to differentiate into plasma cells, which are probably terminal cells (as are erythrocytes) and die without reproducing themselves. The consequence of introducing a sufficiently high concentration of immunogen over a long enough period (several days are required) would be to telescope this process and to cause all the available competent cells and the 'memory' cells to differentiate to plasma cells, by a process of 'suicidal proliferation', and so to exhaust the supply of cells able to respond to the same immunogen on a later occasion. Any antibody produced would normally be undetected because of the overwhelming amount of antigen. It has not been proved that such an explanation is correct, but it is at least consistent with our present knowledge.

It has already been emphasized that immunogens differ enormously in the readiness with which they induce paralysis, and that this depends very much on the physical state in which they are presented. For example bovine gammaglobulin, which is often used as an experimental immunogen, can cause paralysis of adult mice in microgram and of rabbits in milligram doses provided that all aggregated material has been removed—whereas if aggregated material is present it is quite a powerful immunogen even in much higher doses. Flagellin, the purified protein from the flagella of salmonella organisms, is a very powerful immunogen in rats over a wide dose range, whereas a smaller degradation product derived from it causes paralysis in quantities as low as 10^{-9} g. or less. Although any immunogen probably causes paralysis of some cells, the overall effect is generally to stimulate a response, and this is increased by the use of adjuvants.

Specific Immunological Tolerance Produced by Administration of Chemical Sensitizing Agents

It will be discussed later in this book how many chemical agents, such as picrylchloride, which react readily with the body proteins can render these immunogenic by becoming attached as hapten determinant groups (p. 204), and can elicit both cell-mediated immunity and antibody production. The remarkable observation was made that if large amounts of such agents are administered to animals by mouth without touching the skin of the body or the lips, or if they are injected into a mesenteric vein, a state of specific immunological unresponsiveness results such that subsequent application of the agent to the skin causes no immunological response. A possible but at present only hypothetical explanation is that when administered as described the agents combine with proteins of the plasma or the intestinal tract, but that in their passage through the liver all material capable of selective uptake by macrophages is removed. That which escapes to come into contact with immunologically competent lymphocytes acts comparably to the bovine gammaglobulin mentioned above from which aggregated material has been removed, and causes paralysis rather than immunization.

Recovery from Immunological Paralysis

As already mentioned, if no more of the immunogen is administered the capacity to respond eventually returns in a normal animal. There is some evidence that it does so in a piecemeal fashion, and that when the immunogen has a number of different determinants (as most have) responsiveness to one determinant may return before that to another—resulting in a state of partial or 'split' tolerance. Recovery of responsiveness has been found to be greatly but not indefinitely delayed if the tolerant animal has been thymectomized. It can be greatly speeded up, however, by transfusion of normal lymph node or spleen cells (from a syngeneic animal)—an observation which indicates, incidentally, that there is nothing wrong with the internal environment of a tolerant animal such as to prevent cells from responding provided that they are available to do so. In some cases the return of responsiveness has been somewhat accelerated by measures which stimulate regeneration of stem cells and of lymphocytes, such as moderate doses of X-rays. Another way of restoring responsiveness—or 'breaking tolerance' as it is sometimes termed—is to immunize the animal intensively with an immunogen which is antigenically similar to that used to produce paralysis but has some additional determinants towards which the animal is normally responsive. This last method can in fact be used to cause an animal to make antibodies against its own tissue components, and will be referred to again in connection with autoimmune disorders in Chapter Fifteen.

Following the general line of explanation used previously, the recovery from paralysis is considered to be due to the recruitment of new cells competent to respond to the immunogen, which have arisen from precursors which were unaffected by the immunogen at the time when this was present, and were presumably immunologically incompetent stem cells. Evidently the presence of a thymus greatly facilitates the process. To explain the breaking of tolerance by stimulation of a response to a cross-reacting immunogen is more difficult. A possible explanation is that a response is induced to determinants on the original immunogen which are normally not 'recognized' and consequently caused neither paralysis nor stimulation. Although this has been verified, it is not, however, a complete explanation.

Paralysis By Immunogens Which Resist Degradation

Some bacterial capsular polysaccharides, such as those of pneumococcus type III, and some synthetic polypeptides made from the unnatural (D-) form of amino acids, are very resistant to digestion by the enzymes present in the bodies of mice and rabbits. (This may be true for other species also, but has not been tested in them.) It has been found that whereas small amounts (one microgram or less) of such materials elicit a rapid antibody response in mice, administration of larger quantities leads apparently to a long-lasting specific immunological paralysis. No antibody is detectable in the blood even by such very sensitive methods as protection against death after challenge with a minimal number of pneumococci, and no antibody formation is apparently induced by further immunization. Recovery from paralysis eventually occurs, and it has been reported that this is often heralded by the spontaneous appearance of small amounts of circulating antibody.

Immunological paralysis by pneumococcal capsular polysaccharides was the first form of paralysis to be clearly recognized and accepted as such. It now appears, paradoxically, that it is a different phenomenon from the forms of central paralysis discussed hitherto. The reason is that despite the absence of circulating antibody after a paralysing dose of the immunogen, cells making antibody can be detected by testing suspensions of washed lymphoid tissue cells *in vitro*. Antibody does not appear in the circulation because it is mopped up by retained antigen as fast as it is formed. It has been shown that indigestible immunogens of the kind under discussion are taken up rapidly and extensively by phagocytes, and are retained in them for weeks or months, being only slowly broken down or excreted from the body. However, there is evidence that the immunogen is also continuously released from the phagocytes, so that it circulates for a while before being taken up by these cells again. It is thus available to combine with circulating antibody and the complex so formed is rapidly removed by phagocytes, which digest the antibody but retain the immunogen. Whether or not antibody is detectable in the blood will consequently depend upon the balance between the amount made and the amount of antigen available to mop it up.

How far paralysis of this kind, which may be termed 'peripheral' as opposed to 'central', is important biologically is not known. However, it should be pointed out that when animals are immunized by whole pneumococci, rather than purified capsular antigens, they make a good antibody response. This is probably because the organisms, weight for weight, are much better immunogens, stimulating more antibody-forming cells, and perhaps because their associated capsular antigen is better retained or digested within the phagocytes.

CELL-MEDIATED SPECIFIC IMMUNITY

This form of immunological response, and the cellular events which accompany it, are discussed in detail in later chapters. It is sufficient here to state that the response involves the formation of a population of 'sensitized' lymphocytes able to interact specifically with the antigen so as to elicit the phenomena of delayed-type hypersensitivity (Chapter Twelve), and that this property is apparently independent of extracellular antibody. The response occurs typically when the immunogenic stimulus is a living allograft or when a small quantity of an inert immunogen is deposited in a depot (e.g. in the skin) from which it is only slowly released. An especially effective way of doing this is to apply to the skin a reactive chemical, such as picryl chloride or a derivative of oxazolone, which combines with the skin proteins and confers on them a powerful new antigenic determinant group which renders them immunogenic. However, responses of this type form a more or less important component of many responses in which specific antibody formation also occurs. They are markedly increased by mixing the immunogen with certain bacteria or bacterial products (such as the cell walls of mycobacteria, p. 253).

In this chapter we shall describe briefly only those aspects which throw light upon the nature of the response itself. Following the local introduction of an immunogen into an unsensitized animal the first changes are detected in the lymphoid tissue draining the site. After a delay, or lag period, of two or three days there begin to appear in the thymus-dependent areas of the lymph nodes or spleen large pyroninophilic 'blast' cells. During the following days these cells divide (about once in 24 hours in guinea-pigs) giving rise to more cells of the same kind and to small lymphocytes.

Evidence that this is the sequence of events comes from local or systemic administration of a brief 'pulse' of radioactive thymidine, which is incorporated into the nuclei of cells engaged in DNA synthesis at the time of administration. Since the radioactive DNA is divided among the daughter cells, these can subsequently be traced by autoradiography (p. 404). Some large pyroninophilic 'blast' cells and the daughter lymphocytes have been shown to leave the node *via* the efferent lymphatic vessels, whence they enter other nodes and into the general circulation. The animal becomes demonstrably sensitized—i.e. it can manifest specific reactivity characteristic of cell-mediated immunity—from the time when this has occurred, and it is presumed that the sensitized lymphocytes are those which arose in the course of the stimulated cell division. If the nodes draining the site of locally administered immunogen are removed by dissection in the early stage of proliferation, development of cell-mediated immunity is delayed or even prevented (provided that the immunogen does not persist). Furthermore, transfer of the draining nodes, taken when cell proliferation is at its height, to a syngeneic animal confers cell-mediated immunity upon the recipient, in which it may persist for many weeks without further stimulation. No cell proliferation of the type described takes place when the immunogenic stimulus is administered to a specifically tolerant animal. This indicates that the changes are the result of a specific interaction with the immunogen. If the cell proliferation is prevented by some antimitotic agents, which can be used in doses which avoid general toxic effects on the animal, sensitization is prevented.

It has already been pointed out that thymectomy or other procedures which result in the absence of thymus-derived lymphocytes greatly diminish or abolish the capacity to develop cell-mediated immunity. The conclusion is that the response is due to interaction of specifically competent thymus-derived cells with the immunogen, in such a way as to cause these to differentiate into large pyroninophilic blast cells, which divide and give rise to an increased population of daughter lymphocytes which are in turn also able to react with the immunogen. It is not certain whether these daughter lymphocytes have an increased capacity to react (e.g. more or more avid 'receptors' on their surface), though it is possible that this could result from selective stimulation of the more reactive progenitors. However, there is considerable evidence that they retain a very sharp specificity—that is, they only interact effectively with determinants on immunogens identical with or very similar to those which stimulated their formation in the first place. These determinant groups have been shown, by indirect means, to be much larger than the determinant groups with which most circulating antibodies are able to combine. The phenomenon will be discussed under the heading 'carrier specificity' in the section dealing with antibody formation (p. 133). It implies that stimulation occurs as a result of interaction between the postulated receptors and a relatively large part of the surface of the immunogen.

There is some doubt whether the initial interaction between immunogen and responsive lymphocytes takes place within the lymph node or spleen—in which case some of the immunogen must reach these organs—or whether the interaction takes place peripherally, at the site where the immunogen is deposited (e.g. the graft bed or the skin) and is followed by migration of the lymphocytes to the thymus-dependent areas of the draining nodes, as preferred sites for subsequent proliferation. Experiments in which rat thoracic duct cells were perfused through the vascular supply of an allogeneic rat kidney and then returned to the donor rat showed that the latter became sensitized to a subsequent skin graft from the allogeneic rat. This would indicate that peripheral sensitization can occur, but does not prove that it is the only mechanism.

Although the development of cell-mediated immunity is often accompanied by antibody formation against the same immunogen, this does not invariably take place. Furthermore, no convincing evidence has so far been obtained that the large pyroninophilic 'blast' cells or their daughter lymphocytes secrete antibody. These 'blast' cells are sometimes termed 'immunoblasts'—although they are more distinguishable by their function than by their morphology from other primitive cells of the haemopoietic series. They have a large round or oval nucleus, with loosely arranged chromatin and one or two prominent nucleoli; the cytoplasm contains numerous large mitochondria and a prominent Golgi apparatus, but the most striking feature is the large number of ribosomes which are arranged in rosettes or clusters of 3 to 8, and the absence of the endoplasmic reticulum which characterizes a protein-secreting cell (Plate 3.3, between pp. 148–9).

Once cell-mediated immunity has developed it persists for a long time, even though the stimulus (e.g. an allograft) has been removed. This is in agreement with the proposition that the cells involved are long-lived lymphocytes, which continue to recirculate. When the immunogen is introduced on a second occasion a similar process occurs in the lymphoid tissues to that which follows the first introduction, but it takes place rather faster and more intensively. However, there is also a considerable reaction at the site where the immunogen is deposited, due to the local interaction of sensitized lymphocytes which accumulate there. This is described in Chapter Twelve, and will not be discussed further here.

Cell-mediated Immunity and the Lymphocyte Transformation Reaction in vitro

It was described above (p. 97) how long-lived lymphocytes can be stimulated to differentiate and divide *in vitro* under the influence of certain mitogenic agents. A similar transformation, although involving a smaller proportion of the lymphocytes, occurs *in vitro* without the use of mitogenic agents under the following circumstances:

1. When peripheral blood or lymph node lymphocytes (but not thymocytes) from a previously sensitized animal are incubated with fairly high, but non-toxic, concentrations of the specific immunizing agent. There is still some uncertainty whether this transformation is correlated with the presence of cell-mediated immunity rather than of circulating antibody, but the evidence increasingly suggests that it is so.
2. When peripheral blood lymphocytes from two allogeneic strains of animal (or from two human individuals who are not identical twins) are cultured together. Some degree of transformation occurs even when neither donor has been sensitized, for example by a graft, against the other, but is increased when one or both donors were previously sensitized. It has been shown, by treating one or the other set of cells with specific inhibitors of RNA synthesis, that the stimulation is mutual, and by genetic experiments that the stimulation depends upon differences in transplantation antigens (see Chapter Thirteen).

These findings suggest that the transformation reaction is a counterpart to the stimulation of cell-mediated immunity occurring *in vitro*, although under the usual cultural conditions it does not proceed to completion. The observation that among the cells from a previously unsensitized animal there are some which can react to allogeneic transplantation antigens could be taken to indicate that pre-existing specifically competent cells must be present, and it might be expected that their numbers could be calculated by measuring the proportion of cells which transformed. However there is evidence that when specifically sensitized cells interact with the immunogen some factor is released which causes mitosis of unsensitized lymphocytes, and it is consequently not possible from such experiments to decide what proportion were stimulated specifically.

SPECIFIC ANTIBODY FORMATION

The complex nature of antibodies and the detailed features of the cells involved in antibody formation form the subject of separate chapters, which should be read in conjunction with the present. As in the previous section, we shall consider here only those aspects which are relevant to understanding the general nature of antibody responses. It is convenient to consider separately the sequence of events following first contact with an immunogen, before 'memory' (or 'primed') cells are present—the primary response—and the sequence following subsequent contact, when primed cells and usually some specific antibody have been formed—the secondary (or 'booster') response. Nevertheless it commonly happens when immunization is carried out in practice that the immunogen persists in the body for long enough to convert a primary into a secondary response with no hard and fast separation between them.

Before proceeding further some general points need to be made. The first is that two main kinds of antibody need to be considered, which differ in their size and in other important properties discussed in Chapter Four. For convenience they are often referred to in terms of their approximate sedimentation coefficients, namely as 19S immunoglobulins (IgM) and 7S immunoglobulins (mainly IgG and its subclasses). The second point is that conclusions drawn from any study of the formation of antibodies are likely to be influenced greatly by the sensitivity of the methods used for their detection. For example, if 19S antibody is much more active than 7S antibody in a particular test (such as lysing erythrocytes or killing bacteria) the response might appear to consist predominantly of 19S molecules even though equal numbers of 7S molecules were made. The introduction of methods which enable specific antibody formation by single cells to be measured (see Chapter Nine) has considerably modified earlier ideas about the dynamics of antibody responses. A third point is that the most readily interpreted information about antibodies has come from the use of immunogens possessing a minimum number of different kinds of determinants, and especially from those into which a number of similar and strongly antigenic determinant groups have been introduced by chemical reactions *in vitro*. In this way it has been possible to study the response to a single kind of determinant rather than to a mixture. Furthermore it is easier, for technical reasons, to measure the avidity (or association constant—see p. 179) of the antibody and thus to obtain an idea of the degree of exactness with which it fits the antigenic determinant. It is an important characteristic of many antibodies that they will react not only with the immunogen which stimulated their production but also with other molecules bearing similar determinant groups, even though these molecules may not themselves be immunogenic. The significance of this will appear later.

The Primary Response

The sequence of events in primary responses has almost always been studied using potent immunogens such as sheep erythrocytes, viruses (including bacteriophages) or bacterial antigens, but there is no reason to suppose that the general pattern of response does not hold true, with quantitative differences, for other immunogens also.

The time course of onset and the duration of the response varies markedly with the amount and nature of the immunogen and the route by which it is administered. One of the factors involved in this variability may be the extent to which the immunogen persists in the body and remains available to convert a primary response into what is effectively a secondary response, but this is not the only factor. At the risk of over-simplification the following general statements may be made. They relate to a single administration of the immunogen, without added adjuvant materials:

1. Very small amounts of a powerful immunogen tend to elicit the formation of a rapid but transient 19S antibody response with little or no detectable 7S response, although there is usually some generation of 'memory' cells.
2. As the dose of a powerful immunogen is increased the size of the 19S response increases to a maximum, but it remains relatively transient. In addition to the 19S response a 7S response also becomes apparent, whose onset occurs a little later but whose duration is much longer than the 19S response, especially at the higher doses. At the same time 'memory' cells are generated, as discussed below (p. 132).
3. When less powerful immunogens are used the primary 19S and

7S responses are less marked compared with the generation of 'memory' cells.

The results of experiments which illustrate some of these points are given in Fig. 3.2A, B and C. Particularly striking is the difference in time scales between 3.2A and C (days) and 3.2B (weeks).

The rising serum antibody levels reflect the appearance and

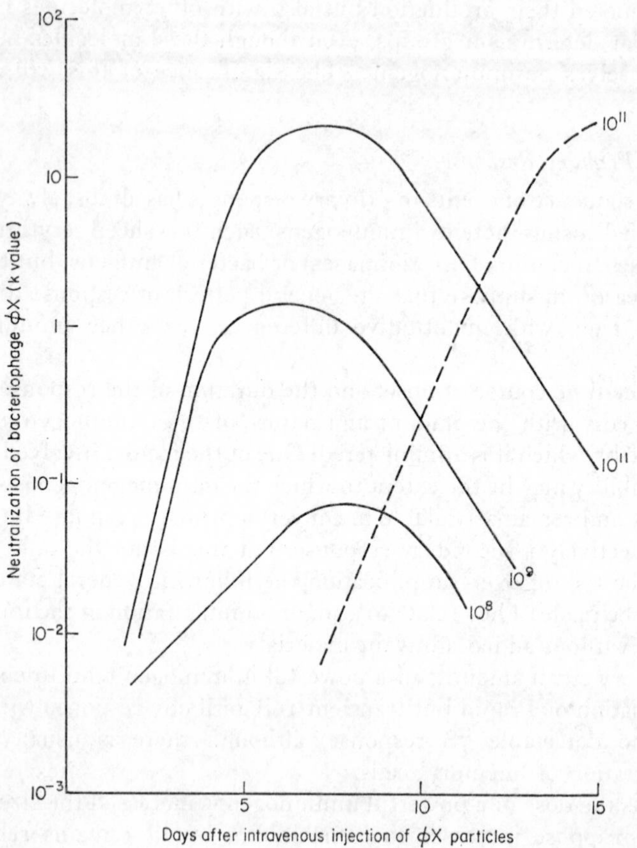

FIG. 3.2A. Serum antibody response in guinea-pigs after primary intravenous injection of graded numbers of phage particles. No 7S response was detectable following administration of the lower doses of phage.

——————— 19S antibody. — — — — — — 7S antibody.

[From Uhr J.W. and Finkelstein M.S., *Progress in Allergy*, 1967, **10,** 43, published by S. Karger, Basel/New York.]

proliferation of antibody-producing cells. It is discussed further in Chapter Seven how such cells first appear in the lymphoid tissue where the immunogen settles. When sheep erythrocytes are injected intravenously they become concentrated in the spleen, and this organ is responsible for the bulk of the antibody produced during

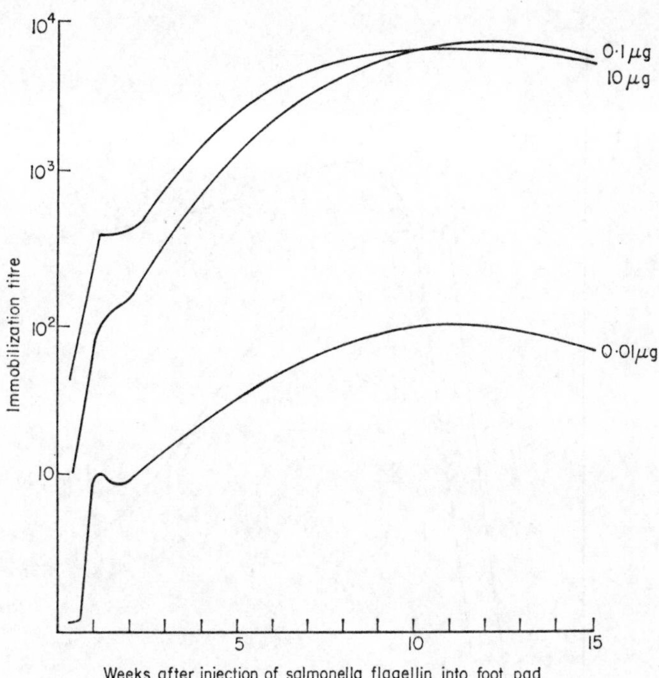

FIG. 3.2B. Serum antibody response in rats after primary injection of graded doses of Salmonella flagella into the footpad. The early response is predominantly 19S antibody but by 11 days the antibody is largely or entirely 7S. Note that the scale of the abscissa is in weeks. [Adapted from Nossal G.J.V., Ada G.L. and Austin C.M., *Australian Journal of Experimental Biology and Medical Science*, 1964, **42**, 286.]

the first days of the response. By examining the antibody-forming cells in the spleens of mice killed at various intervals after a standard dose of sheep erythrocytes the time course of their appearance can be followed. An experiment illustrating this is shown in Fig. 3.2D, which may be compared with 3.2C.

There is a short *lag* period of roughly 12 hours before the number of 19S antibody-forming cells begins to rise above the basal level found in normal animals. The number then increases *exponentially* for 2 or 3 days, after which it declines more slowly. A similar phenomenon is observed in the case of the 7S antibody producers, but the lag period is longer (this is actually an oversimplification,

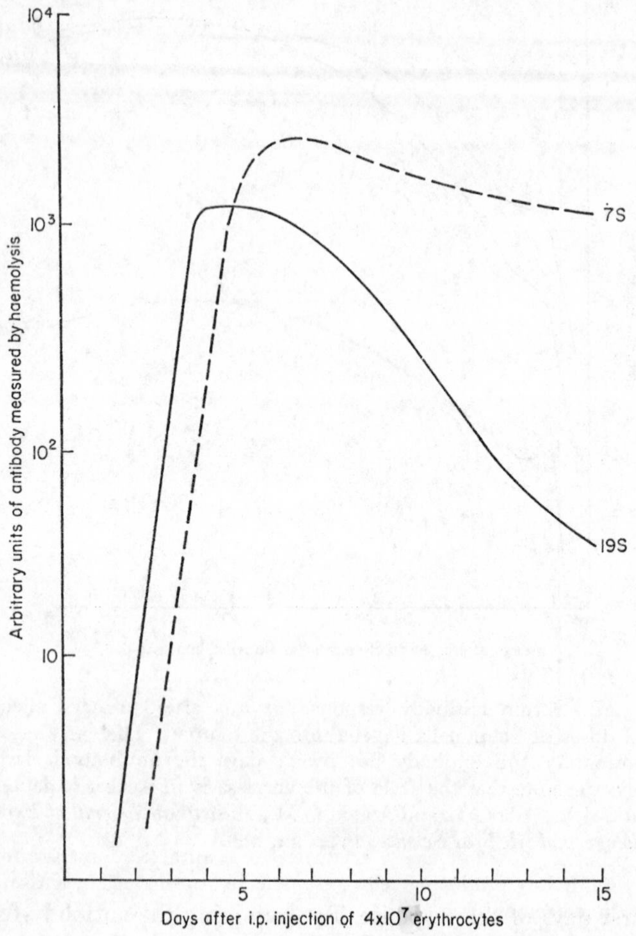

FIG. 3.2C. Serum levels of 19S haemolysin and 7S haemolysin (enhanced by anti-mouse Ig) in mice after administration of 4×10^7 sheep erythrocytes intraperitoneally. [Curves drawn from data kindly supplied by Mrs H.R. Anderson.]

because the duration of the lag period differs for cells producing antibodies of the various IgG subclasses). The increase in the number of 19S and 7S antibody-producing cells has been shown in many experiments to be mainly due to cell multiplication with a

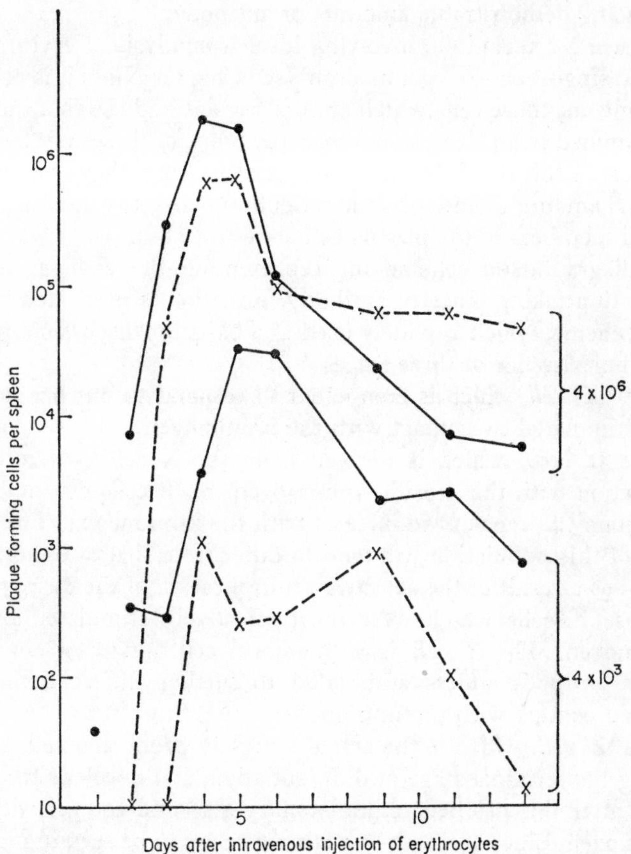

FIG. 3.2D. The number of antibody-secreting cells in the spleen of mice after different doses of sheep erythrocytes administered intraperitoneally. The 7S antibody producing cells were detected by the use of anti-mouse Ig to enhance haemolysis.

——— 19S antibody-producing cells.

– – – – 7S antibody-producing cells.

[Modified from Wortis H.H., Taylor R.B. and Dresser D.W., *Immunology*, 1966, **11**, 603.]

mean generation time of 7–8 hours, which is about the maximum rate of cell division for mammalian cells; however, in the case of the cells producing 19S antibody there is also evidence that in the early part of the response some antibody-producing cells must be recruited *without* cell division from a population which were not previously producing demonstrable amounts of antibody.

By using a technique involving local haemolysis of erythrocytes around single cells in a gel medium (see Chapter Nine) it is possible to single out those cells which are making antibody so that they can be examined in an electron microscope. Some of these cells have the appearance of small lymphocytes, except that they contain an unusual amount of endoplasmic reticulum, whereas others are more typical members of the plasma cell series (p. 288).

A diagrammatic scheme for representing the changes in cell population taking place in antibody formation is presented below. This scheme, which is widely used as a basis for discussion, postulates the existence of three stages:

The '*X*' *cell*, which is competent to respond to but has not yet been stimulated by contact with the immunogen.

The '*Y*' *cell*, which is derived from the X cell as a result of interaction with the specific immunogen. Such cells can multiply, and retain the capacity to interact with the immunogen. The reactivity of this population will tend to differ from that of the original X cells as a result of the selective multiplication of the descendants of those X cells which were most effectively stimulated by the immunogen. The Y cell is a 'memory' cell and does not itself secrete antibody unless stimulated to further differentiation by renewed contact with the immunogen.

The '*Z*' *cell*, which is the actual antibody-producing cell, representing the terminal stage of differentiation, and develops from the Y cell after this has been stimulated by a second contact with the immunogen. Since antibody-containing cells can be seen in mitosis, the Z cells are presumably also capable of multiplication, although the plasma cells finally produced are possibly end cells.

The Z cell can readily be identified, by immunofluorescence for example, but the Y and X cells are hypothetical in the sense that their existence is deduced only by inference. However, they are presumably to be found among the population of lymphocytes, for reasons given earlier in this chapter.

Without considering the very important problems of where and how interaction with the immunogen occurs, and of how cells arise making different classes of antibody, a variety of the possible pathways in which antibody producers and 'memory' cells arise are illustrated in Fig. 3.3. In this figure the different pathways illustrated

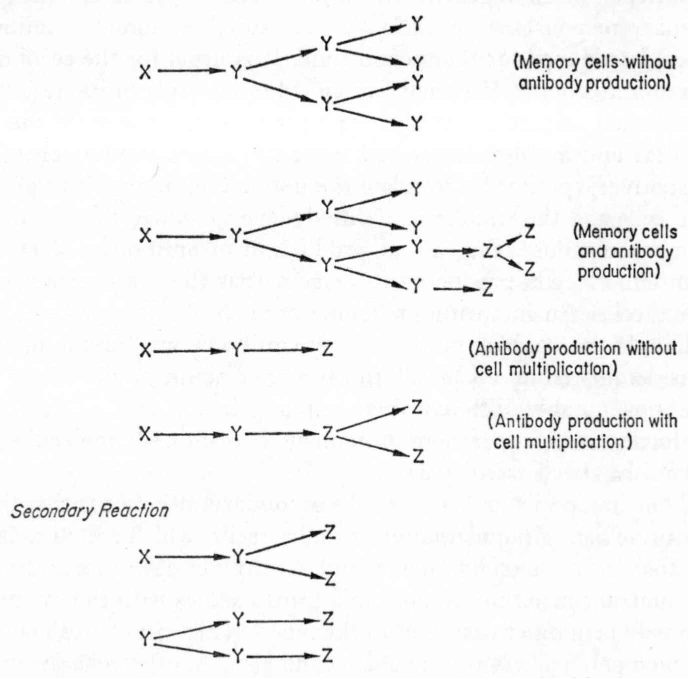

FIG. 3.3. Hypothetical scheme for the changes in the population of cells involved in primary and secondary antibody responses.

are cut short quite arbitrarily, and the extent to which proliferation may continue along any given pathway probably depends upon the amount and persistence of the immunogen.

'Memory' Cells and the Secondary Response

The difference between a primary and a secondary or subsequent antibody response after the primary has had time to die away is that repeated contact with the original immunogen elicits a brisker and more extensive antibody formation (Fig. 3.1). Furthermore, a quantity of immunogen which caused only a feeble or undetectable primary response can evoke very substantial amounts of antibody when introduced for the second time. It is usual for the secondary response to consist of a relatively short burst of 19S antibody (rather like the primary response, although the total amount made may be greater) and a much larger and more prolonged production of 7S antibody. Experiments to relate the population of antibody-producing cells and the circulating antibody levels confirm that, as in the primary response, the rate of production of antibody reflects the numbers of cells producing it—except that there are many more active cells. An interesting outcome of such observations was that although the rate of production of antibody was found to vary considerably from cell to cell, the average amount produced per cell was not notably different between a primary and a secondary response (an average rate of more than 1000 antibody molecules per second has been calculated).

The characteristic feature of the secondary response is that there is a pre-existing population of 'memory' cells, which are stimulated by the immunogen to divide and to differentiate into antibody producers. Since the response to a third contact with the immunogen may be greater than that to the second (Fig. 3.1) a fresh supply of 'memory' cells is presumably made also. Another characteristic feature, which is discussed further below, is that repeated stimulation with the same immunogen often leads to the production of antibody with increased avidity.

19S and 7S Antibody

It has been pointed out that both primary and secondary antibody responses involve the production of 19S and 7S antibody, and that 19S antibody is usually detectable a day or two before 7S and its production is relatively transient. These observations have been taken as suggesting that cells which start by making 19S antibody may switch over to making 7S antibody. Such a phenomenon would pose theoretical problems and is very difficult to demonstrate experimentally, although an experiment has been recorded which suggests that it may occur. However, a switchover of this kind cannot take place as a rule, since the development of some 7S producing cells has been observed to take place in primary responses to sheep erythrocytes as rapidly as that of 19S producers. It seems more probable either that different precursor cells exist for each form of immunoglobulin, or possibly that any one cell may be able to produce any form of immunoglobulin but that the form produced depends upon the manner in which the cell interacts with the immunogen. It has often been noticed that when an immunogen is on a relatively large particle (e.g. on an erythrocyte or bacterium or adsorbed on to latex) or is itself a very large molecule the proportion of 19S antibody elicited and the duration of its formation are increased. A proportion of the lymphocytes in a normal population can be shown by very sensitive techniques to contain and to synthesize 19S immunoglobulin, and it may be (though this is not proved) that some cells of this kind are stimulated directly by the immunogen to become 19S antibody secretors.

'*Carrier Specificity*'

It was mentioned earlier that antibody against a determinant present on the immunogen which elicited its formation will usually combine equally, or almost equally well with a similar determinant attached to a different molecule. It might be expected therefore—if the postulated 'receptor' on the responding cell (the 'memory' cell in the case of the secondary response) resembled the antibody which the cell can be caused to make—that reinjection of any immunogen bearing the same determinant as the original would suffice to elicit a secondary response. In practice this has been repeatedly found not to happen. Only when the *original immunogen* (or something resembling it very closely in respect not only of the particular determinant group concerned but of all others) is readministered does a secondary response occur, with enhanced antibody production against the determinant. When a similar amount of the same determinant on another kind of carrier molecule is used the antibody response to the determinant is characteristic of a primary stimulation—i.e. similar to that which would be expected in an animal receiving this immunogen for the first time.

These important observations have been interpreted in two ways. One possible conclusion is that the 'receptors' on the memory cells, like that on the original immunologically competent cells, are only capable of combining effectively with an area of the immunogen which includes but is larger than the determinant. A similar postulate was already made in relation to carrier specificity in cell-mediated immunity (p. 508). In the case of antibody formation this postulate would imply that the antibody secreted had a different (narrower) specificity from that of the receptor. Although there is no reason at present for excluding this possibility it undoubtedly complicates what began to look like a reasonably simple story! Another possible conclusion depends upon the evidence mentioned earlier that antibody production depends upon or is facilitated by the cooperation of two cells, one derived from the thymus and the other, which actually makes antibody, from the bone marrow. If the thymus-derived cells had the carrier specificity postulated for those involved in cell mediated immunity whereas the specificity of the bone marrow derived cells was similar to that of the antibody which they produce, the overall specificity would still show the effect of the carrier. Unfortunately it is not possible at present to indicate whether either of these explanations is true.*

The Change in Affinity of Antibodies on Repeated Immunization

When a complex immunogen with a variety of different determinant groups is administered repeatedly it might be expected that antibodies would be made to begin with mainly against the most immunogenic determinants, but that with time antibodies would appear against other minor determinants also. This is indeed what commonly happens. Furthermore the mixed population of antibodies present in the serum of an animal which has been subject to a prolonged course of immunization reacts as though the total antibody were more avid—e.g. its combination with the antigen becomes less readily reversible. Such observations, however, tell us nothing about the affinity of the antibodies against any given determinant group, and information about this comes best from the use of immunogens with artificially attached strong determinants such as the dinitrophenyl group whose association constant with antibody can easily be measured.

It has been found that when an animal is immunized with dinitrophenyl bovine gamma-globulin (DNP-BGG), for example, it makes a mixture of antibodies against DNP with a wide range of affinities. When the initial dose of immunogen is small the amount

* See p. 146.

f antibody is small but the average affinity is high; when the initial .ose is large, more antibody is made but its average affinity is low. f repeated doses of immunogen are given, spaced in time so that the response to each dose has declined before the next administration, the average affinity of the antibodies is greater after each dose. These observations are explained by the supposition that the 'memory' cells at each stage are stimulated when they interact with those parts of the immunogen which contain the determinant groups. If the determinant groups are already combined with antibody (produced as a result of previous responses) the 'memory' cells may not be able to interact effectively. However, since antigen–antibody combinations are reversible the receptors on the cells can compete with the antibody, and those cells with receptors which have a higher affinity than the antibody will have a greater chance of being stimulated than those with a lower affinity. Thus there will be a continuous selection of those 'memory' cells with affinities greater than that of antibody currently present, and it is presumed that these cells are the precursors of cells which in turn will make even more avid antibody. This is a special example of the general phenomenon, that antibody can inhibit immunization (see e.g. p. 260). It may be remarked that implicit in this explanation is the assumption that the specificities of the responsive cell and the antibody which it makes are similar.

The Interaction of Antibody Precursor Cells with Immunogens

Since this subject is discussed at greater length in Chapter Seven it is necessary here only to record the following points in summary form:

1. Powerful immunogens such as sheep erythrocytes may interact with specific immunologically competent cells directly, and can even stimulate a primary response when added to spleen cell suspensions cultured *in vitro*. However weaker immunogens are apparently much more, and perhaps only effective after they have been ingested by macrophages. There is some evidence that the actively immunogenic material avoids degradation within the macrophages and is stored in these cells in some form which facilitates interaction with immunologically competent cells for period of days or possibly even weeks.

2. When a population of lymphocytes containing 'memory' cells—e.g. thoracic duct cells from a previously primed animal—is treated

with the immunogen *in vitro*, washed and then transferred to another animal which cannot itself respond, extensive antibody production occurs in the recipient. This indicates that memory cells can be stimulated by direct interaction with the immunogen.

3. Antibody-forming cells are not found in the thymus-dependent areas of lymphoid tissues. Early in a primary response they occur predominantly in the medullary areas—though they may spread elsewhere, and even into the bloodstream.

4. Immunogens administered for the first time to an animal become ingested sooner or later by macrophages. These cells are abundant in lymphoid tissues, especially in the medullary areas.

When specific antibody is already present, as a result of previous immunization by the immunogen itself or by some other immunogen which cross reacts with it, the immunogen becomes localized not only in macrophages but also on specialized reticular cells in the primary nodules and germinal centres. The immunogen may be retained on the reticular cells for long periods of time, and is probably held on their surface by antibody.

5. Antibody formation is nearly always accompanied by a marked increase in the size and number of germinal centres in the lymphoid tissue draining the site where the immunogen is deposited. This enlargement can first be recognized shortly after the time when antibody-forming cells first become detectable in the medulla. Germinal centres in the spleen can persist and contain actively dividing cells for weeks after antibody-forming cells have disappeared from the medulla. It is not known for certain what happens to the offspring of the dividing cells. Under certain experimental conditions specific antibody-forming cells can clearly be demonstrated within splenic germinal centres, but more usually no such cells are discernible in these structures either in spleen or lymph nodes. One possibility is that some of the cells produced in germinal centres migrate out and differentiate into plasma cells in the red pulp or medulla, but there is at present no direct evidence for this, and the function of these obviously important structures is still largely a mystery.

A description, at present hypothetical, of the sequence of events occurring when immunologically competent cells interact with an immunogen might be given along the following lines: The interaction may occur either with the immunogen directly, but more usually after it has been ingested by macrophages, and can lead to the formation of 'memory' (Y) cells and of antibody-synthesizing (Z) cells. The latter, when they occur, are first observable in the medulla. It would seem reasonable to suppose that this is the site in which stimulation of the immunologically competent cells actually occurs, but because of the demonstrated mobility of lymphocytes into, out of and within lymphoid tissues such an inference must be treated with caution. 'Memory' or Y cells can react with immunogen which is freshly supplied or remains available from the initial stimulus. One place in which the immunogen can be shown to persist for a long time is on or in the 'dendritic' cells within the germinal centres and this is possibly a site for continuous stimulation of more memory cells or of antibody producers.

The Precursors of Antibody-producing Cells

In an earlier section (pp. 94–110) evidence was presented that the precursors of antibody-producing cells are found in the population of lymphocytes, but that immunoglobulin production and germinal centre formation are not dependent upon the presence of the thymus to the same extent as is the development of cell-mediated specific immunity. It appears, however—though the evidence here is at present very incomplete—that when thymus-derived lymphocytes are absent the stimulation of specific antibody formation by some immunogens is less efficient than in a normal animal. This suggests that thymus-derived cells are somehow involved in interaction with these immunogens, even though lymphocytes derived from the bone marrow, and perhaps multiplying in germinal centres (again, there is no direct evidence for this) are able to transform into the antibody-producing cells. Some support for this comes from the evidence relating to carrier specificity mentioned above, which indicates that the receptors on 'memory' cells involved in cell-mediated immunity and in antibody production have similar specificities. However, there is also evidence that an already primed animal can be stimulated to make a secondary antibody response against a determinant group present on the original immunogen by administering the same determination on a different carrier, but in very much larger quantities than would be required if the original immunogen were administered a second time. This implies that the precursors of cells producing specific antibody against the determinant can be stimulated directly—albeit inefficiently—by the determinant itself. If this is true, the role of the thymus-derived cells in antibody formation can be described, though not explained, as that of making more efficient the interaction between the potential antibody-producing cell and the immunogen.

NON-SPECIFIC SUPPRESSION OF IMMUNOLOGICAL RESPONSES

The induction of specific paralysis or tolerance by immunogens has already been discussed. It has also been mentioned that the presence

TABLE 3.1

Ways of suppressing immunological responses

A. *Specific:*	1. Immunological paralysis. 2. Masking of determinants on the immunogen by excess of specific antibody.
B. *Non-specific:*	1. Destruction of stem cells and lymphocytes by lethal doses of X-irradiation (requires replacement of stem cells). 2. Neonatal thymectomy, or adult thymectomy + sublethal X-irradiation (suppresses cell-mediated specific immunity more regularly than antibody formation). 3. (in birds). Bursectomy + sublethal X-irradiation (diminishes antibody formation rather than cell-mediated immunity). 4. Destruction of circulating long-lived lymphocytes by antilymphocyte serum (diminishes cell-mediated immunity more than antibody formation). 5. Drainage of thoracic duct lymphocytes (effects similar to those of antilymphocyte serum but generally less prolonged). 6. Destruction or inhibition of lymphocytes by large doses of corticosteroids (other metabolic effects of corticosteroids are a serious hazard). 7. Destruction of lymphocytes by sublethal doses of X-irradiation (although lymphocytes are peculiarly susceptible to X-rays, other cells are damaged also). 8. Prevention of the cell differentiation and multiplication required for the development of immune responses, by antimetabolites which interfere with DNA, RNA or protein synthesis (such interference is generally not specific for cells involved in immune responses). 9. Interference with uptake and retention of the immunogen by macrophages, e.g. by 'blockade' of the reticulo-endothelial system or by high doses of X-rays (such interference affects the response to some weak immunogens, but is not of general application).

of *specific* antibody can mask determinant groups on an immunogen and so prevent their interaction with specifically competent cells Some practical applications of these phenomena are considered in later chapters. We are now in a position to review briefly, in the light of what has been set out concerning the nature of immunological responses, how these may be inhibited by *non-specific* means. Such means in general require either that the sources of immunologically competent cells or the cells themselves be destroyed, or that these cells be prevented from undergoing the differentiation and multiplication which is involved in the exhibition and amplification of their specific immunological capacity. A list of some of the experimental procedures which have been found effective is given in Table 3.1. The only non-specific means of suppressing immunological responses which are presently of practical importance in medicine are those involving selective removal or inhibition of lymphocytes (B. 4, 5 and 6) and those involving the use of antimetabolite drugs, some of which show a certain degree of selectivity for cells engaged in immune responses (B. 8). They are discussed more fully in Chapters Twelve and Thirteen.

THE NATURE OF IMMUNOLOGICAL DIVERSITY

Perhaps the most striking and fascinating feature of immunological responses is that they can be made, and be specific for, an apparently unlimited variety of different determinants including many synthetic chemical groups which are not known to occur naturally. Ehrlich, in his Croonian Lecture in 1900, attempted to explain the origin of antibodies by postulating that the cells of the body had receptors or 'haptophores' capable of capturing specific nutrient substances or, undesirably, toxic agents. He suggested that toxins interacting with the cells caused them to produce an excess of the specific haptophores for the toxins, which were shed into the circulation and became detectable as antibodies. This hypothesis appeared to become untenable when it was discovered that antibodies could be made not only against toxins but also against such compounds as arsanilic acid or various synthetic dyes which were very unlikely to occur in nature and were not necessarily even toxic. Instead the view became generally accepted that antigens must somehow instruct cells to synthesize antibody proteins which had a structure complementary to the antigen, so that they fitted one another, metaphorically as a key fits a lock. Although it was recognized in principle that the materials which a body can make are determined by its heredity, in the case of antibodies the number of different possible specificities seemed to be so great that to postulate hereditary control for each and every one would demand the existence of an improbably—or even impossibly—large number of hereditary factors. Furthermore, although Nature was recognized as being prodigal and wasteful, it seemed improbable that hereditary provision would be made for antibody responses to materials which were never likely to be encountered except under the artificial conditions of laboratory experiments. Thus, despite the fact that no detailed mechanism could be envisaged for it, antibody production came to be regarded as an exceptional process in which globulin molecules were folded, during or after their synthesis, around a template provided by the antigen, so as to possess a unique stable complementary configuration. Such ideas were not unreasonable at the time when they were put forward. However advances in our knowledge of the genetic control of protein synthesis and of the structure of antibody molecules themselves have recently made the earlier ideas untenable. Perhaps the first indication that they would have to be revised came from the studies of adaptive enzyme formation in bacteria—a process which has a marked analogy to antibody formation. The capacity to form adaptive enzymes was clearly shown to be genetically controlled, and it was also demonstrated that in every case where synthesis of adaptive enzymes could be evoked by 'inducers' (usually, but not always, the substrates of the enzymes) the uninduced bacteria were capable of making small but detectable amounts of the enzyme. In other words, the synthesis of specific protein which was switched on by the inducer involved not a new process but one which was already determined by the genome of the organism. A more direct indication came from studies of the structures of a number of proteins, including some enzymes, from which it became clear that the detailed folding of these very complex molecules was uniquely determined by the amino acid sequences of the peptide chains of which they were composed. (This was subsequently shown to be true for some purified antibodies, whose peptide chains could be unfolded in the presence of high concentrations of urea and yet which could regain their specific antibody structure when allowed to refold spontaneously in the *absence* of the antigen.) Such observations made it very improbable that globulin molecules could acquire specific antibody properties as a result of folding round an antigen template, but probable rather that each antibody also had a unique amino acid sequence which determined its specificity.

Evidence has indeed been furnished that antibody-forming cells may contain no antigen molecules, or certainly too few to act as templates for antibody synthesis. More important however has been the development of modern concepts of the mechanism of protein synthesis. It appears to be a general rule that the polypeptide chains of proteins are synthesized by assembly of amino acids on polyribosomes in a sequence coded for by messenger RNA; and (except in the case of RNA viruses) that the messenger RNA is coded for by DNA in the genome. Consequently, if each antibody has a unique structure (and hence a unique peptide sequence) it must be coded for by one or more genes present in the genome. The only escape from this conclusion would be if the antigen, instead of itself acting as a template, could either affect the synthesis or the reading of messenger RNA so as to cause a protein with a complementary structure to be formed. No convincing or even plausible suggestion as to how this could come about has so far been put forward. The hypothesis that antigen *instructs* cells to make antibody has perforce fallen into disfavour.

The alternative hypothesis is that an immunogen *selects* cells which are genetically already able to respond to it—e.g. which already possess genes coding for the synthesis of specific antibody—and stimulates them to express their particular genetic potential by differentiation and division. Such an hypothesis, which in some way resembles Ehrlich's original suggestion, was put forward by D.W. Talmage in 1957, and developed by F.M. Burnet and J. Lederberg in 1958 as the 'clonal selection' hypothesis. They suggested that any given immunologically competent cell was genetically determined to respond to one determinant (or possibly two, to allow for alleles), but that since the very large total population of immunologically competent cells contained many different cells each able to respond to a different determinant, the animal as a whole could respond to a very wide variety of different immunogens. This hypothesis, although it avoids the difficulties of instructive hypotheses mentioned above, still has to face the problems of how the genome of an individual could contain sufficient genetic information to code for making all the enormous variety of antibodies which are known to be possible, and of how it comes about that individual cells only express one or two of these possibilities. However clonal selection in some form appears to provide the only means of accounting for many of the features of immunological responses, which have indeed been discussed in earlier sections of this chapter in terms of such a mechanism.

Before going further, some observations may be noted which are relevant to the problem of whether any given immunologically competent cell can respond to more than one determinant.

(a) Several studies have been made in animals immunized with two or three separate and distinct immunogens or with a single complex immunogen containing two distinct determinants, with the object of determining whether individual cells make antibody with more than one specificity. Such experiments are technically difficult and require very careful controls to ensure that any antibody detected in or around a cell was actually made by the cell itself. The conclusion from most studies has been that nearly all cells made antibody with a single specificity, although a variable but small proportion appeared to have two specificities. In the light of separate studies which indicate that individual cells do not make at one time more than one kind of immunoglobulin allotype (see Chapter Four, p. 159), and of the fact that neoplastic (myeloma) cells make one immunoglobulin unique to their clone (Chapter Eight, p. 337), there is a tendency to regard the observation of double antibody producers as probably due to technical artefact.

Other experiments on antibody responses made to two distinct immunogens by spleen cells cultured *in vitro* have shown that it is possible to kill or inhibit selectively the cells responding to one immunogen while leaving unaffected those able to respond to the other.

Observations of this kind indicate that a competent cell only embarks upon a single immunological response at a time, and that different cells respond to different immunogens. They do not prove, however, that a cell is *only* competent to respond to one particular determinant.

(b) There are other observations which suggest that individual immunologically competent cells may be able to respond to several determinants. These fall into two groups: firstly those in which the proportion of lymphocytes responding to a particular primary antigenic stimulus appears to be inordinately high, and secondly those in which two immunogens are presented together and the one suppresses the response to the other.

We do not know to how many different determinants any animal can respond, but few persons would guess that the number was below 10^4 and most would set it much higher. If each lymphocyte could respond only to a unique determinant, it would be expected that when an immunogen with a small number or only one kind of determinant was presented to a population of lymphocytes for the first time (i.e. before 'memory' cells had accumulated) the proportion of cells responding would be very small—no greater than the chance that any cell happened to be competent to respond to that determinant. In several instances where the proportion of cells responding has been measured, notably in graft *versus* host reactions (see Chapter Thirteen), this has been found to be surprisingly high, even up to half. The graft *versus* host reaction may be exceptional, because of the possibility that the response has some features which are not strictly immunological (see allogeneic inhibition, p. 597). However, in the supposedly primary response to sheep erythrocytes made by rabbit peritoneal lymphocytes or suspensions of mouse spleen cells cultured *in vitro* as many as one per cent of the cells have been found to make detectable amounts of specific antibody. Taken at their face value these findings would imply that individual cells must be capable of specific stimulation by more than one kind of immunogen. The validity of this inference is weakened however by evidence that the rabbit cells may already have been primed by cross-reacting immunogens, and that the mouse cells had undergone several mitotic divisions before their capacity was tested.

The second phenomenon referred to above is known as antigenic competition. It has repeatedly been observed that when two different immunogens, each of which can elicit a primary response on its own, are mixed and administered in the same amounts and by the same route the response to one of them may be largely or wholly suppressed. Such a finding would not be expected if competent cells could respond only to a unique determinant, since the presence of a different immunogen should not affect them, and it also implies that cells can be competent to make more than one response. It does not prove this, however, because there is a possibility that the phenomenon is not due to pre-emption of cells by one immunogen or the other but rather to competition for sites of multiplication or for some other limiting factor.

There are grounds for supposing that each cell before stimulation cannot be competent to respond to *all* determinants. For example, neonatally thymectomized mice make diminished or no primary antibody responses to some immunogens but normal responses to others, in a rather random manner. There are also conceptual difficulties, such as how to account for specific immunological tolerance or paralysis. On the assumption that all cells were competent to respond to all immunogens, a mechanism would be required for selectively blocking the responsiveness of every cell to any immunogen used to cause paralysis (including all 'self' components) while leaving all other possible responses intact.

Although the weight of evidence is increasingly in favour of the competence of individual cells being restricted to one or two, rather than a larger number of responses, it may at present still be wise to reserve judgment on this question.

MODELS FOR THE ORIGIN OF VARIETIES OF ANTIBODY

Once it is accepted that each specific immunological response is under separate genetic control, regardless of whether immunologically competent cells make one or more kinds of antibody, the problem remains how the very large number of genes required could have arisen. There are two possibilities, consideration of which needs to take into account the current knowledge about immunoglobulin structure outlined in the next chapter. The main features of this may be simply summarized by stating that immunoglobulins are composed of pairs of polypeptide chains, the smaller, or light (L) chains being common to all immunoglobulins and the larger, or heavy (H) chains varying according to the class of immunoglobulin. Each L and each H chain has a constant part whose amino acid sequence is similar from one immunoglobulin molecule to another, and a *variable* part whose amino acids at many positions along the chain differ in different molecules. The antibody specificity is due to the arrangement of amino acids in the variable part, which is unique for each antibody.

One possibility is that separate genes controlling the synthesis of all possible L and H chains are present in the zygote, and consequently in every diploid cell in the body—even though only a single pair of genes, one for the L and one for the H chain, may be expressed by any one cell at a given time. The other possibility is that the zygote contains relatively few genes controlling immunoglobulin synthesis (there must be enough for all the genetically controlled allotypes of each kind of L chain and of each class of H chain), but that the great diversity of immunoglobulins arises as a result of somatic mutations occurring in lymphocytes or their precursors during the lifetime of the individual.

The general structure of immunoglobulins must be singularly well adapted both to permitting the possibility of variation in conformation of the antibody-combining site and allowing the molecules as a whole to fulfil their numerous biological functions (see Chapter Four), since the amino acid sequences of L and H chains have been found to show a remarkable degree of similarity in species as far apart as man, the mouse, the rabbit and the horse. This argues a great degree of evolutionary stability for the overall structure. However, we run into difficulties when it comes to considering whether genes controlling the detailed structures of the variable parts of the L and H chains required to make all possible specific antibodies could also be stable during the evolution of even a single species. If genes for all possible antibodies are present in the zygote from which each individual arises, many genes must be present controlling the synthesis of antibodies which are most unlikely ever to have been required by or of evolutionary value to that individual's ancestors. It is difficult to see how, without positive selection, genetic drift could have been avoided, resulting during the course of evolution in the loss of genes controlling antibodies useless to the species as a whole. For this and some other reasons the 'germ line' hypothesis is considered unlikely to be valid.

The somatic mutation hypothesis provides an attractive alternative, but although the occurrence of somatic mutations is well recognized as a rare phenomenon (about one in a million) in many kinds of cell, the frequency of mutation required to explain the origin of antibody diversity is quite exceptionally high. Furthermore, even if somatic mutation were to occur unusually frequently among the rapidly dividing lymphocyte population from which immunologically competent cells derive, there is a difficulty in explaining how one part of the L and H chains is subject to variation, while the other part is not. This is because the biochemical evidence indicates that these chains are each formed in one piece—rather than that the variable and constant parts are formed separately and joined later—

so that their synthesis is presumably controlled by one cistron each. A quite unusual genetic mechanism would be required for frequent mutations to take place in one part of the cistron and yet to leave the rest unaffected. In order to explain a very high mutation rate confined to that part of the cistron controlling the synthesis of the variable part of the L and H chains, the ingenious hypothesis has been put forward that there exists a 'scrambler' gene (or generator of diversity, suitably abbreviated to GOD), which causes frequent crossing over in that part of the cistrons controlling synthesis of the variable parts. The detailed genetic arguments whereby it might be possible to account for the evolution of genes controlling the synthesis both of the L and H chains (including their polymorphic forms) and of the scrambling mechanism, in terms of a primordial gene which underwent successive duplications and translocation, are beyond the scope of this book.

They may be found in the review by E.S. Lennox and M. Cohn referred to in the bibliography for this chapter.

Since the first printing of this edition was prepared definitive studies in mice have confirmed the clear distinction between lymphocytes derived from stem cells which develop into lymphocytes during residence in the thymus, and then go on to populate other lymphoid tissues, and lymphocytes derived from stem cells which colonize lymphoid tissues without passing through the thymus. The former have become commonly known as T-lymphocytes and the latter as B-lymphocytes (because the stem cells originate in the bone marrow in adult life and because they appear to correspond to the lymphocyte population dependent on the Bursa of Falricius in birds). T-lymphocytes possess surface antigen(s) distinct from B-lymphocytes, and can be distinguished by the use of specific antisera against the *theta* antigen. In mice T-lymphocytes make up almost all the lymphocytes in the thymus, 80–85 per cent of those in the thoracic duct, 70 per cent in blood and lymph nodes, 30–35 per cent in the spleen and peritoneal cavity. They do not make circulating antibody and it is uncertain whether they have detectable immuno-globulin at their surface. B-lymphocytes make circulating antibody and have readily detectable immunoglobulin at their surface. Although B-lymphocytes with appropriate immunoglobulin receptors can interact directly with antigenic determinants, they are stimulated to make antibody much more effectively (and perhaps only) when T-lymphocytes capable of interacting with other determinants on the antigen are also available. Such cell-cell cooperation is the basis of the 'carrier effect' described on p. 134, but its detailed mechanism is uncertain. Both B- and T-lymphocytes can be 'memory' cells. Immunological paralysis can be induced readily in T-lymphocyte but less readily in B-lymphocyte populations.

FURTHER READING

BURNET F.M. (1959) *The clonal selection theory of acquired immunity*. Cambridge University Press

CELL COOPERATION IN THE IMMUNE RESPONSE. *Third Sigrid Juselius Symposium*, Helsinki, ed. Ann Cross, Academic Press 1971

COLD SPRING HARBOR SYMPOSIA ON QUANTITATIVE BIOLOGY (1967) **32**, '*Antibodies*' (a) Evolution and genetics of antibodies, (b) Differentiation and cellular events

COOPER, M.D., GABRIELSEN A.E. & GOOD R.A. (1967) Role of the thymus and other central lymphoid tissues in immunological disease. *Ann Rev. Med.* **18**, 113

DRESSER D.W. & MITCHISON N.A. (1968) The mechanism of immunological paralysis. *Adv. Immunol.* **8**, 129

EHRLICH P. (1900) On immunity with special reference to cell life. *Proc. Roy. Soc. London* **66**, 424

ELVES M.W. *The Lymphocytes*. Lloyd-Luke, London 1966

GOOD R.A. & PAPERMASTER B.W. (1964) The ontogeny and phylogeny of the adaptive immunity. *Adv. Immunol.* **4**, 1

GOWANS J.L. & MCGREGOR D.D. (1965) The immunological activities of lymphocytes. In *Progr. Allergy* **9**, 1

HASEK M., LENGEROVA A. & VOITISKOVA M. (eds) (1962) *Mechanisms of immunological tolerance*. Publishing House of Czech Acad. Sci. Prague

LENNOX E.S. & COHN M. (1967) Immunoglobulins. *Ann Rev. Biochem.* **36**, 365

LESKOWITZ S. (1967) Tolerance. *Ann. Rev. Microbiol.* **21**, 157

LING N.R. (1968) *Lymphocyte stimulation*. North Holland, Amsterdam

MEDAWAR P.B. (1960) Theories of immunological tolerance. In *Cellular Aspects of Immunology*. Ciba Foundation, Churchill, London

MILLER J.F.A.P. & OSOBA D. (1967) Current concepts of the immunological function of the thymus. *Physlol. Rev.* **47**, 437

MITCHISON N.A. (1967) Immunological paralysis as a dosage phenomenon. In *Regulation of the Antibody Response* [Ed. Cinader B.] Chapter II, pp. 54–67, C.C. Thomas, Springfield, Ill.

NOSSAL G.J.V. (1962) Cellular genetics of immune responses. *Adv. Immunol.* **2**, 163

NOSSAL G.J.V. (1967) Mechanisms of antibody production. *Ann Rev. Med.* **18**, 81

NOSSAL G.J.V. (1967) Effects of radiation on antibody formation—current views. *Atomic Energy Review* **5**, 3

PINCHUCK P. & MAURER P.H. (1967) Genetic control of the immune response. In *Regulation of the Antibody Response* [Ed. Cinader B.] C.C. Thomas, Springfield, Ill.

SMITH R.G., MIESCHER P.A. & GOOD R.A. (eds) (1966) *The Phylogeny of Immunity*. University of Florida Press, Gainesville

SMITH R.T. (1961) Immunological tolerance of non-living antigens. *Adv. Immunol.* **1**, 67

SORKIN, E. (ed.) (1968) *The Immune Response and its Suppression*. Karger, Basel/New York

WARNER N.L. & SZENBERG A. (1964) The immunological function of the bursa of Fabricius in the chicken. *Ann Rev. Microbiol.* **18**, 253

WOLSTENHOLME G.E.W. & KNIGHT J. (eds) (1963) *The Immunologically Competent Cell*. Ciba Foundation Study Group. Churchill, London

CHAPTER FOUR

Immunoglobulins

It has already been mentioned that specific immunity is bound up with the presence of circulating antibodies. The purpose of this chapter is to consider what antibodies are.

The blood of all animals contains a variety of proteins which are capable of combining more or less specifically with, and inhibiting, a number of known physiologically-active agents (if they were not active agents the odds are that such inhibitors would not be detected, and there may in fact be many more than have been recognized hitherto). Examples are the inhibitors of proteolytic enzymes present in the body such as trypsin, plasmin or thrombin, or the factor (probably an enzyme) causing increased capillary permeability which is released in damaged tissues, or of the spreading factor hyaluronidase; and of various extraneous proteolytic enzymes produced by some non-pathogenic bacteria such as *Bacillus subtilis*. Inhibitors of this kind are presumably of importance in the homeostatic mechanisms of the body, but they are not antibodies. They differ from antibodies inasmuch as they are already present in the blood of normal animals, and their production is little influenced by introducing from outside more of the substance which they inhibit. Furthermore, they are found, when characterized, to be α- or β-globulins, and are chemically and physically quite distinct from antibodies.

Antibodies (with the possible exception of 'natural' antibodies, which are discussed on p. 49) are characteristically formed as a specific response to the introduction into the tissues of the body of soluble materials which are recognized as foreign by the body. Their characteristic property is to combine, under physiological conditions, with the material in response to which they were formed. The various ways in which this combination can be detected, and its physiological importance, are discussed in Chapters Eight, Nine and Ten, and the factors which determine whether a given foreign substance will stimulate antibody formation—i.e. will act as an antigen—are considered in Chapter Six.

Our concern in this chapter is with the physical and chemical properties of antibody molecules and the relationship of these properties to their special functions. During the past five years a great deal of new knowledge has been gained about the *general* properties of antibodies, even though we still do not know in detail to what structural arrangement any single antibody owes its capacity to combine with the antigen which elicited its formation. To present this new knowledge in a reasonably concise form has not only required a complete revision of the matter in earlier editions of this book but has also—unfortunately—made any attempt at an historical approach largely impossible.

After Tiselius had shown in 1937 that plasma proteins could be separated, on the basis of their mobilities in an electric field, into four main groups, namely albumin and α-, β- and γ-globulins, it was soon observed that antibodies occurred either in the γ- or, in ungulates especially, in the β-globulins. This was deduced from a study of sera taken from animals hyper-immunized against a particular antigen, so that a large proportion of the plasma protein consisted of specific antibody. When samples of serum were compared by electrophoresis both before and after the antibody had been removed by specific precipitation with antigen it was possible to see which components had changed. Fig. 4.1 illustrates what happens with a rabbit serum containing large amounts of antibody against the capsular polysaccharide of pneumococcus Type III, when the antibody is removed by adding sufficient polysaccharide to precipitate out all the antibody. It is obvious that the only component to be significantly reduced is the γ-globulin. It is also possible to compare serum samples taken from an animal at the beginning of a course of immunizing injections and at various time intervals during the course when its antibody level is rising. An experiment of this kind is illustrated in Fig. 4.2, but in this instance the serum was obtained from a horse undergoing immunization against diphtheria toxoid, and the serum component which appears to change is not the slower moving γ-globulin but a component lying between the γ- and the β-globulins. This component is

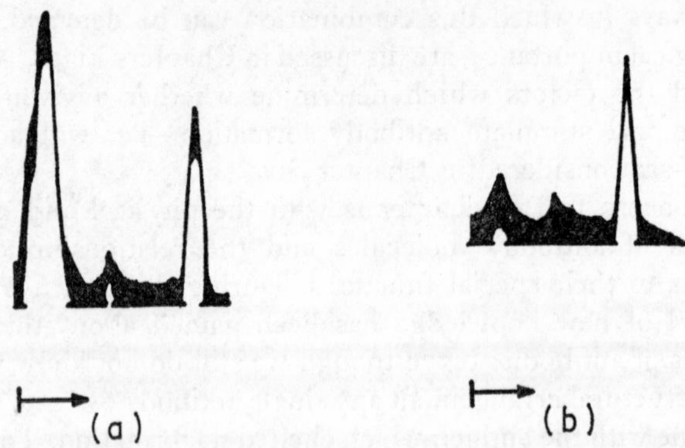

FIG. 4.1. Electrophoretic pattern of rabbit antiserum against *Streptococcus pneumoniae* Type III, (a) before and (b) after removal of antibody by specific precipitation with capsular polysaccharide. The only protein removed is γ-globulin. [N.B. This serum contained 45 mg per ml of specific antibody—an unusually large amount.] The arrows indicate direction of migration. The leading peak is albumin.

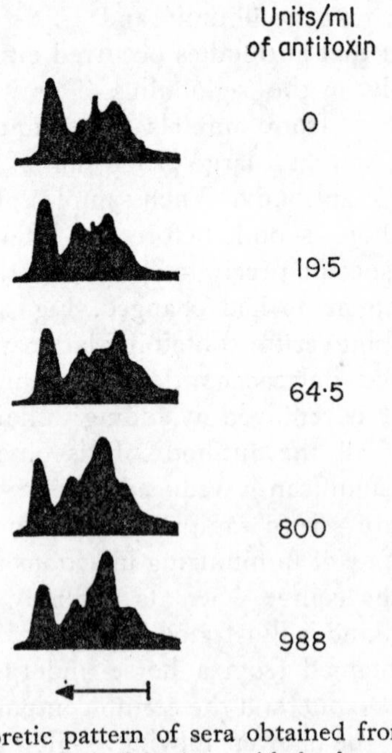

Units/ml of antitoxin

0

19·5

64·5

800

988

FIG. 4.2. Electrophoretic pattern of sera obtained from a horse at various stages of immunization with diphtheria toxoid. As the antibody level increases there is a rise in the fast-moving γ-globulin.

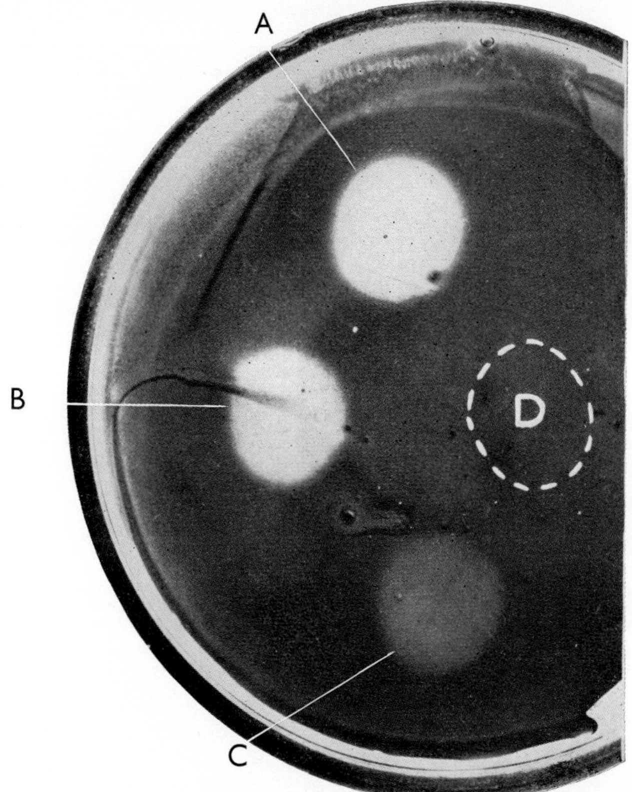

PLATE 2.1. *In vitro* demonstration of activity of lysozyme from various body fluids on *Micrococcus lysodeikticus*. Drops of undiluted tears (A); crystalline preparation of lysozyme from egg white, 40 micrograms per ml (B); saline extract of polymorphs (C); human sweat (D) were placed on a confluent growth of *M. lysodeikticus* on nutrient agar. The action of the enzyme in A, B and C is shown by clear zones due to lysis of the organisms within a few minutes of application.

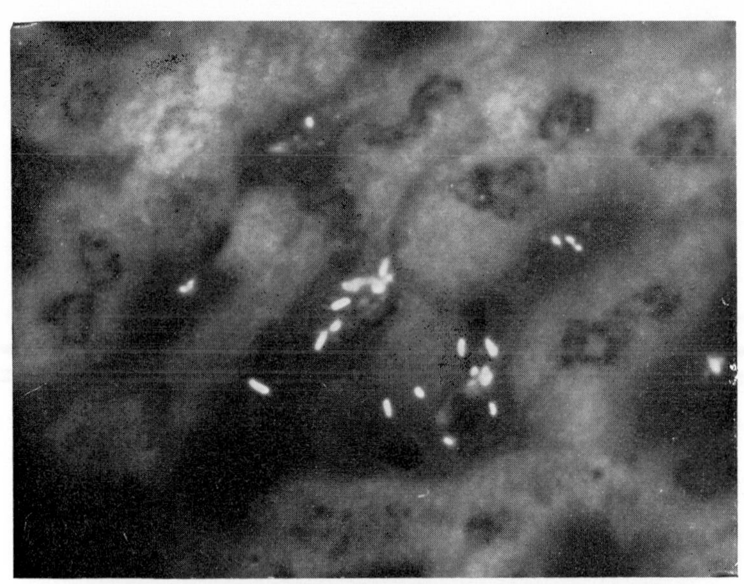

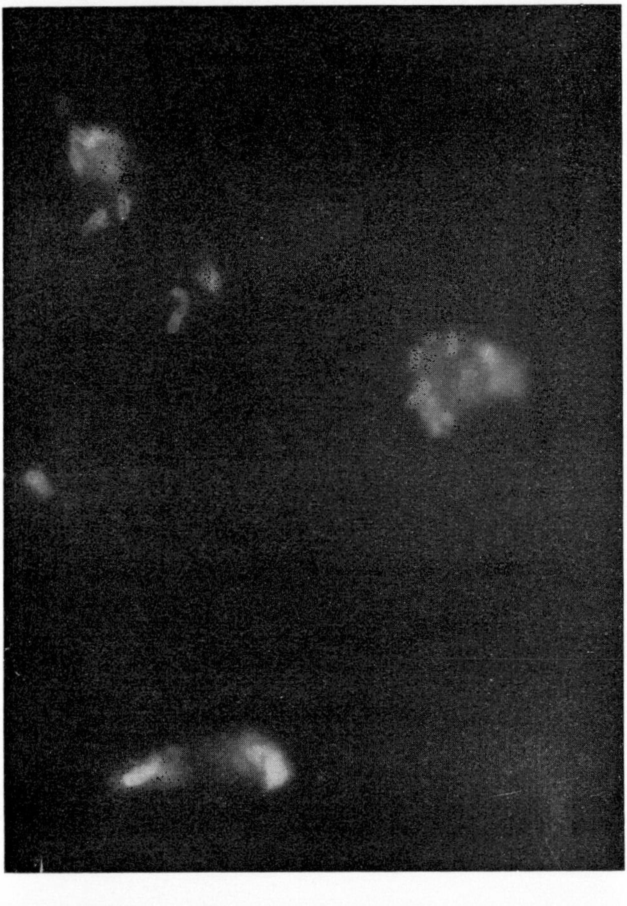

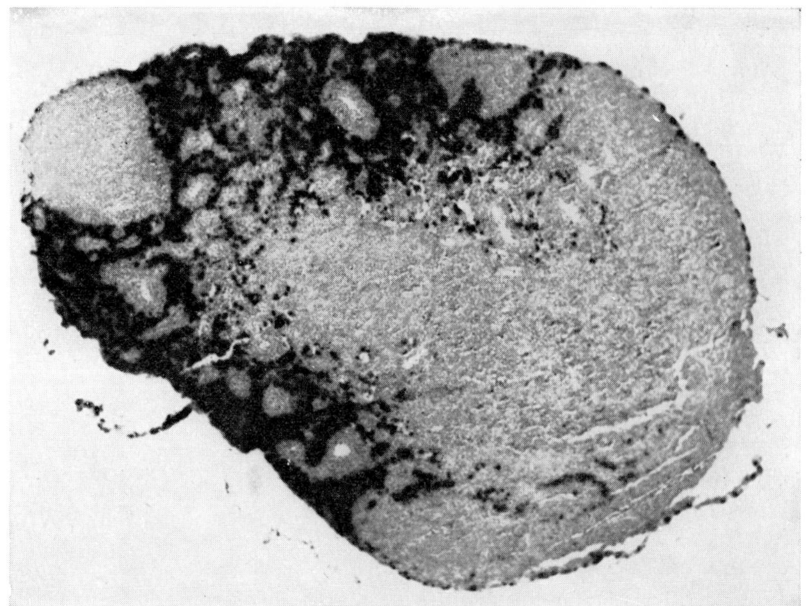

PLATE 2.4. Cross section of the draining popliteal lymph node of a mouse which had been injected in the hind footpad with a small quantity of a highly radioactive synthetic polypeptide. The section had been treated with photographic emulsion, and developed after sufficient time for the weak β-rays emitted by the radioactive material to activate the emulsion. The radioautograph reveals the localization of the antigen by the overlying silver grains (black).

Antigen arriving via the lymphatic vessels is extensively trapped in macrophages lining the medullary sinuses and along the marginal sinus. Little antigen is seen in the cortex of the lymph nodes (unless the mouse has previously been specifically immunized). Particulate materials, such as colloidal dyes or carbon, and microbes are trapped in a similar manner to that shown in this Plate. ($\times 90$)

PLATE 2.2. (*Top left*) *Fluorescence micrograph. Clearance of organisms by the reticulo-endothelial system in the liver.*

Liver of mouse showing uptake and disintegration of organisms in the Kupffer cells 15 minutes after intravenous injection of living *Proteus vulgaris*. Frozen section stained with fluorescein-labelled antiserum to 'O' (somatic) antigen of *P. vulgaris*. ($\times 800$)

PLATE 2.3. (*Opposite*). High power view of another area of the liver to demonstrate that already at 15 min extensive disintegration of the bacteria has taken place. (Magnification $\times 1{,}200$)

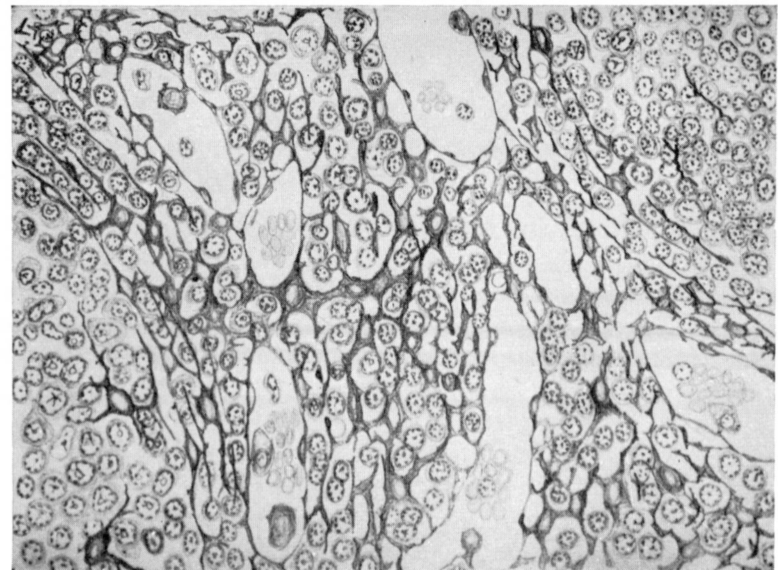

Plate 2.5. Drawing to illustrate the organization of the reticulo-endothelial system in the rabbit spleen as shown by the silver impregnation method of Weil-Davenport. Note different morphological types of macrophages (free and sessile sinus macrophages; stellate cells forming a network throughout the pulp strands; dendritic microglia-like cells at edge of lymphoid nodules).

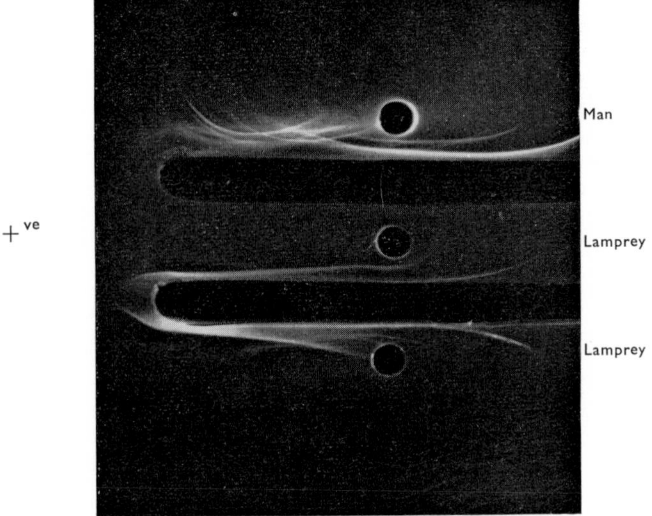

Plate 3.1. *Immunoglobulin in lamprey serum*

Rabbit antiserum prepared against whole lamprey serum was used to test for the presence of a component corresponding to the immunoglobulin of mammals. In this plate the immunoelectrophoretic pattern obtained is shown, and compared with that obtained with human serum and a rabbit antiserum against it. An arc of precipitation is visible in the region of

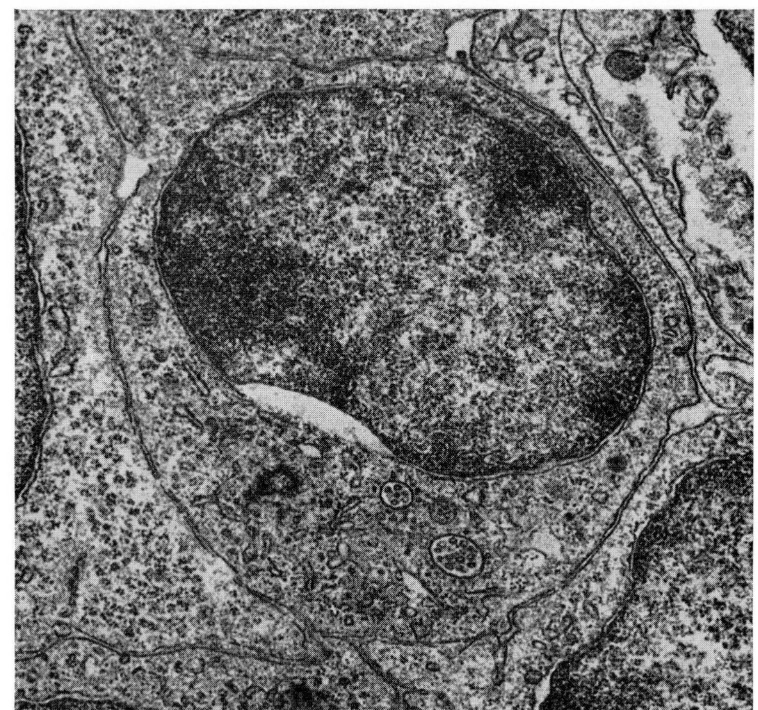

PLATE 3.2 (a). *Small lymphocyte* within lymph node (× 20,000) Electron micrograph. Note oval nucleus with condensed chromatin nodes around the nuclear membrane. No nucleolus obvious. The cytoplasm contains scanty single ribosomes. Below the nucleus is a centrosome (appearing as a dark ring); the collection of smooth surfaced lamellae and vesicles which comprise the Golgi apparatus; and two multivesicular bodies.

[The white area separating the nucleus from the nuclear membrane is an artefact]

PLATE 3.1 (*cont.*)
slowest electrophoretic mobility, corresponding to the immunoglobulin as given by the human serum. (Arcs in the region corresponding to albumin and α-globulins are not revealed in this experiment, since such proteins would have moved beyond the antiserum troughs towards the anodal end).

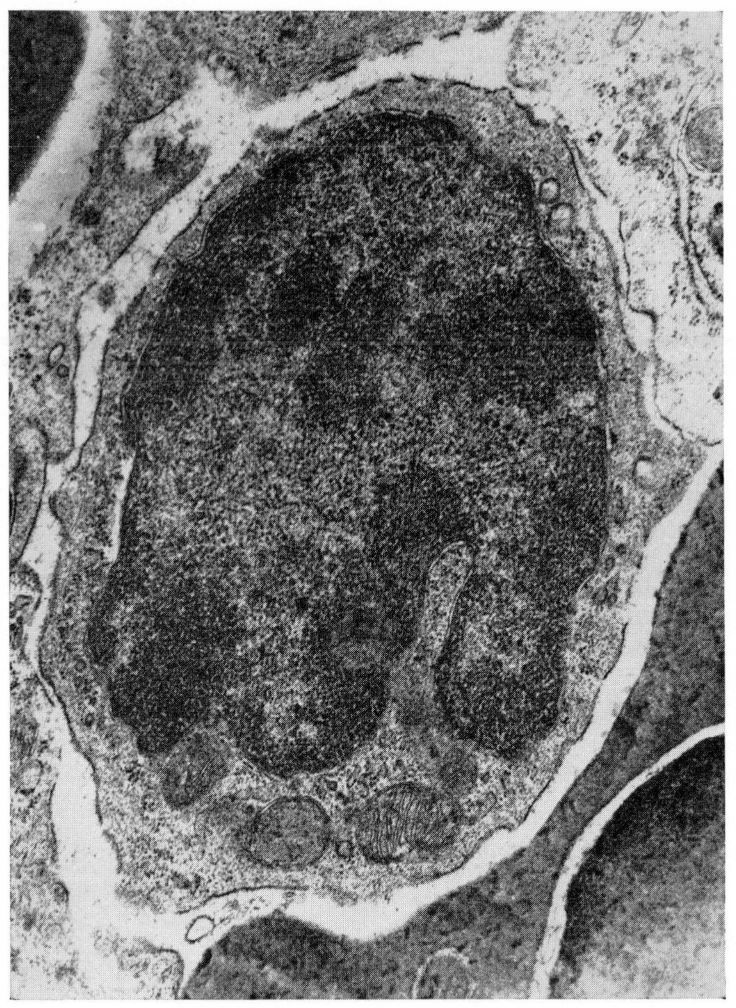

PLATE 3.2 (b). Small lymphocyte: another example from lymph node (×20,000). This form of small lymphocyte shows an indented nucleus and three mitochondria (transected in different planes). Other cytoplasmic features resemble those of the cell shown in Plate 3.2 (a).

[Preparations of Dr. J. Gordon]

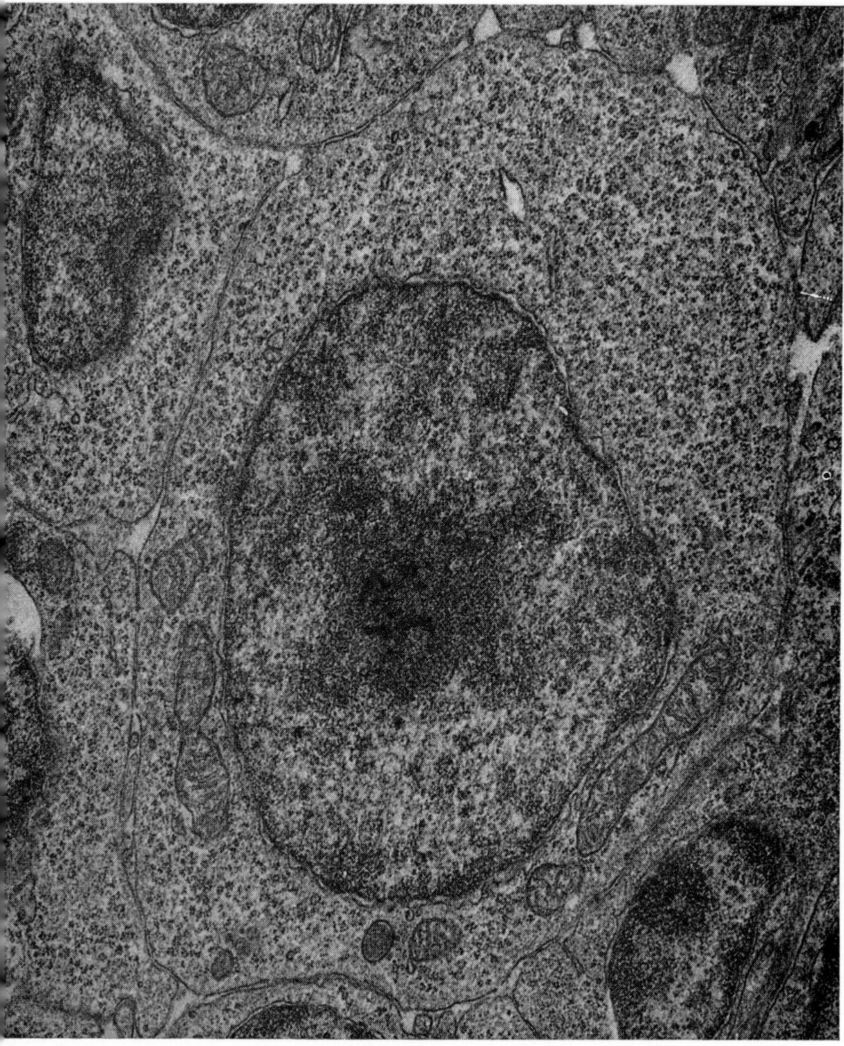

PLATE 3.3. *'Large' lymphocyte: lymphoblast, large pyroninophilic 'blast' cell* (×15,000). Electron micrograph. Note oval nucleus with prominent, complex nucleolus. Several mitochondria immediately surround the nucleus. This cell-type typically has a small Golgi element although none is apparent in this section. The cytoplasm is packed with ribosome clusters.

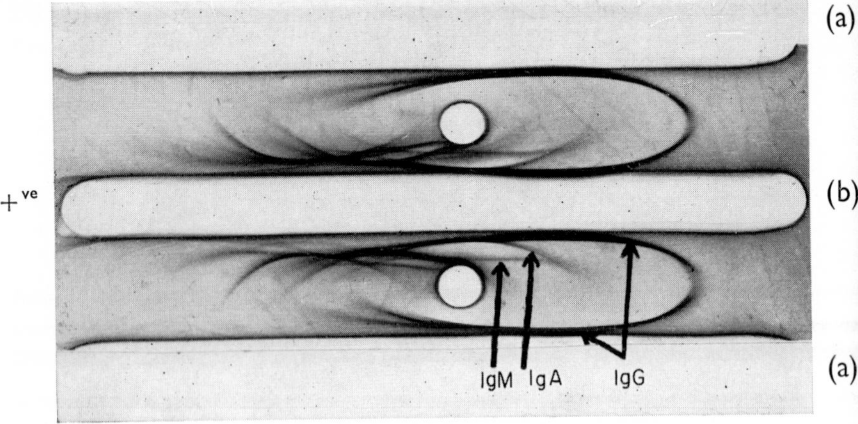

PLATE 4.1. Immunoelectrophoresis of human Igs.

Immunoelectrophoresis of human serum against (a) monospecific antiserum reactive with IgG. Note that the anodal end of the line is split into two obvious tails (corresponding to different sub-classes), (b) reactive against a number of human globulins. The precipitin arcs corresponding to IgG, IgM and IgA are designated.

PLATE 4.2 (*Facing*). Electrophoresis of light chains in urea glycine gel pH 7.8.

(*a*) from normal human IgG (2 samples) and IgM.

(*b*) L-chains of immunoglobulins of various species; rabbit, guinea-pig, cow, horse, baboon, man. Note that all species show similar banding (rabbit light chains do not show banding under these conditions, but do so if the pH is lowered).

(*c*) L-chains of normal human immunoglobulin (positions 1 and 7) and various myeloma proteins. Note that the L-chains of the myeloma proteins contain only one main component.

[Photographs kindly supplied by Professor S. Cohen.]

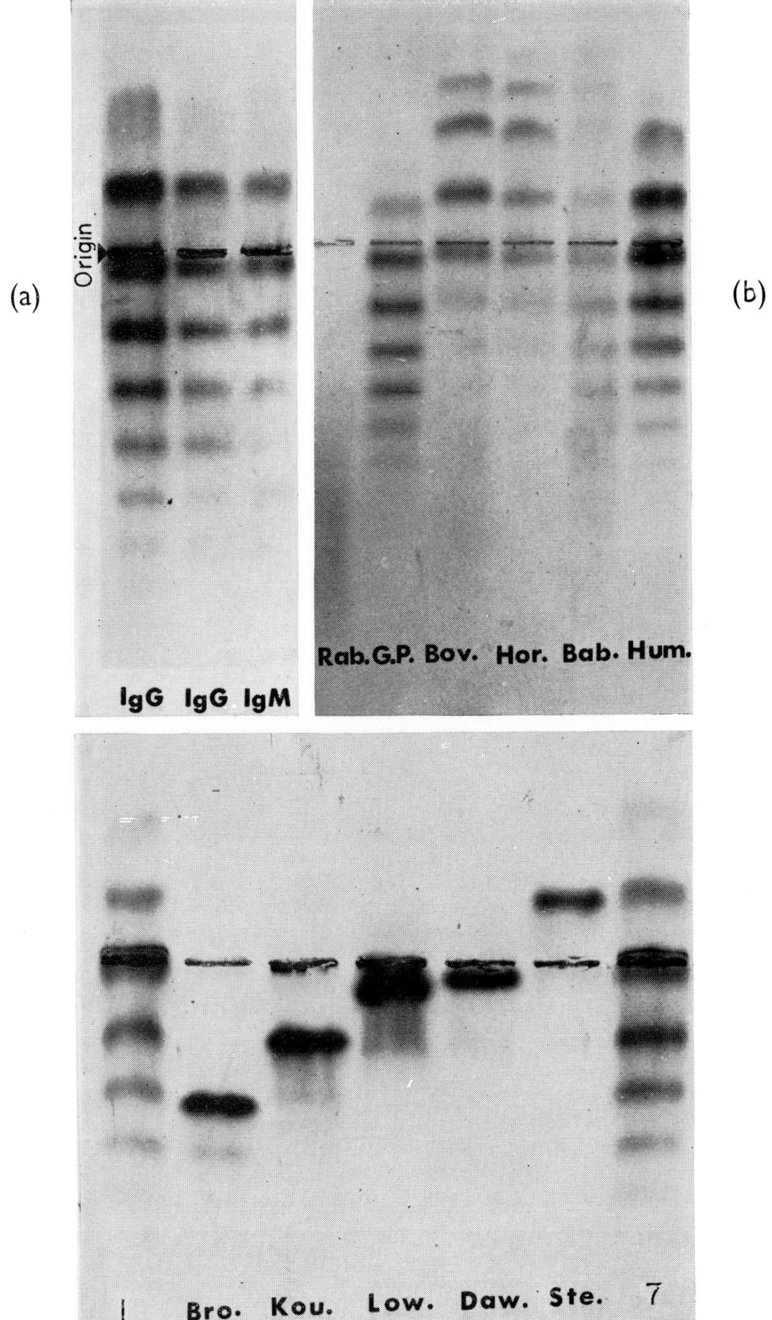

(a)

(b)

(c)

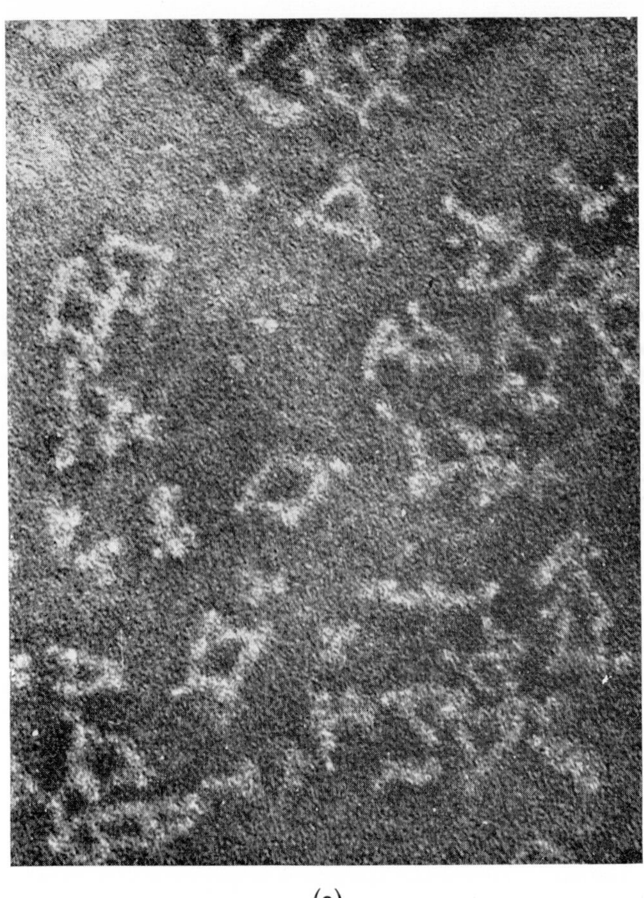

(a)

Plate 4.3 (*a*, *b*, *c*). Electron micrograph of rabbit IgG molecules revealed by negative staining.

The IgG is specific antibody against a bivalent dinitrophenol hapten. The IgG molecules are linked together by the bivalent hapten molecule (invisible in the picture).

(*a*) *Above*—Intact antibody molecules. Aggregates of 3 form a triangle, of 4 a square, of 5 a pentagon etc. Note the projections at the corners which represent the Fc portion.

(*b*) *Facing, top*—The same antibody after treatment with pepsin to split off the Fc portion. Note that similar shapes are formed lacking the projections at the corners.

(*c*) *Facing, bottom*—Diagram to illustrate how the bivalent hapten lies in relation to antibody. ($\times$300,000)

[Photographs kindly supplied by the late Dr. R. C. Valentine.]

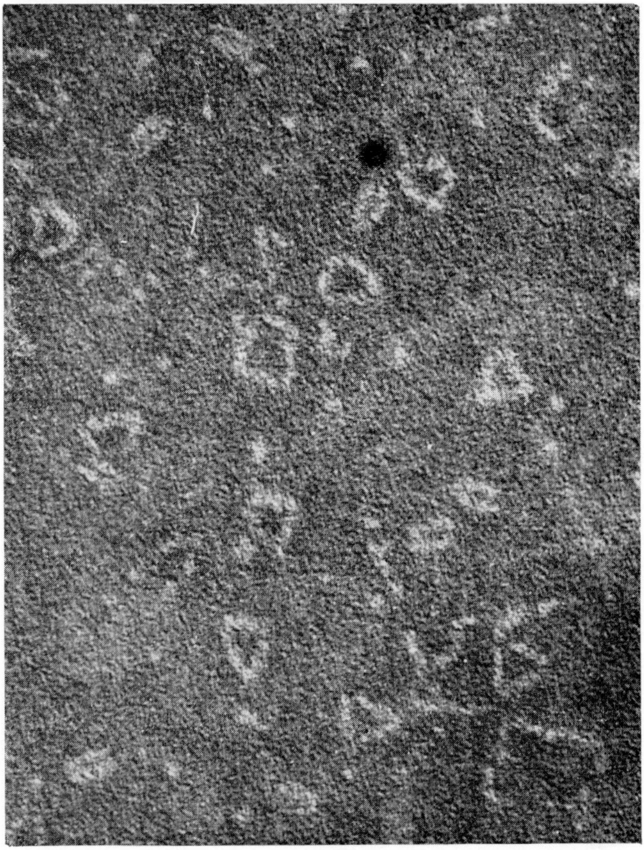

(b)

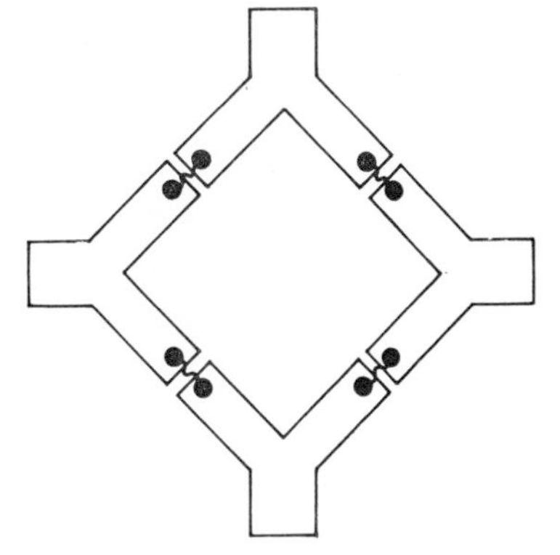

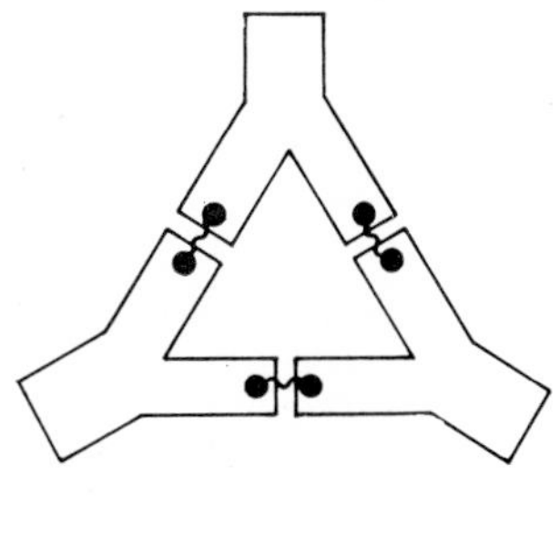

(c)

(a)

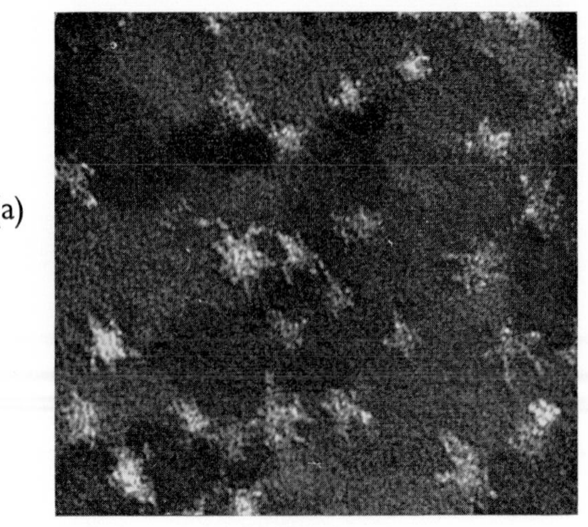

(b)

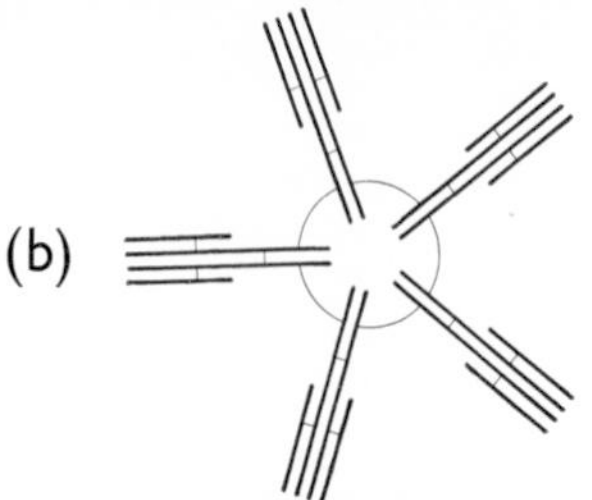

(c)

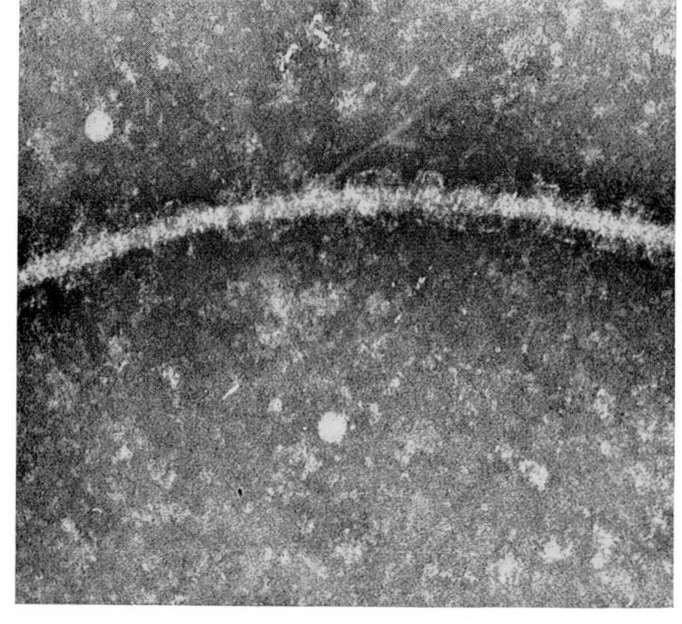

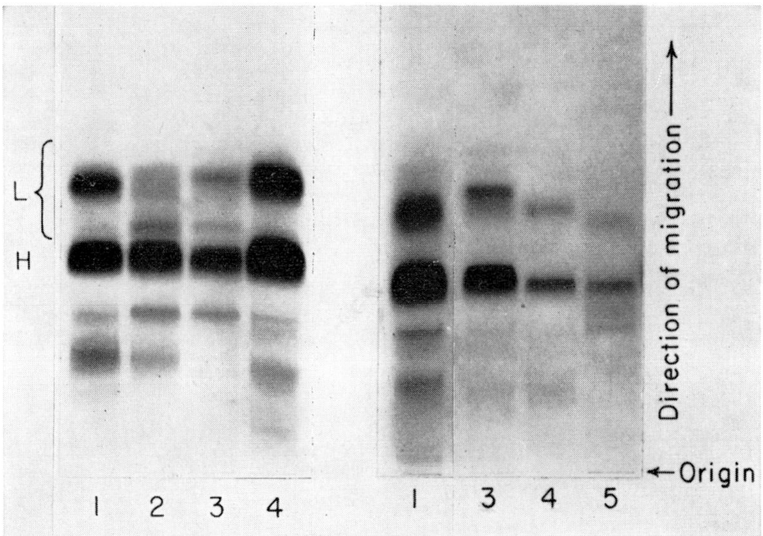

PLATE 4.5. Starch gel electrophoresis of purified human antibodies, after reduction to free H and L chains. (The electrophoresis was performed in *acid* urea solution, which gives less clear separation of the L chains than would the conditions used in Plate 4.2).

(*a*) 1-4 antibodies to dextran from different individuals.

(*b*) 1-5 antibodies to teichoic acid from different individuals.

Note that the L chain region shows multiple discrete bands, which differ in position in each individual. Whole normal IgG gives a broad continuous band over the L chain region when examined in this way; each antibody represents a different restricted population. [Modified from Edelman, G.M. and Kabat E.A., *J. exp. Med.* **119,** 443, 1964].

PLATE 4.4 (*a*, *b* and *c*) (*facing page*). Electron micrograph of IgM molecules revealed by negative staining.

(*a*) Normal bovine IgM. Molecules are seen from above and not attached to antigen. Note that some show the presence of 5 'arms' (× 280,000).

(*b*) Diagram illustrating probable arrangement of *L* and *H* chains in IgM. They are joined by disulphate bonds whose exact position is uncertain.

(*c*) Bacterial flagellum with attached IgM antibody, shown up by negative staining technique. The antibody molecules seen from the side resemble staples attached to the flagellum. (× 225,000).

[Photograph (*a*) kindly supplied by Dr. A. Feinstein and photograph (*c*) kindly supplied by Dr. R. R. Dourmashkin.]

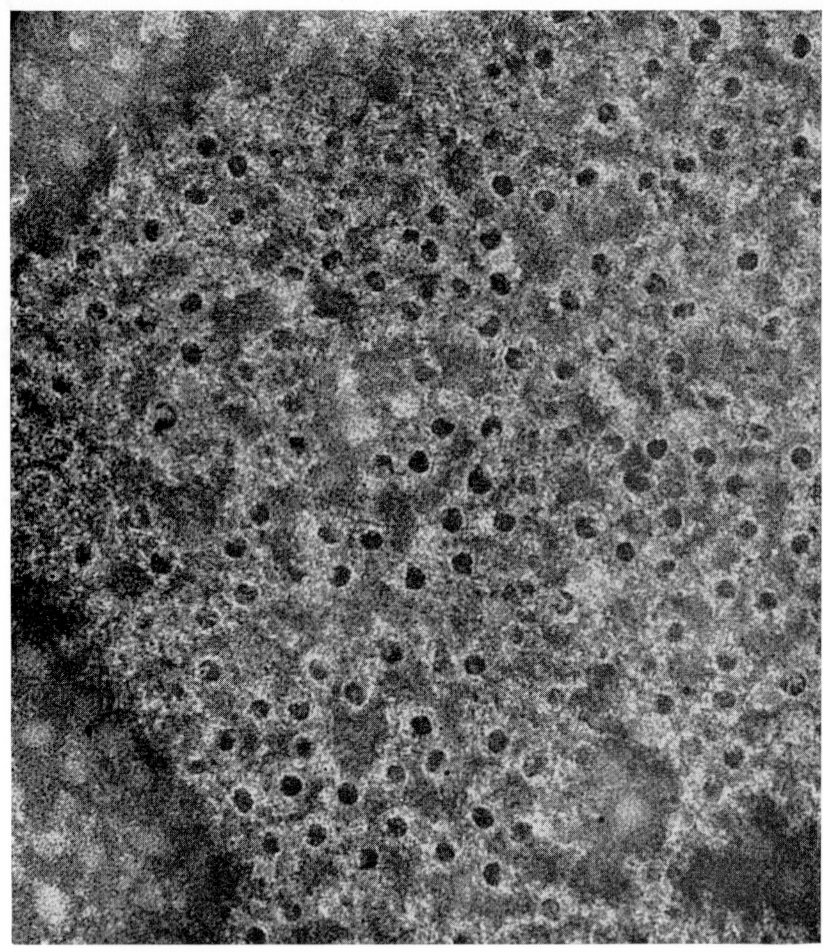

PLATE 5.1. Pits (holes) in the red cell membrane caused by the action of antibody and complement. Electron micrograph showing part of a human red cell membrane negatively stained with phosphotungstate. The red cells were treated with an autoantibody derived from a case of haemolytic anaemia, and human complement. The dark circles are pits in the red cell membrane filled with phosphotungstate and consequently more opaque to the electron beam. Each pit measures about 100 Å in diameter. The pits represent sites of damage produced by the last stage of complement action. (Magnification ×250,000.)

[Photograph by Dr. R. R. Dourmashkin.]

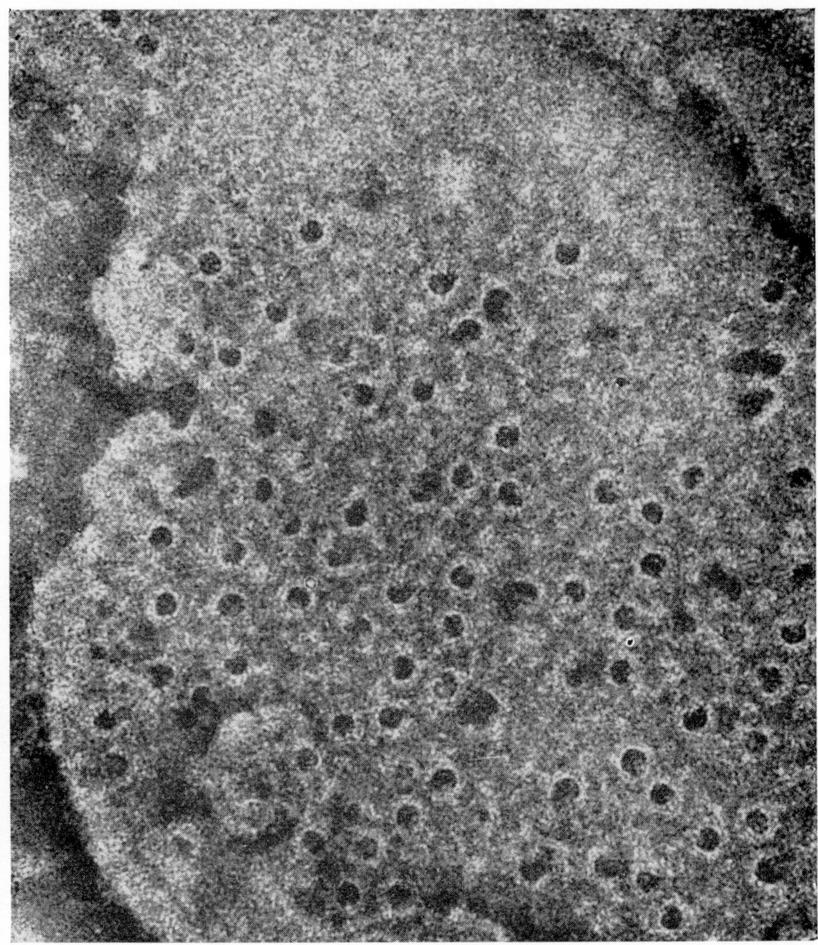

PLATE 5.2. Effect of antibody and human complement on *Shigella shigae*. The bacteria were treated with rabbit antibody against the 'O' somatic antigen and human complement, and examined as described in Plate 5.1. The pits or holes in the outer membrane are closely similar to those on the red cell membrane. (Magnification $\times 250{,}000$.)
(Photograph by Dr. R. R. Dourmashkin.)

PLATE 5.3. Demonstration of chemotactic effect of antigen/antibody complexes in the presence of complement. The plate shows filter membranes which have been cleared and stained to show cells which have migrated into them. Experimental design is explained in the text on p. 199. Antigen/antibody complexes were mixed with (A) heat inactivated serum (B) fresh serum. Chemotactic activity is only evident when fresh serum is present.

[Photograph provided by Dr. H. U. Keller.]

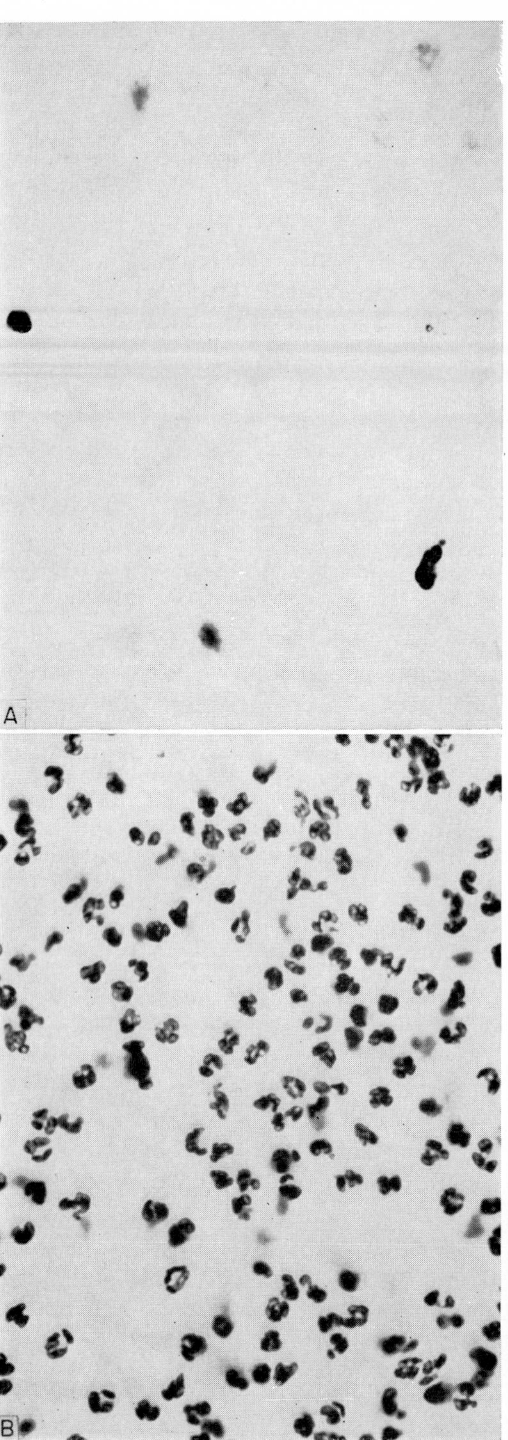

sometimes named T-globulin or, more non-committally, fast or γ_1-globulin. Such results might at first sight appear to be contradictory, or to imply some essential difference between antibodies against different antigens in rabbits and horses, but although there are real differences in the chemical and physical properties of the different antibodies they are not of fundamental importance. In several species of animal antibodies can be formed which may either have properties similar to those illustrated in Fig. 4.1 or similar to those in Fig. 4.2, and other antibodies have properties intermediate between the two.

The fact is that the class of protein to which antibodies belong differs from most other plasma proteins in not being homogeneous, but rather consists of a family of closely related proteins, with overlapping physical and chemical properties. While differing between themselves in various ways which are discussed below they still resemble each other much more than they do any other kind of protein, and are all products of a line of cells whose mature member is the plasma cell, and which have many cytological features in common (see Chapter Seven). To illustrate what is meant by 'a family of closely related proteins' two examples may be given. The first is the separation of plasma proteins by electrophoresis in two dimensions. This consists in essence of first separating the plasma proteins into their main groups by means of electrophoresis on a paper strip, and then causing them to migrate out of the paper into a buffered starch gel by applying an electric field at right angles to the original direction. The starch gel acts as a molecular sieve, retarding different proteins according to their sizes, and in this way a further sharp separation of many components is obtained. Figure 4.3 is a drawing of such a preparation, stained to locate the various protein fractions, and it shows clearly how the γ-globulin forms a long drawn-out trail, instead of a relatively discrete spot. The second illustration comes from the use of immuno-electrophoresis described more fully in Chapter Nine. This technique consists in first separating the plasma proteins by electrophoresis in an agar gel, and then allowing antiserum (prepared against as many as possible of the constituents of plasma) to diffuse from a trough cut in the agar in a direction parallel to the line of protein migration. As each component of the plasma meets its appropriate antibody diffusing towards it, a precipitate is formed in the agar gel along the line where they meet. Since the antibodies are quite specific for each different protein, and do not interact, a separate line is formed for each plasma constituent for which antibodies are present in the antiserum. When, however, two components are antigenically similar (in the sense that some or all of the antibodies against the

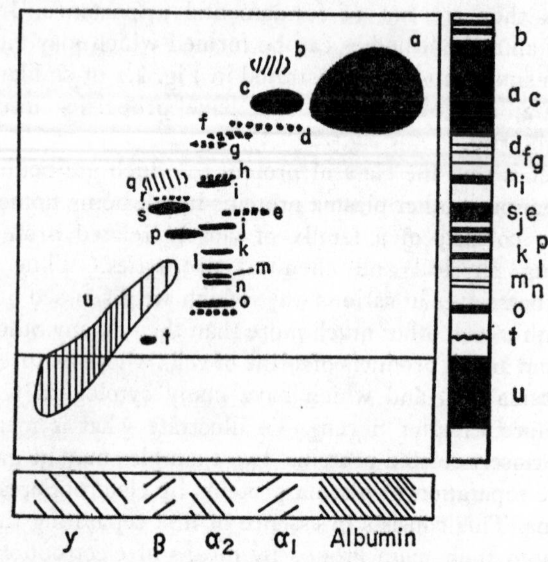

FIG. 4.3. A diagrammatic representation of the results of a two-dimensional electrophoresis experiment with serum of haptoglobin type 2-1 and transferrin type C. The corresponding filter-paper electrophoresis separation is shown below the two-dimensional diagram; the corresponding one-dimensional starch-gel separation is shown to the right. The zones which have been specifically identified are: *a*, albumin; *b*, acidic α_1-glycoprotein 'orosomucoid'; *h*, *j*, *k*, *l*, *m*, *n*, haptoglobins; *o*, heat-labile glycoprotein 'Sα_2-globulin'; *s*, transferrin C; *t*, high molecular weight β-liproprotein; *u*, γ-globulins. Note the drawn-out shape of the γ-globulin zone. [From Smithies O. (1959) *Advanc. Protein Chem.* **14**, 83.]

one will also react with the other), their lines of precipitate will fuse together either partly or wholly. Plate 4.1 (p. 150) shows how this very powerful technique works in practice, and also illustrates how the line corresponding to γ-globulin extends through the β-globulins and even into the α-globulins. It may be seen that the γ-globulin line has 'tails' coming off along its length. These are only visible when appropriate antisera are used, but they indicate that the γ-globulin, acting as an antigen in another species, is not entirely homogeneous. Although most of the antibodies against the γ-globulin react with all the material (irrespective of its electrophoretic mobility), some of the antibodies only react with part of it. By various procedures which utilize the differences in ionic charge, shape, size or solubility between one protein and another the antibody-containing fractions of plasma proteins from any species of animal such as man can be separated into a number of distinct components whose properties can be compared. In respect of their overall amino-acid composition, a parameter which generally differs markedly between different plasma proteins, the components all prove to be very much alike although not identical. When used as antigens to immunize another species they usually elicit antibodies which cross react extensively with each of the other components, although again they are not antigenically identical. They all contain some complex carbohydrate built into their structure, but in man the amount in the different components varies from about 3 to about 10 per cent by weight. Most of the components have a molecular weight about 150,000 and when their rate of sedimentation under the force produced by high-speed centrifugation is measured they have a sedimentation coefficient of about 7 Svedberg units ($S_{20}=7$). However, components can sometimes be detected with sedimentation coefficients of 9S or 11S, and there is always a sizeable component with molecular weight about 900,000 and sedimentation coefficient 18–19S. When this was first recognized it was termed β-macroglobulin (β_{2M}) or γ_1-macroglobulin, to distinguish it from the α-macroglobulin which is not associated with antibody activity.

It became increasingly clear that attempts to designate these antibody-containing proteins in terms of their physicochemical properties measured by electrophoresis, etc. could never be satisfactory, and in 1964 international agreement was obtained to include them all in a single generic term '*Immunoglobulin*' based on their common properties, and to subdivide them into classes (and even subclasses) based on their differences. The classes of human immunoglobulin presently recognized are set out in Table 4.1. It is important to recognize that this complexity is not confined to man. Somewhat similar classes and subclasses have been found in several widely different mammalian species in which they have been carefully looked for, such as the mouse, the rabbit, or the horse. Multiple classes of immunoglobulin exist also in the teleost fishes, and even primitive elasmobranch fishes such as the dogfish possess at least two classes. In the more primitive species fewer classes have been found, and macroglobulin appears to be the principal immunoglobulin.

Further consideration of the properties of immunoglobulins is made very much simpler by taking into account recently acquired knowledge about their structure. However, much of this knowledge was acquired by the study not only of normal immunoglobulins, or of purified antibodies specific for a given determinant, but also of certain abnormal immunoglobulins known as *myeloma* proteins. It is necessary to digress a little to discuss the latter. As mentioned in Chapter Eight they are produced, often in very large amounts, by the overproliferation of homogeneous clones of plasma cells which have acquired the capacity to grow apparently unchecked while retaining their ability to synthesize and secrete their characteristic immunoglobulin product. Although only very few myeloma proteins have so far been shown to combine specifically with any of the many antigens tested, there is every reason to believe that they are all typical immunoglobulins in other respects, and may in fact have antibody properties if only we knew how to recognize them. The myeloma protein produced by any one myeloma in a given patient or experimental animal is not only relatively easy to isolate in a reasonably pure state because there is a lot of it present in serum, but it is usually quite homogeneous, i.e. all the molecules are identical. Different myelomas arising in different subjects are never

TABLE 4.1

Known classes of Human Immunoglobulin (Ig)

	IgG	IgA	IgD	IgM	IgE*
Molecular weight	150,000	150,000 and 400,000	150,000	900,000	? 190,000
Approx. sedimentation coefficient (S_w^{20})	7	7	7	18–19	
% carbohydrate	3	10	?	10	? 10·9
Normal serum concentration (g/100 ml)	0·6–1·5	0·02–0·5	<0·001–0·014	0·05–0·2	0·06–1·0 × 10^{-}

* The evidence for the existence of IgE is discussed on p. 174.

found to be completely identical with one another when they are examined carefully in respect of several parameters such as their electrophoretic mobility, amino acid and carbohydrate content, and antigenic structure. However, if the properties of a large number of *unselected* myeloma proteins from different individuals are averaged out, they are found to correspond very closely to the properties of the total serum immunoglobulins in any one normal individual. Furthermore, the frequency with which myelomas producing a given kind of immunoglobulin arise in a large population of people reflects the average abundance of each kind of immunoglobulin in the serum of normal people drawn from the same population. Thus myelomas have provided a unique source of homogeneous but representative immunoglobulins, which are suitable for analysis by physicochemical and immunological methods. Another important point is that certain myelomas synthesize not only whole immunoglobulin molecules but also smaller fragments of these, which are excreted as a form of Bence-Jones proteins in the urine, from which they are readily isolated. By contrast with myeloma proteins the immunoglobulin fractions isolated—however carefully—from normal serum have invariably proved to be mixtures of closely similar but nevertheless heterogeneous molecules, and consequently less suitable for detailed analysis.

THE LIGHT AND HEAVY CHAINS OF IMMUNOGLOBULINS

We may now return to the question of the structure of the immunoglobulins. It was discovered in 1961 by G.M. Edelman and M.D. Poulik that when immunoglobulins were treated in strong urea solutions with agents, such as mercaptoethanol, which reduce disulphide (—S—S—) bonds to the —SH + HS— form, they regularly fell apart into a number of small components. These they subsequently showed to consist of two groups of polypeptide chains differing in size. The smaller was termed by them the light (L) and the larger the heavy (H) polypeptide chain. The components separated in this way were not soluble in ordinary aqueous media and had lost their immunological activity. However, in the following year R.R. Porter and his colleagues succeeded in obtaining the components in the absence of urea by reducing only five disulphide bonds, stabilizing these by alkylation, then making the solution weakly acid (to prevent the components from recombining) and separating the products by a filtration technique which depended on molecular size. The two components so obtained retained much of their biological activity. They corresponded to the light and heavy chains of Edelman and Poulik, but were termed by Porter the 'B' and 'A' chains. The molecular weight of the B (light) chains from rabbit γ-globulin was shown to be 20,000 and that of the A (heavy) chains 52,000. From evidence based on the relative proportions of the components and on their chemical and serological properties, Porter put forward a diagrammatic structure for rabbit γ-globulin made up of two A and two B chains.

All subsequent work has confirmed the general validity of this structure, not only for the IgG of rabbits but also that of man and several other species. It is now generally agreed that the chains shall be called Light (L) and Heavy (H) and that their molecular weights are about 25,000 and 50,000 respectively. Porter's diagrammatic structure is shown in Fig. 4.4.

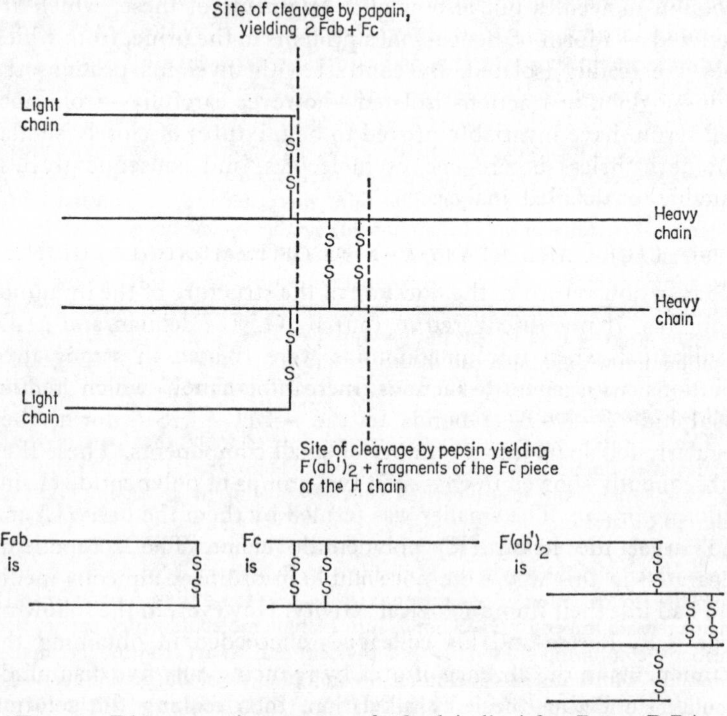

FIG. 4.4. Diagrammatic structure of γG-globulin (after Porter R.R.). (N.B. The number of disulphide bonds joining the H chains varies from one to five according to the subclass.)

It will be seen that each L chain is attached at one end (the carboxy terminal end*) by one S—S bond to a H chain, and that the two H chains are also linked together by S—S bonds. Two of these last are indicated but their number may vary from one to five according to the class or subclass of Ig. The diagram indicates why after rupture of a small number of S—S bonds the molecule falls apart into its component chains.

Cleavage by Proteolytic Enzymes

Before the chain structure of Ig was known it had already been discovered that the proteolytic enzymes papain and pepsin, which hydrolyse peptide bonds specific for each enzyme, could split IgG antibodies into large fragments which retained much of the biological properties of the starting material. The analysis of these fragments and the interpretation of their significance by Porter in 1959 laid the foundation of much of the subsequent work on immunoglobulin structure. The effects of these enzymes are readily understood in terms of the diagrammatic structure of Fig. 4.4, on which the sites of cleavage are indicated.

Papain splits the molecule into three *pieces*. Two, termed *Fab*, are identical, and consist of the L chain linked with the amino-terminal* part of the H chain, by a single S—S bond. The third piece, termed *Fc*, consists of the C-terminal portions of the H chain joined together by one or two S—S bonds. The Fab pieces, if prepared from specific antibodies, each carry one of the two antigen binding sites of the original molecules. Since the Fab pieces are *univalent* they cannot agglutinate particles nor form a lattice structure with antigens so as to lead to specific precipitation (see Chapter Nine), but their combination with antigen can readily be shown in other ways. Disruption of the S—S bond separates the L chain from the N-terminal part of the H chain, which is termed the *Fd* piece.

The Fc piece has no antibody activity, but contains that part of the H chain which determines various other biological properties, such as ability to fix complement, and it also carries some of the allotypic markers. These are referred to later.

The main product of treatment by *pepsin* is termed $F(ab')_2$. Because the site at which pepsin cleaves the H chains is on the other side of the S—S bonds from the site of action of papain, the two L chains and the Fd parts of the H chains remain linked by S—S bonds into a single molecule which carries both antibody combining sites. It is thus bivalent and, apart from being smaller, combines with antigens (including precipitation or agglutination) much as would the original molecule. However, the $\mathrm{F(ab')_2}$ lacks most of the Fc part

* The terms amino or N-terminal and carboxy or C-terminal are explained in the Glossary.

of the H chain, which is split by pepsin into a number of smaller fragments, and has lost those biological properties associated with this piece. By graded reduction of the S—S bonds the F(ab′)2 can be dissociated into two Fab′ pieces resembling Fab, or ultimately to free L chains and Fd′ pieces.

THE POLYPEPTIDE CHAINS OF Ig AND THEIR RELATIONSHIP TO Ig CLASSES

The foregoing discussion may seem somewhat remote from the practical problems of how antibodies behave, but electron microscopy of IgG antibodies and some of their fragments (Plate 4.3) reveals that their actual shapes correspond remarkably well with those predicted from Fig. 4.4. Furthermore, application of similar methods of analysis to other classes of Ig has revealed that they also are composed of equal numbers of H and L chains and that their general structure follows the same pattern as IgG.

Various purified immunoglobulins, usually myeloma or Bence-Jones proteins, have been used as antigens to immunize animals of another species. The antisera obtained have been suitably absorbed with isolated H or L chains or enzymically produced fragments of Ig, and so rendered specific for the L or H chains of the protein used for immunization. Such specific antisera may be used as tools for qualitative or quantitative comparison of the antigenic determinants of other immunoglobulins. The results have shown that in all classes of Ig the L chains are very similar, whereas the H chains show major differences from class to class. Furthermore within a class (defined both by physicochemical properties and by the major H chain differences) there are found minor but consistent differences which enable clear subclasses also to be recognized. Examination of many urinary Bence-Jones proteins—which as mentioned above are the homogeneous products of myeloma cells—has shown that these consist solely of L chains, either single or joined together in pairs by S—S bonds. However in man there are two quite distinct types of Bence-Jones protein which, although similar in size, are built up from very different amino acid sequences and differ antigenically. The L chains corresponding to them are termed $\varkappa$ and λ types, and the relative frequency with which $\varkappa$ type Bence-Jones proteins are found is about twice that of the λ type.* In the

* Three slightly different forms of $\varkappa$ chain ($\varkappa_1$, $\varkappa_2$, $\varkappa_3$) occur, and other minor variants of $\varkappa$ and λ chains are likely to be discovered in future, but they need not concern us here.

serum of all normal people, however, in each class of Ig *both* types of L chain occur, in the proportion 70 per cent κ and 30 per cent λ, but any one Ig molecule in any given class contains *either* κ *or* λ type L chain.

It has been agreed internationally that the Greek letters γ, α, μ, δ and ε shall be used to designate the H chains of the Ig classes IgG, IgA, IgM, IgD and IgE. By this means it is possible to write abbreviations indicating both the L and H chain types, and the number of each in the molecules, as indicated in Table 4.2. Thus IgG molecules are either $\kappa 2\gamma 2$ or $\lambda 2\gamma 2$, whereas human IgM molecules, which contain 10 L and 10 H chains probably arranged in subunits resembling IgG molecules, are written $(\kappa 2\mu 2)5$ or $(\lambda 2\mu 2)5$.

Table 4.2 shows the present classification of human immunoglobulins on the basis of their component polypeptide chains. Although Bence-Jones proteins are traditionally regarded as pathological products, trace amounts have been found in the serum of normal individuals. The table refers to four subclasses of IgG distinguishable by antigenic differences in their H chains into γG1, γG2, γG3 and γG4. Normal human serum contains all four subclasses. The antigenic determinants by which they are recognized may occur on either the Fc part (γG1 and γG2) or the Fd part of the H chains.

It is worth emphasizing that complexity of this kind is not confined to human Ig. Two kinds of L chain have been demonstrated in the mouse and the guinea-pig, and will probably be found in other species also. Multiple classes of H chain, akin to those of man, have been shown to exist in many mammalian Igs. The possible biological significance of this is discussed later in this chapter.

IMMUNOGLOBULIN ALLOTYPES

The antigenic specificities discussed above, which distinguish one class of Ig from another but which are represented in all normal individuals of a given species, are sometimes referred to as *isotypic* specificities. There are however two other sorts of antigenic specificity, first recognized by J. Oudin, while working with rabbit Ig, which are of considerable importance. These are *allotypic* and *idiotypic* (Gk 'allos', other; 'idios', private, and 'tupos', imprint). *Allotypic* specificities are those antigenic specificities which are

TABLE 4.2

Classification of human immunoglobulins in terms of L and H chains

	Bence-Jones proteins	IgG	IgA	IgM	IgD	IgE
Antigenic determinants						
Common (L chain)	κ or λ	κ, λ	κ, λ	κ, λ	κ, λ	? κ, λ
Specific (H chain)	none	γ	α	μ	δ	ε
Relative abundance 70%	κ or κ_2	$\kappa_2\gamma_2$	$\kappa_2\alpha_2$	$(\kappa_2\mu_2)_5$‡	?*	?
30%	λ or λ_2	$\lambda_2\gamma_2$	$\lambda_2\alpha_2$	$(\lambda_2\mu_2)_5$		
Antibody activity	–	+	+	+	?	+
Subclasses with distinct antigenic determinants on H chains. Figures in parentheses indicate relative abundance within the class of Ig		IgG 1† (70–80) IgG 2 (13–18) IgG 3 (6–8) IgG 4 (3)	At least two subclasses identified	Two probable subclasses identified	?	?

* At the time of writing IgD has been insufficiently examined to give figures for relative abundance. Antibody activity is probable but not certain.

† These subclasses prior to 1966 were termed γ_2b, γ_2a, γ_2c, γ_2d respectively (see *Bull. Wld. Hlth. Orgn.* **35,** 953 (1966)).

‡ $\kappa_2\mu_2$ and $\lambda_2\mu_2$ are also found in some individuals with increased plasma IgM concentrations, and occur regularly in elasmobranch fishes.

different in different *groups* of individuals within the same species, while *idiotypic* specificities are peculiar to a single kind of antibody made in a *single* individual member of the species. Both kinds of specificity are most easily revealed by immunizing a large number of animals of a species with Igs from other individual animals of the same species. Such specificities can also be revealed by immunizing animals of another species, but tend to be obscured by the antibody response made against determinants other than those responsible for the allotypic or idiotypic specificity.

In the Igs of rabbits and mice a large number of allotypes have been identified, and their presence has been shown by breeding experiments to be controlled by well defined genes which have several allelic forms. Human Ig allotypes, for obvious reasons, cannot be studied by deliberate immunization of one person with Ig or myeloma protein from another person. Such immunization does occur occasionally however as a result of blood transfusion, and quite commonly as a result of the passage of maternal IgG across the placenta into the foetus. Although it might be expected that in such a situation the child would be born immunologically tolerant of its mother's IgG (see Chapter Thirteen), it has been found that when there is a genetically controlled difference between the mother's and the child's IgG allotypes the child may make weak (or rarely potent) anti-allotype antibodies. Anti-allotype antibodies may also be found in the sera of patients with rheumatoid arthritis and certain other diseases characterized by the formation of Rheumatoid Factors (see Chapter Fifteen). Such factors behave like antibodies to IgG and are sometimes specific for allotypic determinants. Finally, antisera against allotypic determinants of human Ig can fairly readily be obtained by using human myeloma proteins to immunize monkeys, or, better, anthropoid apes, whose own Igs are already chemically and antigenically rather similar to those of man.

Evaluation of the allotypic specificity of a human Ig is usually not done by the more obvious methods of precipitation or agar gel diffusion (see Chapter Nine) but by a roundabout method which is more sensitive and economical with the test materials. The method involves preparing indicator particles coated with an Ig whose allotype is known. Such particles (usually Rh positive red cells coated with an appropriate non-agglutinating antibody) are agglutinable by antibody to the chosen allotype. In the test the ability of Ig of unknown allotype to block the agglutination is determined.

InV Allotypes

The allotypic specificities designated InV were first described in 1962. They are associated with L chains of Ig, and may therefore be found in Bence-Jones proteins and in immunoglobulins of all classes, as well as on the Fab pieces derived from them.

The InV allotypes are apparently confined to κ type L chains; there may well be a similar system related to λ type L chains, but no antisera are presently known able to detect it. At present three InV allotypes have been defined which are termed, by international agreement, InV (1), InV (2) and InV (3). In the populations studied InV (1) and InV (2) are as a rule found together. There may also be a fourth allotype since some κ type L chains are not typable by using the currently available antisera. These allotypes are considered to be controlled by alleles at a single genetic locus. The distinction between InV (2) and InV (3) has been found to be uniformly correlated with whether leucine or valine is present at position 191 in the 'invariable' part of the κ type L chain (see p. 165). No special amino acid substitution has yet been detected to correspond with InV (1).

Gm Allotypes

The Gm allotypes are genetically controlled antigenic specificities associated with the H chain of human IgG. The first examples were detected by the use of rheumatoid arthritis sera in 1956. Unlike the InV allotypes the Gm allotypes are confined exclusively to the IgG class. (It is quite possible that some parallel system of allotypic specificities will be found in the H chains of other Ig classes also—this is known to happen, for example, in the mouse and the rabbit.)

For several years only a few Gm 'groups', as they were first called, were known. Recently however the search for others has been intensified and new ones are being revealed every year. They are now named Gm (1), Gm (2) etc. roughly in the chronological order of their discovery. Gm (1) represents the former Gm a, Gm (2) was Gm κ, Gm (3) was Gm b^2, Gm (4) was Gm f, and so on. At the time of writing more than 20 distinct Gm allotypes are recognized. While the available information is changing so fast it is difficult to make valid general statements. The following specific statements are based partly on conclusions drawn from studies made on the mixed population of IgG molecules present in the whole serum from large numbers of individuals and from chosen families, and partly on studies of individual IgG myeloma proteins (which are assumed to be a truly homogenous population of molecules).

(a) Gm allotypes are genetically controlled variations occurring in several regions of the H chains of IgG.

(b) Some Gm specificities always occur on separate myeloma proteins in members of a particular ethnic group but may occur together on the *same* myeloma protein in members of another group. For example in Caucasian (white-skinned) people Gm (1) and (5) behave as allelic characters and are found on separate IgG molecules, whereas in negro people they are inherited together and occur on the same molecules. Similarly Gm (1) and (4) commonly occur together in Chinese people but not in Europeans.

(c) Particular Gm allotypes are confined to a particular subclass of IgG. For example Gm (1), (2), (3), (4) have been found exclusively on IgG1 molecules, whereas Gm (5), (6) and (10)–(14) have been found only on IgG3 molecules.

(d) The antigenic sites of most Gm allotypes are located on the Fc pieces of the H chains, but some are on the Fd pieces and may even only be detectable when the Fd piece is combined with a L chain to form Fab. There is evidence that certain pairs of allotypes, one of which is on the Fc and the other on the Fd piece (e.g. (1) and (17)), always occur together on the same H chain. This implies strongly that the H polypeptide chain must be made as a whole, rather than from two chains joined together later.

(e) There is at present no evidence that any particular specific antibody-combining site is associated with any particular Gm group.

The Gm allotypes provide a striking and complex example of the phenomenon of *genetic polymorphism*, in which the synthesis of a given kind of protein is controlled by a number of allelic genes. Separate genes must exist which control the synthesis of H chains for each of the IgG subclasses, and for those controlling the IgG1 and IgG3 subclasses at least there must exist several alleles. An explanation of the control of two Gm factors either by the same gene or by two different genes according to the individuals or ethnic groups may be sought in terms of intra-cistronic crossing-over (see Glossary).

THE PROPERTIES OF INDIVIDUAL CLASSES OF IMMUNOGLOBULINS

Bence-Jones Proteins

Bence-Jones proteins were first described by H. Bence-Jones in 1847, as albuminous substances occurring in the urine—typically in cases of multiple myelomatosis—which had the characteristic property of coagulating when the urine was heated to 60° but of redissolving at higher temperatures (about 80°). It has already been mentioned that these proteins are in fact Ig light chains, produced in excess by the myeloma cells, and they get into the urine because their small size permits them to be filtered through the glomerulus. They commonly occur in urine as dimers, linked via those S—S bonds which would link them to the H chains in the whole Ig molecule. Bence-Jones proteins—i.e. excess of L chains—are not secreted by all myelomas (Table 4.3). However, when they are made they may be produced in enormous amounts, and patients (or mice) who excrete large amounts in their urine are subject to severe renal damage, often associated with amyloidosis. Some myelomas are found both in man and mice (see p. 341) which synthesize only L chains and no, or a minimal amount of, H chains.

TABLE 4.3

Incidence of Bence-Jones protein excretion in myelomatosis and pathological macroglobulinaemia

Class of paraprotein	Percentage of total cases	
	With Bence-Jones protein	Without Bence-Jones protein
IgG	15	32
IgA	6	14
IgM	1	13
Bence-Jones protein alone	20	

[From Osserman E.F. and Takatsuki K. (1963) *Medicine* 42, 357.]

Apart from their diagnostic implications, Bence-Jones proteins are of great interest because they represent homogeneous L chains, and can be isolated in sufficient amounts for detailed chemical analysis. The homogeneity of such proteins is well illustrated by Plate 4.2, a, b, c, following p. 148, which shows the pattern of bands produced when L chains from the normal Igs of various species are subjected to electrophoresis on starch gel in slightly alkaline 8 M urea solution. Each band represents a collection of L chains differing in electric charge from those in the other bands. Whereas normal Ig L chains show many distinct bands (about 10 in man), a given Bence-Jones protein usually forms a single band. Different Bence-Jones proteins form bands in different positions, corresponding to one or other of the bands of normal Ig L chain. It should be mentioned that the position of L chain bands analysed in this way has not been correlated with any other known property, such as whether they are κ or λ type or derived from any particular specific kind of antibody.

Most of the Bence-Jones proteins whose amino acid sequences have been analysed in great detail have so far been of the κ type, derived either from man or from various transplantable myelomas of mice. It is a remarkable fact that the amino acid sequences of the κ type L chains from the two species have proved to be very alike.

The total number of amino acid residues is 214 (the number in λ chains is also about the same). Comparison of several κ chains has shown that the carboxy-terminal halves of the molecule in each are virtually identical, the only amino acid differences being a substitution mentioned above of leucine for valine at position 191, which is associated with the InV allotypes 2 or 3. This half of the molecule, which ends in a cysteine residue whose —SH forms an S—S bond with the H chain, is sometimes called the 'invariable' half (see Fig. 4.5, p. 169). The amino-terminal half (107 amino acid residues) has, however, been found to vary markedly from one Bence-Jones protein to another. Even in the 20 or so proteins examined carefully at the time of writing there have been found at least 32 positions in which amino acid variations occur, and presumably many more will be found as more proteins are analysed. At some positions up to four different amino acids have been found in different proteins. Many of the variations are such as would be expected to result from single step mutations, according to current genetic theories, but others would require more than a single step.

The interpretation of these findings is very difficult. If the immunoglobulins of any individual are considered to be made up of a mixture of molecules with different L chains, of which the Bence-Jones proteins constitute just a few homogeneous samples, how are all the various amino acid sequences in them determined? It is nowadays accepted that each different polypeptide sequence is coded for by a different gene, so it follows that each individual must possess many different genes controlling L chain synthesis. We do not know whether these are already present in the germ line, or whether they arise by somatic mutation during growth and development of the individual, in which case different genes could be present in different cells capable of synthesizing immunoglobulins (see p. 144).

Heavy Chains

Heavy chains by themselves are essentially laboratory artefacts although it is convenient to discuss something of their structure at this stage. However, a rare clinical condition has been described, associated with a generalized lymph node enlargement and a low serum level of immunoglobulins, in which an abnormal protein is present both in blood and urine. The protein has many of the properties of the Fc piece of IgG H chain, and lacks L chains, or antibody activity. It does not cross-react immunologically with κ or λ Bence-Jones proteins; nor does it cross-react with the H chains of IgA or IgM. The condition has been termed 'heavy chain disease', but what the fundamental lesion is which leads to the production of incomplete H chains is not at present known (see also p. 344).

As already described on p. 157, H chains may be split by papain into a carboxy-terminal Fc piece and an amino-terminal Fd piece. The main properties which distinguish one class of Ig from another, and which are discussed in relation to each class below, are associated with the Fc piece. The carbohydrate moiety is also on this piece. Even when prepared from the IgG of whole serum the Fc piece(s) can readily be crystallized, a fact which implies that the amount of variation from molecule to molecule is likely to be small. Despite the known presence of numerous allotypic determinants on the Fc piece of human IgG, amino acid and peptide analyses (mainly done on rabbit IgG Fc pieces) indicate that much of this part of the H-chain is of a very constant composition for all the IgG molecules. Furthermore there is a striking similarity between the amino acid sequences of the Fc piece of rabbit IgG and those of the Fc pieces of human or horse IgG. Even more remarkably, this similarity extends to the 'invariable' half of human or mouse Bence-Jones proteins also.

The Fd pieces are much more difficult to isolate in a pure state, and less analytical work has been done on them. However, there is already evidence that the situation is somewhat akin to that which obtains for L chains. The amino-terminal portion show a large number of variations in the amino acid sequences, whereas the carboxy-terminal portion is relatively invariable. Furthermore the 'invariable' portion of the Fd piece appears to be rather similar from one species to another, at least in man, the rabbit and the horse. It is discussed below (p. 182) how the specific antibody combining site is associated with the Fd piece of the H chain, and it is a reasonable hypothesis that it is the variable amino acid sequence at the amino-terminal ends of the H chains which determines the specific structure of this site.

Amino acid sequence studies made on H and L chains have revealed that there are numerous regions of the chains in which identical or very similar sequences occur. This applies to the Fc piece and the 'invariable' part of the Fd piece of H chains, and the 'inavariable' part both of κ- and λ-type L chains prepared from four mammalian species. Since such similarities are far too great to have occurred by chance, these findings have led to the interesting speculation that both L and H chains may have arisen by duplication of a common ancestral gene followed by independent mutations giving rise to the present L and H genes in each species. Since the H chain is twice the size of the L chain, a second duplication of the gene must also have occurred so as to give rise to a primitive H chain gene whose product would have been a single chain equivalent to two L chains joined end to end. By repeated independent mutations the final result could be what is now found, namely H chains whose carboxy- and amino-terminal portions had only a partial sequence in common either with each other or with L chains.

Immunoglobulin G (γG)

The main biological properties of human IgG are listed in Tables 4.1, 4.2 and 4.4. It is the form in which antibodies occur most abundantly, and cells making IgG are usually found in all sites where synthesis of immunoglobulin occurs (see Chapter Seven). IgG exchanges readily between the blood and the extravascular fluid. Its half life in the body, which represents the balance between synthesis of new and catabolism of old molecules, is about 20 days.

TABLE 4.4
Some Biological Properties of the Main Classes of Human Ig

	IgG	IgA	IgM
Distribution between extravascular fluid and blood (% intravascular)	44	40	70
Turnover rate (% of total pool per day)	3	10–15	10–15
Average concentration in normal serum (g/100 ml)	1·07	0·25	0·077
No. of antibody combining sites per molecule	2	2	5* or 10
Complement fixation	+	–	+
Selective secretion by seromucous glands	–†	+	–
Passage across placenta	+	–	–
Presence in milk	+	+	– or trace

* Evidence based on examination of a few specific antibodies. A symmetrical molecule made from 10 H and 10 L chains might be expected to have 10 combining sites.
† IgG is present to a variable extent, but no selective secretion mechanism is involved.

However, IgG appears to be unique among the immunoglobulins in that the rate of catabolism (the *fraction* of the total intravascular IgG catabolized daily) increases with the concentration of IgG in the blood, above a fairly low level. Other immunoglobulins are not so affected, and the fraction catabolized daily is roughly constant, irrespective of their concentration in the blood. A consequence of this is that when IgG levels are markedly raised—e.g. by a myeloma making IgG or in chronic infection with malaria or leishmania—the half life of all the IgG may be much shorter than usual. A person with four times the usual serum level of IgG, for example, will have to synthesize all his IgG at about eight times the normal rate to maintain this level. If he continues to make a given antibody only at the normal rate, its absolute level in the blood will drop to one-eighth. This phenomenon provides at least a partial explanation of why patients with IgG myelomas are liable to suffer from antibody deficiency syndromes. The control of the catabolic rate has been shown to depend upon the Fc piece of the IgG H chain, as does also the property of transmission across biological membranes.

In all mammalian species studied IgG passes from the mother to the foetus, although the detailed mechanism varies with the species. In birds IgG is present in the yolk at the time of laying and is absorbed into the embryo chick during its growth in the egg. This aspect is considered at greater length in Chapter Eight.

When aggregated by interaction with antigen, or by other means such as gentle heating or chemical cross-linking agents, IgG initiates the chain of reactions known as complement fixation (see Chapter Five). This also depends upon some property associated with the Fc piece. Since complement fixation which promotes phagocytosis and killing of microbes is an important element in the biological effectiveness of antibodies, apart from direct neutralization of toxins etc., this property endows IgG with extra significance for the overall protection of the organism against infection. It has already been mentioned (p. 159) that IgG contains at least four subclasses. The detailed biological significance of these is not known, but it is unlikely that they would all have withstood evolutionary selection pressure and still be present in all normal individuals if they did not each at some time in recent evolutionary history confer some biological advantage. The only differences between the subclasses which have been identified as present—and for these a direct biological advantage is not obvious!—is that the IgG1 molecules fail to elicit reversed passive cutaneous anaphylaxis in the guinea-pig (see p. 396) whereas the other subclasses will do so, and IgG4 molecules do not fix complement.

At this point it is relevant to consider how the structure of IgG antibody molecules is suited to their function of combining with a wide variety of antigens of all shapes and sizes. In Plate 4.3 (following p. 148) are shown electron microscope photographs of purified IgG antibody against a simple determinant group (dinitrobenzene) which has been allowed to combine with a synthetic short chain antigen molecule at each end of which is one identical determinant group. On the same plate is a similar picture of the same antibody treated with pepsin to remove the Fc piece and leave the bivalent $F(ab')_2$ fragment. It is evident that the antibody combining sites are at the ends of two arms (Fab), with a knob at the middle corresponding to the Fc piece. The two arms behave as though they were flexibly hinged together, so that the combining sites can be at a variable distance apart up to the whole length of the molecule (about 230 Å). This property remains after the Fc piece has been digested away. Fig. 4.5 shows how the diagrammatic structure of Fig. 4.4 can

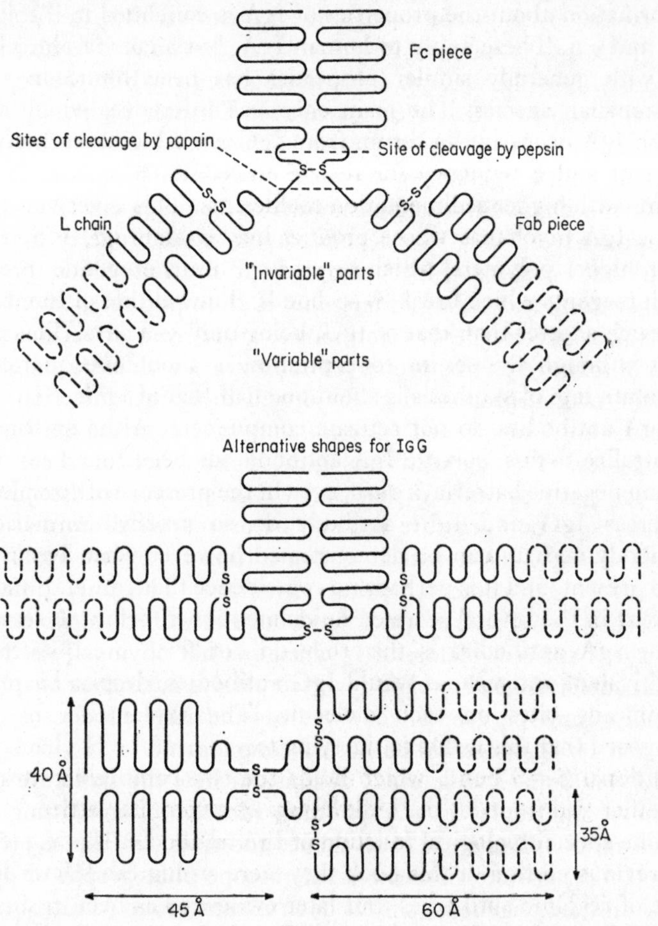

FIG. 4.5

be redrawn to include some of the facts about IgG discussed in the previous sections. The diagram is, of course, fanciful but it illustrates how the relation of the Fc piece to the rest of the molecule (and perhaps its effectiveness in activating complement) might be altered by combination with an antigen.

Immunoglobulin A (γA)

In many ways IgA resembles IgG and was in fact for a long time confused with IgG, despite the difference in electrophoretic mobilities, until specific antisera became available for detecting it. General information about the properties of IgA is contained in Tables 4.1, 4.2 and 4.4. These apply to human IgA, but a comparable class of Ig with generally similar properties has been found in several mammalian species. The main chemical differences which distinguish IgA occurring in serum from IgG are a higher carbohydrate content and a tendency for the 7S molecules to polymerize into forms with higher sedimentation coefficients. This is very evident in some IgA myelomas whose product may contain 9S, 11S, 13S or even higher polymers, which revert to 7S units on gentle treatment with reagents which break S—S bonds. The half life of human IgA is much shorter than that of IgG, being only 5–6 days. This means that although the serum concentration is about one quarter, the absolute rate of synthesis is about one half that of IgG.

IgA antibodies do not activate complement. Although they can neutralize toxins, specific IgA antibody has been found not to kill Gram negative bacteria *in vitro*, even in the presence of complement, whereas IgG and IgM antibody do so readily. Anti-bacterial antibody activity can be demonstrated however when lysozyme is also present, and it is perhaps no coincidence that IgA and lysozyme coexist in the several secreted fluids mentioned below. A feature of some IgA antibodies is that they do not form precipitates with multivalent antigens, as would IgG antibodies, despite having two combining sites on each molecule. The explanation has been proposed that this is due to the tying together of the H chains by an additional S—S bond, which holds the two combining sites close together and impedes the building up of a complex lattice.

The special biological function of IgA antibodies is a mystery. In a previous edition of this book they were strong candidates for the role of reaginic antibodies, but later evidence has been against this (see below). However, interest in them has been reawakened by the demonstration that IgA is the predominant immunoglobulin in a variety of secretions such as colostrum, parotid saliva, tears, nasal mucus and tracheobronchial washings. Furthermore there is indirect evidence of some selective passage of IgA into the lumen of the small intestine, which is corroborated by the observation that plasma cells containing IgA are very prominent, and outnumber those containing IgG, in the intestinal villi. Secreted IgA in saliva and colostrum differs from that in serum by being predominantly in a polymerized (11S) form, and in containing a distinct additional component attached to the molecule. This component, whose molecular weight is about 50,000, appears to be synthesized in the parotid gland epithelial cells (and probably in the epithelial cells of other glands secreting IgA, though this has not been proved at the time of writing), and to become attached to IgA in the process of secretion. The IgA itself may either be synthesized locally by plasma cells in the tissue itself or arrive *via* the blood supply from elsewhere in the body. Evidence that local synthesis of IgA takes place is provided by the observation that tissue cultures of normal parotid gland can make IgA, but even more strongly by the observation that IgA iso-antibodies against red blood cells may be readily detectable in colostrum but absent from the plasma.

The demonstration that IgA is selectively concentrated in certain secretions leads naturally to the suggestion that IgA antibodies play a protective role at mucous surfaces. Furthermore the secreted form of IgA appears to have a somewhat increased resistance to digestion by proteolytic enzymes and to reducing agents, which might be expected to improve its survival in the environment of the gut. Evidence for the presence of 'copro-antibodies' dates back almost fifty years, and even before then it was contended by Besredka that immunization against intestinal pathogens was most effective when these were introduced so as to elicit a local intestinal immunity. The validity of such suggestions is still unproved, but they are likely to be re-evaluated in the light of current knowledge.

Immunoglobulin M (γM)

We have already discussed in Chapter Three how IgM antibody tends to be made very early in an immunological response, and to be present rather transiently in the blood when the antigen is soluble, although IgM antibody can be formed over much longer periods of time in response to at least some particulate antigens. It was suggested on phylogenetic and ontogenetic grounds that the IgM response was more primitive than those responses giving rise to other classes of Ig. A further point of interest is that most, if not all of the 'natural' antibodies (p. 49) against bacterial and cellular antigens have been found to belong to this class. We shall see below that the structure of IgM appears to be adapted for protective activity against microbes and other large antigens which have a repeated antigenic motif on their surface.

Some of the properties of human IgM are set out in Tables 4.1, 4.2 and 4.4. IgM in normal individuals is distributed predominantly within the bloodstream, presumably because of its large size, which hinders escape through capillary vessel walls in the absence of some local inflammation. Like IgA it is broken down in the body more rapidly than IgG, a half life of 5–6 days. It does not cross the placenta and is present only in insignificant amounts in milk or other secretions. The cells which synthesize IgM are distributed throughout the lymph nodes and spleen in much the same way as those which synthesize IgG. They may be indistinguishable morphologically from cells making other Igs, but sometimes have a distinctive appearance of large pyroninophilic lymphoid cells termed by some authors 'lymphocytoid plasma cells' (see p. 295), and are stained strongly by a general stain for carbohydrate such as periodic acid-Schiff reagent. This is especially obvious in the condition of pathological macroglobulinaemia (Waldenström). This condition in many ways resembles multiple myeloma, but the infiltrating cells in lymphoid tissue and bone marrow make IgM rather than other Igs, and do not occur in the local bone-eroding tumour masses which characterize multiple myeloma. Another difference from myelomas, whose significance is hard to assess, is that the pathologically over-produced macroglobulins can sometimes be shown to be specific auto-antibodies, especially antibodies against the I antigen of red blood cells (see Chapter Fifteen).

Despite its large molecular weight (about 900,000) IgM has been shown in several species to have a structure basically similar to that of other immunoglobulins. However, instead of two H and two L chains each molecule has ten H and probably ten L chains. The H and L chains are linked to each other by S—S bonds in the same general way as in IgG, but there are additional S—S bonds linking the Fc portions of alternate heavy chains, so as to produce a molecule with a central shallow cylindrical portion and five radiating arms. When the S—S bonds are broken by reducing agents such as mercaptoethanol the molecule falls apart into subunits composed of two H and two L, or even one H and one L chain. In blood of elasmobranch fishes IgM molecules containing two pairs of chains are normally present as well as those containing five pairs, and in some humans with high plasma IgM levels molecules of the form $\kappa_2\mu_2$ or $\lambda_2\mu_2$ also occur. These are probably the forms in which IgM is put together in the cell, polymerization to the ten-chain form occurring during secretion.

It might be expected, by analogy with IgG, that each pair of H and L chains would comprise one antibody combining site, and that each IgM antibody molecule would have ten identical sites. Present evidence suggests that some IgM antibodies have ten but others only five effective sites. In any case, it is certain that each molecule is multivalent. This means that IgM antibodies are singularly well adapted to combine firmly, by means of at least five combining groups, to any antigen which has a repeating pattern of antigenic determinants close together on its surface. Some examples of antigenic structures which have just such a pattern of determinants are the capsules of pneumococci, the cell wall 'O' antigens of Gram-negative bacilli, bacterial flagella or viruses whose outside consists of a regular close-packed arrangement of capsids. Even if each individual combining site is not particularly 'avid' (i.e. it has a relatively small association constant—see p. 179), the combined action of multiple sites will increase the avidity of the whole molecule very greatly. Plate 4.4 (following p. 148) shows electron micrographs of IgM antibody molecules attached to some structures of the sort mentioned above. The IgM molecules are seen only in relief in Plate 4.4B, and are probably distorted by combination with the antigen. When IgM antibody combines with antigen in this manner it activates complement, and does so in such a way as to be very effective in causing a local lesion in the underlying cell membrane, if the antigen lies on or very close to a cell surface. The mechanism of this is discussed at greater length in Chapter Five. It is sufficient to state here that a single IgM antibody molecule attached to the surface of a cell, such as a red cell, which is incapable of repairing its membrane, can activate complement so as to lyse the cell. This is in contrast to IgG antibodies, which can also cause cell lysis with complement but which appear only to do so when two antibody molecules become attached very close together on the same surface. Consequently many (hundreds or thousands) more IgG molecules per cell are required to produce the same amount of damage as a single IgM molecule. On the other hand, when the antigen is not associated with an organized cell surface but is, for example, an ordinary protein possessing a variety of different antigenic determinants, the IgM antibody is clumsy and has no special advantage. Its multiple combining sites, which are commonly each of low avidity, cannot all attach to the same antigen molecule, and they readily dissociate. Consequently for neutralizing bacterial toxins, or protecting against infection of cells by viruses, for example, IgG antibodies, which are usually more avid, are likely to be more effective.

Recent studies with purified rabbit IgM antibodies have borne out these predictions. Compared with IgG antibodies against the same 'O' surface antigen, the IgM antibodies were found, on a weight basis, to be more than 20 times as active in agglutinating salmonella organisms, more than 100 times as potent for complement-dependent killing of them, and almost 1000 times as efficient for opsonization. Similar findings have been reported with antibodies against red blood cells (though it must be noted that in man both IgM or IgG red cell iso-antibodies are often apparently incapable of causing red cell lysis, for reasons not understood). When it comes to neutralizing diphtheria toxin or a small virus such as poliomyelitis, however, IgM antibodies have been found less effective than IgG.

In mice, but not so far in man, a form of IgM antibody against salmonella typhimurium has been described which is cytophilic for macrophages—i.e. which attaches very firmly to these cells, and confers upon them a greatly increased capacity to ingest and kill virulent organisms. Whether this is a phenomenon of general occurrence remains to be shown.

Immunoglobulin D (γD)

The existence of this class of human immunoglobulin was recognized from the study of certain very rare forms of myeloma. However the presence of IgD, in variable but usually small concentration, has been confirmed in the plasma of normal persons, and it has been shown to be predominantly intravascular and to have the shortest half life (about 3 days) of any of the immunoglobulins. Little is known about the biological properties of IgD and no specific antibody activity has yet been shown to be associated with this class.

Immunoglobulin E (γE)

Strong presumptive evidence for the existence of a fifth class of human Ig has been obtained in the course of attempts over many years to characterize 'reagins'. These are the heat labile skin-sensitizing antibodies responsible for anaphylactic type of immediate hypersensitivity in several species, such as man, monkey, dog, rat and rabbit (see Chapter Eleven). Such antibodies have proved notoriously difficult to separate from those of other classes, especially from IgA, and yet the correlation between the behaviour of reaginic activity and that of any of the known immunoglobulins was never complete. Very recently it has been shown firstly that antisera specific for the H chains of human IgG, IgA, IgM or IgD are without effect upon the activity of reaginic antibodies in human serum; secondly that antisera can be prepared in rabbits, against a selected $\gamma 1$ globulin fraction of serum, which will specifically react with reaginic (anti-ragweed) antibodies without reacting with any of the other four classes of Ig; and thirdly that specific antisera against human L chains react with reaginic antibodies as with other kinds of Ig. This evidence taken together indicates that reaginic antibodies are indeed immunoglobulins but differ from the other classes by virtue of their H chains. Although purified reaginic antibodies have not yet been isolated in sufficient quantity for chemical study they have been assigned provisionally to a fifth class, IgE. A myeloma was described in a patient in 1967 which appears to be typical of the new class. That is, the myeloma protein reacts with antisera specific for reaginic antibodies and not with antisera specific for IgG, IgA, IgM or IgD; and when mixed in low concentrations with serum containing reaginic antibodies it can block the characteristic fixation of the latter in the skin. Since the myeloma protein has a high carbohydrate content (10·9 per cent) and a molecular weight about 190,000, it seems likely that these properties will also prove to be characteristic of reaginic antibodies.

Apart from their heat lability (complete inactivation in one hour at 56°), susceptibility to treatment with mercaptoethanol and their very marked property of becoming attached firmly to certain tissue cells, notably mast cells, of the *same* species (homocytotropic—p. 436) little is known about IgE antibodies. They are evidently present in only very small amounts in serum; they have not been shown to precipitate with antigen nor to fix complement, but it is possible that this reflects the low concentrations at which they have been tested rather than any intrinsic property of the molecules. Certain inhaled antigens such as pollens, or infection with helminths, appear particularly to elicit reaginic antibody formation, but many other antigens can also do so. The biological activity of reagins is discussed at length in Chapter Eleven. No clear cut protective function has yet been discovered for them, though there is some evidence to associate their presence with recovery from and protection against helminth infections.

Other Possible Classes of Immunoglobulin

The great majority of myeloma proteins can be assigned to the known classes of immunoglobulin, and, as has already been mentioned, the relative frequency of their occurrence in each class is well correlated with the relative proportion of cells producing Ig of class in normal individuals. If the frequency of distribution of myeloma proteins is accepted as paralleling that of normal immunoglobulins, this implies that it is unlikely that any more major classes of Ig remain to be discovered. However, the unexpected discovery of IgE described above is an indication that there may well exist other minor classes still unrecognized.

CYTOPHILIC ANTIBODIES

The term 'cytophilic' has been used to describe immunoglobulins which have been shown to have a special tendency to become attached to the surface of certain cells by virtue not of their antibody combining sites but of some other configurational property of the rest of the molecule—usually, and probably always, a property of the Fc portion of the heavy chain. One example of cytophilic antibodies is provided by those of the class IgE referred to above. Such antibodies attach rather firmly to mast cells, and possibly to other cells, of the species from which they are derived but not to the cells of unrelated species. Their biological significance is discussed further on pp. 435–49 in Chapter Nine.

A second example is provided by antibodies present in the serum of guinea pigs which attach specifically to guinea-pig macrophages. These occur in a class of immunoglobulins whose counterpart in man is uncertain, but which might be considered, so far as present knowledge goes, to be a subclass of IgG. Similar antibodies have also recently been described in primates. Their significance is discussed again in Chapter Nine (pp. 381–3) and Chapter Twelve.

A third example, which was the first to be recognized, is provided by antibodies which appear in the serum of rabbits during the course of immunization and which attach to certain cells of the spleen or of peritoneal exudates (probably macrophages) of the same species. They can be detected by placing suspension of cells in contact with the serum, then washing the cells, and subsequently showing that the cells have picked up this antibody on their surface by their ability to bind the specific antigen (which for convenience may be labelled with, for example, radioactive iodine). Cells treated with similar amounts of antibody which is not cytophilic retain very little of this on their surfaces, and after washing combine with antigen to a very much lesser extent. The content of cytophilic antibody in sera with similar levels of total antibody may vary widely. Apart from knowledge of their existence, very little information is available about the biological significance of cytophilic antibodies in the rabbit or about the circumstances under which they are made.

The three examples cited above all refer to antibodies which attach to cells of the same or closely related species, for which the term 'homocytotropic' has been coined (see p. 436). Antibodies in other immunoglobulin classes can often be shown, by similar methods, to attach instead to cells of unrelated species, and are termed 'heterocytotropic'. The latter phenomenon obviously has no fundamental biological importance, though it is of theoretical interest and relevant to a variety of experimental situations.

Cytophilic properties are only likely to be detected when specifically looked for, and systematic studies of the conditions which determine whether or how a particular immunoglobulin will attach firmly to a particular kind of cell have not been reported.

THE SPECIFIC ANTIBODY-COMBINING SITES OF IMMUNOGLOBULINS

The previous sections have dwelt on the general structure of immunoglobulins and on some aspects of their heterogeneity, but have only incidentally discussed their most important function, namely their ability to combine specifically with the determinant groups on antigens. In the sections which follow we shall consider the nature of the combining sites and the way in which they might be formed.

Most natural antigens, even when pure, are very complex and contain a mosaic of quite distinct antigenic determinant groups. Immunization with such antigens is liable to elicit antibodies against each of several determinants, and analysis of the resulting mixture of antibodies is unnecessarily complicated. For this reason the most precise information has been obtained by using for immunization proteins to which small, strongly antigenic chemical groups (haptens) have been attached artificially (this procedure is discussed at greater length in Chapter Six). In principle, by immunizing an animal against a hapten-protein conjugate H-A, and using for testing a conjugate of the same hapten with a quite unrelated protein H-B, or even using the free hapten itself, it is possible to study exclusively the interaction of the hapten with antibodies against it, uncomplicated by antibodies against other parts of the antigen molecules. From such studies it appears unequivocally that all IgG antibodies have two combining groups with identical specificity. 'Hybrid' molecules capable of combining two distinct antigenic groups have never been found naturally, although it is possible to make them in the laboratory by recombining one H-L chain pair from one antibody with one H-L chain pair from another antibody, and when made in this way they have the properties expected.

Antigen–antibody Interaction

The size of that part of an antibody molecule which is involved in combination with the antigen has been estimated in several cases. In the case of an uncharged polysaccharide antigen such as dextran (a polymer of repeating units of α 1 : 6 linked glucose) it has been shown that the size of the antigenic determinant group varies with the particular antiserum examined. When molecules consisting of short chains of the same repeating units are tested to find what is the shortest chain which competes most effectively with the whole antigen, this turns out to contain of the order of three to six glucose residues. In the case of the rather simple protein silk fibroin, by a similar method it can be deduced that one of the determinant groups has some 8 to 12 amino acid residues in it. By arguing that the size of the antibody combining site must be similar to that of the antigenic determinant it can be concluded that only 10 to 20 amino acids are involved out of the 1500 or so which compose the whole IgG molecule.

The combination between antigen and antibody is reversible and does not involve stable chemical bonds, although formation of some reversible hydrogen bonds may sometimes occur. It is thought that the three dimensional arrangement of amino acids at the antibody combining site is such that it presents a surface pattern complementary to the hapten, or to the particular determinant group on the antigen. A diagrammatic representation of how this might occur is given in Fig. 4.6. The forces which bind the two together are in the main partly due to the presence of oppositely charged groups in close contact (ionic bonding), and partly to van der Waals forces—forces which act between molecules independently of their charge, and whose strength falls off very sharply (approximately as the 6th power) with the distance between them. The strength of such forces in holding the antigen and antibody together will clearly depend very greatly on the goodness of fit and the nearness to which the components can approach to one another. The forces are usually maximal at physiological conditions of pH and ionic strength, and at pH values below 3–4 or above 10·5 they are often so much weaker that antigen–antibody complexes dissociate. Since most antibodies remain stable at these pH values, advantage can be taken of this fact to prepare almost pure antibody from the complexes.

Despite the weakness of the forces holding antibody and antigen together the combination is extraordinarily specific, and quite minor arrangements of the atoms in the antigen determinant group will greatly reduce or even abolish its ability to combine with the original antibody. Antibodies even against a given determinant made in a single animal can vary markedly in the strength with which they combine, or their avidity, depending presumably upon minor alterations in the goodness of fit. Such variation is commonly expressed in terms of the *Equilibrium Constant Ko* derived from the classical expression for the Law of Mass Action,

$$\mathrm{Ko} = \frac{[\mathrm{AbH}]}{[\mathrm{Ab}]\,[\mathrm{H}]}$$

Where [Ab] = antibody concentration in mols/litre at equilibrium
[H] = hapten concentration in mols/litre at equilibrium
[Ab H] = concentration of antibody-hapten complex in mols/litre at equilibrium

Ko is expressed in units of litres/mol, and the higher its value the greater the affinity of the antibody. In practice, values for Ko may vary from 10^5 to 10^{12} even for antibodies against a single hapten group.

It is usually found that when an animal is first immunized against a hapten the earliest antibodies formed have lower Ko values than those formed later, although there is often quite a wide range of avidities at all stages. When the immunizing antigen is an ordinary complex protein the earliest antibodies are usually not only less avid but they are also more highly specific for that protein—in the sense that they cross-react little, if at all, even with closely related antigens (e.g. sheep plasma albumin and goat plasma albumin might be considered as closely related, being chemically similar and

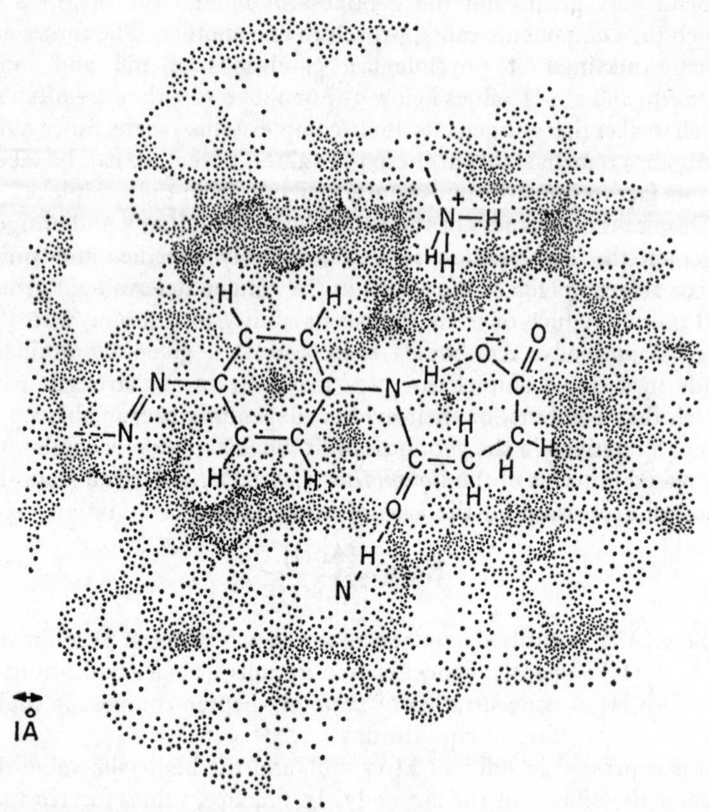

FIG. 4.6. Diagram to illustrate the shape of the combining site of a molecule of antibody against the hapten group p-azo-succinanilate, and the shape of the hapten group itself, of a related hapten (fumaranilate) which is known to cross-react strongly, and of another hapten (maleanilate) which cross-reacts very weakly. The importance of the close fit of the hapten group to the combining site is well brought out. [From Pauling L. (1948) *Endeavour* 7, 43.

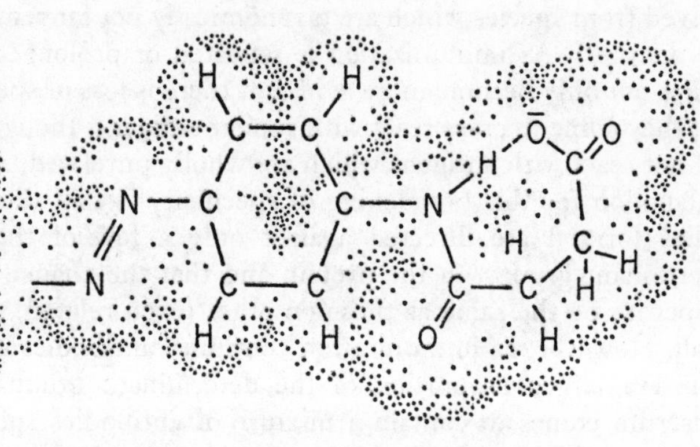

Hapten group of ovalbumin-p-azo-succinanilate

Fumaranilate (cross-reacts strongly)

Maleanilate (cross-reacts very weakly)

derived from species which are taxonomically not far removed from one another). As immunization is repeated or prolonged the antibodies not only become more avid, but there is loss of specificity, so that they come to cross react with similar antigens, though they still will not react with antigens which are wholly unrelated. A plausible explanation for this broadening of specificity is that the first antibodies formed are directed against only a few of the different determinant groups on the protein and that the chance that these happen to be the same as those on other (even related) antigens is small. However, as immunization continues antibodies are formed against a larger proportion of the determinant groups, and the antiserum comes to contain a mixture of antibodies specific for a variety of different determinants, some of which are common to related antigen molecules.

The Site of the Antibody-Combining Group

Antibodies against a given antigenic determinant may be found in any of the classes of immunoglobulin IgG, IgA, IgM and often in IgE. They can also apparently be associated (though not necessarily in the same individual) with any of the L chain or H chain allotypes. Thus there is no evidence on these grounds that any particular recognized combination of L and H chains is responsible for a particular antibody specificity. Nevertheless, it is very unlikely that antibody activity could be due to some special way of refolding of these chains selected, let us say, by the antigen from a variety of possible alternative configurations in which they might exist. In the first place, according to current ideas about protein structure, the folding of a polypeptide chain is uniquely determined by the order of its constituent amino acids; and in the second place it has recently been shown that the folding of purified specific antibodies can be completely unmade (by treatment in strong urea solution after reducing the S—S bonds) in the absence of the antigen, and yet when the unfolded antibody is allowed to regain its shape it also largely regains its specific combining power. This observation implies very strongly that the specific shape of the combining sites is determined by the specific sequences of the amino acids which make up the polypeptide chains of the antibodies.

As has already been mentioned, the combining sites are on the Fab pieces of the antibody molecule. It has been a matter of some controversy as to whether they are associated with the H or the L chain, or with both—the controversy arising mainly because it has been technically difficult to obtain H chains completely separate from L chains and still in a soluble form. However, this has now been achieved for several purified IgG antibodies, and it can be stated with certainty that isolated L chains have never been found to combine specifically with haptens or larger antigens. Isolated H chains, however, have been shown to retain some of the ability to combine specifically with haptens, although they do so less well than the original antibody. When H chains from a purified specific IgG antibody are simply mixed in solution with L chains a stable complex is formed, and it has been shown that mixture with L chains from the original antibody restores the combining capacity more effectively than does admixture of L chains prepared from nonspecific IgG or from a different antibody. It appears, therefore, that the antibody specificity is primarily associated with the H chain, but that the combining power is enhanced when the proper L chain is associated with it. The degree to which the presence of both specific H and specific L chains is required for antibody activity varies with the antibody under study, and in some instances the isolated H chains alone have been found to possess very little combining power.

Association of H and L Chains

It was stated above that simple mixture of isolated specific H and L chains helped to restore antibody activity. This may appear remarkable in view of the fact that in the intact molecule the chains are joined together by S-S bonds. Nevertheless it has been found that L chains and H chains, even when prepared from the IgG of different species, will associate together by non-covalent bonds to form firm complexes which behave in most respects like intact immunoglobulin. Studies with H and L chains from different human myeloma proteins (labelled with radioactive isotopes) have shown, however, that there is usually a marked preferential association of H and L chains derived from the same protein. Furthermore it has been shown that the two chains are synthesized separately within an immunoglobulin secreting cell, and there is suggestive evidence that the H chain is released from the polyribosome upon which it is made simultaneously with becoming attached to the L chain. Such a mechanism would ensure that in a normal cell the synthesis of both chains was synchronized—and might explain why over-production of L chains is not uncommon but that of H chains is exceedingly rare.

The Heterogeneity of Antibodies

Antibody against a defined hapten group can be produced within many of the different Ig classes, subclasses or allotypic specificities.

In other words, antibody of the same specificity can be made of a variety of classes or allotypes. This is not, however, the whole story. Examination of purified specific antibody against any given determinant group, made even by an individual animal, usually shows that the L chains have an additional heterogeneity, revealed by the pattern of electrophoresis in starch gel. Plate 4.5 (following p. 148), which may be compared with Plate 4.2, shows the behaviour of some purified human antibodies when examined by electrophoresis in starch gel at an acid pH. Although the separation and banding of L chains is less well marked under these experimental conditions than it would be under those used in Plate 4.2, it is evident that the various antibodies differ from each other in the distribution of their L chains even when the antibodies are against the same antigen. However, the L chains from purified antibodies are nearly always less complex than those of whole immunoglobulin from the same individual. This implies that only some of the possible combinations of L and H chains are used to make any given antibody.

In studies made using anti-hapten antibodies, notably in the guinea-pig, there appears to be some restriction of particular L chain combinations to particular antibodies—and the same may apply to H chains, though these have been less thoroughly examined—but the restriction is only partial. It is conceivable that the variability observed is partly artefactual, in the sense that antibodies even against a single determinant are known to be heterogeneous in their affinities, and that if an antibody population were isolated whose combining sites were truly homogeneous the chains would prove homogeneous also—but on this there is at present no evidence.

Implications for Theories of Antibody Formation

The evidence from myelomas is strongly in favour of the idea that these are homogeneous clones of immunoglobulin-secreting cells and that the cells synthesize a unique product characteristic of the clone. Other evidence obtained from immunofluorescent studies of various lymphoid tissues, made with specific antisera against different L or H chain allotypic determinants, indicates in general that the normal cells synthesizing Ig are—at a given moment—also making a unique product. It must be stated, however, that there is still some uncertainty whether the same cell can contain IgG and IgM simultaneously. It is also less certain whether any single cell making antibody against a given antigenic determinant can at the same time make antibody with a different specificity. In most studies made on animals simultaneously immunized with two antigens, or even with a single antigen possessing two or more easily distinguishable determinants (e.g. 'O' antigens of salmonella strains), it has been found that the great majority of individual cells make antibody against one antigen or the other, but a few cells appear to contain antibody against both. Such studies are technically very difficult, and it is hard to assess the significance of the exceptions. On the whole the evidence is strongly in favour of each cell making a unique product—that is, a single allele controlling the H chain and a single allele controlling the L chain are expressed at any given time. If this is so, the multiplicity of immunoglobulins in the plasma must reflect a corresponding multiplicity of clones of cells, each of which is expressing different genes, to synthesize them.

When we consider the present evidence about the detailed structure of immunoglobulins it is apparent that there are two different categories of heterogeneity. One relates to classes and allotypes, which appear to be properties of the 'invariable' regions of the H and L chains, with which are associated a limited number of genetically controlled minor variations. It is plausible, and even reasonable, to suppose that there have been sufficient biological advantages conferred by the possession of antibodies with these various properties to have ensured their survival during the course of evolution. The second relates to the potentiality of immunoglobulins to have antibody combining sites specific for an enormous range of antigenic determinants, and appears to depend upon the 'variable' regions of the H and L chains, where the number of possible variations is evidently very large. If the specificity of each antibody depends upon a definite amino acid sequence in the variable region, and if—as is currently accepted—every different amino acid sequence is coded for by a different gene, then it has to be accepted that there is a very large number of different genes which control the synthesis of the 'variable' parts of the H and L chains. Present evidence also indicates that both H and L chains are synthesized as complete polypeptide chains—i.e. there is no indication that the 'variable' and 'invariable' regions are synthesized separately and joined later—and this means that for each difference in the 'variable' region accompanied by each difference in the 'invariable' region there must be a separate controlling gene. The total number of different genes required to code for all the possible antibodies in all the possible classes and subclasses of Ig thus appears, as it is sometimes put, almost astronomically large. A logical extension of this argument would suggest that antibody against a given determinant in a given animal might be a unique protein, not found in other members of the same species. Experiments which show that idiotypical immunoglobulins (p. 161) are sometimes produced in response to antigenic stimuli—such as immunization of rabbits with *B. proteus*—indicate that this suggestion is not wholly fanciful.

Since the total number of different genes required is not known, even within an order of magnitude, it is impossible to state definitely at present whether they could all be accommodated within the genome of stem cells from which antibody-producing cells arise. Once it is accepted, however, that each different Ig is coded for by a different gene it becomes necessary either that all the genes should be so accommodated, or that mutant genes should arise by somatic mutation during the growth and development of each organism. Several attempts have been made to suggest mechanisms in which a large number of mutations could arise in those parts of the gene which code for the variable portions of the H and L chains—for example breakage of one chromosome of a pair followed by a repair process in which faulty copying occurs—but these remain purely hypothetical. It would probably be fair to state that at present there is no consensus of opinion strongly favouring either the view that all possible immunoglobulins are already coded for in the genome of the zygote or that the multitude of controlling genes arises by somatic mutation. If the first view were correct, all immunologically competent cells should be at some stage multipotent and able to respond to any antigen (although they might become committed to one particular response once their development has been triggered by a particular antigenic stimulus); if the second were correct, immunologically competent cells would be expected at all stages to be restricted to being able to respond in only one or a relatively limited number of ways. This subject is discussed at greater length in Chapter Seven, in which is considered the way in which antigen sets off an immune response.

FURTHER READING

BOYD W.C. (1966) *Fundamentals of Immunology*. Interscience, London

BOYDEN S.V. (1963) Cytophilic antibody. In *Cell-Bound Antibodies* (Ed. Amos B. and Koprowski H.). Wistar Institute Press, Philadelphia

BULL. WLD. HLTH. ORG. (1964) *Nomenclature for Human Immunoglobulins* **30**, 447, 450

BULL. WLD. HLTH. ORG. (1965) *Notation for Genetic Factors of Human Immunoglobulins* **33**, 721–4

COHEN S. & PORTER R.R. (1964) Structure and biological activity of immunoglobulins. *Adv. Immunol.* **4**, 287

COHEN S. & MILSTEIN C. (1967) Structure and biological properties of immunoglobulins. *Adv. Immunol.* **7**, 1

FAHEY J.L. (1962) Heterogeneity of γ-globulins. *Adv. Immunol.* **2**, 42

HERZENBERG L.A., MCDEVITT H.O. & HERZENBERG L.A. (1968) Genetics of antibodies. *Ann. Rev. Genetics*

JAROSKOVA L. (ed.) (1964) *Molecular and Cellular Basis of Antibody Formation*. Publishing House Czech. Acad. Sci. Prague

KELUS A.S. & GELL P.G.H. (1967) Immunoglobulin allotypes of experimental animals. *Progr. Allergy*. **11**, 141

KILLANDER J. (ed.) (1967) *Gamma Globulins, Structure and Control of Biosynthesis*. Nobel Symposium **3**, Almqvist and Wiksell. Stockholm

LANDSTEINER K. (1945) *The Specificity of Serological Reactions*. Harvard University Press

MARRACK J.R. (1938) *The Chemistry of Antigens and Antibodies*. Special rep. ser. Medical Research Council. No. 194 (H.M.S.O., London)

MÅRTENSSON J. (1966) Genes and immunoglobulins. *Vox Sang*. **11**, 521

PORTER R.R. (organizer) (1966) A Discussion on the chemistry and biology of immunoglobulins. *Proc. Roy. Soc. B*. **166**, 113

PORTER R.R. (1967) The structure of antibodies. *Sci. Am.* **217**, No. 4, 81

POTTER M. & LIEBERMAN R. (1967) Genetics of immunoglobulins in the mouse. *Adv. Immunol.* **7**, 92

SINGER S.J. (1957) The specificity of antibodies. *Sci. Am.* (October 1957)

WILLIAMS C.A. & CHASE M.W. (eds) (1967) *Methods in Immunology and Immunochemistry*. **1**, Academic Press, New York

CHAPTER FIVE

Complement and other Auxiliary Factors

In a wide variety of situations in which interaction of antibodies with antigens occurs within the body, the biological consequences depend not only on this primary interaction, but even more upon the secondary activation of a complex system of non-specific factors present in blood and tissue fluids, and known collectively as Complement. The Complement complex (abbreviated conventionally to C′) acts as a final common pathway for many of those effects which are the result of antigen–antibody interaction *per se* in a specific situation, such as inflammation, rather than the result of interaction of a particular antibody with a particular antigen, such as toxin neutralization. C′ is also responsible for the direct killing by antibody of complex microbes such as bacteria, and an important factor in assisting their phagocytosis and intracellular digestion. In addition to C′, the blood may contain various other components which can be secondarily involved in immune reactions, and some components which behave as antibodies but are not elicited by a specific antigenic stimulus. Such are conglutinin, immunoconglutinin, 'C-reactive substance' and properdin. In this chapter we may conveniently consider these various substances together, although there is no other necessary connection between them.

COMPLEMENT

Historical

Time and again it has been found that fresh blood serum has properties which are no longer present when the serum has been left to stand at room temperature for a day or two, or has been heated at 56°C for half an hour. Bordet in 1898 first observed that rabbit antisera against sheep red cells, which when fresh would lyse the cells in high dilution, lost their haemolytic power on ageing or on being heated. He found, however, that the haemolytic activity was completely restored by adding fresh normal serum from several species of animal, but not by old or heated normal sera. This heat-labile activity present in normal serum was at the time named 'alexine', though this was gradually replaced by the name 'Complement'. Although complement activity is commonly tested for and measured in the same system that Bordet used, namely by its capacity to enable antiserum against sheep red cells (in practice antiserum against the Forssman antigen in the red cell surfaces) to cause haemolysis, there are many biologically important phenomena in immunology in which the same or a similar complement activity is involved. These include killing of bacteria by serum antibodies, opsonization, immune-adherence and conglutination, lysis of normal or of tumour cells by antibody against antigen on their surface, and the activation of serum by antigen–antibody complexes to cause inflammation, or to produce 'anaphylatoxin' (see Chapter Eleven). It would clearly help our understanding of these phenomena if we knew what complement is and how it acts.

Complement is a physical substance, or rather a number of substances which interact in a definite sequence, in a manner analogous to the blood clotting system—although there is no evidence that complement and blood clotting have any components in common. When antigen and antibody react to form a complex in fresh serum, some components of complement become actually bound up with the complex. For example, if to a quantity of antiserum which has previously been heated at 56° for half an hour to destroy complement (i.e. 'inactivated'), an amount of antigen is added just sufficient to precipitate all the antibody, the precipitate formed can be washed and the amount measured quite accurately. If the process is repeated in the presence of inactivated normal serum essentially the same amount of precipitate will be recovered, but if it is done in the presence of fresh normal serum the amount of precipitate will be significantly greater, owing to the fact that complement components have been precipitated also. Furthermore, brief incubation of fresh normal serum with preformed antigen–antibody complexes removes its complement activity—this being the process of 'complement fixation'. A number of older observations were put together and elaborated by Pillemer and his colleagues twenty-five years ago. They showed that human or guinea-pig sera appeared to contain at least four distinct components, all of which were required for the haemolytic activity of complement to become manifest. This observation was made as a result of treating serum in various ways, each of which was thought to destroy one component while leaving the remainder more or less intact. The components so defined were as follows:

C_1'—heat labile—present in the euglobulin fraction of serum (precipitated at low ionic strength and pH 5·2).

C_2'—heat labile—present in the α- and β-globulin fractions of serum.

C_3'—heat stable—inactivated by treatment of serum with yeast cell walls ('Zymosan').

C_4'—heat stable—inactivated by treating serum with ammonia or hydrazine.

The corresponding components from the sera of different species could largely replace one another, but they were present in different proportions in different species. Thus in guinea-pig and human serum C_3' was the limiting factor, when haemolysis was studied, and C_1' and C_4' were present in relatively great excess, whereas mouse serum was low in C_2' but contained quite a lot of other components. Attempts to purify the active materials by the methods then available were only partly successful, but they sufficed to show that these complement components between them could not account for more than 1 per cent of the total serum protein, and possibly much less. It has since been found that C_1' is a complex of three components linked together, and that C_3' in human and guinea-pig serum is a mixture of six separable components! However, these earlier separations provided a foundation upon which M.M. Mayer and his colleagues were able to build up a consistent theory about the order and manner in which the components of complement interact to produce the end effect—this being lysis in the presence of guinea-pig C′ of sheep red cells, sensitized by rabbit antibody against the Forssman antigen on the cell surface. (This particular system was chosen for reasons of convenience, but there are good grounds for supposing that a similar sequence of events operates in other systems in which C′ is involved). Mayer took it as a starting assumption that lysis of the red cell could be the consequence of acquiring a single site of irreversible damage, or 'hit', at the cell surface which locally destroyed its osmotic properties. This would allow free diffusion of ions (K out and Na in) and also permit water to flow in to balance the very high colloid osmotic pressure of the haemoglobin, which has a concentration of about 35 g/100 ml in the intracellular water. Methods were devised for measuring independently the activity of each of the currently known C′ components. From a mathematical analysis of the rates of lysis of red cells treated serially with the known C′ components it was possible to deduce that haemolysis must be due to a sequence of reactions, each of which was initiated by the one preceding it—and that the C_3' reagent, which acted last, must itself be a complex of two or more active substances.

The validity of the hypothesis that a single site of damage causes a leak in the cell membrane has later been confirmed by demonstrating that the action of C′ actually produces holes in the membrane visible in the electron microscope (see Plate 5.1 following p. 148). It is an intriguing fact that the holes produced by the action of complement on other types of mammalian cell or even on a bacterium are similar in size and appearance (see Plate 5.2, following p. 148). In the particular system studied by Mayer the number of holes on a single cell lysed by C′ was shown to correspond very closely with the number of 'hits' predicted.

The Present Concept of Complement Action

Based on the knowledge that C′ works by the sequential activation—or serial triggering—of different components, and using modern methods of protein fractionation to separate these components, it has been possible to work out the order of the reactions which end by producing sites of damage on a cell and other effects. The sequence is shown diagrammatically for human C′ in Fig. 5.1, but it is essentially the same for guinea-pig C′. In this figure a simplified numbering of the various components is used rather than the designations given to them at the time of their discovery, when the order of reactions was uncertain. Some of the properties of the individual C′ components, so far as they are known at present, are listed in Table 5.1. The sequence looks—and is—complicated, and the various stages will each be discussed briefly.

SA: Antibody of the right kind attaches to antigen on the cell surface (or forms a complex with antigen in solution). As already mentioned in Chapter Four (p. 172), one molecule of IgM or two adjacent molecules of IgG antibody can be sufficient to initiate C′ activation. However, IgA and probably IgE do not do so. There are also marked species differences discussed below (p. 437) which appear to depend on the Fc pieces of the H chains.

An essential step seems to be that the Fc parts of the H chains should become in some way distorted or exposed by combination with antigen (see Fig. 4.5), and that more than one pair of such H chains should be arranged at a suitably short distance apart. Thus antigen–antibody complexes activate C′ most efficiently when mixed at about the equivalence ratio (see Chapter Nine), but fail to do so when the antigen is present in such excess that no lattice structure is formed. Furthermore, if IgG antibodies are prepared artificially with a normal structure of 2 H and 2 L chains but with only one combining site, they cannot form a lattice structure at any ratio of antigen to antibody, nor do they activate C′. (Such artificial antibodies have been prepared by separating the H and L chains from a purified specific antibody and allowing them to recombine with H and L chains from non-specific IgG so as to form hybrid molecules with only one specific combining site.) However, non-specific IgG aggregated not by antigen but by gentle heating (63° for 10 minutes), or cross-linked chemically by means of tetrazotized benzidine, has been shown to activate C′ quite well. The presence of aggregated IgG in preparations of human immunoglobulin for injection is, in fact, the main reason why such preparations cannot be administered intravenously without special precautions (see Chapter Sixteen).

$SAC'1_a$: The first stage is attachment of $C'1_q$ to the Fc portion of the H chain, followed by $C'1_r$ and $C'1_s$. This requires calcium ions to be present, and Ca″ probably acts as a link binding the whole C′1 complex together. $C'1_s$ in plasma is a pro-esterase (i.e. in an inactive form), but during the course of attachment it becomes converted by some unknown mechanism to an active *esterase*, which is responsible for initiating the next stages. C′1 is also convertible by other means to the esterase form, and in the plasma of normal people there is an inhibitor of this enzyme. These are discussed on p. 196.

$SAC'1_a4$: $C'1_a$ converts C′4 to an altered form, somewhat smaller, which can attach to the cell surface or to an antibody–antigen complex, while at the same time part of the C′4 is inactivated.

$SAC'1_a42$: C′2 becomes attached to C′4 and is acted on by $C'1_a$,

TABLE 5.1
Properties of Human Complement Components

	$C'1_q$	$C'1_r$	$C'1_s$	$C'4$	$C'2$	$C'3$	$C'5$	$C'6$	$C'7$	$C'8$	$C'9$
Synonym			$C'1$ esterase	β_{1E} globulin		β_{1C} globulin	β_{1F} globulin				
Sedimentation coefficient rate (Sw)	11·1	7	4	10	6	9·5	8·7	5–6	6–7	8	4
Electrophoretic mobility	γ_2	β	α_2	β_1	β_2	β_1	β_1	β_2	β_2	γ_1	α_2–α_1
Serum concentration (mg/100 ml)	2–3	?	?	3–5	<1	80–150	3–5	<1	?	?	?
Thermolability (56° for 30 min)	+	+	+	0	+	0	+	0	0	+	+
Congenital deficiency occurs in man					+						
mouse							+				
rabbit								+			

[Adapted from Müller-Eberhard H.J., Nilsson U.R., Dalmasso A.P., Polley M.S. and Calcott M.A., *Arch. Path.* **82**, 205, 1966.]

being cleaved in the process, and at the same time converted to an active enzyme. For this Mg″ ions are required. The active complex is C′42, and $C'1_a$ can now be lost or removed artificially (e.g. by treatment with the calcium-complexing agent ethylenediamine tetra-acetate, EDTA) without affecting subsequent stages. Activated C′2 is probably an esterase; it is unstable, and decays quite rapidly (half life about 7 minutes at 37°) to a distinct inactive form $C'2_i$, as shown in Fig. 5.1.

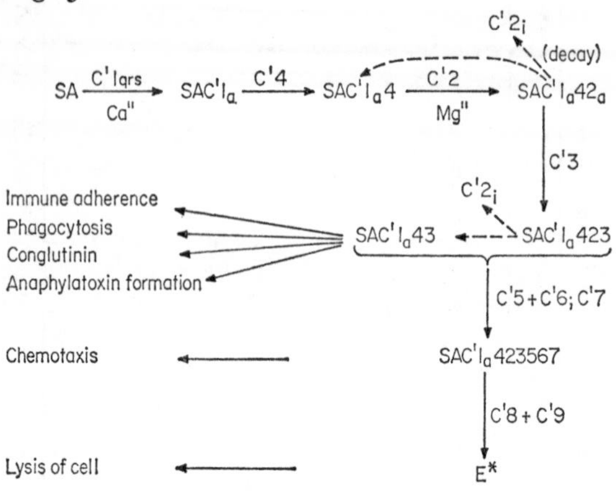

FIG. 5.1. Decay of activated C′2 to a distinct inactive form C′2.
S = antigenic site on cell; A = antibody; C′1,2 etc. = complement components; C'_a = activated form; C'_i = inactive degradation form; E* = damaged cell.

$SAC'1_a423$: The C′3, which is the most abundant component in human plasma, is converted by the active C′42 complex to an active form which rapidly attaches itself to the adjacent cell membrane. In the case of human C′ it is usual for a large number of activated C′3 molecules to become so attached—that is, there is a multiple activation at this stage. When activation occurs in free solution, and the C′3 does not become attached to a cell membrane, it is apparently further converted to an inactive form C′3. During the course of such conversion, *anaphylatoxin* (see Chapter Eleven) is generated.

The complex SAC′1423 has several biologically important properties, and is involved in *immune adherence*, *phagocytosis* and *conglutination* which are discussed later in this chapter.

SAC′1_a423567: Relatively little is known at present about the way in which the next three components C′5, C′6 and C′7 act. When guinea-pig C′ is employed it is possible to show that interaction of these components with SAC′1_a423 must occur seriatim, whereas with human C′—although the three components can be separated—they appear to act together. There is some evidence that the activated C′7 acts directly on the cell membrane, without becoming permanently attached. The cell membrane is still intact at this stage. When the C′ complex is activated as far as C′7 by antigen–antibody complexes in serum a *chemotactic factor* is liberated, discussed on p. 199.

E*: After the stage SAC′1_a423567 the last two identified components of C′ act in turn, though very little is known about how they do so. The end result is that the cell membrane is irreparably damaged and that small molecules leak in and out. In the case of a red cell this leads to osmotic swelling and rupture, whereas in the case of other cells disorganization following disturbance of the internal environment leads to rupture of lysosomes and death without gross swelling. Gram negative bacteria are both killed and rendered susceptible to digestion of the cell wall by lysozyme.

The lesions can be seen in the electron microscope as holes in the membrane, whose diameter is about 103Å with human C′ and about 88Å with guinea-pig C′. These holes are of similar size and appearance whether they are formed by the action of C′ on red cells or tumour cells or Gram negative bacteria (Plates 5.1 and 5.2, following p. 148). They appear to be due to local disruption of the continuous surface lipid layer by micelle formation, due to some alteration of the phospholipid component, but how this is brought about is still unknown.

Inhibitors of Complement

Complement activation can be inhibited *in vitro* by reagents which complex Ca″ or Mg″ (such as citrate or EDTA); by heat inactivation of various components which are heat-labile (Table 5.1); C′4 and C′3 are destroyed by ammonia or hydrazine; and other components are destroyed by various agents, such as alkyl phosphonates, which combine with the active sites on esterases and block them. Interestingly the latter agents have no effect on native C′1 or C′2, which exist as proesterases, but act only after these have been converted to the active forms.

There are also present in human serum naturally occurring inhibitors, of which the best characterized is a heat-labile α_2-neuramino-glycoprotein which inhibits $C'1_a$. Its function may be to limit the duration of the effects of C′ activation, although it may be more important as an inhibitor of plasma kallikrein (see p. 435, Chapter Eleven). In a rare condition, '*hereditary angioneurotic oedema*', this inhibitor is lacking, and the subjects are liable to recurrent attacks of acute circumscribed non-inflammatory oedema, unassociated with any specific allergic episodes. This condition is dangerous because it is liable to lead to death from acute oedema of the pharynx and glottis.

Two other natural inhibitors have been described. One is a heat stable inactivator of C′3, which is reported to be about the same size as serum albumin. The other is an inactivator of C′6, which is heat labile and may be an enzyme. Their biological functions are not known.

Complement Deficiencies

It is uncertain in which cells or tissues most of the C′ components are made, because of the difficulty in identifying and measuring them. However C′1 has been shown to be made in the human colon and ileum, probably by epithelial cells, and C′3 is certainly made largely or exclusively in the liver. C′3 exists in different allotypic forms, distinguishable by their electrophoretic mobility, which are characteristic for any given individual. In a patient who received a liver transplant his C′3 changed from the allotypic form present before his own liver was removed to the form characteristic of the liver donor. C′2 is thought to be made by macrophages, but perhaps by other cells also. Little is known about the rates of synthesis and turnover, so that it is uncertain whether a low level in disease results from increased destruction or decreased synthesis. Nevertheless, it is commonly found that the overall level of haemolytic complement falls markedly in conditions such as acute and chronic glomerulonephritis, serum sickness, and systemic lupus erythematosus in which it is known or suspected that excessive activation by antigen–antibody complexes takes place.

Certain hereditary deficiencies occur of individual complement components, similarly to deficiencies of components of the blood clotting system. Although at present they are very rare this may be because serum complement activity is not commonly examined and techniques for measuring the activity of individual components have only recently become available.

C′1 deficiency, apparently due to lack of the $C'1_q$ component, has been found in an infant born with the condition *thymic alymphoplasia* (see Chapter Eight, p. 325).

A condition of hereditary deficiency in C′2 has recently been described in apparently healthy persons, in whom haemolytic C′ activity was found by chance to be absent. Perhaps not surprisingly the condition, though rare, has been discovered more commonly among persons who work in immunological laboratories than in other sections of the population whose serum C′ activity is less liable to be tested at random. In this condition only the C′2 level in serum is very low (though C′2 dependent reactions such as immune adherence and bactericidal activity are not much impaired). The condition behaves as an autosomal codominant trait—i.e. it is not sex linked, and heterozygous individuals have about half the normal C′2 levels. A secondary C′2 deficiency occurs in subjects with hereditary angioneurotic oedema, owing to continuous activation and spontaneous decay, due to the uninhibited action of $C'1_a$ (see above).

An absolute C′5 deficiency occurs in certain inbred strains of mice, and an absolute C′6 deficiency has been found in an inbred strain of rabbits. Again, the animals appear to remain in good health. Sera from the strains have been very useful in studying the biological activities of these two components.

Species Differences in C′

C′ activity, which functions with antibody from the same species, has been observed in blood from many species of mammals, of birds, of fishes (including elasmobranchs such as the shark) and amphibia. In many instances (e.g. between man, pig, mouse, guinea-pig) the components are functionally interchangeable from one species to another, although not always with equal efficiency. However, in other instances antibodies against red cells from one species (such as chickens, sheep or goats) do not activate human or guinea-pig C′ so as to cause cell lysis. The reasons for this are not at present understood.

Antibodies Against C′: Immunoconglutinins

Antibodies against C′ can readily be elicited by injecting purified C′ components, or antigen–antibody complexes which have attached the different C′ components, into another species. Such hetero-antibodies have proved useful in helping to identify C′ components in serum fractions, for example, and for detection by means of immunofluorescence (see Chapter Nine) of fixed C′ in tissues at the site of antigen–antibody interactions.

The existence has recently been established of a very interesting group of antibodies against complement which result from autostimulation by fixed, but not by native C′ components. These are the *immunoconglutinins* (I-K), first recognized in 1930 by O. Streng. When homologous or autologous fixed C′ is injected into an animal, or when its own C′ is activated within the body (e.g. during an infection in which antibodies are produced against the invading microbes, or by repeated injection of bacteria) antibodies are produced against some of the altered C′ components, which are presumably recognized as 'foreign'. These antibodies are predominantly IgM, and appear to be directed against fixed C′3 or C′4 and possibly other components. I-K activity is detected by using particles such as red cells or yeast, coated with C′, as indicators which are agglutinated by the I-K. An increase in I-K activity is in fact a quite sensitive indicator of recent C′ fixation occasioned by infection.

A peculiarity of such antibodies is that they react not only with fixed C′ of the same species, but also with corresponding components of other species. This confirms a similarity of structure of C′ components of different species which might be inferred from the fact that they can replace one another functionally, and points to an interesting analogy to Rheumatoid Factors (Chapter Fifteen, p. 621) which behave as auto-antibodies against altered Ig which can react with Ig of a wide variety of other species. It has already been stated in Chapter Four that Igs of different mammalian species have marked structural resemblances.

The biological significance of I-Ks is not clear. There is experimental evidence that the presence of I-K helps to protect mice against otherwise lethal infections with small numbers of virulent organisms, but does not protect against lethal doses of relatively avirulent organisms. It is possible that I-K acts by attaching to complexes which have already fixed C′ and so in turn increasing the amount of C′ fixed.

Immune Adherence and Phagocytosis

Immune adherence is the name given to a quite striking phenomenon wherein particles, such as bacteria, coated with antibody or smaller antigen–antibody complexes stick tightly *in vitro* to platelets of many species or to the erythrocytes (but not platelets) of primates. Such adherence does not occur in the absence of C′ and has been shown to depend upon attachment of C′3 to the complexes. Apart from the usefulness of the phenomenon as a very sensitive indicator of the presence of antibody, there is evidence derived from tissue culture studies that particles or complexes adherent in this way are more readily engulfed by phagocytes. The detailed mechanism is not known, but it may involve maintaining opsonized objects and phagocytes in contact with one another after collision.

It is still an open question whether C′ promotes phagocytosis in any way other than by immune adherence. In the absence of serum phagocytosis of inert particles can take place quite vigorously. In the presence of serum phagocytosis of particles such as bacteria is undoubtedly promoted by specific antibodies (opsonins); some of these may be heat labile, so that their activity is diminished when heating at 56° is used as the means of inactivating C′ in the serum. Nevertheless, in certain systems involving 'natural' serum antibodies the opsonization effect on increasing phagocytosis appears to be potentiated by C′ (probably up to C′3). This could be due to a stabilizing effect of C′ uptake on weak antigen–antibody bonds, an effect for which there is some experimental evidence.

Chemotaxis of Neutrophil Polymorphs

Antigen–antibody complexes *in vivo* or suspended in fresh serum are powerfully chemotactic for neutrophil polymorphs. This is evident from studies on Arthus-type reactions (see Chapter Eleven, p. 449), but can also be examined *in vitro* by means of a simple device consisting of a chamber divided into two sections by a fine perforated filter membrane which has pores large enough to allow proteins etc. to diffuse freely through, and large enough to allow polymorphs to migrate into them, but too narrow to let the polymorphs squeeze their way right through. When such a chamber, containing a suitable medium with leucocytes in one half and a chemotactic agent in the other, is incubated at 37° the chemotactic activity can be measured in terms of the numbers of leucocytes which migrate into the membrane (Plate 5.3, facing p. 159). In this way it has been shown that antigen–antibody complexes in the presence of complement induce the formation of a potent agent chemotactic for neutrophil polymorphs. By using serum from C′6 deficient rabbits as a source of C′, and supplementing this with partly purified later C′ components, evidence has been obtained that activation as far as C′7 is required for leucotactic activity to be elicited. However, further studies have cast doubt upon whether complement activation to this stage represents the normal physiologically important mechanism whereby chemotactic factors are liberated by antigen–antibody complexes. It has been found that potent chemotactic agents for polymorphs and macrophages can be obtained from fresh normal serum (including that of C′6 deficient rabbits) by simple physical methods of separating protein fractions, but that when the fractions from normal serum are recombined the activity becomes no longer detectable. This implies that active materials are normally present in whole serum but combined reversibly with an inhibitor. The alternative hypothesis to explain activation of chemotaxis by complexes is that these somehow remove or inactivate the inhibitor.

Conglutinin

The phenomenon of conglutination consists in the firm clumping by serum from ruminants of particles such as red cells or bacteria which have adsorbed complement. In the early studies by Ehrlich, Bordet and especially Streng the C′ was derived from a species whose C′ would not lyse sensitized particles—e.g. horse C′—and was termed 'conglutinating', as opposed to haemolytic complement. The interpretation of this phenomenon gave rise to prolonged controversy, which has only recently been resolved, largely by the work of R.R.A. Coombs and his colleagues.

Conglutination is brought about by *conglutinin*, a natural constituent of the serum of many (but not all) bovidae. Conglutinin has been isolated, and proves to be a large protein molecule, molecular weight about 700,000, which is unusually long and thin, so that it has an unexpectedly low sedimentation coefficient, about 7S or less. It has no relationship to immunoglobulins, and its concentration is quite small (about 1 mg/100 ml). In the presence of Ca″ it combines firmly, but reversibly, with *conglutinogen*, a polysaccharide-rich constituent found in yeast cell walls, and in *Histoplasma capsulatum*, but not in many bacteria. It also combines, in the presence of Ca″, with fixed C′3 from several species, but there is evidence that it may require an additional serum factor ('conglutinogen activating factor') distinct from the components of haemolytic C′.

The phenomenon of conglutination provides a useful serological tool for demonstrating fixation of C′, especially by antibodies of certain mammalian species (including some human antibodies) which fix conglutinating C′ (especially horse C′) well whereas they may fix haemolytic C′ poorly. It also suggests that some polysaccharide structure may be an important constituent of C′3 from different species. The biological importance of bovine conglutinin is not known, though it may provide a natural mechanism of immunity against yeasts and certain fungi.

Properdin

Properdin is the name given by Pillemer to a factor obtained from normal plasma which was able in the presence of C′ to kill various bacteria and viruses. Properdin could be isolated by treating the plasma in the cold with a preparation of yeast cell-wall material ('zymosan'), and recovered in an impure form from the complex with zymosan. The preparation behaved as a macroglobulin, but differed from known IgM antibodies by apparently being active against a wide variety of microbes. Not surprisingly its nature was a subject of some controversy, which has been resolved by later evidence that several of the activities attributed to properdin were due to a mixture of small amounts of 'natural' specific IgM antibodies concentrated by the isolation procedure. However, a residue of activity still remained unaccounted for, and further purification recently revealed that a distinct protein was also present, which was not Ig and could truly be called properdin. This protein has a molecular weight of 230,000, and like conglutinin is relatively long and thin. It reacts with zymosan in the presence of Mg″ ions and complement, but does not itself clump C′-coated cells. Its biological significance is not known.

C-Reactive Proteins

In the blood of humans and rabbits during an acute infection, or other conditions accompanied by fever and tissue destruction, there is a transient appearance of so-called 'acute phase proteins', known as *C-reactive protein* and *Cx-reactive protein* respectively. These are characterized by their ability to form precipitates, in the presence of Ca″ ions, with the group-specific C-carbohydrate of pneumococci resembling those obtained with specific antibody. Complement is not involved in this reaction. The proteins have been isolated and found not to be immunoglobulins but β-globulins, and specific antibodies have been made against them by immunizing other species. By use of such antibodies it has been shown that the proteins are not present in detectable amounts in the blood under normal conditions; furthermore, by immunofluorescent staining Cx-reactive protein could be demonstrated in myocardium damaged by various means. Although this finding might suggest that the Cx-reactive protein was found locally as a result of tissue breakdown, it is more likely that it represents a local accumulation from the bloodstream since studies based on the incorporation of radioactive amino acids into specific proteins by a wide variety of tissues indicate that Cx-reactive protein is made exclusively in the liver. Blockade of the reticulo-endothelial system by intravenous injection of colloidal thorium dioxide ('thorotrast') prevents the appearance of Cx-reactive protein which normally follows injection of pyrogens (p. 227). Although the 'acute phase' proteins have been the object of much study we are still ignorant whether they have any biological role or how their synthesis is switched on and off.

The Biological Significance of Complement

The summary account given above of the activation of C′ by antigen–antibody interaction, and of various auxiliary substances which also act *via* C′, suggests that the C′ complex plays an important part in the responses to and protection against microbial infection, acting as a final common pathway for elicitation of a restricted number of responses initiated by a wide variety of possible antigen–antibody interactions. By virtue of serial activation of each step by that which preceded it, with a possible multiplication at the C′3 stage, coupled with a natural inhibitor of free $C'1_a$ and a fairly rapid decay of $C'2_a$, the system seems to have built-in devices for ensuring local while avoiding generalized activation which might be harmful. A fair analogy may be sought in the complex chain of reactions leading to blood coagulation. The fact that essentially similar C′ systems have been found in a very wide variety of species suggests that the system is evolutionarily rather stable; it implies that each C′ activity—even cell lysis after nine steps—has conferred some significant biological advantage in recent evolutionary history, though it must be admitted that what we recognize in the laboratory may not be the truly important effects. A stumbling block in the way of this thesis is the existence of hereditary C′ deficiencies, which do not notably impair survival. In the case of human C′2 deficiency, which does not appear to be absolute, it may be that there is enough C′ activity to meet the exigencies of present-day living. The C′5 and C′6 deficiencies in inbred strains of mice and rabbits respectively appear, however, to be absolute, and our thesis can only be maintained if it is conceded that the activities mediated by these and later components can be dispensed with by animals reared under laboratory conditions.

FURTHER READING

COOMBS R.R.A., COOMBS A.M. & INGRAM D.G. (1961) *The serology of conglutination in relation to disease.* Blackwell Scientific Publications, Oxford

HUMPHREY J.H. & DOURMASHKIN R.R. (1969). The lesions in cell membranes caused by Complement. *Adv. Immunol.* **11** (in preparation)

LACHMANN P.J. (1966) Conglutinin and immunoconglutinins. *Adv. Immunol.* **6,** 479

MAYER M.M. (1961) Complement. In *Experimental Immunochemistry*, Kabat E.A. and Mayer M.M. 2nd edition. C.C. Thomas, Springfield, Ill.

MIESCHER P.A. & GRABAR P. (eds) (1968) Complement. In *Immunopathology* **5,** Schwabe and Co. Basel/Stuttgart

MÜLLER-EBERHARD H.J., NILSSON U.R., DALMASSO A.P., POLLEY M.S. & CALCOTT M.A. (1966) A molecular concept of immune cytolysis. *Arch. Path.* **82,** 205

MÜLLER-EBERHARD H.J. (1968) Chemistry and reaction mechanisms of complement. *Adv. Immunol.* **8,** 2

NELSON D.S. (1963) Immune adherence. *Adv. Immunol.* **3,** 131

RAPP H.J. & BORSOS T. (1966) Complement research. *J. Amer. Med. Assn.* **198,** 1347

SCHUR P.H. & AUSTEN K.F. (1968) Complement in human disease. *Ann Rev. Medicine* **19,** 1

WOLSTENHOLME G.E.W. & KNIGHT J. (eds) (1965) *Complement.* Ciba Foundation Symposium. Churchill, London

CHAPTER SIX

Antigens: Immunogens and Haptens

THE term antigen has commonly been used, and was used in earlier editions of this book, to include both materials which could bring about an immunological response and materials which could react with antibody or cause a specific reaction in an animal which has already made an immunological response. These two properties are often associated with the same materials, but not invariably so. For example, the purified capsular polysaccharides of pneumococci do not cause the production of antibody in rabbits, although the capsulated whole organisms can do so very well; nevertheless, the purified capsular materials react with antibodies once these have been made, equally as well as the same capsular materials still attached to the parent organism. For this reason it is convenient to use the term *immunogen* for a substance which is able to bring about immunological responses *de novo.* Those substances which can react with preformed antibody or evoke specific immunological reactions in a pre-immunized animal, but are unable to bring about an immunological response *de novo*, are referred to as *haptens* (see Glossary). This term was introduced for the purpose by Landsteiner. It has sometimes been restricted to describe the specific chemical groupings on such materials which are responsible for their interaction with antibody. However, the specific groupings are better described as hapten *determinant groups*. The term *antigen*, which has long been in common use and is likely to remain so, is still a useful term to describe loosely any material which is able to bring about a specific immunological response or to be involved in specific immunological reaction *in vivo* or *in vitro*.

It will already be evident from the preceding paragraph that the definition of what constitutes an immunogen is circular, since it depends upon demonstrating that any particular material can elicit an immunological response specific for that material in some species of animal. In general the immunological response elicited is antibody production, but there is no reason for excluding a delayed-type hypersensitivity response (see Chapter Twelve) which in certain species such as man or the guinea-pig may be a more sensitive indicator of immunogenicity than is the production of antibody. It is usual to find that if in some species one type of immunological response can be produced by suitable choice of route and method of administration the other type can be produced also.

The first essential for a material to be immunogenic is that it should contain chemical groupings which are not present in the substances which normally have access to the *immunologically competent cells* (see Glossary) of the animal which is to be immunized. This question is discussed at greater length in Chapters Three and Seven, but it is sufficient to state here the well-known fact that animals do not as a rule make an immune response against constituents of their own bodies. For a chemical grouping to be 'foreign' to an animal does not necessarily imply that it should contain entirely different building blocks—amino acids, for example—but only that their arrangement should be such that at least part of the surface of the molecules presents a configuration which is unfamiliar to the organism. Since molecules have a three-dimensional structure it is easy to conceive that complex molecules such as proteins or polysaccharides, built up of many residues, will be folded so as to present surface arrangements which are peculiar to themselves. Alternatively, 'foreignness' can be a property which depends upon the presence in a molecule of chemical groupings which are entirely unfamiliar to an organism such as when p-phenyl-arsonic acid groups are artificially introduced into proteins. The antibody response is determined by the foreign groups on the antigenic molecule. When such determinant groups have been introduced artificially, and can readily be recognized, they are commonly termed hapten groups (from Greek 'haptein' = to grasp); there is no logical reason why the naturally occurring antigenic determinant groups should not also be considered as hapten groups, but at the present state of our chemical knowledge their structure, with few exceptions, has not been adequately defined. Examples of hapten groups will be given below.

A second essential is that the material should have a sufficiently great molecular weight. This statement is based on empirical observation rather than on any theoretical reasoning. It is easy to conceive that the larger a molecule is the greater chance it will have of comprising unfamiliar antigenic determinant groups on its surface; also that large molecules are less readily lost from the body, e.g. by excretion in the urine (although smaller molecules may in fact be retained by becoming complexed with plasma proteins). Neither of these reasons, however, is sufficient to account adequately for the failure of molecules with molecular weight below about 1000 to act as immunogens. The smallest natural molecules against which antibody has been made are about 1000 M.W. (oxytocin, vasopressin, angiotensis I). Antibodies against foreign insulin (M.W. about 6000) can be fairly regularly obtained provided that adjuvants, such as Freund's adjuvant (see Chapter Seven), are used in conjunction with it. Proteins such as the enzyme ribonuclease (M.W. 14,000) are moderately good antigens with adjuvants, but poor without; whereas proteins with M.W. 40,000 or over, such as ovalbumin, are usually powerful immunogens. Very large proteins, such as the insect or crustacean respiratory pigment haemocyanin, or tobacco mosaic virus (M.W. 1,000,000 or more) are better still. In the case of carbohydrates the situation is in general similar. Thus in man dextran with a mean molecular weight less than 100,000 is not immunogenic, whereas highly polymerized dextran, with M.W. 600,000 or more, can undoubtedly cause antibody formation although it hardly differs chemically from the less polymerized form. In apparent contradiction to these statements is the fact that many quite simple chemical compounds, such as picryl chloride, or even formaldehyde, can produce sensitization when applied to the skin, or inhaled or injected. In such cases, however, the immunogenic material consists not so much of the materials themselves as of compounds which they form very readily, by chemical reaction under physiological conditions with proteins of the skin or with plasma proteins, for example, thereby introducing foreign hapten groups into the animal's own proteins and so producing artificial antigens within it. Some illustrative examples are discussed in greater detail below.

Apart from the size of a molecule and its possession of surface groupings not present in the test animal, other properties are important in determining whether or not it will be a good immunogen. In general proteins are good immunogens in any species, but the form in which they are presented and the route of administration may be critical factors. It is pointed out in Chapter Seven that adjuvants prolong the period during which the immunogenic stimulus is effective by forming depots from which the immunogen is slowly released, and they may also be effective by causing it to come into contact with more of the right kind of cells. In the case of proteins, which tend to be readily broken down by enzymes in the phagocytic cells, prolongation of effective contact in this way (or repeated administration) may be particularly important. Another property of proteins which determines their immunogenicity is their content of the amino-acid tyrosine. Gelatin, for example, which has a very low tyrosine content ($<0{\cdot}1$ per cent) is a very poor immunogen, but if a few extra tyrosine groups (2 per cent) are artificially conjugated on to it, it becomes a good immunogen although the antibodies which it evokes still react with the native gelatin. The explanation for this is probably that tyrosine groups confer rigidity on the neighbouring parts of the molecule and thereby 'sharpen' the definition of the potential determinant groups, whose configuration may be otherwise rather ill defined.

There must be many other unknown properties also involved in determining whether or not a given material will be immunogenic, or to which components of a mixture an animal will respond best. An illustration of this may be taken from consideration of accidental sensitization of human beings to horse dander. The soluble part of this material has been shown to contain about half its weight as horse serum albumin, and about half as a mixture of several globulins, which are all apparently rather similar and all rich in carbohydrate. Presumably a handler of horses inhales and absorbs them all—yet tests of a number of persons sensitive to horse dander showed that only one of the globulins present was responsible for the sensitivity. Whether this particular material is especially stable against drying and against light, or whether it possesses some other unknown property, is quite undetermined.

In the case of polysaccharides an important consideration in determining whether or not they are immunogenic is the species of animal in which they are tested. For example, the polysaccharides which compose the capsules of pneumococci, and are responsible for their type-specificity, can be isolated and purified. Each type of capsular polysaccharide consists of very long chains of different sugars, amino-sugars, or uronic acids linked in a characteristic way (e.g. Type III polysaccharide is composed of units of a disaccharide made of glucose and glucuronic acid—to be precise—of 1 : 4 linked D-glucose and 1 : 3 linked D-glucuronic acid). They are very often almost indigestible by the enzymes of the phagocytic cells of the body, and after injection into an animal can be shown to persist unchanged in the tissues (e.g. within liver Kupffer cells) for many weeks. Such substances would appear to possess all the qualifications needed for being good immunogens; and indeed in man and in mice they are so; yet injection of the same material into rabbits yields no antibody. If, however, rabbits are injected with killed encapsulated pneumococci, or with an artificial complex composed of pneumococcus polysaccharide and a protein derived from *Shigella shigae*, abundant antibody is produced, which reacts with the capsular polysaccharide rather than with the other constituents with which it was mixed.

The commonest way in which foreign polysaccharides are introduced intact into the body is in the form of bacteria and their products, which are efficient immunogens even in rabbits, and the failure of purified polysaccharides to stimulate antibodies is more in the nature of a laboratory artefact.

In view of the fact that polysaccharides are made up of units of sugars it might seem surprising that these could be put together in enough different ways to provide a wide diversity of structures. However, recent developments in the chemistry of polysaccharides have shown that the variety of potential building blocks (pentoses, hexoses, heptoses and their derivatives) and of the linkages joining them is quite sufficient to ensure that a very large number of different molecules can be constructed, with determinant groups foreign to the body and therefore potentially antigenic.

By and large, lipids are not antigenic, and antibodies against typical lipids such as fatty acids and triglycerides are not known. However, the material responsible for the Wassermann reaction has the properties of an antibody and reacts with a substance, cardiolipin, which has been isolated in pure form and confirmed by chemical synthesis to be diphosphatidyl glycerol. It appears, therefore, that a lipid may occasionally act as an immunogenic determinant, although the exact nature of the immunogen which acts as a stimulus for the Wassermann antibody is not known. In so far as steroids may be classed as lipids, they also are not known to be immunogenic in normal circumstances. Nevertheless, there is some evidence that steroids artificially conjugated to proteins may give rise to antibodies with specificity directed against the attached steroid group. This is, however, a special case in which the steroid is acting as a determinant group, rather than as an immunogen *per se*.

It was considered for many years that nucleic acids were not immunogenic, since repeated injections of crude or purified nucleic acids (both DNA and RNA) into experimental animals did not elicit antibodies demonstrable by unequivocal tests. However, the knowledge that in human auto-immune diseases, such as systemic lupus erythematosus (p. 626), antibodies to DNA were undoubtedly present in the serum led to renewed attempts to elicit such antibodies by experimental means. Immunization of rabbits with ribosomes was shown to result in the formation of antibodies which would react specifically with natural and synthetic polyribonucleotides; and immunization with a bacteriophage T4, which contains an unusual DNA in which glucosylated 5-hydroxycytosine replaces cytosine, elicited antibodies against the phage DNA. However, the latter antibodies reacted only with single-stranded denatured DNA, not with the native double-stranded form, and proved to be specific for DNA molecules containing the unusual base.

What appears to be a general method for eliciting antibodies against DNA or RNA has recently been discovered. This consists in using complexes formed by mixing the negatively charged nucleic acids with a strongly positively charged protein such as methylated bovine serum albumin (MeBSA), which must itself be a good immunogen. In the complex the nucleic acids are protected from the rapid enzymic degradation which they would otherwise undergo in the body, and the MeBSA acts in some way as a carrier (see p. 250). The antibodies which result resemble the human auto-antibodies mentioned above, in that they react much more strongly with denatured single-stranded than with native nucleic acids—suggesting that in native nucleic acids the immunogenic groups are concealed within the double strands—and are not specific, in that they will react with DNA or RNA from a number of different species. This probably implies that antibodies are formed against a variety of the base sequences present in nucleic acids.

Antibodies specific for individual purine or pyrimidine bases, or for nucleosides containing these, can be elicited by immunizing animals with synthetic polypeptides to which the appropriate compounds have been linked chemically and act as determinants. Such antibodies will also react with denatured single-stranded DNA or RNA by virtue of exposed bases in them, but do not react with native nucleic acids.

There is no evidence that animals immunized against nucleic

acids or their constituent nucleotides suffer from any pathological consequences.

The Distinction Between Antigens and Immunogens

It is pertinent at this point to return to the distinction which was drawn in the opening paragraph of this chapter between immunogens and antigens. We have already met two clear instances in which materials which interact perfectly well with preformed antibodies are not able to elicit their formation. The first instance was provided by purified pneumococcus capsular polysaccharides, which do not act as immunogens in rabbits (though they do so in mice), and the second by various nucleic acids which are only immunogenic when combined with some suitable carrier. Additional examples of this last phenomenon were well known to the early immunologists, who gave the name 'schlepper' to various materials—of which a frequent example was pig serum—capable, when mixed with otherwise non-immunogenic substances such as cardiolipin or alcoholic extracts of the Forssman antigen (p. 225), of converting these into full immunogens. (The mechanism of action of such carriers is discussed further in Chapter Seven, p. 251.)

A further example of this distinction arises from the small size of the molecules involved. Thus when two or more benzyl penicilloyl (BPO) groups (the common determinants in penicillin allergy) are attached to a short polypeptide chain the molecule is too small to act as an immunogen, but is nevertheless able to interact demonstrably with antibodies and to elicit, for example, cutaneous anaphylaxis in an already sensitized animal.

Genetic Factors Determining Immunogenicity

It is becoming increasingly recognized that genetic factors play a part in determining whether or not immunological response is evoked, even by materials which are both large enough to be immunogenic and contain determinant groups foreign to the body. The role of such factors is not usually obvious when complex proteins are employed as immunogens, owing to the wide variety of determinant groups which these contain. It is more apparent when relatively simple proteins, such as insulin, or synthetic polypeptides containing only one or two varieties of amino acid are used, and these are tested in inbred strains of animals. Two distinct ways have been recognized in which genetic factors may operate:

(a) A particular determinant group may fail to elicit an immunological response in one strain of animal but may do so in another, even when the rest of the antigen molecule is the same. One example is provided by the observation that when two strains of guinea-pigs are immunized with bovine insulin the antibodies made in one strain are against a different determinant on the insulin from those made in the other strain.

(b) A determinant group which is a potent immunogen when attached to one kind of carrier molecule may—in a given strain of animal—not be immunogenic when attached to a different carrier molecule. For example, if benzylpenicilloyl groups are attached to a synthetic polymer made from L-lysine, the conjugated material is immunogenic and elicits antibody against the BPO groups in all animals of one strain of guinea pigs, but in none of another. Nevertheless, all animals of both strains could make antibodies against BPO when this was attached to a different carrier protein. When tested in random-bred guinea-pigs the same compound was immunogenic in about 40 per cent of animals; by selective breeding from those which responded and those which did not the capacity to respond was shown to behave as though it was as an autosomal Mendelian dominant trait.

It appears then that both the capacity to 'recognize' a particular determinant group, and the capacity to respond to a determinant group attached to a particular kind of molecule can be genetically controlled. It is uncertain how far such observations are of general significance, since most antigens are too complex and most breeds are genetically too heterogeneous for such effects to be obvious in ordinary immunization procedures. Nevertheless the findings are of great significance for theoretical ideas about the nature of the immune response, and are considered again on p. 248.

Immunogens in Relation to Immunological Paralysis

It was pointed out in Chapter Three that potential immunogens can cause specific paralysis as well as immunization. Paralysis is liable to result when an immunogen is administered, without adjuvants, (1) in very small amounts continuously over a long period of time; (2) in larger, normally immunogenic amounts to an animal whose capacity to respond is handicapped by immunosuppressive agents; (3) in amounts great enough to cause exhaustive stimulation of all the cells able to respond. Some immunogens can cause specific immunological paralysis when administered in a single dose of a few micrograms to mice or rabbits. These are materials which are only very slowly degraded in the body, and can persist within macrophages, from which they are continuously released in minute amounts over many weeks. Examples are polypeptides composed of the D- (unnatural) form of amino acids, and the purified capsular polysaccharides of Type I or III pneumococci.

THE NATURE OF ANTIGENIC SPECIFICITY

Having briefly considered the general properties of antigens (i.e. immunogens and haptens), it is necessary to consider in greater detail what determines antigenic specificity. This has been and continues to be subject to intensive study, mainly by means of antigens containing artificially attached hapten groups, which are chosen either so as to be easy to recognize and to estimate or so as to test the importance of particular chemical groupings. By these means it is possible to determine the importance of certain structural features of the molecule in determining its antigenic specificity. The general procedure is to conjugate the hapten by a diazo- or a peptide linkage to free amino or tyrosine groups on a protein; the protein is usually some foreign protein readily available in purified form, such as bovine γ-globulin, but the serum proteins of the animal to be immunized can also be used, since they become immunogenic by virtue of the attached hapten groups. The experimental animals are given one or more courses of injections of the conjugated protein, until they form sufficient precipitating antibody for subsequent testing. At this stage the serum of a rabbit immunized with, say, bovine γ-globulin–hapten conjugate (BGG–Hapt) will usually contain:

(1) antibodies against antigenic groupings in the original BGG,

(2) antibodies against the hapten determinant group,

(3) (possibly) antibodies against modifications of the BGG produced by the presence of the attached hapten or by other chemical reactions occurring during conjugation.

The serum of a rabbit immunized with rabbit serum protein–hapten conjugates will obviously not contain antibodies in category (1) but will contain antibodies in category (2) and, possibly, (3).

Antibodies against the carrier foreign protein of type (1) can be removed by adding an excess of this protein, so that they are either precipitated or remain in solution as soluble complexes (in antigen excess). Antibodies of type (3), if present, could be removed by adding the same protein conjugated in the same way but with an unrelated hapten. The antiserum after absorption in this way contains only antibodies against the hapten determinant group, and it can be tested for its ability to react with proteins to which the same or related hapten groups have been attached. Comparison of the capacity of an anti-hapten antiserum to react with different hapten determinant groups attached to proteins can be made in three ways:

(a) The amount of antibody precipitated at the equivalence point by proteins conjugated with the original immunizing hapten is compared with the amount precipitated by the same proteins conjugated with related haptens. The nearer the immunological relationship (i.e. the greater the capacity to interact with the antibody combining groups) the nearer will the amount of antibody precipitated by the related hapten–protein conjugate approach to that precipitated by the original hapten–protein conjugate.

(b) The antiserum is first tested with the related hapten–protein conjugate, and all antibody precipitable by this conjugate is removed and estimated. The antiserum is then tested with the original hapten–protein conjugate. Any further precipitate is due to antibodies which could react with the latter, but not with the former.

(c) The hapten determinant group combined with a simple amino acid, such as glycine or lysine, can combine with antibody but does not form a precipitate, since not only is it small but it carries only one determinant group, so that no precipitable lattice (see Chapter Nine) can be formed. The simple hapten can, however, compete with the hapten–protein conjugate for the antibody and, at a given concentration in a given system, will prevent precipitation of antibody by the hapten–protein conjugate. The relative abilities of different haptens to combine with the antibody can be compared by determining the minimal concentrations required to prevent precipitation in a standard system.

There are several variants of these methods, and between them they enable a quantitative measure to be made of the degree of resemblance between hapten groups modified in different ways, and of the ability of antibodies to discriminate between one determinant group and another. The results obtained by many able workers, of whom Karl Landsteiner was perhaps the most outstanding, have shown that antibodies are often capable of showing a quite extraordinary degree of specificity (comparable to that of enzymes) and of distinguishing between small differences in the shape of the hapten, especially in the position of charged groups. At the same time small chemical variations can be introduced into the structure of a hapten, in such a way as hardly to alter its shape and distribution of electric charge, without greatly affecting its capacity to interact with its specific antibodies. Some illustrative examples are given below. They are taken from Landsteiner's classical book *The Specificity of Serological Reactions*, published in 1946.

TABLE 6.1 (after Landsteiner)

	Antigens from:		
	L-tartaric acid	D-tartaric acid	*meso*-tartaric acid
Precipitation by immune sera against:	COOH HOCH HCOH COOH	COOH HCOH HOCH COOH	COOH HCOH HCOH COOH
L-tartaric acid	+ + ±	o	⩲
D-tartaric acid	o	+ + ±	⩲
meso-tartaric acid	±	o	+ + +

Two examples of very great specificity are given in Tables 6.1 and 6.2. In Table 6.1 are shown the interactions of proteins conjugated to the dextro, laevo and meso isomers of tartaric acid (by a diazo-reaction with the corresponding aminotartranilic acids) with antisera prepared by immunizing rabbits with a different carrier protein conjugated with one or other of the different forms of tartaric acid. In Table 6.2 are shown the reactions of antisera obtained by Avery and Goebel against simple sugars, which had been converted first into p-aminophenol-glucosides which were then coupled to proteins. The antisera could distinguish sharply between glucose and galactose, even though these differ only by the interchange of

H and OH on one carbon atom! Para-aminophenol α-glucoside and p-aminophenol β-glucoside, which differ only in the manner of linking to the aminophenol group and present the same surface configurations, but at a different angle, were also compared; the antisera cross-reacted strongly, but even in this case a quantitative distinction was possible. The examples illustrate how fine are the distinctions in shape of antigenic determinants which can evoke corresponding differences in the antibody combining groups. (Not

TABLE 6.2

Reactions of antisera with isomeric glucoside protein conjugates

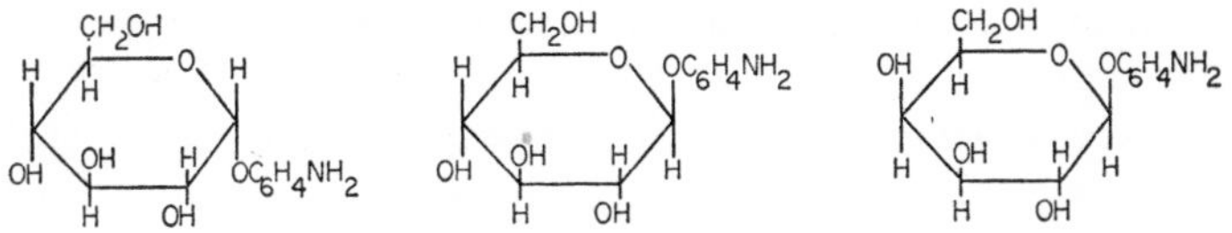

	Antigens from:		
	p-aminophenol α-glucoside	p-aminophenol β-glucoside	p-aminophenol β-galactoside
Antisera against			
α-glucoside	+ + +	+ +	0
β-glucoside	+ +	+ + +	0
β-galactoside	0	0	+ + +

\+ = precipitation

all variations are equally important, and some other minor modifications, which produce little alteration in its shape and distribution of electric charge, can be introduced into the structure of a hapten without greatly affecting its interaction with specific antibodies.) At the same time it must be recognized that the combining sites on the antibodies formed against a given hapten group are not all perfect fits, and that any given antiserum is likely to contain a mixture of antibodies whose combining sites range from those which permit a very close approach of the given hapten, giving sharp specificity and strong binding forces, to those which are less well adapted, and have less specificity and weaker binding forces. On the proportion between the different kinds of antibodies will depend the extent and the sharpness with which the antiserum can distinguish between related haptens.

It is a matter of considerable interest to know how large is the antigenic site involved in combining with antibody. In the case of highly charged hapten groups such as sulphanilic acid, or picryl groups, the specificity is apparently determined practically by these hapten groups alone, irrespective of how they are attached to the carrier protein—i.e. the important part of the molecule is not much larger than the benzene ring. In the case of uncharged polysaccharides such as dextran (see p. 206) it has been shown that the size of the determinant group varies with the particular antiserum examined, but is of the order of three to six glucose residues, while in the case of a rather simple protein, silk fibroin, it is probable that one of the antigenic combining sites has some eight to twelve amino-acid residues in it.

The Size of Immunogenic Determinants: Carrier Specificity

As has been explained earlier, it is usual to study specific antibody responses to a particular hapten determinant group by using as the immunogen a carrier protein to which several identical hapten groups have been conjugated, and to study the anti-hapten antibody by means of materials containing the same hapten conjugated to a different carrier protein, or sometimes by using the hapten molecule by itself (p. 212). The great majority of anti-hapten antibodies examined have been found to combine almost equally well with the hapten, irrespective of whether it was attached to the carrier protein originally used for immunizing or to a different carrier protein. Antibodies formed very early after immunization have been found, however, to combine more strongly, or even exclusively, with the hapten on the original carrier—suggesting that the specificity of the earliest antibodies is directed towards a larger structure composed of the hapten plus part of the protein molecule in its immediate neighbourhood.

This phenomenon is termed 'carrier specificity'. Its importance lies in the fact that carrier specificity is a very marked feature both of the secondary antibody response and of delayed type hypersensitivity to a hapten. Thus if an animal is given a single primary immunizing injection of hapten–protein A, and later challenged with a second injection of the same conjugated material there is a marked secondary response characterized by a sharp increase in the *specific anti-hapten antibody*. If the material used for the challenge injection consists of hapten–protein B, however, there is no such sharp rise in anti-hapten antibody but only the slower and more gradual increase characteristic of a primary injection. In other words, even though the primed or 'memory cells' (p. 102) produced by the priming injection could respond to a second injection by making specific anti-hapten antibody, they are only caused to do so by hapten–protein A and not by hapten–protein B. The implication is that the primed cells recognize a determinant larger than the hapten, containing both hapten and a neighbouring part of the surface structures of protein A.

In the case of delayed type hypersensitivity the situation is very similar, except that detectable anti-hapten antibody is not involved. Guinea-pigs, for example, sensitized to hapten–protein A give delayed type responses to this material but not to hapten–protein B. Such observations have given rise to the suggestion that both cells primed for antibody production and the sensitized cells responsible for delayed type hypersensitivity have 'recognition sites' which interact effectively only with a determinant group larger than the hapten, although the latter may be the dominant factor in determining specificity. It is of interest in this connection that some studies with synthetic polypeptides have indicated that the smallest molecules which can act as immunogens are also the smallest which can act as antigens for eliciting delayed type hypersensitivity.

As already stated, most of our knowledge of the nature of antigenic determinant sites has come from studies of artificially conjugated haptens. Recent progress in the chemistry of proteins, whereby a few proteins have been broken down into smaller fragments, some of which could be separated and examined independently, has confirmed the existence of distinct determinant groups on different parts of the molecule. Furthermore, the fragments, when used as immunogens to stimulate antibody formation, have been found to evoke not only antibodies which react both with the fragment and the parent molecule but also antibodies which react *only* with the fragment. This means that splitting the parent molecule has revealed new potentially antigenic groups which were previously hidden within the molecule, and implies that only those groups at the surface are able to stimulate antibody formation—a fact of some importance in relation to theories of antibody formation.

HAPTEN–PROTEIN COMPLEXES AS SENSITIZING AGENTS

The foregoing discussion, although largely theoretical, is intended to give some insight into the nature of antigenicity. It should also make it possible to understand not only how immunological specificity is achieved but also how, despite such specificity, the sharing of identical or closely similar antigen determinant groups by different molecules can lead to unexpected cross-reactions between apparently unrelated antigens—e.g. between oxidized cotton and pneumococcus Type III capsular polysaccharide, or human group A red cells and Type XIV pneumococci. Nevertheless the study of artificially conjugated haptens is not wholly academic, since the opportunity for such conjugates to be formed within their bodies is not uncommon among inhabitants of countries with highly developed drug and fine chemical industries, and even primitive peoples cannot evade contact with reactive materials elaborated by certain plants such as poison ivy. For example, during the Second World War, workers in explosive factories often became sensitized to picryl proteins because they absorbed 'tetryl' (trinitrophenylmethylnitramine) which contains the picryl group, through their skin, so that it was able to combine with their epidermal proteins and render these antigenic by virtue of the attached hapten groups. Certain hair dyes, in contact with the skin of the scalp, can act in the same way, and so can certain forms of marking ink (made from aniline dyes). Several drugs are able to react with proteins, either as they are administered or after conversion to reactive derivatives in the body. Two which appear to have a special affinity for some constituent of platelets, and against which sensitization is liable to cause thrombocytopenic purpura, are sedormid (allylisopropylacetylurea) and quinidine; these are discussed at greater length in Chapter Eleven. A particularly striking example is penicillin, the incidence of sensitization to which has reached such proportions that up to 1 per cent of persons receiving it parenterally are liable to have sensitization reactions ranging in severity from mild urticaria to anaphylactic shock. Recent experimental work has indicated that the material which reacts with the body proteins (in this case the plasma proteins) is not penicillin itself, but breakdown products, such as benzylpenicillenic acid, which is rather readily formed from penicillin in acid solution, and can become chemically linked to proteins under physiological conditions in several ways.

It is fortunate, and somewhat surprising, that the incidence of clinically important drug sensitization is not greater.

Alteration of Antigens Without Affecting their Antigenicity—Toxoids

The modifications of proteins by attachment of hapten groups discussed hitherto have been such as to produce new and additional antigenicity, and often to mask to a greater or lesser extent the antigenicity of the original protein. It is, however, possible to treat many proteins with formaldehyde, under mild conditions, so that their free amino groups are blocked by conversion to methylene compounds ($CH_2 = N—$), and other groups (e.g. indol nuclei and imidazol rings) become involved in cross-linkages, without any great alteration of their antigenicity. The electric charge on the proteins is, of course, changed, but they often remain soluble at physiological pH. When such proteins possess a biological activity, such as toxicity, this is commonly (though not always) destroyed by such treatment, and the toxin is converted to a 'toxoid'. Toxoids of this kind are extremely useful for immunization purposes, since they confer the same immunity as would the toxin, but, being non-toxic, they can be administered in very much greater amounts even to a non-immune subject. There are several other modifications of proteins which can be made without destroying their immunogenicity, but they have no practical advantage over formaldehyde treatment. However, it should be mentioned that loss of toxicity or other activity without loss of immunogenicity—so called 'toxoiding'—can occur in certain instances apparently spontaneously. One way in which this can happen is by oxidation by atmospheric oxygen of —SH groups which are essential for the biological activity of the protein in question; but since this process may be reversible, it is not of practical interest.

The reason why formaldehyde treatment has so little effect upon antigenicity is presumably because the extra groups added to the molecule are small, and do not greatly alter its surface structure, even though they affect the net charge. However, formaldehyde is not entirely without effect, and especially if proteins have been reacted extensively with it, they acquire an added antigenic specificity. Antisera against them will cross-react with other formaldehyde-treated proteins (even though there is no cross-reaction between the native forms), and, for example, a rabbit can make antibody against its own serum proteins after they have been modified by such treatment. This is the reason why sensitization to formaldehyde may occur in persons who are exposed to it so that they absorb it through the lungs or through the skin.

Denaturation

When proteins are denatured by various means (e.g. by heating, or by treatment with strong solutions of urea or guanidine) a proportion of the bonds which hold together the molecule in its normal three-dimensional shape are broken, and the molecule becomes rearranged in a new shape, in which the amino-acid chain is not broken, but the secondary linkages which control the way in which the chain is folded (largely hydrogen bonds and S—S bonds) are reformed in a more haphazard manner. The result is that some or all of the original antigenic determinant groups on the surface are destroyed, and new arrangements appear in their place. Denatured proteins lose most, or all, of their original antigenic specificity, and acquire new specificities instead. It has been found that denatured proteins often cross-react with one another immunologically—presumably because the sorts of rearrangements which are most stable and which occur most readily, once the original configuration is broken, are likely to be to some extent the same for different proteins.

SOME ANTIGENS OF PRACTICAL IMPORTANCE

The foregoing brief outline of the general nature of antigens and of the features which determine antigenic specificity might be expected logically to lead up to a discussion of the detailed character of antigens derived from bacteria, viruses, red cells, etc., which are of practical importance in medicine. Unfortunately, the time has not yet arrived when this can be done, both because of the difficulties which have been experienced in obtaining such materials in a sufficiently pure state for chemical analysis and because of the extremely complicated nature of the molecules involved. Nevertheless, a start has been made, and it is now possible at least to indicate general features, and sometimes details, about many substances which would have been impossible twenty years ago.

BLOOD GROUP ANTIGENS

Distinct red blood cell groups are found in many species of

mammal, but only in man has their nature been examined extensively. Although they are present in the envelope of red cells, and on the surface of many other cells (e.g. epithelial cells and even on human tumour cells maintained for many generations in tissue culture), they are very difficult to isolate from such sources. However, they are secreted as water-soluble substances in mucous secretions—saliva, gastric juice, colonic mucus, pseudomucinous ovarian cyst fluids—of about 80 per cent of people, and from these fluids they can be obtained in large amounts and with relative ease. Persons whose fluids contain the blood group substance corresponding to their red cell groups ('A' substances from groups A_1 and A_2; 'B' substance from group B; a hybrid 'AB' substance from group AB; 'H' substance from group O) are termed 'secretors'. Those whose fluids do not contain their blood group substance are termed 'non-secretors'; their fluids are very similar to those of secretors, and they have, in all but a small proportion, been found to contain another blood group substance with the serological specificity of the Lewis (Le^a) blood group. About 1 per cent of all persons secrete fluids which have none of these blood group specificities; the nature of this material is not yet known, but it is chemically very similar to the others, and may represent the primary material from which the others are derived (see below).

All the purified blood group substances so far isolated are large molecules (M.W. about 200,000 to 1,000,000), made up of 75 per cent of a complex polysaccharide and 25 per cent of a polypeptide, and form viscous solutions in water. The polysaccharide chains are apparently tightly integrated with the peptide units, and disruption of either part of the molecule destroys its serological specificity. Irrespective of their blood-group specificity, each material contains four sugar components, L-fucose, D-galactose, D-glucosamine and D-galactosamine, and the same fourteen or fifteen amino acids. There are, however, small differences between the amounts of each sugar present in the different materials, which relate to extremely important differences in the structure of the terminal groups on the carbohydrate chains, and determine their serological specificity. The way in which these differences have been worked out is extremely complicated, but the method has consisted essentially in (1) testing the activity of the blood group substances after stepwise degradation of their carbohydrate chains by chemical or enzyme action, studying at each stage what group is split off, and (2) testing possible hapten groups (e.g. L-fucose which inhibits H activity; α-N-acetyl-galactosaminoyl-(1→3)-galactose which inhibits A activity). The criterion usually employed is their ability to inhibit the serological activity of antibody against red cells of the various blood groups. The test systems are worked out with red cells of known specificity, using either natural or immune iso-agglutinins, or certain specific agglutinins which, for unknown reasons, are present in animal sera and plant seed extracts (e.g. eel serum contains anti-H; *Vicia cracca* seeds contain anti-A activity).

In this way it has been found that the blood group substances all owe their specificity to definite groups at the ends of the carbohydrate chains, and that by splitting off these groups in the right order the specificity of some of the blood group substances can be changed in a definite sequence. In so far as they are known, the groups responsible, or probably responsible in part, for the specificities of the different blood groups are listed in Table 6.3. This also

TABLE 6.3

Nature of groups determining blood group specificities in man

Antigen	Antiserum	Determinant Group
human A	human anti-A	α-N-acetylgalactosaminoyl-(1→3)-galactose
human B	human anti-B	D-galactose is important. Possibly α-D-galactosyl-(1→3)-galactose
human H	anti-H (eel serum)	L-fucose
human Le^a	human anti-Le^a	O-β-D-galactose joined (1→3) and α-L-fucose joined (1→4) to D-N-acetyl glucosamine
degraded human blood-group substances	horse anti-pneumococcus type XIV	O-β-D-galactosyl (1→4)-N-acetyl glucosamine

includes the interaction between degraded human blood group substances and horse antiserum against Type XIV pneumococcus, since this cross-reactivity regularly appears when blood-group substances are degraded sufficiently far. In Table 6.4 are listed some of the known changes in specificity brought about by specific bacterial enzymes which split off individual sugar molecules. The implications of the facts in this table are that as the end groups which confer one specificity are removed, pre-existing groups conferring a different specificity are revealed.

TABLE 6.4

Changes in serological activity of blood group substances during splitting by bacterial enzymes

(a) enzyme from *Clostridium tertium*
A substance⟶H-active substance
(b) enzyme from *Trichomonas foetus*
B substance⟶H-active substance + galactose⟶Le^{a} active substance⟶substance with Type XIV pneumococcus specificity + fucose

A working hypothesis has been proposed which accounts for these complex interrelationships, and includes the known immunochemical and genetical facts. It supposes that all persons can make a basic precursor blood group mucopolysaccharide, and that the final stages of synthesis are controlled by genes which control the formation of new chemical structure, conferring the various blood group specificities, in an orderly fashion. Thus a gene (L′), perhaps by adding *a*-L-fucose units, converts the precursor substance, which has pneumococcus type XIV serological reactivity, to Le^{a} substance; another gene (H) converts the Le^{a} substance to H substance, by adding further fucose units, but by a different link. There are secretor genes (*Se*, *se*) which function at the level of the conversion of the precursor or Le^{a} substance into H substance. The *Se* gene may be considered as activating the H gene, or alternatively the *se se* genes may suppress its action (in *se se* individuals no H substance is found). After this stage changes are controlled by A, B and O genes which respectively control the modification of H substance to A substance, or to B substance, or are inactive. Each L′ or H gene has an inactive allele (l′ or h). By suitable combinations of the different genes the occurrence of various combinations of Le^{a}, A, B and H substances actually observed can be accounted for.

This picture, complex though it is, is incomplete and much remains to be filled in. For example, there are undoubtedly minor differences between the structure of A substance in persons whose blood group is A_1 and in those of blood group A_2. Furthermore, materials can be prepared from hog or horse stomach linings which have serological specificities and general properties very like those of human A, B and H substances and yet whose serological properties differ in certain tests. The blood group substances A and B occur in the stroma of red cells probably as glycolipids, that is compounds containing the carbohydrate part of the molecule joined through sphingosine to fatty acids.

Recent evidence suggests that some other specific blood group determinants in man may be associated with complex carbohydrate macromolecules in a generally similar manner to the A, B, H and Lewis specificities. For example, substances with M and N specificities have been obtained from red cell stroma and from meconium. They contain a variety of amino acids, and a high proportion of sialic acid (N-acetyl neuraminic acid); the latter appears to be an important determinant since treatment with influenza viruses or neuraminidase prepared from *vibrio cholerae* destroys the serological activity. The P_1 antigen of the P blood-group system has not yet been isolated from red cells, but a substance with a similar specificity occurs in sheep hydatid cyst fluid and proves to contain a carbohydrate structure whose main serological determinant is α D-galactose.

Little is known of the nature of other blood group characters such as Rhesus factors, the substances responsible for which have not been found in water-soluble form in secretions and tissue fluids. Nevertheless, blood group substances have been considered at some length since they illustrated how complex antigens can be studied and how their heredity may be controlled.

Furthermore, they are of great practical interest for blood transfusion; for medico-legal experts (who use the evidence of blood groups in cases of disputed parenthood, etc.); for ethnographers (who can trace the relationship of different races to one another by studying the relative prevalence of different blood groups); and even for archaeologists inasmuch as blood group substances have been shown to survive such processes as mummification.

HETEROPHILE ANTIGENS

'Heterophile' is the name given to several groups of antigens which occur in cells or fluids of apparently unrelated animals and microorganisms, and which are so closely related immunologically (presumably by virtue of similar or identical haptenic groups) that they cross-react extensively with antibodies against any one member of the particular heterophile group. Their nature is not known, although attempts at purification indicate that they are perhaps mucopolysaccharides associated with lipid; they are usually recognized by virtue of the antibodies to which they give rise. As expected, animals of a species which already possesses a heterophile antigen in its tissues or fluids will not produce antibodies against this antigen, whereas animals which do not contain the antigen will do so readily—and in fact they may normally contain heterophile antibodies, apparently occurring naturally but more probably due to stimulation by micro-organisms which possess the antigen.

An example of a heterophile antigen is the well-known Forssman antigen, which is present in the red cells of many species (a list of some of them is given in Table 6.5) as well as in some bacteria such

TABLE 6.5

Presence or absence of Forssman-type antigen in red cells of some common animal species

Forssman^{+ve}	Forssman^{-ve}
Horse	Man
Sheep	Monkey
Dog	Rabbit
Cat	Rat
Mouse	Guinea-pig (kidney cells are +ve)
Fowl	Duck

(N.B. Although the Forssman antigens have marked antigenic similarity to one another, they are not necessarily identical.)

as pneumococci, certain strains of dysentery and paratyphoid bacilli, *Neisseria catarrhalis*, *Clostridium welchii*, *Pasteurella lepiseptica* and others. It probably represents part of a material which forms a structural unit in cell walls, and is used by the many Forssman-positive species; but the material is not necessarily identical in each, and in fact clear differences between Forssman antigens from different sources can be demonstrated despite the fact that they cross-react.

Another heterophile antigen is related to the human blood group B and is found in various strains of *E. coli* (e.g. O86); another related to blood group O (H substance) is detected when antisera are used, prepared against dysentery organisms in goats; the cross-reactions between Type XIV pneumococcus capsular polysaccharide and blood group A, or degraded blood group substances of other groups, have already been mentioned. This list is not exhaustive, and as more systems are investigated still more cross-reacting materials of this type are certain to be found. It is not improbable that antigens of this kind are responsible for the formation of natural iso-agglutinins. If, from infancy onwards, people are subjected to stimuli (from the gut or respiratory tract) by bacterial antigens with blood group specificities A and B, they will react by producing antibodies against those to which they are not naturally tolerant (i.e. a group A person will produce anti-B, and so on). That this is the true explanation has not been proved in man, but evidence to support it comes from germ-free animals (e.g. chicks, or piglets reared without colostrum). Normal, non-sterile chicks and piglets very early develop antibodies which agglutinate human group B cells, but germ-free animals do not. However, if the latter are fed with pure cultures of *E. coli* O86 (which has the group B antigen), they very soon develop anti-B antibodies. Furthermore, such heterophile antibodies commonly occur in the macroglobulin fraction, just as do natural red cell iso-agglutinins.

Apart from their intrinsic interest, heterophile systems are practically important both because they can confuse serological diagnosis and because, in certain instances, they can also be put to diagnostic use. Examples of the latter are the Weil–Felix reaction for typhus (agglutination of *Proteus* OX19); the agglutination of streptococcus strain MG in patients with primary atypical pneumonia; and the Paul–Bunnell reaction for infectious mononucleosis, in which antibody is formed which reacts with a heat-stable antigen on sheep red cells which is shared by ox cells but not by guinea-pig kidney (i.e. is not Forssman antigen).

LIPOPOLYSACCHARIDE ANTIGENS OF GRAM-NEGATIVE BACTERIA

Many Gram-negative bacteria have been found to contain in their cell walls complex antigens composed of carbohydrate, lipid and a protein or polypeptide-like material. Each of the three components is associated with properties of the complexes, the carbohydrate determining the somatic 'O' antigen specificity, the lipid being implicated in the endotoxin properties, and the protein being important for the immunogenic (as opposed to antigenic) properties in rabbits. These substances have been named Boivin antigens after the French worker who first isolated them by extraction of dried organisms with trichloroacetic acid, followed by further purification steps.

They are of especial interest because of their unique properties. More or less irrespective of the bacterial species from which they are obtained, highly purified Boivin antigens (often termed 'endotoxins') injected intravenously into man or into laboratory animals cause characteristic effects. These are:

(1) In sufficient doses (from about 30 micrograms to several milligrams per kg, depending on the species), death. Rabbits and mice are particularly susceptible.

(2) Leucopenia, followed by a leucocytosis.

(3) Fever. Some animals (e.g. rabbit and man) are extremely susceptible, and as little as 0·02 μg/kg will produce a definite rise in temperature, whereas other animals require more. Contamination with Boivin antigens (which are rather stable to heat) is in fact a common cause of pyrogenic reactions following intravenous infusions. The interaction of the 'endotoxin' with the tissues (leucocytes and other cells) of the recipient releases an endogenous pyrogenic material, whose nature has not yet been established.

(4) The Shwartzman reaction (see Chapter Eleven).

(5) Very small doses stimulate phagocytosis by cells of the reticulo-endothelial system. Larger doses initially depress phagocytosis, but if the dose is not too great, this is followed by a phase of increased phagocytic capacity, and increased non-specific resistance to injection. (See Chapter Two.)

(6) Antibody production against unrelated antigens injected at the same time is often increased. This might be a consequence of the increased phagocytic activity (5). However, other cell systems are also stimulated. Thus there is a marked increase in size of the germinal centres within the Malpighian bodies of the spleen. This is associated with great mitotic activity in cells which appear to be derivatives and/or precursors of lymphocytes.

At the same time, the Boivin antigens from each bacterial species carry the 'O' somatic antigen specificity characteristic of the bacteria in question. These complex antigens can be broken down by relatively mild chemical treatments according to the following scheme:

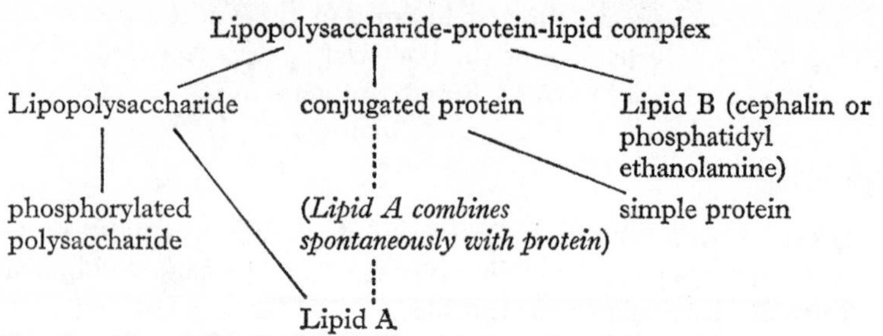

Properties (1) to (5) listed above have often been associated with fragments of the original antigen containing Lipid A, but recent evidence suggests that they depend rather on some yet unidentified structure in the intact molecule. The whole complex is immunogenic but once the conjugated protein has been split off the fragments are found to have lost this property. The specificity of antibodies induced by Boivin antigens is due to the polysaccharide part, and both the lipopolysaccharide moiety and the polysaccharide (which contains bound phosphorus) will precipitate specifically with the antibody, although they will not elicit antibody production.

Much work has been done on the structure of the polysaccharides in relationship to their role in the serological classification of Gram-negative bacteria of the *coli-salmonella* group according to the Kauffmann-White scheme and its extensions. The basal structure of the cell wall appears to be the same in all *Salmonella*. It consists of a polymer of a heptose phosphate linked via ketodeoxyoctonic acid to Lipid A (a derivative of poly-N-β-hydroxymyristioyl-D-glucosamine phosphate esterified with long-chain fatty acids). To the heptose phosphate are linked in 'rough' (Ra) variants galactose and glucose; in less 'rough' (Rb) variants there are additional chains of galactose, glucose and N-acetylgalactosamine; in 'smooth' strains the side chains are further elongated by addition of O-specific determinants composed of a number of repeating units each containing a variety of linked sugars or amino sugars (Fig. 6.1). Besides galactosamine, mannose, fucose or rhamnose each repeating unit includes, as a rule, one or more 'special sugars', i.e. sugars not found in the basal structure. These special sugars, which play an important role in the serological specificity, include the recently described 3 : 6 di-deoxyhexoses tyvelose, abequose, paratose and colitose named after the strains (*S-typhi*, *S. abortus equi*, *S. paratyphi* and *Escherichia coli*) from which they were first isolated. By conjugating colitose to a carrier protein, and using it to immunize goats, it has even proved possible to obtain antisera which will agglutinate some, though not all, of the strains whose Boivin antigens contain this sugar—an interesting development which suggests the possibility of eventually being able to produce tailor-made, non-toxic, immunizing agents.

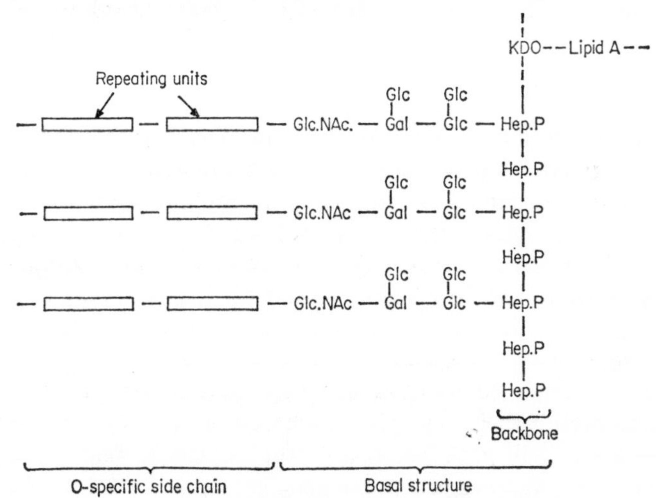

FIG. 6.1. Schematic representation of the polysaccharide moiety of an O-antigen (*Shigella flexneri*).

Glc.NAc = N. Acetyl glucosamine; Gal = galactose
Glc = glucose; Hep.P = Aldoheptose phosphate
KDO = ketodeoxooctonic acid

Structural studies of this type have led to the identification of the sequences that are involved in the serological specificity and cross reactivity and have shown that it is the easily available peripheral or surface units which are the important determinants of immunological specificity. Smooth to rough mutation is the result of enzyme defects that block the O-specific terminal side chains with the consequent exposure of the underlying R-determinants in the basal structure. From studies of the enzyme defects found in many R-mutants and from the structures of the incomplete lipopolysaccharides that result, it has been possible to gain insight into the genetic control of the biosynthetic pathways for these very complex macromolecules and to map these successfully on the bacterial chromosome.

The attachment of bacterial viruses such as bacteriophage depends on cell wall receptors whose specificities and cross-reactions for phage attachment are in many ways similar to those found by immunological means. Bacteriophage lysis or 'phage-typing' is an important practical procedure for the identification of bacteria. Elucidation of the antigenic structures involved should, moreover, illuminate the important problem of how viruses attach to and enter cells.

Histocompatibility Antigens

Histocompatibility (or H) Antigen is a term used to describe material present in the surface and internal membranous structures of the cells of an animal which is able to immunize another animal of the same species so that grafts of tissue made from one animal to the other are destroyed by a specific immunological reaction. Such antigens are *iso-antigens*, being completely identical only in genetically identical individuals (i.e. in uniovular twins in outbred animals, or in individuals of the same inbred strain). Although no one claims to have isolated histocompatibility antigens in a form sufficiently pure to permit their definitive characterization, they require to be discussed briefly both because of their intrinsic importance and because their analysis provides a good example of the application of immunological and genetic principles.

Our main knowledge of histocompatibility antigens comes from studies made in mice, both because many inbred (isogeneic) strains have been developed, and because within these strains a large variety of transplantable tumours have appeared, which have been extensively used in cancer research. The presence of H antigens is essentially detected by their capacity to immunize a host animal so that it will subsequently reject a graft of tissue containing the same H antigens at an accelerated tempo (for further discussion of graft rejection see Chapter Thirteen). However, H antigens can also evoke circulating antibodies as well as delayed type hypersensitivity, and their presence can consequently be detected by a variety of tests which depend on their interaction with specific serum antibody—e.g. agglutination or complement-dependent lysis of cells bearing the same H antigen, complement fixation or immunofluorescent staining. For a species in which inbred animals are available, such as the mouse, the number of gene loci controlling histocompatibility antigens can be estimated by crossing two inbred strains and grafting transplantable tumours or normal tissues from the parent strains to the members of an F_2 generation. In this way it has been found that there are at least 14 histocompatibility loci in the mouse, named H-1, H-2, H-3 etc. The H-2 locus controls what are called 'strong' antigens—i.e. those which evoke a powerful and rapid response—and the other loci control relatively weak antigens. Each locus which has been studied carefully has been found to control a number of alleles characterized by different combinations of specificities. There are 18 identified alleles at the H-2 locus, and probably others unidentified; five alleles have been reported at H-1; and multiple alleles at H-3.

The cellular distribution of H-2 antigens has been examined carefully. They occur in virtually all kinds of adult cells, including tumours, but are more abundant in some (e.g. lymphoid cells) than in others such as red cells; they also occur in embryo cells. Chemical studies have been held up by the fact that these antigens are destroyed by many extraction procedures, and purification is difficult. However, it appears that they are probably glycoproteins, normally associated with lipids, present in the walls and other membranous structures (e.g. endoplasmic reticulum) of cells, and that several antigenic specificities are carried on the same molecule. If this is true, then there is a general similarity to the 'O' antigens of Gram-negative bacteria or the ABO blood group antigens of man, which are also cell surface components and on to which different and multiple immunological specificities are added by the ordered attachment of carbohydrate residues.

Histocompatibility antigens in Man have been studied extensively in relation to organ transplantation and by experimental skin grafts in volunteers, but of course direct genetic studies on inbred strains are impossible. Much has been learned, however, from studies of *leucocyte antigens*, whose presence or absence appears to correlate well with the antigenic behaviour of tissues used for grafting, and may well correspond in general to the H antigens of mice. Leucocyte antigens are usually examined in peripheral blood leucocytes or in platelets, by similar methods to those used in mice, usually by cytotoxicity or agglutination tests. The antisera are obtained mostly from women who have become immunized during pregnancy by cells or materials which must have leaked from the foetus across the placental barrier. Such antisera must each be tested against a large sample of randomly chosen donor cells before a pattern of antibody activity emerges by which the expected complex mixture of leucocyte antigens can be analysed—nowadays with the help of a computer. At present at least twelve leucocyte antigens can be distinguished, and ten of these appear from family studies to belong to one complex allelic system reminiscent of the H-2 system in mice. Reference banks of suitable antisera are being collected so that the tissue types of prospective donors for grafting operations can be chosen to be as close as possible to those of the recipient. Experience with kidney grafting has shown that when this is done the long term survival rate is much improved, irrespective of other immunosuppressive measures.

SPECIFIC CAPSULAR POLYSACCHARIDES

Micro-organisms such as pneumococci and *Haemophilus influenzae* in their smooth (virulent) forms are coated with capsules consisting of polymers of complex polysaccharides of high molecular weight, which differ from the materials mentioned above in not being associated with protein or lipid components. The capsular polysaccharides from many of the thirty-two main types of pneumococci and some of the haemophilus types have been isolated and analysed chemically. Although their detailed structures have not been elucidated in most cases, it is clear that the specificities of pneumococcal polysaccharide are due to structural units composed of hexoses, hexuronic acid, amino-sugars, etc., in the same sort of way as the blood group substances. Those of *H. influenzae* types a, b and c are apparently due to polymers of glucose phosphate, ribose phosphate and galactose phosphate respectively.

Not all antigenic capsular materials are polysaccharides, however. *B. anthracis*, for example, has a capsule composed entirely of the unnatural dextro-form of glutamic acid, polymerized in the form of a polypeptide linked *via* the γ-carboxyl group. The capsules of the related non-pathogenic *B. mesentericus* and *B. subtilis* are similar but contain L- as well as D-glutamic acid.

As will be described in Chapter Ten, antibodies against capsules of pneumococci and influenza bacilli (but not anthrax bacilli) are protective. During the course of experiments on immunization of experimental animals with pneumococcus capsular polysaccharides, which are only decomposed very slowly in the body, it was observed by Felton that whereas 0·1 or 1 μg injected into a mouse caused a good antibody response, larger amounts such as 50 or 500 μg elicited no antibody whatsoever. Furthermore, after treatment with such large doses it was impossible during a period of many months to elicit an antibody response to the particular pneumococcus polysaccharide even by using whole killed pneumococci for immunization. The antibody-forming mechanism was in fact paralysed, and this paralysis was specific since the response to other antigens (and even unrelated pneumococcus polysaccharides in small amounts) was quite normal. This was the first occasion on which the phenomenon of specific immunological paralysis was recognized. This has been discussed at greater length in Chapter Three and on p. 211.

OTHER BACTERIAL ANTIGENS, TOXINS, ETC.

It is not possible in the compass of this volume to consider in detail antigens from other medically important bacteria such as streptococci, staphylococci, corynebacteria, acid-fast bacilli, etc. In general, antigens bound up with cell walls appear to be complex mucopeptides, with or without lipid; capsules are polysaccharides or polypeptides; 'slimes' may contain complex proteins, but their composition is largely unknown. The principles which govern their antigenic behaviour are the same as those which have already been discussed. Secreted bacterial products—exotoxins, enzymes, etc.—are nearly always proteins and even when several different materials are produced by a single strain of bacteria each material has been found to possess distinct antigenic specificity. They will not be considered at greater length here since several of the more important are discussed in Chapters Ten and Sixteen.

VIRUS ANTIGENS

All animal and plant viruses have been found to be composed largely of either deoxyribosenucleoproteins or ribosenucleoproteins. In some viruses this is associated with lipid, and sometimes traces of carbohydrate, which are derived from the normal constituents of the cell in which the virus is formed and are in a sense adventitious. The essential part of the virus which is able to divert the synthetic mechanisms of host cells to reproducing new virus particles is the nucleic acid. The nucleic acid can be split off from the protein and lipid and may by itself, under suitable and rather artificial circumstances, actually infect susceptible cells so as to bring about reproduction of the complete virus. The protein, and lipid when present, are only associated with the ability of the virus to attach to and to penetrate susceptible cells, and with protecting its essential nucleic acid from destruction by deoxyribo- or ribonucleases. During the course of virus reproduction it appears that the macromolecular components from which it is made up are probably produced in the cell haphazard, some of them in excess of requirements, and that these join together afterwards to form complete virus; in the course of doing so, some of the components become buried beneath the surface. When antibodies are produced they are often formed both against the whole virus and against the component parts (which are antigenically distinct from one another). It may thus come about, according to the complexity of the virus, that several distinct antibodies are formed, and that only some of these react with the whole virus, while the others will only react with extracts of infected cells or with the virus after it has been partially broken up so as to reveal components lying beneath the surface. Obviously the latter antibodies will have no protective function. The specificity of antibodies against viruses has always been found to be determined by the protein (or perhaps carbohydrate, when present) which they contain, and never by the nucleic acid. This is in accordance with the failure of nucleic acids to act as antigens, except in special circumstances (p. 209). It might be predicted, therefore, that if viruses were to exist under any circumstance as infectious nucleic acid, without any protein coating, they could be present together with anti-viral antibody and yet not be inactivated by it. Some specific virus antigens are mentioned in Chapters Ten, Fourteen and Sixteen.

A point of considerable interest is that antibodies against viruses often persist for a very long time after infection, in the absence of any known re-exposure to the antigen—longer than would be expected from experience with most other antigens. In certain instances (e.g. Rickettsiae, adeno-, herpes, hepatitis viruses) there is good clinical or experimental evidence that the viruses can persist intracellularly, and, although the antibody prevents any general spread in the body, it is probable that small amounts of antigen are released periodically and maintain immunization. In the case of others, such as mumps, measles and perhaps poliomyelitis, repeated contacts (with or without subclinical infection) may occur from the environment and act as secondary stimuli. However, instances are known in which neither intracellular persistence of virus nor repeated contact from outside are at all probable, and yet measurable antibody has persisted for many years. The explanation may lie in the fact that virus neutralization tests are extremely sensitive, and can detect very minute amounts of antibody, so that antibody is observed with such systems at a stage when it would apparently have disappeared if measured by the less sensitive techniques used for other antigens. It may be, however, that viruses are for yet unknown reasons more efficient immunizing materials than are other antigens.

ANTIGENS OF PLANTS: PLANT LECTINS

Plants are, not surprisingly, rich sources of antigens, which have been the subject of considerable study for purposes of taxonomic classification and, to some extent, of identification. Their interest from the point of view of this book lies partly in the fact that some of these antigens, such as those of pollens, are important in hay fever and asthma (see Chapter Eleven), and partly that plants have been found to contain polysaccharides capable of interacting with antibodies against a number of human blood group antigens, and are presumably either chemically similar to these or possessed of a similar surface configuration. Since such polysaccharides are often more readily extractable than are blood group antigens, and are obtainable in greater amounts, and since their chemical structure is sometimes known, they have proved to be useful immunochemical reagents. For example, materials with the specificity of the H antigen of human erythrocytes are found in extracts of yew trees and in sassafras; materials with Rh (D) specificity are found in lilac and forsythia twigs.

An unexpected finding, whose biological significance is obscure, is that plants also contain proteins which behave like natural specific antibodies against certain polysaccharide antigens—though these proteins, which are termed *lectins*, resemble immunoglobulins in no other way. The lectins which are recognized (and there are probably many more unrecognized) are those which have been found, by trial and error, to interact with mammalian erythrocytes. For example, extracts of the seeds of *Lotus tetragonolobus* react with human H antigen, extracts of *Vicia graminea* agglutinate group N erythrocytes, and extracts of *Phaseolus limensis* or of *Dolichos biflorus* agglutinate cells of group AB. These lectins are useful to haematologists because of their sharp specificity. Other plant extracts, e.g. from castor beans, lima beans, red kidney beans or from American-pokeweed, behave as *phytohaemagglutinins*. That is, they agglutinate erythrocytes of a number of mammalian species (though there is a certain specificity according to the phytohaemagglutin used). They also contain distinct substances which act as mitogenic agents, causing mitosis of lymphocytes *in vitro*, which have been referred to on p. 97.

FURTHER READING

BOYD W.C. (1963) *Fundamentals of Immunology*. Interscience, London

DAVIES D.A.L. (1968) 'Transplantation Antigens' in *Human Transplantation*, (ed. Rapaport F.T. and Dausset J.) Grune and Stratton, New York

DUMONDE D.C. (1965) Tissue specific antigens. *Adv. Immunol.* **5**, 30

GOLDSMITH K.L.G. (1959) (ed.) Blood groups. *Brit. Med. Bull.* (No. 2) **15**, 89–170

HEIDELBERGER M. (1956) *Lectures in Immunochemistry*. Academic Press, New York

KABAT E.A. (1956) *Blood Group Substances*. Academic Press, New York

KABAT E.A. & MAYER M.M. (1961) *Experimental Immunochemistry*. C.C. Thomas, Springfield, Ill.

KARUSH F. (1962) Immunologic specificity and molecular structure. *Adv. Immunol.* **2**, 1

LANDSTEINER K. (1945) *The Specificity of Serological Reactions*. Harvard University Press, Cambridge, Mass.

LANDY M. (Convenor) (1961) Symposium on bacteriol endotoxins. *Bacteriol. Rev.* **25**, 427

LEVINE L. & STOLLER B.D. (1968) Nucleic acid immune systems. *Progr. Allergy* **12**, 161

LUDERITZ O., STAUB A.M. & WESTPHAL O. (1966) Immunochemistry of O and R antigens of *Salmonella* and related *Enterobacteriaceae*. *Bact. Rev.* **30**, 192

McCARTY M. & MORSE S.I. (1964) Cell wall antigens of gram-positive bacteria. *Adv. Immunol.* **4**, 249

MARRACK J.R. (1938) *The Chemistry of Antigens and Antibodies*. Special rep. ser. Medical Research Council No. 194. HMSO London

MORGAN W.T.J. (1960) Croonian Lecture: A contribution to human biochemical genetics: the chemical basis of blood group specificity

PLESCIA O.J. & BRAUN W. (1966) Nucleic acids as antigens. *Adv. Immunol.* **6**, 231

PRESSMAN D. & GROSSBERG A.L. (1968) *The Structural Basis of Antibody Specificity*. W.A. Benjamin, New York

SELA M. (1965) Immunological studies with synthetic polypeptides, *Adv. Immunol.* **5,** 30

SPRINGER G.F. (1967) 'The relation of microbes to blood group-active substances'. In *Cross-reacting Antigens and Neoantigens.* Williams and Wilkins Co., Baltimore

STACEY M. & BARKER S.A. (1960) *Polysaccharides of Micro-organisms.* Clarendon, Oxford

VAN HEYNINGEN W.E. (1950) *Bacterial Toxins.* Blackwell Scientific Publications, Oxford

WATKINS W.M. Blood-group substances. *Science* **152,** 172

WILLIAMS C.A. & CHASE M.W. (eds) (1967) *Methods in Immunology and Immunochemistry* **1,** Academic Press, New York

(See also suggestions for further reading, Chapter Thirteen)

CHAPTER SEVEN

The Fate of Antigen and the Process of Antibody Production

THE problem which faces us in this chapter is how the cells deal with the injected immunogen and how this becomes a stimulus for the synthesis of immunoglobulin molecules which are so specifically tailored that they combine with the molecules of the antigen and with these alone. We should recognize at the outset that the cellular systems responsible for the synthesis of these antibodies are highly complex; only a small fraction of the injected dose of antigen is concerned in the effective stimulation of cells to produce antibody; only a minute proportion of the cells which are caused to multiply in the lymphoid tissues of the body will be involved in the actual synthesis of antibody; and only a proportion of the resulting production of immunoglobulin molecules are specific antibodies reactive with the antigen.

In addition to considering the first synthesis of antibody resulting from the injection of an immunogen, we have to consider the cellular mechanisms responsible for the changed synthetic response which characterizes second and subsequent injections of immunogen (these altered characteristics of later responses have already been explained in Chapter Three). Great practical importance attaches to the factors determining the build-up in the magnitude of the immune response. In man, a second stimulus given before the lapse of ten days or so from the first will fail to result in a typical rapid and enhanced antibody response. With increasing intervals of time, the secondary responses become built up over several months. Figure 7.1 shows the analogous phenomenon in the guinea-pig. In the immunization of children it is important that *time* be allowed for

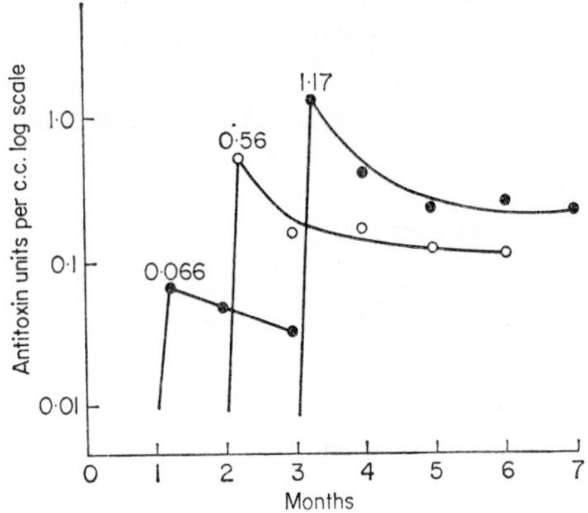

FIG. 7.1 Mean antibody responses (International units per ml) of groups of guinea-pigs stimulated by reinjection of alum-precipitated diphtheria toxoid at 1, 2 or 3 months after primary stimulation with similar material.

Note that the response after 3 months is greater than that after shorter time intervals.

With this antigen, after the initial peak, a high level of antitoxin is maintained for several months. [Barr, Mollie and Glenny A.T. (1945) *J. Hyg., Camb.* **44**, 135.]

the build-up of the effect of previous stimuli in order to derive the maximum immunizing effect from the subsequent injections of prophylactic vaccines and toxoids. The use of additives to the immunogen injection mixture, i.e. substances generally referred to as *adjuvants*, may also be of crucial importance for this process.

The practical aim, for example, in a diphtheria immunization programme is not only to produce circulating antitoxin, which will be the means of immediately neutralizing toxin absorbed from the site of the diphtheria membrane in the throat, but also *potential immunity* or *immunological memory*, i.e. the ability to respond swiftly and strongly to the small amounts of toxin produced in the initial stages of an infection. There is good evidence that all members of our community have fairly frequent contact with toxin-producing diphtheria organisms (possibly once or twice a year at least). When good potential immunity exists, each such small immunogenic dose will act as a boost and so appreciable levels of antitoxin can be maintained in the circulation indefinitely. With a high level of potential immunity, a boost of antibody production can be obtained with a minute dose of antigen. Thus, even the small amount of toxin in one Schick test dose (1/1,000 Lf or 0·0000003 mg) will serve to act as a booster, although such a tiny dose is quite unable to cause antibody production if given as a primary stimulus.

The Cellular Fate of Injected Antigens

The destination of antigens in the various cells of the body has been much explored, since it was argued that the cells which handle the antigen must either themselves be among those that make the antibody or must act in an essential way to prepare the immunogen to become the effective stimulus of the actual antibody-producing cells. The specific resistance acquired by the body after an injection has been regarded as due to the stimulus of one or more antigenic components of the infecting organism and substantial efforts have been made to reproduce the effects of infection by injecting the extracted and purified antigen(s). A knowledge of the destination of these would be of great importance since the degree of resistance attained may well depend on the way such antigens are presented to the antibody-producing tissues. It often happens, especially with virus infection, that the highest degree of immunity follows recovery from a severe infection with the virus. A natural, mild or subclinical infection can often result in almost as effective immunity. But with, for instance, vaccinia virus even the mildest methods for inactivating the virus result in failure to produce effective immunity following injection of such killed material. We have to find out, for practical purposes, how to present the antigens to the important cells for the purpose of securing good immunity, and, for theoretical reasons, we would like to know which recipient cells are the important ones for this immune response. It is even possible to induce the wrong kind of response and do harm to the body by a misguided immunogenic stimulus. Attempts to immunize the host against a neoplasm may thus result in the paradoxical *enhancement* of the tumour growth (see Chapter Fourteen). This result is interpreted as the stimulation of a particular type of antibody in the absence of other protective components (cellular or humoral) of the immune response.

A study of these problems involves consideration of tags for identifying immunogenic molecules. The ideal label should allow the tracing of the immunogen without, of course, altering the physical properties or the antigenic activity of the labelled substance. It should also be without toxic effect of its own on tissue cells. Thus a radioactive label should not be so concentrated within the cell as to halt or modify mitosis. We do not want to use a label which will itself persist in tissues after the breakdown of the antigen. Ideally, immediately this happens, the released label should diffuse away and be excreted. Many labels fall short of these requirements and the results obtained by their use are of questionable value for our purposes.

There have been many careful studies of the fate of coloured proteins. The first of these was by Sabin, who gave to rabbits small repeated doses of alum-precipitated ovalbumin coupled to a dye (R-salt azo benzidine) by various injection routes. The dye accumulated principally within the system of phagocytic cells, which had been defined for many years previously by Aschoff and termed the Reticulo-Endothelial system (see Chapter Two). These findings bolstered the belief that the cells of the reticulo-endothelial system were concerned in the manufacture of antibody. In default of other rivals, it was readily assumed that the cells which take up immunogens also produce antibody.

This belief that the reticulo-endothelial cells manufacture antibody was supported by Sabin's observations on the phagocytic cells of the omentum. After intraperitoneal injection these cells were found to take up the dye-labelled protein precipitate into their digestive vacuoles. Later the dye was seen to be removed from the particles and these disappeared—presumably by an enzymic digestion process. Next the cells shed some of their cytoplasm. This property of the macrophages within connective tissue had been known for a long time. Indeed Ranvier had named such cells *clasmatocytes*: the 'shedders of cytoplasm'. Soon afterwards antibody was found in the serum and the near coincidence of shedding of cytoplasm and appearance of antibody gave rise to the belief that antibody was liberated in the shedding process.

Other evidence for the same view was derived from the effects of 'blockade' of these cells in cutting down antibody production. Such blockade was effected by repeated intravenous injection of carbon particles, which loaded the cytoplasm of the macrophages and interfered with the uptake of antigen. In the last analysis, however, this merely suggests that the route of the antigen lies through the macrophage and does not necessarily indicate this as the actual producer of antibody.

Although recent work has led to the rejection of the cells of the reticulo-endothelial system as producers of antibody, nevertheless the processes of immunogen uptake, retention and catabolism by these cells is regarded as being of central importance to the immune response. In order that the immunogen should be able to act as a stimulus for antibody production it, or fragments of it, might reasonably be expected to persist within cells for at least a day or so. Therefore interest attaches to the further studies with arsenic- and dye-labelled proteins and more recently with radioactively labelled proteins showing that persistence is possible at certain sites in the body. In this respect the experiments of McMaster with blue-azo-labelled bovine γ-globulin injected into mice were outstanding, in showing that traces of this dye persisted in the Kupffer cells and in the mesenteric lymph nodes for as long as 120 days after the injection of about 3 mg of azo-protein. Interesting as it is, this result is suspect since the entity which is localized (the dye) is not the immunogenic part of the complex and may not reasonably be taken to indicate the fate of the latter. Another approach to detection of persisting immunogen is by the method of fluorescein-labelled specific antibody (Coons' technique). This method (Chapter Nine) consists in the specific 'staining' of antigens by carrying out a precipitin test *in situ* on a tissue section, prepared in such a way as to leave the antigens intact and able to react with the applied solution of fluorescein-labelled antibody, and then studying the sections under the fluorescence microscope. The method has the strategic advantage that the immunogen can be localized so long as it remains able *to combine with antibody*.

An early use of this method showed that pneumococcal and other bacterial capsular polysaccharides, which were injected in 0·5–10 mg amounts into mice, could subsequently be located in the macrophages of the spleen, lymph nodes and liver, and in the pulmonary interstitial cells and the endothelium of the kidney and to persist for at least 75 days. Later experiments with injections of native proteins such as ovalbumin and human γ-globulin into mice showed that they could not be detected longer than a few days or a week at the most, although at the earlier times the pattern of localization in cells and tissues corresponded in general to that obtained with polysaccharides and dye-labelled proteins. The persistence of bacterial polysaccharides appeared significant since when pneumococcal polysaccharides were injected into man (even in such small quantities as 50 μg), antibody production was shown to continue for as long as 8 years. Moreover, some of the injected subjects failed to show an increase in antibody when a second injection was given, indicating that they were already fully stimulated. The result is significant in showing how an immunogenic entity (bacterial polysaccharide) can be highly indigestible by macrophages, and remain intact and potent for stimulation of antibody production over a very long period of time.

A further technique for study of persistence of immunogens in the tissues is based on the ability of organ extracts from immunogen-injected animals to sensitize new recipients for a primary or secondary response. The results, as they apply to protein antigens, show considerable variation. Some, such as diphtheria toxin, remain in an immunogenic state for 3 weeks, others such as haemocyanin from the keyhole limpet remain as potent immunogens for only 3 days. However, extracts of organs from animals immunized up to 40 days previously with the haemocyanin could inhibit haemocyanin–anti-haemocyanin precipitation. This implies that this protein immunogen can persist in a partially catabolized or modified form for many multiples of the time during which it is immunogenic when tested in a secondary host.

Yet another approach, which overcomes certain of the disadvantages of the foregoing methods, may be considered in relation to the controversial issue of the persistence of protein antigens. Rabbits will produce no antibody if they receive an immunogenic stimulus 1–2 days after irradiation. When such rabbits are left and re-stimulated with the same antigen (staphylococcal toxoid) after a lapse of 6 or 8 weeks, a primary rather than a secondary response occurs, showing that the protein antigen could not have persisted after the recovery from the X-ray damage for otherwise it would have induced a primary response and re-stimulation would have given a secondary response. A rather similar experimental approach has been used for study of the decay *in vivo* of the protein human serum albumin (HSA). Presensitized lymphoid cells were transferred to non-lethally X-irradiated host mice, which had been injected with HSA at various intervals previously. In the dose used, this immunogen did not stimulate a detectable primary response. Antibody appearing after cellular transfer was therefore produced as a result of immunogenic stimulation of a secondary response. Very rapid decay of immunogenicity was found, the half-life of which was virtually identical with that of HSA as measured in the circulation (see below), i.e. 17 hours.

Much information is available concerning the disappearance of specific or labelled proteins after their injection into the bloodstream. Fig. 7.2 (A) shows the disappearance curve for horse diphtheria antitoxin in the rabbit. It should be pointed out that this 'antibody' is also capable of acting as an antigen. Its use here is as an antigen which is capable of being accurately estimated by its reaction with diphtheria toxoid. Experiments carried out as early as 1923 show that the antigen disappears from the blood in three separate phases. Approximately half of the protein disappears rapidly from the blood within 24 hours. It is generally agreed that this first rapid phase represents equilibration with extra-vascular plasma proteins. Thereafter, there is a steady decline which follows an exponential curve, i.e. a constant fraction of the amount present is eliminated in unit time. When this second phase is plotted semi-logarithmically, i.e. logarithm of antigen remaining (ordinate) against time (abscissa) the result is a straight line. This phase usually lasts about 6 to 7 days and appears to be the elimination of the foreign protein by the normal catabolic processes. This exponential fall then suddenly changes to a third phase of accelerated loss. This occurs as a result of the production of antibody to the foreign protein acting as antigen, and the combination of antigen and antibody with complex formation leads to uptake by the cells of the reticulo-endothelial system and rapid elimination from the circulation.

When the horse diphtheria antitoxin was injected into a sensitized rabbit (i.e. one that had already received a previous injection) the duration of the exponential second phase was shortened to 3 days or less, as shown by curves C and D in Fig. 7.2. Also the third phase of accelerated loss was even more accelerated resulting in total loss of detectable antigen within 24 hours.

These events, as obtained by the assay of antitoxin activity, have been confirmed and extended by the use of radioactive labelled antigens. The results of Dixon and his colleagues using bovine γ-globulin labelled with ^{131}I as antigen in rabbits are shown in Fig. 7.3. Firstly they compared the rate of removal of the bovine-globulin with that of the recipient rabbits' own γ-globulin similarly labelled and reinjected. In the normal rabbits, once equilibrium between the vascular and extra-vascular labelled proteins was established, the rate of catabolism as shown by the appearance of protein breakdown products containing ^{131}I in the urine was the same for both proteins. This continued until the end of the fourth day, after which the antigenic bovine γ-globulin was eliminated at a greatly increased rate (see also Fig. 7.4, curve C), whereas the decline of the animal's own γ-globulin proceeded at the same slow rate. Antibody (indicated by the black column) was present in the animal's serum on the seventh day.

In immune rabbits, with circulating antibody at the time of injection, the rate of elimination and metabolism of the antigen was greatly increased, starting immediately after injection (Fig. 7.4, curve A). In immune rabbits, sensitized by a previous injection, but given sufficiently long before so that circulating antibody was very low, the rapid phase of elimination began on the second day (curve B). The relation of the rapid elimination phase to the production of circulating antibody was further shown by the use of X-irradiated animals (curves D and E). In those receiving sufficient doses of

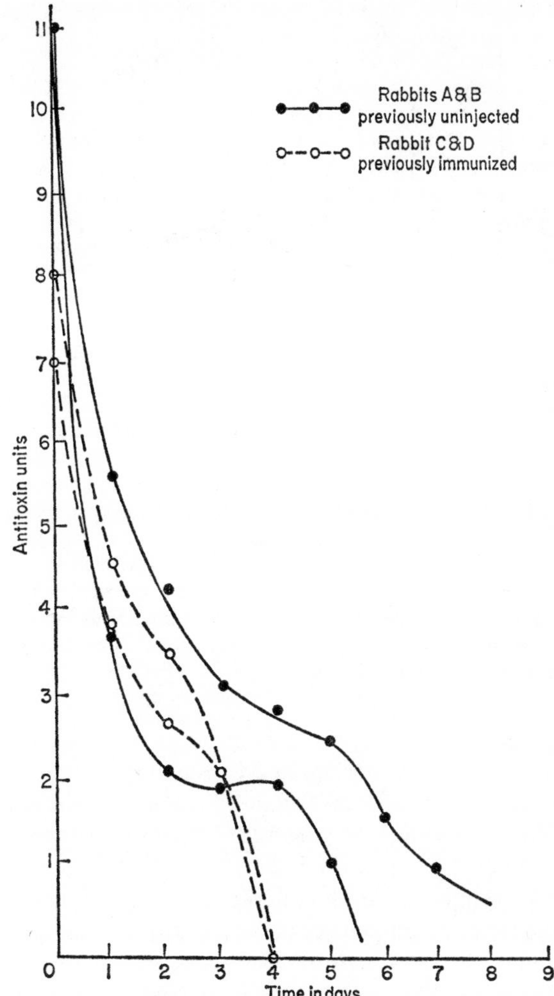

FIG. 7.2 ●—●—● Disappearance of horse diphtheria antitoxin from the blood of two normal previously uninjected rabbits A and B after intravenous injection.

○--○--○ Disappearance of horse diphtheria antitoxin from the blood of two rabbits C and D, previously sensitized to horse serum (intravenous injection). [Data from Glenny and Hopkins (1922) *J. Hyg. Camb.* **21**, 142.]

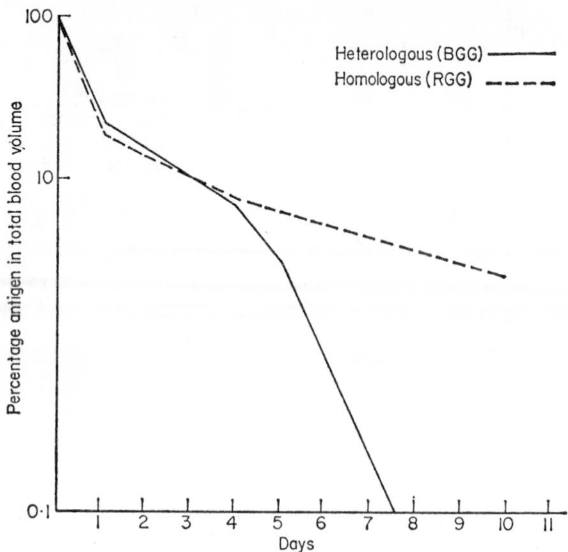

FIG. 7.3. Disappearance curves of heterologous (bovine) γ-globulin (solid line) and autologous (rabbit) γ-globulin (dotted line) after intravenous injection. Note the increased rate of disappearance which sets in on the fifth day in the case of the heterologous antigen.

X-rays to prevent completely the immune response of antibody production (curve E) no accelerated elimination phase occurred and the slow decline continued throughout (exactly like the curve for the rabbits' own γ-globulin). As a result of such experiments it is clear that when labelled proteins are injected an antibody response results which leads to the rapid destruction of most, if not all, of the antigen and that breakdown products (mainly free iodide and traces of small iodotyrosine-containing peptides) appear promptly thereafter in the urine. These facts indicate that the newly produced antibody unites with antigen to form complexes (which may be in the form of an actual precipitate or in a soluble form), which are taken up by the reticulo-endothelial system and then rapidly hydrolyzed by some proteolytic process. Also, in experiments in which labelled rabbit antibody was injected into rabbits first, followed by the homologous antigen, it could be shown that the antibody itself was also caught in the same destructive process with the rapid appearance of labelled breakdown products in the urine.

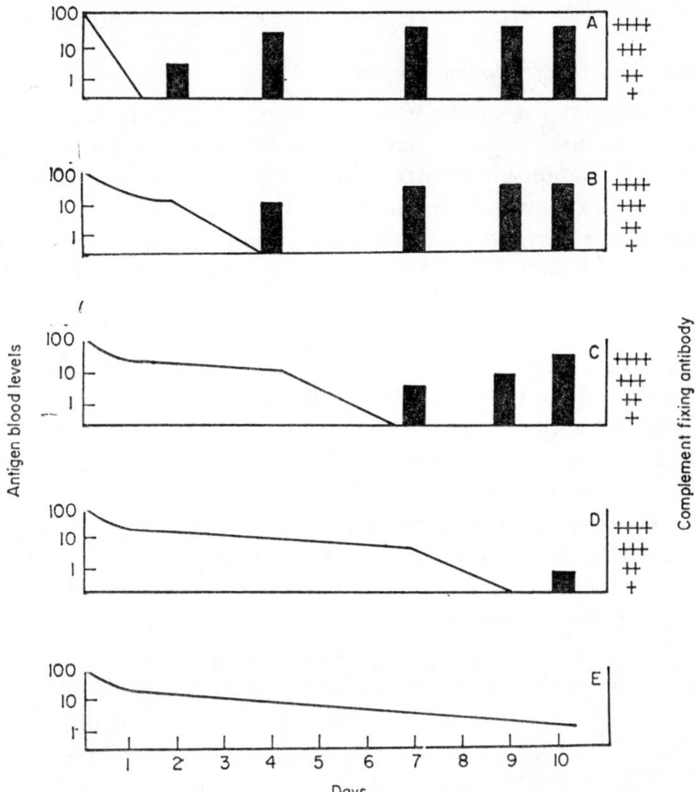

FIG. 7.4. Disappearance curves of antigen (^{131}I-labelled bovine γ-globulin) in relation to the antibody response in rabbits.

A. previously sensitized animal with circulating antibody to bovine γ-globulin at the time of injection.

B. previously sensitized animal with no circulating antibody to bovine γ-globulin at the time of injection.

C. normal rabbit not previously immunized.

D. normal rabbit irradiated whole-body with 200 r X-rays.

E. normal rabbit irradiated with 500 r X-rays.

[From Dixon, Talmage and Maurer (1952) *J. Immunol.* **68,** 693.]

EFFECTS OF VARIOUS FACTORS ON ANTIBODY FORMATION

Genetic Control of Immune Responses

Many early studies of the genetic transmission of the capacity to give an immune response have shown that there is a statistically significant relationship between the ability of parents and offspring to respond to a given immunogen. From these studies Mendelian segregative patterns were not, however, evident, due presumably to the structural complexity of the immunogens used. What is needed for such studies is a kind of unit immunogenic response, i.e. an antibody or other immune response specifically directed to a single determinant. When a standard protein immunogen such as bovine serum albumin is injected into mice of different pure inbred strains, the resultant antibody responses never have been found to yield 'all or nothing' interstrain differences of response. The group responses for two different mouse strains always overlap. The explanation of this is that the anti-BSA response is the sum of a set of responses to numerous antigenic determinants, i.e. configurations of, perhaps, four or five amino acids scattered over the surface of the molecule.

Much clearer results showing marked interstrain differences of response were obtained when guinea-pigs were immunized with pork insulin which is a natural small protein capable of being regarded as a univalent antigen. More recently tenfold differences were found between the antibody responses of two pure-bred mouse strains CBA and C57 black, using a branched chain synthetic polypeptide antigen (TG)AL made up of tyrosine, DL alanine, glutamic acid and lysine.

Detailed analysis of the mechanism underlying these differences has become possible by the use of such synthetic polypeptide antigens, since their structure can be varied at will. It appears that two distinct mechanisms may be involved:

(1) The difference between responding and non-responding strains depends upon the capacity of their immunologically competent cells to recognize and respond to the *determinant group*. Responsiveness behaves as though it were controlled by one or more autosomal dominant genes. An obvious explanation would be available if it could be shown that non-responding strains were naturally tolerant to the determinant because it was present on some component of their own tissues; however, this is

ruled out by the observation that F_1 hybrids between the two strains, which would possess antigens of both parents, can respond perfectly well.

(2) The difference depends upon the ability or inability to respond to any determinant attached to a particular kind of *carrier* molecule. Animals which can respond to many different haptens when attached to a variety of carrier molecules fail to respond to the same haptens when attached to certain simple carrier molecules (e.g. poly-L-lysine in one strain of guinea-pigs, or poly-L-tyrosine in another). The capacity to respond is again determined by an autosomal dominant gene. In this instance it appears that non-responders lack the capacity to carry out some essential (but unidentified) step in handling the carrier molecule. We know too little about the detailed mechanisms of immune responses to be able to indicate how or at what stages such genetic control may be effected.

Association of Antibodies with Particular Allotypes

When individuals are stimulated to make antibodies against an immunogen possessing only a very few different kinds of antigenic determinant (e.g. Rh-incompatible erythrocytes or dextran) or when the antibodies to a single determinant on an immunogen can be studied separately (e.g. to the hapten on a hapten-carrier protein complex), it is not uncommon to find that the antibodies occur only among a very restricted range of the immunoglobulin allotypes which are present in the serum of that individual (see Chapter Four). This implies that cells making immunoglobulin of a particular allotype are more readily stimulated by a particular immunogen, and it might be inferred that only immunoglobulins with a given L or H chain allotype were capable of assuming the conformation required to produce a given specific combining site. The allotypic variations have been identified as occurring in the 'constant' regions of the L and H chains, but some of them are certainly associated with the Fab part of the antibody molecule and could conceivably influence the shape of the 'variable' regions. If this were so it would provide an obvious mechanism for genetic restriction of specific antibody formation. Although a very refined analysis of antibody specificities may ultimately show that such a mechanism is operative, present evidence indicates that in different individuals similar antibody specificities may be associated with a variety of different immunoglobulin allotypes. The reason for the tendency towards restriction in any one person is not known.

ADJUVANTS

Many simple proteins are poor immunogens when injected alone. Thus when the protein exotoxin of the diphtheria bacillus (which has been modified by formalin to produce non-toxic 'toxoid') is injected intravenously into a rabbit, little antibody results. The protein circulates and is slowly broken down by and lost from the body. Adjuvants (L. *adjuvare*: to help) are substances which when mixed or combined with the immunogen act to increase the immunological response.

The practical advantages of measures to increase antibody levels or to increase protective immunity are such that most observations on the action of adjuvants have been limited to antibody formation. However, adjuvants may also affect other aspects of the immune response. They may, for instance, markedly increase cell-mediated hypersensitivity. This result may be a nuisance to the physician who seeks prophylaxis of an infective disease but may in other circumstances prove to be beneficial as a means of increasing the resistance of the body to a neoplastic growth. It is important also to realize that adjuvants do not merely act to increase all types of immunological responses. Even in the field of antibody production, particular immunoglobulins may be specifically increased by certain adjuvants (see examples below).

In the past the discovery of new adjuvants has been a process of trial and error. The following list is a witness to the great variety of substances used as adjuvants: tapioca, aluminium hydroxide, aluminium phosphate, mineral-oil emulsions, saponin, calcium alginate, beryllium sulphate, silica, endotoxins of Gram-negative bacteria, exotoxins of Gram-positive bacteria, acid-fast bacilli, *Bordetella pertussis* and vitamin A.

Influence of the Carrier on Immunogenicity: Adjuvant Effects which are Built into the Immunogen

An immunogenic protein is currently conceived to be provided with a surface which is divided like a mosaic into the 'determinants' or surface configurations of four or five or more amino acids. The determinants ascertain the specificity of the immune response. The rest of the molecule is regarded as without influence on specificity but nevertheless able to influence the antibody response both qualitatively and quantitatively. The influence of these factors can be explored by the use of haptens, which are small, chemically defined molecules which are capable of inducing the formation of antibody only when attached to a large protein molecule. If the hapten is attached to a foreign or heterologous protein carrier it will generate a better antibody response (hapten specific) than when attached to a protein derived from the species injected. The ratio of haptens to protein is also important. If the number of haptens attached to a single protein is in the range of 3–5, antibodies to the hapten are formed more regularly and in greater amount than if fewer hapten groups are attached to the same protein.

The nature of the carrier can also determine the immunoglobulin type of the resulting antibody. When an acidic protein, e.g. diphtheria toxoid, is injected into a rabbit, the resulting antibody appears in the first peak eluted by chromatography, i.e. among the more positively charged immunoglobulins. With lysozyme, a strongly basic protein, the antibody appears in the second peak, i.e. among the more negatively charged immunoglobulins. The molecules of antibody from the two peaks differ in their heavy-chain peptide components.

It is therefore clear that many non-specific factors relating to the molecules of the immunogen can affect the quality and quantity of the resulting response. This allows one to understand how molecular aggregation produced by heating a protein solution at 70° can convert a non-antigenic to an antigenic preparation, whereas centrifuging a protein solution at 50,000 **g**, by removing aggregated molecules, can render the subsequently injected material less likely to provoke an immune response.

Soluble Versus Particulate Antigens

The immunogenicity of many soluble antigens is enhanced if they are adsorbed to particulate matter, e.g. diphtheria toxoid is commonly adsorbed to a colloidal suspension of aluminium hydroxide or aluminium phosphate before use as an immunogen. Other particles used as adsorbents for immunogens are collodion, polyvinyl pyrrolidone and tridymite or bentonite (particles of diatomaceous earth).

In addition to their effect of increasing and prolonging the antibody response, proteins adsorbed to particles such as bentonite and injected intravenously cause a prolonged and increased production of antibody in the form of macroglobulin.

The use of aluminium hydroxide and subsequently aluminium phosphate as an adjuvant for diphtheria toxoid became universally adopted in the prophylaxis of diphtheria in man. By this means substantial reduction and even eradication of the disease was achieved in many countries. Such alum-precipitated antigens are injected *subcutaneously* and under these conditions give rise to high antibody levels which persist for a long time. Alum-precipitated antigens give rise to a firm local granuloma which develops over 2–3 weeks at the site of injection and consists in the main of macrophages which have accumulated around the mineral salt deposit. The antigen is released only slowly from such a subcutaneous 'depot'. The later the release of antigen the greater will be the number of available primed or 'Y' cells upon which the antigen could exert a stimulus for the production of antibody (Chapter Three). In other words, the delay in absorption by a so-called '*depot effect*' allows the secondary response mechanism to come into play. The main value of such mineral adsorbents is in relation to the primary response. Aluminium phosphate precipitated toxoid could not be shown to have any advantage over soluble toxoid as judged by the serum levels attained in a secondary response in man. The cellular mechanism involved in this adjuvant activity are discussed in a later section of this chapter.

Antibody as an Adjuvant

It has been explained above how diphtheria toxoid injected intravenously into a rabbit usually fails to produce an antibody response. By mixing the toxoid with antitoxin as an under-neutralized mixture a marked adjuvant effect can be obtained. Similarly the injection of sheep erythrocytes together with a small amount of 19S antibody to them increases the cellular response (as judged in a plaque assay technique: Chapter Nine) and 19S antibody production.

The outcome of these experiments would be expected to depend on the ratio of antibody to antigen injected. With diphtheria toxoid it was found that, above a critical level of antitoxin, the result was consistently an interference with immunogenicity. Another important determinant for such an adjuvant effect of antibody is the avidity of the antibody used. It has been observed how very low concentrations of high-affinity antibody, but not low affinity antibody, increased the antibody formation against a dinitrophenyl-protein conjugate in rabbits.

It remains to be seen how important this effect of antibody may be in the natural process of initiation of an immunological response. Theoretically it is possible that natural antibodies may be essential for the induction of antibody formation to certain antigens.

Water-in-oil Emulsions with and without Added Mycobacteria

Immunogenic water-in-oil emulsions are usually prepared by the use of a mineral oil, an emulsifying agent such as lanolin or Arlacel A (mannide mono-oleate) and an aqueous solution or suspension of the antigen. On mixing, a white creamy emulsion forms consisting of tiny water droplets containing the antigen surrounded by mineral oil. When killed mycobacteria are added, they are usually mixed in with the mineral oil since they are lipophilic. The mixture, which includes mycobacteria, is referred to as Freund's complete adjuvant.

Simple water-in-oil adjuvant mixtures without mycobacteria (referred to as Freund's incomplete adjuvant) appear to have two main effects. First, the local destruction and elimination of the antigen are retarded. Thus, the antigen of *Shigella* bacilli was still detectable 22 weeks after injection into mice. The destruction of antigen in such an emulsion is gradually achieved by the peripheral invasion of foamy macrophages. Secondly, the oil facilitates the dispersal of antigen. The early granulomatous tissue at the site of injection can be surgically removed at 14 days without any diminution of the subsequent antibody response, and excision at 30 minutes after injection still allows a good antibody response. Presumably the adjuvant effect is mainly dependent on the release of antigen from the depot at the injection site and from the widely disseminated foci of water-in-oil emulsion within the lymphatics and lymph nodes.

The addition of mycobacteria (or related organisms such as *Nocardia* spp.) is essential in such emulsions for pronounced sensitization of the delayed type to result (Plate 7.3). It is also the case that mycobacteria are essential in the Freund adjuvant injection mixture for the experimental production by tissues, like brain, thyroid and testis, of the auto-allergic organ specific diseases such as encephalitis, thyroiditis and orchitis. Presumably, the second statement follows logically from the first, since sensitization of the delayed-type is essential for the production of the disease. These statements are based on experiments in the guinea-pig. In this species, the addition of mycobacteria leads to the biosynthesis of different immunoglobulins. Thus, as seen from Plate 7.3, ovalbumin injected in water-in-oil emulsion leads to an antibody response at 3 weeks which is virtually entirely confined to γ_1-globulin. Where mycobacteria are added to the water-in-oil emulsion of ovalbumin, the synthesis of slow or γ_2-immunoglobulin becomes greatly enhanced. γ_1-globulin differs from γ_2-globulin in its heavy chain. In the guinea-pig, adjuvants such as aluminium phosphate act to increase γ_1-immunoglobulin without increasing γ_2-immunoglobulin (and do not have the effect of increasing delayed-type hypersensitivity).

The active principle of the mycobacteria in so far as the adjuvant effect on circulatory antibody and delayed type hypersensitivity is contained in a fraction extractable with chloroform from human-type strains of *Mycobacterium tuberculosis* known as wax D. The principal chemical components of wax D are glycolipids and peptidoglycolipids, of which the latter are responsible for biological activity. The molecule of peptidoglycolipid is composed of mycolic acids (β-hydroxy branched chain fatty acids with an alkyl chain (C_{24}) in the α position and an empirical formula of $C_{84}H_{168}O_4$) esterified with a polysaccharide (composed of arabinose, galactose and mannose) which is linked to a peptide moiety composed of D- and L-alanine, D-glutamic acid and α, ϵ, di-aminopimelic acid. The adjuvant molecule also includes glucosamine, galactosamine and muramic acid; in this and its other features it has many chemical analogies with the mucopeptide of the bacterial cell wall. The intact molecule is presumably highly surface-active and hydrolyses to the lipophilic mycolic acid and the hydrosoluble glycopeptide, neither of which possess adjuvant activity.

The mode of action of Freund's complete adjuvant has not been convincingly elucidated. The main problem is to account for its unique effect in leading to a high degree of delayed-type hypersensitivity. By cannulating the efferent lymphatics from such a granuloma it can be shown that it is the site for the transit of very large numbers of lymphocytes. Presumably the conditions under which these re-circulating cells encounter the immunogen within this epithelioid and giant cell granuloma are crucial for inducing such cell-mediated immunity. Thus it was shown many years ago that injection of a protein antigen into the granulomatous tissue at the site of local infection with living tubercle bacillus led to the development of marked cell-mediated immunity. The adjuvant effect on serum antibody levels could be secondary to the stimulation of delayed hypersensitivity, since when antigens are injected into animals which are undergoing a delayed-type response to another antigen they stimulate increased antibody responses. Thus the persisting mycobacteria in a Freund complete adjuvant mixture may act as a continuous stimulus of delayed-type hypersensitivity reactions which maintain the animal in a more inducible state for antibody production to other immunogens. The cell-mediated responses which follow the use of Freund-type complete and incomplete adjuvant are described in a later section.

Surface-active Agents

In seeking for a lowest common denominator of adjuvant effect, attention has been attracted to a large number of surface-active molecules among a list of recognized adjuvants. More recently a search for adjuvant activity which was conducted among a large number of various aliphatic nitrogenous bases resulted in the discovery of many adjuvant active compounds (quaternary ammonium compounds, guanidines, benzamidines and thiouroniums). Activity depended upon a combination of basicity and a long aliphatic chain of twelve or more carbon atoms. Such adjuvants tend to be haemolytic and to cause damage to cells in tissue culture. It is suggested that their activity is concerned with their ability to alter cell membranes. Indeed, many adjuvants (silica, endotoxin from Gram-negative bacterial species, vitamin A, saponin) are known to be able to disrupt lysosomes within amoeboid macrophages.

Gram-negative Bacteria

The earliest concepts of the existence of this adjuvant effect appear to have stemmed from observations in the field of *non-specific vaccine* therapy. There are many instances on record of striking therapeutic benefit following injections of TAB vaccine (a mixed suspension of killed *Salmonella typhi* and *paratyphi A & B*). The central phenomenon of immunological interest is that purified lipopolysaccharide preparations from a wide range of Gram-negative bacterial species (*Salm. typhi*, *Bordetella pertussis*, *Brucella melitensis* etc.) when injected intravenously together with protein antigens cause greatly enhanced subsequent formation of antibody. Endotoxin does not require to be injected at the same site as antigen. It is important, however, that for maximum effect endotoxin be given at the same time or within six hours after injection of the antigen. Linkage of the adjuvant effect to the toxic ability of the latter is indicated by the fact that when rabbits are rendered *tolerant* to endotoxin by repeated dosage, so that injection fails to be followed by the usual stress symptoms, the adjuvant effect was annulled at the same time.

The adjuvant effect of *Bordetella pertussis* micro-organisms has also been attributed to their content of endotoxin or phenol extractable lipopolysaccharide. More recently a protein has been obtained by a method which would not be expected to extract endotoxin. This has shown adjuvant activity as well as the ability to induce a greatly heightened sensitivity to histamine in injected mice. This histamine-sensitizing factor (HSF) differs from endotoxin by being heat-labile. *Bordetella pertussis* organisms have a selective ability to increase the formation by the rat of 'mast-cell sensitizing antibody' —a cytophilic immunoglobulin, which may possibly correspond to IgE in man in possessing a high ability to sensitize rat mast cells over a long time period and to give rise to passive cutaneous anaphylaxis (see p. 437).

Maturation of the Immunological Response: the Influence of Age

Young infants are relatively deficient in antibody-forming capacity and until recently the foetus *in utero* was regarded as totally deficient in all immunological activity. The human infant will normally start its life with a level of immunoglobulin in its blood which is almost completely derived from its mother and is approximately equal to the normal adult concentration. In animals with a type of placenta which does not permit the transfer of antibodies, the serum at birth may be almost totally devoid of immunoglobulin. Thus piglets which are removed by caesarian section and prevented from obtaining maternal colostrum have only 20–30 μg per ml of γ-globulin. This small amount of protein could be shown to be formed by the newborn piglet by injecting ^{35}S-labelled methionine which became incorporated into the γ-globulin; however, this protein has not been shown to have the character of antibody.

Although the newborn of man and other species respond poorly, if at all, to many immunizing procedures it is now clear that a mammalian foetus can respond to many types of immunogenic stimuli before birth. Presumably the inability to find plasma cells in a normal foetus merely reflects the protection afforded by the normal placenta against extraneous antigens. When this barrier is breached by the *Treponema pallidum* or *Toxoplasma gondii*, the human foetus responds by a precocious development of lymphoid tissues and impressive collections of plasma cells at the sites of infection. Toxoplasmic newborn infants may also show non-maternal macroglobulin antibodies in their cord blood. The appearance of the lesions of congenital syphilis only after the 5th or 6th month of gestation has led to the speculation that this may indicate the time of onset of immunological competence in man. The fact that younger foetuses can be infected with treponemes but do not develop the lesions of syphilis has been interpreted as evidence that, in the absence of immunological competence, the pathogenicity of the treponemes is not manifest. In the lamb the earliest antibody response which could be elicited was to bacteriophage by the 35-day foetus, i.e. just about the time that thymocytes first appear in the primitive thymus and before the appearance of functional lymph nodes and spleen. Experiments in the lamb suggest that ability to produce antibody to different antigens appears at markedly different stages of gestation. Antibodies to the protein ferritin were not formed until the 65th day of gestation and antibodies to ovalbumin were not formed until the 125th day. Competence to reject skin homografts developed only at about 80 days' gestation.

The initial antibody response by foetus, premature or full-term infant consists almost entirely of macroglobulin. The antibody first formed when human premature infants were injected with TAB vaccine was macroglobulin (19S) antibody to the flagellar H-agglutinogen, in contrast to older children and adults in whom the major production was 7S (IgG) immunoglobulin. When antigen in Freund-type adjuvant was injected into the foetal calf, large amounts of immunoglobulin were produced while antibody only just reached detectable levels.

The most important source of early antigenic stimulation in nature is usually the bacteria of the gut. In so-called germ-free animals which are deprived of living (but not dead) bacteria in their food and environment generally, the lymphoid tissue in relation to the gut is considerably less developed than in a normal animal. This deficiency affects the development of germinal centres in the lymphoid nodules of Peyer's patches and there is also a relative deficiency of plasma cells. Germ-free animals possess lower levels of γ-globulin in their serum than normal animals. In the 2–3 week old rabbit the production of γ-globulin, as shown by *in vitro* culture of isolated tissues, is confined almost entirely to the appendix. As will be discussed below, in the adult many other tissues are active in γ-globulin production (e.g. bone marrow, spleen and peripheral lymph nodes).

Nutrition

It would be logical to expect that antibody formation would be greatly impaired by starvation. However, studies made on prisoners of war or cachectic hospital patients do not suggest that this occurs, although the concentration of the serum albumin may be considerably depleted. Experimental studies in the rat have consistently reported that a deficiency of the B vitamin pyridoxine impairs antibody production. In the guinea-pig ascorbic acid deficiency was associated with decreased production of diphtheria antitoxin.

Endocrines

Antibody production can be influenced experimentally by hormone administration. The administration of cortisone from the onset of immunization undoubtedly decreases antibody formation to a low level in mice, rabbits and rats. The effect as shown in the rat varies with the dose of antigen used, with the amount of cortisone administered and especially with the time and duration of administration in relation to the antigen. To produce maximal effects on the primary response cortisone has to be injected at least 2 days before antigen injection and continued up to that day. When soluble corticosteroid preparations are injected over a single 4-hour period, the maximum depression of haemolysin production in the rat was observed when the drug was started 10 hours before injection of immunogen. Since recovery from such dosage is rapid the cortisone must produce its damage during a short period of the inductive phase, within a few hours of the injection of immunogen.

There is a general resemblance between the effects of cortisone and moderate doses of whole body X-radiation (see p. 565) if allowance is made for the much slower recovery after the latter treatment. Both types of immunological depression can be counteracted by injections of cells or cell fractions containing DNA or RNA breakdown products, even those derived from a different species. In the doses often used experimentally, e.g. 4 mg/100 gr., cortisone causes lymphopenia and pronounced depletion especially of small lymphocytes from the lymphoid tissue (including the thymus) of rabbits, rats and mice. A cytotoxic action of cortisone on rat lymphocytes has been demonstrated *in vitro*. Man, monkey and the guinea-pig are, however, relatively resistant and in man ordinary therapeutic doses have been found not to diminish the antibody response.

Nevertheless, cortisone in amounts of about 1 μg/ml is apparently essential for antibody formation of tissues maintained *in vitro*. Tissue culture medium will not support antibody formation in the absence of cortisone, so that serum from animals killed quietly in the morning before any excitement, supports antibody synthesis less than serum from animals which were stressed before they were bled.

Cortisone, dehydrocortisone, prednisone, prednisolone and pituitary adrenocorticotrophic hormone have been used extensively in man to depress immunological responses, especially those thought to be dependent on delayed-type hypersensitivity mechanisms and homograft rejection. Their undoubted effectiveness in many clinical situations in man cannot be attributed with certainty to any specific immunological effect. All similar corticosteroids possess marked general anti-inflammatory effects, owing perhaps to a vasoconstrictive action that leads to reduction in blood flow, decreased capillary permeability and lessened diapedesis.

Further consideration of the effects of corticosteroids is given in Chapter Two and on p. 543.

X-rays and Radiomimetic Drugs

The term radiomimetic is applied to drugs whose general biological effects are similar to those of X-radiation. In general they fall into the class of alkylating agents, which interfere with cell division by combining with DNA. The model for this group of drugs is nitrogen mustard. The suppressive effects of these substances on antibody production and other manifestations of the immune response are considered in Chapters Three and Fourteen.

REGULATION OF THE IMMUNOLOGICAL RESPONSE BY ANTIBODY

In Chapter Eight, in relation to the subject of myelomatosis, a feedback mechanism will be described for regulating the concentration of IgG in the circulation. This mechanism operates by increasing the catabolic rate of IgG when the serum concentration is abnormally increased. The mechanism appears to be selective for IgG so that increased serum IgG increases catabolism of IgG but not IgA or IgM. However, this mechanism cannot distinguish one *antibody* from another and since a specific antibody occupies usually only a tiny fraction of the total serum immunoglobulin, this particular mechanism must play only a minor role in the precise regulation of the immunological response.

However, many studies exist to indicate that the level of serum antibody can act to regulate the rate of antibody synthesis. The need for such a control mechanism seems apparent, at least for those antigens which are not readily metabolizable by the body and which could persist indefinitely as immunogenic stimuli. It has long been known that mixing antigen with excess antibody can prevent the antibody response. This might be expected to depend on a mechanism of steric hindrance—the antibody acting to cover the determinant groups of the immunogen molecule. However, it is apparent that not all antigenic sites in the molecule need to be bound by antibody for suppression to occur. Thus, a threshold for this effect is difficult to demonstrate and diphtheria toxoid–antitoxin floccules with an average molecular composition of $Ag\text{-}Ab_3$ are apparently as effective in preventing antitoxin formation as complexes with average molecular composition $Ag\text{-}Ab_5$ (a single molecule of diphtheria toxoid has a minimum of 6–8 sites for combination with antitoxin).

It seems to be a general rule that antibody formation to strong immunogens is less easily suppressed than to weak ones. In man the formation of antibody to the weak Rhesus immunogen on erythrocytes can be very effectively suppressed by an injection of antibody (see Chapter Eight). Sensitization of a Rhesus negative mother involves the leakage of Rhesus positive erythrocytes across the placental barrier. Such leakage occurs in small amounts throughout pregnancy, although a much greater quantity of immunogen is normally released in the third stage of labour. Immunization against the Rhesus (D) antigen can be prevented by anti-D serum administered in the immediate postpartum period.

In some studies the suppression induced by antibody has been remarkably specific. Thus, the passive immunization of mice of a certain pure strain with antibody against certain antigenic determinants of mouse cells from a different pure strain resulted in suppression of antibody only against those antigens against which antibodies were present in the anti-serum. A normal immune response was observed against other antigenic determinants present on the same incompatible cells. Also, in the case of a hapten-carrier conjugate, suppression of antihapten antibody formation only occurs when antibody to the hapten is used and does not occur with antibody to the carrier. However, an important example exists of an equally striking *non-specific* suppression of the immunogenicity of red cells in man. Thus it is well established that Rh negative mothers with Rh incompatible pregnancies become immunized against the foetus more often if mother and child are ABO compatible than if they are incompatible. Experiments in humans have demonstrated that passive transfer of antibodies against A or B blood groups to Rh-negative recipients of Rh-positive cells containing the corresponding A or B group suppressed antibody synthesis against the Rh antigens. In this case it is possible that there is a different mechanism: the antibody-coated erythrocytes may be selectively and rapidly removed by the Kupffer cells of the liver, where they are soon broken down and so unable to stimulate antibody formation against any of their component antigens.

Suppression of a secondary response by antibody is more difficult to achieve than suppression of primary antibody formation. This difference is probably related to the fact that smaller doses of immunogen are sufficient to stimulate antibody formation in primed than in uninjected animals, and is also to be expected from the progressive increase that occurs in the average binding affinity for antibody with time after immunization. Thus the population of cells primed for the secondary response would be equipped with receptors which are more avid for antigen and more difficult to inhibit by antibody.

The ability of a given population of antibody molecules to suppress the immune response would be expected to depend upon the binding affinities of the antibodies used. It has been clearly shown with hapten-protein conjugated immunogens that the ability of an antiserum to the hapten (DNP-lysine) to suppress is related to its avidity, high-affinity antibody being capable of causing suppression at far lower concentrations than low-affinity antibody. Another important factor is the dose of antibody used. Antibody may act as an adjuvant and lead to the formation of excess serum antibody (see p. 252). Thus it has been found that very low concentrations of high-affinity antibody, but not low-affinity antibody, increased the expected antibody response in rabbits. The determination of which effect of antibody will predominate probably depends on many factors but if large amounts of antibody with high binding affinities are used, suppression will normally occur.

THE SITES OF ANTIBODY PRODUCTION IN ADULT ANIMALS

It might be argued that, since all cells grow, they all have the chemical apparatus for synthesis of protein. Therefore, why should not all cells have the ability to make antibody? However, there is good evidence that antibody production is the concern of specialized lymphoid tissues (other than the thymus in mammals) such as the spleen, lymph nodes and bone marrow. Thus in the rare human disease, the Swiss type of hypogammaglobulinaemia (Chapter Eight) in which a failure of development of the thymus is associated with defective development of all the lymphoid organs of the body, all immunological responses, including antibody production, graft rejection and delayed-type hypersensitivity, are lacking. Similarly, more or less selective damage to the lymphoid tissues by X-rays, nitrogen mustard, anti-lymphocyte sera and cortisone result in diminished immunological responses of all the above categories.

Broadly the situation seems to be that if antigen is injected repeatedly intravenously antibody is produced mainly in the spleen, lung and bone marrow. When antigens are distributed by lymphatics from a local focus of infection or following injection of antigen, antibody is made predominantly in the group of regional draining lymph nodes. Under certain circumstances, and especially when the antigen is mixed with the so-called adjuvants, subcutaneous injection is followed by local granuloma formation and often antibody formation takes place locally in such granulomata.

Of the various lymphoid tissues, the thymus and bursa of Fabricius in the bird stand in a unique position, in so far as neither is active in the production of antibody or cells immediately concerned in delayed hypersensitivity, but either provide the cells necessary for seeding other lymphoid tissues or control by the production of hormones the development of the latter. Some authors have therefore envisaged the existence of two levels of organization of the lymphoid tissues of the body: *central* exemplified by bursa and thymus and *peripheral* exemplified by spleen and lymph nodes. The bone marrow is difficult to allocate since it possesses some of the attributes both of a central and a peripheral lymphoid organ.

Antibody Formation by the Spleen

In extraction studies in which the whole organ is ground up and an aliquot portion analysed for antibody content, it has been repeatedly shown that at certain times after an intravenous injection of various antigens, there are higher levels of antibody extractable from the spleen than are present at the same time in the serum. This was not the case after subcutaneous injections, when the antibody was higher in the serum, and, in this case, apparently was formed mainly elsewhere.

Further evidence for the spleen as a site of antibody production comes from studies of the effects of splenectomy. The splenectomized rat is found to make little or no antibody when small amounts of particulate antigens are injected into the bloodstream. If antigen is injected intraperitoneally or intradermally the splenectomized rat equals the intact animal. In humans also the production of haemolysins and haemagglutinins following the injection of small doses of foreign red cells intravenously was far less in splenectomized patients than in controls.

These results would appear to stress the role of the spleen in forming antibody to antigens which are particulate and distributed *via* the bloodstream. Therefore, in human haemolytic disease, when antibodies occur against antigenic components of erythrocytes it would be logical to expect that the spleen plays a foremost role in their production.

Antibody Formation within Lymph Nodes

The major evidence for lymph nodes as producers of antibody was derived from the classic approach of McMaster & Hudack. They controlled the possibility that the antibody which was extractable from lymph nodes was the result of seepage into an inflamed node of antibody which had been formed elsewhere, by injecting two different antigens of killed bacilli, one into each ear of a mouse. The injections would, of course, cause the regional nodes of both sides to become more permeable than normal, but the antibodies of the two kinds would have an equal chance to concentrate in the inflamed area. In point of fact it was found that agglutinins to the antigen injected in the right ear appeared earlier and in high concentration in the lymph nodes draining that ear, but not in the lymph nodes draining the other ear. Conversely, in the cervical nodes of the left side antibodies appeared first to the antigen injected in the left ear, and not to that injected on the right side.

Further evidence for the fact that the main production of antibody occurs in the grouping of lymph nodes in the region draining the lymph from the site of injection will be considered later, when the contribution made by the local granuloma and the individual cells involved is considered. But it should be stressed that the method and route of administration of antigens determines which tissues predominate in antibody production. Thus the adjuvant administered with the immunogen plays a major role in determining the pattern of tissues involved in the response (see section later in this chapter on antibody production under the influence of adjuvants).

Local Production of Antibody

The foregoing discussion concerning the spleen and lymph nodes has stressed that the preliminary fixation of the antigen is an important factor in determining whether a tissue manufactures antibody. It is possible to summarize the vast amount of work which has investigated the possibility of local production of antibody by the general statement that, providing methods are used which secure the local fixation of the antigen, almost any tissue is found capable of accumulating antibody-producing cells.

The problem can be approached by the same technique which was used to show antibody production in lymph nodes, i.e. by extraction of the local tissue, and finding that the antibody titre of the extract is greater than in the plasma. The same objection occurs, as with the lymph node studies, that antibody has merely become concentrated rather than synthetized in the local tissues, but the same device of injecting two antigens, one at the site of study and one elsewhere, can control this concentration effect.

A second approach was to transplant tissues from immunized animals to non-immunized recipients and to show that antibody appeared in the recipient at about the time that it would have appeared in the donor. Fatty tissue, after local injection of alum-precipitated diphtheria toxoid, was transplanted into the omentum of rabbits, with results as shown in Fig. 7.5. It will be noted that whereas the 10-day transplant produced antibody from the beginning, the 3-day transplant required a day or two to get going—behaving as it would have done in the donor. It may be objected that the antigen persisting in the tissue transplanted could induce the recipient to form antibody anyhow. But such primary formation would not start until a much longer time had elapsed following the transfer. It should be realized that the antibody in this case is apparently not formed by the fat cells but by the cells of the granulomata which develop about the alum-precipitated toxoid antigens. An important aspect of the local production of antibody is whether this is possible within the organs which house antigen-containing fluids such as the bladder, uterus and mammary glands.

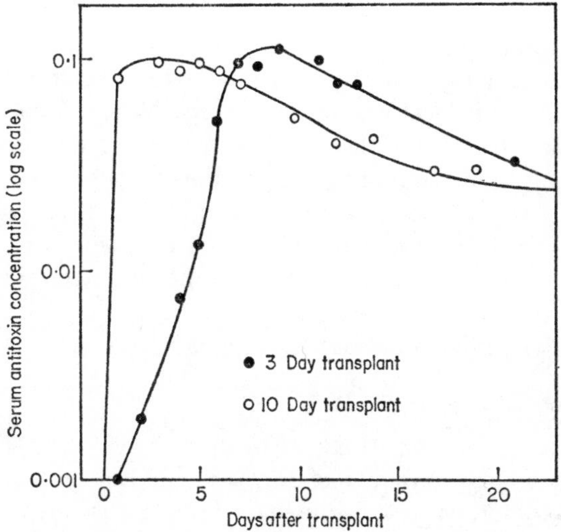

FIG. 7.5. Local production of antibody by a fat transplant. Serum antitoxin rises in two rabbits, which received a 3-day and a 10-day transplant into the omentum. Each donor was injected primarily with 60 Lf diphtheria A.P.T. Twenty-eight days afterwards a secondary injection of 12 Lf diphtheria was made into the interscapular fat. [From Oakley C.L., Warrack G.H. and Batty I. (1954) *J. Path. Bact.* **67,** 485.]

After the introduction of *Trichomonas* and *Brucella abortus* into the uterus and vagina, it is possible to extract antibody from the walls of these organs. There is also evidence that, when *Br. abortus* is introduced into the 'milk cistern' of one quarter of a cow's udder, agglutinins to this antigen appear in the milk from that quarter well in advance of agglutinins from other quarters, suggesting very strongly that antibody can be formed in a local sector of the udder. The problem of such local antibody production has recently assumed new interest and complexity from the demonstration that γA globulin is the predominant immunoglobulin type in human parotid saliva, colostrum, nasal and lacrymal secretions. The γG/γA ratio in this group of fluids is less than one, whereas in normal human serum this ratio is approximately six. Moreover, γA of colostrum and saliva differs from serum γA since; first, it is more highly polymerized and consists principally of a component with a sedimentation coefficient of 11S; secondly, it is not disrupted by disulphide bond reduction in the absence of urea; and thirdly, saliva and colostrum γA has an additional antigenic determinant. *In vitro* culture has revealed that both salivary and mammary tissue can incorporate ^{14}C-labelled amino acids into newly synthesized γA *in vitro*, although this approach is unable to indicate what fraction of the total γA is locally produced *in vivo*. When immunization is systemic it seems likely that most of the production derives from circulating plasma immunoglobulin, but an additional 'transport piece' of the γA molecule must be added during the selective transport of this polymeric form of γA by the glandular epithelium. However, recent evidence obtained from volunteers given living influenza virus intranasally indicates that after such local challenge much of the antibody in nasal secretions is in fact made locally.

Antibody Production in the Liver

Several of the plasma proteins are formed in the liver, which would appear to be the only site of formation of the plasma albumin, various β-globulins and fibrinogen. Thus an isolated rat's liver, when perfused with ^{14}C-lysine, vigorously incorporated this radioactive amino acid into these three fractions of the plasma proteins, but showed little or no incorporation into γ-globulin. Contrariwise, the perfusion of the eviscerated carcase of the rat produced plasma proteins with the mobilities of γ-globulins only. Since antibodies are usually associated with the γ-globulin fraction of serum, this evidence argued strongly against the role of the liver in antibody production.

Another way to study the proportional activity of the different tissues in the synthesis of antibody is to measure the incorporation of radioactive amino acids into the antibody formed by various tissues taken from antigen-injected animals and maintained in tissue culture. The technique consists in the incubation of tissue slices in a nutrient medium over a period of 4–5 hr, in the presence of ^{14}C-labelled amino acids. At the end of the incubation period the antibody produced is isolated by specific precipitation and estimated quantitatively by its count of emitted radiation. Although such a method does not, without numerous assumptions, give a true estimate of the absolute rate of synthesis, the technique is valid for comparing one tissue with another and one method of immunization with another. By allowing for the total weight of the tissue in the animal, the relative contributions of the different tissues can be easily calculated.

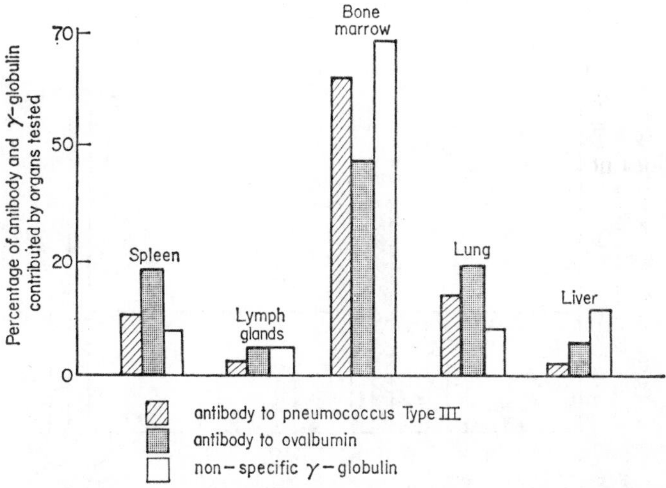

FIG. 7.6. Percentages of antibody and of non-specific γ-globulin contributed by different tissues to overall synthesis in a rabbit hyperimmunized by intravenous injections of alum-precipitated ovalbumin and pneumococcus type III capsular polysaccharide. [Askonas B.A. and Humphrey J.H. (1958) *Biochem. J.* **68,** 252.]

The results of this method are shown in Fig. 7.6 for the different organs of a rabbit hyper-immunized with intravenous injections of killed pneumococcus type III and alum-precipitated ovalbumin. It will be seen that these results confirm the above evidence of a relatively insignificant production of antibody by the liver. Moreover, this method of administration of antigen (by intravenous injection of a particulate antigen) would be expected to favour the role of the liver, since under these circumstances the phagocytes of the sinuses trap a very high proportion of the antigenic material. As is seen in Figs. 7.6 and 7.7, when the antigen is injected intramuscularly into a rabbit or subcutaneously into a guinea-pig, the liver plays an even smaller role.

As will be seen later, antibody production within the liver can usually be correlated with the presence of invading cells forming scattered periportal granulomata. The true hepatic parenchymal cell does not seem capable of forming antibody.

Antibody Formation in the Bone Marrow

The scattered nature of the bone marrow has resulted in this tissue receiving less attention from the ablation and isolation techniques

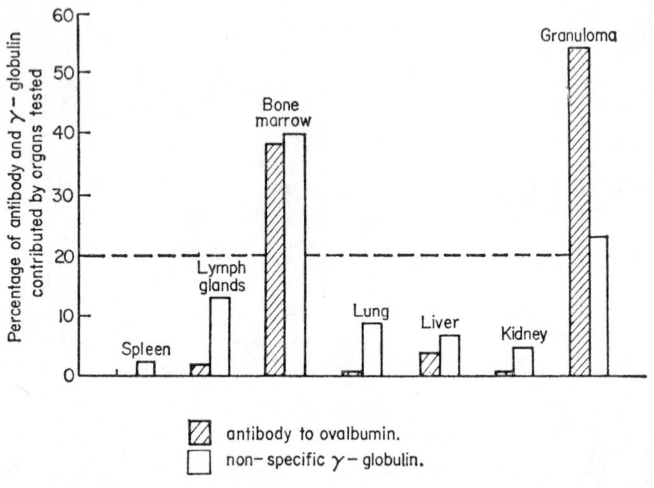

FIG. 7.7. Percentages of antibody and of non-specific γ-globulin contributed by different tissues to overall synthesis in a rabbit, immunized by intramuscular injection of ovalbumin in Freund's adjuvant. [Askonas B.A. and Humphrey J.H. (1958) *Biochem. J.* **68,** 252.]

of the experimental pathologist. In the experiments quoted in the previous section, the significant contribution of the eviscerated carcase of the rat to the synthesis of γ-globulin was interpreted as depending upon the activity of the bone marrow chiefly.

In the tissue culture experiments, as illustrated in Figs. 7.6, 7.7 and 7.8, the bone marrow, by all three methods of antigen administration, made a major contribution to the overall calculated antibody synthesis. The activity per unit mass of this tissue was never strikingly high, but the total bulk of the bone marrow so far outweighs that of the other lympho-reticular tissues that its importance for antibody production ranks relatively high. The immunoglobulins made by the bone marrow of the guinea-pig in these experiments were $7S\gamma_1$ and γ_2 anti-ovalbumin. In other experiments,

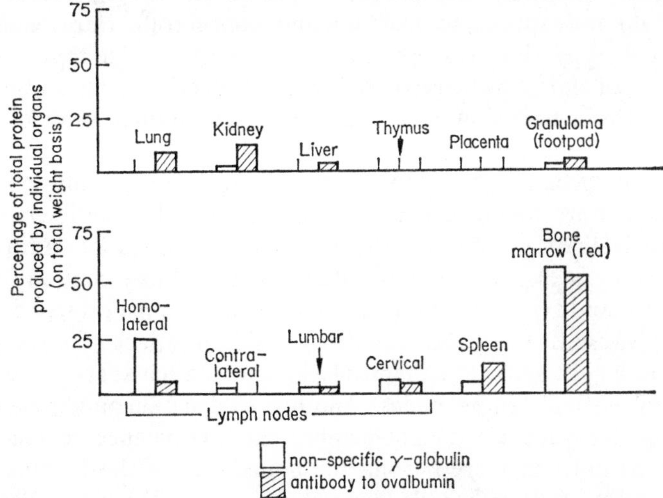

FIG. 7.8. Percentages of antibody and non-specific γ-globulin contributed by different tissues to the overall synthesis in a guinea-pig immunized by injection into the footpad of an oily emulsion of ovalbumin in Freund-type adjuvant mixture. [Askonas B.A. and White R.G. (1956) *Brit. J. exp. Path.* **37,** 61.]

using a suspension of bacteriophage X174 as immunogen, bone marrow taken at 8–10 days after injection appeared to produce a very high proportion of the 19S (IgM) immunoglobulin antibody as calculated from the relative activity of the isolated tissues in culture. In this case the biosynthetic activity for IgM antibody per unit mass of tissue attained higher levels in bone marrow than in lymph nodes or other tissues tested.

Antibody Formation in the Thymus

Most workers seem agreed that little antibody is made in the thymus (see Fig. 7.8), although by sensitive methods, such as radioimmunoelectrophoretic analysis of cultured glands, some synthesis of immunoglobulin can be detected. But even when particulate or other antigens are repeatedly injected in a vein, extraction of the thymus fails to reveal any more antibody than similar extractions of muscle, and there is no production of plasma cells or germinal centres. Such a behaviour could result if antigen failed to reach the thymic cells or if there was a lack of a proper receptor system for antigens. Although macrophages are present in histological sections, they do not appear to take up and concentrate intravenously-injected trypan blue (except after X-ray damage). The thymic cells have been shown to be separated from connective tissue and blood vessels by a basement membrane and a continuous layer of epithelial-reticular cells. However, this epithelial layer does not offer an absolute barrier to soluble antigens, since ferritin and labelled albumin were found to pass into the gland. When antigens were injected directly into the thymus large numbers of antibody-containing cells (as demonstrated by the fluorescent-antibody method) and typical lymphoid nodules with germinal centres can be seen to result. The explanation may reside in a lack of a receptor system for antigens. The thymus lacks sinuses such as are present in the spleen and lymph nodes. Another explanation might be that thymic lymphocytes do not acquire the competence to react to antigens until they are beyond the boundaries of the thymus and have interacted with cells derived from bone marrow. Several claims to have demonstrated the competence of transplanted populations of such cells in antibody production and graft-*versus*-host reactions have been made. Some experiments have, however, shown a relatively low activity when equal numbers of the thymic cells are compared with equal numbers of spleen or lymph node cells. Small lymph nodes are often embedded in the thymus surface and provide an experimental hazard in such experiments, so that it has been claimed that the low levels of activity shown by the transplanted cells are actually due to contaminant cells.

Antibody Production in the Central Nervous System

Somewhat similar considerations apply in the case of the central nervous system, which also shows no uptake of intravenously injected vital dyes or carbon particles, due presumably to the existence of a hypothetical 'blood-brain' barrier. In point of fact, potential antigenic components appear to exist within the normal brain which when injected into the extra-neural parts of the body give rise to antibody production. This argues that the brain must lack the power of responding under normal conditions to antigens within its substance. This may be associated with the lack of a system of lymphatics in the brain draining into lymph nodes. However, when once an immune response is established to the antigens of the brain by repeated injection into the animal of brain tissue, this immune response can react upon the antigens already present in the brain and cause damage (disseminate allergic encephalomyelitis).

Homografts are often well tolerated when grafted into the normal brain, presumably since no immune response is forthcoming. However, animals who have made a successful response resulting in the rejection of a graft from a given donor which was in this case implanted on the skin of the animal, can also react against skin grafts from the same source which are implanted into its brain.

One might argue from this that if the mechanism for the immune response were set up by antigen absorption outside the central nervous system the presence of antigen within the system could then cause an immune response and possibly antibody production.

Certainly, in neurosyphilis the Wassermann reaction is occasionally positive in the cerebrospinal fluid and negative in the bloodstream. Monkeys injected intracerebrally with poliomyelitis virus demonstrated the highest antibody titres in the body within the anterior horns of the spinal cord and little or no antibody in the blood. In such inflammatory conditions the cells which are associated with antibody formation elsewhere in the body—macrophages, lymphocytes and plasma cells, may accumulate in the lesions of the nervous tissue and would provide the most probable cellular site of the formation of such antibody.

ANATOMY OF THE LYMPHO-RETICULAR TISSUES

LYMPH NODES

These flattened ovoid or kidney-shaped structures, varying in size from a few millimetres to more than a centimetre across, are present along the path of collecting lymphatics. Through them the lymph flows on its way to the main lymphatic trunks of the neck and their union with the veins. The point of exit for efferent lymphatics and veins and point of entry for arteries is shown as a small indentation called the hilum. Lymph nodes attain their highest organization in mammals. Birds have no well developed lymph nodes but merely loosely organized foci of lymphoid tissue at intervals along the side of the lymph vessels.

The subsequent description will limit itself to an outline of the structural components of a lymph node of *man*. It should be realized that besides a variation between species, the lymph nodes of different areas of the same animal vary greatly even in the normal. Germ-free animals have small underdeveloped nodes but 'normal' animals are continuously exposed to a wide variety of antigenic stimuli and thus show a wide degree of morphological variation. In the rat nine distinct histological patterns have been described for nodes removed from different sites of healthy animals.

The afferent lymphatics of a mammalian node, which are several in number, enter the *capsule* of a node at points scattered over its convex surface (Plate 7.1, following p. 276). Lymphatic vessels leave the node at the hilum. From the inner surface of the capsule a number of *trabeculae* project into the node and divide the contents irregularly into compartments.

The lymphoid tissue of a lymph node is occupied by a delicate meshwork of fibrils within which lie the principal cells of the node; the lymphocytes. This mesh or *reticulum* consists of fibrils over the surface of which are extended the *reticular cells*. The cytoplasm of the latter ensheathes the fibres of the extracellular reticulum and extends as delicate branching processes to join apparently with similar processes of other cells. The ordinary haematoxylin and eosin section mainly reveals the nuclei of such reticular cells.

The collection of cells forming the lymphoid tissue proper is separated from the capsule by the marginal lymph sinus. While it is common for sections of nodes to show circular areas of lymphoid tissue between two radially arranged sinuses this appearance is fortuitous and misleading in suggesting that this 'primary nodule' or 'follicle' is a sphere which is walled off by sinuses. The mass of lymphoid tissue within a node is continuous, being pierced but not interrupted by the lymph sinuses.

Lymphocytes are the most conspicuous of the free cells lying within the reticulum in a lymph node. Within the uniform mass of cells the lymphocytes are often grouped into large *nodules*, especially in the outer layer or *cortex* which occupies the whole surface of the organ with the exception of the hilum. By a curious tradition these nodules are referred to as 'follicles' (i.e. small sacs) although they are indeed solid spheres of cells. Ehrich referred to them as 'primary nodules' (1946). In the central region of the node and in the vicinity of the hilum the mass of lymphocytes is divided into anastomizing cords of cells (the *medulla* or *medullary* cords), separated by lymph sinuses.

The organization of the lymphocytes within the medullary cords and cortical follicles is related to the arrangement of blood vessels. Arteries enter the node at the hilum and the branching arterioles running outward from the hilum in the trabeculae reach the follicles of the cortex and break up into a rich capillary plexus (left half of Plate 7.1). These now group into venules which run into larger veins in the trabeculae. In the cortex each primary nodule is traversed by an arteriolar branch whose capillary branches supply the nodule. The periphery of the nodule is characterized by a condensation of the reticulin network which extends throughout the remainder of the gland. The nodule itself is almost devoid of reticulin fibrils.

The cortical reticulum is arranged as a rather open meshwork of fibres which enclose spaces of average diameter 20 μ. The reticulum of the medulla is characterized by much smaller, slit-like spaces with an average diameter of 6·8 μ. This clear-cut difference between cortical and medullary organization as disclosed by silver staining probably indicates that cell-exchange and mobility is greater in the former than the latter.

The lymphoid nodules of the cortex may become the site in stained sections of pale-staining, circular or oval areas. These are the *lymphocytopoietic* or *germinal centres*, which include cells which are generally larger, with more basophilic or pyroninophilic cytoplasm, and with nuclei which are larger and paler (leptochromatic) than the surrounding small lymphocytes of the cortex. Some of the included cells show prominent nucleoli and some are in mitosis. These appearances of this specialized part of the primary nodules led Flemming (1885) to regard these as foci of intensive division by large lymphocytes (haemocytoblasts) to produce medium and small lymphocytes, and to justify the name: germinal centre. In addition to the proliferating lymphocytes such centres often contain scattered macrophages with abundant cytoplasm enclosing DNA-rich irregular bodies often referred to as Flemming's tingible bodies. Another cell which is scattered throughout the germinal centres and only becomes revealed clearly by special staining procedures is the dendritic macrophage (Chapter Three). Some authors use the term 'secondary nodule' for those primary nodules which contain germinal centres.

Germinal centres are absent at birth from the nodes of a healthy human foetus, but soon make their appearance after birth and increase in size and frequency during childhood. They are maximal in size and number at about the time of puberty and thereafter decline. Superficial nodes such as the inguinal always tend to have smaller germinal centres than the deep nodes such as those along the vessels of the neck. They are particularly large in the nodes which drain the gut. They can vary in size up to 1 mm in diameter. All but the smallest centres indicate their recent, sudden growth by producing a compressed periphery of reticular fibres and a surrounding ring of aligned closely packed small lymphocytes. Internal to the nodular cortex, with its germinal centres in varying grades of maturity, are the 'tertiary nodules' which form vaguely demarcated masses abutting at their internal limits on the region of the medullary cords. These, unlike the 'primary nodules', are penetrated by reticulin fibrils. They are not the site of germinal centres, and they are not traversed by arterioles but have a blood supply from veins, the endothelium of which is of a characteristic raised cuboidal type (venules of Schulze). In the rat, corresponding *post-capillary venules* have been described which transmit small lymphocytes across their walls into the cortical lymphoid tissue. The wall is often seen to be infiltrated with small lymphocytes which are in the subendothelial connective tissue and *within* the endothelial cells. This fact argues a specific mechanism for transporting the small lymphocytes from blood to the lymphoid tissue of the tertiary nodules. While in inflammatory states granulocytes and monocytes can cross the same vessel wall, these cells always pass between and not through endothelial cells.

The lymphatic tissue based on the tertiary nodules may be so developed that it stretches as a continuous broad intermediary zone between the outer cortex and the region of the medullary cords. It is sometimes referred to as the 'intermediate' or 'para-cortical' zone. This is the zone of lymphatic tissue which becomes selectively depleted of small lymphocytes after thymectomy (thymus dependent area) and after experimental prolonged drainage of the thoracic duct. Within this zone occur the cellular changes which accompany the induction of a state of delayed hypersensitivity as in a node draining an allograft or skin treated with a contact sensitizing agent (see Chapter Twelve).

The afferent lymphatics penetrate the convex surface of the capsule at several points and open into the subcapsular lymph sinus immediately beneath it. This sinus continues around the periphery of the gland to open into efferent lymphatics at the hilum and it is possible that in a normal gland the major part of the lymph flow takes place through the subcapsular sinus (see Plate 2.4, following p. 150). Normal lymph nodes are relatively inefficient filters; bacteria and other particles injected into normal animals may pass through them rapidly to reach the bloodstream. However, in states of local inflammation cells carried by the lymph through any node tend to aggregate in the hilar sinuses before the outlet 'simulating a log jam at the narrow outlet of a mill pond' (W.B. Wood) and this cellular mass greatly enhances the normal filtration power of the node.

Spleen

The spleen is a lymphoid organ which reacts vigorously to blood-borne antigen, especially when this is of particulate nature. However, it also includes many functions other than providing the site for differentiation of immunologically competent cells. It includes specialized vascular spaces (*sinuses*) and specialized vascular structures (ellipsoids) which serve to clear the blood of foreign particles and damaged or effete blood cells. At certain stages of embryogenesis, it provides a site for the transformation of haemopoietic stem cells into erythrocytes, myelocytes and thrombocytes. In adult man this function (of extra-medullary myelopoiesis) may be revived in certain pathological conditions.

In this cursory survey of its anatomical organization the distribution of the lymphoid elements will be traced by following the blood vessels. The human spleen is enclosed by a capsule of dense connective tissue several millimetres thick. From the internal capsular surface a network of trabeculae subdivides the organ into communicating compartments. The branches of the splenic artery enter the hilum and pass along the trabeculae, with which they branch, becoming smaller in diameter. When an artery has decreased to about 200 μ diameter it leaves the trabecula and becomes surrounded by a cylindrical sheath of lymphatic tissue or white pulp. It is now termed the *central arteriole of the white pulp.* In its course through the white pulp this arteriole gives off numerous capillaries which supply the lymphatic tissue of the sheath. The central arteriole itself branches, and as it approaches the limit of the white pulp it branches into several small straight vessels called *penicillary arterioles.* Each of these is provided with a characteristic spindle-shaped thickening of its wall, the *Schweigger-Seidel sheath* or *ellipsoid.* Strictly speaking the vessel here is a capillary since the sheath consists of an endothelium of tall cells surrounded immediately by a layer of large pale cells, a basement membrane and a further layer of pale cells. The capillary may divide within the sheath. The ellipsoids vary in prominence in different species. They are particularly developed in dogs, cats, birds and the domestic pig. They are not apparent in the rabbit and the rat. Man has relatively small ellipsoids and not every penicillary vessel bears one.

After leaving the ellipsoid the route of the blood is subject to dispute and probably alternative routes exist. The ellipsoids are usually at the edge of the white pulp, surrounded, in some species, by a thin prolongation of the white pulp, in what is termed the marginal zone. After this the blood is involved in the *red pulp.*

The red pulp is made up of two entities: the *splenic sinuses* and the *splenic cords.* The splenic sinuses are long vascular channels of variable diameter since they can be collapsed or open. The lining cells are elongated spindle-shaped cells lying with their long axis parallel to the sinus. They are bounded by a network of reticular fibres forming a very loose basement membrane, the fibres of which pursue a generally circular course—so that they correspond to the hoops which in a barrel bind the staves (or sinus-lining cells) together. The sinus-lining cells in cross-sections of the spleen present a cuboidal shape. They lie against one another's lateral surfaces but are without desmosomes or other attachments. Indeed, they may easily be separated from one another and blood cells are often found traversing the gap. The splenic cords constitute the bands of tissue lying between sinuses. They are continuous tissue honeycombed by sinuses. They are traversed by a network of reticulin fibres and accompanying stellate reticulum cells (Plate 2.5, following p. 150). The spaces between these represent a vascular space into which arterioles leaving the white pulp and marginal zone enter. Circulating cells may be held in the cords: erythrocytes, lymphocytes and granulocytes, etc.

As stated above, the route of circulation of blood through the spleen is controversial. Several pathways may be necessary in order to account for the fact that red cells labelled with carboxy-haemoglobin or ^{51}Cr traverse the spleen at widely different rates. Some of the alternatives are as follows. The vessels emerging from the ellipsoids enter sinuses. From the sinuses the blood is conveyed by venules to veins in the trabeculae (so-called closed circulation). Sphincteric action at the distal end of the sinus could slow the flow, resulting in sludged erythrocytes, the plasma escaping into the pulp. Alternatively the vessels from the white pulp may open directly into the spaces of the red pulp (so-called open circulation). Yet again, lateral channels have been postulated to exist in the ellipsoidal wall whereby blood cells could directly enter the pulp.

The white pulp is divisible into *periarterial lymphatic sheaths* and *lymphatic nodules.* On a fresh section of the spleen the white pulp shows up as circular or elongated grey areas (0·5 mm diameter) against the red pulp. These areas are often called Malpighian bodies, which can refer either to transected lymphatic sheaths or nodules. The nodules may be either solid spheres of small lymphocytes within the lymphatic sheath, often at bifurcations of the central arteriole, or similar nodules including germinal centres. The latter resemble the corresponding structure in the lymph nodes. The peripheral zone of small lymphocytes which surrounds the centre and constitutes the remainder of the nodule is sometimes called the *mantle zone.* Immediately beyond there exists, particularly in hyper-immunized animals such as the rabbit, a compact rim of the red pulp which is relatively free of sinuses and includes many reticular cells, haemocytoblasts and plasma cells. This is the so-called *peri-follicular envelope.*

The Thymus

The thymus is a large lymphoid organ which in most mammals is located in the upper anterior mediastinum of the chest. In some species (the chicken and guinea-pig) it is in the neck. Embryologically the thymus arises from *epithelial* outgrowth of the third and fourth branchial pouches, around which *mesodermal* elements aggregate. Earlier *in vitro* experiments have strongly suggested that during ontogeny the epithelial cells differentiate, under the inductive influence of the mesenchymal cells and proliferate to form the precursors of the lymphoid cells. Recent experiments in the chick using chromosome markers suggest that it may not be the epithelial cells themselves which produce thymocytes but rather that they furnish an inductive environment for the differentiation of blood-borne stem cells. In its post-natal existence at least the thymus accepts into its structure new blood-borne cells, mainly from the bone marrow.

In man, the thymus varies greatly in size and weight at different ages. During foetal life it forms a much higher percentage of the body weight than at any time afterwards. The thymus becomes predominantly lymphoid late in foetal life and preserves this histological form throughout childhood. Thereafter the lymphoid component gradually decreases, a process which proceeds gradually and continuously throughout life under normal conditions (age involution). During the course of neoplastic or infectious diseases the normal slow involution may be suddenly and greatly accelerated.

The histological unit of the thymus is the *lobule* and it is a striking feature of the organ in a variety of animal species that, although the absolute size may vary widely, the size of the thymic lobules remains remarkably similar. Each lobe therefore is made up of a number of angular lobules 1–2 mm across. The lobules appear in a section totally separate from one another. This is misleading since all are joined together in the centre of the organ. In reality the thymus is like a branching coral in which the long finger-like processes of the medulla are covered with a rather uniform, thick layer of cortex, while the processes are bound together by the connective tissue of the capsule and septa.

The thymic lobule may be visualized as a sponge of reticular *epithelial* cells, in the interstices between which are embedded aggregates of tightly packed lymphoid cells. The epithelial meshwork is densest in the central region or *medulla* of the lobules, which has an almost non-lymphoid appearance. In places in the medulla the epithelial cells are aggregated into whorled patterns (the Hassall's corpuscles). A central lumen has also been described for the corpuscles, which sometimes also yield a striking immunofluorescent reaction for immunoglobulin (IgG). This suggests that they may be derived from the occlusion of capillary segments with resulting inspissation of their contents. Another hypothesis is that they represent persisting thymo-pharyngeal ducts. The epithelial cells are united by desmosome bridges, and they contain granules of sulphated mucopolysaccharide. They are not phagocytic. Myocytes

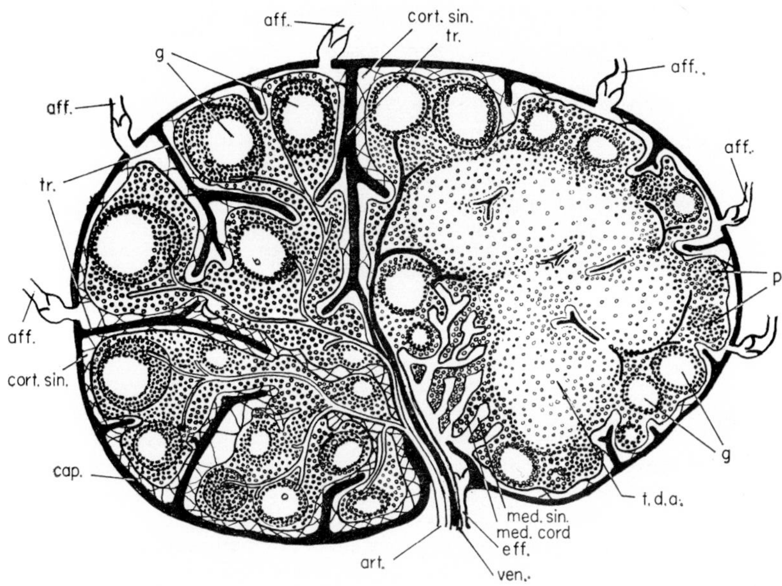

PLATE 7.1. Diagrammatic representation of a typical lymph node of an adult man. On the left side of the diagram the arteries are shown as they enter the hilum, travel in the trabeculae, branch and leave to enter the dense lymphoid tissue of the cortex. On the right side of the diagram is the system of veins. Also, on the right side the section passes through cortex, showing lymphoid nodules with germinal centres, thymus dependent area (t.d.a.) and medulla.

p. 'primary' lymphoid nodules of cortex.
g. germinal centres within "secondary' lymphoid nodules of cortex.
t.d.a. complex of 'tertiary' nodules (the *thymus dependent* or *paracortical* zone).
cap. capsule
tr. trabeculae
cort. sin. cortical sinus
med. cord. medullary cord.
med. sin. medullary sinus
aff. afferent lymphatic
eff. efferent lymphatic
art. artery
ven. vein.

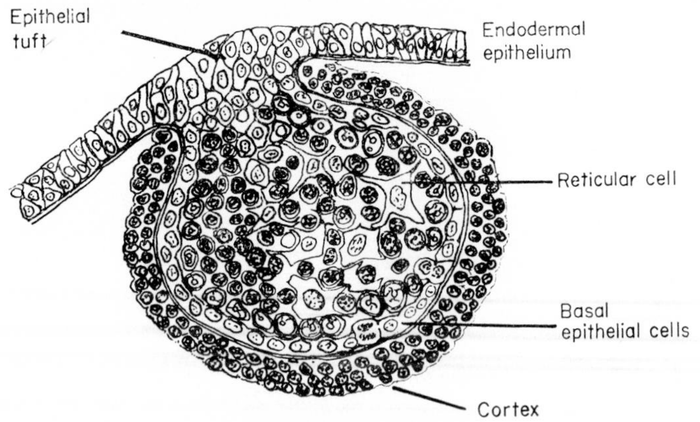

PLATE 7.2. Diagram of the structure of a lymphocytopoietic 'follicle' in the Bursa of Fabricius of a chicken. *Note.* Cortex composed of several layers of packed small lymphocytes; basement membrane continuous with the basement membrane of the endodermal epithelium; basal layer of epithelial cells continuous apparently with the cells of the endodermal epithelium; and the central zone of larger, often basophilic cells with scattered reticular cells. This structure deserves the name 'follilce' since it appears to be a hollow sphere or cup into which cells are budded from the basal epithelial cells.

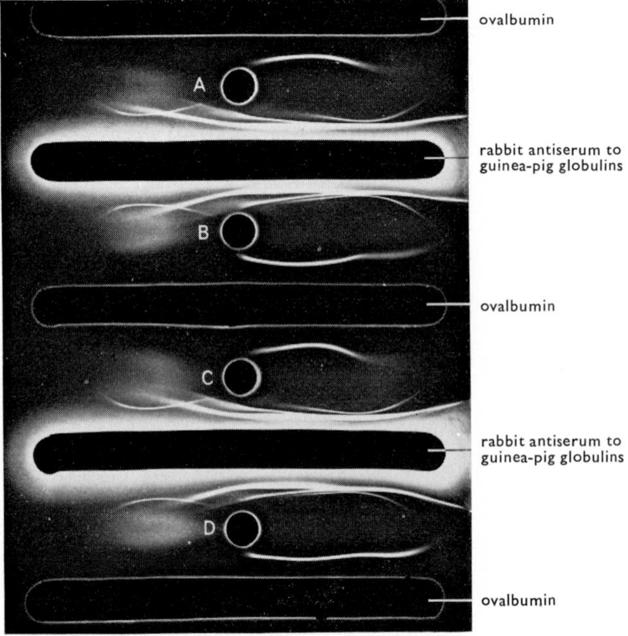

PLATE 7.3. (*Caption facing*).

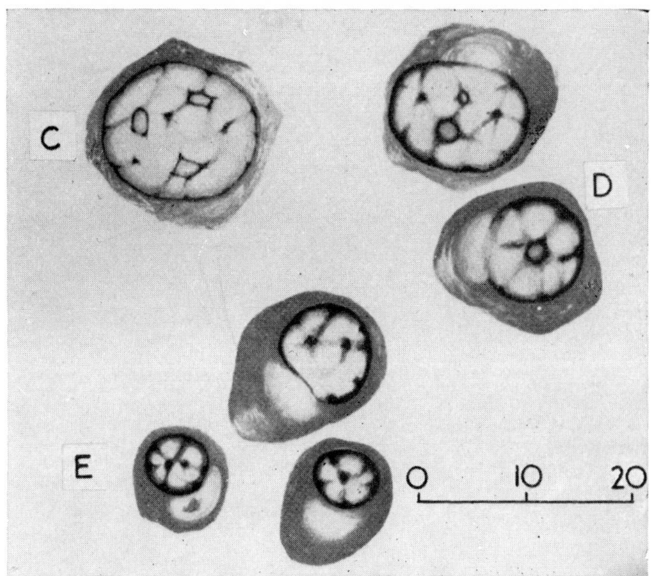

PLATE 7.4. Types of antibody-forming cell seen in fixed, paraffin embedded and sectioned tissues which have been stained with the methyl green-pyronine method (DNA: nuclear chromatin blue-green; RNA: cytoplasm, excluding zone of Golgi apparatus, and centres of nucleoli red).

C haemocytoblast (transitional cell, plasmablast).
D immature plasma cells.
E mature plasma cells.
Scale in microns.

PLATE 7.3. (*Facing page*). Agar-gel immuno-electrophoresis. The direction of migration of serum albumen from the starting wells (A B C D from above down) is to the left.

A, C. Sera of guinea pigs immunized with ovalbumin in mineral oil (Freund incomplete adjuvant).

B, D. Sera of guinea pigs immunized with ovalbumin in mineral containing peptidoglycolipid from a human strain of *Mycobacterium tuberculosis*.

Note: The double precipitin arcs (γ_1 and γ_2) of anti-ovalbumin in the case of sera B and D and the absence of the slower moving (γ_2) arc in the case of sera A and C.

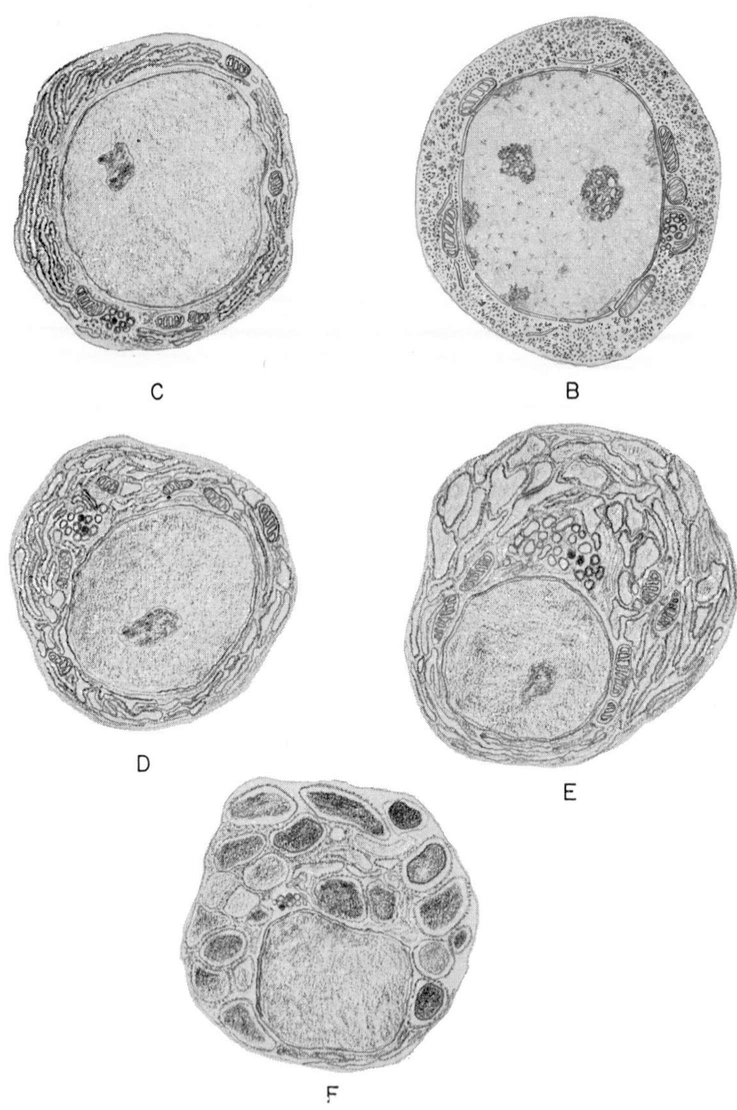

PLATE 7.5. (*Caption facing*).

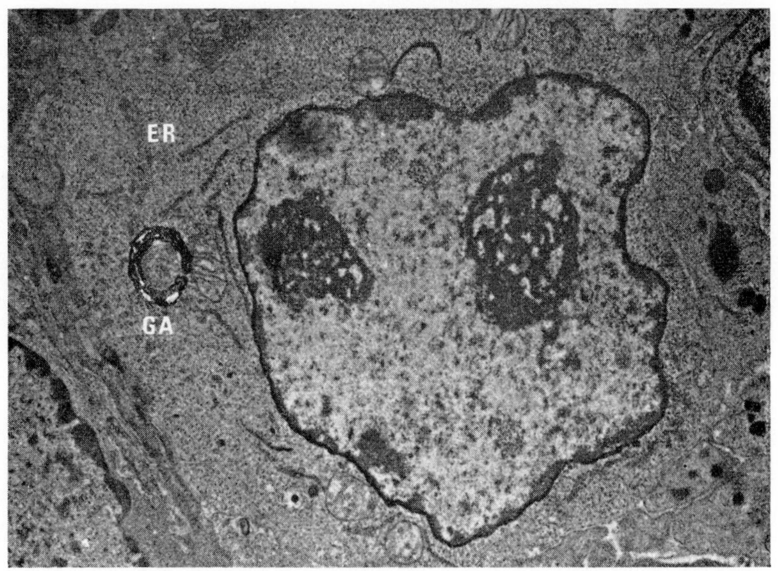

PLATE 7.6 (A). Electron micrograph. Localization of antibody in the cytoplasms of an early (stage 1) haemocytoblast. The antigen in this case is an enzyme: horse radish peroxidase. Sections of rabbit spleen have been prepared 2-4 days after a secondary injection of antigen. The fixed cells were incubated with peroxidase (antigen) to obtain the coupling of this enzyme to the antibody in the cells. The site of peroxidase was then revealed by incubation with 3,3-diaminobenzidine and hydrogen peroxide, the resulting histochemical reaction being shown by a black precipitate. The antibody in this cell is present in the perinuclear space, two segments of ergastoplasm (arrows) and the Golgi apparatus (GA). Several ergastoplasmic lamellae (ER) are present which do not contain antibody. ($\times$ 8,400.)

[Preparation of Dr. Elizabeth Leduc, reproduced with the permission of the editors *Journal of Exptl. Medicine.*]

PLATE 7.5. Diagrammatic representation of maturation stages in the plasma-cell series, as seen in electron micrographs of tissue fixed with osmium tetroxide (cf plate 7.4).

B haemocytoblast (stage 1) (the cytoplasmic RNA is in the form of single ribosomes and ribosomal clusters) see plate 7.6.

C haemocytoblast (stage 2) (plasmablast) (the cytoplasmic RNA is partly organized on membranes of the endoplasmic reticulum).

D immature plasma cell: See plate 7.6B.

E mature plasma cell: see plate 7.6C.

F mature plasma cell with cytoplasmic Russell bodies.

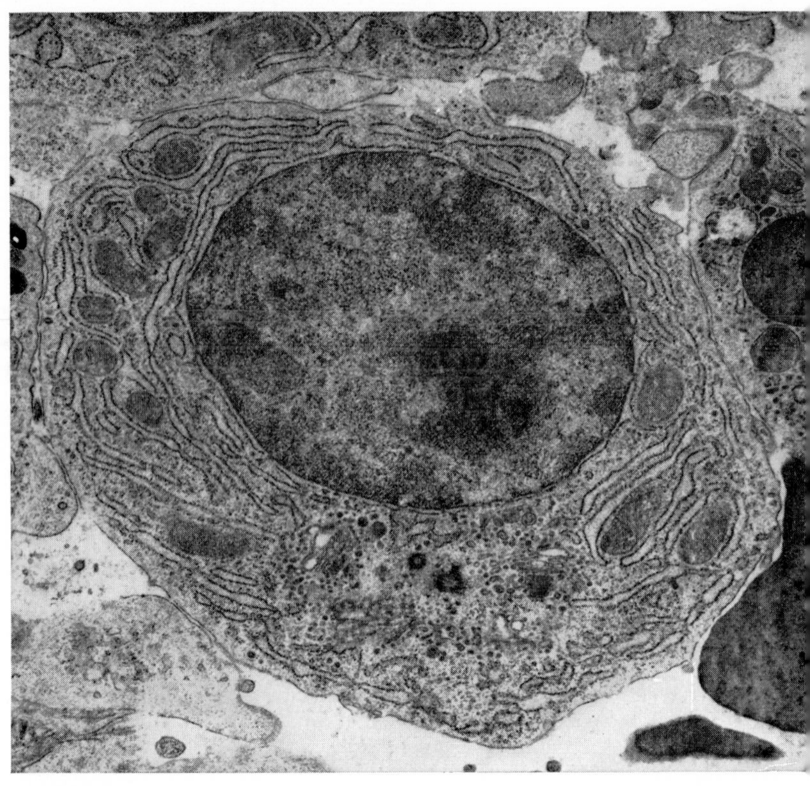

PLATE 7.6 (B). Electron micrograph. Immature plasma cell. *Note* extensive Golgi apparatus and asymmetrical position of nucleus. The two dark rings are part of the centriole. The cytoplasm is occupied by flattened ergastoplasmic lamellae and mitochondria. The cisternae are bounded by membranes 70 Å thick whose outer surface is studded with RNA granules 150 Å diameter. Nucleus with prominent nucleolus. (× 20,000.)

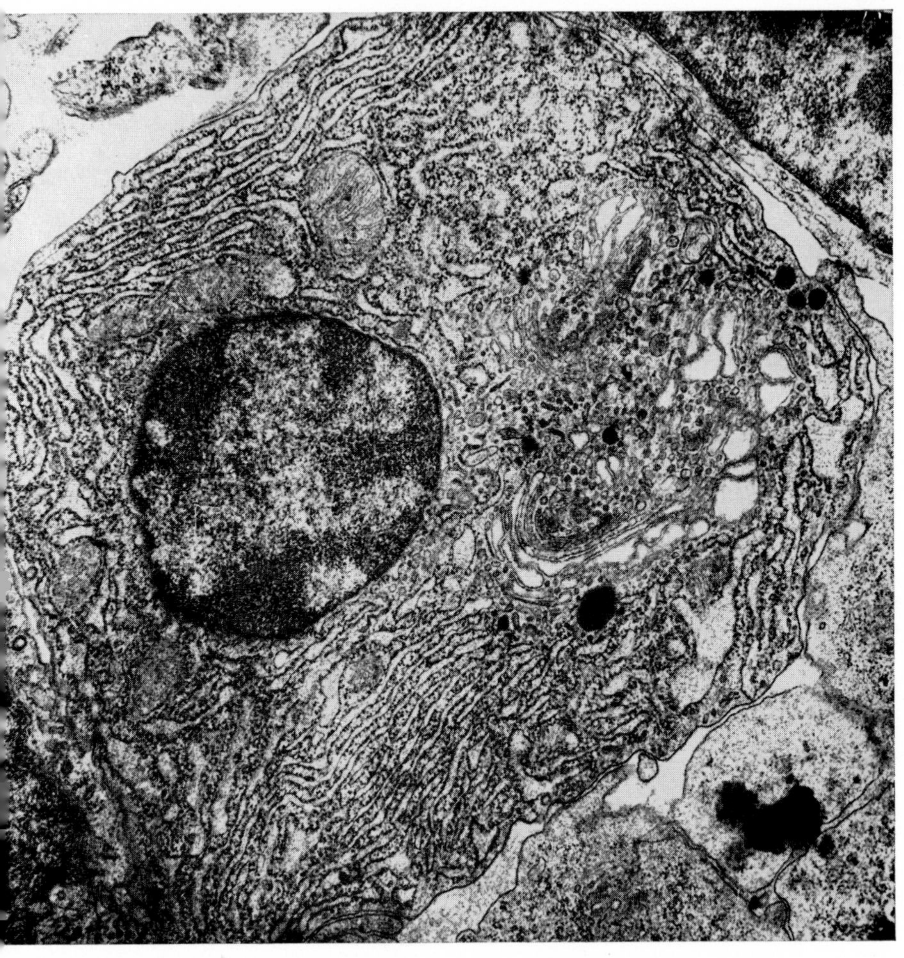

PLATE 7.6 (C). Electron micrograph. Mature plasma cell. *Note* flattened and expanded ergastoplasmic lamellae. Contracted nucleus with peripheral dense chromatin clumps. No nucleolus. (× 35,000.)

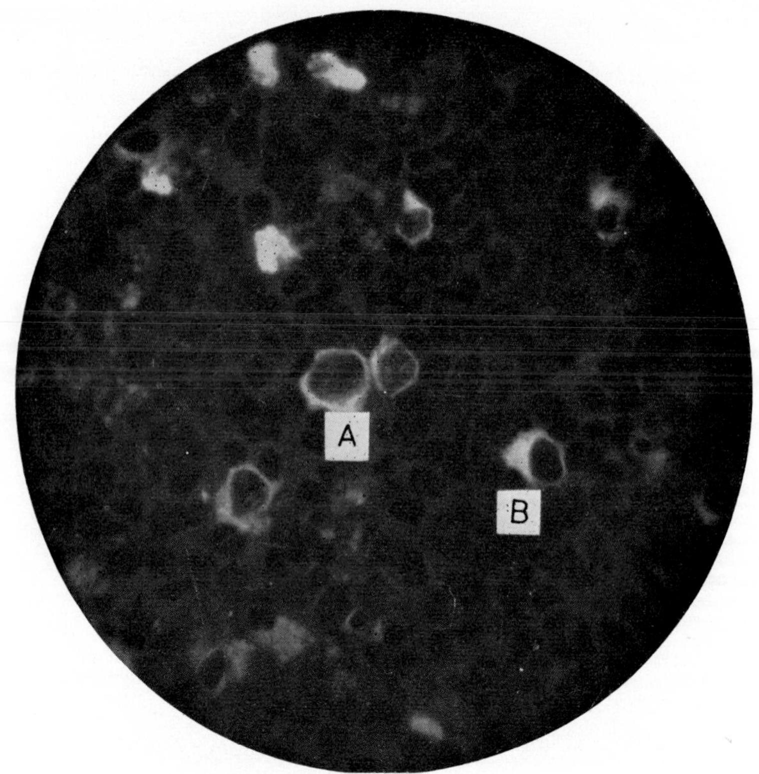

PLATE 7.7. Fluorescence micrograph. 'Sandwich' technique used to demonstrate diphtheria antitoxin in regional lymph node of a rabbit 6 days after a *first* injection of 20*Lf* diphtheria toxoid into the foot pad.

A. Haemocytoblast B. Immature plasma cell. Antibody is distributed throughout the cytoplasm. (× 560.)

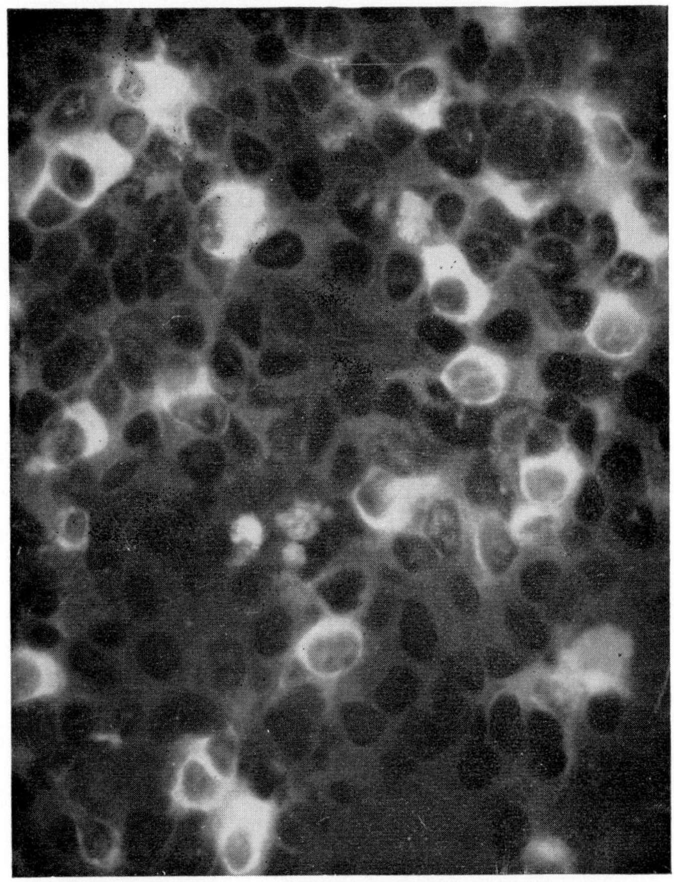

Plate 7.8. Fluorescence micrograph. 'Sandwich' technique used to demonstrate diphtheria antitoxin in regional lymph node of a rabbit 4 days after a *second* injection of 20*Lf* diphtheria toxoid into the foot pad.

Many more cells contain antibody than in Plate 7.7.

Antibody appears throughout the cytoplasm and in irregular areas within the nuclei of some cells. The cells are mainly immature plasma cells, together with a few mature plasma cell types. (× 1050.)

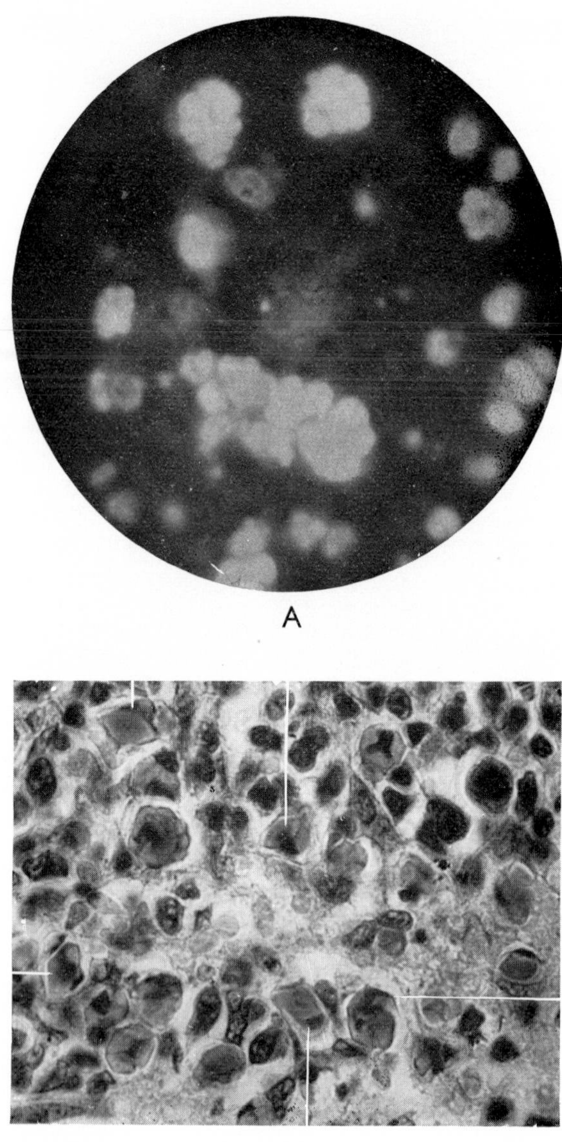

PLATE 7.9. A. Fluorescence micrograph. Russell bodies appearing as clusters of brilliantly fluorescent round objects within the cytoplasm of plasma cells. From a lymph node 6 days after a secondary stimulus with ovalbumin. 'Sandwich' technique as in Plate 7.7. and 7.8. (×720.)

B. A similar area from the medulla of a lymph node stained with haematoxylin and eosin. The Russell bodies here take the form of lozenge-shaped crystalline inclusions (see lines). (×675.)

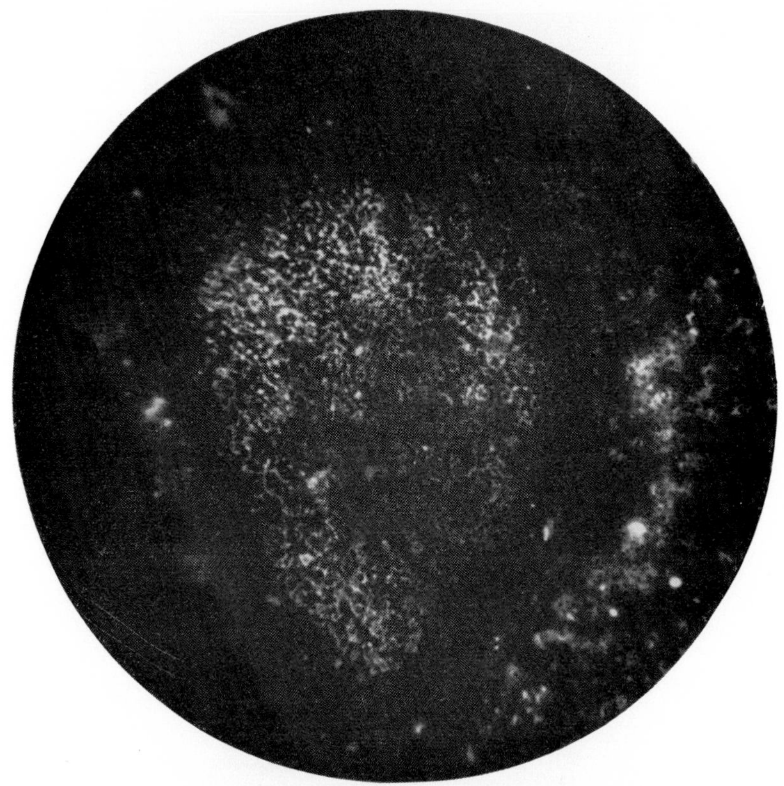

PLATE 7.10. Fluorescence micrograph. Rabbit popliteal lymph node. Lymphoid nodule showing antibody within and between the cells of the germinal centre. Secondary homolateral subcutaneous antigenic stimulus in foot 3 days previously. 'Sandwich' technique for diphtheria antitoxin. ($\times$180.)

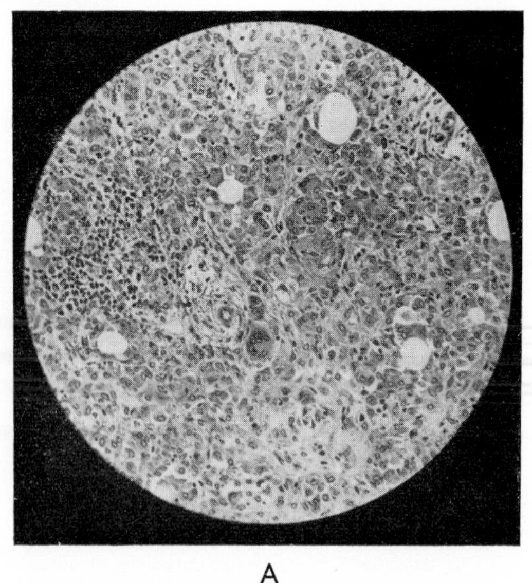

A

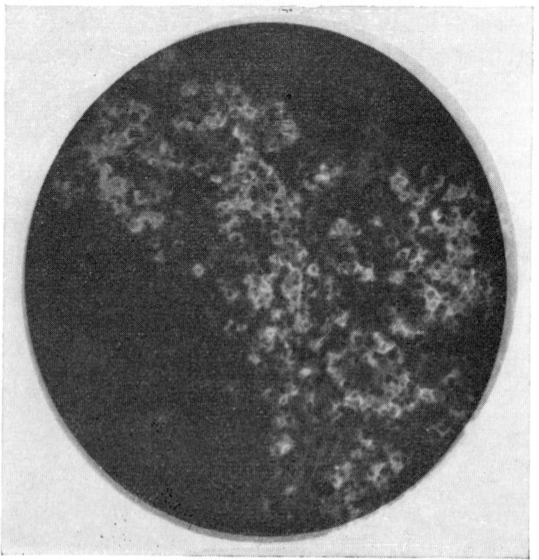

B

Plate 7.11 A. and B. Section of granuloma at local site of injection of Freund-type adjuvant mixture in a guinea-pig. The tissue consists mainly of epithelioid and giant cells, with few or no plasma cells. (× 80.)

B. Fluorescence micrograph of distant lymph node (contra-lateral) node from the same animal. Numerous antibody-containing plasma cells occupying the medullary strands of this lymph node. (× 120.)

[Askonas, B. A. and White, R. G. (1956) *Brit. J. exp. Path.* **37,** 61.]

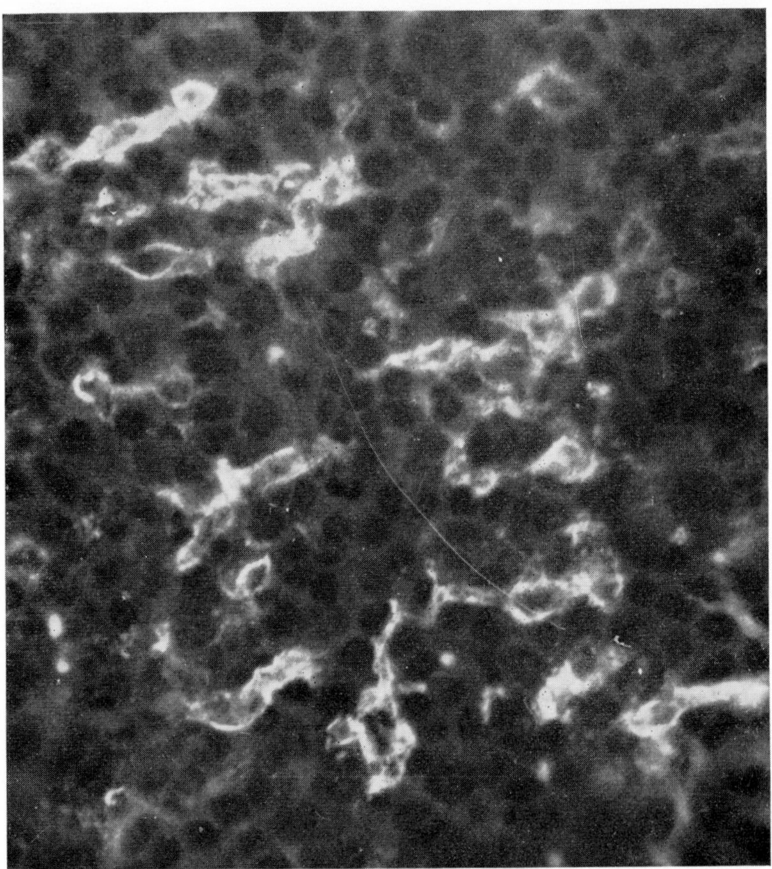

PLATE 7.12. Fluorescence micrograph. Antigen-bearing dendritic cells within a germinal centre. Section of spleen of chicken which had been injected intravenously six days previously with 10 mg of human serum albumin (HSA). Section treated with fluorescein-labelled anti-HSA to reveal HSA on surface of cell body and dendritic extensions of cells scattered among the lymphocytes (non-fluorescent) of the germinal centre. ($\times$ 960.)

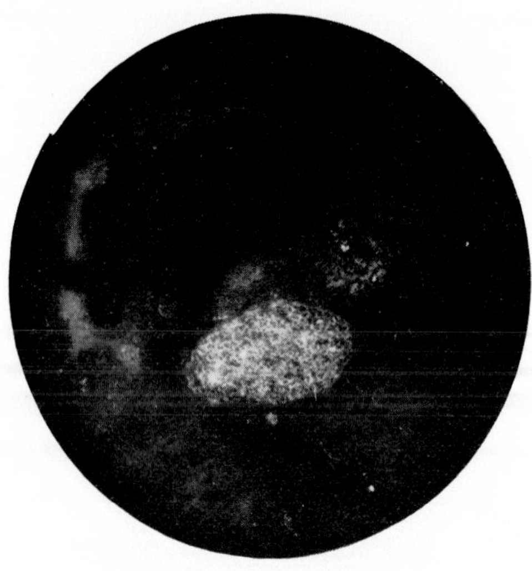

Plate 7.13. Fluorescence micrograph. Section of the spleen of a chicken which was injected with 1 mg of human serum albumin (HSA) 14 days previously. Section treated by the 'Sandwich' technique i.e. a first layer of antigen (HSA) and a second layer of fluorescein-labelled anti-HSA to reveal antibody to HSA. Two germinal centres contain fluorescent antibody-containing cells. The larger centre is made up of cells, almost all of which have a content of anti-HSA. *Note* also an almost total absence of antibody-containing plasma cells in the red pulp regions of the spleen at this time. (×160.)

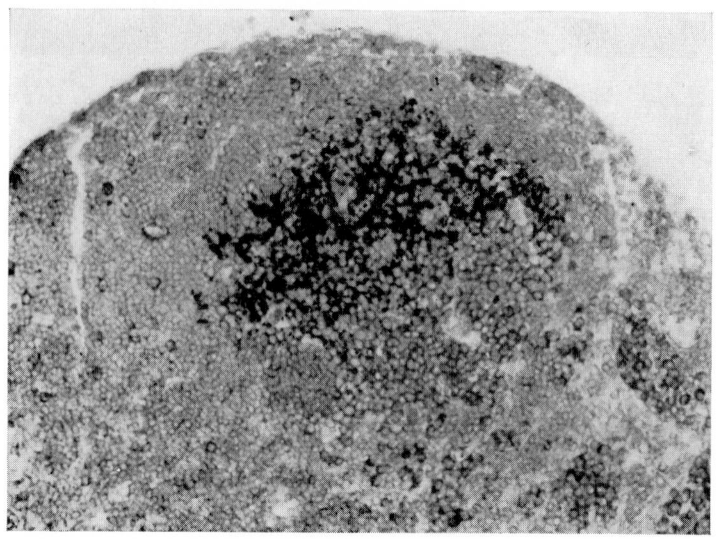

Plate 7.14. (*Caption facing*).

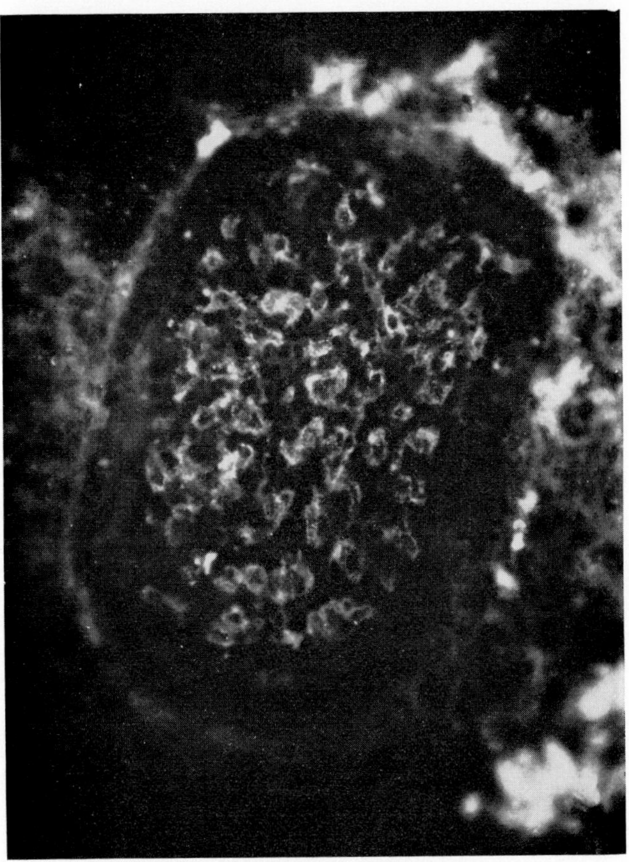

PLATE 7.15. Fluorescence micrograph. Section of spleen treated by fluorescein labelled rabbit anti-chick γ-globulin to reveal localization of chicken γ-globulin to the surface of scattered dendritic cells within a germinal centre at 8 days after an intravenous injection of 10 mg human serum albumin (HSA). *Note* that the pattern of chicken γ-globulin resembles that shown for antigen (HSA) in plate 7.12. ($\times 450$).

PLATE 7.14. Autoradiograph. Section of popliteal lymph node of mouse showing localization of injected antigen to the germinal centres of the cortex. The antigen was a synthetic co-polymer of L-tyrosine, DL-alanine, L-lysine and L-glutamic acid—(T,G) -A—L which was heavily radio-labelled with ^{125}I, and injected into a footpad. The localized antigen at eight days after a secondary injection is shown by the black grain clusters in the peripheral half of the germinal centre. ($\times 190$.)

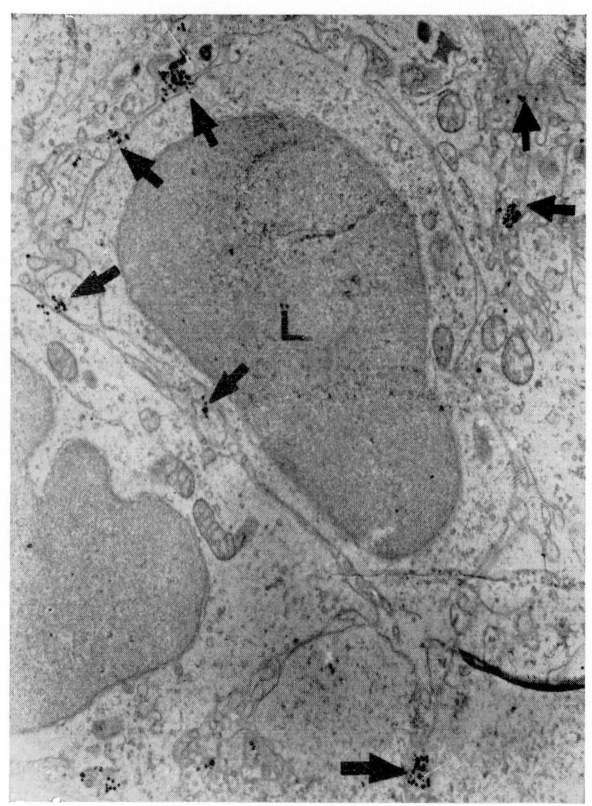

PLATE 7.16. Electron microscopic autoradiograph of a lymphocyte (L) within the germinal centre of a popliteal node of the rat. ^{125}I-labelled *Salmonella adelaide* flagella had been injected into the footpad a few days previously. *Note* the localization of radio-iodine labelled antigen to discrete spots (arrows) at the periphery of the lymphocyte just beyond the cytoplasmic membrane. Presumably these grain foci correspond with the sectioned dendritic processes of cells with the morphology shown in plate 7.12. ($\times$10,800.)

[Preparation provided by Dr. Judith Mitchell.]

(or myoid cells) have long been known to occur in the thymus of certain animal species, and the presence of skeletal muscles fibres in neonatal and adult human thymus has also been reported recently.

The cortical epithelial meshwork is filled by dense aggregates of small lymphoid cells. These cells are very uniform in size and are on the whole slightly smaller and more uniform than the cells of the cortex of a lymph node. The thymic cortical cells exhibit intense mitotic activity whereas mitoses are uncommon in the medullary lymphoid cells. This cortical population (mouse data) is made up of 1 per cent large lymphocytes (haemocytoblasts >11 μ) 10 per cent medium lymphocytes (7–11 μ) and 89 per cent small lymphocytes (<7 μ). The use of autoradiographs prepared by incorporation into the DNA of tritiated thymidine shows that the large lymphocytes divide every 6·7 hours and the medium lymphocytes every 8·2 hours. Most thymic small lymphocytes are not dividing and fail to incorporate the tritiated thymidine. The replacement rate of the thymic cortical population of small lymphocytes is far more rapid than that of small lymphocyte populations in the lymph nodes and it is estimated that replacement is completed every 3–4 days. Unlike lymphocytes in the cortex of lymph nodes or in the white pulp of the spleen, the lymphocytes of the thymus cortex (or medulla) are not normally organized into germinal centres. The cortical thymocytes are highly sensitive to X-irradiation, and several times more so than the medullary thymocytes. The epithelial cells, by contrast, are strikingly resistent. The organization of blood vessels and lymphatics contrasts markedly with that of spleen or lymph nodes. The arteries enter through septa and supply numerous branches to the medulla. The blood supply of the cortex is derived from arterioles which run along the junction of cortex and medulla. From there, capillaries run outwards to the capsule and return to drain into venules running in company with the arterioles in the corticomedullary junction. The capillaries display several unique features. The endothelium forms a complete layer surrounded by a broad basement membrane, rich in collagenous fibres, and an outer layer of epithelial cells. The latter usually forms a complete investment of the vessel but occasional gaps in this have been described. There appear to be no afferent lymphatic vessels to the thymus. Efferent lymphatics leave the medulla to enter the septa and drain into mediastinal nodes. In the medulla lymphatic vessels may envelop medullary veins. No lymph or blood sinuses occur in the thymus.

The relation of the bone marrow as a source of cells for the thymus is critical for the economy of this organ. In the mouse which has been lethally irradiated and subsequently restored with syngeneic marrow cells bearing a chromosomal marker (see Chapter Nine, p. 404), the marked marrow cells appear not only in the bone marrow, but also in the thymus and lymphoid tissues. If, in addition to marked marrow cells, such a mouse is given marked lymphoid cells from the nodes of an adult mouse, cells of the latter type appear initially in the lymph nodes (not in thymus or bone marrow), but are later replaced in the lymph nodes by cells bearing the bone marrow marker. This evidence suggests that cells of the bone marrow which are able to differentiate to the future lymphocytes of lymph nodes (at least those of the thymus dependent areas) probably circulate to the thymus and, after a temporary residence, during which they multiply, pass on to populate the lymph nodes.

The Bursa of Fabricius

The bursa is a round or pear-shaped dorsal diverticulum from the posterior wall of the cloaca. The mucous membrane lined with pseudostratified epithelium has finger-like longitudinal folds or *plicae*, which in the more advanced stages of development are high and resemble villous projections. The plicae are thickened by numerous lymphoid nodules each with a central medullary portion and an outer cortical portion. These nodules appear at the plical surface between the 13th and 21st day of embryonation as epithelial thickenings. It is claimed that the mass of lymphoid cells which compose the mature nodule develop by direct differentiation from the epithelial cells.

Within the first week after hatching, the nodules have already developed the adult pattern of cortex and medulla. In this they are unlike the germinal centres of the spleen, which appear several weeks later, presumably as the result of stimulation by antigens of the bird's environment. Their structure also obviously differs from that of a germinal centre in spite of a superficial similarity. Thus throughout their functioning period the nodules of the bursa maintain an intimate association with the epithelium of the gut wall (Plate 7.2). A thin basement membrane underlies this epithelium and extends as a continuous sheet around the medullary portion of the nodule. Within and closely associated with the basement membrane is a row of basal epithelial-like cells which blends at the plical surface with the cells of the surface epithelium. The medulla of the nodule is composed predominantly of small lymphocytes. A network of stellate cells runs between the latter. The peripheral region of the medulla is more compact with larger and more immature basophilic cells. The basal epithelial-like cells show frequent mitotic figures and the histological appearances have suggested that they are continuously differentiating into lymphoblasts. However, the evidence from use of chromosome markers is that the early basophilic lymphocytes appearing in the bursal anlage are immigrants, presumably stem cells from the yolk sac.

The bursa resembles the thymus in the time course of its development and subsequent involution. Involution begins between 7 and 13 weeks in the chicken, and coincides with the onset of puberty. Indeed, the bursa can be caused to involute by injecting the young bird with androgenic hormones and can be prevented from developing by testosterone injection into the fertile egg at the 5th day of development. In this latter case, the bursal primordium becomes highly vacuolated and remains as a convoluted short duct without forming the bursal vesicle. The effect is not restricted to the bursa since, at hatching, the size of spleen and thymus is also reduced.

Gut-associated Lymphoid Tissue

Accumulations of lymphoid tissue are found at many sites in the mucous lining of the digestive tract. In man the entrance to the pharynx is 'guarded' by a ring of lymphoid tissue, mainly aggregated to three organs, the *lingual*, *palatine* and *pharyngeal tonsils*. The traditional view that this tissue acts protectively against the microbes of the environment is supported by the evidence that by gargling a solution of diphtheria toxoid a secondary antitoxin response can be induced in a person who is already primed to diphtheria antigens. The tonsils are collections of epithelial pits which are surrounded by lymphoid tissue. The lymphatic tissue is similar in appearance to the cortex of a lymph node, consisting of nodules of lymphocytes which often enclose a germinal centre. The epithelium dips into the subjacent lymphoid tissue in the form of tubules or *crypts* which bifurcate at their ends. The epithelium of the crypts is invaded by numerous lymphocytes, which pass through the epithelium to become 'salivary corpuscles'.

Peyer's patches are areas of lymphatic tissue, numbering 30–40, which are located primarily in the lamina propria of the small intestine. They occur in man only occasionally in the duodenum, and are most numerous in the proximal part of the ileum. Structurally they resemble the lymphoid tissue of the tonsils. Large lymphocytopoietic or germinal centres are usually present in the lymphoid nodules. Peripherally they may extend beyond the muscularis mucosa, being limited by a thin capsule of regicular fibres; centrally they are separated from the gut lumen only by the epithelium, which is characteristically infiltrated heavily with large lymphocytes. Besides the Peyer's patches, which measure 1–2 cm by 8–12 mm, there are numerous, small nodules of lymphoid tissue or *solitary follicles* scattered all over the intestinal wall (0·5–3 mm diameter).

The *appendix*, a blindly ending evagination of the caecum in man, has in its wall an almost continuous layer of lymphatic tissue resembling that of the tonsil.

THE CELLS INVOLVED IN ANTIBODY PRODUCTION

On the basis of the evidence discussed above that antibody production is the especial concern of tissues like the spleen, bone marrow and lymph nodes, and that a granulomatous accumulation of similar cells always precedes antibody biosynthesis by organs like skin or adipose tissue, it becomes possible to narrow the field somewhat in regard to the individual cell types which are responsible.

The preceding section will have given some idea of the complexity of the organization of many different cell types within the various lymphoid tissues. This histological detail is relevant but is inadequate since it fails to make the obvious point that many cells are mobile and repeatedly arrive and depart.

In order to simplify the problem, the lymph nodes and spleen can be regarded as an organization of three essential cell types: lymphocytes, macrophages and plasma cells. Obviously the reticular tissues are not merely a hodge-podge of such cells and their precursors. Apparently they have a very precise arrangement. Presumably streams of selected cells are admitted to specific compartments of the lymphoid tissues where co-ordinated activity results between the cell types and interaction with antigen results in the creation of antibody-producing cells, or the effector cells of cell-mediated hypersensitivity. The cells concerned in the latter responses are known to be under the influence of the thymus and to be guided into the tertiary nodules (or thymus dependent areas) where they differentiate under the influence of the immunogen to 'blast' cells. These cellular reactions are discussed in Chapter Thirteen.

By the insertion of a catheter into the thoracic duct and by drainage of the emerging cells it is possible to deplete the animal of the ability to undergo a primary antibody response (see Chapter Three). Thus cells essential for this response are present within the pool of re-circulating small lymphocytes. The problem of the primary response in antibody production may, therefore, be simply stated as the organization necessary to allow a liaison between some of the members of this re-circulating pool of small lymphocytes and the immunogen molecules. It is next necessary to discuss the role of the macrophages in the initial manipulation of this antigen.

Role of the Macrophage in the Initial Manipulation of Antigen

Ideally the data given previously on the cellular fate of antigens ought to have enabled us to trace the immunogen from the time of its entry into certain appropriate cells until the time at which antibody is produced. However, it is really only with particulate bacillary antigens that we can point definitely to a specific receptor cell type—the macrophages of the reticulo-endothelial system. Actually the microphages of the blood also receive such bacillary antigens, but since they are believed to be rather impermanent end-cells they are generally considered unsuitable for a role in antibody production.

The role of the macrophage in antibody production is far from clear. In all the histological situations in which antibody production has been described: local production in various injected tissues, regional production following distribution of an antigen by lymphatics and general production following introduction of the immunogen into the bloodstream, there is a correlation between the presence of macrophages demonstrably containing the injected antigen and production of antibody. However, there is an obvious discrepancy between the ability of a tissue to take up antigen and its ability to synthesize antibody. This is clearly so for the liver which, as discussed above, will accept 90 per cent of an intravenous dose of particulate antigen and yet contributes only a small fraction to the subsequently synthesized antibody. In the rat which has been injected with ^{125}I-labelled flagellin the lymphoid organs take up only a small percentage of this. Thus total lymph nodes and spleen contained about 4 per cent of the injected radioactivity 4 hours afterwards. Moreover the radioactivity drops rapidly after a few hours to a fraction of this figure.

In a variety of situations it is possible to show that the macrophages neither contain nor synthesize antibody. Thus the local granuloma which develops in a guinea-pig after injection of Freund-type adjuvant mixture makes comparatively little antibody, although this tissue is packed with hypertrophic macrophages, some of epithelioid type. Studies with the fluorescent antibody technique on this granuloma and on the granuloma following injection of alum-precipitated immunogens show that the macrophages are devoid of antibody, which can be readily detected in other cells present which belong to the plasma-cell series.

It could be argued that most *morphological* studies of the fate of antigen are misleading since the dose of an antigen necessary to provoke antibody formation is far less than that used for these experiments. In the classical studies with pneumococcus polysaccharide referred to above the amounts injected ranged from 0·5 to 10 mg per mouse. The dose necessary to produce immunity is 0·5 μg—a thousandfold lower dose. In point of fact, doses of 1 mg and upwards produce immunological paralysis rather than immunity. Doses as small as 10 and 100 nanograms of the protein flagellin cause peak antibody titres in the rat and doses as small as 100 picogram (·0001 μg) occasionally cause antibody production in this species.

Evidence such as the foregoing has led to the alternative view that the macrophage acts to catabolize antigens and by this function seems to protect the antibody-producing cell from exposure to excessive antigen which would result in paralysis. Indeed, it could be argued that any cell which took in a large dose of antigen would be precluded thereby from antibody formation.

If, therefore, it is accepted that macrophages do not form antibody it still has to be decided whether antibody production is totally independent of these cells or whether certain steps of processing the immunogen by macrophages are a necessary preliminary for the stimulus and biosynthetic activity of the real antibody production.

Another question for which it would be reasonable to seek an answer is whether antibody production can continue after the antigen has been totally catabolized. Three observations provide suggestive data. First, it is found that antibody only continues to be produced for really long periods of time when the antigen consists of relatively indestructible substances such as pneumococcal (and other bacterial) capsular polysaccharides. Secondly, when antibody production to a protein antigen is prolonged by the use of adjuvants such as alum-precipitated antigens there is at the same time an obvious persistence of demonstrable protein within the macrophages. Thirdly, it generally seems to be the case that antibody production drops sharply following the elimination by the body of the major part of the antigen. Antibody production therefore appears at first sight to depend on persisting antigen. However, this matter cannot be regarded as settled, since some studies have shown the persistence of antibody production at a low level for months after the presumed complete disappearance of antigen.

Using a technique for selecting and isolating single antibody-producing cells from the lymphoid tissues of mice which were injected with bacterial antigens, it is possible to investigate their immunogen content at the same time as they are known to be producing antibody (see Chapter Nine). This is accomplished by using flagellin which was heavily labelled with ^{125}I and by preparing autoradiographs of the isolated antibody-producing cells. The sensitivity of the method was such that only a few molecules of antigen per cell could have been detected. None was found associated with such cells. However, information on this point is conflicting, since other studies exist to show that immunogenic ferritin molecules can be detected in cells of the same general morphology as antibody-producing plasma cells. The first of the above data would, if accepted, provide a clear indication that the antibody-producing cells can be brought into action either by transient contact with immunogen or after it has been processed by another type of cell. The most direct evidence that macrophages are involved in antibody production has been provided with an *in vitro* culture system which requires the sequential action of two cell populations. It was shown that the direct introduction of T2 phage (as immunogen) to teased out lymph node cells did not result in antibody synthesis nor was any antibody formed by a culture of rat peritoneal macrophages after injection of phage. However, by allowing the interaction of antigen and macrophages to occur as a first step and secondly the interaction of this material with lymph node cells, synthesis of specific anti-phage resulted.

In later experiments T2 phage was incubated with peritoneal macrophages for 30 minutes and a phenol (RNA containing) extract of this mixture was later added to the rat lymph node cells. This period of contact was found to be optimal and longer periods of contact of immunogen and macrophages led to no greater antibody synthesis. Since the donors of the lymph node cells themselves had a low titre of anti-phage activity, it remains an open question whether this production of antibody represents a primary or a secondary response.

The nature of the phenol-soluble RNA-containing material which could stimulate the lymph node cells has not been finally elucidated. The extract has been clearly shown to contain antigen fragments capable of reacting with phage antibody. One possibility is that the activity of the extract depended upon a complex of antigen (or antigen fragment) and RNA. In experiments with haemocyanin, RNA-bound antigen extracted from macrophages was shown to be highly immunogenic when administered to primed mice. The enhanced immunogenicity was lost if the material was treated with RNAase. This suggests that some macrophages do 'process' antigen, linking it with RNA, so that the complex acts as a 'super antigen' when added to immunologically competent cells; however, it is possible that such complexes are artefacts of the extraction procedure, and not really significant biologically. Another possibility which has received some experimental support is that the extract contains an informational-type RNA. However, the molecular size of the RNA material obtained free from antigen was too small to be a messenger RNA of a size which would code for a light or a heavy chain.

It is nevertheless a valid experimental observation that a number of protein antigens are much more immunogenic when administered in living macrophages than in their native form. This activity is correlated with the persistence in the macrophages of a small fraction of the antigen, which escapes the degradation to which most of the material is subjected, and appears to be retained at some site where it remains accessible to stimulate immunologically competent lymphocytes. The apparently enhanced immunogenicity may well be due, at least in part, to the prevention of concomitant immunological paralysis (see Chapter Three). A point which requires emphasis is that in the case of a number of powerful immunogens (usually very large molecules, or particulate materials) there is good evidence that direct interaction with immunologically competent cells to give a primary antibody response can also occur, without the intervention of macrophages. In fact prior phagocytosis by macrophages may actually diminish the primary response to such immunogens.

The cells which have served as macrophages in most such experimental studies *in vitro* have been the 'exudate cells' which are washed out from the peritoneal cavity after introduction of a mild chemical irritant. It is beginning to be apparent that the degradative capacities of phagocytic cells differ widely according to their type and tissue source. For example, when *E. coli* micro-organisms are introduced into polymorphs, peritoneal macrophages or alveolar macrophages and then tested for immunogenicity, this is found to be destroyed by the first two types of cells far more quickly than by the alveolar macrophages. In other studies employing sheep cells the Kupffer cells of the liver were found to degrade this antigen rapidly and completely whereas macrophages of the spleen retained active antigen.

In studies which will be detailed below (see section on germinal centres) a type of 'dendritic cell which is possibly a variant type of macrophage' is described which can retain high concentrations of antigens for periods of many weeks or months. This cell-bound antigen is likely to be the stimulus for the proliferation of lymphocytes and the occasional development of antibody-producing cells within the germinal centre.

Role of Plasma Cells in Biosynthesis of Antibody

There can be little doubt that the bulk of antibody is produced by cells belonging to the differentiating line of cells whose mature member is the plasma cell. Plasma cells are not prominent members of the lymphoid tissues of normal healthy animals—apart from those draining the gut—but when powerful immunogens such as bacillary vaccines (especially those containing many mixed types of micro-organisms) or horse serum are injected repeatedly into the bloodstream, the medullary or pulp strands of the spleen become infiltrated with cells which are larger than the small lymphocyte and have prominent basophilic cytoplasm.

These cells, which vary in appearance, as do the various maturing members of the erythrocyte or leucocyte series of cells, have a very distinctive mature member, long recognized as a common cell in various chronic granulomas such as, say, syphilitic gummata and referred to by pathologists as the *plasma cell.* The nucleus is small, round or slightly oval and has an eccentric position. In the nucleus as seen in sections of fixed, embedded tissue stained with haematoxylin, the chromatin is distributed as regular particles around the inside of the nuclear membrane, producing the so-called 'clock-face' nucleus. Mitoses are rare. The cytoplasm is strongly basophilic appearing a deep blue when stained by Romanowsky dyes such as Leishman or Giemsa. Another staining method (Unna-Pappenheim or methyl green-pyronin method) colours the cytoplasm a bright red and leads to the term pyroninophilic for the same basophilic areas of cytoplasm which owe this staining effect to their high content of ribonucleic acid (Plate 7.4, following p. 276).

The work of Caspersson and his Scandinavian colleagues (1940–50) had focused attention on the association between cytoplasmic ribonucleoprotein and protein synthesis in protein-secreting glands such as the pancreas and salivary glands. In the plasma cell, the accumulation of ribonucleic acid in the cytoplasm strongly supports the role of this cell as a unicellular protein-secreting gland. Other cells of the lymphoid tissues may, of course, show basophilia: for instance, the haemocytoblasts, myelocytes and erythroblasts. However, in these cases only the young and rapidly dividing, undifferentiated cells are basophilic or pyroninophilic, presumably since these are vigorously synthesizing protein for growth. Precursors of such cells as the granulocytes, the lymphocytes and erythrocytes all lose their cytoplasmic nucleic acid with the process of differentiation. The plasma cell, on the contrary, maintains basophilia as a mature cell. Moreover, the electron microscope shows that the ribonucleoprotein of a young actively growing and dividing cell is organized differently from that of a mature protein-secreting cell (see below).

Using the methyl green-pyronin method Fagraeus and others have defined the developmental stages of the family of cells found in reticular tissues after antigen injections. Plate 7.4 shows diagrammatically the individual cell types of the plasma cell series. The early cell in the series (C) referred to as the *transitional cell* by Fagraeus, when stained by the methyl green-pyronin method or by Romanowsky dyes is indistinguishable from the *haemocytoblast*—the precursor cell of the erythrocytic and leucocytic series of cells. We can use the term haemocytoblast or 'blast' for this cell of the plasma-cell series, not because we think it identical with the precursors of red cells and leucocytes (indeed, by other methods it is readily distinguishable) but merely to stress the fact that by the above staining procedures it is not distinguishable from them. At the next defined stage (D), termed the immature plasma cell, the large circular leptochromatic nucleus of the haemocytoblast stage has become smaller, its chromatin strands have condensed and the prominent pyroninophilic nucleoli have become less conspicuous. In this cell a definite clear area (containing the Golgi apparatus) can be made out against the nucleus. In the final stage (the mature plasma cell, E, which is sometimes referred to as the Marschalkó type cell) the process of condensation of nuclear chromatin has gone further to produce the small, round and eccentric nucleus. The cytoplasm of the mature plasma cell is deeply basophilic except for a prominent bean-shaped area overlapping the edge of the nuclear area. This area corresponds with the Golgi apparatus, which is a prominent cytologic feature of all protein-secreting glandular cells, e.g. pancreas, thyroid and salivary gland (Fig. 7.9).

The electron microscope shows that the basophilic area of the cytoplasm of the immature and mature plasma cell is occupied by a complex system of parallel membranes (the endoplasmic reticulum, or ergastoplasmic membranes) (Fig. 7.9; Plates 7.5, 7.6B&C, following p. 278). The basic details of the endoplasmic reticulum are common to plasma cells and to the cells of other protein-secreting glands. The electron micrographs also reveal the Golgi element as a highly characteristic collection of membranes, with basic similarity between the plasma cell and the cells of the protein-secreting glands. By way of contrast, the small lymphocyte (Plate 3.2) and the large pyroninophilic lymphoblast (Plate 3.3) have cytoplasm which is almost devoid of ergastoplasmic membranes: the Golgi zone is also quite tiny.

The unit of the endoplasmic reticulum, as seen in sectioned cells, is a pair of opposed membranes seen in profile. These are regarded as making up a system of intercommunicating sacs or cisternae, which extend throughout small or large areas of the cytoplasm or sometimes may almost fill the whole cytoplasm. The membranes extend up to the nucleus and may be continuous with the outer membrane of the double nuclear membrane. Similarly the cell membrane may dip into the cell and continue as an ergastoplasmic membrane; also, these membranes are considered to be continuous with the Golgi membrane (Fig. 7.9). The lumen of the membranes (the sacs of cisternae) can be empty or sometimes occupied and distended by proteinaceous material—the secretion of the cell. The membranes are fairly uniformly about 70 Å thick, and on their outer surfaces show regularly spaced granules or projections 150 Å diameter (Pallade granules, ribosomes). Beyond the membranes and between adjacent similar structures is the *cytoplasmic matrix*, which includes similar granules occurring in clusters (polyribosomes) or singly, and which appear to be freely scattered between the cisternae of the whole reticulum. The Golgi apparatus consists of a collection of smooth-surfaced sacs (which are possibly identical with lysosomes) and lamellated membranes.

The lamellated membranes are peripheral while the granules are usually at the centre of the Golgi zone. The specific functions of the Golgi apparatus are not clearly known, though it seems to be concerned with secretion. It is likely that it supplies the membranes of the cell (both lysosomal membranes and ergastoplasmic membranes) and this may account for its prominence in the plasma cell, which is liberally provided with them.

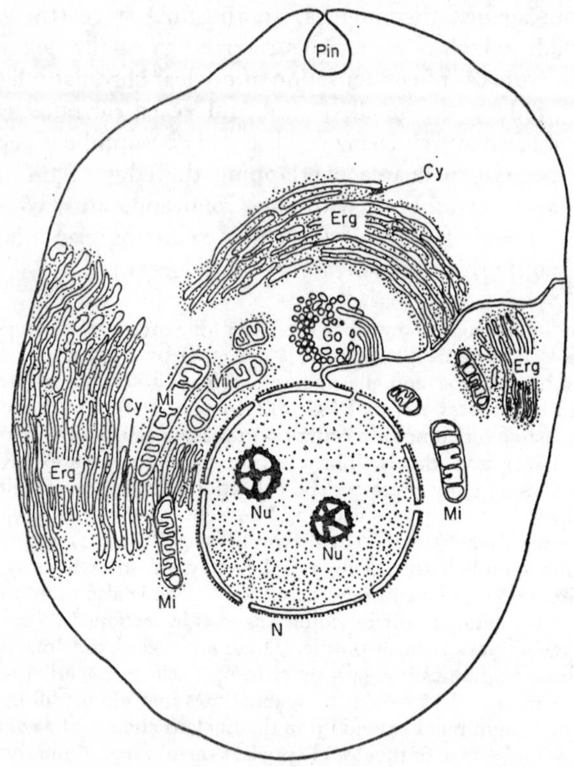

FIG. 7.9. Schematic diagram of the ultrastructure of a typical protein-secreting cell as revealed in an electron-micrograph of an ultra-thin section of osmic-acid fixed tissue.

- B Nucleus with nucleoli (Nu).
- Go Golgi complex.
- Mi Mitochondria.
- Erg Membranes of endoplasmic reticulum or ergastoplasm with attached ribonucleoprotein granules (RN).
- Cy Cytoplasmic matrix.
- Pin Pinocytotic invagination of cytoplasmic membrane about to form a vesicle.

In cells which synthesize protein but do not release it from their cytoplasm and do not require that the protein be membrane-bounded, the endoplasmic reticulum is scanty and the Golgi apparatus is inconspicuous. Such a cell is the erythroblast which synthesizes and retains within its substance haemoglobin. The characteristic reactive cells of delayed hypersensitivity reactions (or cell-mediated hypersensitivity) (see Chapter Twelve) are of this second type (pyreninophilic blast cells or large lymphoid cells of the thymus dependent areas).

The haemocytoblast stage of the plasma cell series is also at first a cell of this type, and is scarcely distinguishable from the 'large pyroninophilic' cell of delayed hypersensitivity reactions. However, even at this stage it may be distinguished by special techniques (see below: detection of antibody to horseradish peroxidase) by the presence of antibody in the perinuclear space. Later the haemocytoblast of the plasma cell series develops an extensive endoplastic reticulum consisting of flattened cisternae. This stage has been distinguished as the *plasmablast* by some writers.

The actual presence of specific antibody within the cytoplasm and nuclei of plasma cells was first clearly demonstrated by a modification of the fluorescent antibody method of Coons and his colleagues. This method (see Chapter Nine and Fig. 9.11c) is referred to as the 'sandwich' technique, since appropriate frozen sections, suspected of containing antibody, are first treated with a dilute solution of antigen. The sites of the resulting antigen–antibody union can then be revealed, after a brief wash to get rid of unattached antigen molecules, by exposing the section to fluorescent homologous antibody, and final inspection of the section under a fluorescence microscope.

The results of this technique (Plates 7.7 and 7.8) show that antibody is present in all of the designated stages of the plasma cell (haemocytoblast, immature and mature plasma cell) and has a distribution which corresponds with the cytoplasmic distribution of the basophilia (or the endoplasmic reticulum as seen in the electron micrographs).

Rather recently the distribution of antibody to horse ferritin in plasma cell derivatives of an immunized rabbit was studied by exposing formaldehyde-preserved lymph node sections to ferritin, thus obtaining specific antigen-antibody precipitates which could be visualized in electron micrographs. The iron molecules of the ferritin are electron-opaque and have a distinctive intramolecular arrangement which permitted the localization of this antigen-antibody complex in the cisternae of the endoplasmic reticulum.

Even more precise intracellular localization of antibody has been achieved by use of horseradish peroxidase as an immunogen in rabbits. A solution of the enzyme is applied to appropriate sections of lymphoid tissue from an injected animal and the site of bound antigen is then revealed by the histochemical technique for oxidase activity, i.e. incubation with hydrogen peroxide and a substrate diaminobenzidine tetrahydrochloride. As seen from Plate 7.6A antibody first appears in the perinuclear space of the haemocytoblast and in the lamellar or peripheral part of the Golgi apparatus.

With development of the ergastoplasmic membranes, antibody accumulates in the cisternae. The large, almost spherical accumulations of antibody in mature plasma cells remain within distended, ribosome covered cisternae.

Sometimes, and under circumstances which are not fully understood, antibody can occur in mature plasma cells as conspicuous spherical cytoplasmic granules, referred to as *Russell bodies*. These appear in conventional sections stained by haematoxylin and eosin as hyaline eosinophil spheres, or sometimes lozenge shaped crystals, and in fluorescent antibody 'sandwich' preparations as brilliantly fluorescent spheres (Plate 7.9 A & B, following p. 276. In the electron micrographs each Russell body can be seen to be bounded by a membrane of the endoplasmic reticulum; presumably, therefore, the body arises by a process of aggregation and condensation of the protein which is retained within the cell instead of being secreted from it. (Plate 7.5F)

The antibody-containing cells which are detected by the fluorescent antibody method in primary and secondary responses are apparently exactly alike. The difference lies in the paucity of antibody-containing cells involved in the primary response (Plates 7.7 and 7.8). Scanty, isolated cells of haemocytoblast form may be seen in regional lymph node, on the 4–5th day after a first injection of protein (diphtheria toxoid) into a rabbit's footpad. On the 7th or 8th day the number of cells has increased and they are mainly immature and mature plasma cells. In a secondary response the tempo is quickened and the first antibody-containing cells may be seen at 30 hours. By the third day there are large numbers of immature plasma cells (hundreds in a section of the medulla of the node in contrast to 5–15 of such cells in a primary response at the same time). In the secondary response to fluid diphtheria toxoid, after a peak of 5–6 days, the number of antibody-containing cells rather suddenly declines. At the peak the vast majority are immature plasma cells. At the twelfth day of this secondary response only a few scattered mature plasma cells remain. These facts suggest that most plasma cells live for a few days only, and are probably end cells. In mice stimulated by antigen in Freund's adjuvant, an injection of tritiated thymidine resulted in no labelling of mature plasma cells at 1 hour later. After 8 hours 80 per cent were labelled, suggesting a life span of about 8–12 hours for most of these cells.

The early cells, the haemocytoblasts, are dividing rapidly. At the peak of the secondary cellular response, at 4–5 days, the majority of antibody-containing cells (immature and mature plasma cells) are not synthesizing DNA as shown by their inability to incorporate tritiated thymidine. They also contain stable RNA as judged by their inability to incorporate tritiated uridine. However, mature plasma cells rapidly incorporate labelled leucine into protein.

On the basis of this histological evidence it seems that mature plasma cells for the most part are brought into existence in the medulla of the lymph nodes as the result of mitotic activity on the part of the haemocytoblasts and immature plasma cells, and then live a short life without active division and die in the one place. No good evidence exists that they escape in large numbers into the blood or lymph, and nothing to suggest positively that they change into a different cell. It seems unlikely that immunological memory can be a function of persisting plasma cells.

Systemic Migration of Cells During the Immunological Response of a Fixed Tissue

Thus far the lymph node or spleen, which is the site for an immunological response, has been considered as a static organ. When a lymph node is stimulated by antigen there is a greatly increased exodus of cells *via* the efferent lymphatics. Under certain circumstances, as when influenza virus vaccine is used as a local stimulus, the cells emerging in the lymph from the region node include immature and mature typical plasma cells. However, this is unusual and it seems to be the case that plasma cells, which can be found in large numbers in the medullary strands of the node near to the sinuses, rarely leave the lymph nodes. The cells usually found in the efferent lymph of a stimulated node are a particular type of basophilic lymphoid cell; they differ markedly in appearance from the cells in either the afferent or efferent lymph of an unstimulated node.

In the unstimulated popliteal node of a sheep, the efferent lymph contains 5,000–15,000 cells per cmm, which are mainly small, with a few large lymphocytes. The cells of the afferent lymph are far fewer (200–500 per cmm) and of markedly different cellular composition. Thirty per cent of these cells are macrophages while the rest are mature, medium and small lymphocytes with occasional large lymphocytes and eosinophils. Within a few minutes of the injection of antigen into the drainage area of the popliteal node, the number of cells in the efferent lymph falls, so that in the next 24 hours the count of cells is only 20–30 per cent of normal. After 60 hours or so the cell population of the efferent lymph increases and includes young, very large cells with basophilic cytoplasm. These are haemocytoblasts which account for up to 10 per cent of the cells in the lymph.

Over the next few days many smaller, intensely basophilic cells appear in the efferent lymph. When the lymph node undergoing this response was perfused with tritiated thymidine, it was found that all the basophilic cells of the efferent lymph became labelled. This contrasts with the situation in an unstimulated node where only about 1 per cent of the cells of the efferent lymph become labelled. Thus it would seem that normally large numbers of cells pass through the node, and since they do not come from the afferent lymph they presumably derive from the blood (the re-circulating pool of small lymphocytes). During an immune response, however, the efferent basophilic cells appear to be formed within the node itself.

It is significant that many of the cells of the efferent lymph are found by electron microscopy to be primitive undifferentiated haemocytoblasts with many free polyribosomes and only an occasional rough double membrane of endoplasmic reticulum in their cytoplasm. They are a rapidly dividing population as judged by the frequency of mitoses. No cells with the ultrastructure of true plasma cells are usually found. The suggestion is that the emerging cells are unrelated to the immediate production of antibody in the local node—although they can be shown in suitable plaque assays (see Chapter Nine) to be capable of forming antibody. Rather, they may function by colonizing remote lymph nodes, transforming after arrival into plasma cells or becoming memory cells (or Y cells).

In conformity with this hypothesis, when the efferent lymph which contained these basophilic cells was drained away by a cannula, systemic immunity as shown by a titre of agglutinins failed to develop in the serum of the sheep. This could not be explained merely in terms of the loss of antibody in diverted lymph. It can therefore be concluded that the basophilic cells of the efferent lymph may act to propagate the immune response into the remote non-regional lymph nodes. Support for this was provided by other experiments showing that the cells of the diverted efferent lymph can initiate an immunological response when injected into a twin sheep.

CELLULAR ORIGIN OF DIFFERENT CLASSES OF IMMUNOGLOBULINS

The question whether the same cells make IgM and IgG or other immunoglobulins has already been discussed in Chapter Three (p. 132). We return here to the morphological aspects of the question. Several investigations of the biosynthesis of IgM have suggested that a cell type different from the plasma cell was responsible. Most studies of patients with macroglobulinaemia have drawn attention to the presence of large cells (16 μ diameter) with a lymphocyte-like nucleus, and a rather narrow rim of basophilic cytoplasm containing a para-nuclear clear area resembling that of a plasma cell. Electron micrographs show the presence of endoplasmic reticulum throughout the cytoplasm. These cells have been termed '*plasmacytoid lymphocytes*'.

Further evidence that cells of this type are associated with bio-synthesis of macroglobulins has come from a study of the newborn infant, which can form macroglobulin specific antibody when injected with Typhoid-Paratyphoid vaccine in spite of a lack of typical plasma cells in its tissues. However, other authors have described the presence of IgM in typical immature and mature plasma cells in human lymph nodes and spleen in surgical biopsy material from cases of rheumatoid arthritis.

The cells from human lymph nodes of cases of macroglobulinaemia have often been noted to contain eosinophilic inclusions in their nuclei which appear a bright purple after periodic-acid Schiff staining. Immunofluorescence studies with specific anti-IgM have shown this material to be macroglobulin.

Cells which contain IgA immunoglobulin (as revealed by fluorescein-labelled specific antibody to IgA) appear to possess the typical morphology of members of the plasma cell series. However the cells which occur in human cases of IgA myeloma can be recognized as distinct from other plasma cells by their so-called *flaming* cytoplasm, i.e. a diffuse and intense eosinophilia of the cytoplasm when stained by Romanowsky dyes. These flame cells were frequently accompanied by so-called *thesaurocytes*, i.e. cells which have a cytoplasm occupied by globular eosinophilic masses separated by tenuous basophilic trabeculae. The substance of these masses gives a strongly positive response with periodic-acid Schiff reagent, and presumably these distinctive appearances of flame cells and thesaurocytes depend upon the high content of carbohydrate in the IgA secretion as it lies within the distended sacs of the endoplasmic reticulum of the plasmacytoma cells.

CELLULAR IMMUNE RESPONSES INVOLVING THE CORTICAL NODULES AND RESULTING IN GERMINAL CENTRE FORMATION

In spite of the conclusive demonstration of the association of plasma cellular responses with antibody production it should be stressed that the accumulation of differentiating members of the plasma cell family in the medullary strands of the lymph nodes or the pulp of the spleen is only one of the reactions produced in reticular tissues by antigen. Another prominent histological effect is the production of germinal or lymphocytopoietic centres in the Malpighian bodies of the spleen after intravenous injection and in the cortical lymphoid nodules of lymph glands after subcutaneous injection. Many investigations have been made of the reaction in the spleen following repeated intravenous injections of bacillary vaccines or foreign protein (such as horse serum).

The earliest changes are to be seen at 3–4 days after injection at sites near a branch of the central arteriole of the white pulp. Foci appear of about 25 cells (in sections) which are larger than the surrounding small lymphocytes, with slightly basophilic cytoplasm and leptochromatic circular nuclei. Mitoses among such cells proclaim these as foci of intense cellular division which enlarge into round areas which (at 6 days) are sharply differentiated from the surrounding zone of darkly staining small lymphocytes since they are composed of larger, paler and slightly more basophilic cells. The rapid enlargement of the focus of proliferating cells seems to compress the surrounding tissue, so that the cortical small lymphocytes appear in neat parallel circumferential rows around the periphery of the *germinal centre*.

In the germinal centre at 6 days the cells consist of primitive reticular cells (cells with long, oval nuclei with a delicate nuclear membrane, small chromatin nodes and no nucleoli), activated reticular cells (cells with more rounded leptochromatic nuclei; small basophilic nucleoli and a stellate, slightly basophilic cytoplasm), haemocytoblasts and smaller cells with less pyroninophilia than the latter (medium lymphocytes). Many cells contain mitotic figures. At a later date (10 days) the cells are mainly medium lymphocytes and with increasing time the average cell size decreases. Macrophages with phagocytosed Feulgen positive (i.e. DNA) inclusions ('tingible corpuscles') are also present, although their extent varies in different animal species. They are, for instance, not very prominent in the chicken or the rabbit spleen. In the centres of human lymph nodes following local inflammation, they are very prominent, being scattered throughout the germinal centres to produce the so-called 'starry sky' appearance.

The major function for the germinal centres seems to be the intensive production of lymphocytes. The synthesis of so much nucleoprotein in the form of cell nuclei should reflect a high turnover of phosphorus, and by the use of autoradiograph preparations made after injection of radioactive phosphate, very high levels of phosphorus uptake are observed in such centres. The data from autoradiographs would put the peak of activity in such a centre at about 10 days. How long after an immunogenic stimulus active cell division continues is unknown. The exact destination of the cells which are being produced so vigorously in such centres is also unknown. It is difficult to escape the conclusion that they eventually add themselves to the stock of cells in the node or spleen, although the presence in the centre of macrophages with DNA inclusion indicates that a proportion may die *in situ*. Experiments with the palatine tonsil of the rabbit using tritiated thymidine labelling of the centre cells after an intravenous dose of this DNA precursor strongly suggested that labelled cells migrate out from the centres on to the epithelial surface and transform to cells with the general appearance of small lymphocytes.

Further evidence that the process of germinal centre formation is connected with the process of antibody production is as follows. In human immunological deficiency diseases, inability to synthesize immunoglobulins and specific antibodies is in general associated with absence of germinal centres from the lymphoid tissues. In thymic aplasia (Di George syndrome) germinal centre development and immunoglobulin (including some antibody) bio-synthesis remain normal in the presence of deficiencies of cell-mediated hypersensitivity mechanisms (see Chapter Eight). The neonatally bursectomized chicken subsequently shows a severely depressed immunological response to several antigens and at the same time lacks a normal development of splenic germinal centres, which fail to increase in number after injection of immunogens. Chickens which are hatched and reared in a sterile environment have lowered serum 7S and 19S immunoglobulin levels, have few plasma cells in their lymphoid tissues and a striking reduction in germinal centres, especially in the lymphoid tissue of the intestinal tract. Contrariwise, germinal centres are still present in the lymph nodes and spleens of germ-free mice. However, all strains studied of even germ-free mice carry leukaemia virus and some strains carry mammary tumour virus, so that the occurrence of germinal centres may reflect the activity of such viral agents.

Nevertheless, the exact role of the proliferative activity of the cells of the centre in relation to the immune response is still far from clear. Although under many circumstances of an immune response, germinal centres are caused to appear without their component cells having any content of antibody (as revealed by the fluorescent antibody technique), under certain circumstances antibody makes its appearance in a reticular pattern between the cells of the centre (see Plate 7.10) and actually within the centre cells (Plate 7.13). Thus in the hyperimmunized rabbit it is not uncommon to see such antibody in the germinal centres of the spleen and lymph nodes.

The first evidence relating the immunogen to these events in the germinal centre was derived from experiments in chickens. It was found that for the first 24–30 hours after an injection intravenously of the protein immunogen (human serum albumin) no fluorescence indicating the presence of this substance could be detected within the spleen. But at 48 hours after injection antigen was present on the bodies and cytoplasmic dendritic extensions of certain elongated cells within the white pulp of the spleen. Antigen was not visible in the red pulp cells, apparently since it had already been catabolized to below the threshold necessary for detection by the fluorescence method. Antigen-bearing cells, at first outside the germinal centres, subsequently appeared in sections from animals killed at 6 days after injection (Plate 7.12) wholly within germinal centres. Antigen could be detected on such dendritic cells within germinal centres for at least 25 days. This persistence of immunogen in and on the dendritic germinal centre cells argues a significant role for this small fraction of the total injected antigen in specifically stimulating the cellular proliferation of the germinal centre. Further evidence that this proliferation involves immunologically competent cells with a specific reactivity to the antigen is shown by the fact that a small proportion of the germinal centres later contain a high proportion of antibody-containing cells (Plate 7.13). Such antibody-containing centres were present from 14 days onwards and could still be found at 45 days after a primary injection.

Similar experiments have been carried out in rats with radio-iodine-labelled whole flagella or the protein flagellin as immunogen and in mice with both a tritium and a radio-iodine-labelled synthetic multichain polypeptide (TG)AL composed of tyrosine, glutamic acid, alanine and lysine. These experiments also show a localization in autoradiographs of labelled immunogen in a lacelike or dendritic pattern within the germinal centres (Plates 7.14 and 7.16). Such localization is especially intense in previously primed animals, but was found to occur to some extent in unprimed mice, irrespective of whether they made antibody detectable in the circulation or whether they were primed for a secondary response. It is evident therefore that germinal centre localization of antigen is not a *sufficient* condition for immunogenicity, although it could nevertheless be a *necessary* condition.

An intense and proportionately greater concentration of antigen within germinal centres occurred in actively sensitized rats already possessing circulating antibody. This observation raised the question of the role of antibody in the localization process and the subsequent experimental data derived in mice, rabbits and chickens strongly supported the necessary role of antibody in this localization process. Thus, animals which have been made specifically tolerant to the protein antigen concerned have been found not to localize antigen to the germinal centres. Further, by the use of fluorescent antibody to the μ or γ chain of immunoglobulin of the species concerned, it can be shown that immunoglobulin is also present in the germinal centres and occurs in a similar pattern to that of the localized specific antigen (Plate 7.15).

Although carefully searched for by immunofluorescence methods, complement has not been detected in a similar situation within the germinal centre.

Much work requires still to be done in order to define the nature of the cell within the white pulp which accepts the antigen–antibody complex on to its surface. Present views are that this cell may be a selected type of macrophage which is deficient in hydrolytic activity towards immunogens and probably deficient in lysosomes. In their morphology these cells appear to resemble the microglia of the brain which have for a long time been linked functionally and by certain silver impregnation methods to typical macrophages (compound granular corpuscles). The presence of persisting antigen in association with elongated dendritic processes of cells within the germinal centres has been confirmed by an autoradiographic method applied to electron micrographs of rat centres after injection of radio-iodinated flagellin (Plate 7.16).

In the rat the first portion of the popliteal node to show antigen was the circular sinus, closely followed by the appearance of antigen in the macrophages lining the medullary sinuses. Antigen-laden macrophages appeared to migrate from the region of the circular sinus into the germinal centre of the primary lymphoid nodules of the cortex.

The sequence of events in the chicken spleen during a primary response is that *medullary* collections of plasma cells first make their appearance and, coincidentally or slightly later, a rise occurs in the serum antibody. This biosynthesis in the medulla would seem to provide the antibody necessary for the localization of antigen to dendritic cells in the white pulp of the spleen. At the time that Ag/Ab complexes are demonstrable in the blood, the first antigen-bearing cells appear around the ellipsoids (or Schweigger-Seidel) sheaths. The complexes segregate from the blood to the periphery of the ellipsoids where they are loaded on to the surface of dendritic cells. These subsequently migrate in the white pulp along the penicillary arterioles (Fig. 7.10), and appear at 3 days after antigen injection as small, spherical collections mixed with somewhat greater numbers of lymphoid cells. The appearances in a sequence of histological sections suggest that antigen-bearing dendritic cells attract to their surface and agglutinate with lymphoid cells bearing a complementary immunoglobulin receptor. The initial sphere of cells then enlarges by transformation and mitosis of the enclosed lymphoid cells.

While the immunological function of the germinal centre is far from clear, possibly the most plausible role which can be suggested for it is in relation to the multiplication of memory cells. Evidence in support of this comes from two sources. In the rabbit the presence of antibody-containing cells within germinal centres could be induced by a second dose of antigen, if this was given in the same region as the primary and at a time (18 days) when the germinal centre was well developed. Thus the primary antigen injection appeared to endow cells of the germinal centre with the capacity to respond to a secondary antigenic stimulus with antibody formation.

Secondly, the distribution of 'primed' or 'Y' cells occurring in the white or red pulp compartments of the spleen of a rabbit making a primary response to sheep erythrocytes has been investigated by a method in which fragments of each kind of tissue were dissected out and challenged *in vitro* with sheep red cells. After a further 4–5 days of maintenance *in vitro* the number of antibody-producing cells in each culture was estimated by a plaque assay technique (Chapter Nine). The white pulp showed a secondary rise in the number of

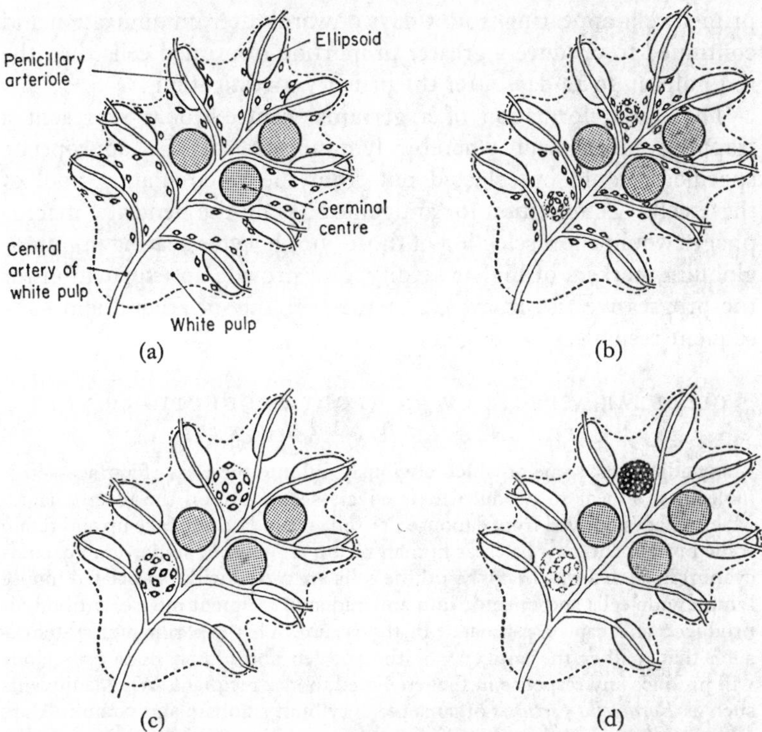

FIG. 7.10. Diagram illustrating successive findings at increasing intervals of time after an intravenous injection of 10 mg human serum albumin (HSA). White pulp is demarcated by the dotted line. The central arteriole of the white pulp gives rise to a leash of penicillary arterioles which diverge to the ellipsoids situated in the marginal zone at the edge of the white pulp.

(a) Section of spleen at 48 hrs. Antigen-bearing dendritic cells distributed around the ellipsoids and along the penicillary vessels. Germinal centres which are present lack any content of antigen.

(b) Section of spleen at 88 hrs. Antigen-bearing dendritic cells have formed small clusters in the angles between the diverging penicillary vessels. More antigen-bearing cells remain along the penicillary vessels. Mature germinal centres which are shown as hatched circles show no content of antigen.

(c) Section of spleen at 6 days. All of the antigen-bearing dendritic cells have clustered within a germinal centre with well-demarcated periphery. None are present outside the germinal centres.

(d) Section of spleen at 18 days. *Note* appearance of antibody-containing cells throughout whole extent of a germinal centre. Other centres are devoid of antibody-containing cells but some show a faint residual pattern of antigen on the included dendritic cells.

primed cells appearing from 5 days onwards after immunization and continued to produce a greater proportion of primed cells than the red pulp up to 12 days after the primary investigation.

The initial formation of a germinal centre would represent a trapping mechanism whereby lymphocytes of the appropriate specificity could be selected out from the re-circulating pool of these cells. Competition for antigenic sites on the dendritic macrophages would allow selection of those lymphocytes bearing immunoglobulin markers of higher avidity, and provide an explanation for the progressive rise in avidity in the antibody of second and subsequent responses to antigen.

CELLULAR ASPECTS OF ANTIBODY PRODUCTION UNDER THE INFLUENCE OF ADJUVANTS

Many adjuvants, some of which obviously fall into the class of surface-active molecules, appear to produce their effects selectively on the macrophages. Macrophages derived from a mouse peritoneal exudate will take up and retain some protein antigens (such as human serum albumin or spider-crab haemocyanin) in such a way that when these cells are mixed with dissociated mouse lymph node cells and injected into an irradiated recipient mouse, antibody is produced and can be estimated in the serum. This experimental system is such that neither the antigen nor the antigen and lymph node cells alone will produce any response in the irradiated mouse recipient. When adjuvants such as *Bordetella pertussis* organisms, beryllium sulphate and vitamin A are added to the macrophages as the first stage in this experiment, they cause a greater eventual response in the recipient irradiated rat. The same adjuvants have a negligible effect when added to the lymph node suspension. This suggests that macrophages which have taken up the adjuvants may somehow be able to stimulate lymphocytes in the direction of antibody formation by some additional means which is not specific for any particular immunogen.

Other adjuvants may cause their effects by stimulating a more effective proliferation of the antibody-producing cells or of the primed memory (or Y) cells. In the case of bacterial endotoxin, local granuloma formation is not an essential component of activity. However, it is claimed that intravenous injection of a rabbit with a protein antigen and endotoxin causes accelerated mitotic division of the germinal centre lymphoid cells and eventual enlargement of the centres far beyond those of controls receiving antigen alone. It is envisaged that endotoxin may act by causing the liberation from damaged cells of nucleic acid precursors. The desoxyribonucleic acid breakdown products which are active in these systems are dialysable oligoribonucleotides and oligodeoxyribonucleotides. Ionizing radiation can also enhance antibody formation when administered a few hours after immunization (see Chapter Thirteen) and it is a plausible hypothesis that this effect may similarly be mediated through DNA breakdown products, which have been shown to be active in this respect. Yet again colchicine gives an adjuvant effect which is similar to endotoxin. This is surprising for a drug which is widely known as an antimitotic agent but again its adjuvant effect may depend on cell damage with the release of nucleic acid metabolites.

Mineral Adsorbent Adjuvants

Aluminium hydroxide (or phosphate)-precipitated antigens act to produce a local granuloma. As judged by the presence of antibody-containing cells revealed by the fluorescent antibody method, antibody production proceeds partly within the granulation tissue which develops at the site of injection and partly within the regional lymphatic nodes. The first production of antibody occurs in the regional nodes, and antibody-containing cells only appear in the area of injection after 14 days, by which time the assembled macrophages, microphages, lymphocytes and plasma cells become neatly organized into a small nodule. In its centre is a mass of aluminium salt infiltrated with macrophages. At 14–21 days this central mass still contains antigen. More peripherally is a broad zone of macrophages packed with aluminium salt. These cells are devoid of either demonstrable antigen or antibody. Antibody-containing plasma cells are present mainly in the adventia of vessels in the young fibrous granulation tissue just beyond the macrophage zone, and presumably derive from cells which reached there from the circulation. The adjuvant effect of aluminium phosphate is interpreted as due partly to the delay in absorption of antigen from the local site of its injection, which results in prolongation of the stimulus to the regional nodes. Comparing the cellular responses in the popliteal node of a rabbit injected in the footpad with 10 Lf of aluminium phosphate precipitated diphtheria toxoid and a much larger dose (150 Lf) of soluble toxoid, antibody-containing plasma cells, as revealed by the fluorescent antibody method, had almost completely disappeared from the node at 3 weeks whereas with the precipitated toxoid the cellular response was still evident at 4 and 5 weeks. Antibody-containing plasma cells also persist for at least 2 months in the periphery of the local granuloma and presumably their production makes an important contribution to the adjuvant effect.

Freund-type Adjuvant

The cellular response to water-in-oil adjuvant mixtures varies considerably with the experimental animals and the account given below relates to the guinea pig, which develops a high level of delayed-type hypersensitivity. At 2–3 weeks following the subcutaneous injection of antigen in *incomplete* Freund-type adjuvant, a soft and ill-defined local granuloma is present at the site of injection. Section shows this to be composed of fibrous granulation tissue surrounding oil vesicles. The granulation tissue includes numerous macrophages, their cytoplasm bulky with vesicles containing mineral oil (foamy macrophages). Ingested antigen can be detected in the area of such granulomata for many weeks, and it seems clear that the locking away of the immunogen in the watery vesicles of the mineral-oil emulsion serves to delay its absorption and elimination from the locality of injection. Antibody-containing plasma cells are also present in such granulomata in both guinea-pigs and rabbits. Presumably, like alum adjuvants, the incomplete Freund mixture derives its main effects from a prolongation of the antigenic stimulation of regional lymph nodes, as well as from some contribution by the local granuloma itself.

With the complete adjuvant the subcutaneous granuloma becomes a large, sharply demarcated, rubbery-firm mass. If the injection is made anywhere near the surface, ulceration often occurs by the fourteenth day. On section, instead of the foam cells mentioned above, there is seen a solid proliferation of epithelioid cells and giant cells (Plate 7.11A) which produces a tissue very similar to a tuberculous granuloma. The macrophages or epithelioid cells do not show a content of antibody. However, more remote nodes (Plate 7.11B) as well as the spleen contain impressive collections of antibody-containing plasma cells. Besides a widespread action on plasma cells, the addition of mycobacterial wax D (or peptidoglycolipid) effects a pronounced stimulation of macrophages, locally and in remote organs. The lungs, for instance, show disseminate sub-pleural miliary macrophage granulomata. These effects are dependent on the dose of peptidoglycolipid used and correlate with the observed adjuvant effects on serum antibody levels and delayed-type hypersensitivity. At a dose level of peptidoglycolipid which is optimal for adjuvant effect, neither the local granuloma nor the regional node was important in antibody production since both were composed almost exclusively of fibroblasts, macrophages and epithelioid cells with only occasional antibody-containing plasma cells.

FURTHER READING

Brachet J. (1961) The living cell. *Sci. Am.* **205**, No. 3, 50

Campbell D.H. & Garvey J.S. (1963) Nature of retained antigen and its role in immune mechanisms. *Adv. Immunol.* **3**, 261

Feldman J.D. (1964) Ultrastructure of immunologic processes. *Adv. Immunol.* **4**, 175

Freund J. (1951) Effect of paraffin oil and Mycobacteria on antibody formation and sensitization. *Amer. J. Clin. Path.* **21**, 645

Good R.A. & Papermaster B.W. (1964) Ontology and phylogeny of adaptive immunity. *Adv. Immunol.* **4**, 1

Holub M. & Jarošková L. (eds) (1960) *Mechanisms of Antibody Formation.* Publishing House Czech. Acad. Sci. Prague (distributed by Blackwell, Oxford).

Humphrey J.H. (1969) The fate of antigen and its relationship to the immune response. In *The Immune Response and its Suppression.* [Ed. Sorkin E.] Karger, Basel

Jarošková L. (ed.) (1964) *Molecular and Cellular Basis of Antibody Formation.* Publishing House Czech. Acad. Sci. Prague

Munoz J. (1964) Effect of bacteria and bacterial products on antibody response. *Adv. Immunol.* **4**, 397

Nossal G.J.V. (1962) Cellular genetics of immune responses. *Adv. Immunol.* **2**, 163

NOSSAL G.J.V. (1967) Mechanisms of antibody production. *Ann Rev. Med.* **18,** 81

NOSSAL G.J.V. (1967) Effects of radiation in antibody formation. *Atomic Energy Review* **5,** 3

SHAFFER J.H., LO GRIPPO G.A. & CHASE M.W. (eds) (1959) *The Mechanisms of Hypersensitivity*. Henry Ford Symposium. Churchill, London

SHANDS J.W. (1967) The immunological role of the macrophage. In *Modern Trends in Immunology* [Ed. Cruickshank R. and Weir D.M.]. Butterworth, Edinburgh

WHITE R.G. (1963) Factors affecting the antibody response. *Brit. med. Bull.* **19,** 207

WHITE R.G. (1963) In *The Immunologically Competent Cell.* Ciba Foundation Study Group No. 16 [Ed. Wolstenholme G.E.W. and O'Connor M.] p. 15. Churchill, London

WHITE R.G. (1967) Antigen Adjuvants. In *Modern Trends in Immunology* [Ed. Cruickshank R. and Weir D.M.]. Butterworth, Edinburgh

WIGZELL H. (1967) Studies on the regulation of antibody synthesis. In Cold Spring Harbor Symposium on Quantitative Biology. '*Antibodies*' Vol. **32,** 507

WOLSTENHOLME G.E.W. & O'CONNOR M. (eds) (1960) *Cellular Aspects of Immunity*. Ciba Foundation Symposium, Churchill, London

CHAPTER EIGHT

Clinical Aspects of Immunoglobulin Metabolism

Aberrations of Immunoglobulin Production and Immunity

THE first part of this chapter is concerned with the distribution and fate in the body of immunoglobulins including, of course, specific antibodies. There is no evidence that in these respects specific antibodies behave in any way differently from nonspecific immunoglobulins of the same class (or subclass) and what will be written about the one applies equally to the other.

THE DISTRIBUTION OF ANTIBODIES IN TISSUES

Immunoglobulins, including antibodies, are made predominantly in the spleen and lymph nodes, from which they may enter the blood directly or by way of efferent lymphatics. Apart from those immunoglobulins which pass directly into the secretions of apocrine glands, all arrive sooner or later in the bloodstream, wherein they circulate around the body and come into equilibrium with immunoglobulins in the extravascular tissue spaces. The total amount of extracellular immunoglobulin in the body is termed the *total pool*, that within the bloodstream is the *intravascular pool*, and that outside the bloodstream in the tissue spaces and lymphatic vessels is the *extravascular pool*. This last pool is complex, and includes a number of pools whose rate of exchange with the blood varies widely, from that in the wall of the intestine which exchanges rapidly, that in the skin which exchanges more slowly, that in muscle which exchanges slower still, to that in tendons which exchange very slowly indeed. In the absence of inflammation immunoglobulin introduced into the bloodstream in man takes almost a week to reach equilibrium, though the process is half complete in a day or two. Where capillary permeability is increased locally, by inflammation for example, interchange between the blood and tissues is much faster and the concentration of antibody approaches that in the plasma. The proportion at equilibrium of the total pool of an immunoglobulin which is present outside the bloodstream depends upon the immunoglobulin class. For IgG, IgA and IgM in man it is about 0·55, 0·6 and 0·3 respectively. These figures reflect the relative ease with which molecules of IgG and IgA can cross uninflamed capillary vessel walls and fenestrae compared with the larger molecules of IgM. The actual concentrations of immunoglobulin in the extra-vascular extracellular tissue fluids vary with the vascularity of the site from about 0·8 × the plasma concentration in the peritoneal cavity to as little as 0·06 in an avascular tissue such as a tendon.

Immunoglobulins are normally barely detectable in *cerebrospinal fluid*, since they are held back by the choroid plexus and meningeal vessels. The level rises when there is meningeal inflammation, or an actual leak of blood, and in certain conditions such as multiple sclerosis or neuro-syphilis or the rare Bing-Neel syndrome (see p. 342). in which cells making immunoglobulin are actually present within the brain. As already mentioned in Chapter Four, IgG and especially IgA are present in exocrine gland secretions, such as milk, saliva, tears, nasal and bronchial mucus and in the intestine. The term 'antiseptic paint' has been used to describe the antibodies secreted externally in this way and indeed there is evidence that persons deficient in IgA in exocrine secretions are more liable to sialitis, chronic bronchitis etc. than are normal persons. The special question of transfer of immunoglobulins from mother to foetus or infant is discussed separately below (p. 312).

CATABOLISM OF IMMUNOGLOBULIN IN MAN

Along with other plasma proteins immunoglobulins are continuously being destroyed and replaced in the body. When the pool size remains constant the rate of destruction and synthesis are just balanced. The process of destruction is generally considered to be due to endocytosis or pinocytosis (see Glossary) of the proteins by phagocytic cells, followed by intracellular digestion. The cells responsible have not been identified, but there is good evidence that they must be mainly in or close to the bloodstream.

The catabolism of immunoglobulins can be studied by transfusing a small amount of material with an easily detectable label, such as a specific antibody activity or a radioactive isotope such as iodine-131, and following its rate of elimination from the bloodstream or from the body. This is possible because once such a labelled molecule has been broken down the label is lost, either by destruction of the specific antibody activity or by a rapid elimination of radioiodine *via* the urine. When such a study is made catabolism is found to take place *exponentially*. That is, it can be expressed in the form

$$C = Co\ e^{-kt}$$

where C = the amount present at time t, Co = the amount present initially (t = 0), t = time, and k is a constant. Some curves depicting the elimination of an intravenously administered trace dose of iodine-131 labelled human IgG from the blood and the body of a normal adult human subject are shown in Fig. 8.1. The curves are plotted on a semi-logarithmic scale—i.e. if the expression given above is obeyed the curve of elimination may be expected to be a straight line. Also shown is a plot of the amount of radioiodine excreted each day in the urine, expressed as a percentage of the total amount of labelled IgG present in the bloodstream at the same time.

It may be assumed that the total pool of IgG in the body remained constant (i.e. the subject's plasma levels of IgG were not fluctuating significantly) during the period of study; that the small amount of iodine-131 labelled IgG injected did not appreciably increase the pool; and that the cells catabolizing IgG could not distinguish between labelled and unlabelled molecules, so that the behaviour of the labelled IgG is a fair representation of what happened to all the IgG present in the blood at the time of the intravenous injection. If we consider the curve depicting the intravascular radioactivity, the first point to notice is that there is an early rapid fall in the amount of the labelled IgG in the blood. Since the total amount in the body hardly changes during this period this rapid fall must largely represent passage of labelled IgG out of the blood into the tissues; and eventually—after about 10 days—equilibrium is reached between the blood and all the various extravascular tissues. From now onwards the curve is a straight line, and the exponential nature of the catabolism becomes evident. The time taken for the amount of labelled IgG in the blood to fall by half is now approximately constant and is termed the *half life*—in this instance equal to about 15 days.

The bottom curve in Fig. 8.1 (after the variations in daily urine collection have been smoothed out) shows that the amount of radioiodine excreted daily in the urine corresponds to 8–9 per cent

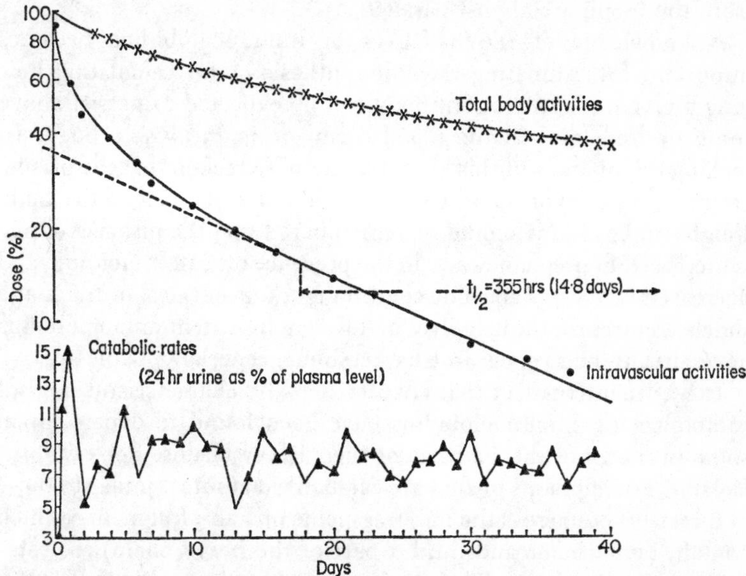

FIG. 8.1. Catabolism of normal human IgG labelled with ^{131}I in man. Trace quantities of radioactively labelled IgG were injected intravenously and blood samples and urine samples taken at regular intervals during the next 38 days. The radioactivity in the urine is due to free iodine liberated by the breakdown of the labelled protein. The total body radioactivity was measured in a whole body counter designed to measure γ-rays.

The curves illustrate the total activity retained in the body (upper curve) the amount of radioactive protein in the plasma (middle curve) and the daily output of radioactivity in the urine plotted as a percentage of that in the plasma at the same time (bottom curve).

of the labelled IgG in the blood. Since rather more than half the IgG is in the tissues, this daily catabolism represents about 4 per cent of the total body pool. The top curve shows the total radioactivity retained in the body, measured by means of a whole body counter. The fact that it is not parallel to the exponential portion of the curve of intravascular radioactivity, as might be expected, is due partly to the fact that there is a lag between passage of labelled IgG from the blood to the tissues and its return, and partly to retention by the thyroid glance of some of the radioiodine set free by the breakdown of the IgG. When similar studies are performed in experimental animals, in which uptake of radioiodine by the thyroid is blocked, the curves representing disappearance from the body and from the blood are almost parallel.

A knowledge of the half-lives of immunoglobulins becomes important for estimating rates of synthesis or for calculating how long a given quantity of antibody can be expected to persist above some desired level in the bloodstream or in the whole body. In making calculations of this kind it is useful to reckon that the plasma volume (in litres) of a normal adult is about 4 per cent of the body weight (in kg) but it should be remembered that the plasma volume is increased in pregnancy and in the presence of water retention, and decreased in various anaemic conditions and in surgical or traumatic shock. Figures for the half-lives of different human immunoglobulins have already been given in Chapter Four, especially Table 4.4.

It was mentioned in that chapter that the characteristic rates of catabolism of immunoglobulins have been found to depend upon some property of the Fc parts of their heavy chains. For example, isolated Fc fragments of IgG are catabolized at rates similar to those of intact IgG, whereas the Fab fragments or Fab'_2 fragments (which contain light chains and the Fd part of the heavy chain) are catabolized much faster. This is an important consideration when immunoglobulin preparations, which may have been 'refined' by pepsin treatment, are used therapeutically.

In several species, including man, the catabolic rate of IgG—i.e. the proportion catabolized daily—increases with the concentration of IgG in the blood. This phenomenon is peculiar to IgG, and is not observed with IgA and IgM or with other plasma proteins such as albumin, whose catabolic rates are essentially independent of their concentration in the plasma over the range which has been studied. Since IgG molecules are also selectively transferred across the gut and/or across the placenta in the same species it is tempting to try to find a common mechanism to explain these phenomena. One hypothesis is that pinocytosis of droplets containing all the plasma proteins takes place at a steady rate, and that the proteins once ingested are rapidly degraded unless specially protected from digestion. In the case of IgG special receptors are postulated on the walls of the pinocytotic vesicles, which bind the IgG, protecting it from catabolism, and at the same time are involved in transfer of the IgG across the cells or permit its return intact to the surrounding fluid. Any IgG taken up in excess of the amount required to saturate the receptors is broken down in the ordinary way. The existence of such a mechanism has not been proved, but it could account for what has been observed.

Increased Catabolism of Immunoglobulins

There are a few conditions in which production of immunoglobulins or of specific antibodies may be normal or even increased but in which the rate of loss or catabolism is so great as to lead to an antibody deficiency with clinical effects comparable to those in the antibody deficiency syndromes described below (p. 328). These conditions may be separated into two categories, on the one hand loss by general leakage of plasma proteins from the body and on the other increased breakdown of immunoglobulins without increased leakage.

Excessive chronic loss may occur *via* the kidney in severe nephrotic states, *via* the small intestine in the state of protein-losing enteropathy and *via* the skin after extensive burning. In all such conditions there is a general leakage of plasma proteins and the loss of albumin is often proportionally greater than that of immunoglobulins. The effects of overall protein loss are usually more striking than those of antibody deficiency, but the possibility of the latter needs to be borne in mind.

Excessive catabolism of immunoglobulins confined to IgG occurs when the plasma level of IgG is raised. This can occur as a result of repeated or prolonged infections, of which malaria in a hyperendemic area provides a notable example, or in the presence of an IgG myeloma. The plasma levels of IgG in chronic infections may reach four times the normal, and be accompanied by an 8-fold increase in catabolic rate, so that specific antibodies must be produced in correspondingly greater amounts to reach the same levels as in normal persons. This usually presents no problem. However, in myelomatosis the IgG levels may rise to eight or ten times normal level, and the overall increase in IgG catabolism may be so great that IgG antibody synthesis, which is not accelerated (and may actually be diminished), fails to keep pace and an antibody deficiency occurs sufficiently serious to lower resistance to infection.

In such cases transfusions of normal immunoglobulins may be required, in addition to any measures taken to diminish the synthesis of myeloma proteins.

PASSAGE OF ANTIBODY FROM MOTHER TO FOETUS AND INFANT

Within its mother's womb the foetus is protected not only from the outside world but also from antigenic stimulation except by such allotypically foreign maternal proteins as may cross the placenta and, rarely, by congenital intrauterine infections such as with rubella virus or *Treponema pallidum.* The human foetus can probably make antibody throughout the second half of pregnancy, as is evidenced by the discovery at such time of mature plasma cells in the tissues of foetuses with congenital syphilis or toxoplasma infection, and the detection of macroglobulin antibodies (which would not normally cross the placenta) in the cord blood taken at delivery from infants infected with toxoplasma or rubella *in utero*. Experiments with foetal monkeys and sheep have shown clear evidence of the capacity from mid-gestation onwards to make at least some antibody to certain antigens. However, in the absence of antigenic stimulation the amount of immunoglobulin synthesized before birth is extremely small, and the newborn infant, relying only on its own resources, would be ill equipped to face the many potentially infective agents of the environment into which it is born. The problem is solved by supplying the young animal with a ready made stock of its mother's antibodies either across the placenta before birth or through the milk immediately after. The relative importance of these pathways varies with the animal species concerned, and is mainly a function of the type of placenta. Placental structures differ markedly in the number of layers or the thickness of foetal and maternal tissue which are interposed between the two circulations. The number varies to some extent with the stage of gestation, since the erosion of maternal tissues is a gradual process, but the main types of placentation and the layers present towards the end of pregnancy are those listed in Table 8.1.

The ease with which substances cross from the maternal to the foetal circulation is correlated partly with the thickness as well as the number of the intervening placental membranes. It is clear that direct passage of proteins is unlikely to occur in those species which have several intervening layers of cells, and indeed it might only be expected in those which have no maternal layer and only minimal foetal layers (man, monkey, rabbit, guinea-pig and mouse). There are, however, other possible routes. If the yolk sac is large (as it is in the rabbit, rat or guinea-pig—though it is rudimentary in the human) and becomes exposed during gestation to the uterine lumen,

TABLE 8.1
Type of placenta

	Epithelio-chorial	Endothelio-chorial	Haemo-chorial	Haemo-endothelial
Maternal tissue:				
Endothelium	+	+	−	−
Epithelium	+	−	−	−
Foetal tissue:				
Chorion	+	+	+	−
Endothelium	+	+	+	+
Examples	Horse, pig, cattle	Cat, dog	Man, monkey	Rabbit, guinea-pig, rat

(Tissues making up the separation membrane in the four principal types of placentation.)

then a large area of potentially absorbing membrane exists which might take up any maternal proteins which pass into the lumen. As will be seen below, in certain species this route has been shown to be important. In birds, antibodies are transmitted from the hen into the yolk of the egg, from which they are absorbed via the yolk sac membrane of the embryo chick without any loss of antibody throughout the period before hatching. IgM antibodies are not absorbed in this way, but remain in the yolk sac until its contents are finally emptied into the gut and thence into the chick just before hatching. This ingenious device ensures that these antibodies, whose half-life is relatively short, are available when they are most needed by the chick.

TRANSFER OF ANTIBODIES IN UTERO

At one end of the scale no transfer of antibody from the maternal blood to the foetus occurs *in utero* in cattle, horses, pigs or sheep, whereas at the other end the young of man, monkey, rabbit and guinea-pig are born with plasma antibody levels about equal to those of their mothers. In between come dog, rat and mouse which receive some, but not all, of their antibodies *in utero*. The situation is summarized in Table 8.2.

TABLE 8.2
Transmission of passive immunity in mammals

Species	Prenatal	Route	Postnatal	Duration of gut absorption
Man, Monkey	+++	transplacental	o or ±	negligible
Rabbit, Guinea-pig	+++	absorption via yolk sac splanchnopleur from uterine lumen	o or ±	negligible
Rat	+	absorption via yolk sac splanchnopleur from uterine lumen	+	20 days
Mouse	+	absorption via yolk sac splanchnopleur from uterine lumen	+	16 days
Dog	+	absorption via yolk sac splanchnopleur from uterine lumen	+	10 days
Ox, goat, sheep, Pig, Horse	o	—	+++	36 hours

Modified from Brambell F.W.R. (1958) *Biol. Rev.* 33, 448–531

Knowledge about passage of antibody from mother to offspring is fairly readily obtained by comparing the levels of actively or passively induced antibodies in the mother with those in the child at birth or when delivered by Caesarian section. Other proteins can be traced by labelling them with a radioactive isotope, such as ^{131}I, and injecting them into the mother and observing to what extent they pass into the foetus. By administering them into various compartments of the mother or foetus (e.g. the blood, the uterine lumen, the amniotic cavity or the exocel) an indication can be obtained of their route of absorption.

In monkeys, and probably in man also, IgG and its contained antibodies pass across the placenta from mother to foetus during the second two-thirds of the gestation period. This passage is selective, in the sense that IgG is transferred, but not IgA or IgM (including the red cell isoagglutinins, which could damage the foetus) or IgE, and albumin is also transferred to a lesser extent but apparently other plasma proteins are not. The direction of transfer of immunoglobulin and albumin is reversible, and materials injected into the foetus reach the mother's circulation, undergoing a similar selection in the process. A foetus is, of course, born with a full supply of albumin, α- and β-globulins, but these have largely or entirely been made by the foetal tissues (mainly the liver) themselves.

In rabbits and guinea-pigs, which have a well-developed yolk sac, the general pattern is much the same in regard to which proteins are transferred, but the route is different. In these species plasma proteins from the mother pass freely to and from the lumen of the pregnant uterus, whence they are absorbed selectively into the foetal circulation via the yolk sac splanchnopleur. Dogs, rats and mice, so far as present evidence shows, behave similarly. A point of theoretical interest, and of some practical importance, is that for immunoglobulin to be absorbed into the foetus it must be intact. As already mentioned in Chapter Four, antibodies can be broken down by papain treatment into F(ab) fragments with the antibody-combining groups and the Fc fragment with no antibody activity. The former are not transmitted whereas the latter is. Since IgA and IgM are not readily transmitted across the placenta, and are known to differ structurally from IgG in respect of their H chains, it is likely that transmissibility depends upon some structural feature unique to the Fc-fragment end of the H chain (see Fig. 4.4). This fact should eventually provide a clue to understanding the cellular mechanism of transmission, but its practical implication is that passive immunization of a mother near term (e.g. with diphtheria antitoxin) will not immunize her offspring unless crude rather than enzyme-treated ('refined') antitoxin is used. In cattle, horses and pigs no transfer of antibody *in utero* occurs.

ANTIBODY TRANSFER BY MILK

Antibody has been found to a variable extent in the milk of all species in which this has been examined. When transmission of antibody also occurs *in utero* the route *via* the milk may be relatively unimportant, but in those species (e.g. ruminants) whose placental structure prevents this, the antibodies received in the milk during the first days after birth are vitally important for the survival of the young animal in the highly infectious world into which it is born. The process by which antibodies pass in this complicated way from the mother's blood to the baby's sets some biological problems which are among the most interesting of the many which surround the neonatal period: these are firstly how the antibodies get into the milk, and secondly how they are absorbed intact from the gut of the suckling animal during its first days of life.

Antibody in Colostrum

The first milk, before lactation proper sets in, is termed colostrum. It differs both in appearance and composition from ordinary milk, and contains mainly immunoglobulins and albumin, with relatively little of the characteristic milk proteins such as casein or β-lactoglobulin. The immunoglobulins in human colostrum are IgG and IgA. Some of the IgA may be synthesized *de novo* from amino acids in the mammary tissue itself, since antibodies are occasionally found in milk which can combine with specific red cell antigens even though such antibodies may be absent from the blood. However, by the use of radio-isotope tracer methods it has been shown in the rabbit that the IgG and part of the IgA, as well as the albumin, are derived from the mother's blood.

Antibodies which accumulate in the colostrum represent a concentration of those present in the mother when colostrum is being secreted, i.e. during the weeks immediately preceding the birth of the young. The mechanism whereby this highly selective concentration of immunoglobulins is brought about is largely unknown, but for IgG may well be similar to that which determines selective passage across the placenta or the gut wall. In the case of IgA transport into the milk, colostrum, saliva and other exocrine secretions involves association of the IgA molecules with a separate and distinct protein ('transport piece') which is formed in the epithelium of the secreting gland. As has already been mentioned in Chapter Four, such secreted IgA occurs in a polymeric form, M.W. about 600,000, probably composed of 3 molecules of IgA and one of 'transport piece'. Extensive synthesis of immunoglobulin *de novo* does not normally occur in the mammary gland itself, but local antibody synthesis may be much increased in the presence of chronic local infection (e.g. chronic mastitis).

In man the amount of antibody provided by colostrum is quite small, but in ruminants, whose young are wholly dependent upon such antibody for protection in the early days of life, the amount is very considerable.

Antibodies in Milk

Once full lactation has begun the milk proteins are predominantly casein and lactoglobulins, but small amounts of immunoglobulin (1–2 per cent of the total protein) derived from the mother's blood are still present. These include antibody, but are normally of no significance, except perhaps for local protection, since, as will be discussed below, the infant no longer absorbs them. Milk may, however, contain quite large amounts of antibody when there is an infection of the ducts and alveoli of breast or udder. Particularly in cases of bovine mastitis, caused by chronic infection of the udder with *Streptococcus agalactiae*, it has been found that antibody is produced by accumulations of plasma cells in the udder tissue, and antibody against the streptococci can be found in the milk even when none is detectable in the blood.

ABSORPTION OF ANTIBODY FROM THE GUT

The new-born calf or rat can absorb from the gut the antibodies in its mother's colostrum or milk almost completely, and they pass into the bloodstream without first being broken down to peptides and amino acids as they would be later on. By feeding serum or milk containing antibodies not already present in the baby, or by feeding proteins labelled with radioactive isotopes, it has been shown that absorption from the gut is selective, and that rather the same sort of selection occurs as takes place when plasma constituents pass into the colostrum or from the mother to the foetus—namely a preferential passage of IgG (not IgA or IgM) and, to a lesser extent, of albumin. Although immunoglobulins of the same species are absorbed best, those from other species are absorbed also, and in any one species of animal the immunoglobulins of other species can be arranged in a characteristic order according to the readiness with which they are absorbed from the gut.

The extent to which absorption by this route can occur is strikingly brought home by comparison of the serum of a new-born calf before first suckling and two days later. In the first case immunoglobulin is virtually absent, and in the second the level is of the same order as that in adult sera (Plate 8.1). It has long been known by farmers that when calves do not get colostrum in the ordinary way they rapidly succumb to a diarrhoeal condition, known as 'calf scours', due to coliform organisms which are harmless in the protected animal.

After a period of time, which varies from 36 to 48 hours in the horse or goat to about 18 days in the rat, absorption of antibodies and other proteins intact from the gut greatly diminishes and finally virtually ceases (see Table 8.2). In the rat, where the question has been studied most, it is found that absorption stops when the cells lining the villi of the small intestine change from a state of very active pinocytosis (ingestion of droplets of the surrounding fluid, to form cytoplasmic vacuoles) to a state in which they have the normal characteristics of such cells in the adult. Administration of cortisone can accelerate the change by as much as 7 days, and cuts short antibody absorption at the same time.

IMMUNOLOGY OF ANTIBODY TRANSFER FROM MOTHER TO FOETUS

The beneficial aspects of antibody transfer *in utero* and of absorption from the milk in the first days of life have been recognized since the classical, and remarkably complete, studies by Paul Ehrlich at the end of the last century. The possibility that harm might also result was only recognized much later, when the rhesus (Rh) blood groups and their relationship to haemolytic disease of the newborn were discovered.

The general problem of the foetus as a homograft is discussed in Chapter Thirteen, and the only aspect which will be discussed here is that of immunization of the mother by foetal erythrocytes. In man, despite the frequent occurrence of ABO blood group incompatibilities between the mother and her offspring, damage to the foetal red cells by transmission of iso-agglutinins is very rare. That this is so is probably largely due to the fact that macroglobulin antibodies (in which the iso-agglutinins are exclusively found, except after artificial immunization with purified iso-antigens) are not transmitted across the placenta; but it may also be due to the fact that when an ABO incompatibility already exists, any foetal red cells which get into the mother's circulation become promptly coated with pre-existing antibody and are destroyed in the liver without providing much antigenic stimulation. When the mother is Rh-negative, and becomes immunized by Rh-positive foetal cells (especially when there is no ABO incompatibility), antibodies are formed in the mother which include IgG as well as IgM and IgA. The former cross the placenta and can cause haemolytic anaemia and other damage to the foetus. In man, antibody in the milk is relatively unimportant in this connection, since the amount is small and absorption is small also.

PREVENTION OF RHESUS ISO-IMMUNIZATION

Although blood group incompatibilities other than Rh may occasionally give rise to haemolytic disease of the newborn by a similar process of immunization of the mother with foetal red blood cells, by far the most important is the Rhesus D antigen. It is very rare for a Rh negative mother to become immunized against her first Rh positive offspring *during* pregnancy, and even more uncommon for the first child to come to any harm from maternal antibody. However, if mothers in Britain are followed up after bearing their first Rh incompatible baby, about 15 per cent can be shown to develop Rh antibodies. During subsequent pregnancies with Rh positive infants the mother's Rh antibody levels are liable to rise much higher, and the risk of damage to the baby by IgG antibodies is correspondingly greater. Studies of the passage of foetal red blood cells into the mother's circulation are not difficult to carry out since foetal cells, irrespective of their blood groups, mostly contain foetal haemoglobin which is more resistant to treatment with alkali than is the haemoglobin in adult red cells. Until the mother develops antibodies, foetal red cells which have entered the mother's blood circulate in the same way as the mother's own red cells. Consequently blood smears taken from the mother at intervals through pregnancy, and treated with dilute alkali, can be used to estimate how many foetal cells have entered her circulation. Such studies have shown that leakage of foetal blood cells may occasionally occur towards the end of gestation, but that the quantity of cells is usually very small, and inadequate to evoke a primary antibody response, though sufficient to evoke a response in a mother who is already primed. During labour or following surgical delivery with rupture of foetal vessels, however, larger leakages are quite common. This accounts for the finding that primary immunization tends to occur at the time of delivery rather than before. It has also made possible a measure to prevent such immunization which is of great practical and theoretical interest.

It was mentioned above that Rh iso-immunization occurs much less frequently when there is also an incompatibility in the ABO blood group system than when there is not. This suggested that if the mother already had antibodies against antigens in the foetal red cells, but was not already immunized by the Rh antigen, the foetal red cells failed to be immunogenic. The effect was therefore tested of administering human anti-Rh antibodies shortly after childbirth to Rh negative primiparae who had borne Rh positive infants, and in whom foetal cells were shown to be present, and it was found that in no instance did the mother become immunized. Very extensive trials in women and in male volunteers have shown that administration of human IgG Rhesus antibody intramuscularly within 24–48 hours of delivery or of injecting Rh positive cells effectively prevents Rhesus iso-immunization (see Table 8.3). The amounts of antibody

TABLE 8.3

Effect of administration of anti-Rh(D) immunoglobulin to Rh negative mothers shortly after giving birth to Rh positive infants

The mothers' serum was tested for the presence of anti-Rh antibodies (attributable to active immunization by their infants' red cells) six months or more after parturition.

	Total	Anti-Rh present	% immunized
Treated group	1137	2	0·18
(subsequent pregnancy*)	92	2	2·2
Untreated group	885	78	8·8
(subsequent pregnancy*)	83	19	23

* Subsequent pregnancy, without further anti-D administration.

(Figures kindly supplied by Prof. C.A. Clarke from a survey of results from the U.K., U.S.A. and Germany up to 1968. Various doses of anti-D were used in the different trials.)

needed to neutralize the usual leakage of Rh positive cells from the foetus are quite small—200 micrograms are probably more than sufficient—and have been shown to be less than the amounts which would be required to combine with all the Rh antigenic determinants on the foetal cells. We appear to be dealing with a very practical example of so-called feed-back inhibition by antibody of primary immunization (see Chapter Seven, p. 259). At present it is uncertain how far the mechanism involves masking of antigenic sites on the red cells or their rapid clearance from the blood after combination with antibody. What seems certain is that administration of anti-Rh immunoglobulin concentrates is likely to become routine prophylactic treatment for women at risk. The supply of such antibodies could currently be met by blood donations from women who have already been immunized by pregnancy, but as the prophylactic measures take effect further supplies are likely to require donations from actively immunized Rh negative men or women who have reached the menopause.

HAEMOLYTIC DISEASE OF THE NEWBORN IN OTHER SPECIES

Haemolytic disease of the new-born occurs also in mules, thoroughbred horses and in pigs. In the horse, immunization occurs during pregnancy against foetal red cell antigens inherited from the sire but absent from the mare, in much the same way as in Rhesus iso-immunization in man. The sow, however, generally does not become naturally immunized by pregnancy, but is readily immunized by a commonly used vaccine against swine fever which consists of pooled whole blood taken from infected animals. In so far as this contains antigens possessed by the foetus and not by the mother, the consequences of such artificial iso-immunization are equally damaging. Since antibodies are not transmitted *in utero* the young are born healthy, but haemolytic anaemia and jaundice develop within one or two days after ingesting the mother's colostrum, which is rich in immune iso-antibodies. Colostrum from another mare or sow can be quite harmless.

OTHER CONSEQUENCES OF TRANSFER OF INTACT PROTEIN ACROSS THE PLACENTA OR ABSORPTION FROM THE GUT

(a) *Transfer of Other Iso- and Auto-antibodies*

When red blood cells leak from the foetus to the mother foetal leucocytes may do likewise, and indeed pregnancy is the commonest cause of the appearance of leucocyte isoagglutinins. These are discussed more fully in Chapter Six, but it may be mentioned here that if a mother has a high level of IgG antibodies against antigenic determinants on her baby's leucocytes the child may be born with leucopenia which may last for as long as ten weeks. Auto-antibodies may also be transferred to the foetus during gestation from mothers with such diseases as systemic lupus erythematosus, idiopathic thrombocytopenic purpura, myasthenia gravis or thyrotoxicosis. The degree to which the various auto-antibodies are responsible for disease is considered at length in Chapter Fifteen. However, there is strong evidence that high maternal levels of anti-platelet antibodies, or of 'long acting thyroid stimulator' (an antibody against thyroid microsomal antigens), may be accompanied by transient affection of the corresponding tissues of the infant at the time of birth and during the weeks that follow.

(b) *Immunization Against Maternal IgG*

Maternal IgG is often not identical with the IgG made by the infant in respect of the genetically determined allotypic determinants such as Gm groups discussed in Chapter Four. Since the foetus is flooded with its mother's IgG throughout most of pregnancy, and for some months after, and since it is known that immunological tolerance is readily produced by administration of quite small amounts of many soluble foreign proteins before or shortly after birth, the reader who has followed the argument in Chapter Three might expect that a state of tolerance would develop towards such allotypic determinants. In fact a considerable proportion of children aged 3 to 4 years have been found to possess antibodies specific for Gm determinants present in their mother's IgG but absent from their own, and these must have arisen as a result of immunization by maternal IgG. When the allotypic determinant absent from the child but present in the mother is Gm (1), as many as 70 per cent of the children develop antibodies against this determinant. Such antibodies are usually only present at quite low levels, and they have little known practical consequence except to provide a source of Gm specific antisera and to raise so far unsolved theoretical problems.

(c) *Immunization Against Proteins Absorbed from the Gut*

At the time during the neonatal period when proteins from the mother's milk are absorbed intact from the gut foreign proteins with similar characteristics may also be absorbed when administered by mouth. Experimentally it has been shown that sufficient foreign protein may be absorbed by a rat or mouse to produce a state of immunological tolerance (see Chapter Thirteen), and indeed the period during which immunological tolerance can be produced most easily corresponds rather closely with the period during which absorption of intact protein can take place. Alternatively, if foreign proteins are first ingested somewhat later, but before absorption intact has completely ceased, such proteins may cause immunological sensitization. Although in man intestinal absorption is minimal it may account for the fact that many infants fed on cow's milk have antibodies to milk proteins in their blood, and may in this way acquire the preliminary sensitization which leads to infantile eczema, or, rarely, 'cot death' (see Chapter Nine).

IMMUNOLOGICAL DEFICIENCY DISEASES

In the sections which follow we shall discuss various disorders of the immunological apparatus, some of which lead to quantitatively or qualitatively deficient production and others to specialized over-production of immunoglobulins. Many of these result in a failure to resist infection but immunity may also fail because of deficiencies in functions of the reticuloendothelial system other than those involving specific responses by immunologically competent cells. Although this subject has been discussed in a general way in Chapter Two, it may be useful for the sake of clarity to summarize at this stage without discussion some of the principal defects met in human beings. Deficiencies in the phagocytic mechanism can occur on the one hand from diminished numbers of microphages or macrophages, or on the other hand from their inadequate function, which may take several forms. They are most commonly recognized in childhood, since many of them are congenital. All are rare, but the least rare are listed below.

NON-SPECIFIC FAILURE OF IMMUNITY DUE TO DEFECTIVE PHAGOCYTIC MECHANISMS

(a) QUANTITATIVE DEFICIENCIES

Congenital Neutropenia

In theory, and possibly in practice, immunization of a mother by the child's leucocytes can occur *in utero*, and result in a more or less severe neutropenia due to transferred maternal antibody. Such a neutropenia is likely to be transient. There are also described two genetically determined conditions in which the number of neutrophils fluctuate around a low or very low level. One, termed *infantile agranulocytosis*, is inherited as a recessive trait and usually proves fatal, whereas the other, *benign chronic granulocytopenia of children*, is a dominant character but—as its name implies—is less severe. Children with marked neutrophil deficiency are liable to have foul necrotic lesions of their tonsils, due to spirochaetes and fusiform bacilli, and to suffer recurrent severe staphylococcal infections.

Acquired Neutropenia (Agranulocytosis)

Various causes are described, including neutropenia induced by drugs; by toxins (e.g. benzol poisoning); accompanying aplastic anaemia; or secondary to invasion of the bone marrow by tumours or to sclerosing diseases. Drug induced agranulocytosis is discussed further in Chapter Eleven (p. 478). Damage to the bone marrow due to large doses of ionizing radiation or of radiomimetic drugs represents potentially the most important cause of neutropenia at the present time.

Quantitative Deficiency of the reticulo-endothelial (macrophage) system resulting from splenectomy (or congenital splenic hypoplasia) or from invasion by neoplastic tissue. When this occurs the subjects are unduly liable to suffer overwhelming bacterial infections, and are notably susceptible to meningococcal septicaemia.

(b) QUALITATIVE DEFICIENCIES

Chronic Granulomatous Disease

This is a sex-linked recessive condition characterized by increased susceptibility to infection early in life by microbes of relatively low virulence in normal persons. Severe suppurative and granulomatous inflammatory responses occur together in children whose specific immune mechanisms are apparently adequate.

The defect is in the function of neutrophil leucocytes, which ingest microbes normally but fail to kill them. This failure is associated with an absence of the activation of the hexosemonophosphate shunt which normally follows phagocytosis, and it can be tested for in individual cells by a histochemical technique. Female carriers of the mutant gene have been found to possess two populations of polymorphs, one defective and one normal, suggesting that one or other of the X-chromosomes is inactive, as predicted by the Lyon hypothesis.

Chediak-Higashi Syndrome

A rare disease of children characterized by a tendency to chronic infections and defective pigmentation of skin, hair and eyes. There appears to be an underlying abnormality of intracellular organelles including lysosomal granules and melanin granules. Survivors tend to develop reticuloses (see Plate 8.2, following p. 404).

SPECIFIC FAILURES OF IMMUNITY

These may be divided into two broad categories—those which involve failure of the synthesis of some or all of the immunoglobulins and those which involve a failure of cell-mediated specific immunity. Consideration of the pathogenetic mechanisms involved is made more intelligible by the experimental observations on birds and mammals which indicate that lymphoid tissues are functionally separable into two components (see Chapter Three). One population is thymus-dependent and is responsible for cell-mediated specific immunity; another is thymus-independent and contains the precursors of plasma cells involved in immunoglobulin synthesis. In birds the latter population differentiates in the bursa of Fabricius. (It has been suggested that an analogous function in mammals may be served by some of the lymphoid tissue along the gut, but this remains to be conclusively demonstrated.) There is at present no evidence to indicate whether or not the functional cells which make up the two components are derived from a common stem cell, but it is a reasonable hypothesis that a single stem cell could become functionally differentiated in different ways under the local influence of hormones or other environmental factors in different sites.

This approach has some useful predictive value when considering the various kinds of immunological deficiencies outlined below. Thus patients with failure of the thymus-dependent system alone may be expected to have normal germinal centres, normal numbers of plasma cells and normal levels of each of the immunoglobulins, but to show defective cell-mediated specific immunity and to lack lymphocytes in the 'thymus dependent' areas of lymphoid tissues. Such is the case in *thymic aplasia*. Patients with failure of the thymus-independent immunoglobulin producing system will lack germinal centres and plasma cells and will not make immunoglobulins, but will have a normal thymus and relatively normal numbers of lymphocytes in their lymphoid tissues and unimpaired cell-mediated specific immunity. Such are the patients with *infantile sex-linked recessive agammaglobulinaemia*. When both systems are defective (e.g. in consequence of a genetic defect involving all lymphoid stem cell development) the picture will be that revealed by patients with *autosomal recessive alymphocytic agammaglobulinaemia*.

The conditions mentioned above represent the most clear cut and extreme examples, and it is not easy to compress within this general scheme all the syndromes described. Furthermore, some of the syndromes are not so clearly defined that their characteristic clinical and pathological features, or their names, can be set down with certainty. Nevertheless a tentative classification is needed, and one based on the report of a Study Group of the World Health Organization (see Further Reading for this chapter) is attempted below.

TABLE 8.4

Syndromes showing failure of Specific Immunity with Thymus Abnormalities

Syndrome	Probable heredity	Thymic development	Other developmental abnormalities	Peripheral lymphoid tissue	Blood lymphocytes
Reticular dysgenesis	?	Rudimentary epithelial elements only	Absence of all leucocytes	Absent	All leucocytes absent
Alymphocytic agammaglobulinaemia (Swiss-type agammaglobulinaemia; thymic alymphoplasia)	autosomal recessive	rudimentary; epithelial cells variable	—	absence of lymphocytes and of germinal centres	very low
Hereditary lymphopenic immunological deficiency	X-linked recessive *or* autosomal recessive	hypoplastic; grossly deficient in lymphoid cells and Hassall's corpuscles	—	gross deficiency of lymphocytes, but foci present in spleen and lymph nodes	low but variable
Thymic aplasia (thymic agenesis) (Di George syndrome)	?	absent	failure of development of epithelium of 3rd and 4th pharyngeal pouches (including parathyroids)	lymphocytes absent in paracortical areas. Germinal centres present	low but variable
Ataxia telangiectasia	autosomal recessive	embryonic type, No Hassall's corpuscles	telangiectasia, especially in cerebellum	lymphocytes absent from paracortical areas	slight decrease

TABLE 8.4 (*cont.*)

Syndrome	Cell-mediated specific immunity	Immunoglobulin production	Antibody production	Survival
Reticular dysgenesis	? absent	? absent	? absent	brief
Alymphocytic agammaglobulinaemia (Swiss-type agammaglobulinaemia; thymic alymphoplasia)	absent	all classes very deficient	absent or very deficient	brief
Hereditary lymphopenic immunological deficiency	deficient response to some antigens but not to others	Always abnormal, but class involved and direction of change variable	deficient response to some antigens but not to others	brief; usually die of fungal or virus infection
Thymic aplasia (thymic agenesis) (Di George syndrome)	absent	all classes normal	partially deficient	brief (usually recognized by neonatal tetany)
Ataxia telangiectasia	deficient response to some antigens but not to others	usually abnormal, but class involved and direction of change variable (often IgA deficiency)	deficient response to some antigens but not to others	may appear late. Associated telangiectasia; cerebellar ataxia; ovarian dysgenesis in females

SYNDROMES WITH DEFECTIVE DEVELOPMENT OF THE THYMUS

Several syndromes have been described, associated with greater or lesser degrees of thymus deficiency. Some of these deficiencies appear to affect the development of other tissues besides lymphoid tissues, and may involve some unrecognized general step in cellular differentiation. It is not always possible to make hard and fast divisions between the syndromes, and the literature is confused by the use of several terms to describe the same condition. A provisional classification is given in Table 8.4, although it is recognized that further studies may lead to some other classification. The common feature of all the conditions in which development fails of thymus lymphocytes is failure to show delayed type hypersensitivity. Immunoglobulin production (and plasma cell development) is frequently depressed, but by no means invariably so. The capacity to form specific antibodies in response to natural or experimental stimuli is apparently more defective than is immunoglobulin synthesis, and this deficiency is a major cause of early death. In many ways the syndromes are reflected in the behaviour of neonatally thymectomized mice (see Chapter Three). No perfectly consistent explanation is available, but the findings support the hypothesis that delayed type responses involve thymus-dependent cells and that immunoglobulin production can be effected by cells which do not originate in the thymus, but whose ability to synthesize specific antibodies depends upon some function of the thymus, possibly related to its epithelial cells. In the absence of defective function of the thymus the generation of diversity (p. 145), required for synthesis of a wide spectrum of different antibodies, appears to be missing or restricted.

IMMUNOGLOBULIN DEFICIENCIES WITHOUT THYMUS ABNORMALITIES

There are a number of conditions in which immunoglobulin production is defective, but in which no primary thymus abnormality is recognized. There are either primary or secondary to other conditions, and are listed below:

Congenital sex-linked (Bruton type)
Primary acquired (late onset)
Selective immunoglobulin deficiencies
(Dysgammaglobulinaemia)

Secondary acquired (generally due to leukaemia or myeloma)
Transient, in infancy.

Congenital Sex-linked Immunoglobulin Deficiency (Agammaglobulinaemia)

This was the first form of hypogammaglobulinaemia to be recognized and was described in 1952. It affects males, and is usually first recognized at 4–6 months of age, when the maternal immunoglobulin acquired before birth has virtually disappeared from the circulation. The afflicted children lack all forms of immunoglobulin, the overall levels lying below 50 mg/100 ml. Plasma cells are absent from their lymphoid tissue, which is reduced in bulk—pharyngeal lymphoid tissue being strikingly and almost diagnostically diminished. The thymus structure is normal; circulating lymphocytes are not notably diminished (though there may be neutropenia); lymphoid tissue contains cortical lymphocytes, but germinal centres and lymphoid follicles are lacking. Delayed-type responses are usually unimpaired. A fair experimental analogy is provided by chickens which have been bursectomized at birth or *in ovo*, and a very close analogy by chickens which have been bursectomized and exposed to 600 r whole body irradiation, in which plasma cells and immunoglobulins are lacking, but delayed type responses are little if at all impaired (see Chapter Three). Patients who survive this disease have an increased tendency to develop leukaemia, but whether there is a causal connection is not known.

Primary Acquired Immunoglobulin Deficiency

A more common form of immunoglobulin deficiency affects adults of either sex who were previously apparently normal. Its onset occurs most commonly between 30 and 50 years of age. All classes of immunoglobulin are generally affected, and the overall level is commonly 10–200 mg/100 ml. Antibody responses are undetectable or very feeble, though they may nevertheless suffice to afford protection against second infections with viruses such as measles or poliomyelitis. Peripheral lymphocytes are apparently normal, and delayed-type hypersensitivity is not impaired. Plasma cells are absent from the bone marrow and lymphoid tissues, and the latter usually lack germinal centres, though rarely these are hyperplastic and resemble those seen in the condition known as *giant follicular lymphoblastoma*. The thymus usually has no obvious abnormality, but some 10 per cent of cases have thymomas which are epithelial rather than mesenchymal in type.

It is quite likely that the syndrome of primary acquired immunoglobulin deficiency includes several different diseases, and that they are not truly acquired, in the sense that they are specifically due to some agent acting late in life. Family studies have shown that close relatives of the patients are liable to an unusually high incidence of hypergammaglobulinaemia, myeloma, systemic lupus erythematosus, idiopathic thrombocytopenia, rheumatoid arthritis and isolated immunoglobulin deficiencies. This suggests that in at least some instances there is an unknown genetic abnormality concerned with the regulation of immunoglobulin synthesis.

Selective Immunoglobulin Deficiencies (*Dysgammaglobulinaemia*)

A variety of syndromes has been described under the general term dysgammaglobulinaemia which involve selective rather than absolute immunoglobulin deficiencies, coupled with heightened susceptibility to infection. Their relationship to the congenital sex linked deficiency of all immunoglobulins (agammaglobulinaemia) described above is uncertain, and since evidence about the presence or absence of thymus abnormalities has often been lacking it is not possible to be sure whether some of the cases assembled under this heading may not properly have belonged to the group of immunoglobulin deficiencies listed in Table 8.4. Nevertheless each syndrome appears to be sufficiently characteristic to warrant at least a provisional classification as set forth in Table 8.5. Most authors agree that peripheral blood lymphocytes are normal or only moderately decreased in number in these conditions and that lymphocytes are not notably absent from lymphoid tissues. Delayed-type responses when tested for have usually been normal but sometimes diminished or absent—a variability which suggests that more than one aetiology is involved. The interesting suggestion has been made that the selective immunoglobulin deficiencies represent defects in the genetic control of the synthesis of the H chains specific for one or more immunoglobulin classes (complete absence of all immunoglobulins being perhaps due to failure to make L chains, which would prevent any complete immunoglobulin molecules from being made at all). This speculation is difficult to reconcile with the fact that inheritance of some forms of selective deficiency appears to be sex-linked, whereas the inheritance of allotypes on the H chains (and

TABLE 8.5

Classification of selective immunoglobulin deficiencies (Dysgammaglobulinaemias)†

Type	Age at onset	Sex occurrence	Special clinical features*	Antibody responses	Immunoglobulin levels IgG	IgM	IgA
congenital or acquired	usually infancy but also any age	usually but not always males	enlargement of spleen, liver and lymphoid tissue	poor	very low or absent	markedly raised	moderately diminished
congenital	infancy	males		very poor	normal	very low or absent	very low or absent
Wiskott–Aldrich syndrome	infancy	males	eczema; thrombocytopenia	normal or decreased (especially IgM)	normal	low	raised

* All cases have increased susceptibility to infections.

Modified from Stiehm E.R. and Fudenberg H.H., *Amer. J. Med.* **40**, 805 (1966).

† The term 'dysgammaglobulinaemia' is unsatisfactory since there is no general agreement concerning its *raison d'être*. The concept of inefficient gammaglobulin seems to have arisen from the occurrence of patients with history of recurrent infections who had normal or raised total immunoglobulin levels in their serum. Immunological deficiency has been envisaged to depend upon either selective deficiency of one of the immunoglobulin classes or of a segment of the spectrum of the varied specificities of the antibody or by replacement of the normal immunoglobulins by molecules without function as antibodies.

presumably of the whole H chain genes) is not, but it is mentioned because it illustrates a possibly fruitful approach to understanding the aetiology of such disorders.

The Wiskott–Aldrich syndrome is included under the heading dysgammaglobulinaemia because of the very marked susceptibility to infections, depression of IgM and absence of isoagglutinins, and the markedly raised IgA levels. In addition there is characteristically moderate to severe eczema, and an unexplained thrombocytopenia. However, antibodies against some bacterial antigens are made normally, though antibodies against viruses tend to be decreased. The morphology of lymph nodes and their response to antigenic stimulation have been reported normal, and so has phagocytosis of bacteria by polymorphs. In families affected by this remarkable sex linked recessive disease as many as half the male children may die from infections in infancy. However, treatment with normal IgG (see below), even when supplemented with normal IgM, has not been so successful as it has in the case of primary or secondary agammaglobulinaemias, and there may be some other important but unrecognized factors in the aetiology of this disease.

Secondary Acquired Immunoglobulin Deficiency

Normal immunoglobulin production is profoundly diminished, sufficient eventually to produce complications attributable to antibody deficiency such as those described below, in about half of all cases of chronic lymphatic leukaemia. The most obvious explanation for this is that the lymphoid organs become so extensively infiltrated by leukaemic tissue that immunoglobulin-producing cells are crowded out and/or that there is competition for essential nutrients. However, it is also possible that the same change in the lymphoid cells which leads to malignant proliferation also blocks their differentiation into plasma cells; thus an early effect of Friend virus infection, which ultimately leads to leukaemia in mice, is to diminish antibody production.

Severe antibody deficiency is a not uncommon complication of multiple myeloma, especially of those cases in which IgG myeloma protein is present in very large amounts. An important factor is the greatly increased rate of catabolism of all IgG which results when the level of IgG is markedly raised even by a single component belonging to this class. This can result in much diminished levels of IgG antibodies even when their rate of synthesis is undiminished.

However, other factors such as those cited above in chronic lymphatic leukaemia may also be operative.

Physiological Immunoglobulin Deficiency in Infancy

It has already been explained that newborn infants largely rely on maternal immunoglobulin. On the very rare occasions when the mother is herself deficient in IgG the infant will lack this supply, and if untreated will remain virtually unprotected until it begins to make its own antibodies. Most infants begin to make significant amounts of immunoglobulin after 4–12 weeks, and achieve normal immunoglobulin levels by their own efforts some time between 6 and 9 months, by which time maternal immunoglobulins have disappeared from their circulation. Occasionally (for reasons unknown) antibody formation in the infant is delayed in onset or slow in progress, and its supplies may fall to a dangerously low level after the first months before they eventually recover.

CLINICAL MANIFESTATIONS OF IMMUNOGLOBULIN DEFICIENCY DISEASES

Increased susceptibility to infections of many kinds is the hallmark of all the diseases discussed above, although in particular syndromes there may be additional features such as those due to developmental defects, e.g. of the parathyroid glands or of blood leucocytes. The age of onset of manifest illness depends upon whether the deficiency is congenital or acquired later in life, but is rarely earlier than the third or fourth month, owing to the protection afforded by maternal antibodies. Illness is heralded by any one of a variety of bacterial infections, such as repeated attacks of meningitis, repeated bouts of pneumonia, furunculosis or pyodermia, sinusitis or otitis media. The individual pattern of infection is unpredictable, but the most frequent site to be affected is the respiratory tract. The organisms involved in these infections are primarily the so-called pyogenic (or pus-forming) bacteria: *Staphylococcus aureus*, *Streptococcus pyogenes*, *Streptococcus pneumoniae*, *Neisseria meningitidis* and *Haemophilus influenzae*. It is also apparent that fungal infections are also common in these cases, especially involving *Candida albicans* which can give rise to mouth infection (thrush), tracheitis or enteritis. There is a suggestion that patients lacking IgA antibody are particularly susceptible to chronic infections of the respiratory tract mucosa, which would be in line with the postulated role of secreted

IgA as an 'antiseptic paint' mentioned in Chapter Four. In those syndromes in which there is no associated deficiency in cell-mediated specific immunity the response is normal to the common virus infections of childhood such as measles, rubella, chicken pox, mumps and virus infections of the upper respiratory tract, although attacks of viral hepatitis often take a severe form. Vaccination with vaccinia virus produces no unusual reaction, and such patients respond normally to BCG and show no undue susceptibility to clinical tuberculosis. However, when there is also marked deficiency in cell-mediated specific immunity associated with thymic abnormality, the resistance to viral infectious may be defective and thus vaccination against smallpox may result in severe necrosis at the site of vaccination (*vaccinia gangrenosa*) or in progression to generalized vaccinia; measles infection may fail to resolve and the rash may persist for weeks or even months. Likewise BCG vaccination may result in generalized miliary tuberculosis.

It would appear that the thymus-dependent lymphopenic states, whether or not the immunoglobulins are defective, are particularly associated with a susceptibility to virus infections. In them also a striking incidence of mucous membrane infections by *Candida albicans*, and of urinary tract infections by *Pseudomonas pyocyanea* has been recorded.

The patients most fully studied have been those with severe deficiency of all the immunoglobulins, who have survived beyond infancy and in whom the disorder has first appeared in adult life. Their antibody responses to immunization with typhoid vaccines or with diphtheria or tetanus toxoids are usually undetectable or very poor. Nevertheless, such individuals do not suffer from recurrent virus infections. In point of fact, when extremely sensitive tests for antibody to virus vaccines, such as poliomyelitis, are used it can be shown that even these patients can make detectable amounts of specific antibody. Since, so far as we know, interferon production is normal, and since even minute amounts of antibody can prevent virus infection of cells, these probably suffice. Why the patients with the Wiskott–Aldrich syndrome should suffer from repeated virus infections despite relatively intact immunoglobulin production and cellular resistance mechanisms is without explanation. As has already been mentioned, other factors may be involved in this condition.

Pneumocystis Carinii Pneumonia

Patients with immunoglobulin deficiency appear to be more than usually susceptible to a strange form of pneumonia associated with the presence in the lung of a rare protozoon, *Pneumocystis carinii*. In the normal person this infection leads to an interstitial pneumonia with a viscous alveolar exudate, plasma cells being prominent among the inflammatory cells. It is significant that in cases of immunoglobulin deficiency the *Pneumocystis* pneumonia occurs without plasma cells being present in the interstitial cellular exudate.

Ability to Develop Delayed-type Cutaneous Hypersensitivity

As was indicated above in the classification of immunoglobulin deficiency diseases, those cases in which there is a primary thymus abnormality fail to show the normal response to BCG vaccination and to develop a typical positive Mantoux reaction. Similarly, when simple chemical compounds such as 2,4-dinitrofluorobenzene are applied in vesicant doses to the skin, such patients do not develop typical contact sensitivity to a subsequent patch test; homografts of human skin have also been shown to survive for prolonged periods of time, sometimes for the abbreviated lifetime of the patient.

By contrast most cases of immunoglobulin deficiency show normal responses to BCG vaccination, they develop contact sensitivity, and they reject skin homografts after the usual or sometimes a somewhat prolonged time interval. This clear-cut separation between failure to make antibodies and ability to develop delayed type hypersensitivity has been used as an argument that free antibody plays no part in the phenomenon of delayed type hypersensitivity. Furthermore, it has been shown that such hypersensitivity developed in individuals with extreme immunoglobulin deficiency can be transferred to non-sensitized normal individuals by subcutaneous injection of the patient's leucocytes, but cannot be so transferred by even large amounts of serum.

INVESTIGATION OF PATIENTS WITH PRIMARY IMMUNOLOGICAL DEFICIENCY SYNDROMES

These syndromes, though rarely encountered, are of the greatest interest because of the light which they can shed upon the nature of the immunological response, and ultimately on the way in which the deficiencies might be corrected. The examination of such patients should therefore include whenever possible:

(a) Family studies through three generations for any abnormality of immunoglobulins or immunoglobulin function. Enquiry should be made for parental consanguinity, a high incidence of which suggests autosomal recessive inheritance.

(b) Careful search for prenatal infections or other prenatal influences.

(c) Chromosome analyses on all patients. These should be made on peripheral blood cells as well as cells from some other site. Such studies would be of interest in their own right and would help to establish the existence of chimaerism. For the same reason history of twinning or previous transfusions should be elicited and a search for mosaicism of blood groups should be made.

(d) A search for linkage or association with known genetic markers.

(e) Quantitative determinations of all classes of immunoglobulins and a search for qualitative immunoglobulin abnormalities in patients and relatives.

(f) Observations in patients and relatives of immune responses to a standard panel of weak and strong antigens. Living virus or bacterial vaccines should *not* be used. Tests for ability to develop contact hypersensitivity.

(g) Serial counts of circulating lymphocytes and lymphocyte function tests *in vivo* and *in vitro*.

(h) X-ray of the thymus region and biopsies of the rectum and a peripheral lymph node. Post-mortem examination should include the thymus and all lymphoid organs.

TREATMENT

The basis of treatment is the use of an appropriate antibiotic to control infections and regular administration of pooled human immunoglobulin, which may be expected to contain antibodies against the great majority of the natural pathogens present in the community. Injections may be given at a dosage of 100–200 mg/kg body weight each month. In Britain it is usual to give ether-fractionated immunoglobulin. Only IgG is effectively replaced by this procedure, and deficiencies in IgA and IgM remain. However, such treatment is effective in most cases of straightforward immunoglobulin deficiency. In other cases, such as the Wiskott–Aldrich syndrome, which do not respond satisfactorily to this regimen, even when IgM has been purposely added as well the prognosis has not been markedly improved. Vaccination is contraindicated owing to the danger of progression to generalized vaccinia or to vaccinia gangrenosa. Should these occur they may be treated with interferon or N-methylisatin-β -thiosemicarbazone. It is also necessary to stress the dangers attending the use of blood transfusions for cases with deficiencies of cell-mediated immunity. Rigorous precautions must be taken to avoid serum hepatitis, and any syringes used for injecting these patients must be carefully checked for sterility.

Attempts have been made to correct some of these deficiencies by means of grafts of thymus or lymphoid tissue. Such attempts are beset by the danger of causing graft *versus* host reactions if adult lymphoid tissue or cells are used (see Chapter Thirteen), and foetal tissues have therefore generally been employed. The problem differs for the different types of immunological deficiency. Failure of foetal thymus to restore cases of Swiss-type (or combined) deficiency indicates a defect in this disease of multipotent cells derived from the bone marrow. Use of maternal (unmatched) marrow cells in such a case resulted in fatal graft-*versus*-host disease. Recently, success has attended the use of sibling bone marrow closely matched for histocompatibility. In the case of thymic aplasia (Di George syndrome) restoration with a graft of foetal thymus has recently been reported. Delayed-type hypersensitivity reactions and ability of lymphocytes to transform with phytohaemagglutinin were dramatically restored soon after grafting and since the graft consisted of female cells into a male it could be established that the transforming cells were the recipient's own leucocytes.

ABERRATIONS OF IMMUNOGLOBULIN SYNTHESIS

MULTIPLE MYELOMA (PLASMACYTOMA)

We have already discussed in Chapter Four how over-proliferation may occur of cells synthesizing a constant and uniform immunoglobulin product, and apparently derived from a single clone of neoplastic plasma cells which have retained their characteristic synthetic ability. In that chapter it was stressed how much our understanding of the immunoglobulin classes and of the heterogeneity of the immunoglobulins within each class owes to the immunochemical analysis of such neoplastic cell products. We shall now consider multiple myeloma and certain allied conditions from a more clinical point of view.

The condition occurs in persons, especially males, over 40 years of age. Characteristically there is an increase in total plasma proteins (to 10 g or more per 100 ml instead of the usual 6·5 to 8·0 g), due to an increase in the concentration of immunoglobulin. Electrophoretic or immunoelectrophoretic examination of the serum reveals the presence of an unusually sharp Ig peak, usually in the region of the γ-globulins but sometimes in that of the β-globulins (Plate 8.3). The peak is due to the myeloma protein, which because of its homogeneity is not spread over the range covered by the rest of the immunoglobulins. By the use of suitable specific antisera it has been shown in a large series of cases that about 55 per cent of the patients had an IgG myeloma protein, about 23 per cent IgA, and less than 1 per cent had IgD. IgE is exceedingly rare, and in fact only a single presumptive case has so far been reported. The remainder of the series had Bence-Jones proteins (see below) only. Although the characteristic protein and its electrophoretic behaviour varies markedly from patient to patient, in any one person it remains the same throughout the course of the disease. Such increased immunoglobulin production is associated with multiple tumours composed of plasma cells, which are typically found in the bones and give rise to punched out transparent areas in X-ray pictures.

Bence-Jones Proteins

In about half the cases there also appears a quite unusual protein in the urine ('Bence-Jones proteinuria') named after its discoverer in 1848. This finding is of great diagnostic importance since, apart from the rare occurrence of a similar protein in the urine in cases of macroglobulinaemia (see below) and leukaemia, its secretion in significant quantities is unique to this disease. Bence-Jones proteins are precipitated on heating urine to 50–60°C, especially when the pH has been adjusted to lie within 4 to 6, which is the iso-electric range; on further heating above 80° they go back into solution, but reappear on cooling.

The Bence-Jones proteins of different patients are not identical. As has already been explained in Chapter Four, they represent either monomers or dimers of the light chains of the myeloma protein, which are over-produced as a result of unbalanced synthesis of light and heavy chains. No two light chains of individual immunoglobulins have yet been shown to be identical. However, the Bence-Jones protein secreted by any one patient remains the same throughout the course of the disease, and is always found to belong either to the κ (of which there have recently been found to exist three subtypes) or λ type. As was mentioned above, in about 20 per cent of cases of multiple myeloma Bence-Jones protein may be the sole secreted produce of the myeloma cells. Such proteins may be excreted *via* the urine in large quantities, but are not usually evident on routine electrophoretic examination of the serum. The reason is that, being small molecules (about 20,000 molecular weight if monomers or about 40,000 if dimers) they readily pass through the renal glomeruli. It has also been shown—by isolating Bence-Jones protein from a patient's urine, labelling it with radioactive iodine and reinfusing it into the bloodstream—that these proteins are also rapidly broken down in the body, much faster than whole immunoglobulin molecules with their H chains intact. This observation implies that the daily production of Bence-Jones proteins is substantially greater than would be deduced from the amount lost in the urine.

Patients who excrete Bence-Jones protein over prolonged periods of time are especially liable to develop *amyloidosis*, usually of the 'primary' type with infiltrations of the heart, tongue, skin and gastrointestinal tract rather than of the liver, spleen and kidneys. However, renal damage is not uncommon in chronic myelomatosis, and the urine is then liable to contain an excess of other plasma proteins in addition to Bence-Jones protein.

It should be pointed out that the secretion of excess free light chains in the course of immunoglobin synthesis is not wholly a pathological phenomenon. If the plasma and urine from healthy people is examined after extensive concentration and suitable fractionation, a very small amount of free light chains can be detected. These are not the result of breakdown during fractionation, but indicate that even in the normal population of cells synthesizing immunoglobulin there are some in which synthesis of H and L chains is not perfectly balanced.

Antibody Production in Multiple Myeloma

Patients with myelomatosis, especially if they make large amounts of IgG myeloma protein, are very often poor producers of antibody. They may in fact suffer from repeated infections much as do persons with immunoglobulin deficiency syndromes and may require repeated transfusions of immunoglobulins from normal persons in order to keep them free from intercurrent infections. The probable reasons for this have been discussed above (p. 332). Many unsuccessful attempts have been made to immunize these patients with antigens such as tetanus toxoid, and to seek whether antibody activity would be found in the myeloma protein. This is not surprising if, as is now accepted, myeloma cells represent the products of clones of cells which differ from other plasma cells only by virtue of the fact that they have undergone malignant change, and have acquired the capacity to proliferate unchecked without losing their ability to synthesize and secrete their characteristic immunoglobulin. Whatever hypothesis is adopted about the initiation of specific antibody formation, there is no evidence to suggest that a plasma cell once engaged in immunoglobulin production can be switched by antigen towards making specific antibody against that antigen. If the plasma cell was already engaged in making a specific antibody when it underwent the change which gave rise to a clone of neoplastic cells, it would be a matter of chance whether the antibody would ever be identified as such. In the previous edition of this book it was written that we might expect that sooner or later, either haphazard or as a result of systematic testing with many antigens, a myeloma protein will be shown to possess specific antibody properties. This has now been shown in a very few instances, and individual myeloma proteins have been described which react specifically, though weakly, with antigens as common in the environment as streptolysin O on the one hand and as (presumably) uncommon as dinitrobenzene on the other.

Morphology of Myeloma Cells

The morphology of myeloma cells varies greatly from patient to patient. The cytoplasm may be extensive and deeply basophilic, with a juxta-nuclear clear area, so that the appearance corresponds well with that of immature or mature plasma cells seen in a normal immune response. However, as would be expected of a neoplasm, many types yield cells which are rather unlike a normal member of the plasma cell family. There are two diagnostic features of importance. The sternal puncture will show a large number of basophilic cells resembling plasma cells. However, it must be realized that since tumour tissue occurs as nodules it is possible to sample normal marrow even when the disease is present. Also one must be aware that some infections can cause marked increases in plasma cells in the bone marrow. The second feature is that X-ray examination demonstrates characteristic punched-out areas, without evidence of bone regeneration, in the ribs, spine, clavicle, skull and the shoulder and pelvic girdles. In a small proportion of cases osteoporosis occurs diffusely.

Myelomas in Mice and Other Species

Myelomas occur spontaneously though rarely in other species, and have been described especially in domestic or laboratory animals which live to a fair age and/or are subject to careful pathological examination, as is the case with dogs and mice. Of especial interest are myelomas which arise in inbred strains of mice, since these can often be maintained by transplantation within the same strain, in the form of subcutaneous or ascites tumours, for many generations. When this is done, the transplanted tumours continue to secrete the myeloma protein characteristic of the original, thereby demonstrating forcibly the stability of the cell lines once they have differentiated into immunoglobulin producing cells. The possibility of propagating such myelomas indefinitely has been of the greatest assistance in experimental work directed to the study of immunoglobulin structure and its variability. Equally important has been the discovery that in certain strains of mice—notably Balb/C—the injection of sterile liquid paraffin intraperitoneally is followed several months later by the development in about half the animals of multiple plasma cell tumours in the peritoneal cavity. These tumour nodules can be propagated separately in individual normal mice of the same strain, and in their new hosts they not only grow as typical myelomas, secreting characteristic myeloma proteins, but different nodules from the same animal may have quite distinct products. Just as in Man the range of myeloma proteins appears to extend over the whole spectrum of normal immunoglobulins, and the frequency of occurrence of any particular myeloma protein (identifiable by class or allotypic markers) corresponds approximately to the prevalence of cells producing similar proteins in the tissues of normal mice. However, such mouse myelomas tend more frequently to produce L chains only. An interesting feature of all mouse myelomas which have been examined in the electron microscope is that they contain large numbers of cytoplasmic particles which look like virus particles; however, it has not proved possible to induce myelomas by injecting cell-free filtrates of the tumours into other mice, and the significance of the virus-like particles is not clear.

All in all, the experimentally induced mouse myelomas provide the strongest evidence that such tumours arise from random malignant transformation of cells competent at the time of transformation to make one characteristic immunoglobulin product. As in human myelomas the question arises whether any or all of the experimental mouse myelomas produce identifiable antibody; a systematic search, using a very wide range of antigens, has revealed that recognizable antibody activity can be ascribed to a substantial proportion of the induced myelomas. The specificities range from a pneumococcal carbohydrate to salmonella 'O' antigens, but the commonest specificity recognized is against the hapten dinitrobenzene. This is a surprising finding, but it must be noted that the affinity constants are nearly all low, and it seems likely that reactivity with this hapten is in a sense accidental, even though the specificities are marked. Indeed some of the antibodies against dinitrobenzene also react with certain purine and pyrimidine derivatives, and the suggestion has been put forward that they might primarily be autoantibodies against nucleic acid components.

MACROGLOBULINAEMIA

In about 10 per cent of patients in whom there is pathological overproduction of immunoglobulins without evident cause, the abnormal protein proves to be IgM. This disorder is associated with the name of Waldenström, who in 1944 first described three patients whose serum was unusually viscous at room temperature and contained increased levels of immunoglobulin. Ultracentrifugal analysis of the sera of these patients demonstrated the presence of large amounts of a protein having a sedimentation coefficient of 19–20 Svedberg units. The main clinical features in these patients were epistaxis and gingival haemorrhages, and moderate general enlargement of the lymph nodes. The bone marrow contained an excess of large basophilic lymphocytes. Waldenström proposed a new syndrome—*macroglobulinaemia*.

Since this time many cases have been discovered with greatly elevated levels of IgM and have been assigned to this syndrome, but they vary greatly in respect of the clinical abnormalities. Some examples have presented with neurological symptoms and have been associated with extensive cerebral infiltration with reticulum cells (microgliomatosis) giving rise to the so-called Bing-Neel syndrome. Most of the cases are between 50 and 70 years of age and the disease is commoner among males.

Many clinical laboratory abnormalities are described along with the presence of increased IgM levels in the serum. The presence of the macroglobulin molecules leads to ready clumping of the erythrocytes, reflected in a markedly raised sedimentation rate. The clumping of the red cells often makes it difficult or impossible to count cells in a haemocytometer, and gross rouleaux formation is frequently seen in peripheral blood smears.

The macroglobulins of this disease are insoluble in distilled water, so that when serum is allowed to drip into a beaker of distilled water there is an immediate development of a white cloud of precipitate. In accordance with their extremely high molecular weight and high sedimentation velocity the small cloud of precipitate rapidly settles to the bottom of the beaker. This test (Sia test) is often positive in multiple myeloma, systemic lupus erythematosus, as well as in certain chronic infective diseases with raised immunogloublin such as tuberculosis, kala-azar and chronic malaria. Macroglobulins are occasionally *cryoglobulins*, i.e. their solution reversibly forms a jelly or crystals when placed at a low temperature (0–4°C), but even without demonstrable cryoglobulins the blood is often noticeably viscous. The extent of this increased viscosity varies from patient to patient, but it may be so great as seriously to embarrass the circulation. When this occurs marked clinical relief is obtained by removing as much of the macroglobulin as possible by withdrawing whole blood and returning the separated red cells (plasmapheresis).

Macroglobulins contain three or four times the carbohydrate content of normal serum γ-globulin, and blood smears from cases of macroglobulinaemia often stain positively with the periodic-acid Schiff technique. In macroglobulinaemia up to about half of the total serum protein can be in the form of IgM. In spite of this, these patients do not often show gross defects in their serum content of IgG, nor suffer from increased susceptibility to infection (Bence-Jones proteinuria is very uncommon).

The histological picture in the bone marrow, lymph nodes and spleen is usually described as a hyperplasia of lymphocytes. Some authors use the term 'lymphocytoid' which would seem to indicate that they experience difficulty in saying whether the cells are lymphocytes or plasma cells. Definite plasma cells may sometimes occur in the bone marrow and also in the peripheral blood in the later stages of the disease, and it is described how the histological appearances of the lymphoid tissues may change from a lymphocytosis to a plasma-cell reaction during the course of the illness. As with multiple myeloma, no exogenous antigen has yet been found to exist either as a simulus for the production of these globulins or as capable of combining with them as antibodies. However, in a few instances the increased macroglobulin has been shown to consist largely or wholly of material which could be classed as autoantibody (Chapter Fifteen)—namely cold erythrocyte agglutinins, rheumatoid factor, or antinuclear factors.

According to one view the disease is fundamentally a lymphosarcoma which includes cells which have the capacity to synthesize macroglobulin or acquire this following the occurrence of a somatic mutation. As in the case of the myeloma and Bence-Jones proteins, the macroglobulins from different cases differ antigenically from one another although these differences are not absolute and many antigenic determinants are shared. Presumably immunological differences among macroglobulins must reflect genetic differences in cells synthesizing these proteins, and such differences may be accounted for by somatic mutation yielding clones of what are essentially neoplastic cells. Such mutation might occur independently or be the result of X-rays or mutagenic chemicals, as these are used commonly in treatment. Some regard the disease as a variant of myelomatosis, and practical difficulties in distinguishing these two conditions are not uncommon. The Bing-Neel syndrome (coincidence of macroglobulinaemia and central nervous system involvement) appears to result from involvement of the brain and spinal cord with the same kind of cellular infiltration as is described in the lymphoreticular tissues in the globulinaemia of Waldenström.

HEAVY CHAIN DISEASE

A very rare but interesting disease has been described with an unusual immunoglobulin abnormality and unique and distinguishing features. The disease has appeared in males over 40 years of age, who rapidly developed generalized tender swellings of lymph nodes, usually with splenomegaly, suggesting a diagnosis of malignant lymphoma. However, lymph node and bone marrow biopsies showed proliferation of plasma cells, lymphocytes, reticulum cells and marked infiltration with eosinophils. The patients were unusually susceptible to bacterial infections, and had an unusual oedema of the palate and uvula. Examination of the plasma revealed marked deficiencies of IgG, IgA and IgM, but the presence of a sharp electrophoretic peak typical of a fast moving myeloma protein. The patients had proteinuria, but unexpectedly the urinary protein was not shown to be Bence-Jones protein but proved instead to be identical with the abnormal plasma protein. Studies of these proteins showed that they totally lacked L chain determinants but had the immunological properties of H chains of IgG and the syndrome was termed 'heavy chain disease'. However, further examination has revealed that the abnormal proteins resemble the Fc piece of H chains rather than the whole H chains. It appears that the abnormal plasma cells not only do not make L chains but make a defective H chain. The reason for this is not at present known.

A different form of heavy chain disease, *alpha chain disease*, has been described in which lymphoma involving the intestinal tract is accompanied by the production of large amounts of defective α-chains, apparently analogous to the defective γ-chains described above. This rare condition has so far been observed only in Arab patients.

A puzzling feature of human and mouse myelomas is that although some secrete a balanced mixture of H and L chains (i.e. complete immunoglobulins), some secrete complete immunoglobulins and excess free L chains, and some secrete free L chains only, none have been found which secrete free H chains. This has led to the suggestion that if there is defective production of L chains then free H chains cannot be made. However, it is known that free H chains tend to aggregate and become very insoluble. Examination of some morphologically typical mouse myelomas which apparently secreted neither H nor L chains has revealed that intracellular inclusion bodies were present which behaved immunologically as aggregates of H chains. Thus it appears that true H chain producing myelomas can exist but that they are unlikely to be identified by the discovery of H chains in the blood or urine.

'MONOCLONAL GAMMOPATHY'

A considerable number of patients, perhaps 20 per cent of all those discovered to have abnormal increases in immunoglobulin other than those due to recognized infections, cannot be placed clinically in the categories of multiple myeloma or macroglobulinaemia. Nevertheless, the immunoglobulin increase is usually due to the presence of a homogeneous protein (as judged by electrophoresis both of the whole protein and of its L chains) such as is observed in myelomatosis. Bence-Jones proteinuria, however, is absent. These patients have been grouped together under the general heading (introduced before the current nomenclature of immunoglobulins) 'monoclonal gammopathies'.

One group of such cases can be separated in which the immunoglobulin abnormality (usually increased IgG) is associated with lymphosarcoma or lymphatic leukaemia. Such patients frequently have depressed levels of normal Ig, and are unduly susceptible to bacterial infections. In recent years successful long term *in vitro* cultivation has been achieved of lymphoma tissues, and good evidence has been given to show that such cells can synthesize moderate amounts of immunoglobulins even *in vitro*. It seems probable that the immunoglobulin increase observed *in vivo* is in fact produced by the enormous number of neoplastic lymphoid cells present in such patients.

A further group of cases have associated neoplasms, commonly involving the gastrointestinal tract. The primary tumours are often found to be heavily infiltrated with plasma cells, but whether these represent an immunological response to tumour antigens or to a viral agent, or to materials absorbed from the intestinal lumen is not known.

Finally about a third of the cases of 'monoclonal gammopathy' are not associated with any neoplasm and their course is essentially benign. Plasma cells are increased in bone marrow and lymphoid tissues, but do not form invasive masses. Such cases generally occur in relatively elderly people, and probably form a heterogeneous collection. Although the causes are unknown there is certainly a marked tendency for such conditions to run in particular families, and they may be associated with multiple myeloma, systemic lupus erythematosus, or rheumatoid arthritis occurring in the same families. This suggests an underlying hereditary disorder in the control of immunoglobulin production. Some associations with other rare diseases are also striking. For example, the presence of an abnormal basic γG immunoglobulin with an unusually low electrophoretic mobility has been reported in all of a series of patients with *papular mucinosis* (*lichen myxodematosus*), a skin disease characterized by the appearance of large lichenoid papules which eventually spread over the whole body. Another abnormal immunoglobulin which complexes with β-lipoprotein has been reported in several cases of *xanthomatosis* with raised plasma cholesterol levels. Whether these are essentially auto-immune conditions (see Chapter Fifteen) is not known.

'MONOCLONAL' RESPONSES TO INFECTION

Occasionally in man, and more commonly in rabbits, intensive infection or immunization with antigenically homogeneous bacterial carbohydrates results in massive production of antibodies which appear to be homogeneous electrophoretically and in respect of their L chains. When the immunogenic stimulus ceases to act, however, the antibody level falls away and the electrophoretically homogeneous immunoglobulin disappears from the serum. This phenomenon is presumably due to antigenic stimulation of one or a very limited number of clones of cells, and is probably related to the production of idiotypic antibodies referred to in Chapter Four (p. 186).

Cryoglobulinaemia

Cryoglobulins are immunoglobulins which precipitate from the serum on cooling and redissolve on warming. These are commonly noticed accidentally when sera are left standing overnight in the refrigerator. The precipitates are usually amorphous, but occasionally they form pseudo-crystals, which is an indication that the cryoglobulins must be very homogeneous. They are not common, and usually occur as IgM in cases of macroglobulinaemia or other conditions with very elevated IgM, though they may occur as IgG in cases of multiple myeloma or of 'monoclonal gammopathies' and —in experimental animals—as a result of hyperimmunization. It is possible that cryoglobulins owe their markedly temperature dependent solubility in isotonic salt solution to some chance arrangement of their tertiary structure, and that they are part of the spectrum of immunoglobulins normally synthesized. Unless present in supranormal concentration, however, their presence would go unnoticed. However, it is also possible that cryoglobulins are complexes of autoantibody against IgG and the subject's own IgG, with the peculiarity that the autoantibody only combines effectively in the cold (as occurs with 'cold' agglutinins, which are also autoantibodies—see Chapter Fifteen). It has been clearly shown that complexes of IgM autoantibody and IgG, which only precipitate on cooling, occur in the plasma of certain cases of thrombotic thrombocytopenic purpura.

An apparently distinct condition in which cryo-precipitation occurs follows the acute damage due to intravenous administration of bacterial endotoxin. In this case the precipitate consists of complexes between altered fibrinogen (fibrinogen B) and acid mucopolysaccharides derived from the tissues.

FURTHER READING

BRAMBELL F.W.R. (1958) The passive immunity of the young mammal. *Biol. Rev.* **33**, 488

CLARKE C.A. (1968) Prevention of Rhesus Iso-immunization. *Lancet* **2**, 1 (6th July).

COHEN S. (1963) Gamma Globulin Metabolism. *Brit. Med. Bull.* **19**, 202

COHN M. (1967) Natural history of the myeloma. *Cold Spring Harbor Symposia on Quantitative Biology. Vol. 32* 'Antibodies', pp. 211–21

Genetics of the Immune Response. *Wld. Hlth. Org. tech. Rep. Series.* No. 402 (1968)

GOOD R.A., KELLY W.D. & ROTSTEIN J. (1962) Immunological deficiency diseases. Agammaglobulinemia, hypogammaglobulinemia, Hodgkin's disease and sarcoidosis. *Progr. Allergy* **6**, 187

KAUGER E. & MAUER A.M. (1966) Neutropenia of childhood. *J. Pediat.* **69**, 147

OSKI F.A. & NAIMAN J.L. (1966) *Hematologic Problems of the Newborn.* Saunders, Philadelphia

SOOTHILL J.F. (1968) 'Immunity Deficiency States'. In *Clinical Aspects of Immunology* [Eds. Gell P.G.H. and Coombs R.R.A.]. Blackwell, Oxford

The Suppression of Rh immunization by passively administered human immunoglobulin (IgG) anti-D (anti-Rh). *Bull Wld. Hlth. Org.* **36**, 467

VAHLQUIST B. (1958) The transfer of antibodies from mother to offspring. *Advanc. Pediat.* **10**, 305

WALDENSTRÖM, J.G. (1968) *Monoclonal and polyclonal hypergammaglobulinemia—Clinical and Biological Significance.* Cambridge University Press

CHAPTER NINE

Serological Aspects of the Antigen–Antibody Reaction: the Detection and Measurement of Antigen and Antibody

STUDIES of the interaction of antigen and antibody are of great importance, since apart from allowing an understanding of how antibody acts to promote resistance, they provide methods for diagnosis of infective disease and for the identification of infectious agents. Also, when a specific antibody can be produced against them, sundry other biological entities which bear no relation to infectious disease can be detected and measured, such as, for example, hormones and enzymes. Our problem usually involves the detection or estimation of one of the components when the other is available and known. Antigen is used to detect antibody and *vice versa*. But it should be realized that the combination as it first occurs is an invisible reaction and all the common practical *in-vitro* serological procedures, such as precipitin formation, bacterial agglutination, bacteriolysis, haemolysis and so on, are dependent upon secondary manifestations of the primary union of antibody and antigen (an exception is the fluorescent antibody method). Some of them may also require the simultaneous presence of one or more additional reagents such as the components in normal serum called *complement*. Before proceeding to consider the serological procedures in use for detection or estimation of antigens and antibodies in biological fluids, it is necessary first to consider some of the features of this primary reaction.

CHARACTERISTICS OF THE UNION OF ANTIBODY WITH ANTIGEN

(1) The reaction is specific, or relatively so.

(2) The *Unitarian Theory* of antibodies was proposed by Zinsser. He regarded it as unreasonable to divide antibodies into agglutinating, precipitating or haemolytic types, since it could be shown that the same antibody could perform all these functions. However, in individual cases, a certain antibody may fail to accomplish a particular reaction. Thus certain antibodies fail to precipitate with their homologous antigen. They are known as *non-precipitating antibodies*. But this is a failure not of a primary union between the two, but of the secondary effect of aggregation of the combination and visible precipitation.

(3) The *precipitin* reaction is between large antigen molecules, and the *agglutination* reaction between large particles, such as bacteria, and large antibody molecules. The reaction occurs by the close approximation of the *surface* of the antigen and antibody molecule so that a union takes place over a portion of the surface of one, with a complementary area on the surface of the other.

(4) The union is *firm* but in general *reversible*.

(5) Antigen and antibody combine in varying proportions. The alternative view that antigen and antibody combine irreversibly in a fixed proportion by a chemical bond (as carbon combines with chlorine to form CCl_4) was previously held by Ehrlich. It was soon found, however, that when equal amounts of an antitoxin were added successively to a given amount of toxin they neutralized a smaller proportion of toxin at each addition. Ehrlich, therefore, was forced to the conclusion that toxins contained a wide variety of components with different affinity for antitoxin, a view which became untenable with increasing experience, and which gave way to the concept of a combination in which widely varying proportions of antigen and antibody could participate.

The combination in multiple proportions depends upon the fact that both antigen and antibody are multivalent. Antibody valencies are generally restricted to two per molecule (except in the case of IgM, when the number is 5 or 10) but antigen valencies may exceed 200, although they are more usually around 50 to 10 per molecule.

(6) The union between antigen and antibody is a chemical one due to the combination of the specific reactant groups of the two reagents.

The nature of the forces which bind together antigen and antibody have been discussed previously in Chapter Four. It is necessary here only to point out that combination occurs between a localized and relatively *small* part of the surface of the antibody molecule and a correspondingly small part of the antigen, and that the firmness of this union depends upon how closely these surfaces can approach one another and the size of the areas involved. In other words the antibody sites must fit the antigen sites as exactly as possible, and although small variations in these sites can occur without spoiling the fit too badly, most variations will prevent it completely. The combination therefore shows a very high degree of specificity. Ehrlich's analogy was of the fitting of a lock and key.

As regards the forces involved, these depend partly upon the nature of the antigen. The extremely short range Van der Waals forces and hydrogen bonds are probably the most important, but when the antigenic grouping has a positive or a negative charge it has been shown in certain instances that the reactive site on the antibody contains a grouping with an opposite charge, and so electrostatic (Coulomb) forces are also involved. The strength of these will be affected by the pH and ionic strength of the medium in which the antigen–antibody reaction takes place.

THE PRECIPITIN REACTION

The problem now arises of the way in which the union of antigen and antibody gives rise to a precipitate or to the agglutination of cells. The antigens in the *precipitin* reaction are solutions of molecules which are usually protein or carbohydrate in nature. This is in contrast with an *agglutination* reaction, in which the antibodies are directed against antigens at the surface of relatively large *particles* (foreign cells such as erythrocytes or micro-organisms).

Precipitation is a reaction which occurs rapidly under optimal conditions and may be complete within a few seconds. The visible precipitate contains both the antigen and the antibody as components (as well, sometimes, as components of normal sera, such as complement, if they are present in the reacting system; complement, however, is not necessary for the union of antigen and antibody). The essential evidence for the actual presence of antigen was first supplied by von Dungern, who made use of a marked antigen, haemocyanin, which is blue in the oxidized state. Thus, when this copper-containing protein combined with colourless antibodies formed as a result of the previous injection of crab serum (which contains haemocyanin) into a rabbit, the precipitate formed became distinctly blue when exposed to air.

Lattice Hypothesis

In 1934 Marrack stated a concept describing the reaction between antigen and antibody resulting in precipitation, in terms of the building up of aggregates of large size. Marrack pointed out that if the antibody has more than one valency it would be possible for the antigen and antibody to be bound together in the form of a coarse 'lattice'.

In order to fit theory with practice it is necessary to understand something of the quantitative considerations involved in the union of antigen and antibody. The first studies in this field were the work of Heidelberger who originally made use of the purified capsular polysaccharide of the Type III pneumococcus as antigen, for the reason that it contained no nitrogen. The reaction was followed by adding increasing amounts of antigen to a constant amount of antiserum. After allowing time for complete reaction to occur, the precipitates were washed free of uncombined reactants and the total nitrogen content estimated by the Kjeldahl method. Since this antigen is free of nitrogen, all the nitrogen in the precipitate derives from antibody. For a protein antigen, the determination of antibody in the precipitate requires that the antigen component be subtracted from the total weight of the washed precipitate. Thus, a reaction curve as shown in Fig. 9.1 can be plotted. This shows that the amount of antibody precipitated increases to a maximum with increasing addition of antigen and then rather suddenly declines so that in extreme antigen excess no precipitate is formed.

The curve can be divided into several zones. In the zone OP (the zone of *antibody excess*) antibody can be detected in the supernatant solution after the precipitate has been completely deposited and separated. To the right of point P, in the zone PB (*equivalence zone*) neither antigen nor antibody can be detected in appreciable quantities in the supernatant fluid. Beyond B is the zone of antigen excess, in which free antigen can be detected in the supernatant, and in which with increasing quantities of antigen complete inhibition of precipitin formation often occurs. It was found in fact that a very slight excess gave the maximum amount of precipitable nitrogen.

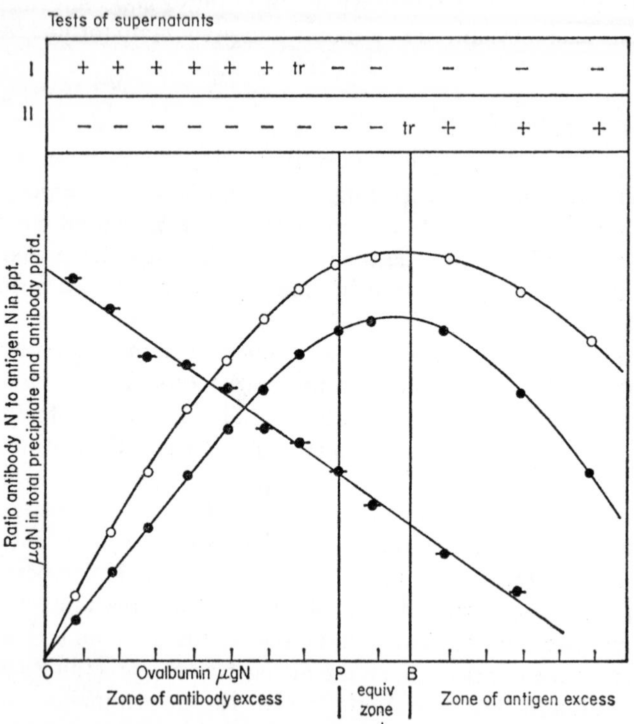

FIG. 9.1. Quantitative course of the precipitin reaction between ovalbumin and rabbit anti-ovalbumin. Abscissa: amount of antigen added expressed as nitrogen (N).

o——o——o total weight of N in precipitate.

•——•——• weight of antibody N in precipitate.

+——+——+ ratio of antibody N to antigen N in precipitate.

Results of tests on supernatant fluids obtained after separation of precipitate with: in line I, antigen (ovalbumin), and in line II, antibody. tr = trace.

Optimal Proportions in Antigen–Antibody Precipitation

If a series of tubes are set up with increasing amounts of antigen added to a constant amount of antiserum in each tube, it can be seen that the opacity increases along the row to a certain point and then falls off. It is possible to pick out a tube in which the precipitate appears sooner and in greater amount than in any of its neighbours. The opacity which at first develops in this tube will increase more quickly and will break up into flocculi sooner. The characters of this zonal effect were investigated originally by Dean and Webb, who termed the antibody : antigen ratio that gave most rapid flocculation, the *optimal proportion*. For a given antiserum and antigen the ratio was constant for all dilutions of the reagents.

An important result of such studies is that the precipitate varies in composition according to the proportions of antigen and antibody in the reacting mixture. If antibody is present in excess the precipitate will contain relatively more of this component, and *vice versa*. This point is illustrated according to the lattice hypothesis in Fig. 9.2, in which the assumption (nowadays supported by much

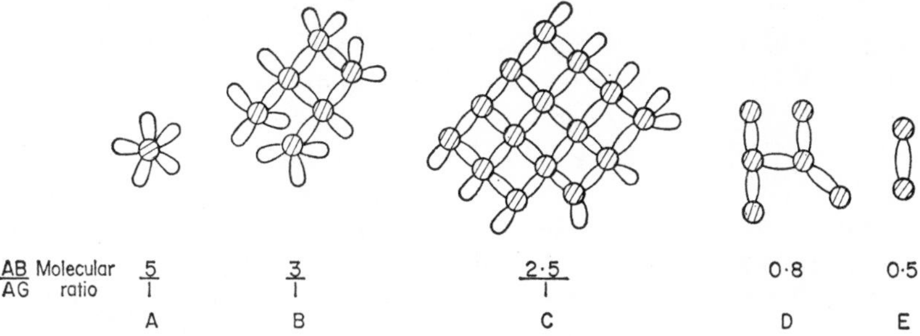

FIG. 9.2. Diagram of hypothetical arrangement of antigen (shaded) and antibody (white) molecules in antigen–antibody complex, according to the lattice hypothesis.

A extreme antibody excess with all valencies (5) of antigen satisfied by excess antibody.
B moderate antibody excess.
C 'optimal proportions'.
D antigen excess.
E extreme antigen excess with both valencies of antibody satisfied.

[Modified from Pauling L. (1940) *J. Amer. chem. Soc.* **62**, 2643.]

independent evidence) is made that the antibody is bivalent and the antigen multivalent. It can be seen that if the valency of antigen is N and the antibody is 2, there will be increasing chances of building large aggregates up to a point where the $\frac{AB}{AG}$ ratio is around $\frac{N}{2}$.

This mode of combination of two substances to form a compound of variable composition according to the proportions in which they are mixed has no counterpart in the chemical reactions of small molecules, but is more akin to the polymerization of plastics. It is, of course, essential that the antigen be multivalent and the antibody at least bivalent for the lattice hypothesis to work in this way. It is of great interest that it was possible to make large synthetic haptens with two or more specific combining groups which were precipitated by antibody, suggesting the formation of compounds of the kind —H—AB—H—AB—H—which accords with the lattice hypothesis. On the other hand, similar haptens with only one combining group are never apparently precipitated by homologous antibody.

Another test for the hypothesis was provided by the following experiment, which supports the idea that the lattice principle is also at work in the agglutination reaction. Type I pneumococci which were exposed to *excess* of antibody were washed until detectable free antibody no longer appeared in the washings. Then the resuspended organisms were found to be reagglutinated by the addition of fresh Type I pneumococci or of free Type I-specific polysaccharide. Reagglutination did not follow the addition of the heterologous Type I pneumococcus polysaccharide or whole organisms. This can be interpreted as a demonstration of the role of intermediate links of antigen in building up aggregates.

The hypothesis also allows a possible explanation of 'incomplete' antibodies which sometimes occur naturally, and which are able to combine with antigen but not to form a precipitate. These could be univalent and thus unable to link two antigens together. However, other explanations are possible. The precipitation from solution might be regarded as a consequence of mere aggregation, but Marrack has also stressed the importance of the fact that hydrophilic polar groups of both antigen and antibody molecules become involved in the interaction and are no longer able to interact with the surrounding molecules of water, so that their water solubility is much decreased.

Precipitation and agglutination reactions are highly dependent upon the electrolyte concentration of the medium. Although the combination of soluble or particulate antigen with antibody can occur in the total absence of electrolyte the system will not proceed to precipitation or agglutination unless a minimum concentration of salt is present. Thus if one takes a bacterial suspension and adds antibody to it, the suspension condition of the organisms will not change in the absence of electrolyte. If the still evenly distributed bacteria are now sedimented from the mixture in a centrifuge, it can be shown that antibody leaves the solution with it, for if enough bacteria were used the supernatant fluid will be found to have lost the ability to agglutinate additional antigen even if salt is added to the system. Also, if the centrifuged deposit of bacilli is resuspended in saline they quickly agglutinate. Such evidence of the influence of salt calls into question whether the aggregation phase of the precipitation or agglutination reactions is really dependent upon specific linkages, as demanded by a lattice hypothesis. An experimental demonstration of this is provided by allowing two distinct particulate antigens to be agglutinated in a mixture of their homologous antisera. If aggregation were non-specific, the formation of mixed agglutinates would be expected. In point of fact, separate agglutinates of each antigenic type have usually been found to result from such experiments. Indeed, when mixed agglutinates do occur, e.g. of skin epithelial cells and erythrocytes, when placed in an appropriate antiserum, this has been taken as evidence for the presence of similar antigenic groups on both cell surfaces.

Reversibility of Antigen–Antibody Union

Antigen–antibody combinations are reversible. This can be shown by the use of radioactively-labelled antibody in either precipitin or agglutinating systems. Thus when, say, Rh-positive erythrocytes are acted on by an Rh antiserum the antibody combines with the cells, which can be washed free from uncombined antibody by centrifugation and resuspension in fresh normal saline. If such cells are now suspended in a solution of radioactively-labelled antibody, the latter will slowly take up on the cells and displace the non-radioactive antibody molecules which appear in solution. The same happens with a precipitate of antigen and antibody, which when made with, say, labelled antibody, is washed and suspended in unlabelled antibody. It will, without changing in total weight, gradually exchange its labelled for the unlabelled antibody.

The rate of such exchange varies with different antibodies, even when in combination with the same antigen. When a 'good fit' has been established between antigen and antibody, as might be expected, the speed of the changeover is relatively slow. The same effect is shown by the *Danysz phenomenon*. Thus, if a constant amount of diphtheria toxin is added to a constant amount of antitoxin, the toxicity of the mixture varies according to the way in which the addition is made. If to a given amount of antitoxin, the equivalent amount of toxin is added all at once, the mixture is non-toxic. If the same amount of toxin is added in two fractions, with an interval of 15 minutes or more between each addition, the mixture will be highly toxic. The fraction of toxin added earlier unites with more than its equivalent amount of antibody, so that there is insufficient antibody to neutralize the later fractions and no appreciable redistribution of antibody occurs during the time of the experiment. The ease of dissociation of a toxin and its antibody depends on the *avidity* of the antitoxin. Thus with an avid antibody the amount of *toxoid* required to release a given amount of *toxin* from combination is found to be much greater than that required for the same toxin combined with non-avid antibody. In the case of antitoxins required for therapy, highly avid antibody is obviously most desirable. In some instances antibody can be dissociated from a complex with a soluble antigen, such as, for example, pneumococcus polysaccharide, by greatly increasing the electrolyte concentration. Apparently the salt ions compete for the sites of the antibody union with the polysaccharide ions. Incidentally, all the latter remains in the precipitate under these conditions, so that advantage can be taken of these findings to prepare pure free antibody.

No precipitate is formed in precipitin reactions when antibody is added to a considerable excess of antigen. If the antigen–antibody combination were fully reversible the precipitate should dissolve in a strong solution of antigen. The time taken for this to occur is variable but eventually all systems will redissolve.

As might be expected, antibody will dissociate more readily at higher temperatures and in some erythrocyte systems, e.g. the combination of sheep erythrocytes and glandular fever antibody, the antibody (here a 19S antibody) can be easily recovered by raising the temperature of the agglutinated corpuscles to 56°C. Use has been made of this property for recovering almost pure antibody from serum.

THE MEASUREMENT OF ANTIBODY AND ANTIGEN

From consideration of the nature of the antigen–antibody interaction as outlined above, a wide variety of different methods for measuring or detecting antibody or antigen have been devised. Some of these possess great sensitivity (see Table 9.1), but the choice of

TABLE 9.1

Sensitivity of various methods of detecting or determining antibodies

Method	*μg of antibody—N/ml
Specific precipitation:	
(a) Qualitative—'ring' test	3–5
in gels	5–10
(b) Quantitative—micro-Kjeldahl nitrogen	10
Colorimetry (Folin and Ciocalteu)	4
Bacterial agglutination:	0·01
Bactericidal (with optimum complement)	
turbidimetric	0·001
viable count	0·00001
†*Haemagglutination* (adsorbed antigen)	0·003–0·006
†*Haemolysis* (lytic antibody + complement)	0·001–0·03
Complement fixation	0·1
Flocculation test (*syphilis*)	0·2–0·5
Toxin neutralization:	
(Diphtheria antitoxin in rabbit skin)	0·01
Passive anaphylaxis:	*Total antibody required* (*μg N*)
Whole guinea-pig	30
Guinea-pig uterine muscle	0·01
Guinea-pig skin (passive cutaneous anaphylaxis)	0·003
Skin transfer (Prausnitz-Küstner) in man	0·01

* Multiply by 6·25 to obtain antibody protein.

† Higher degrees of sensitivity can be achieved by examining small numbers of indicator cells under the microscope.

any one will depend upon the nature of the antigen, its purity and availability, and the degree of precision and the nature of the information required. Some of the techniques more commonly employed for diagnosis, follow-up or research are discussed in some detail below.

The Meaning of 'The Titre'

A procedure which is commonly applied in, for instance, the agglutination and the complement-fixation reactions is to measure the concentration of antibody in serum by adding a constant amount of antigen to each of a row of tubes containing antiserum, serially diluted so that, for instance, each tube in the series contains 1 in 10, 1 in 20, 1 in 40, 1 in 80, 1 in 160, etc., dilution of serum.

The antigen in an agglutination reaction is usually a certain amount of a suspension of bacteria or of red cells. After the mixtures are made up in the tubes, they are incubated appropriately and then scanned to detect the end-point. In an agglutination test this is usually the last tube in the series showing clumping of the suspension which is just visible to the naked eye. In a titration of rabbit anti-sheep haemolysin, the rabbit antiserum is diluted in a series of tubes, each of which contains a constant number of sheep red cells and an adequate amount of complement. Here the end-point may be the last tube showing complete haemolysis of the red cells (or, for more accurate work, the tube is chosen which shows lysis of about half of the erythrocytes). The last tube in the series which shows the desired effect may be regarded as containing one arbitrary unit of antibody. The 'titre' should be a measure of the number of antibody units per unit volume of the original serum. Therefore if the last tube showing a reaction contains 1 ml volume, and the serum in this tube is diluted 1 in 640, the titre of the serum is 640 units per ml of serum.

The serological titration methods possess several inherent disadvantages. They do not measure antibody in absolute weight units. Also, the unit which is arbitrarily chosen for, say, a bacterial suspension bears no relation to the similarly chosen unit for a suspension of a different bacterium. Thus, if the agglutination titre for a pneumococcal suspension is 500 units per ml and for a suspension of typhoid bacilli is 1,000, it would be quite false to conclude that the weight of typhoid antibody per ml of serum is twice that of the pneumococcal antibody. In practice the titration is set up in doubling dilutions. This means that in a comparison between two antisera to the same antigen, at least a two-tube difference must be achieved before the conclusion is justified that one has more antibody than the other. This may involve a four-fold increase in the amount of antibody.

IN VITRO METHODS

1. PRACTICAL PROCEDURES INVOLVING PRECIPITATION

The precipitin reaction may be used qualitatively or quantitatively. The great sensitivity of the precipitin reaction (as of all the other serological procedures), together with its specificity, renders this test of great value in detecting and identifying various protein or polysaccharide antigens. Thus precipitin tests are of great practical importance in detecting the adulteration of foodstuffs, or in their forensic application to the differentiation of human and animal blood and seminal stains. In the laboratory generally, these tests are eminently suitable for the detection of even minute amounts of impurities present in biological preparations. Using potent antisera it is possible to detect as little as 1 μg of a protein antigen by this technique.

A classical use of the precipitin reaction is its employment for the identification of the species from which a protein is derived. The early studies of Nuttall (1904) showed that when blood sera from numerous animal species were used to elicit antibodies in other species, the reaction was strongest with the kind of serum used for immunization, whereas when sera from other species were used as antigen, the intensity of the reaction was found to parallel the degree of zoological relationship. The specificity of antisera prepared against, say, human serum varies, but at the highest dilutions at which it still gives a precipitin test, no reaction would be expected against the serum of other animal species such as the horse, dog, sheep, chicken, goose, etc., although it is probable that a reaction would be found with the serum of the higher apes. In case the antiserum is found to react with any of the non-human samples, it may be rendered specific by absorption. That is, some of the cross-reactive heterologous antigen is added, the precipitate is removed, and the absorbed serum is then deprived of its power to react with this heterologous material.

Studies of this kind, although they gave important information, were more complicated than meets the eye because injection of whole serum gives rise to antibodies against several of the protein components, each of which is antigenically quite distinct. Thus the comparison was in fact not between one protein from a species and a similar protein in another species, but between whole families of proteins in each.

MAINLY QUALITATIVE PROCEDURES

(a) *The ring test.* This is the simplest form of the precipitin reaction, and is carried out by placing one fluid (the antigen) over the other (the antibody) in a narrow tube (Fig. 9.3). By this interfacial technique the reaction is visible as the formation of a white disc or plane at the junction of the two perfectly clear fluids. It has been pointed out above that when mixtures of antigen and antibody are prepared the precipitin reaction may be inhibited under conditions of excess of antigen. Under the conditions of the ring test the reaction takes place over a wide range of concentrations as the antigen and antibody diffuse into one another. Even so, a number of different dilutions of antigen should be tested. Each precipitin test should be accompanied by control tests, such as immune serum plus saline, normal serum plus antigen. No precipitation should occur in such control tubes.

(i) *Ring test*

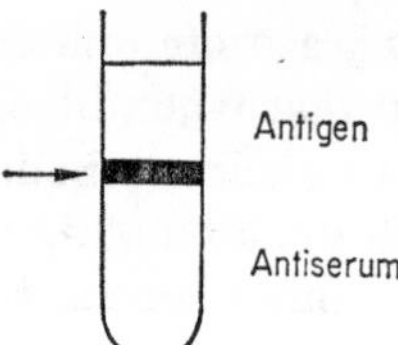

Antigen solution is carefully layered over antibody. In the case of a positive reaction a disc of white precipitate forms at the junction of the two fluids (arrow).

(ii) *Agar diffusion*

a. Single diffusion in one dimension (Oudin procedure).

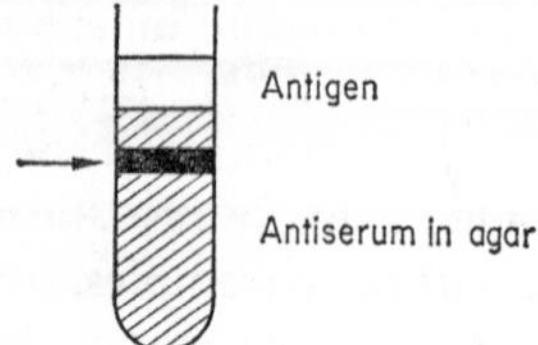

Antigen solution is placed above column of antibody incorporated in agar. The arrow denotes the site of a precipitin band in the agar.

b. Double diffusion in one dimension (Oakley-Fulthorpe procedure).

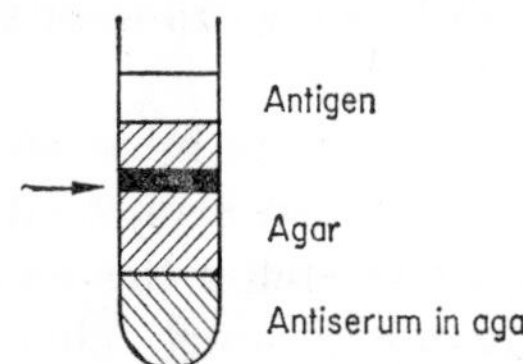

Antibody is incorporated into agar. A column of agar is superimposed and antigen solution placed above. The arrow marks the site of a precipitin band in the agar.

c. Double diffusion in two dimensions (Ouchterlony procedure).

Reaction of identity | Reaction of partial identity

The precipitin band which forms between antiserum (S) and known antigen (A_I) inclines towards and joins up with that between S and unknown antigen (A_{II}). Evidence is thereby provided that $A_I = A_{II}$.

The precipitin band which forms between antiserum (S) and homologous antigen (Ho) involves some component which gives a reaction of identity with a cross-reacting heterologous antigen (He) and some component which does not, and which in consequence forms a 'spur'.

FIG. 9.3. Precipitin tests (qualitative).

(b) *Agar diffusion methods.* Greater precision and the ability to recognize the multiplicity of components of mixtures of antigens and antibodies are achieved by allowing the reactants to diffuse together in agar gel. A simple procedure is to allow *single diffusion* in one dimension (*Oudin procedure*). This generally involves the incorporation of the antiserum into the agar and layering antigen solution above in a tube. An equal volume of the antiserum is warmed and added to molten 0·6 per cent agar, and carefully poured into the tube to form a column of 3–5 cm length. After the agar has solidified, the antigen solution is layered over the surface of the agar. After a few hours to a few days, depending on the concentration of the reactants, bands of precipitate form in the agar and as diffusion continues each band appears to move slowly down the length of the tube. This is the result of precipitation taking place at the advancing front of the antigen. As more antigen diffuses in from above, the rise in concentration may be sufficient to dissolve the precipitate behind the advancing front leading to apparent movement of the band. With mixtures of antigens and antibodies several bands are usually obtained, since the various factors such as molecular size and relative concentration of the reactants will differ for different systems. Excluding various artefacts, with any given mixture of antigens and antibodies, the number of bands obtained will indicate the minimum number of separate antigen–antibody systems that are present. A variation in the procedure is to allow both antigen and antibody to diffuse towards each other from both sides of a column of agar: *double diffusion in one dimension*. See Fig. 9.3 (ii b).

Single Diffusion in Two Dimensions (*Halo Formation*)

In this technique 1–2 per cent molten agar is mixed with antiserum and poured to form a uniform layer. Antigen solution is introduced into circular wells cut into the agar. At a suitable concentration ratio of matching reactants, ring-shaped bands of precipitate (haloes) will form concentrically about the wells.

As the diffusion process goes on, the diameter of the rings will gradually increase. In this plate technique, unlike the Oudin procedure, the migration ceases comparatively soon. The reason is that the amount of the antigen (if this is in the well) is small compared with that of the antibody. A quantitative method developed by Mancini *et al.* (1965) (Quantitative radial immunodiffusion) uses the measurement of the area of the halo after the diffusion of the antigen has ceased. Melted 3 per cent agar gel buffered at pH 8·6 is mixed with an appropriate amount of specific antiserum and poured as a 1 mm thick layer. After the agar has set wells of 1 mm diameter are punched out. An accurately measured volume of antigen is introduced into each of the wells by means of a micropipette. After incubation in a damp atmosphere the diameter of the halo is measured after migration has stopped. A series of dilutions of standard antigen is usually set up as a reference on the test plate. For a given concentration of the antigen (in the well) the diameter of the halo ring bears a linear relationship to the initial concentration of the antiserum (in the plate).

This method has been adopted for the quantitative estimation of different classes of immunoglobulins in serum and other body fluids, employing antisera specific for the heavy chains of Ig. It is most accurate for the estimation of low levels of immunoglobulins, as in the case of serum from subjects with hypogammaglobulinaemia. Provided that uni-specific antiserum is available, the method can be used to measure the concentration of any protein in almost any mixture, and is of wide application.

Double diffusion in two dimensions (*Ouchterlony method*)*:* This method has the further advantage that various antigens and antisera can be directly compared. Given a known antigen, it may allow the direct identification of this antigen in an unknown mixture. The various reactants may conveniently be placed in the wells which can be cut out with a cork borer from a 5 mm layer of agar in a flat Petri dish. A band will form in the agar between a well which contains antigen and one which is filled with the homologous antiserum. The band forms where antigen and antibody come together in optimal proportions. It will form first at the point at which the two wells are closest and later extend at both ends. In the pattern set up in Fig. 9.3 (ii c) the unknown preparation of antigen A_{II} is compared for its reactivity with a known antiserum to antigen A. It can be seen that the band of precipitation between A_I and its antiserum S curves round to join up exactly with the corresponding band formed between A_{II} and S, thus providing evidence that the well A contains an antigenic component which is identical (at least in its immunological reactivity) with A_{II}.

If two cross-reacting antigens He and Ho are placed in adjacent wells as in Fig. 9.3 (ii c) there is a similar fusion of the bands but the homologous antigen (Ho) shows an additional 'spur' projecting out beyond the point of fusion. This is because it is able to react with the antibody molecules which have not been caught up in the precipitate with the cross-reacting antigen (He) and have diffused past the precipitin line (*reaction of partial identity*).

The position of the band between antigen and antibody wells will depend on the relative concentration of the interacting molecules. When either antigen or antibody is in considerable excess the band cannot form in the agar between the two wells, but a precipitate will form in the well containing the weaker component. Titration of antigen or antibody may be made by placing serial dilutions of one component in a series of circumferential wells (see below under Quantitative Procedures).

A special example of the double diffusion method in two dimensions is Elek's method for demonstrating the toxigenicity of a given strain of *Corynebacterium diphtheriae*. A strip of filter paper is soaked in diphtheria antitoxin and embedded in agar in a Petri plate, as shown in Plate 9.1, following p. 404. At AB is streaked a known toxigenic strain of *C. diphtheriae*. With the growth of toxin-producing organisms the toxin diffuses outwards from the culture and at right angles to the line of diffusion of the antitoxin from the filter paper. At points along the paths of their cross-diffusion, antigen and antibody will be at optimal proportions, and a line of precipitate will form in the agar at these sites. Such a line, which arises from a positive toxigenic organism XY, will give a reaction of identity with, and so join with, the similar line which arises from the reaction between the antitoxin and the known toxigenic strain AB.

Immuno-electrophoresis

By combining a double diffusion method (Ouchterlony) with the electrophoretic separation on the same agar plate Grabar and Williams developed a method whereby mixtures of proteins can be analysed on the basis of both their antigenic and electrophoretic properties. By using this technique human serum can be resolved into more than thirty distinct antigenic proteins. After electrophoresis in agar, ditches are cut in the agar parallel to the direction of migration and on each side of the spread-out electrophoretic components. Thus (Plate 9.2, pp. 406–7) the serum is placed in the well at A and after the time required for electrophoresis, the ditches XY and WZ are cut and filled with antiserum. After 1–3 days or longer a series of bands appears in the agar, each a band of precipitation with a distinct antigen in the separated serum. Each electrophoretic region, such as the α-, β- and γ-globulins, gives rise to multiple overlapping bands. It is of interest that the γG gives a long line extending into the α_2 region. In other words, despite the broad range of its mobility, the γG acts as a single antigen. The γA line crosses or is confluent with this main (or γG) line in the α_2, β and γ_1 region but emerges towards the cathode end as an independent arc inside the γG line. It is close to and may be confused with transferrin. The antibody-containing fraction of high molecular weight globulins (S = 19) separates as a distinct band in the fast γ- (γ_1-) or slow β- (β_2-) globulin region, as a rule well within the γ-globulin line. This has received the designation γM macroglobulin. Other examples are shown in Plates 9.3 and 9.4, following p. 404.

A variety of methods have been developed for the identification of the lines corresponding with components of the electrophoresed serum or other protein mixture:

(I) a particular line can be identified by employing a suitable mono-specific antiserum in a separate parallel trough on the other side of the serum well (Fig. 9.4 I)

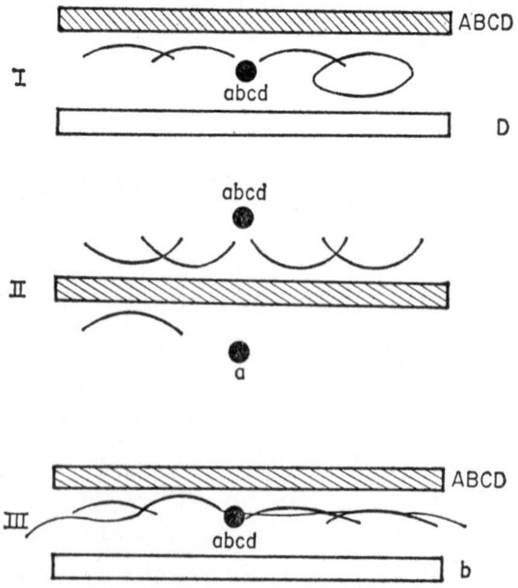

FIG. 9.4 (I–III). Three methods for the identification of the lines corresponding with components of the electrophoresed serum or other protein mixture (see text).

(II) if the pure component of the serum is available this can be electrophoresed simultaneously from another serum well (Fig. 9.4 II)

(III) the pure component of the serum can be placed in a parallel trough. This will result in the corresponding arc in the serum mixture developing extensions at its ends which continue into precipitin lines parallel with the additional trough (Fig. 9.4 III).

Radio-immunoelectrophoresis

This is a very sensitive method for the qualitative detection of antibodies to a given antigen (e.g. a peptide hormone), provided that this is available in purified form and can be labelled at high specific activity with a γ-ray emitting isotope such as ^{131}I. The method also permits identification of the immunoglobulin class in which the antibodies are present.

Immunoelectrophoresis of the test antiserum is carried out in the usual way, using for development an antiserum which can distinguish as many classes of Ig as possible. However, a dilute solution of the highly radioactive antigen is added to the developing antiserum in the trough. The antigen diffuses into the gel together with the anti-Ig, and part of it becomes trapped by any specific antibody present in the immunoglobulin precipitate arc. When development is finished, the gel is washed very thoroughly to remove all unbound antigen, and (usually after drying) it is placed in contact with sensitive X-ray film. The resulting autoradiograph shows the presence of antigen on one or more of the immunoglobulin–precipitin arcs.

QUANTITATIVE PROCEDURES

The customary titration procedure in which the minimum amount of serum necessary to bring about a certain visible reaction with a constant amount of antigen is used cannot be applied to the precipitation reaction. Thus, in a series of tubes set up in this way, the tubes containing the higher dilutions of serum will be in the zone of antigen excess, in which precipitation gradually becomes inhibited with increasing Ag : Ab ratio. In these tubes precipitation fails to occur, despite the presence in them of antibody. Indeed, if the amount of antigen in each tube is reduced the precipitation reaction will go further along the series of antibody dilutions.

Valid quantitative procedures are mostly based on the *optimal proportions* precipitin determination. If a constant amount of serum is placed in a row of tubes and decreasing amounts of antigen are added to these, then by observing the tube which first shows flocculation the mixture is determined in which antibody and antigen exist in *optimal proportions*. The tubes on either side of the optimal proportions tube flocculate later, and so on, the reaction spreading to more distal tubes later still. Another feature of the reaction in the optimal proportions tube is that when precipitation has gone to completion, the supernatant fluid, when tested for residual antigen and antibody, usually contains neither. In the tubes on the left of this, the supernatants contain residual antigen; in those to the right, residual antibody only. This test can give a relative idea of the antibody content of a serum when compared with other sera of the same kind. Thus, if two antisera against the same antigen show optimal flocculation, in one case in the tube containing 1·0 mg of antigen and in the second in the tube containing 0·5 mg, the first serum contains roughly twice as much antibody as the second. The answer is only an approximation since the combining ratio of antigen to antibody at optimal proportions varies somewhat with different antisera.

The quantitative procedure of Heidelberger allows the determination of precipitating antibody in absolute units of weight. An optimal proportions determination is first made as outlined above. Then, in order to select conditions such that all the antibody is precipitated, a slight excess of antigen over that present in the optimal proportions tube is used. Precipitation is allowed to proceed to completion over several days at 4°C. The supernatant fluid should, of course, show the presence of free antigen and absent antibody when tested with antigen and antibody respectively in a precipitin test. The precipitate obtained is washed thrice with ice-cold buffered saline to free it from adhering non-specific serum constituents, and the total nitrogen content determined by Kjeldahl analysis. If an antigen is used such as a pneumococcal polysaccharide, which is free from nitrogen, the nitrogen value of the precipitate will correspond with the antibody nitrogen value. Where a protein antigen is used, a slight deduction must be made—the nitrogen content of the added antigen, which makes up usually about 10–15 per cent of the precipitate.

The Heidelberger quantitative precipitin analysis can only be applied if the antigen used is homogeneous. When multiple individual antigen and antibody systems are present no tube can be selected in which all the antibody is precipitated. Some allowance must also be made for the addition of components of complement to the precipitate. If necessary complement can be removed from the serum by prior addition of the calculated amounts of a heterologous antigen–antibody system.

Non-precipitating antibody. Antibody is rarely homogeneous with regard to its ability to precipitate with antigen. This was first clearly shown when small amounts of antigen were added serially to the antiserum until no more precipitate was formed. It was found in the case of anti-ovalbumin rabbit serum that such serial addition yielded only 78 per cent of the antibody which was precipitable by the addition of the adjusted amount of antigen in one portion. The 'incomplete' or 'non-precipitable antibody' (22 per cent of the total) would co-precipitate if an antigen–antibody precipitate were formed in the solution by addition of fresh whole antiserum and antigen at optimal proportions.

Non-precipitating antibodies are probably present as a proportion of the antibody in all sera. They will not be revealed unless some such procedure as outlined above is used. Here, by serial precipitation, the normal precipitating antibody is made to compete with the non-precipitating antibody, so that all of it is removed before the incomplete has a chance to co-precipitate. Incomplete antibodies can also be revealed by *blocking*, i.e. when added to antigen before adding precipitating antibody they will interfere with the normal precipitate formation of the latter.

Incomplete antibodies may form a large proportion of the antibody formed in the early stages of immunization. More concerning their activity will be found in the section on *agglutination* later in this chapter, particularly in reference to Rh antibody.

As previously discussed in relation to the lattice hypothesis, the temptation to regard such antibody as univalent is hardly justified since although it will not precipitate with antigen alone, the addition of complement will sometimes result in precipitation.

Toxin–Antitoxin Reaction: the 'Flocculation' System

Some serological systems, of which certain toxin–antitoxin reactions are an example, behave in a curiously different fashion from that described above, in that distinct flocculation may occur over a very narrow range of relative Ag : Ab concentrations and perhaps only one tube in the series may show flocculi. Fig. 9.5 is a typical example of such a 'flocculation' reaction as shown by diphtheria toxin and horse antitoxin. In both antibody and antigen excess regions flocculation is inhibited. Inhibition in the antibody-excess zone is referred to as a 'prozone', and is accounted for by the presence of sufficient non-precipitating antibody to cause inhibition of precipitation in this region of the curve. In regions of higher antigen concentration such antibody acts to increase the bulk of the precipitate formed between antigen and precipitating antibody.

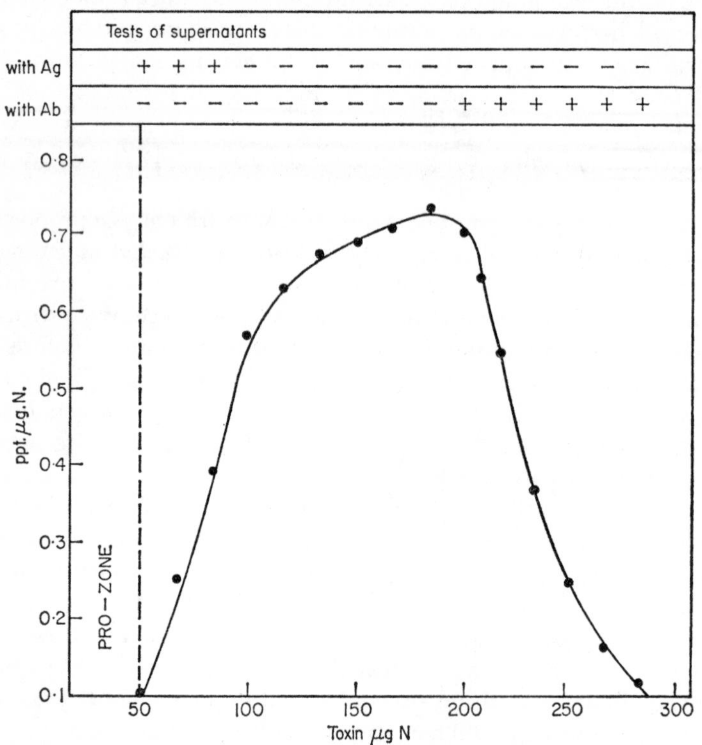

FIG. 9.5. Flocculation-type reaction curve of diphtheria toxin and antitoxin derived from the horse. The curve was obtained by adding increasing amounts of toxin to a constant quantity of antitoxin.

Ordinates: weight of thrice-washed precipitates express as μg N.

Abscissae: weight of toxin added in μg N.

Farr's Method (the Ammonium Sulphate Method to Measure Antigen-binding Capacity) and its Modifications

The precipitin test and most of the serological tests for antibody measure the capacity of an antiserum to produce secondary effects such as precipitation, agglutination and complement fixation rather than measure the capacity of an antiserum to bind antigen. Some antibodies do not precipitate and some only precipitate under particular high concentrations of salt or in the presence of complement components. Hence the value of a method which directly measures the antigen-binding capacity of serum.

Very small amounts of antibodies against antigens, such as serum albumin, that are not precipitable with half saturation with ammonium sulphate, can be measured by the antigen-binding capacity method of Farr. The antigen is labelled with ^{131}I; doses of antigen containing, say, 0·2 μg N are mixed with varying dilutions of antiserum in a total volume of 1 ml and kept at 4° for 30 minutes. An equal volume of saturated ammonium sulphate is added; antigen combined with antibody is precipitated. The precipitate is washed with half-saturated ammonium sulphate, and the antigen contained in it is estimated by its radioactivity. The antigen-binding capacity (ABC-33) is the number of μg of labelled antigen N bound per ml of undiluted antiserum and is calculated in μg per ml serum by multiplying the reciprocal of the dilution of antiserum required to precipitate 33 per cent of the antigen by 0·33 times the antigen added, i.e. 0·2. Thus, if a serum could be diluted so that 0·001 ml bound 0·33 of 0·2 μg of antigen, the antigen-binding capacity would be 66 μg per ml.

The 33 per cent precipitation end-point was arbitrarily selected because spontaneous precipitation does not occur at this degree of antigen excess, but enough of the ^{131}I activity is in the precipitate to permit accurate counting procedures.

Much experience has shown that antibody globulin does not release, bind or exchange appreciable amounts of labelled or unlabelled BSA after half-saturation with ammonium sulphate and the antigen–antibody equilibrium appears to be 'frozen' under these conditions.

Farr found that 1 μg of antibody N, measured by a quantitative precipitin test, bound about 1 μg of bovine serum albumin providing that dilution of the antiserum produced little effect on its capacity to bind antigen. If the binding capacity of the antiserum was much reduced by dilution, the ABC found was much less.

This particular technique is only applicable when the antigen is not itself precipitated by the concentration of ammonium sulphate used to precipitate out the antibody. A more general method, applicable to any antigen which can be labelled with radioactivity, is to precipitate the antibody by means of an antiglobulin antiserum prepared in another animal species. Thus, for human antibody, rabbit antihuman γ-globulin could be used to precipitate the bound antigen. This method has the disadvantage of requiring a lot of expensive antiserum and also freezes the antigen–antibody interaction more slowly than the procedure of adding $(NH_4)_2SO_4$.

An advantage of this general method is that it can be used with labelled haptens as well as simple protein antigens, and that it can be made extremely sensitive by employing very small amounts of antigen or hapten of high specific radioactivity. In fact, under these conditions as little as 5 μl of the test serum can be used, with a corresponding saving of anti-Ig.

II. PRACTICAL PROCEDURES INVOLVING AGGLUTINATION

In the case of agglutination, particulate, rather than soluble, antigens are brought together by antibody. The particles concerned—bacteria, yeasts, erythrocytes—are in general large enough to be seen under the microscope. Indeed, in observing agglutination we can watch the formation of bacterial clumps under the microscope. But usually in quantitative titrations the macroscopic method, in which the flocculation of the suspension is observed with the naked eye, or with the aid of a hand lens, is employed.

The mechanism of clumping has been envisaged in two different ways. Under the microscope the cells in, say, an erythrocyte suspension are seen not to be distributed in truly random manner, but to be at almost exactly equal distances from each other, almost certainly held apart by electrical repulsion. On this view, all that is required of antibody in order to clump such a suspension is to combine with and partially cover the surface of the erythrocytes so that their surface potentials are reduced. Another, possibly more important, alteration in the surface is the transformation of its hydrophilic character to a more hydrophobic character. The importance of electrolytes in determination of clumping is shown by the fact that if bacteria are allowed to react with an agglutinating antiserum in a salt-free medium there is usually no agglutination of the bacterial cells. That the antibody unites with the antigen may be shown by demonstrating its absence from the supernatant fluid after centrifugation of a mixture in which bacteria are present in excess or by adding an electrolyte to the suspended cells, when agglutination occurs.

According to another view the visible agglutination is the result of the linkage by antibody molecules of antigen at the surface of both particles. Here the clumping is brought about by a specific bond, and if this view is correct the agglutination of one kind of cell ought to be entirely independent of the agglutination of other serologically unrelated cells. In other words, if one mixes two independent cell-antibody systems the clumps formed should consist entirely of one kind of cell. On the whole, when diluted antisera are used, the results agree with this prediction. But, at the same time, it should be recognized that non-specific factors such as the presence of other colloids or electrolytes are also of importance.

The sensitivity with which the agglutination reaction can detect antibody varies over a wide range. Thus some bacterial agglutination reactions are highly sensitive and the titre of O agglutination of typhoid bacilli of a patient who is convalescent from typhoid fever may be 1 : 10,000 when the serum contains less than 190 μg of antibody nitrogen. Thus the sensitivity of the reaction is 0·02 μg Ab.N. Contrariwise the agglutination of capsulated pneumococci requires a relatively large amount of antibody, because the antibodies are used against the large amount of polysaccharide on the surface of the cells. The agglutinin titre of an antiserum which contains about 10 mg of antibody/ml may be 1 : 120; so that the sensitivity of this test is 0·08 mg/ml, i.e. an amount readily detectable by a simple ring test in gel (see Table 9.1). All agglutination reactions tend to detect IgM antibodies with greater sensitivity than IgG antibodies.

Titrations involving antibody may be carried out with dead or living bacteria or erythrocytes by diluting out the serum and observing the titre at which the desired degree of agglutination is achieved. In bacteriology one of the best known applications of the agglutination reaction is the *Widal Test* in the investigation of suspected infection by *Salmonella* organisms in diseases such as typhoid, paratyphoid and food poisoning. A positive agglutination reaction can be expected to appear during the second week of typhoid or paratyphoid fevers. In the performance of the test, the selection of organisms is usually designed to cover all those bacterial species which might cause a continued pyrexia of the enteric type. Thus those which are included in such a test in this country are *Salm. typhi*, *Salm. paratyphi*, and *Br. abortus*. Both of the first two species contain both flagellar and somatic antigens. The bacterial suspensions which are used are H-suspensions, which have been treated with formalin to preserve the H-antigens and annul the reactivity of the O-antigens and O-suspensions which have been treated with alcohol to destroy the H-antigens of the flagella and preserve the O-antigens. Where it is desirable to seek antibody against Vi antigen, suspensions of organisms selected to contain this antigen and treated in such a way as to preserve it, are set up with serum dilutions and incubated at 37°C. This procedure is recommended in the detection of carriers of *Salmonella typhi*, since immunization with phenol-treated vaccines does not induce the formation of Vi antibody. While most cases of enteric develop serum antibody to both H- and O-antigens, some cases fail to develop H-agglutinins. Incubation of the tubes in a water bath at 56°C for 2 hours is sufficient for H and for 4 to 24 hours for O. The tubes should be only half immersed in order to stimulate mixing by convection.

Caution is required in the interpretation of such tests. In areas where enteric is not endemic a titre of 50 for H and 100 for O may be taken as diagnostic of typhoid or paratyphoid, providing the patient has not had a previous attack of enteric fever and has not been vaccinated with TAB vaccine. Since in either of these two cases the flagellar H-agglutinin may persist in the blood at a considerable titre for many years, evidence based on this alone is not acceptable, but the O agglutinin due to inoculation soon sinks to titres below 50 and therefore an O titre of 100 or more is usually a valid indication of present infection. However, the somatic antigens of the different bacterial species have common components, and it may be impossible to decide which specific species is involved.

More dependable evidence of infection can be obtained by testing two samples of sera with a week or so between the dates of their collection, and thus demonstrating a rise in the titre. However, it is necessary to stress the need for the two sera to be tested simultaneously and for the difference in titre to be at least fourfold since under ordinary circumstances the experimental error of an agglutination test is 100 per cent (the tubes are usually set up in doubling dilutions).

Slide Agglutination

This simple qualitative test is widely used for blood grouping, for the rapid identification of bacterial species and in flocculation tests for syphilis.

A typical agglutination procedure for determining the blood group is as follows. A drop of an approximately 4 per cent erythrocyte suspension is placed within each of the areas of two circles on a glass slide. To the one a drop of known blood group A serum (containing agglutinins for B cells) and to the other a drop of known blood group B serum (containing agglutinins for A cells) is added. The drops on the plate are mixed by rocking and observed over 5 minutes for the presence of agglutination. The pattern of reaction given with the blood of various groups is shown in Table 9.2.

Prior to the transfusion of blood, besides the knowledge that the donor and recipient are compatible in respect to blood group, cross-matching must be done, by mixing the serum of the recipient with the cells of the donor and *vice versa.* If agglutination is absent from both mixtures the bloods are compatible.

TABLE 9.2
Pattern of agglutination observed with red cells and various sera of the human *ABO* system

Blood group	Serum from Grp. A individual (anti-B or β)	Serum from Grp. B individual (anti-A or α)	Cellular content of antigens	Content of iso-agglutinins in serum
O	–	–	none	α and β
A	–	+	A	β
B	+	–	B	α
AB	+	+	A and B	none

+ = agglutination

FURTHER ADAPTATIONS OF PRECIPITATION AND AGGLUTINATION TESTS

Two factors limit the usefulness of the precipitin test. First it is theoretically possible to run into difficulty with non-precipitating antibody. Secondly, the test is relatively insensitive when used for detecting antibody. In the majority of sera, although some of the antibody is non-precipitating, there is usually a sufficient proportion of precipitating antibody to allow co-precipitation of an antibody when the latter combines with antigen. Non-precipitating antibody will not produce agglutination either, and the practical aspects of the problem of their detection in certain naturally occurring antisera will be taken up below.

The precipitin test provides an extremely precise method for the quantitation of antibody when amounts of more than 10 μg N per ml of serum are present (see Table 9.1). Below these levels antibody can neither be measured nor detected with accuracy. An immune serum which will give detectable precipitin reactions at a dilution of down to 1 in 10 may be diluted several thousand times and still achieve agglutination. The limitation of the agglutination test derives from the fact that it can only be applied if the particle can be found or manufactured with the homologous antigen at its surface. It was shown that collodion particles coated with, e.g., egg albumin were agglutinated by extremely high dilutions of anti-ovalbumin sera even though they gave precipitin reactions only at very low serum dilutions. This allowed the exploitation of the exquisite sensitivity of the agglutination reaction and paved the way for many similar *passive agglutination tests*, in which various types of particle were used with specific antigens stuck to their surface.

In recent years the range of usefulness of the haemagglutination reaction has been considerably extended by the observation that erythrocytes could absorb various polysaccharides and that after treatment with tannic acid, which acts as a mordant, they would also take up, at their surface, many protein antigens. Thus antibodies to the polysaccharide antigens of tubercle bacilli can be detected and titrated in the sera of animals and humans by the use of erythrocytes coated with polysaccharides derived from the tubercle bacillus (Keogh procedure). The use of tannic-acid treated erythrocytes, usually derived from sheep's blood (Boyden procedure), has been applied to the detection and titration of antibodies to bacillary proteins (e.g. tuberculoprotein), hormones in blood and urine (pituitary growth, thyrotrophic and gonadotrophic hormones), sundry viruses (see below), and various tissue antigens (thyroglobulin, auto-antigens of cardiac muscle, auto-antigens of the brain involved in allergic encephalomyelitis, etc.). An example is illustrated in Plate 9.5 (following p. 404).

In addition, polystyrene latex suspensions have become available which are of a uniform particle size and easily preserved over long periods. These have in many cases replaced the use of the technically erratic collodion particles mentioned previously. The *Latex particle test*, which has proved of such usefulness in the follow-up and diagnosis of cases of rheumatoid arthritis, employs latex particles coated with human γ-globulin, and the agglutination which is observed with the sera of such patients is attributed to the presence of an antibody to denatured γ-globulin in them. (See further discussion in Chapter Fifteen.)

Furthermore, it is possible to titrate antigen in solution by its capacity to react with antibody and so inhibit the antibody from agglutinating the coated cells. Thus the levels of growth hormone in human sera can be estimated by the ability of the growth homrone in such sera to inhibit the agglutination by hyperimmune rabbit antisera of growth-hormone sensitized tanned sheep erythrocytes. This is termed a *haemagglutination inhibition test*. It can be extremely sensitive, but great care must be taken to exclude the effect of non-specific factors.

In the field of blood group serology the use of antisera to human γ-globulin has greatly extended the use of agglutination techniques and enabled the detection of antibodies with unique characteristics. Thus in 1944 it was found that the Rh-negative mothers of erythroblastotic infants often possess antibodies which are incapable of causing agglutination of erythrocytes under the ordinary conditions of serological titration. But these antibodies could reveal themselves by a blocking action. Thus, if the serum were mixed with appropriate erythrocytes no visible reaction occurred, but if a known agglutinating serum for the same cells were subsequently added to the mixture, these also failed to cause aggregation. This failure is due to the *non-agglutinating*, *incomplete* or *blocking antibody* occupying the combining sites of the red cells.

Coombs, Mourant and Race revealed another method for detecting such antibodies by adding an antibody against human γ-globulin to the red cells previously treated with blocking antibody. The bivalent antiglobulin serves to cross-link and so to aggregate the globulin-coated erythrocytes; see Fig. 9.6 I. On the basis of these facts blocking antibody was often termed '*univalent*'. (This is, strictly speaking, a functional use of the term, and is not supported by the known facts concerning the molecular structure of antibodies.) In consequence of its one effective combining group presumably such an antibody could unite with antigen but could not form cross-links with other antigen sites on other red cells.

However, the matter is not quite so straightforward as this. First, it was found that many samples of incomplete or blocking antibody would bring about agglutination if the test were carried out in serum or in a solution of serum albumin rather than in saline. Secondly, certain methods of pretreating the red cells will render them susceptible to agglutination by incomplete antibody. Pretreatment with trypsin or the filtrate of a culture of cholera vibrios (containing RDE or receptor-destroying enzyme) will do this.

It has become possible to recognize degrees of incompleteness of agglutinating antibody:

Grade 1. Conventional antibody which acts in saline.

Grade 2. Antibody with capacity to block, which agglutinates in the presence of albumin, and which can also be demonstrated by the antiglobulin test.

Grade 3. Acts similarly to the last but lacks the capacity to block.

I Detection of an "incomplete" or non-agglutinating antibody by means of anti-human gamma-globulin

Antigenic receptor sites on surface of erythrocyte

Hypothetical uni-valent antibody combining site for anti-human gamma-globulin

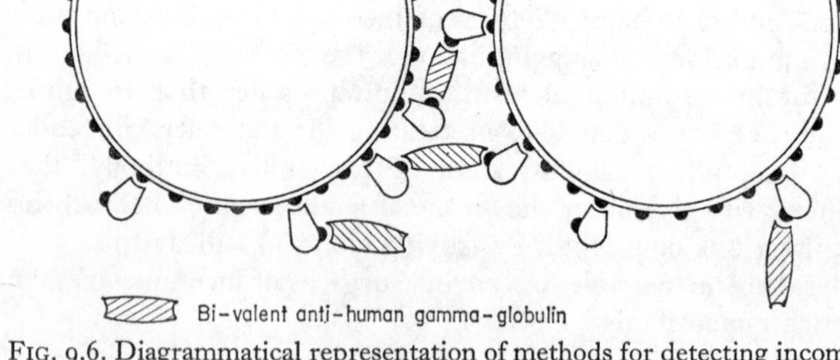

FIG. 9.6. Diagrammatical representation of methods for detecting incomplete erythrocyte antibodies.

I. By means of anti-human-γ-globulin reagent. The effectively univalent antibody might combine with the red-cell receptors and thus block further antibody reaction at these sites, but could not cross-link with other red cells. The result is non-agglutination. The addition of bivalent anti-human-γ-globulin reagent allows cross-links to form between the molecules of univalent antibody.

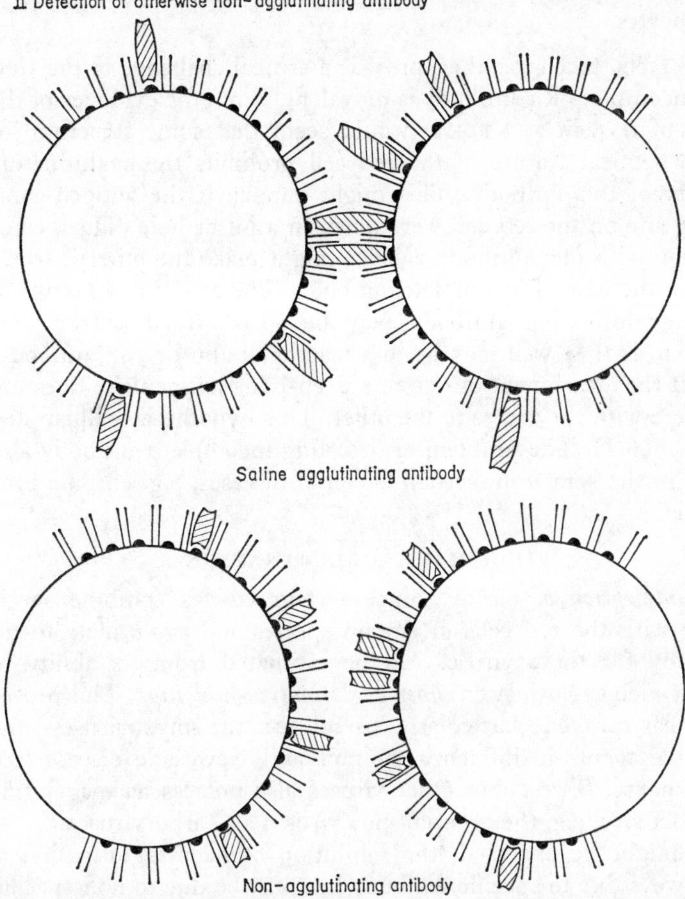

Antibody which is non-agglutinating in saline on account of steric hindrance with projections from the erythrocyte surface. Such antibody could work if the projections were removed by pretreatment of erythrocytes with enzymes. Such projections need not interfere with the action of anti-human γ-globulin in forming cross-links by the mechanism illustrated in Fig. 9.6 I.

II. By means of enzyme-treated erythrocytes. The antibody which achieves agglutination of normal erythrocytes in saline is presumed to have widely separated combining sites. Antibody which is non-agglutinating under these conditions is shown as smaller molecules which are prevented by the surface erythrocyte projections from combining with another erythrocyte receptor site after linkage with a first site on another erythrocyte. Removal of the surface projections by enzyme treatment is followed by agglutination. Such projections need not interfere with the action of anti-human-γ-globulin in forming cross-links by the mechanism of section I above.

Grade 4. Antibody which agglutinates enzyme-treated erythrocytes.

These facts, taken together, provide a critical challenge to the view that incomplete Rh antibody is univalent. From the evidence of the effect of trypsin and RDE it would seem that some structural or stereochemical feature of the red cell prohibits the agglutinating activity of the antibody. This might happen if the antigen-combining site on the red cell were down in a pit or hole. Thus, combination with one antibody valence might make the other inaccessible in the case of incomplete antibody. The combining groups of saline-agglutinating antibody may be spaced further from one another, as they well may be in a macroglobulin or 19S antibody, so that the attachment of one to a deep-lying antigen site does not interfere with the access to the other. This hypothesis is illustrated in Fig. 9.6 II. The problem of detecting incomplete antibody also arises in the sera from certain bacterial diseases, e.g. chronic brucellosis.

VIRUS HAEMAGGLUTINATION

Haemadsorption of viruses. Since certain viruses combine specifically with the red cells of certain species and agglutinate them, antibody for these viruses can be estimated from its ability to inhibit such agglutination: *haemagglutination-inhibition*. This procedure has proved particularly useful for the myxoviruses—the infective agents in influenza, mumps and Newcastle disease (see also Chapter Two)—but other viruses also possess haemagglutinating activity, e.g. the group of pox viruses and arborviruses.

As might be expected, the inhibition of haemagglutination is not always due to specific antibody but may be due to non-specific factors. With the myxoviruses, these appear to be mucoproteins, with the arborviruses lipoproteins. Since the concentration of the inhibitors in serum may be so high that the specific antibody is masked, sera must first be treated in some way to avoid inhibitor activity. The inhibitors of the myxoviruses can be removed by receptor-destroying enzyme (RDE) from *Vibrio cholerae* filtrates and those of the arborviruses by acetone extraction.

Indirect Virus Haemagglutination

Certain viruses which lack the ability to agglutinate erythrocytes directly can be made to agglutinate erythrocytes by an indirect method, which makes use of antibody and is analogous to that described above for various soluble antigens (Boyden technique). Thus herpes simplex virus can be adsorbed on to sheep erythrocytes whose surface has been treated with tannic acid. When such virus-coated cells are exposed to specific immune serum, haemagglutination occurs.

COLD HAEMAGGLUTININS

These antibodies derive their name from the fact that they are able to agglutinate human group O erythrocytes at 0–4°C but not at body temperature. They are non-specific, in the sense that they will agglutinate erythrocytes from many species, and although they may occur in certain virus diseases bear no relationship with the haemagglutinins previously discussed. They are encountered in a variety of diseases: primary atypical pneumonia caused by *Mycoplasma pneumoniae*, trypanosomiasis, acquired haemolytic anaemia, blackwater fever and occasionally occur in lower amounts in normal blood.

These cold agglutinins may be adsorbed on erythrocytes at low temperatures, and eluted at 37°C. Material prepared in this way has been characterized as a γ macroglobulin.

Since reaction also occurs with autologous erythrocytes such antibodies are auto-antibodies. The antigen sometimes involved is present in nearly all human and animal erythrocytes and has been termed I. A very occasional person lacks this antigen. Instances of acute haemolytic anaemia have been seen to accompany atypical pneumonia. In this latter condition, other aberrant antibodies may occur, especially an agglutinin for a coccal organism: *Streptococcus MG*. There is no evidence to incriminate *Streptococcus MG* as the causal agent of primary atypical pneumonia but the possibility must be envisaged that the pleuropneumonia-like organism (Eaton agent) now considered responsible may share common antigens with the streptococcus or even be derived from it.

In atypical pneumonia the serum titre for cold agglutinins and against *Streptococcus MG* starts to rise about the end of the second week of disease and rises to maximum at about the fourth week.

Further Elaborations of the Agglutination Reaction; Mixed Agglutination and the Antiglobulin Consumption Test

Several factors may render tissue cells unsatisfactory particles to be agglutinated by antibody. First, the cells may be unstable in suspension and agglutinate spontaneously. Secondly, the cells bearing the antigen in question may be only one of a number of different types of cell in a mixture. Thirdly, antigens in a sub-surface position although able to combine with antibody may fail to provide the means for agglutination.

Mixed Agglutination has been specifically applied for the detection on tissue cells of the same antigens as are present on erythrocytes, e.g. the blood group iso-antigens. Thus, for the detection of surface blood group A antigen, cells (e.g. from a tissue culture) are incubated with anti-A serum and then washed. Any antibody which remains adherent to the cells is detected by adding group A red cells and gently centrifuging the mixture. This allows free combining sites on the antibody adherent to the tissue cell to link with the A antigen on the red cell. The adherence of cells indicating a positive mixed agglutination reaction can be seen after gently depositing a drop of the mixed cell preparation on a microscope slide and inspecting in a phase-contrast microscope after sealing under a cover glass (Fig. 9.7).

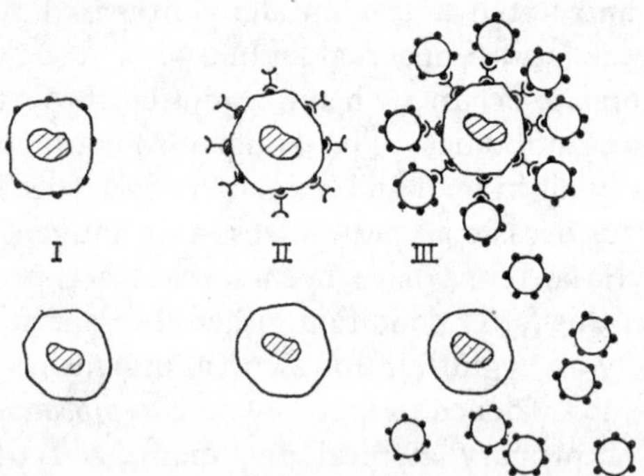

FIG. 9.7. Diagram of the mixed agglutination reaction for the demonstration of an antigen (B) on the surface of tissue culture cells.

I. (above) Untreated tissue cell with B antigen on surface, (below) untreated cell with no B antigen.

II. (Above and below) Cells treated with anti-B and washed.

III. Addition of group B red cells and centrifugation. (above) Mixed agglutination demonstrating presence of B on tissue cells. (below) No mixed agglutination demonstrating absence of B on tissue cells.

The mixed agglutination reaction has been used for the demonstration of the red cell iso-antigens A, B, H, M, N, T, j, and a on leucocytes and platelets. The method is widely used for checking the identity of tissue culture cell lines preserved through many generations *in vitro*. The test can in this instance be applied directly to the cells growing on and attached to the glass of the culture tubes. For forensic purposes the method can be adapted to the detection of blood group antigens on the shed epidermal scales in dandruff and for the detection of human or animal blood on the fibres of cloth. A great advantage of the latter method is that only a minute amount of material is needed for the test.

The Antiglobulin Consumption Test is of particular usefulness in detecting auto-antibodies to leucocytes and platelets which occur in systemic lupus erythematosus and cases of idiopathic thrombocytopenic purpura and leucopenia. The technique depends on the uptake of antiglobulin molecules on to the immunoglobulin which has been taken up by the tissue cell. The *direct* antiglobulin consumption test is able to show the fixation of immunoglobulin *in vivo* on leucocytes and platelets (or mixtures of the two) from cases of SLE and the above diseases. The *indirect* test detects antibodies free in the serum of the same group of diseases, which is able to combine with a suitable suspension of cells *in vitro*. In both direct and indirect forms of the test the cells coated with antibody after washing are mixed with the antiglobulin and the depletion in the level of the antiglobulin antibody is measured by titration against globulin-coated red cells. To obtain the best results the coated cells should be exposed to a critical and small level of an antiglobulin which is specifically directed against the particular globulin class to be detected, i.e. specific anti-IgM if this is the class of the antibody involved in the reaction.

Detection of Cytophilic Antibody

Cytophilic antibody has been defined (Boyden) as a globulin component of antiserum which becomes attached *in vitro* to certain cells in such a way that these cells are subsequently capable of specifically adsorbing antigen. Cytophilic antibody was first described in sera from rabbits immunized with human serum albumin (HSA) and its detection involved the use of ^{131}I-labelled HSA together with suspensions of spleen cells. More recently, cytophilic antibody with affinity for macrophages has been investigated using sheep red cells as antigen and this application will be considered first.

(i) *Method for Demonstrating Cytophilic Antibody to Sheep Red*

Cells. Small well-type chambers (1 cm diameter) were used in Perspex slides. Peritoneal cells were taken from a normal guinea-pig, and counted. A total of 2×10^5 peritoneal cells were placed in each well. The slides were placed at 37° in a moist atmosphere containing 5 per cent CO_2 for 40 minutes to allow the macrophages present to settle on to and attach to the glass. The wells were next rinsed out with tissue culture medium, and 0·1 ml of diluted test serum introduced. After one hour in the cold room the monolayer was washed several times with tissue culture medium (Stage 1, Fig. 9.8). Finally 0·1 ml of a 1 per cent suspension of washed sheep red

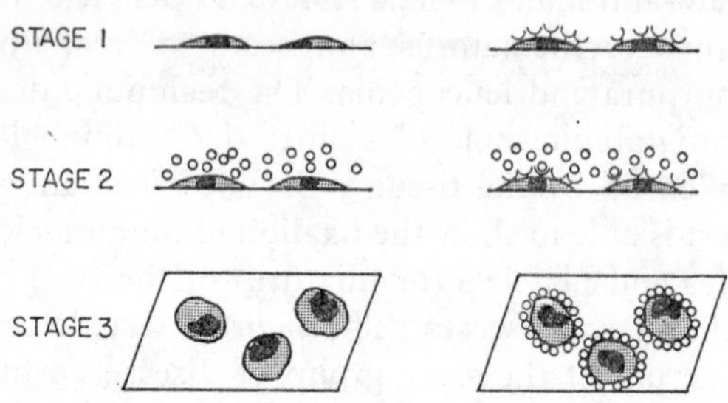

FIG. 9.8. Rosette test for macrophage cytophilic antibody to sheep red cells.

The procedure for the test is illustrated diagrammatically in the following steps:

Stage 1: macrophage monolayer on glass has been exposed to serum and washed. On left, a serum negative for cytophilic antibody to sheep erythrocytes has left naked macrophages. On right, the antibody molecules are left attached.

Stage 2: 1% suspension of washed sheep red cells added to culture.

Stage 3: after inversion of culture in tissue culture fluid the red cells have remained attached to macrophages coated with cytophilic antibody (positive result on right, negative on left).

cells was placed in each well and left to interact for one hour (Stage 2, Fig. 9.8). Slides were then placed upside down in tissue culture fluid to allow the unattached red cells to fall away from the bottom of the well. The result was expressed as the number of red cells adherent to 100 macrophages as seen under a microscope. A positive result involves the formation of characteristic 'rosettes' of sheep red cells adhering to macrophages (Stage 3, Fig. 9.8 also Plate 9.6).

(ii) *Extension of Method for Demonstrating Cytophilic Antibody to Soluble Antigens.* The inconvenience with the above procedure is that the indicator erythrocyte particles are necessarily the same as the immunogen. The method can be adapted to the detection of macrophage cytophilic antibody for soluble antigens by the use of the protein coupling agent bis-diazotized benzidine. The test illustrated in Fig. 9.9 has used as indicator cells sheep red cells to which

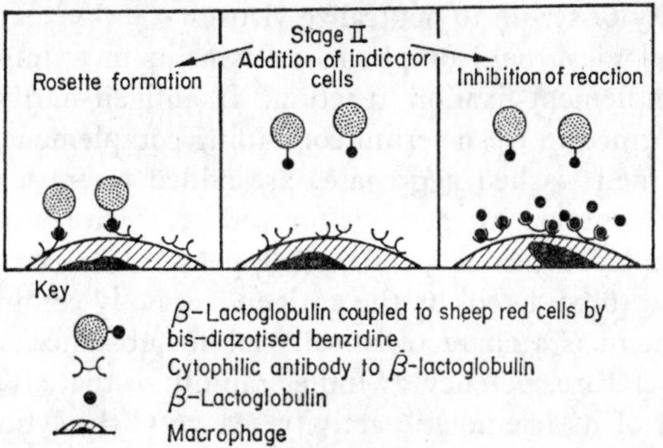

FIG. 9.9. Rosette test for macrophage cytophilic antibody to soluble protein antigens.

The procedure is illustrated diagrammatically for the protein antigen β-Lactoglobulin which has been coupled to sheep red cells by means of bis-diazotized benzidine in order to provide a suitable indicator particle, at Stage 2 of the procedure in Fig. 9.8. A positive result (on left of diagram) is indicated by formation of 'rosettes' of erythrocytes around the macrophages of the monolayer. A negative control is provided (on right of diagram) by addition of soluble protein antigen (β-Lactoglobulin) which specifically inhibits the attachment of the indicator erythrocytes to form rosettes.

β-Lactoglobulin has been coupled with bis-diazotized benzidine. In a positive test rosettes of the indicator cells are formed around the monolayer macrophages. A negative control (shown on right side of diagram) has employed the use of soluble antigen (β-Lactoglobulin) to inhibit the reaction specifically before final addition of the indicator cells.

COMPLEMENT AND COMPLEMENT-FIXATION

As explained in Chapter Five, complement is a group of at least nine serum factors, of globulin nature, which occur in the plasma of all normal animals. It enters into various immunological reactions, and generally speaking it is absorbed by any combination of antigen and antibody.

In concert with the appropriate antibody, complement lyses erythrocytes, kills and sometimes lyses certain bacteria, promotes phagocytosis and immune adherence, and in some cases contributes to the tissue damage in hypersensitivity reactions in the tissues and to the ability of serum to neutralize viruses.

As a serological tool, complement attains its most important role in the complement-fixation reaction. If antigen–antibody aggregates are formed in fresh serum containing complement, or, if previously formed washed aggregates are added to fresh serum, the haemolytic complement activity for red cells with attached antibody (so-called sensitized cells) disappears. The complement is thereby said to be 'fixed' by the antigen–antibody combination.

Complement is a characteristically labile substance and, even at room temperature, potency dwindles rapidly so that after 24 hours little is left of its haemolytic activity. At 56°C the lytic activity is completely destroyed in 20 minutes, and this procedure is routinely used for ridding an antiserum of its normal content of complement before use in serological tests.

Usually the complement of any one species of animal will act with antibody derived from other species, although several exceptions to this rule exist. In many routine complement-fixation tests use is made of guinea-pig serum as a source of complement.

The mechanism of the bactericidal or haemolytic effects of complement is far from clear. Complement does not combine with antigen alone. It has a slight affinity for antibody and will combine strongly with heat-denatured γ-globulin, but with normal antibody strong affinity is not shown until this is in combination with antigen. Studies of immune haemolysis suggest that the relationship between the cell which is disrupted and the complement may be extremely indirect. Thus, if quite unrelated antigen is caused to be adsorbed on the red cell surface, the antibody specific to this antigen together with complement may induce lysis. This makes it unlikely that the complement acts directly on the antigens in the cell surface. Rather, the antigen–antibody reaction occurring in the presence of complement activates enzymes in the complement complex, which can secondarily affect the cell surface. The mechanism is discussed more fully in Chapter Five.

The reaction of complement with the antigen–antibody complex can be made use of to detect or measure either antigen or antibody. For most antigens the fixation of complement occurs without causing any visible effect, and a haemolytic system must be used to detect the final presence or absence of complement.

In order to illustrate the diagnostic qualitative use of the complement–fixation test let us consider its application to the detection of antibody in the serum of say a patient with suspected gonococcal arthritis. We mix the serum (heated to inactivate its own complement), a standardized dose of complement (fresh guinea-pig serum) and gonococcal antigen (a suspension of heat-killed gonococci of several freshly isolated cultures). After time has been allowed for interaction of complement with the possible antigen–antibody complex, the mixture is tested (by addition of an indicator system) for the presence of free complement. The absence of free complement, i.e. fixation of all of the dose of added complement, will indicate a positive test for gonococcal antibody.

The *haemolytic indicator system* used to detect presence or absence of complement is prepared by adding a suspension of sheep red cells in isotonic salt solution to a heated antiserum against them prepared in the rabbit. The suspension of such 'sensitized' cells will undergo haemolysis if added to a solution containing free (unfixed) complement, since the third component of the reaction, given below, is provided. (See also Fig. 9.10.)

Sheep red cells + specific antibody + complement → haemolysis.

The amounts of antigen and of complement to be used in such a test must be determined by previous titration. First, the guinea-pig serum is set up in a series of dilutions against the standard dose of sheep cells sensitized by rabbit antibody. The end-point taken may be the MHD (the minimum haemolytic dose) which refers to the dilution of guinea-pig serum necessary to bring about total haemolysis of all of the dose of the red cells, or for greater accuracy the $C'H_{50}$ (50 per cent haemolytic unit). The latter is strictly preferable since the 100 per cent haemolysis does not furnish a sharply defined end-point. It is common for tests to employ either 2 MHD or 5 $C'H_{50}$ doses of complement. Thus if the test serum fixes 4 units the remaining 1 $C'H_{50}$ will produce 50 per cent lysis of the sensitized cells, and this has proved to be a convenient baseline, so that a fixation of less than 4 out of 5 units will be recorded as a negative reaction. The factors which determine the activity of complement in bringing about haemolysis must at all times be standardized, viz. the number of red cells, the ionic strength, the concentration of magnesium and calcium ions, pH and temperature (37°C).

Secondly the antigen must be titrated by the method of optimal proportions to determine the appropriate dilution to be used in the test. Using a known positive serum, the end-point of the titration is that antigen dilution which reacts with the greatest dilution of the positive serum to give complete fixation of the adopted dose of complement.

Many agents other than antigen-antibody reactions can inactivate complement, so the final test against an unknown serum must be accompanied by certain controls which serve to show that the observed fixation is truly immunological. Often the serum will inactivate complement in the absence of antigen, and it must be shown in every test that neither the serum nor the antigen alone interferes with the haemolytic activity of the complement dose employed. Sera which are contaminated with bacteria are strongly anti-complementary, an effect possibly due to the formation of immune complexes between the micro-organisms and traces of corresponding antibody which may be present in the test serum or the serum serving as a source of complement.

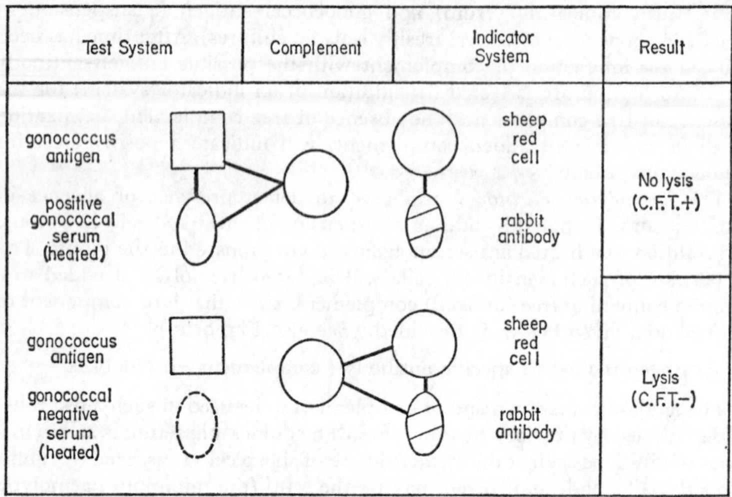

FIG. 9.10. Diagrammatical representation of the complement-fixation reaction.

THE APPLICATION OF THE COMPLEMENT-FIXATION REACTIONS

Complement-fixation possesses the main advantage that the antigen may be either soluble or insoluble. Moreover, relatively impure preparations such as virus preparations contaminated by much tissue debris may serve as adequate antigens.

Complement can enter into the antigen-antibody complex at the earliest stage of combination, and this reaction can occur not only when the proportions of antigen and antibody are unfavourable for aggregate formation but also when the type of antibody is such that aggregation cannot occur, i.e. so-called 'incomplete' antibody. For these reasons, the complement-fixation test may be positive earlier in the course of an infectious disease than the agglutination or precipitin reactions.

Apart from the gonococcal complement-fixation test and the

Wassermann reaction it is nowadays the case that complement-fixation is little used in the diagnosis of bacterial diseases, but they continue to be of great value in many virus infections.

Wassermann Test

Early in the present century Wassermann, using the complement-fixation method which had been described earlier, discovered what has become known as 'Wassermann antibody' in the serum of cases of syphilis. At first foetal liver tissue swarming with *Treponema pallidum* was used as the antigen in the test, and the antibody was regarded as specific for this organism. However, it was soon discovered that this antibody could just as readily be demonstrated using normal liver as antigen, and later it was shown how alcoholic extracts of a wide variety of human and animal tissues could serve as the antigen in the Wassermann test. The antigen commonly used at present is a purified lipid extracted by alcohol from beef heart, the so-called *cardiolipin*, to which lecithin and cholesterol have been added. Otherwise, the plan of the Wassermann reaction follows that of other complement-fixation tests.

Much discussion has centred on the question of whether the serological entity which is detected in the Wassermann reaction is a true antibody, and whether it represents a response to an antigen of the *Tr. pallidum* or possibly to some tissue component which by virtue of the treponemal infection is caused to become antigenic. This extract of normal heart tissues which is active in the Wassermann reaction is referred to as *cardiolipid*. When injected alone no antibody results. However, if absorbed on to kaolin or aluminium hydroxide, antibody may be produced. Thus, cardiolipid is referred to sometimes as a *hapten*. Doubts concerning the cardiolipid-reactive serum component as a true antibody are reflected in the use of the term Wassermann *reagin* for this entity. Most human Wassermann antibody from early cases of syphilis migrates as a γ-globulin, but in late sera from this disease it migrates as a β_2-globulin. In view of the ubiquitous antigen, it seems remarkable that the antibody can exist without combining with and causing widespread tissue damage. However, such damage has never been described, possibly since the antigen is normally *inside* the cells.

The same Wassermann antibody can be detected by direct mixture of syphilitic sera with Wassermann-type antigens which leads to a *flocculation reaction* easily observable through a hand lens or even by the naked eye. Various modifications such as the Kahn, Meinicke, Hinton and other such flocculation tests exist. The flocculation reactions give results which closely parallel those of the Wassermann complement-fixation test. Their great value over the latter lies in their technical simplicity, so that they can be done in laboratories where the complement-fixation test would be an inconveniently complicated undertaking. The Kahn test is of greater sensitivity in detecting syphilitic antibody than the Wassermann, but is also more likely to become positive in non-syphilitic infections. Both the Wassermann and Kahn reactions, despite their great diagnostic value, are less specific than is desirable in an important disease such as syphilis. So-called *biological false-positive reaction* can occur in patients with tuberculosis, leprosy, malaria, glandular fever, infective hepatitis and systemic lupus erythematosus. Indeed, the healthy relatives of patients with systemic lupus may also yield such false-positive results.

Recently, several other tests have been introduced in which the antigens used are derived from treponemata. In the *Treponema Pallidum Immobilization* (TPI) *test*, dilutions of the patient's serum are mixed with a suspension of motile *Tr. pallidum*, which are usually obtained by needle puncture of a syphiloma maintained in the testis of a rabbit. An appropriate dose of complement is added and, after incubation, the test is read by finding the proportion of immobile spirochaetes under the dark field microscope. The test is complicated and expensive, but since it may clarify the diagnostic significance of a false-positive W.R. or Kahn test it is of great practical value. The fluorescent antibody technique (see below) has also been adapted to the same purpose. The test in this case is designed to detect specific treponemal antibody which localizes to a smear of *Tr. pallidum*. Use of a subsequently applied fluorescent-antibody to human γ-globulin and inspection in the fluorescence microscope allows the detection of a positive reaction. This test has the advantages of being convenient, specific and highly sensitive, and is the first to become positive after infection. The immune-adherence reaction (see below) can also be adapted to the same purpose.

IMMUNE-ADHERENCE REACTION: AN AGGREGATION REACTION REQUIRING COMPLEMENT

In the agglutination procedure, as previously discussed, specific aggregation follows reaction of antigen and antibody without the help of any foreign particles. However, many early investigators had noticed that organisms such as *Vibrio cholerae* became entangled in clumps with the blood platelets when introduced into the bloodstream of immunized animals other than primates. Later, it was shown that this interaction could occur with other particles besides platelets, such as erythrocytes of primates, silica and starch granules. Also it was established by *in vitro* tests that complement was essential. In classical agglutination complement is unnecessary. Indeed the reaction is usually done at 56°C and when carried out at, say, 37°C it is found that complement has, if anything, an inhibitory effect.

Spirochaetes, protozoa, filaria, as well as bacteria, have been reported to give the adherence reaction, and the reaction has been successfully used for the antigenic differentiation of species of trypanosomes and leptospirae. Conversely, the adherence reaction has been used with platelets or red cells serving as indicators for the diagnosis of human trypanosomiasis, and of syphilitic infection, in which the adherence reaction and the treponemal immobilization test tend to parallel one another.

The adherence phenomenon might be expected to assist the process of phagocytosis by keeping opsonized objects and phagocytes in contact after collision. Moreover, the adherence of sensitized bacteria to red cells has been claimed to lead to increased uptake of the bacteria by phagocytes. It is easy to imagine that the immune-adherence reaction could operate to the advantage of the body in clearing the blood of microbes, but such hypotheses at present lack the support of any substantial evidence.

FLUORESCENT ANTIBODY TECHNIQUES

From the foregoing discussion of the precipitin technique it will be obvious that this immunological method has proved of great help to the chemist in the specific identification of protein and polysaccharide antigens in solution. Similarly, an obvious approach to the study of such macromolecules in tissue sections is by use of the specific antibody globulin which has been labelled with a colour. This could be applied over a section of tissue so that a microprecipitate would form at the site of the antigen. The main difficulty is the detection of the small amount of dye in such a microprecipitate. For this reason, the method eventually developed by Coons and his colleagues used the fluorescent dyes, anthracene and fluorescein, which could be detected with high sensitivity in a fluorescence microscope; in the case of fluorescein this allows the green fluorochrome to be seen against a background of the natural, usually blue, auto-fluorescence of the tissues. Fluorescein isocyanate and isothiocyanate can be easily linked with antibody globulin to yield a blue-green fluorescent substance. The tissue section used in this work must, of course, be prepared in such a way as to avoid damage to the immunological reactivity of the antigen. In general, polysaccharide antigens might be expected to withstand treatment with the standard histological fixatives and with the organic solvents required for embedding the tissue in paraffin wax. Proteins generally have to be handled rather more gently. Frozen sections of unfixed tissues which have received minimal treatment with ethanol, methanol or acetone are often satisfactory. Alternatively freeze-dried or freeze-substituted tissues can be used, from which the water has been removed either *in vacuo* or by organic solvents (alcohol) at low temperature, followed by infiltration with paraffin.

The simplest application of the technique, which employs a single treatment with labelled antibody followed by a wash in physiological buffer-saline to get rid of the excess of uncombined labelled antibody, is illustrated in Fig. 9.11A. Such a method has been used

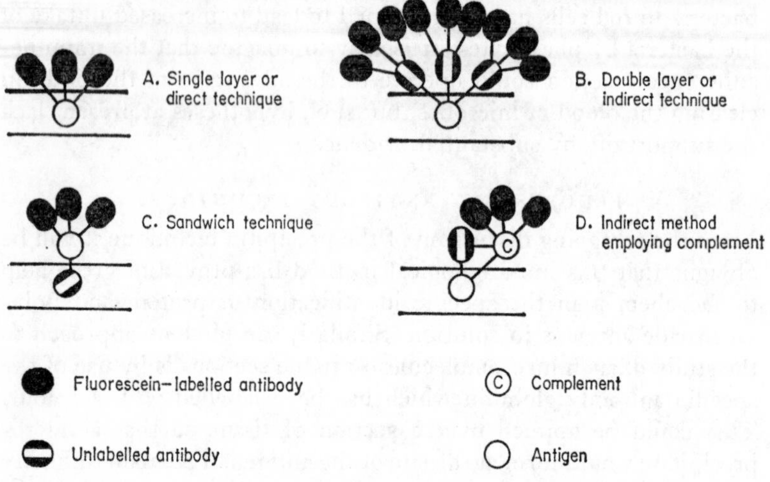

FIG. 9.11. Diagrammatical representation of the various modifications of the fluorescent-antibody method.

A Direct method for demonstrating antigen by the use of a single layer of fluorescein-labelled specific antibody.

B Indirect or double layer technique: unlabelled specific antibody is used first and the material is subsequently treated with fluorescent antibody against γ-globulin. Thus if the first layer employed rabbit antibody, fluorescent antibody against rabbit γ-globulin would be used in the second layer.

C Sandwich technique for the detection of antibody. The section is first treated with a dilute solution of antigen. After a wash to get rid of the excess antigen, the section is exposed to fluorescent antibody.

D Indirect method for detection of antigen employing complement (fresh guinea-pig serum) and rabbit antibody to guinea-pig globulin.

for the identification of injected foreign antigens in tissues (Plate 9.7), e.g. for the detection of particulate viruses as well as their soluble antigens (Plate 9.8, following p. 404) and of bacteria, protozoa and fungal antigens (Chapter Seven).

There exist several modifications of the technique which make use of two or more immunologically linked layers for the demonstration of antigen or antibody. The so-called 'sandwich' technique for the detection of antibody (Fig. 9.11C) employs a primary layer of a dilute solution of unlabelled antigen. After reacting for 30 minutes or so, this is rinsed off with physiological saline, and then exposed to specific fluorescein-labelled antibody. Such a method depends upon the multivalency of the antigen. The reaction of the antigen with the antibody in the tissue section still leaves many possible combining sites for antibody on the sides of the molecule away from the tissue section. Figs. 7.7, 7.8, 7.9A, 7.10, 7.11B, 7.12, 7.13 and 7.15 in Chapter Seven were obtained by the use of such a sandwich technique.

Other double layer techniques have been adapted for the detection of antigen. A convenient approach is to use labelled antiglobulin sera as a second layer in order to detect the sites of localization of an unlabelled specific antibody which was applied as the first layer (Fig. 9.11B). Plate 9.9, pp. 404–5, shows this method employed to detect an interaction between nuclei and an antibody to nucleo-histone present in the serum of a case of systemic lupus erythematosus. The sensitivity of the method is increased by such double layer techniques since each added layer combines as an antibody with subjacent multivalent antigen. The method is also of great convenience in cases where only small amounts of specific antisera can be obtained. Fig. 9.11D shows diagrammatically a double layer technique in which guinea-pig complement is used for the detection of antigen in combination with homologous unlabelled antibody.

The method has been further extended by the use of a variety of different coloured fluorescent dyes such as rhodamine sulphonyl chloride (orange red) and amino-naphthalene-5-sulphonyl chloride (lemon yellow).

Before it can be concluded that a fluorescent image results from the specific localization of the fluorescent antibody to a site of its homologous antigen, various controls must be satisfied. First, the fluorescence must be distinguished from the natural or primary fluorescence of the tissue. As explained above, most natural fluorescence can be distinguished on the grounds of colour from the yellow-green dye fluorescein or from the orange-red rhodamine. In any case the tissue section, untreated by any fluorescent conjugate, provides an obvious control for such natural fluorescence. Secondly, the fluorescence must not arise from non-specific adsorption of any of the mixture of proteins which accompany specific antibody in the material used for conjugation with fluorescent dye. This is usually a crude globulin or γ-globulin fraction of serum. Thirdly, serum will contain many antibodies other than the one intended for coupling with fluorescent dye. Some of these may link specifically with their homologous antigens in tissue. One example would be Forssman antibody which would occur in most rabbit sera and would react with erythrocytes and other tissue elements in a Forssman-positive species like the sheep. Finally a γ-globulin molecule which becomes labelled with more than two or three molecules of fluorescein becomes able to combine with many tissue elements presumably due to its increased acidity.

It will be apparent therefore that most tissues will be brightly fluorescent for non-specific reasons after the use of most crude antibody conjugates. The most widely used methods at present for removing such unwanted reactions are by absorption of the crude fluorescent antibody conjugate with tissue powder suspensions before use, and by chromatographic separation on DEAE cellulose.

Controls to show that any positive staining result is specific for a given antigen can be done as follows. First, the conjugate can be absorbed with the specific pure antigen. The staining result from the use of such an absorbed conjugate should, of course, prove negative. Secondly, it should be possible to block a specific result by prior, or simultaneous, treatment of the section of tissue with excess of unlabelled antibody. Thirdly, the application of a similar fluorescent conjugate of normal serum of the same animal species as that used to provide the labelled antibody should fail to reproduce the fluorescent image.

Immunoferritin Technique for the Identification of Antigens by Electron Microscopy

As in the fluorescent antibody method, conjugated antibody globulin linked to an electron-dense marker, ferritin, can be used for the localization of antigens in tissue sections by formation of a micro-precipitin reaction. The introduction of this method has extended the usefulness of conjugated antibody globulin to the identification and localization of antigens at the ultra-structural level of the electron microscope.

Ferritin can be coupled to antibody globulin by use of metaxylylene di-isocyanate in a two-step coupling reaction (see Fig. 9.12). Other coupling procedures have been suggested, such as p,p′-difluoro-m,m′-dinitrodiphenyl sulphone (FNPS) in a one-step coupling procedure. Since only a part of the globulin becomes labelled, antisera of high specific antibody content must be used, and IgG fractions from a DEAE cellulose column have often been employed. It is advisable to remove free ferritin (e.g. by chromatography) before putting the reagent to use.

Ferritin is an iron-containing protein of high electron density with a molecular weight of 750,000. Its iron content is in the form of an inner core of ferric hydroxide micelles (60 Å diameter) within a protein shell (120 Å diameter). Each molecule of ferritin contains 2,000–3,000 atoms of iron, so that in spite of the low atomic number a high opacity to electrons is attained.

The method is adaptable to many purposes, but requires very careful manipulation of the tissue fixation in order to avoid destruction of the immunological reactivity of the antigen or antibody. Five per cent formalin phosphate at pH 7·2 has proved sufficient for many purposes for a pre-fixation of the tissue. After treatment with the ferritin-conjugated antibody further fixation with osmium tetroxide or glutaraldehyde followed by osmium is essential to obtain preservation of ultrastructural details.

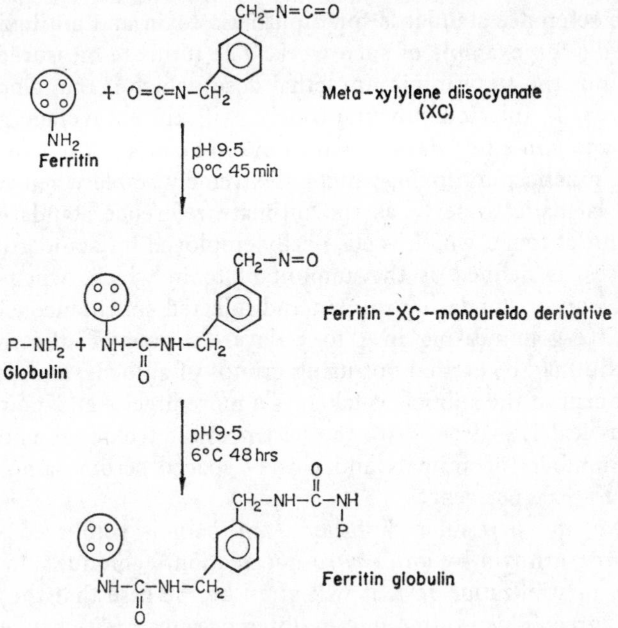

$CH_2-N=C=O$
Ferritin (NH_2) + $O=C=N-CH_2$ Meta-xylylene diisocyanate (XC)
pH 9·5
0°C 45 min
$CH_2-N=O$
Ferritin-XC-monoureido derivative
$P-NH_2$ + $NH-C(=O)-NH-CH_2$
Globulin
pH 9·5
6°C 48 hrs
$CH_2-NH-C(=O)-NH-P$
$NH-C(=O)-NH-CH_2$
Ferritin globulin

FIG. 9.12 (See text).

IN VIVO PROCEDURES UTILIZED FOR THE DETERMINATION OF ANTIGEN AND ANTIBODY

Neutralization of Toxins

Neutralization is of special interest to the bacteriologist and to the clinician because it is the essence of a major protective mechanism in several diseases such as diphtheria, tetanus, botulism and gas-gangrene. Neutralization is of special interest to the immunologist since the biological property which is measured is of more direct relevance to resistance than any provided by *in vitro* methods, such as precipitation or complement-fixation.

Although antitoxin can be estimated in weight units, values which are more closely correlated with the clinically important toxin-neutralizing ability of the serum sample are obtained by employing arbitrary antitoxin units determined from animal protection experiments (see Chapter Ten). In actual practice, in order to secure economy of animals, provisional standardization is first attempted by means of *in vitro* flocculation tests and animal skin tests when these are practicable.

The reference standards for diphtheria toxin and antitoxin may be used as an example of such work. The ultimate measured effect of toxin is the MLD (minimum lethal dose) which is that amount of toxin which, injected subcutaneously, will kill an average guinea-pig of 250 g in 4 to 5 days. Toxins tend to be more or less unstable, and in practice, antitoxin, which is extremely stable when suitably dried, is made to serve as the ultimate reference standard. The L+ unit of toxin, which is classically employed for standardization purposes, is defined as the amount of toxin which, when mixed with 1 unit of standard antitoxin and injected subcutaneously, will kill a 250-g guinea-pig in 4 to 5 days. In practice, the assay of antitoxin may be carried out using groups of animals, and death of 50 per cent of the animals is taken as a more precise end-point than the classical L+ dose. With the best possible technique and using large numbers of animals and closely spaced serum samples the error is ± 10 per cent.

When any particular diphtheria antitoxin is compared with a standard antitoxin by an *in vitro* flocculation technique and by an *in vivo* neutralization test, it will often be the case that the values fail to agree. This is often due to differences in *avidity* between the sera (see Chapter Three), and the ratio between the *in vitro/in vivo* values has been used as a quantitative measure of this.

Neutralization of Viruses

The neutralization reaction derives its importance from the fact of its providing a major protective mechanism in virus infections. The reaction is also of unique use to the immunologist since it enables him to study antigen–antibody reactions at extremely low concentrations of antibody. The infective property of virus can be accurately detected even at very high dilution of infective units. The concentration of antibody necessary to neutralize the infective action can likewise be very low.

The neutralizing action of antibody to bacteriophage has been made the basis for the most sensitive of all techniques for measuring antibody concentration. This action of antibody involves the blocking of the tip of the tail portion of the phage particle. It is here that the phage gains its attachment to the host bacterial cell, prior to injecting its quota of DNA from the head portion. Antibody to phages of Gram-negative bacterial species such as *E. coli* consists of two kinds at least, one for the head and one for the tail. An entire phage particle can absorb about 5000 antibody molecules of which about 1000 are on the tail and presumably only a few of these are required to cover the critical site for adsorption to the bacterium.

Phage particles can be enumerated by counting the number of clearings or *plaques* to which they give rise when introduced into an agar layer heavily seeded with bacteria sensitive to infection. Under favourable conditions, from 50 to 100 per cent of the viable particles form plaques.

Animal virus antibodies can be measured by neutralization, the methods in use for individual viruses depending on the possibilities which exist for demonstrating the infective activity of the virus particles. Since demonstration of infectivity requires the use of living tissues, the host systems used are various whole animals, especially the white mouse, the embryonated hen's egg, and mammalian or avian cell cultures.

The titration of an antiserum involves the testing of a series of dilutions of virus or of immune serum to a given end-point which is generally the dilution at which a certain proportion of the test animals reacts in a given way or dies. The most desirable type of end-point is one based on an assay in which one half of the animals react (or die). A direct determination of this would in general involve such vast numbers of animals that the method would often be impracticable. However, by the statistical method of Reed and Muench (1938), small groups of animals can be used to determine the effect of each of a series of dilutions. The 50 per cent end-point can be based on several types of reactions and is named accordingly. Thus when the death of the animal is used the unit is the LD_{50}, and, when infectivity is concerned, the ID_{50}. With tissue culture methods, the term TCD_{50} represents the dose of virus which gives rise to cytopathogenic change in 50 per cent of the inoculated cultures.

The more recently developed neutralization techniques have been widely employed in the control of virus vaccines (e.g. poliomyelitis), and in epidemiological survey work. They make use of a variety of tissue culture systems; monolayer cell cultures, suspensions of dispersed cells, or by the plaque technique of Dulbecco and Vogt. In the monolayer cell method, use is made of cells, for example HeLa human carcinoma cells growing on glass cover slips in tubes. Serial dilutions of serum, usually in two-fold steps, are tested against a standard dose of virus such as 100 TCD_{50} as determined from prior titrations of a stock virus. Each serum-virus mixture is inoculated into groups of several culture tubes. After the necessary time for incubation, cytopathogenic change is looked for to indicate those virus-serum mixtures containing unneutralized virus, and a 50 per cent end-point can be computed by the method of Reed and Muench. A simple technique which lends itself to surveys for the presence or absence of neutralizing antibody is illustrated in Plate 9.10, following p. 406.

Passive Anaphylaxis

Another *in vivo* method, which is of general usefulness for many antigens and antibodies, and which may be adapted for the estimation of either when the other is available in known quantity, makes use of anaphylaxis in the whole animal or of a local vascular reaction in the skin. Guinea-pigs are usually employed because of their high sensitivity. Intravenous or intraperitoneal injection of a variety of rabbit antibodies, in doses of 0·3 to 0·4 mg/kg, is sufficient to sensitize guinea-pigs so that they all die of anaphylaxis when 1–10 mg of the appropriate antigen is administered intravenously 48 hours later. A more sensitive reaction, which can detect extremely small amounts of either antigen or antibody, was developed by Ovary and is termed Passive Cutaneous Anaphylaxis (PCA). When antibody is under study this is injected intradermally into the back of a guinea-pig. Approximately three hours later the animal is given an intravenous injection of the antigen mixed with a volume of dye solution (0·5 ml of 1 per cent Evans blue in saline). The vascular reaction at the site of the intradermal antibody injection leads to escape of the Evans blue with resultant 'blueing' of a circular area of skin. The reactions can be seen more easily if the animal is killed and the skin reflected to expose the reactions on the inner surface (Plate 9.11, following p. 406). Under the best conditions, the test will detect 0.02 μg of antibody. The test as carried out above serves to estimate 7S antibody only, since it depends on the ability of the antibody to fix in the skin. Macroglobulin antibodies generally, and even 7S antibodies from certain species, are not so fixed (see Chapter Eleven).

METHODS FOR DETECTING ANTIBODY PRODUCTION BY SINGLE CELLS

In order to answer such questions as whether a single cell can make more than one kind of antibody at a time, or how many cells in a given tissue are engaged in antibody synthesis, it is necessary to be able to study antibody production by single cells. Although the fluorescent antibody (sandwich) technique makes it possible to detect which cells contain specific antibody, and even—by using two different fluorochromes—whether they contain antibody of more than one kind, the technique involves killing the cells, and provides at the best only a very roughly quantitative idea of the amounts of antibody present in each cell. Other methods have therefore been sought for examining antibody production by single living cells. Two techniques are described below which have been applied successfully to suspensions of cells made by carefully teasing out from lymph nodes or spleen.

Microdroplet methods

The first depends upon isolating single cells from lymph nodes or spleen by means of a micro-manipulator in tiny droplets of nutrient medium. These can then be placed below a layer of paraffin oil, which serves to keep them apart and to prevent evaporation while they are incubated. Antibody production has been studied against bacteriophages and against flagellar antigens of salmonellae, a known number of test organisms being added to the microdrops at the end of the incubation period. Antibody production against bacteriophages is measured by subsequently plating out on plates of suitable test organisms, and determining how many plaque-producing phage particles have been inhibited; antibody against the salmonellae is determined by observing inhibition of their mobility and noting how many organisms can be added such that they are all immobilized.

By this technique it has been found that the cells of animals simultaneously immunized with two different antigens (e.g. antigenically unrelated phages, or salmonellae with different 'H' antigens) nearly always make antibody with only a single specificity. However, when the donor animals had been subjected to very prolonged immunization with two distinct phages, some cells were also found which contained antibody against both. The cells which were found to make antibody in such studies were almost always typical plasma cells.

Localized Haemolysis by Antibody Synthesizing Cells (*LHG assay*)

Antibody produced by single cells can be detected by immunofluorescence, microdroplet assays and by production of localized haemolysis in gel. In immunofluorescence methods the antibody is detected by means of fluorescein labelled specific antibody (sandwich technique) or rarely, fluorescein labelled antigen (single layer technique). Preparations used in the method include smears and sections of tissue. In microdroplet assays isolated cells are teased out of fresh lymphoid tissue and placed with a micro-manipulator in a fluid droplet. The fluid of the droplet is subsequently assayed for anti-bacteriophage antibody or the specific inhibition of bacterial movement by antibody to the flagellae of *Salmonellae* spp. The LHG assay is, in principle, the same as the plaque technique of the virologist, i.e. a visible plaque is formed round those cells producing antibody. Thus a suspension of sheep cells from a mouse immunized against sheep red cells (SRBC) is mixed with SRBC in a semi-solid medium which is made to form a thin layer. The plates are incubated for a few hours and then complement (fresh guinea-pig serum) is added before the plates are reincubated for a further 40–50 minutes. Lysis occurs around those cells which have produced a specific haemolysing antibody. These plaques are readily visible to the naked eye and can be accurately counted. As originally described, the method could only detect those lymphoid cells producing antibody capable of lysing erythrocytes with high efficiency (mostly IgM) but not other antibodies (IgA, IgG antibodies). These other classes of antibody can be made to produce plaques if an antiglobulin serum is used in addition.

An important technical point is that the solid medium used for suspending the cells must not inactivate complement. Ordinary agar samples cannot be used and either agarose or purified agar with added DEAE-dextran is used. Another procedure uses a gum (carboxymethyl cellulose) instead of a gel. The advantages of this method are that it is possible to use micromanipulative and microscopic procedures. In this medium the macrophages move about.

More recently the method has been adapted for the detection of other antibodies other than those developed against sheep red cells. Sheep erythrocytes can be readily coated at a slightly alkaline pH with various lipopolysaccharides of bacterial origin and these coated cells can be used to detect cells producing anti-polysaccharide antibodies. Similarly, it has proved possible to add protein antigens to tanned erythrocytes for use in the method, and to coat erythrocytes with certain haptenes, e.g. arsanilic acid, and bacteriophage particles.

A further modification of this kind of method is the so-called 'rosette' or 'cluster' technique. While not an LHG assay this procedure identifies the cells containing antibody by means of a suspension of unmodified erythrocytes or antigen-coated erythrocytes. These indicator cells cluster round those cells with antibody on their surface, and can be seen microscopically.

HORMONE DETECTION AND ASSAY

The high sensitivity and specificity of immunological methods have been put to use for detecting the small amounts of hormone present in biological fluids such as blood and urine. These procedures depend upon the availability of anti-hormone sera, which have been shown by appropriate tests to be specific for the hormone to be estimated.

Hormone-coated, tannic-acid-treated erythrocytes are agglutinated by such antisera and the free hormone can be assayed by virtue of its ability quantitatively to prevent specific agglutination (*haemagglutination-inhibition technique*). As seen from Table 9.3 several hormones have been assayed in blood, and human chorionic gonadotrophin has been assayed in urine by this method. This latter forms the basis for a rapid and convenient pregnancy test. Antisera against purified HCG are prepared in rabbits. Even though these usually contain non-specific antibodies, it is a simple matter to get rid of them by absorption with urine from non-pregnant females. Blood cells first treated with formalin and then with tannic acid are used since the formalin renders them extremely stable and

TABLE 9.3
Summary of immunological techniques for detection and assay of hormones

Hormone	Method	Result or sensitivity
Insulin	Chromato-electrophoresis with ^{131}I-insulin (pig) and guinea-pig antiserum	2·5 μμg.
	Haemagglutination-inhibition (bis-diazotized sheep cells)	10–100 mμg.
	Fluorescent-antibody technique	β-cells of pancreatic islets.
Glucagon	Chromato-electrophoresis with ^{131}I-glucagon (pig) and rabbit antibody	3 μμg.
	Fluorescent-antibody technique	β-cells of pancreatic islets.
Growth hormone	Haemagglutination-inhibition (tanned sheep red cells)	1–10 mμg.
	Precipitin method with ^{131}I-labelled growth hormone and rabbit antiserum	1–5 μμg.
	Fluorescent-antibody technique	Acidophil cells of anterior pituitary.
Thyrotrophin	Haemagglutination-inhibition (tanned sheep red cells)	1–10 mμg.
Corticotrophin	Fluorescent-antibody technique	Basophil (R-type) cells of anterior and posterior pituitary.
Chorionic gonadotrophin		
(in urine)	Haemagglutination-inhibition	$<$10 mμg.
(in serum)	Complement fixation	10 mμg.
Parathyroid Hormone	Radio-immunoassay with ^{131}I-parathomone from parathyroid tumours	
Gastrin	Radio-immunoassay with ^{131}I-gastrin (synthetic pentapeptide)	

they can be coated with antigen in the same way as cells treated with tannic acid only. Because the cells are so stable antibodies can be added to them after sensitizing with HCG and the whole lyophilized. When such lyophilized erythrocytes are suspended in saline, a haemagglutination reaction normally takes place, but haemagglutination will be specifically inhibited in the presence of sufficient free hormone in urine, which is also added. In this way it is possible to detect as little as 20–40 units of HCG per litre of urine. As a routine pregnancy test a concentration of cells and antisera is used, such that 600–800 units of HCG are unequivocally detected. In comparison the biological Friedman test requires at least 1000–2000 units per litre of urine if it is to be positive.

Other assay methods, which can be developed to an exquisite degree of sensitivity, depend on the use of a radioactively labelled antigen. These methods are applicable to most materials, but are especially suitable for hormones. They have the common principle that radioactive antigen is added to a solution of antibody and the antigen–antibody complex formed is, by various means, separated from the free antigen and measured by means of its incorporated radioactivity. If, for example, the antigen is soluble in half-saturated ammonium sulphate, it can be separated from the antigen–antibody complex, which will be precipitated by this reagent. Another way of separating free from complexed antigen is selectively to precipitate the antigen–antibody complex by adding an excess of antibody (made in another species) against the γ-globulin of the species in question. A third method is exemplified by an increasingly popular method for the assay of human insulin. In this assay the serum or other fluid containing the hormone is added to a mixture ^{131}I-labelled pork insulin and guinea-pig antibody against pork insulin, so chosen that, in the absence of added insulin, about $\frac{2}{3}$ of the radioactive insulin is bound by antibody. (Pork insulin is chosen because it is chemically very like human insulin, and guinea-pig antibody is used because guinea-pigs make good antibodies against it.) Competition between labelled and unlabelled insulin occurs according to the equation:

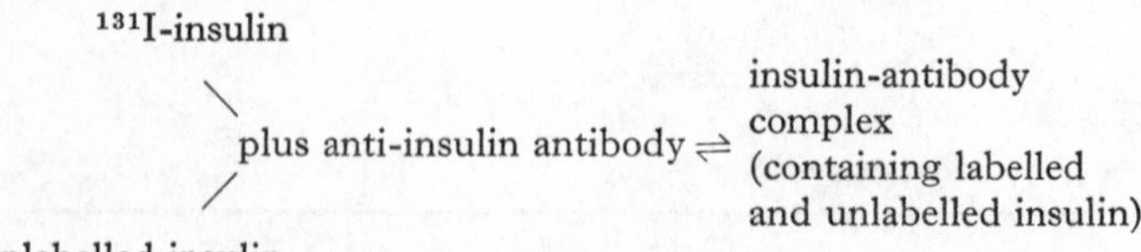

The ratio of bound: free ^{131}I-labelled insulin will vary inversely with the concentration of unlabelled insulin in the system. After equilibration the bound and free ^{131}I-labelled insulin are separated by electrophoresis on paper and estimated from a count of the ^{131}I-label in the two separated zones, and from this the amount of unlabelled insulin in the sample is deduced from a standard curve.

The basic assumption is made in tests of this kind that the material to be assayed can compete freely, and on equal terms, with the labelled antigen. Thus in the case of insulin it has to be shown that ^{131}I-labelled pork insulin is identical in immunochemical reactivity with human insulin when suitable guinea-pig antisera are used. If, as many believe, insulin exists in plasma partly in a bound form the method will succeed in assaying only that portion which is free.

In another recently developed assay procedure for human growth hormone, which is in principle similar to that for insulin, the bound and free hormone are separated by addition of an antibody prepared against the species of gamma-globulin used as an anti-hormone serum. Provided that the labelled hormones can be made sufficiently radioactive, these two tests have a very high degree of sensitivity—in the case of insulin down to about 3 micro-micrograms, or about 250 million molecules.

For the localization of hormones within the cells of relevant endocrine glands, the fluorescent antibody technique has proved of great value in supplementing the results of general histochemical methods. Some of the findings obtained are included in Table 9.3.

METHODS FOR THE STUDY OF ANTIGEN–ANTIBODY BINDING: MEASUREMENT OF AFFINITY (AVIDITY) OF ANTIBODY

Equilibrium Dialysis

This technique is applied to the study of small molecular haptens and antibody, in order to characterize the affinity characteristics or goodness of fit of the native antibody or fractions of antibody obtained after chemical or enzymal treatment. The apparatus required is a dialysis membrane (X in diagram Fig. 9.13) which encloses and restricts the movement of antibody but allows the smaller hapten molecule to pass through freely.

After the necessary time to achieve equilibrium the concentration of the free hapten on both sides of the dialysis membrane will be the same. However, there will be a greater number of haptens in the compartment B containing the antibody since this contains in addition the hapten molecules which are bound to the antibody.

By determining the concentration of bound hapten in relation to the free hapten, the average association constant of the interaction of hapten and antibody can be determined from the equation

$$K = \frac{(Ab\ H)}{(Ab)\ (H)}$$

where (Ab) = concentration of free antibody molecules, (AbH) = concentration of antibody bound to hapten and (H) = concentration of free hapten.

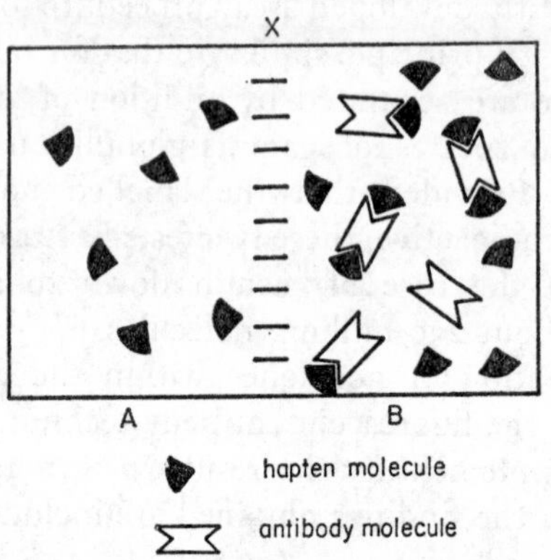

FIG. 9.13. Diagrammatic representation of equilibrium dialysis with distribution of hapten and anti-hapten molecules after equilibrium has become established. *Note* that the membrane X is permeable to hapten but not to the antibody molecules. The concentration becomes equal on both sides of the membrane in respect of free hapten molecules. There is a greater number of hapten molecules in compartment B since in addition to free hapten there are also hapten molecules attached to antibody.

Unlike fluorescence quenching (see below) any hapten which can be conveniently measured in dilute solution can be used. Another advantage is that, unlike fluorescence quenching, it can be performed with γ-globulin fractions rather than purified antibody. Its disadvantages are the relatively large amount of antibody required, the delay before equilibrium is established and the labour involved.

Fluorescence Quenching: Kinetics of Antigen–Antibody Binding and Measurement of Affinity (Avidity) of Antibody

Nearly all proteins fluoresce when exposed to ultra-violet radiation. The emitted rays are mainly in the ultra-violet. Fluorescence is associated with the presence in the protein molecule of three amino acids—phenylalanine, tyrosine and tryptophane. However, in proteins containing all three amino acids the fluorescence spectrum is essentially that of tryptophane, and this holds even for human serum albumin which contains only one tryptophane residue to every eighteen tyrosines. The emission maximum of tryptophane-containing proteins varies between 3300 and 3500 Å. In the case of antibody this fluorescence can be decreased by combination with an organic group (e.g. an hapten) which absorbs ultra-violet energy in the same region as the protein emission spectrum. The most extensive studies utilizing the phenomenon of *fluorescence diminution or quenching* have been with the antibodies to the 2,4 dinitrophenyl (DNP) hapten.

In study of antibody–hapten reactions by the fluorescence quenching method it is essential to use purified antibody. Fortunately, in the case of DNP system, highly purified antibody can be obtained in good yield by elution with 2,4 dinitrophenol from the complex of antibody and an antigen conjugated with DNP groups, when this is done in the presence of a large basic molecule such as streptomycin which precipitates and retains the free conjugated antigen.

In order to calculate binding constants it is necessary to determine by titration of, say, anti-dinitrophenyl antibody with ε-DNP-lysine the diminution in antibody fluorescence when antibody sites are all occupied by hapten (termed maximal quench). At any given total hapten concentration the ratio of the observed quench to maximal quench is taken as the fraction of the antibody sites occupied. Since the total antibody is known the concentration of free and bound antibody sites is readily calculated. The association constant:

$$K_a = \frac{Ab-H}{(Ab_f)\,(C)}$$

where $Ab-H$ is bound hapten or occupied antibody sites, C is unbound hapten and Ab_f is free antibody sites (all expressed in moles/litre). Since the antibody used in the titration will normally be heterogeneous in respect of affinity, Ka values vary continuously throughout the titration of constant antibody with increasing hapten concentration. However, suitable mathematical treatment will yield an average K_a and an index of heterogeneity.

Using fluorescence quenching it has been learned that the range of affinities of DNP antibody extends from at least 10^5 to 10^9. Even purified antibody preparations from single animals have great binding heterogeneity with variations in K_a of at least several orders of magnitude. The average binding affinity of anti-DNP antibody increases markedly with time after immunization (see Chapter Three).

Methods for Studying Cell Migration

Since it is technically not possible to examine the inside of living tissues repeatedly so as to observe the flow of cells through them, nor to recognize individual living cells within them, it has been necessary to devise methods whereby nucleated cells originating in one tissue can be identified elsewhere. The most useful and elegant technique involves the use of a *marker chromosome*. Attempts have been made to follow female cells injected into male mammals (or male cells into female birds) by means of the second sex chromsome, which becomes non-functional and is often detectable as a small chromatin mass (Barr body) at the edge of the nucleus. However, a more reliable marker, discovered in mice, is a translocated chromosome easily recognized by the presence of a short fragment and is named T6. It is replicated regularly at cell division in all somatic tissues of mice which possess it, and causes no evident functional abnormality of these cells. The T6 chromosome has been bred (with considerable difficulty) into pure line (isogeneic) strains of mice, and—apart from this marker—the cells from a mouse possessing the T6 chromosome are identical with corresponding cells of a normal mouse of the same strain. Mice can be made homozygous (T6+, T6+) or heterozygous (T6+, T6−) for the marker, whereas normal mice are (T6−, T6−). If tissue cells from a T6+ strain are transplanted to a T6− strain, the donor cells evoke no homograft reaction and dividing donor cells can be recognized in the recipient by administering colchicine (to arrest dividing cells in metaphase) and examining suitably prepared cell suspensions taken a few hours later.

An alternative method is to use radioactive nucleosides labelled with tritium at very high specific activities. These nucleosides are incorporated into DNA and/or RNA by living cells in the same manner as the unlabelled compounds. Thus ^{3}H-thymidine is incorporated exclusively into the DNA of a cell synthesizing DNA; ^{3}H-adenosine is incorporated into both DNA and RNA; and ^{3}H-uridine is incorporated exclusively into RNA. The label most commonly used is thymidine, because once it has been incorporated into the nucleus of a cell preparing to divide either *in vivo* or *in vitro* the radioactivity remains associated with that cell nucleus, or, if the cell divides subsequently, is shared between the nuclei of the daughter cells. A population of rapidly dividing cells in a particular tissue can sometimes be labelled by exposing only this tissue to ^{3}H-thymidine, but it is more usual to label all the dividing cell populations in an animal by systemic administration of thymidine and afterwards to select cells from the particular tissue for further study —e.g. for transfer to another animal. When it is desired to label cells which are not dividing, or are dividing only slowly, tritium can be introduced by incubating them with labelled adenosine or uridine *in vitro*. The label is mainly incorporated into RNA, which turns over quite rapidly in most cells, but in this form it is unstable compared with a DNA label, and is lost from the cells rather soon.

The labelled cells are usually identified by autoradiography of smears or tissue section (i.e. by using the emitted β-particles to form silver grains locally in a photographic emulsion).

An alternative method is to use radioactive chromium (^{51}Cr) phosphate, which attaches readily and fairly stably to living nucleated cells on incubation together *in vitro*, and apparently does not harm them. The principle is similar to that employed for tagging erythrocytes, and the method could in theory be used for following the fate of lymphocytes in man, as it is already used in practice for studying the fate of transfused erythrocytes.

FURTHER READING

ANGRES G.A., HSU K.C. & SEEGAL B.C. (1967) Immunoferritin technique for the identification of antigens by electron microscopy. In *Handbook of experimental immunology* [Ed. Weir D.M.] p. 527. Blackwell Scientific Publications, Oxford

BOORMAN K.E. & DODD B.E. (1957) *Introduction to Blood Group Serology*. Churchill, London

BOYDEN S.V. (1959) Approaches to the problem of detecting antibodies. In *Mechanisms of Hypersensitivity* [Ed. Shaffer J.H., Lo Grippo G.A. and Chase M.W.]. Henry Ford Symposium. Churchill, London

CRUICKSHANK R. (ed.) (1965) *Medical Microbiology*. Livingstone, Edinburgh

DACIE J.V. (1964) Demonstration of antibodies to erythrocytes: 1. Warm autobodies. 2. Cold auto-antibodies. In *Immunological Methods* [Ed. Ackroyd J.F.] pp. 515–38. Blackwell, Oxford

COOMBS R.R.A., COOMBS ANNE M. & INGRAM D.G. (1961) *The Serology of Conglutination and its Relation to Disease*. Blackwell Scientific Publications, Oxford

COOMBS R.R.A. (1964) Conglutinating complement and its use in serological tests. In *Immunological Methods* [Ed. Ackroyd J.F.] p. 43. Blackwell Scientific Publications, Oxford

COOMBS R.R.A. (1964) The mixed agglutination and mixed antiglobulin reactions. In *Immunological Methods* [Ed. Ackroyd J.F.] p. 443. Blackwell Scientific Publications, Oxford.

COONS A.H. (1956) Histochemistry with labelled antibody. *Int. Rev. Cytol.* **5**, 1

COONS A.H. (1958) Fluorescent antibody methods. In *General Cytochemical Methods* [Ed. Danielli J.F.] pp. 400–22. Academic Press, New York

COONS A.H. (1961) The beginnings of immunofluorescence. *J. immunol.* **87**, 499

CROWLE A.J. (1961) *Immunodiffusion*. Academic Press, New York

GOLDSTEIN G., SLIZYS I.S. & CHASE M.W. (1961) Studies on fluorescent antibody staining. I. Non-specific fluorescence with fluorescein-coupled sheep anti-rabbit globulins. *J. exp. Med.* **114,** 89

GOLDMAN M. (1968) Fluorescent antibody methods. Academic Press, New York

GRABAR P. & BURTIN P. (1960) *L'analyse Immuno-électrophorétique*. Masson, Paris

GRABAR P. (1964) Immunoelectrophoretic analysis. In *Immunological Methods* [Ed. Ackroyd J.F.]. Blackwell, Oxford

HUNTER W.M. (1967) The preparation of radioiodinated proteins of high activity, their reactions with antibody *in vitro*: the radioimmunoassay. In *Handbook of Experimental Immunology* [Ed. Weir D.M.]. Blackwell Scientific Publications. Oxford

INGRAHAM J.S. & BUSSARD A. (1964) Application of a localized haemolysin reaction for specific detection of individual antibody-forming cells. *J. exp. Med.* **119,** 667

JERNE N.K., NORDIN A.A. & HENRY C. (1963) The agar plate technique for recognizing antibody-producing cells. In *Cell-bound antibodies* [Ed. Amos B. and Koprowski H.]. Wistar Institute Press, Philadelphia

KABAT E.A. & MEYER M.M. (1961) *Experimental Immunochemistry*, 2nd edition. C.C. Thomas, Springfield, Ill.

MANCINI G., CARBONARA A.O. & HEREMANS J.F. (1965) Immunochemical quantitation of antigens by single radial immunodiffusion. *Immunochemistry* **2,** 235

MARRACK J.R. (1938) *The Chemistry of Antigens and Antibodies*. Special rep. ser. Medical Research Council No. 194 (H.M.S.O., London)

MARRACK J.R. (1963) Sensitivity and specificity of methods of detecting antibodies. *Brit. Med Bull.* **19,** 178

NAIRN R.C. (1964) *Fluorescent protein tracing*. 2nd edition. Livingstone, Edinburgh

NELSON D.S. (1963) Immune adherence. In *Adv. Immunol.* [Ed. Dixon F.J. and Humphrey J.H.]. Vol. 3, 131. Academic Press, New York

NETER E. (1956) Bacterial hemagglutination and hemolysis. *Bacteriol. Rev.* **20,** 166

OSLER A.G. (1958) Quantitative studies of complement fixation. *Bacteriol.*

OUCHTERLONY Ö. (1962) Diffusion-in-Gel Methods for Immunological Analysis II. In *Progress in Allergy* [Ed. Kallos P. and Waksman B.H.] **vi,** 30

OUCHTERLONY Ö. (1964) Gel-diffusion techniques. In *Immunological Methods* [Ed. Ackroyd J.F.]. Blackwell Scientific Publications, Oxford

OVARY Z. (1964) Passive cutaneous anaphylaxis. In *Immunological Methods* [Ed. Ackroyd J.F.]. Blackwell Scientific Publications, Oxford

PORTERFIELD J.S. (1964) The plaque inhibition test. In *Immunological Methods* [Ed. Ackroyd J.F.] p. 341. Blackwell Scientific Publications, Oxford

RAPP H.J. (1964) The nature of complement and the design of a complement fixation test. In *Immunological Methods* [Ed. Ackroyd J.F.] pp. 1–24. Blackwell Scientific Publications, Oxford

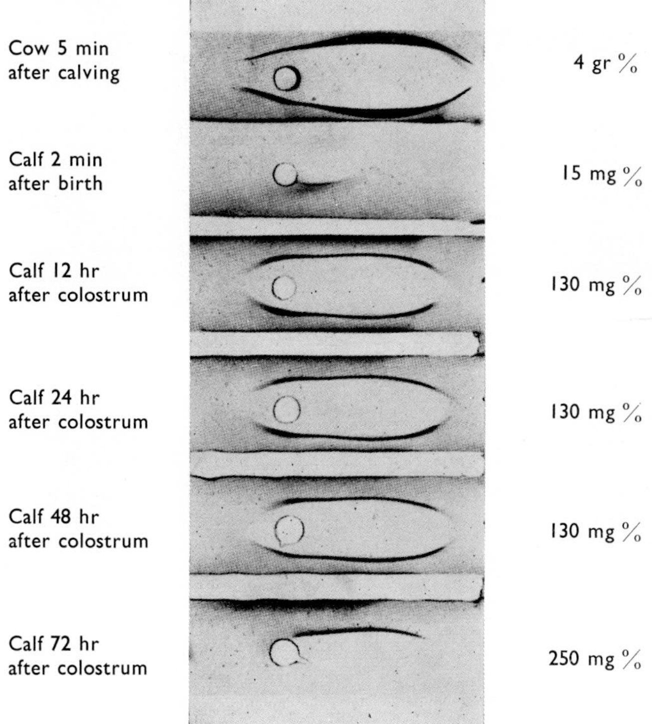

PLATE 8.1. The serum of a cow and her calf were examined by immuno-electrophoresis using an antiserum against bovine immunoglobulin. Before suckling the calf had a negligible amount of immunoglobulin, but this increased rapidly after absorption of immunoglobulin present in the colostrum.

[From de Muralt, G. *La maturation de l'immunité humorale chez l'homme*, Helvetica Medica Acta, Supp. 42].

facing p. 406

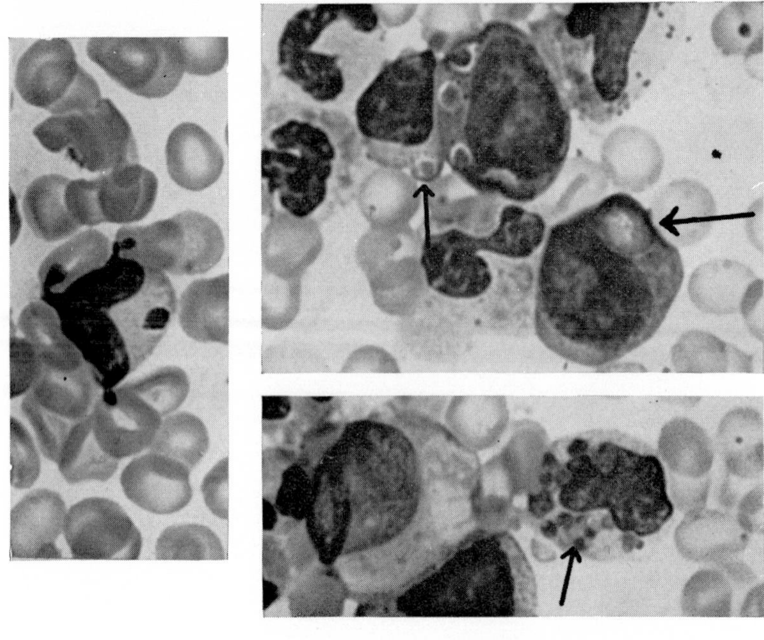

A B & C

Plate 8.2. *Chediak-Higashi syndrome*. In this disease there is a general abnormality of intracellular organelles such as lysosomes and melanin granules, which occur in enlarged and bizarre forms. The peripheral blood granulocytes show a characteristic hypersegmentation of the nucleus. The plate illustrates smears stained by the Romanowsky method from peripheral blood and bone marrow (A) hypersegmented polymorph in the blood (B) and (C) bone marrow cells showing bizarre intracellular granules (arrowed). (×1175)

[Photograph kindly supplied by Dr. J. M. Estevez, Danville, Virginia, U.S.A.]

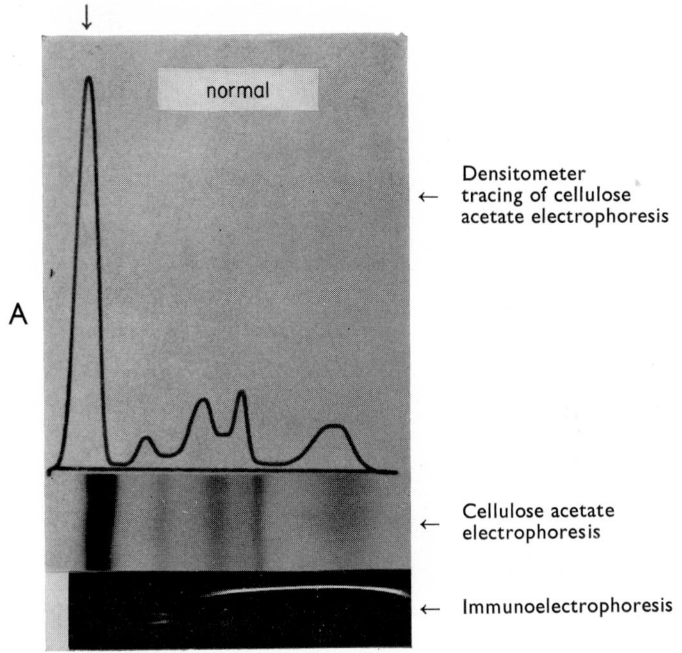

PLATE 8.3. Serum protein patterns in multiple myeloma and macroglobulinaemia.

(A) normal; (B) γG myeloma; (C) γA myeloma; (D) γM macroglobulinaemia; (E) Bence Jones protein (λ chain) myeloma.

For each serum is shown the electrophoretic pattern on cellulose acetate (middle), densitometer tracing (above), and the immunoelectrophoretic pattern developed with a specific antiserum against γ chains (A and B); α chains (C); μ chains (D); λ chains (E). Note that the increased narrow band of myeloma protein is accompanied by a decrease in the rest of the immunoglobulins. (Plates B—E *overleaf*).

(From photographs supplied by Dr. J. C. Hobbs).

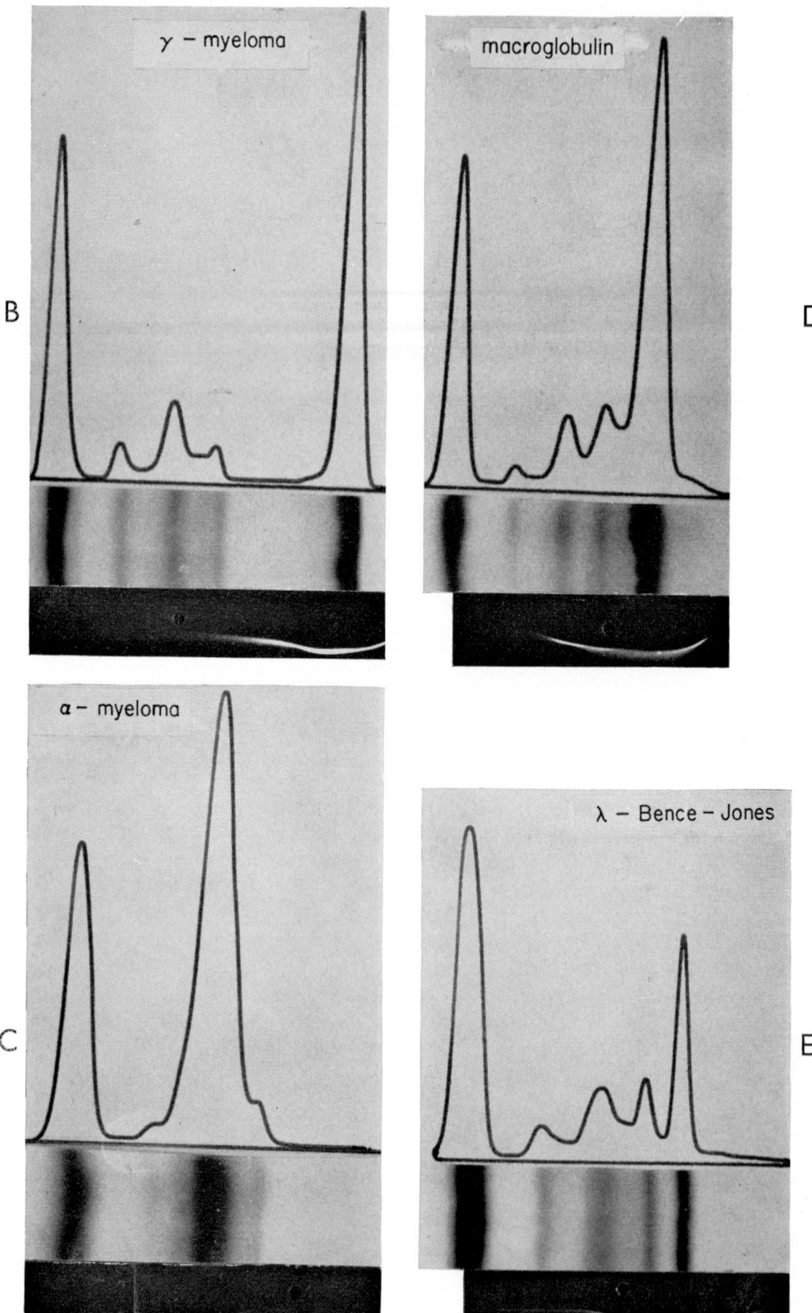

PLATES 8.3 (B-E). *Caption previous page.*

PLATE 9.1. Agar diffusion technique. Elek's method for demonstrating toxigenicity of an unknown strain of *Corynebacterium diphtheriae*. See p. 363 for explanation.

AB culture streak of known toxin-producing *C. diphtheriae*. XY culture streak of strain of *C. diphtheriae* under test.

Cultures of these organisms are streaked at right angles to a strip of filter paper soaked in diphtheria antitoxin and applied to the surface of the agar. With a toxigenic strain the resultant lines of precipitation will develop in the angle between growth streak and filter paper and will incline towards and fuse with the similar lines produced by the known positive culture.

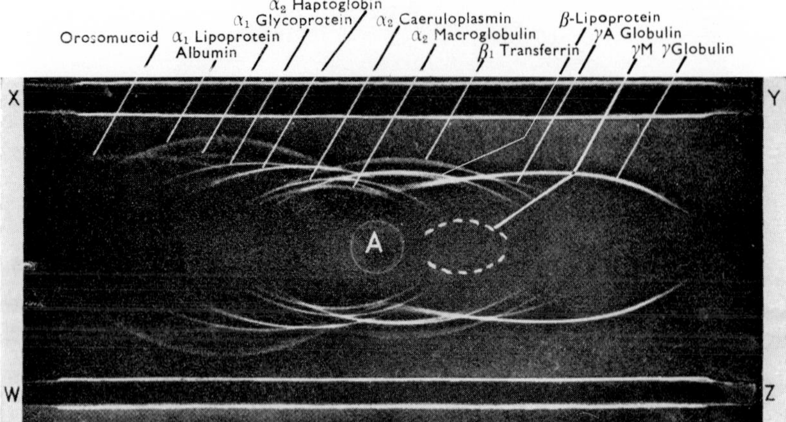

PLATE 9.2. Human serum immuno-electrophoresis. The well A received the serum sample, and the dictation of albumin migration was to the left. Rabbit antibody to whole human serum (a composite of antisera is actually used) was placed in the troughs XY and WZ. Distinct immunological serum components are each indicated by an arc of precipitate with convexity away from the axis of electrophoresis. The nomenclature of such components is at present in a state of flux, but is conveniently based on subdivisions of the Tiselius components.

Group		*Synonyms*
albumin	orosomucoid	pre-albumin
	albumin	
α-globulin	α_1 lipoprotein	
	α_1 glycoprotein	seromucoid
	α_2 haptoglobin	
	α_2 caeruloplasmin	Cu-binding protein
	α_2 macroglobulin	
β-globulin	β_1 transferrin	siderophilin
	γA	IgA
	γM (stippled in)*	γ_1 macroglobulin; 19S γ-globulin; IgM
γ-globulin	γ-globulin	7S γ-globulin; IgG

* The antiserum used for this illustration failed to reveal the presence of γM globulin, but many similar antisera do so.

[Modified from Williams C. A. *Scientific American* (1960)]

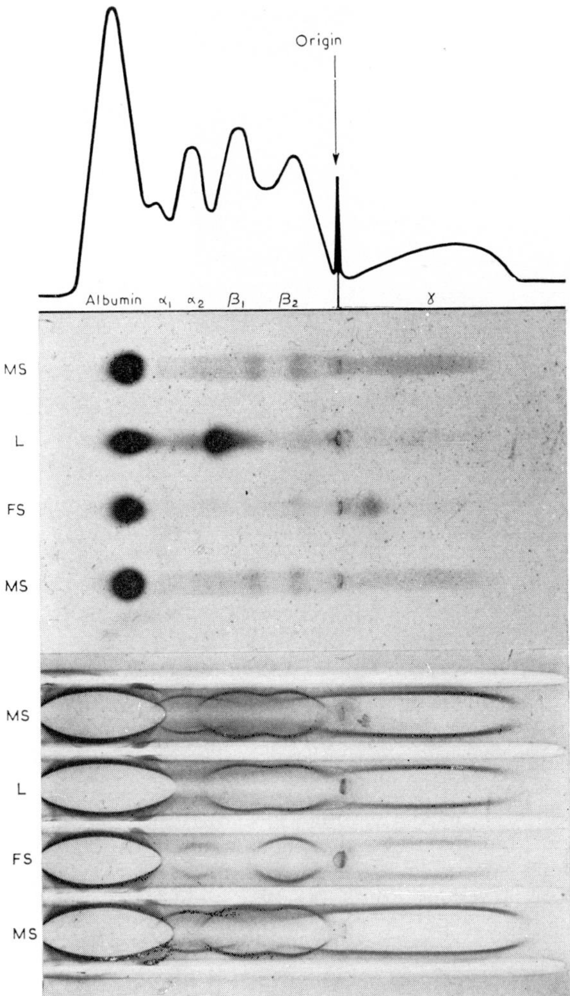

PLATE 9.3. (From above down.) *Tiselius electorphoresis pattern* of the major components in serum (diagrammatic); *zone electrophroesis* in agar of maternal serum (MS), liquor amnii (L), and foetal serum (FS) of a monkey; *immuno-electrophoresis* of the above body fluids. The immuno-electrophoresis patterns were developed by placing rabbit antibody to whole adult monkey serum in the troughs on both sides of each agar strip in which the electrophoretic separation of the individual body fluids was done. Note in particular that the immunoelectrophoresis pattern for liquor amnii shows no precipitin arcs corresponding with the prominent additional component clearly revealed by zone electrophoresis, since antibody against this component was lacking.

[From Bangham, Hobbs and Tee. *J. Physiol.* (1961) **158,** 207.]

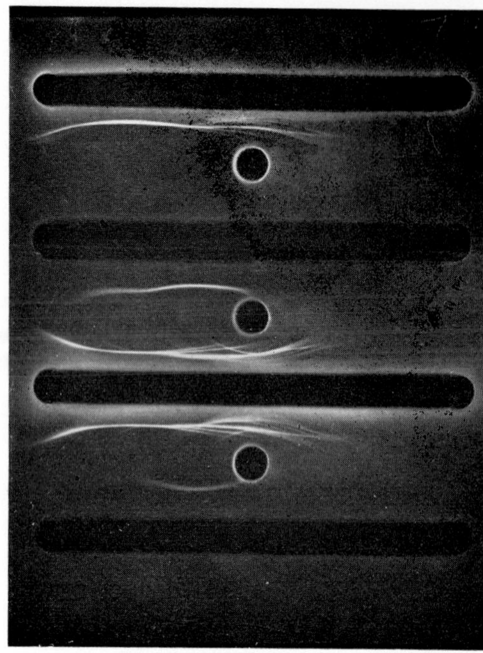

PLATE 9.4. Immuno-electrophoresis of guinea-pig serum to demonstrate antibody to ovalbumin. The electrophoretically separated components of three sera were developed by placing ovalbumin (the homologous antigen) and rabbit antibody against guinea-pig β- and γ-globulin in the troughs alternately as shown. I. (result) No antibody detectable. II. Ovalbumin injected in water-oil emulsion with added mycobacteria, short course of injections over 1 month: result—slow and fast specific antibody components. III. Ovalbumin injected in water-oil emulsion with added mycobacteria, long course of injections over 6 months: result—fast-moving antibody component only.

Direction of albumin migration is to the right.

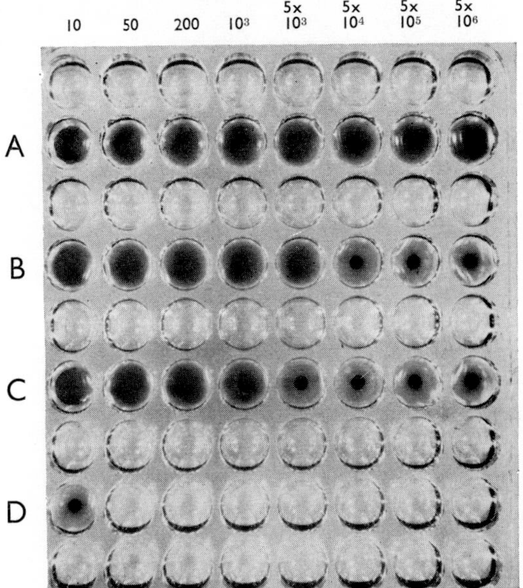

PLATE 9.5. Passive haemagglutination test. Titration of antibody to thyroglobulin in a patient with Hashimoto's disease using tannic-acid treated sheep erythrocytes sensitized with purified human thyroglobulin.

A Complete agglutination (+ +) to serum dilution $1:5 \times 10^6$
B Complete agglutination (+ +) to serum dilution 1:5,000
C Complete agglutination (+ +) to serum dilution 1:200
Partial agglutination (+) to serum dilution 1:1,000
D Thyroglobulin-treated tanned erythrocytes : control minus human serum—no agglutination.

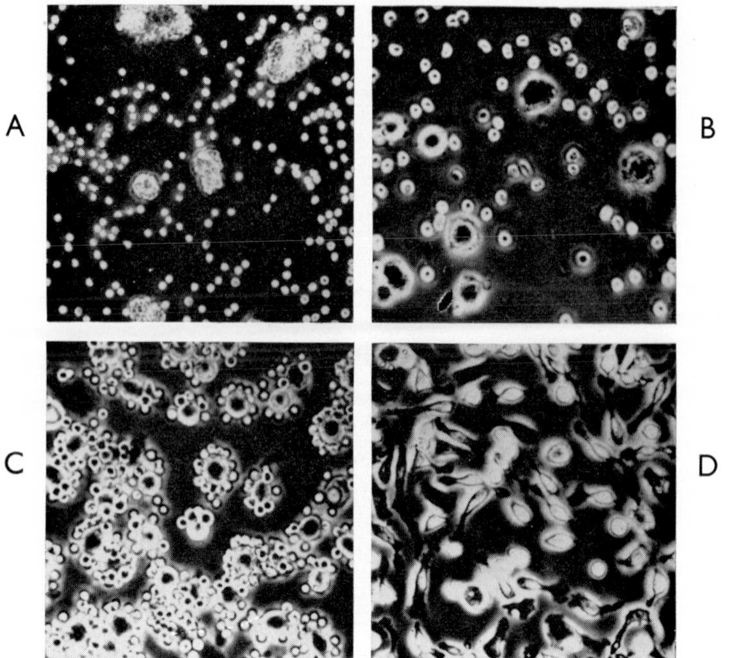

PLATE 9.6. *Rosette test for macrophage cytophilic antibody.*
A and B: Rosette test for cytophilic antibody to sheep erythrocytes of mouse macrophages: A, positive; B, control.
Photographs of result stage (see Fig. 9.8).
C and D: Similar test with guinea-pig macrophages: C, shows a marked positive result for cytophilic antibody with formation of 'rosettes' of erythrocytes around the monolayer macrophages; D, shows a negative control, i.e. no rosette formation.
[Pictures supplied by Dr. D. S. Nelson.]

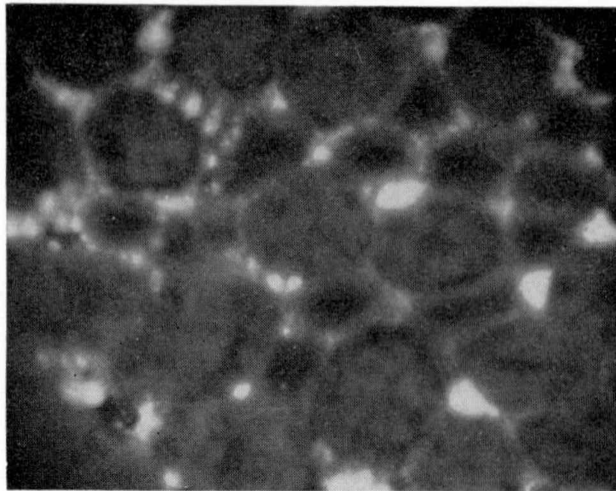

PLATES 9.7. Use of the fluorescent antibody method to trace the fate and distribution of an injected foreign antigen. 5 mg of the capsular polysaccharide antigen of type III pneumococcus was injected intravenously into the mouse. At one week later the animal was killed, and sections of its kidneys

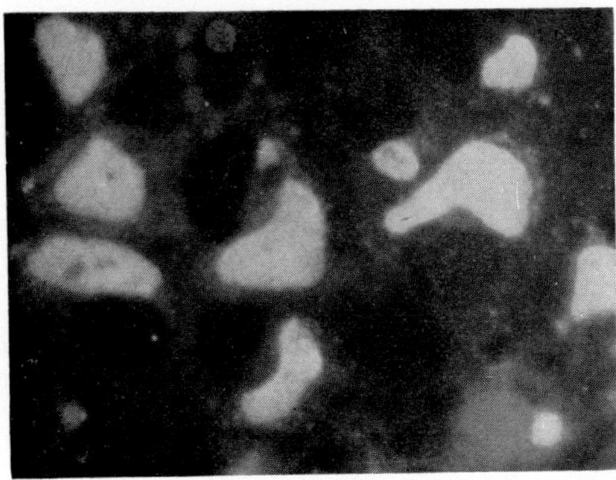

Plate 9.8. Fluorescence micrograph. Use of fluorescent antibody for the visualization of lymphogranuloma venereum virus in the cells of a tissue culture monolayer of HeLa cells. The virus in the cytoplasmic inclusions appears bright. The nucleus and remainder of cytoplasma is black or dull. ($\times$700).

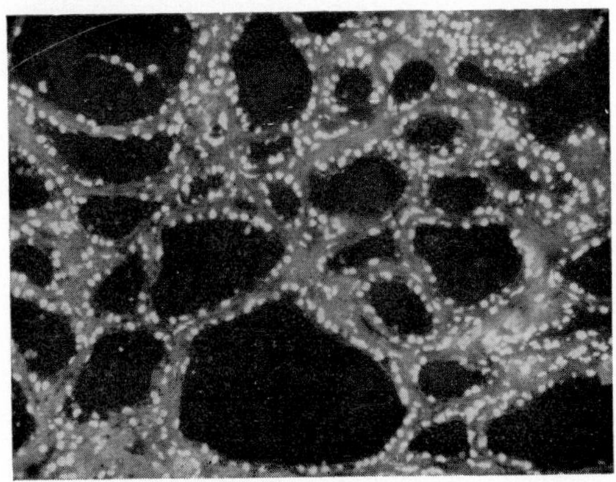

Plate 9.9. Fluorescence micrograph. Method for the detection of anti-nuclear factor in the serum of a patient with systematic lupus erythematosus by the fluorescent antibody technique. A frozen section of human thyroid was treated with:

(i) Unlabelled serum from patient.
(ii) Fluorescein-labelled rabbit anti-human γ-globulin.

The serum was 'positive' for anti-nuclear factor as shown by the bright resultant fluorescence of the nuclei of all the acinar-lining cells. ($\times$150)

Plate 9.7. (*cont.*)
were treated by the direct method using fluorescent antibody prepared in the rabbit to type III polysaccharide of the pneumococcus. The bright areas represent the persisting antigen in the loose connective tissue between the dark circles of the cortical tubules of the kidney. ($\times$160).

PLATE 9.10. Virus neutralization test. A layer of chick embryo fibroblasts growing on the bottom of a flat dish was infected with one of the arbor viruses, and covered with a thin layer of agar gel. The black dots are small porcelain beads filled with different human sera. On further incubation the virus has lysed the fibroblasts at all places except the zones around those beads containing virus-neutralizing antibody. [Preparation from Dr. J. D. Porterfield.]

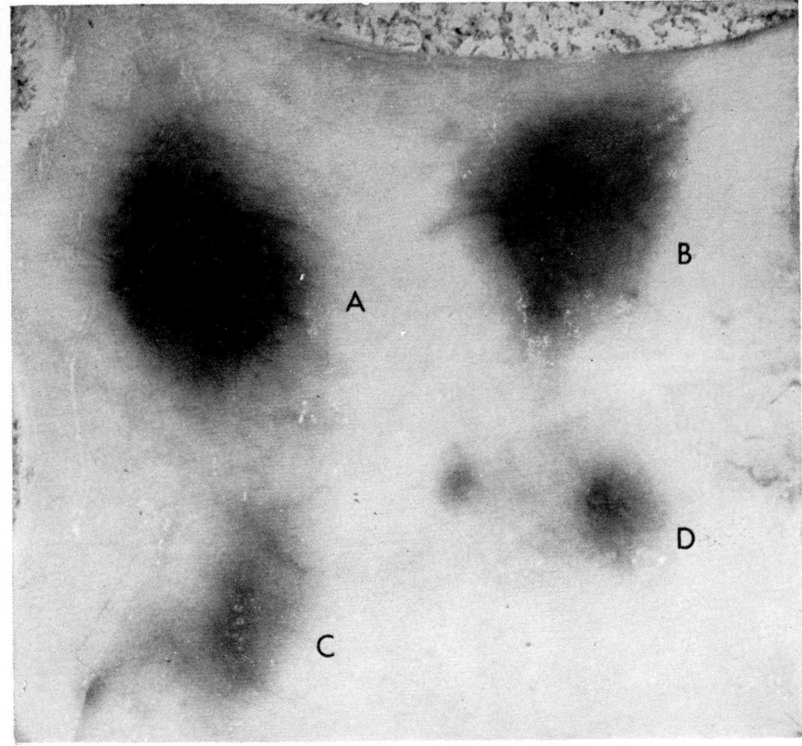

PLATE 9.11. Passive-cutaneous anaphylaxis. The antibody under study (rabbit anti-ovalbumin) was injected intracutaneously into a guinea-pig at four sites over the back in amounts A 10 μg, B 2 μg, C 0·4 μg, D 0·08 μg, each in 0·2 ml volume. Three hours later the animal received an intravenous injection of 100 μg ovalbumin mixed with 0·5 ml of 1 per cent. Evans blue dye in saline. After a further 30 minutes the animal was killed and skinned. The photograph shows the areas of blueing due to capillary leakage on the under surface of the guinea-pig pelt.

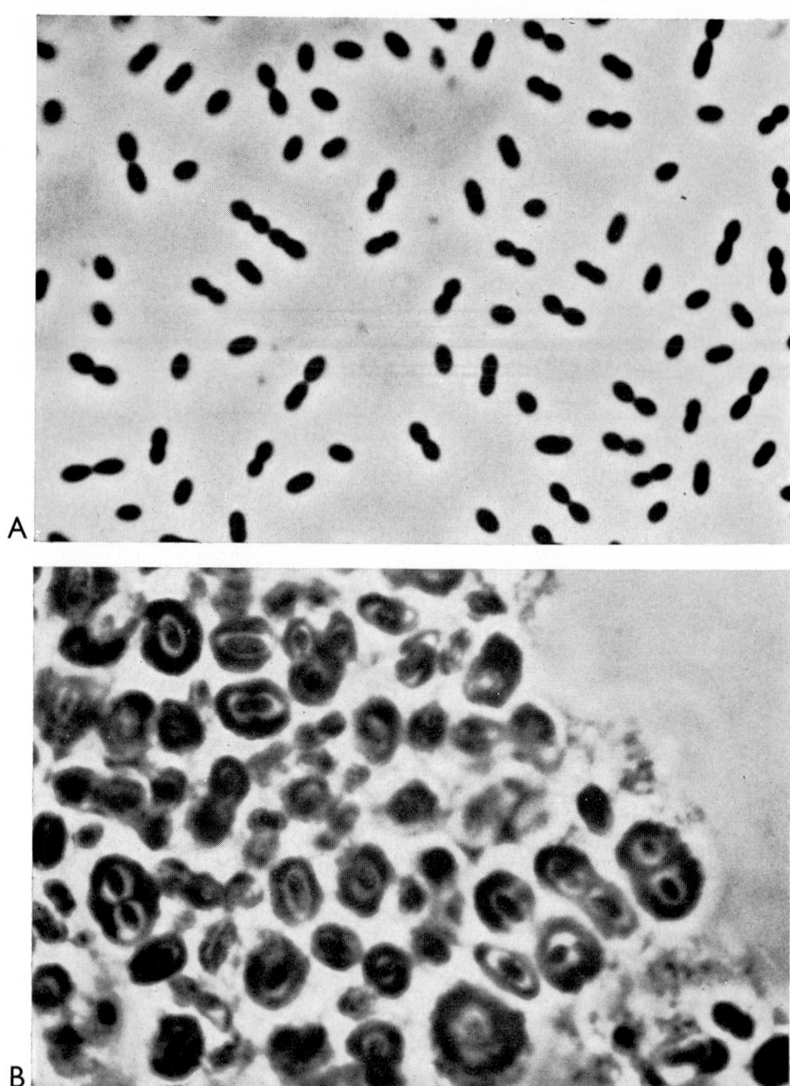

PLATE 10.1. Encapsulated Type III pneumococci: A in normal serum, and B in serum containing antibody against the capsular polysaccharide. Note the aggregation and apparent swelling caused by the antibody, which increases the optical density of the capsules (Neufeld's 'Quellung' phenomenon). (Phase contrast ×2000).

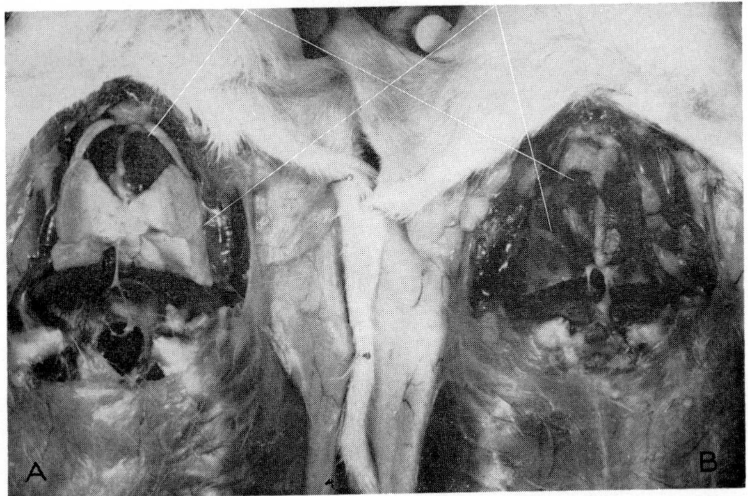

PLATE 11.1. Anaphylaxis in the guinea-pig. Note the greatly distended lungs of the guinea-pig which died from anaphylaxis. The bronchioles are so tightly constricted that even after death the lungs do not collapse by mechanical pressure, or by their natural elasticity when the chest wall is cut away. A. Anaphylactic shock. B. Normal.

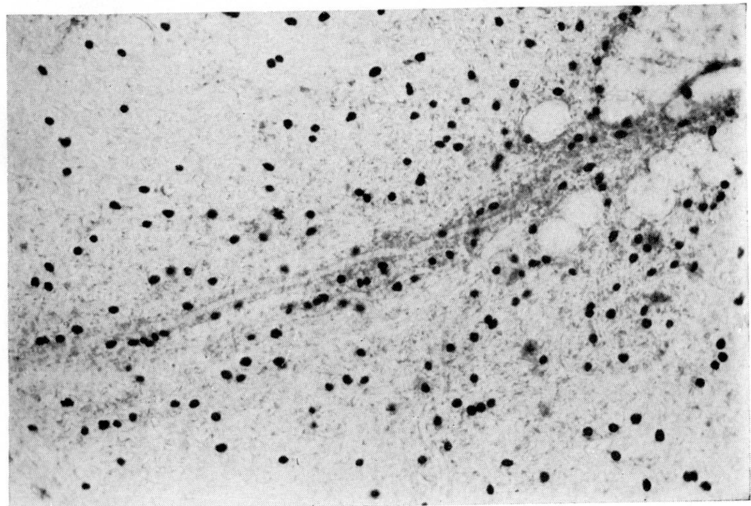

PLATE 11.2. Distribution of mast cells stained by toluidine blue in mesentery of a rat. ($\times 97$).

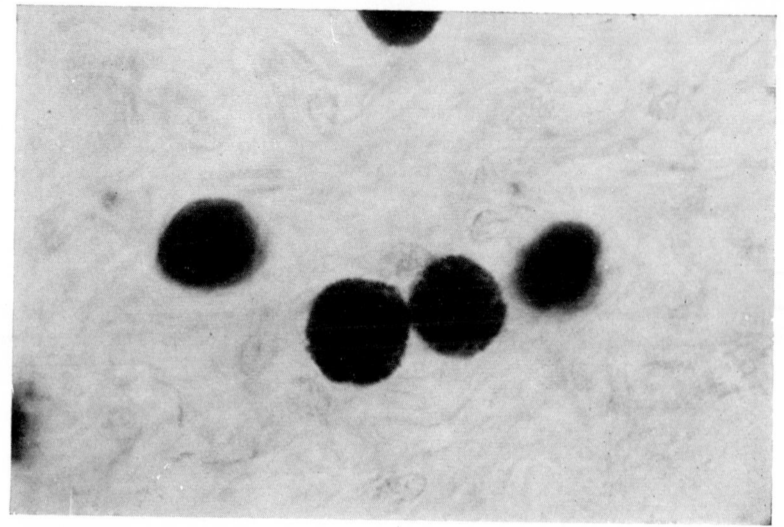

A

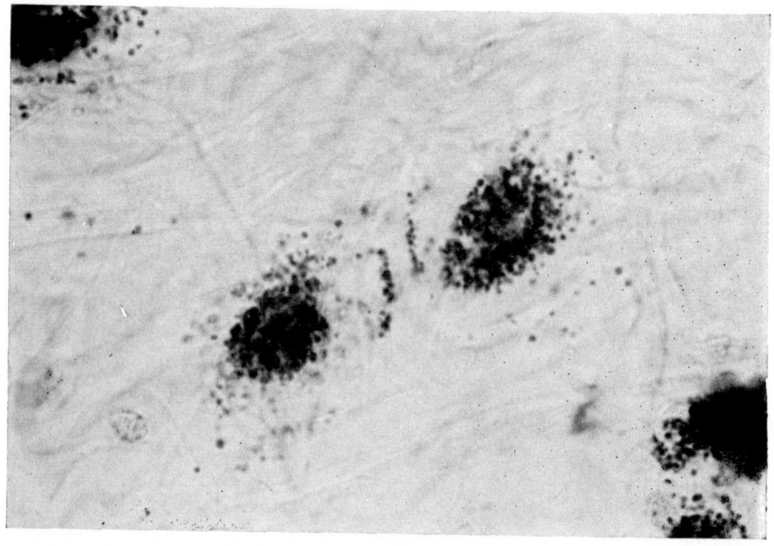

B

PLATE 11.3. Mast cells of a rat (*a*) before, and (*b*) after, antigen-antibody reaction. Toluidine blue stain. (×1,350) Note how the mast cells are disrupted and their granules scattered. This process is accompanied by the release of histamine.

REED L.J. & MUENCH H. (1938) A simple method of estimating 50 per cent end points. *Amer. J. Hyg.* **27,** 493

STAVITSKY A.B. (1964) Haemagglutination and haemagglutination-inhibition reactions with tannic acid and bis-diazotized benzidine-protein-conjugated erythrocytes. In *Immunological Methods* [Ed. Ackroyd J.F.] pp. 363–96. Blackwell Scientific Publications, Oxford

TYRRELL D.A.J. (1964) Demonstration of antibodies to viruses. In *Immunological Methods* [Ed. Ackroyd J.F.] p. 313. Blackwell Scientific Publications, Oxford

WHITE R.G. (1960) Fluorescent antibody techniques. In *Tools of Biological Research* [Ed. Atkins H.J.B.] **2,** 89. Blackwell Scientific Publications, Oxford

WILLIAMS C.A. Jr. (1960) Immunoelectrophoresis. *Sci. Am.* No. 84 (March 1960)

WILLIAMS C.A. & CHASE M.W. (eds) (1967) *Methods in Immunology and Immunochemistry*, Volume I. Preparation of Antigens and Antibodies. Academic Press, New York

WILLIAMS C.A. & CHASE M.W. (eds) (1969) *Methods in Immunology and Immunochemistry* Vol. III. Academic Press, New York

WOLSTENHOLME G.E.W. & CAMERON MARGARET P. (eds) (1962) A Ciba Symposium: *Immunoassay of Hormones*. Churchill, London

WORTIS H.H., TAYLOR R.B. & DRESSER D.W. (1966) Antibody production studied by means of the LGH assay. 1. The splenic response of CBA mice to sheep erythrocytes. *Immunology* **11,** 603

CHAPTER TEN

The Protective Effects of Antibody

THIS chapter is concerned solely with the protective effects of circulating antibody, the effects which are sought by organizers of immunization programmes and by manufacturers of sera and vaccines. Perhaps the most striking evidence that antibodies, whatever their shortcomings, are essential to survival under natural conditions is afforded by children with congenital immunoglobulin deficiencies (Chapter Eight). These children, who can make immunoglobulin (and antibody) in only exiguous amounts, never survived for long before the advent of antibiotics, but suffered from recurrences of pneumonia, skin infections, tonsillitis, etc. from which they eventually perished. With the help of antibiotics and of regular injections of pooled human immunoglobulin, such children can now survive and live reasonably normal lives. Even without being supplied with immunoglobulin from normal people, they do not appear to suffer unduly from virus infections (unless complicated by bacterial infections). The extent to which this may be due to interferon is discussed in Chapter Two.

As has already been shown, the cardinal feature of antibody is its capacity for combining specifically with antigenic material which stimulated its formation or other materials possessing the same antigenic groups. It is worth while to consider in what ways this property results in biological protection of the possessor of the antibodies. There are several, and they are sufficiently distinct to be worth considering separately.

NEUTRALIZATION OF EXOTOXINS

Although the exact mechanisms by which bacteria kill or damage their hosts are usually not known, and are probably complex, in a few instances the damage is due to one main toxin liberated from the organisms during growth (exotoxin) and acting at sites remote from the organisms themselves. Well-known examples are diphtheria, tetanus, botulism and gas gangrene. In an animal which possesses adequate antibodies against these, overt disease does not occur. Other micro-organisms produce a variety of toxins, none of which is lethal in itself—at least in the quantities which are likely to be produced in an ordinary infection—but whose effects add up to produce tissue damage and to paralyse the host's defences. An example is the staphylococcus, which forms one or more haemolysins, two leucocidins, coagulase, fibrinolysin, hyaluronidase, etc. Quite a number of toxins have been identified as specific enzymes and it is a reasonable guess that others will also turn out to be either enzymes destroying the structural integrity of host cells or chemicals which interfere with specific host enzymes necessary for survival.

Antibodies against bacterial, plant or mammalian enzymes have been studied extensively, and it has been found that such antibodies can effectively inhibit the action of such enzymes, provided that these have high molecular weight substrates, such as proteins or polysaccharides. If the substrate is of low molecular weight (e.g. that of penicillinase, or alcohol dehydrogenase), antisera from some animals may inhibit enzyme activity, whereas antisera from others with apparently the same combining power for the enzyme may not. This is probably a question of how far the sites on the enzyme with which the antibody combines overlap with the enzymatically active site. When the substrate is a large molecule, antibody can be attached to an enzyme at a point more remote from the enzymatically active site and still hinder the effective approach of the substrate. Antitoxins are effective in so far as they block that part of the toxin molecule which is responsible for its toxic properties, and neutralize its effects. This can be shown by mixing toxin and antitoxin and then testing the toxicity of the mixture either by a suitable *in vitro* test or by injecting into a live susceptible animal. Provided that sufficient antibody is present no toxic effects are produced. Tests in living animals have shown that antibodies cannot in general prevent the action of toxins once these have become firmly fixed to their substrate in the tissues—antibodies cannot, so to speak, pull them off again. Neither, clearly, can they repair the damage once it has been done. The key point is that toxins which have combined with antitoxins are not able to attach themselves to the tissues and to exert their specific damaging effect.

The protective effect of antibodies against bacterial exotoxins depends upon their being present in the body fluids in quantities sufficient to neutralize toxin elaborated by the invading micro-organism faster than it is produced. In this way the host is kept alive until the invading bacteria have been eliminated by the processes of antibacterial, as opposed to antitoxic, immunity. The essential thing, therefore, is that antibodies should be present at the time of infection or at least be produced before toxin production has got significantly under way. The ideal protection is provided in an animal which has already been actively immunized, since, as discussed in Chapter Seven, even though very little antibody may be present at the time, the introduction of more antigen leads within a short time (2 to 3 days) to the explosive production of more antibody. Alternatively, antibody can be administered prophylactically, either before infection is established, or the toxic symptoms become manifest. Once infection and toxin production are well established (which implies that the host's immune mechanisms are unable to cope sufficiently) passive antitoxin can be administered as a therapeutic rather than as a prophylactic measure. Since antitoxins, to be of use, most be available at short notice, and of high potency, they must in general be derived from animals immunized artificially. As we shall see later, the introduction of foreign serum can be only temporarily effective, and very often leads to complications of its own. A detailed discussion of the practical aspects of active and passive immunization is given in Chapter Sixteen. It is worth while, however, to have some idea of the amounts of toxins and antitoxins which are needed for killing and protecting animals. A list of the potencies of some of the known toxins is given in Table 10.1. These results were obtained by direct injection of the toxins into the test animals, and for obvious reasons similar information is not available for man. Some animals are more susceptible than others to the action of any particular toxin, and this must be borne in mind when extrapolating the figures to man. Nevertheless, they give a proper order of magnitude, provided it is remembered that the experimental direct introduction of toxin into an animal is the most efficient method of administering it, and probably more effective than an actual bacterial infection. The amounts of good, avid antitoxin which could be required to neutralize the lethal dose of toxin in a test tube are correspondingly small—perhaps 10 to 20 times as much as the weight of toxin. In practice, in a live animal, the level of antitoxin has to be considerably higher, in order to achieve adequate local concentrations in the tissues, and depends greatly upon the length of time which has elapsed after the introduction of toxin. This is shown by an experiment made many years ago by Glenny and Hopkins, who tested how much antitoxin was needed to prevent the effects of an intracutaneous dose of diphtheria toxin

TABLE 10.1

Toxicity of some purified bacterial toxins expressed in terms of minimum lethal dose per kg weight of animal

Toxin	MLD/μg	MLD/μMole	Animal
Shigella shigae endotoxin	0·0002	100?	Mouse
Salm. typh. endotoxin	0·02	10,000?	Rabbit
Clostridium welchii α-toxin	0·4	40,000	Mouse
Diphtheria toxin	3·5	245,000	Guinea-pig
Tetanus toxin	1,200	120,000,000?	Guinea-pig
Botulinus toxin type A	1,200	1,200,000,000	Guinea-pig
Botulinus toxin type B	1,200	72,000,000	Guinea-pig

Modified from van Heyningen (1950) *Bacterial Toxins*. Blackwell Scientific Publications, Oxford

just sufficient to produce a characteristic local reaction (the Schick test dose). Although 0·001 units of antitoxin would neutralize this dose *in vitro*, in the guinea-pig it required 10 units of antitoxin administered intravenously within 30 minutes, and 1000 units within 1½ hours to diminish (let alone abolish) the skin reaction. If the antitoxin were administered by a route from which absorption was slower, such as subcutaneously, it was even less effective in countering the effects of toxin once it had become fixed on the tissues. The level of antibody which is considered to represent adequate protection against diphtheria infection in an immunized human is around 0·01 units/ml of serum. This represents about 0·00012 mg of actual antibody protein/ml. Rather exceptionally, people can reach levels of 200 or more units of antitoxin/ml (2·4 mg/ml) which represents an enormous excess, but this is still quite a small fraction of the 10 to 15 mg of total immunoglobulin per ml which are found in the normal person's serum.

PROTECTION BY ANTIBODY IN VIRUS INFECTIONS

The fact that antibody protects against some virus infections is attested to by the widespread use of immunoglobulin for prophylaxis against measles, and by the world-wide efforts made to stimulate antibody production by immunization against poliomyelitis viruses. Nevertheless the role of antibody in protection against some other virus infections is far from obvious. In order to understand these differences it is necessary to consider some general points about virus infections. These have only become obvious in recent years, as a result of the greatly improved techniques for isolating virus from tissue even when present in small amounts. The first important point to recognize is that infection can occur without recognizable clinical symptoms. Protection by antibody is usually considered in terms of protection against overt disease. The second important point is that virus infections can, by and large, be divided into two groups: (*a*) those in which the portal of entry, and the target organs, are at the surface, e.g. influenza and the common cold; (*b*) those virus infections in which the portal of entry is probably the oropharynx, but in which clinical symptoms do not occur until dissemination through the bloodstream has taken place and in which the target organs are different from the portal of entry, e.g. poliomyelitis, measles, hepatitis, mumps, chickenpox and smallpox. There are exceptions, of course, such as rabies, in which the virus is introduced directly into the tissues by a bite and can reach the central nervous system by travelling along nerve trunks or by the bloodstream. In general, groups (*a*) and (*b*) can be distinguished by the length of their incubation periods. This is illustrated in Table 10.2, but it is important to remember that the picture may be confused when several strains of the same virus exist.

Experiments *in vitro* carried out both with bacterial viruses (bacteriophage) and susceptible bacteria, or with animal viruses and susceptible cells in tissue culture, have shown that if antibody is mixed with the virus before the virus is able to come into contact with the susceptible cell, very small amounts of antibody are capable of preventing infection. In the case of bacterial viruses, only two to four antibody molecules appear to be required to attach to critical sites on the tail of a phage and so to prevent it from becoming attached to and able to penetrate the bacterial cell. In the case of animal viruses there is not much quantitative information and, in

TABLE 10.2

Relationship between site of entry, incubation period and duration of immunity after some clinical infections

Disease	Portal of entry	Usual incubation period of clinical disease (days)	Duration of immunity
Viruses:			
Chicken-pox	Respiratory	14–21	lasting
Measles	,,	10–15	,,
Mumps	,,	12–26	,,
Rubella	,,	10–21	,,
Smallpox	,,	7–16	,,
Yellow Fever	Skin (bite)	3–6	,,
Dengue	,,	3–15	,,*
Sandfly Fever	,,	3–6	,,*
Poliomyelitis	Gastro-intestinal	5–35	,,*
Influenzas	Respiratory	1–3	temporary*
Common colds	,,	1–3	temporary*
Rickettsiae:			
Typhus (all kinds)	Skin (bite)	6–15	lasting*
Q Fever	Respiratory	14–26	,,
Bacteria:			
Pneumococcal pneumonia	Respiratory	?	lasting*
Pertussis	,,	7–21	,,
Diphtheria	,,	2–5	temporary†
Plague (bubonic)	Skin	3–6	uncertain
Tularaemia	,,	1–10	lasting
Bartonella fever	,,	16–22	,,

* Immunity is confined to the type or strain causing the first infection. Since more than one strain exists, clinical recurrence may occur with infection by another strain.

† Immunity wanes in the absence of restimulation.

Modified from Macleod C.M. *J. Immunol.* **70**, 421

any case, the size of the virus, upon which depends the number of antibody molecules required to coat it, will be important. There is indirect evidence that the presence of a few million molecules of antibody per ml of blood is enough to protect against poliomyelitis. When once viruses have become attached to their susceptible host cells, just as when toxin has become attached to the tissues, the effect of antibody is much less. Whereas minute amounts of antibody mixed with virus will prevent the attachment of the virus and initiation of infection, very much larger quantities are required to prevent the visible effects of virus (e.g. plaque formation or microscopical cell damage) if the antibody is added after the virus has been in contact with the cells for any length of time. Time now becomes all important. There appears to be a phase during which the virus is attached to the cell but can still be inhibited by enough antibody; once the virus is safely inside the cell and has begun replication, antibody appears to be ineffective. The question whether antibody penetrates in an effective form into the inside of living cells is still a matter of controversy. There is no doubt that antibody already attached to an antigen, e.g. a bacterium, can penetrate or be engulfed by a cell such as a polymorphonuclear leucocyte or a macrophage. What is much less certain is whether antibody applied from outside can reach and affect the fate of a micro-organism which has already become safely established inside the cell.

This is not an easy point to establish, but there is evidence that if peritoneal macrophages have been allowed to take up virulent bacteria—against which they would be protected by antibody administered before or at the same time as the bacteria—they are not protected against intracellular multiplication of the microorganisms by antibody supplied afterwards. Furthermore, fluorescent antibodies against intracellular constituents have not been shown to penetrate living cells in tissue culture, although they can be shown to do so readily, and to combine with the constituents in question, once the cells are dead.

One further point should be made in considering protection by antibody against viruses, namely the fact (mentioned in Chapter Six) that the infective part of a virus is its nucleic acid, and that this is not antigenic. Although viruses normally have a coating of protein, this can be removed artificially in the laboratory and the possibility exists that the same could occur under natural conditions. If this were to happen, infectious virus nucleic acid could coexist with what would normally be protective antibody. Such a situation has not been demonstrated unequivocally to arise in practice, but the possibility is sufficiently real not to be neglected.

With these facts in mind we can now re-examine the role of antibody in some clinical virus infections. Let us consider first those infections in group (*a*), e.g. influenza, about which most is known. There is no doubt that large amounts of passively administered antibody will protect experimental animals, such as mice or ferrets, against clinical infection by influenza virus administered intranasally. Protection, in this case, means that the dose of virus required to produce visible effects has to be very considerably increased. Antibody can therefore have some effect, but in actual infections in animals which have not been hyperimmunized antibody probably plays only a small role in recovery. Unless very large amounts are present, it is unlikely that sufficient will be present on the mucous membranes of the nose or bronchial tree to prevent infection of the cells by the virus. It has been shown experimentally that when the infection is not fatal, virus begins to diminish before large amounts of antibody are detectable. Interferon (Chapter Two), however, can be found abundantly at this stage, and it, rather than antibody, is likely to be the cause of the waning of the infection. The recovered animal will, however, be resistant to further infection for a period of months with the same strain of influenza virus. This resistance is due to antibody, but is only maintained so long as the antibody level is sufficient in the actual tissues which are at risk. Antibody immunity is therefore short-lived.

The best studied example of virus infections in class (*b*) is that of poliomyelitis. In this disease the virus first enters by the alimentary tract, and proliferates in the intestinal mucosa or in the lymphoid tissue of the Peyer's patches and mesenteric nodes. It can do this whether antibody is present in the bloodstream of the host or not, unless very large amounts of antibody are present and some actually gets into the lumen of the gut. (It is probable that IgA antibodies are in fact released into the gut, but their effectiveness in preventing virus multiplication within the gut wall has not been conclusively demonstrated.) The situation at this stage is quite analogous to that in diseases of group (*a*). However, infection of the intestinal tract causes little in the way of clinical effects, and would be unrecognized but for studies carried out by virus isolation from the stools performed during systematic surveys. After an incubation period lasting some days, virus may enter the bloodstream and in the susceptible person be carried to the spinal cord and brain where it can enter and proliferate within the motor nerve cells. Very small amounts of antibody are sufficient to combine with the virus during its passage to or after it enters the bloodstream and to prevent it from being able to attach to the susceptible nerve cells. *Clinical* protection is therefore given by antibody, although the primary invasion by the virus is not prevented. Thus, passive protection by pooled human immunoglobulin is possible in this disease. In the actively immunized person, even though the level of antibody may be quite small at the beginning, it is sufficient to neutralize any virus which begins to get through from the intestinal tract. Such virus in turn stimulates a secondary response on the part of the host, so that by the time that any large amount of virus begins to get through the amount of antibody available to deal with it is correspondingly increased.

The fact that the amount of antibody required to protect against poliovirus is very small indeed is relevant to the problem of how patients with immunoglobulin deficiencies recover from and usually resist reinfection by viruses just as well as do normal people. In respect of the interferon mechanism there is no evidence that such patients are at a disadvantage. Furthermore, it has been shown by the use of very sensitive assay methods that these people do in fact possess antibodies against poliomyelitis after a first infection or after immunization, which are below the level detected by ordinary methods but are still sufficient to prevent repeated *clinical* infection, even though symptomless infection may still occur.

No other virus infections have been studied in such detail as has poliomyelitis. However, on less adequate evidence, it seems fairly certain that many of the common virus infections, with prolonged incubation periods, are similar to poliomyelitis as regards antibody protection and immunity, as is illustrated schematically in Fig. 10.1. These include measles, rubella, chicken-pox, mumps, viruses akin to poliomyelitis such as the Coxsackie group and some adenoviruses. Another group of viruses which are not common in temperate countries, but widespread in tropical and sub-tropical regions, is the arthropod-borne (arbovirus) group. These also follow a similar pattern, and antibody gives a high degree of protection against clinical, though not necessarily against inapparent, infection.

There are virus infections of man which, from the immunological point of view, cannot be fitted in either of the two broad categories discussed above. An example is herpes, and some adenoviruses, which can persist in the body indefinitely in the presence of large amounts of neutralizing antibody. Such viruses appear to have evolved part of the way towards a state of symbiosis with their hosts, in which the viruses can exist intracellularly without damaging the cells in which they live except under exceptional circumstances. The complete state of symbiosis is illustrated by those viruses, in monkey kidney cells for example, which normally do no harm to the cells whatsoever. Their presence remained entirely unsuspected until it was revealed by growing kidney cells in tissue culture *in vitro*. In the abnormal environment so provided the viruses produce cytopathic changes. In the case of herpes simplex the natural history is as follows. In about half of completely unprotected children the

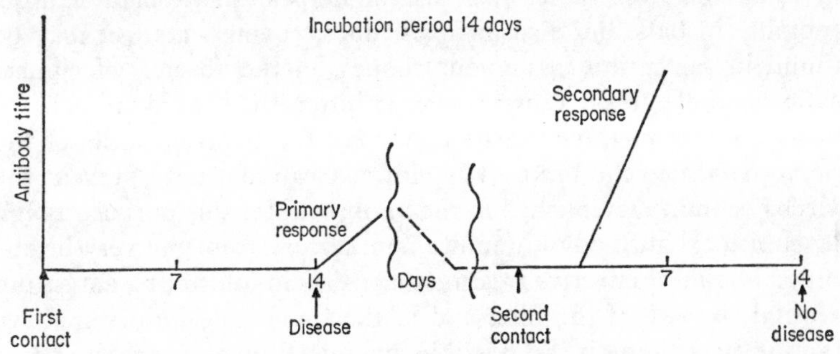

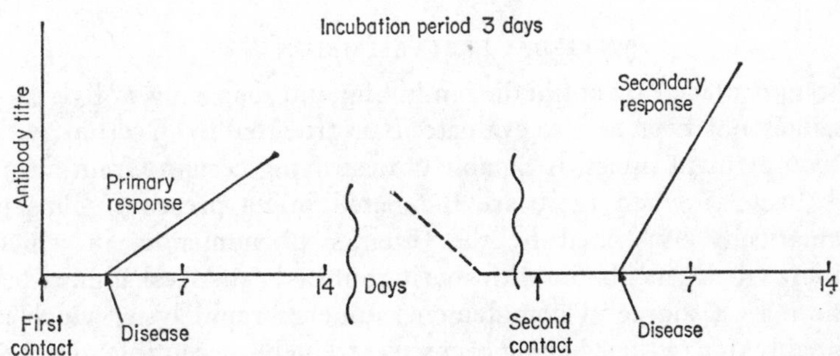

FIG. 10.1. Diagram to illustrate the relationship between the length of the incubation period and the presence or absence of subsequent immunity after a first attack of virus disease. [After Macleod C.M. *J. Immunol.* 70, 421.]

first attack of herpes takes the form of a more or less florid attack of vesicular stomatitis whereas in the other half no clinical signs are apparent. After this, antibodies appear (and can be found in the great majority of the adult population) which are capable when mixed with herpes virus *in vitro* of rendering it non-infective. Nevertheless, the virus persists and mild lesions occur when it is stirred up, by mechanisms unknown, during a high fever, or during other infections such as with the common cold or by ultra-violet radiation. Since herpes virus is rather resistant to interferon it presumably is not prevented from growing even when this mechanism is at work. The explanation of the ability of herpes virus to persist in the presence of antibody appears to be that it spreads from cell to cell, in the skin, or in the central nervous system, without coming outside the cell and being exposed to antibody. Blood-borne invasion is prevented, but local spread is not. In some respects the virus of rabies behaves rather like that of herpes. In its natural hosts (notably in bats, but also in foxes, dogs, coyotes, etc.), it may be found in saliva and in nervous tissues, in the absence of clinical symptoms of rabies. When a man is bitten by a rabid animal, the virus appears to travel fairly slowly *via* the Schwann cells of the nerve trunks to the brain. The aim of treatment is to prevent the virus becoming established in the brain, and for this purpose a high level of local antibody immunity is necessary from the very beginning. The most effective treatment consists in infiltrating antiserum around the site of the bite, and at the same time inducing active immunity as rapidly as possible by injection of preparations of killed rabies virus (see Chapter Sixteen).

ANTI-BACTERIAL IMMUNITY

The part played by antibodies in killing and disposing of live bacteria has not been easy to evaluate. It is true that fresh serum, with its complement intact, is capable of destroying certain Gram-negative bacteria when these are incubated in its presence. This is dramatically illustrated by the 'Pfeiffer phenomenon' in which cholera vibrios incubated with specific antibody and fresh guinea-pig serum (as a source of complement) undergo rapid lysis, which is probably due to their having become extremely susceptible to traces of lysozyme present in the serum. Furthermore, animals which have been given inoculations of killed bacteria show heightened bactericidal activity in their serum. This would appear to indicate that antibody, either 'natural' or immune, in the presence of complement can kill micro-organisms. However, this applies only to a relatively small number of Gram-negative bacteria. Other bacteria, pneumococci for example, can grow perfectly well *in vitro* in the presence of antibody against them. If the antibody is against the capsule of the organism, very often the growth will be of 'rough' organisms lacking the capsule, but growth itself is not prevented. In the same way, protozoa growing in the presence of antibody against them may obviously combine with the antibody in the sense that they are clumped or that their flagella become stuck together, but they are not necessarily killed, and after a while mutant forms may occur, which possess different antigenic constituents on their surface and are no longer affected by the antibody. In the living animal, as opposed to the test tube, bacteria are killed usually after being engulfed by free macrophages or polymorphs, or by the fixed cells of the reticulo-endothelial system. As already discussed in Chapter Two, these cells contain within them powerful bactericidal substances, some of which have already been identified. Most micro-organisms, once they have been taken up by such cells, are killed fairly rapidly (within half an hour or so). The exceptionally virulent micro-organisms, which are discussed below, appear to be able to resist such intracellular digestion. The importance of antibodies directed against bacteria, as opposed to their toxic products, lies in the facilitating of the uptake of these bacteria by the phagocytic cells, and, in the case of certain virulent organisms, in aiding their intracellular digestion. This may best be illustrated by taking two examples.

Pneumococcal Infection

Although an important killer of mankind in our community, the pneumococcus does not produce powerful toxins. The important fact about pneumococci is their possession of a capsule. As already discussed in Chapter Two capsulated pneumococci can multiply freely in a liquid medium in the presence of leucocytes because leucocytes fail to engulf them. If the same pneumococci are made to adhere to a surface (even blotting paper will do) the leucocytes are able to ingest the pneumococci, which are then rapidly killed. In the body fluids, or the fluid-filled alveoli of an infected lung, the necessary surface is not available. The effect of antibody against the capsule is to change their surface so that the bacteria are now readily phagocytosed by the white cells. They no longer multiply unhindered, and so long as the numbers of bacteria are not overwhelming, the infection is rapidly brought to an end. Plate 10.1, following p. 406, shows the effect of antibody on the bacterial capsule. Very small amounts of antibody are sufficient to protect against the introduction of a small number of organisms into the bloodstream. However, once the infection is established the pneumococci produce and release large amounts of capsular substance, which mop up antibody, so that for the organisms themselves to be coated relatively large amounts of antibody have to be given or to be manufactured by the infected person. Serum treatment of pneumonia is not practised now, but it was widely employed during the 1930's, especially in the United States of America, where a wide network of antiserum banks was set up. These consisted of stocks of horse or rabbit serum, and the dose of antibody which was administered to cure was of the order of 500 mg of antibody. Apart from the complications of serum sickness (see Chapter Eleven) the great disadvantage of serum treatment was that there exist 70 or more different pneumococcal types—each with a capsule made of antigenically different material. Although some of these resembled one another fairly closely, in general each type of pneumococcus required a different antiserum, and the type of the organisms had to be known before intensive therapy could begin. For similar reasons a person who has survived an attack of pneumococcal infection by one type is not necessarily immune against subsequent attacks by the other types. Certain types are, however, much more common than others, and in special circumstances active immunization against these more common types may be worth while. For example, during the Second World War, when recruits from all parts of the U.S.A. were thrown together in barracks, infection with pneumococcus Types I, II, V, and VII was frequent enough to be a military nuisance. Recruits were immunized by intracutaneous injection of minute amounts (about 50 μg) of purified capsular polysaccharides from each of these types, and they responded by making, and continuing to make over the course of several years, surprisingly large amounts of antibody. Pneumonia due to these types of pneumococcus virtually disappeared simultaneously, although it continued to occur in an uninoculated control group.

Although pathogenic streptococci elaborate a variety of toxins, which complicate the picture, as regards phagocytosis and killing by leucocytes the story is not very dissimilar from that of pneumococci. Virulent haemolytic streptococci may be phagocytosed by polymorphs in whole blood, but the organisms are not killed, or not completely killed, within the cells and are subsequently ejected and continue to multiply. This resistance to intracellular digestion is associated with the formation of a specific material, the M protein of Lancefield, for if the blood is taken from an animal which has previously been immunized with streptococci possessing M protein of the same antigenic type as the test organism, or in the presence of specific antibodies against the M protein of the streptococci, the organisms are not only phagocytosed more rapidly, but once taken up they are destroyed. It is interesting that of the various structural antigens which have been identified in streptococci, only the M protein seems to confer the property of resisting intracellular digestion, although the possession of a capsule made of hyaluronic acid appears to hinder phagocytosis, much as do the capsules of pneumococci. Once again there are many types of streptococci, each with an antigenically distinct M protein, and therefore there is no reason to suppose that the antibacterial protective effect due to antibodies against one particular M protein will protect against others.

ANTIBODIES IN ENTERIC INFECTIONS

Immunization procedures against typhoid, paratyphoid, cholera, etc., have been practised in man for some 60 years. It is exceedingly difficult to prove unequivocally that such procedures protect, since controlled therapeutic trials are almost impossible. However, the weight of evidence is in favour of a real measure of protection being given. It is obviously very important to ensure that the vaccine used contains the right antigens, and the preservation of a particular antigenic activity in the killing process depends not only upon the presence of that antigen in the original organisms, but also upon the method of killing. The evaluation of these factors presents a peculiar difficulty, because of the impossibility of reproducing in experimental animals the same type of disease as occurs in man. Human enteric infections in the first stage—i.e. the stage at which preventive immunity must act—are confined to the bowel and the bowel wall and its lymphoid tissue. Only at a later stage, when infection is well established, does the bloodstream become invaded. The human pathogens are in general not pathogenic for experimental animals when given by mouth, and the challenge therefore has to be made by some other route, e.g. intraperitoneally. When mice, for example, are tested in this way it is quite easy to show that immunization gives powerful protection, and that the serum of the immunized mouse will confer protection upon other mice. Furthermore, protection of mice can be shown to be associated with antibody against a particular antigen, the Vi antigen, which is destroyed by the formaldehyde treatment often used in preparing vaccines. Unfortunately, although the antibodies evoked by this antigen are protective in mice they do not appear to be so in man. It seems certain that antibody must play a part in protecting against infection when the organism is introduced into the peritoneal cavity or into the bloodstream. What is less certain is that antibody plays the same role in preventing infection when the organism is introduced by mouth, when the main initial proliferation takes place in the intestinal tract. However, it is well established that antibodies can be liberated into the intestinal lumen ('copro-antibodies'). The secretable form IgA (see Chapter Four) is particularly abundant among the antibody-forming cells lying in between the intestinal villi and in the lymphoid cell accumulations such as Peyer's patches, although cells making IgG and IgM are also present. Both IgA and IgG have been shown to occur in the contents of the intestinal lumen, and are probably derived from these local cells. However, some passage of passively transfused antibody has been shown to occur from the bloodstream into the gut in apparently normal animals. These antibodies may be important in neutralizing bacterial toxins locally and in preventing the invasion of the organisms through the mucosa.

Much experimental work has been devoted to the study of immunity against enteric organisms which have been introduced into the peritoneal cavity, and the findings are of sufficiently general application to be worthy of more detailed discussion. The peritoneal cavity of mice contains a large number of macrophages of which part are free, and can be removed by gentle washing, and the rest are present in the milk spots attached to the lining peritoneum and the mesentery. The free macrophages can be kept alive in tissue culture flasks for a few hours at least, without changing their physiological state. The events which follow the introduction of living bacteria into the peritoneal cavity of a mouse can therefore be followed either by treating the peritoneal cavity as a test tube or by using tissue cultures of peritoneal cells, in which case the whole process occurs *in vitro*. Uptake of bacteria is observed by counting the numbers which remain free in the peritoneal cavity or in the supernatant fluid above the macrophages, and the fate of the organisms within the macrophages is observed by washing the cells and then breaking them up and plating out their contents on suitable culture media. Organisms which have been taken up, but have remained alive, will then grow out. In this way it has been shown that if a relatively small number of organisms are introduced compared with the number of cells, avirulent strains of Gram-negative organisms, such as *E. coli*, are rapidly taken up into macrophages (the process is 90 per cent complete within 30 minutes) and are there rapidly destroyed. This occurs in the presence of normal serum, and even faster in the presence of serum of animals which have been immunized against the same strain of *E. coli*, but it is possible that even the normal serum contains small, but sufficient, amounts of 'natural' antibody. The same thing happens with staphylococci, but the process is somewhat slowed down. When virulent organisms are used, e.g. *Salmonella typhi* or virulent strains of

Salmonella typhimurium, uptake in the presence of normal serum is very much slower, although the organisms which are ingested are still rapidly killed within the macrophages. In the presence of antiserum the virulent organisms are treated in the same way as avirulent organisms unless the numbers injected are overwhelmingly large. The course of these events is illustrated in Fig. 10.2. Thus it seems that antibody, by coating the bacteria,

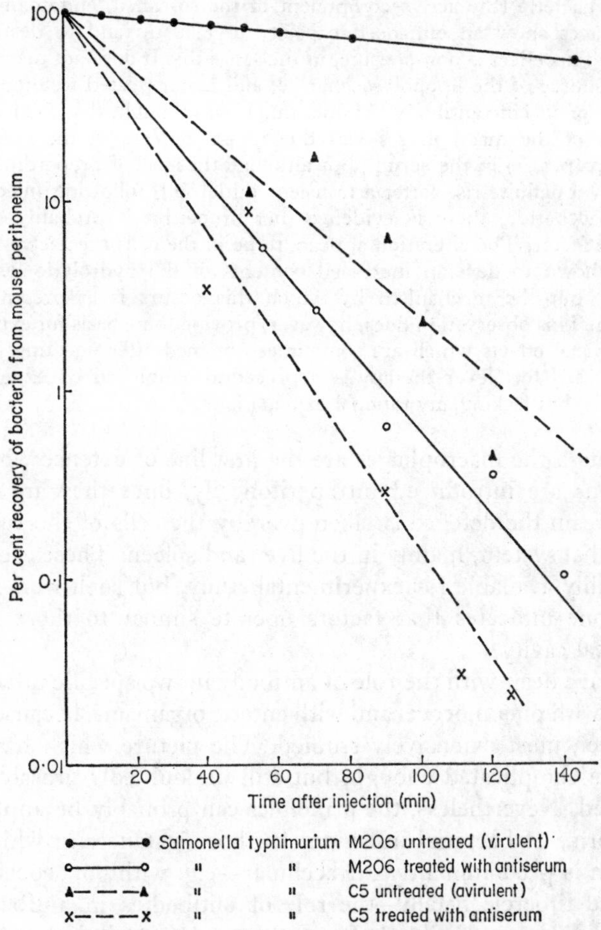

FIG. 10.2. Removal of living bacteria from the peritoneal cavity by macrophages.

Uptake of the virulent strain is greatly accelerated in the presence of antibody, whereas uptake of the avirulent strain is relatively little affected. [Modified from Whitby and Rowley (1959) *Brit. J. exp. Path.* **40**, 363.]

once again facilitates their uptake, and in some circumstances their destruction within the macrophages. The amounts of antibody needed are exceedingly small, being rather less than 1,000 molecules per bacterium, but it is probable that they are ineffective unless some of the components of complement are also present. A very interesting observation which has emerged from this work is that if the mice have been injected a few hours beforehand with 10 to 100 μg of a lipopolysaccharide obtained from the cell walls of Gram-negative bacteria (the active component of the so-called 'endotoxin') their macrophages show an enhanced capacity to take up and to destroy the bacteria. This effect is non-specific, in the sense that it does not matter what was the source of the lipopolysaccharide, and is not related to alteration in the levels of specific antibody. At one time it was thought that the increased efficiency of the macrophages was due to an increase in the content of properdin (p. 201) in the serum, but although the level of properdin does in fact show a definite rise (after a transient initial fall) following injection of lipopolysaccharide, there is evidence that properdin is probably not the operative factor. The alteration appears to be in the cells themselves, which can be shown to develop increased contents of the hydrolytic lysosomal enzymes, but the mechanism by which this occurs is at present quite unknown. This observation does, however, provide some basis for explaining the beneficial effects which are sometimes obtained after injecting typhoid vaccine (used for 'fever therapy')—a procedure employed by experienced physicians, but lacking any rational explanation.

Although the macrophages are the first line of defence when the organisms are introduced intraperitoneally, once they are in the bloodstream the defence is taken over by the cells of the reticulo-endothelial system, mainly in the liver and spleen. These are much less readily available for experimental study, but such work as has been done indicates that factors operate similar to those in the peritoneal cavity.

We have dealt with the role of antibody in two specific infections, namely with pneumococci and with enteric organisms, because these have been most extensively studied. The picture which has been drawn is complicated enough, but still undoubtedly grossly over-simplified. Nevertheless, the principles can probably be applied to other forms of bacterial infection. In those instances in which the infection is predominantly intracellular—e.g. with gonococci, brucella and tubercle bacilli—the role of antibodies in antibacterial immunity is correspondingly less and the role of 'cellular' immunity correspondingly greater. This has been discussed in Chapter Two.

IMMUNITY IN PROTOZOAL DISEASES

The role of antibody in immunity against protozoal diseases is very difficult to evaluate. In animals or man infected with plasmodia or with trypanosomes, antibodies are undoubtedly produced which will visibly react with (e.g. by agglutinating) the infecting protozoa at some stage of their life cycle. However, it appears that the protozoa can in large measure escape the inhibiting effects of antibody. For example, in experimental trypanosome infections there is good evidence to indicate that the surface antigens of the trypanosomes are changed at each succeeding cycle of infection, so that although the antibodies might be capable of dealing with the organisms as they were at the time of original infection, or even during two or three cycles afterwards, they are not capable of inhibiting the trypanosomes during the current cycle. Similarly it can be inferred from the natural history of malaria in hyperendemic areas such as the Gambia that infants are born with sufficient antibody transferred from their mother to maintain them immune from infection for the first 9 months or so of life. From the age of 1 to 5–8 years old, however, they are subject to repeated attacks of malaria after which, if they survive, they appear to be solidly immune and the overt attacks cease. Such immunity persists so long as the patients remain in the hyperendemic area, where they are subject to repeated mosquito bites. If they leave the district to go to a non-malarious area for some years and then return their immunity has waned. If IgG, prepared from the serum of persons who have acquired a solid immunity, is administered to young children in the same area at the beginning of any of their attacks of malaria, it has been found that the attack is brought to an end after one further cycle of red cell infection instead of the expected several cycles. IgG prepared from the serum of persons from non-malarious areas has no such effect. These findings, together with the epidemiological pattern, suggest that there is a humoral immunity, presumably due to antibodies, but that there are many strains of malaria present in the district and that immunity must be developed against all of these in order that the inhabitants shall be free from overt attacks.

Recent work in monkeys infected with *Plasmodium knowlesi* has partly confirmed this supposition. It has been found that plasmodia, similar to trypanosomes, are subject to antigenic variation and that under suitable experimental conditions antigenically distinct variants of the erythrocytic forms occur at each relapse after a single experimental infection. However, the development of immunity depends only partly on antibodies against the relapse variants, but probably more importantly on the gradual build up of antibodies against a 'group' antigen common to all of the variants.

Since gamma-globulin from persons in West Africa will abort malarious attacks in East Africa the plasmodia in each area must be antigenically similar, but it is not known whether those from India or the Far East will also prove similar. The possibility is raised, however, of developing immunity by means of vaccination against at least the asexual erythrocytic form of malarial parasites.

Immunity in Fungal Diseases

Antibodies against fungi and yeasts may be found in the sera of many apparently normal people, as well as in those who have overt infections. In the presence of clinical fungal infections, e.g. due to *Aspergillus fumigatus*, the amounts of antibody may be so great as to be readily demonstrable by precipitin tests. Although there is considerable evidence to implicate such antibodies in the pathogenic effects of pulmonary fungal infections (see Chapter Eleven), there is no evidence that they hinder their spread once infection is established. However, the very fact that patients with immunoglobulin deficiency diseases are so unduly prone to candida and monilia infections indicates that antibodies must play some part in protecting against initial or reinfection.

FURTHER READING*

DUBOS R.J. & HIRSCH (eds) (1965) *Bacterial and Mycotic Infections of Man.* 4th edition. Pitman, London

HALE J.H. (1961) Duration of immunity in virus diseases. *Adv. Immunol.* **1**, 263

HOLLAND J.J. (1964) Viruses in animals and in cell culture. In *Fourteenth Symp. Soc. Gen. Microbiol. Microbial Behaviour* [Ed. Smith H. and Taylor Joan) p. 257. Cambridge Univ. Press, Cambridge

HORSFALL F.L. & TAMM I. (eds) (1965) *Viral and rickettsial infections of man.* 4th edition, Pitman, London

Immunology of Malaria (1968) *Wld Hlth Orgn tech. Rep. Series* **396**

Immunology and Parasitic Diseases (1965) *Wld Hlth Orgn tech. Rep. Series* **315**

ISAACS A. & HITCHCOCK GRISELDA (1960) Role of interferon in recovery from virus infections. *Lancet* **2**, 69

JENKIN C.R. & ROWLEY D. (1963) Basis for immunity to typhoid in mice, and the question of 'cellular immunity'. *Bact. Rev.* **27**, 391

OAKLEY C.L. (1968) Prophylaxis of Microbial Diseases. In *Clinical Aspects of Immunology* [Ed. Gell P.G.H. and Coombs R.R.A.) Blackwell Scientific Publications, Oxford

* See also suggestions relating to Chapter Sixteen.

Soulsby E.J.L. (1962) Antigen–antibody reactions in helminth infections. *Adv. Immunol.* **2,** 265

Taylor A. E. (ed.) *Immunity to Parasites* (1968) Blackwell Scientific Publications, Oxford

Wilson G.S. & Miles A.A. (eds) (1964) *Topley and Wilson's Principles of Bacteriology and Immunity*, 5th edition, Arnold, London

Wood W.B. (1960) Phagocytosis with particular reference to encapsulated bacteria. *Bact. Rev.* **24,** 41

Wright G.P. (1968) Protective Immunity. In *Clinical Aspects of Immunology* [Ed. Gell P.G.H. and Coombs R.R.A.) Blackwell Scientific Publications, Oxford

CHAPTER ELEVEN

Hypersensitivity Mediated by Antibodies

IT is well to begin this chapter by a consideration of the current terminology. The *hypersensitivity* with which we are concerned is an acquired state which develops as a result of exposure to some environmental agent. *Hypersensitivity* is often used as synonymous with *allergy*, although when this term was first introduced by von Pirquet in 1906 it implied simply *an altered capacity to react* (Greek 'allos', other: 'ergon' work or energy). For our purposes allergy is defined as a *specifically induced altered reactivity* in which there is evidence for an underlying immunological mechanism. Moreover, it is inconvenient to use this term in the double-edged manner of its originator von Pirquet, which includes both increased and decreased reactivity. In general, in considering the reaction of the body to an external harmful antigenic agent, the term *immunity* implies a decreased reactivity. It thus becomes convenient to apply the term *allergy* in the restricted sense of an altered reactivity which is increased above the normal.

In speaking of the results of exposure to antigenic stimuli, as they affect the whole body, the term *prophylaxis* is used for the induction of a state of immunity (Gk. 'pro'; 'phulaxis', guarding). *Anaphylaxis* implies the opposite of prophylaxis and denotes a process whereby the reactivity of the whole body is increased to an antigenic stimulus. Anaphylaxis is therefore a specific example of the hypersensitive state.

A useful division of hypersensitivity is into *immediate*-type and *delayed*-type, which is based on the time-scales with which the reactions occur, but actually reflects fundamental differences in mechanism. The immediate-type reactions are those whose first manifestations occur within a few seconds or minutes of the contact of antigen with antibody, although the macroscopically visible effects may not become obvious for minutes or even hours and may not disappear for days. Reactions of this type can be shown always to be associated with serum antibodies. Delayed-type hypersensitivity reactions, however, which are discussed in the next chapter, appear to be independent of serum antibodies and to depend upon sensitized cells.

Anaphylaxis was observed by Richet and Portier in 1902, who found that whereas a first intravenous injection into dogs of an extract of sea anemones, which they were studying, was relatively harmless in small doses, a second intravenous injection some weeks later resulted in violent symptoms and often in death of the dogs. The symptoms came on within a few minutes of the injection and were characterized by weakness, difficulty in breathing, vomiting, defaecation and micturition; in some animals the prostration and difficulty in breathing increased, gasping respiration occurred, and death supervened. In others the symptoms gradually cleared and after an hour or so the animals were more or less normal. Post-mortem examination of those animals which had died revealed greatly engorged livers, intestinal congestion, haemorrhages in the submucosa of the stomach, and lungs which were greatly distended and did not collapse when the chest was opened. This reaction they termed acute anaphylaxis. It is now known that many species of animal, and even some fish which have been sensitized to an antigen, can, in suitable circumstances, respond to reinjection of the antigen by manifesting an acute anaphylactic reaction which differs in detail, but resembles in principle, that first observed in the dog. The second variant of immediate-type hypersensitivity is associated with the name of Maurice Arthus. He found that if he gave weekly subcutaneous injections of foreign serum into rabbits, the first two or three injections produced no injurious result, but subsequent injections caused an inflammatory reaction of increasing intensity with much oedema and even haemorrhage and necrosis. The whole process was much slower than that seen in acute anaphylaxis, and was characterized by invasion of the reaction site by enormous numbers of inflammatory cells, mostly polymorphonuclear leucocytes. The term Arthus-type phenomenon has become generally used to describe the local results of interaction of antigen and antibody when these are accompanied by an inflammatory response rather than by the many acute manifestations of anaphylaxis described above. Although, as has already been remarked, there is often no hard and fast distinction between the two, it is convenient to treat them separately. These subdivisions are listed in Table 11.1.

TABLE 11.1

Biological consequences of immune responses

IMMUNITY

HYPERSENSITIVITY (ALLERGY)

1. *Immediate* (dependent upon circulating antibody)
   (a) *Anaphylaxis:* Results from acute release of short-lived pharmacologically active agents when antigen is reintroduced locally or systemically. Mainly conditioned by interaction of antigen with antibody which is 'fixed' on tissues. (In man, atopic, or reaginic, antibodies are largely responsible.) Can be local (e.g. in the skin) as well as systemic.
   (b) *Arthus reaction:* Severe inflammatory response to formation of antigen–antibody aggregates, especially within vessel walls, when antigen is reintroduced locally. Develops more slowly than anaphylaxis, and often supersedes a local anaphylactic reaction. IgG or γ_2 antibodies are responsible.
   (c) *Serum sickness:* Results from single introduction of a large amount of antigen, so that antigen is still present in the circulation when antibody is made and antigen–antibody complexes are formed in the presence of excess antigen. Manifestations are mainly those of Arthus reaction, since the process is too gradual for effective concentrations of agents responsible for anaphylaxis to occur. IgG or γ_2 antibodies are responsible.
   (d) *Lesions due to antibodies against cells or tissue:* Heterologous or autologous antibodies can either cause complement dependent lysis of the target cells or may cause a transient or persistent local inflammatory response in the target tissue.
2. *Delayed* (bacterial allergy, tuberculin-type sensitivity, contact sensitivity to simple chemicals). See Chapter Twelve.

N.B. The different types of allergic response are classified by some authors as types 1, 2, 3 and 4, corresponding to 1(a), 1(d), 1(b) and 1(c) and 2 listed above. (See Gell, P.G.H. and Coombs, R.R.A. in 'Further Reading')

ANAPHYLAXIS

Before attempting to discuss the mechanism of anaphylaxis in man, it is simpler to consider first the extensive evidence which derives from experimental animals. The animal which is most exquisitely sensitive to anaphylaxis is the guinea-pig, and it has been the chief object of study. The intensity of study to which it has been subjected is probably due not so much to an attempt to solve the mystery of human anaphylaxis, as the fascination of the problem posed by the fact that whereas a first injection of a milligram or even very much less of a substance such as egg albumin is completely harmless, reinjection of another milligram two to three weeks later results in death of the guinea-pig within a few minutes from asphyxia caused by intense constriction of the bronchi and bronchioles. At death the lungs are intensely emphysematous because of hindrance to the exit of air due to constriction of the bronchiolar lumen (Plate 11.1, following p. 406). Light on this was shed by the remarkable researches of Sir Henry Dale who in 1911 to 1914 showed that a great many, but not all, of the symptoms exhibited by the guinea-pig were the same as those produced by the newly discovered pharmacological agent histamine.

Schultz and Dale also showed independently that the uterus of a sensitized guinea-pig, suspended in an organ bath containing nutrient fluid at 37° and oxygenated, would contract upon addition to the bath of a small amount of the substance against which the guinea-pig had been sensitized. This effect was quite specific, unrelated antigens having no action. Furthermore, the uterus having once responded by contraction to the antigen in question, a second addition of the same amount of antigen produced no effect, although a larger quantity might produce a small contraction. In other words, the tissue had become desensitized. Later workers found that other smooth muscles such as strips of intestine would respond in the same way, and muscle from the ileum, which contracts and relaxes much faster than the uterus, is commonly used for detection *in vitro* of sensitization of this kind. Dale showed that the uterus of a normal guinea-pig could become sensitized by perfusing through it serum from a guinea-pig or a rabbit which had been sensitized with a particular antigen. It was later found that perfusion was unnecessary, and simply soaking the tissue in the antiserum would render it sensitized just as though it came from a sensitized animal. (Although guinea-pig, rabbit, dog, monkey, and most human antisera will sensitize guinea-pig tissue in this way, antisera from ruminants or from horses or from chickens do not.) It appears, therefore, that suitable antibodies are somehow taken up by guinea-pig tissues, and that when antigen comes into contact with the antibody on the tissue a sequence of events takes place which causes smooth muscle to contract. We already know that the results of anaphylaxis can be mimicked to a considerable extent by the action of histamine. It has been shown that histamine is in fact released from sensitized tissues within less than a minute after addition of antigen. Rather sensitive techniques are required to demonstrate the histamine, since the amounts released are small, and enzymes are present in the tissues and body fluids which destroy it once it has been set free.

Three questions may now be asked. Is any other pharmacologically active agent besides histamine released? Where does the histamine come from? What is the mechanism by which this occurs?

There are in fact four distinct pharmacologically active agents which are known to appear as a result of antigen–antibody interaction. These are, besides histamine, Slow Reacting Substance (abbreviated to SRS-A), 5-hydroxytryptamine (also known as Serotonin), and a polypeptide known as bradykinin. The origin and action of each of these will be discussed briefly below. It is important to realize that in the body, once they have been released, these agents are active only for a matter of minutes or less. This is because histamine, serotonin and bradykinin are soon destroyed by enzymes present in the body fluids or metabolized; SRS-A is apparently removed by adsorption on to the tissues. Since the amounts of such materials and the sites at which they are released or formed, and the sensitivity of the tissues (such as smooth muscle or capillary endothelium) to them, can all vary markedly from species to species, it is clear that a wide variety of manifestations of anaphylaxis are possible. There may in fact be other unidentified agents also, but those already known are probably sufficient to account for many of the features which we can recognize. Thus a sensitized guinea-pig, which has been protected against the effects of histamine by antihistamine drugs, can still show evidence of damage when antigen is reinjected. Although the very severe bronchial constriction, contraction of smooth muscles and profound fall in blood pressure do not occur, nevertheless the animals look ill and sit huddled in a corner of the cage for an hour or so, and there is in fact a transient fall in blood pressure. Likewise the local changes in capillary permeability which occur when a small amount of antigen is injected into the skin of a sensitized rat cannot wholly be explained in terms of the action of histamine or serotonin. Such effects can probably be explained by the action of bradykinin and/or SRS-A.

Histamine is a base derived by decarboxylation of histidine. It has a powerful action on many (but not all) smooth muscles, causing them to contract rapidly. It also causes vasodilatation, and a very marked increase in capillary permeability in most species, though some (such as man and guinea-pig) are much more susceptible than others (e.g. rat). Histamine occurs in the tissue mast cells and the free mast cells of many species, being present in the large granules of these cells which stain metachromatically with basic dyes such as toluidine blue. Also present in the granules are acid sulphate-containing polysaccharides, which are often but not always a form of heparin, and which are responsible for the metachromasia. Histamine is probably stored in the granules as an ionic complex with a basic protein, which itself binds strongly to the acid polysaccharide, leaving a relatively weak negative charge, such that the histamine can be rather easily displaced by cations such as Na. Mast cells are present throughout the connective tissue, particularly near small vessels, although in some sites they tend to be more abundant than in others (e.g. in the pleura, the liver capsule, the peritoneum, the tongue and the skin around the nostrils and nipples. They are also moderately plentiful in muscular organs such as the gut, the uterus and the heart.) It is not known whether all the tissue histamine is present in mast cells, which on average each contain about $1\text{–}4 \times 10^{-5}$ micrograms, but certainly most of it is. As a result of anaphylaxis some of the mast cells are disrupted, and their granules lie scattered outside the cell or else become invisible because they have lost their metachromatic properties. Such disruption is accompanied by release of histamine and of heparin. The distribution of mast cells in the peritoneum, and the effect of an antigen–antibody reaction occurring on the surface of an isolated rat mast cell, are illustrated in Plates 11.2 and 11.3, following p. 406.

Another source of histamine in certain species is the blood platelets. These also have been shown to release histamine both *in vitro* and in the living animal following antigen–antibody reactions. Although rabbit platelets each contain about 4×10^{-9} micrograms of histamine, the platelets of man, dog or guinea-pig contain less than 10^{-10} micrograms, and platelets are not of general importance as sources of histamine in anaphylaxis.

Serotonin (5-hydroxytryptamine) is a base derived by decarboxylation of tryptophan after the introduction of an –OH group into the indole ring. It causes rapid contraction of certain smooth muscles, and increases capillary permeability (especially in rodents), although its action on larger blood-vessels, unlike that of histamine, is predominantly vasoconstrictor. It is present in most platelets, in amounts which depend upon the species of origin. In rodents it probably occurs in mast cells in some parts of the body (it is also present in mast cell tumours). Serotonin is also formed in brain tissue, in the intestinal wall, and in carcinoid tumours, but in these sites it is irrelevant to anaphylaxis, although it probably fulfils important physiological functions.

Release of serotonin from platelets as a consequence of antigen–antibody reactions has been shown to occur *in vitro* and in the living animal. In most species the amount released contributes little to the picture of general anaphylaxis, although it might be more important as a vasoconstrictor locally. In the rabbit, however, whose platelets are particularly rich in histamine as well as serotonin, the symptomatology of anaphylaxis may partly be accounted for by release of these amines from platelets which accumulate in the lung capillary bed.

SRS-A is at present of unknown constitution, but it appears to be a lipid which usually occurs rather firmly attached to a protein. It is detected by its ability, in minute amounts, to contract certain smooth muscles (including some important ones in the human bronchioles) with a characteristically

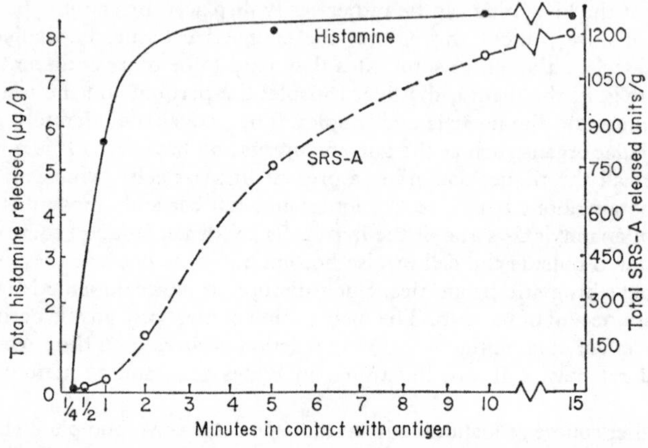

FIG. 11.1. Time course of the release of histamine and SRS-A from fragments of sensitized guinea-pig lung after addition of specific antigen (ovalbumin). [From Austen and Brocklehurst (1961) *J. exp. Med.* **113**, 545.]

prolonged contraction, slow in onset—hence its name, *Slow Reacting Substance*. ('A' means released by anaphylaxis.) This action is not antagonized by the drugs which prevent the activity of histamine or of serotonin. In the tissues of sensitized guinea-pigs, and in sensitized human lung, SRS-A is liberated during anaphylaxis along with histamine, but the time course of liberation of the two substances is different—the peak of release of SRS-A occurring later than that of histamine and release continuing for longer. This is illustrated in Fig. 11.1 which gives the results of an experiment in which fragments of lung taken from a sensitized guinea-pig were incubated at 37° in the presence of the specific antigen, and the amounts of active materials released into the supernatant fluid as time went by were measured. Similar results are obtained when a sensitized lung is perfused with antigen through the pulmonary artery. In the rat, however, SRS and histamine are released independently of one another, and by antibodies of different classes.

The origin of SRS-A is unknown. Unlike histamine and serotonin, it does not appear to exist preformed in cells but is generated as a result of the events set in motion by antigen–antibody interaction, whose nature is discussed below. How far SRS-A is important in the symptoms of anaphylaxis remains to be shown, but it would appear to be responsible for a major part of that bronchial constriction in human asthma which is not antagonized by anti-histamine drugs, and to be the cause of the therapeutic failure of such drugs in this condition.

Bradykinin is another slow-reacting substance, with a powerful contracting action on certain smooth muscles, with a vasodilator action greater than any substance known and quite a marked activity in increasing capillary permeability. Unlike SRS-A, bradykinin has been characterized chemically as a basic peptide made up of the L-forms of nine amino-acids, and has been synthesized. Historically it was at first a pharmacological curiosity, being produced by the action of certain snake venoms or proteolytic enzymes such as trypsin (or plasmin) on a substrate in the pseudoglobulin fraction of blood plasma. More recently it has been shown to be identical with one of another group of pharmacologically active peptides, which were first studied under the name of 'kallidins' and are now generically termed plasma kinins. The kallidins are produced by the action upon a substrate in plasma (a specific α-globulin, *bradykininogen*) of enzymes termed 'kallicreins' (now thought to be esterases) present in apocrine glands. A similar substance is also generated from plasma, on contact with glass or other water-wettable surfaces, by the action of a factor which is probably identical with the Hageman blood-clotting factor.

Bradykinin has almost certainly an important physiological role as a functional vasodilator. It is produced in pathological amounts in the 'dumping' syndrome which sometimes follows operations for intestinal resection. How far it has any importance in determining the biological consequences of antigen–antibody reactions is still uncertain, but it is present in the blood during anaphylaxis in several species of animal and can mimic some of the changes which are not abolished by antagonists of histamine or serotonin and presumably cannot be attributed to these agents. An enzyme capable of forming bradykinin in plasma is released from sensitized guinea-pig lung or skin within a short time when these tissues are perfused with the specific antigen. Bradykinin, generated locally, might be responsible for some of the inflammatory changes accompanying antigen–antibody reactions.

TYPES OF ANTIBODY INVOLVED

Since the appearance of earlier editions of this book a major advance in understanding the differences between anaphylactic and Arthus or serum sickness types of hypersensitivity has resulted from improved methods of separating different classes of antibody, which have revealed that the reactions are mediated by different classes of antibody in different species. As has already been pointed out in Chapter Four the important differences between one class of antibody and another reside not in the nature of the antibody combining sites (the Fab portions) but in the Fc portions of the heavy chains, which determine whether or not the antibody molecule can activate complement, whether it will attach to the membranes of certain cells, whether it is transmitted from mother to foetus, and so on. A clearer understanding has also been attained of the difference between homologous (or autologous) and heterologous antibodies in their capacity to cause the different kinds of immediate type hypersensitivity reactions. It is an empirical observation that when antibodies of a given class cause anaphylactic sensitization in a given (or in closely related) species they fail to do so with anything like comparable efficiency on passive transfer to animals of a second unrelated species; nevertheless, the serum of an animal of the first species may contain antibodies of another class which, while failing to sensitize its own species for anaphylaxis, can do so quite effectively in the second species. This observation has understandably given rise to confusion, and has led to the introduction of new terms to describe the biological behaviour of such antibodies in these special circumstances. The terms are based on the assumption, which is justified below, that anaphylactic sensitization is due to the affinity of the causative antibodies for the surfaces of certain tissue cells, notably mast cells, so that interaction with antigen at these sites damages the cells, causing release of powerful pharmacological reagents, which are responsible for the manifestations of anaphylaxis. The terms are *homocytotropic* (Gk homoios = like, cytos = cell, tropein = to turn towards) for antibodies which sensitize the cells of *the same* species, and *heterocytotropic* for those which sensitize the cells of *another* species. Such antibodies are special examples of *cytophilic* antibodies, which are mentioned elsewhere (p. 381).

A list of the main known characteristics of homocytotropic antibodies of various species is given in Table 11.2. It may be noticed that the antibodies fall into two distinct groups. On the left half of the table are guinea-pig and mouse, in which homocytotropic antibodies are present in considerable quantity in the serum, belong to a class presently termed γ_1, and are relatively resistant to heat and to reduction of their disulphide bonds. On the right half of the table

TABLE 11.2

Characteristics of the homocytotropic antibodies of mammals

	Guinea-pig	Mouse		Rat	Rabbit	Dog	Man
Reactions mediated in species of origin	PCA, SA, *in vitro*	PCA, *in vitro*		PCA, SA, *in vitro*	PCA	PCA, SA	P–K, SA, *in vitro*
Amount of component in serum	++++	++++	trace	trace	trace	trace	trace
Sedimentation coefficient	6·5S	7S	?	sl. > 7S	sl. > 7S	?	Appro. 8S
Heat lability (56° for 30 min.)	± (slight)	–*	+	+	+	+	+
Susceptibility to disulphide bond reduction	±	+°	?	+	+	?	+
Ability to fix C′	–	–	?	–**	–**	?	–**
Persistence at passively sensitized skin site	more than 2 less than 4 days	less than 1 day*	10 days or more	31 days or more	17 days or more	14 days or more	28 days or more
Transfer across maternal-foetal membranes	+	?	?	–	?	?	–
Immunoglobulin class	7Sγ1†	7Sγ1	? IgE	? IgE	? IgE	? IgE	IgE

PCA = passive cutaneous anaphylaxis; SA = systemic anaphylaxis; *in vitro* = sensitization of homologous normal tissue for antigen-induced release of histamine; P–K = Prausnitz–Kustner reaction

* by inference, not tested with isolated 7Sγ1 antibody; ° also required reduction and alkylation

** based on indirect evidence

† The occurrence of a different kind of homocytotropic antibody, resembling those of rat, dog, rabbit and man, has been described in guinea-pigs infected with helminths (ascaris).

(Modified from Bloch K.J. C.I.O.M.S. *International Symposium of the Biochemistry of the Acute Allergic Reactions.* Blackwell, Oxford, 1968) are rat, rabbit, dog and man, in which homocytotropic antibodies are present only in trace amounts in the serum, belong to a quite distinct class (identified in man as IgE), and are very readily inactivated by heat or by reduction. There is some evidence that the mouse shares the characteristics of both groups, and while resembling the guinea-pig in making large amounts of γ_1 antibodies (which are not found in the second group), also makes antibodies resembling those of the second group. Very recently, in response to helminth infections (e.g. trichinella), guinea-pigs also have been found to make homocytotropic antibodies generally resembling those occurring in man. Since Table 11.2 may appear partly to contradict the outline of human immunoglobulins given in Chapter Four, it should be made clear that major classes of antibody apparently similar to most of those of man have been identified in mice, rats, rabbits, dogs and guinea-pigs, but that the guinea-pig differs in that its 7S immunoglobulin is separable into two major electrophoretically distinct classes, named γ_2 and γ_1, which differ in their heavy chains but do not obviously correspond to those of man. They have already been referred to in Chapter Seven (p. 254).

With this necessary introduction, which anticipates some of the discussion in the following pages, we may return to the subject of anaphylaxis.

THE MECHANISM OF ANAPHYLAXIS

The mechanism by which these pharmacologically active agents are released has not been fully worked out even in the much studied guinea-pig. There is probably not a completely unique mechanism involved in the release of any one of them, in the sense that the agent or its precursor may be released rather specifically from the cell which holds it by an antibody–antigen reaction, or some release may follow secondary damage as a result of local vascular occlusion or of the accumulation of inflammatory cells and local discharge of their lysosomal contents. Furthermore, the different agents to some extent have similar effects—e.g. they increase vascular permeability—and in consequence it is possible to elicit some of the features of general or local anaphylaxis in more than one way. However, what may be called the 'true' picture of anaphylaxis is that which is dominated by the explosive discharge of histamine (and serotonin in rodents) derived from tissue mast cells and blood basophils, and it is this reaction which has been the subject of most study. It can be studied in the whole animal, usually the guinea-pig, but is often more conveniently done with isolated tissues as already mentioned above.

The first prerequisite is that antibody of the right class (i.e. a cytotropic antibody) should be adsorbed on to the surface of the target cells, which certainly include mast cells, but may include other cells the result of damage to which is less obvious than is damage to mast cells. The process of adsorption is reversible, and the antibody molecules compete for adsorption with other similar molecules of immunoglobulin (whether specific antibody or not) in the surrounding fluid. In consequence there is a *latent period* before sufficient specific antibody will have become attached to elicit a measurable reaction on further interaction with the antigen. The firmness with which adsorption occurs varies markedly even between antibodies which are all cytotropic, and the more firm the adsorption the longer will be the latent period and the longer will a tissue or animal remain sensitized when antibody is no longer present in significant amounts in the surrounding fluid. The amounts of an effective antibody which must be attached to a tissue so that the anaphylactic reaction can occur are extremely small, being of the order of 0·01 μg, or less, per gm of tissue—and even then much of the antibody is probably attached to irrelevant cells. Such amounts are too small to be detected by ordinary serological methods, but can be measured if the antibody has first been tagged with a radioactive label.

Reversed Anaphylaxis

This is a purely experimental situation in which the antigen is introduced first into a normal animal, and antibody against it is introduced later. For an anaphylactic reaction to result it has been shown that in this case the *antigen* must first become adsorbed to the tissues in the right way. Since there are few, if any, antigens which will do this, other than cytotropic immunoglobulins, reversed anaphylaxis provides a useful experimental means of determining what classes of antibody are likely to have cytotropic properties.

Because anaphylaxis is so sensitive a test for the detection of antibody, the reaction in guinea-pigs is often used as an experimental method—especially in the form of passive cutaneous anaphylaxis, described in Chapter Nine (p. 396). It will, of course, only detect antibodies which are cytotropic for guinea-pig tissues. A list of antibodies from various species whose reaction in guinea-pigs has been tested is given in Table 11.3. It may be remarked that of heterologous antibodies most IgG and subclasses are active, whereas IgA, IgM and homocytotropic antibodies are not. Most ruminant, ungulate and avian antibodies are also inactive. The heterocytotropic antibodies are, on the whole, those which with antigen can activate guinea-pig complement—but this does not signify that complement activation is a necessary step in anaphylaxis since homocytotropic antibodies (in the guinea-pig and other species) do not in fact effect this.

TABLE 11.3

Immunoglobulin class of certain antibodies capable of eliciting local cutaneous anaphylaxis in the *guinea-pig*

(N.B. Some of these were tested by reversed passive anaphylaxis)

	Immunoglobulin Class	
Species	Positive	Negative
Guinea-pig	γ_1	γ_2, ?IgM
Mouse	γ_{2a}	γ_{2b}, γ_1, IgA, IgM
Rabbit	IgG	IgA, IgM, homocytotropic antibody
Dog	IgG	homocytotropic antibody
Monkey	IgG	? (not extensively tested)
Man	IgG1, IgG3, IgG4	IgG2, IgA, IgM, IgD, IgE

A point of considerable interest, which will be referred to again when discussing specific desensitization, is that antibodies of a class which is not cytotropic for a given tissue can often inhibit the activity of cytotropic antibodies of the same specificity—presumably by competition for antigen. A good example of this is the inhibition of the anaphylactic activity of guinea-pig γ_1 antibody by an excess of γ_2 antibody.

When combination occurs between antibody on the surface of the target cell and the antigen (or *vice versa* in reversed anaphylaxis) the cell is damaged and discharges some of its contents. Such damage could conceivably be produced directly by distortion of the cell surface, but this does not seem to be the case, and the sequence of events is much more complicated. Clues which have helped to unravel the process have been obtained from observing the effects of various inhibitory agents upon the release of histamine from isolated tissues or suspensions of basophil cells obtained from the peritoneal cavity or the blood. It has been shown that calcium ions are necessary and that the ionic strength of the medium must not be much greater than physiological, just as in the case of haemolysis of red cells by antibody and complement (see Chapter Five). The presence of added complement is, however, *not* required. By the use of specific enzyme inhibitors it has been found that at least two stages are involved, one of which results in activation of an enzyme with the general specificity of chymotrypsin. In the guinea-pig the release of histamine and the production of SRS–A appear to require activation of the same mechanism, at least in the early stages.

By an ingenious method, using bivalent or (artificially made) univalent antibodies, and monovalent, bivalent or multivalent haptens as antigens, it has been shown that to set these processes in motion it is necessary for a molecule with two or more binding sites to interact simultaneously with (i.e. to *bridge*) two immunoglobulin molecules on the cell surface. This implies that even a small bivalent hapten can evoke an anaphylactic reaction, although—of course—it cannot itself bring about antibody formation.

Species Variation in Anaphylaxis

Although it is probable that the fundamental mechanisms of anaphylaxis are the same in different species, the symptoms and their severity vary markedly from one kind of animal to another. This is partly because the pharmacologically active agents released may differ in quantity and in nature, and partly because the susceptibility of different kinds of animal to known agents such as histamine or serotonin varies very markedly. There is a fairly general correlation between susceptibility to the pharmacological action of histamine and susceptibility to anaphylaxis. Thus rats, for example, can tolerate very large amounts of histamine (hundreds of times more than would be required to kill a guinea-pig) and are highly resistant to anaphylaxis. Furthermore, in this species the production of homocytotropic antibodies is transient and irregular, and generally requires the use of adjuvants such as *Bordetella pertussis*, except in the case of infection with helminths such as *Nippostrongylus braziliensis* when—for reasons unknown—such antibody is produced against some constituents of the parasites over prolonged periods of time.

In rabbits true anaphylaxis—i.e. anaphylaxis due to explosive disruption of mast cells—is rare, since homocytotropic antibody formation is an evanescent phenomenon occurring only near the beginning of immunization and in any case rabbits are resistant to the effects of histamine. However, a syndrome often regarded as anaphylaxis is readily produced by injection of antigen into animals with high levels of IgG antibody. This syndrome is characterized by intense constriction of the pulmonary artery and embarrassment of the pulmonary circulation—which is partly attributable to actual obstruction of the pulmonary capillaries by antigen–antibody aggregates and partly to segregation of platelets in the lungs and the local release of large amounts of serotonin from them. These examples are only illustrative, and other factors hitherto unidentified may be equally or more important.

ANAPHYLAXIS IN MAN

Anaphylaxis in man is fortunately rare, but it may follow parenteral administration, or even ingestion, of quite small amounts of antigen into suitably sensitized subjects. Administration of therapeutic antiserum to a person who is already sensitized against it (sensitization is difficult to predict and may result from previous administration of serum, or even from immunization in earlier life with, for example, toxoid–antitoxin floccules); a prick test, or an injection of a pollen extract; a sting from a bee or a wasp; an injection of an antibiotic such as penicillin or of a local anaesthetic such as procaine; all these take an annual toll in deaths from acute anaphylaxis. The symptoms and signs commonly begin with itching of the scalp and tongue, flushing of the skin over the whole body, difficulty in breathing (due to bronchial spasm and/or oedema of the upper respiratory tract) and symptoms associated with acute hypotension which may lead rapidly to unconsciousness. In such cases only prompt administration of adrenaline or one of its analogues, followed by antihistamines, will prevent death.* In milder cases the respiratory embarrassment gradually clears up, and generalized urticaria appears over the body. The patient commonly has a violent headache.

It should be emphasized that the quantities of antigen required to elicit such symptoms may be extremely small, especially when the effective antigen represents a substantial proportion of the material injected (e.g. as a result of purification). For obvious reasons accurate

* Precautions to be taken are discussed in Chapter Sixteen.

intravenous doses are not known in man, but local anaphylactic reactions can be elicited in some subjects by 0·001–0·01 micrograms of purified pollen antigens, and microgram amounts of potent antigens, such as those from the castor oil plant, have probably killed people. This may seem less surprising when it is considered that 1 microgram of material with molecular weight 12,000 (the order of magnitude of several pollen antigens) contains 5×10^{13} molecules.

HAY FEVER AND ASTHMA

Although systemic anaphylactic reactions are fortunately uncommon, local ones are not. The most familiar is hay fever (vasomotor rhinitis), whose symptoms are produced when the antigen (usually pollen) comes into contact with the mucous membrane of the nose or with the conjunctiva. Another example is asthma, especially of the type known as extrinsic, in which some specific causative factor such as pollen, feathers, animal dander or house dust (the active agent in which is usually found to be moulds or mites) can be identified as the exciting agent. It should be stated at once, however, that asthma is seldom simple, and psychological factors and other types of hypersensitivity (e.g. delayed-type, which is discussed in Chapter Twelve) also play a lesser or greater role. Extrinsic asthma may occur either as a result of the antigen reaching the bronchial tree along the respiratory tract, or *via* the bloodstream—e.g. after absorption from the alimentary canal. Another local anaphylactic manifestation is the urticaria which occurs in susceptible people after eating certain food such as strawberries, fish or nuts. Since in this last instance small amounts of the exciting agents must have been absorbed from the alimentary tract and have travelled through the bloodstream, it is perhaps strictly incorrect to describe the urticaria as a local anaphylaxis. It might more properly be described as a local manifestation of general anaphylaxis in which the skin reaction is the most prominent aspect—particularly susceptible people may get bronchial spasm and intestinal spasm also. Purely local skin reactions can, however, occur as, for example, in the subject who is hypersensitive to dog scurf and whose hand or arm will come up in weals if he or she is rash enough to stroke a dog.

It is a matter of common observation that a tendency to asthma, hay fever, etc., runs in families, and the evidence is good that there is a hereditary basis, although the exact nature of this has not been defined. Clinical hypersensitivity of this type, with a hereditary predisposition, was termed '*Atopy*' by Coca some 40 years ago. Such hypersensitivity is associated with the presence in the blood of specific homocytotropic antibodies to the inciting agent, commonly known as '*reaginic*' or '*atopic*'. Inasmuch as hypersensitivity is always in the first place acquired as a result of contact with an antigen, and depends upon the development of specific antibodies of this kind, the hereditary predisposition may best be considered as an undue readiness to form reaginic antibodies. There is some evidence that, in certain families at least, such a tendency is controlled by a single recessive gene.

Most 'normal' people, even though they exhibit none of the stigmata described above, do make some reaginic antibodies, especially as a result of repeated exposure to suitable antigens. This can be shown by introducing into the skin (e.g. by a scratch or a prick) small amounts of solutions of the sorts of materials which are known to cause symptoms in hypersensitive people. If enough different materials are tried it is found that 80 to 90 per cent of ordinary people give a skin reaction to one or more such substances. Furthermore, 30 to 40 per cent of bakers have been found to give skin reactions to the flour with which they work, and over 20 per cent of cavalrymen (in the days when cavalry used horses) reacted to horse dander.

Such tests must be conducted with great care, since really sensitive people may undergo a generalized anaphylactic attack even when an apparently minute quantity of the allergen has been introduced. A typical skin reaction consists in a local feeling of itching, which is accompanied by the development of a peripheral flare and, at the site of the prick, a weal which commonly increases for 20 to 30 minutes, often producing irregular extensions which have been likened to pseudopodia, and then gradually fades. Although sensitivity may be found to be quite specific for one substance, it is usual to find that people who are hypersensitive will respond to a number of apparently unrelated allergens. By no means all persons with hypersensitivity of this kind suffer from clinical symptoms. This may be because, although they possess reaginic antibodies, these are weaker, or because they also possess 'blocking' antibodies (*vid. inf.*), or because they do not come into contact with the sensitizing material in such a way that it gets to their mucous membrane, but there may be other factors.

There is abundant evidence that histamine is released during local or systemic anaphylactic reaction in man. Thus isolated human tissues (e.g. nasal polyps or pieces of lung removed at operation from persons with hay fever or asthma) have been shown to release pharmacologically large amounts of histamine on contact with the specific allergen *in vitro*; raised histamine levels have been measured in the blood plasma and urine of persons during anaphylactic attacks; antihistamine drugs, which admittedly are not completely specific in their action, are therapeutically effective; and, more indirectly, it has been shown that intravenous administration of certain compounds which are known to release histamine from the tissues in man reproduces many of the features of systemic anaphylaxis. Studies on human tissues *in vitro*, however, have shown that in addition to histamine there are also liberated important amounts of SRS-A. SRS-A is particularly significant because it has a powerful constrictor activity upon human bronchioles (there are great species variations in this respect) and SRS-A is not susceptible to the action of antihistamines.

HOMOCYTOTROPIC ANTIBODIES (REAGINS) IN MAN

Although the mechanism by which reaction between antigen and antibody adsorbed to the target cells sets in train the sequence of events which lead to anaphylaxis has not been studied in man in such detail as in the guinea-pig or the rat, there is nothing to suggest that the mechanisms are not in general similar. As has been outlined in Chapter Four (p. 176) the class of antibody responsible has recently been identified as IgE. Antibodies in this class are normally present in only very small concentrations in the blood; they are unusually sensitive to heat, being destroyed completely in 30 min. at 56°, and to disulphide bond reducing agents; they do not pass from mother to foetus (but they can be passively transferred by blood transfusions!). It is doubtful whether they form precipitates with antigen, though repeated failures to demonstrate precipitation may be due to nothing more subtle than the very low concentration in which they are present. To detect such antibodies, and to distinguish them from antibodies of similar specificity belonging to other classes, has hitherto presented considerable difficulty. Now that a myeloma protein belonging to the IgE class has been discovered, and that antibodies specific for this class can be obtained by immunizing rabbits for example, the problem may be simplified by the use of techniques such as radioimmunodiffusion or indirect agglutination (see Chapter Nine). In fact specific antisera against IgE have been used already to show that the mean concentration of IgE is some six times higher in the serum of subjects with allergic asthma than in comparable controls. However, the one reliable test which has been in use for many years is that described by Prausnitz and Kustner (the P–K test), in which the serum from a sensitized person is injected intracutaneously into an unsensitized person. One or two days later a solution of the allergen is pricked into the same area and into normal skin at a remote site; if reaginic antibodies are present a typical weal and flare, maximal after about 20 min, are produced at the prepared site, while no reaction occurs at the control site. By measuring the size of the reaction to the allergen at sites injected with different dilutions of the reaginic serum it is possible to get a rough comparative measure of the amount of antibody present. As has already been mentioned in Table 11.2, reaginic antibody persists at the prepared site for many days; other kinds of antibody disappear with a half-life of about 24 hours.

Since to perform such tests in human subjects carried a very real risk of transferring hepatitis, attempts have been made to use laboratory animals instead. Only apes and monkeys give positive P-K tests with human reaginic sera, and even in them a dye such as Evans Blue must be injected intravenously to demonstrate local capillary leakage—a striking demonstration of the biological specificity of homocytotropic antibodies. An alternative test, which is difficult to perform consistently, is to use suspensions of normal human leucocytes, of which the relevant cells are the basophils. The cells are incubated in the serum to be tested, and the amount of histamine released on addition of a dilute solution of the antigen is measured. It is a matter of some interest that only leucocytes from certain individuals are suitable for this test—suggesting that individuals may differ in their capacity to become sensitized for anaphylaxis even when known reaginic antibody is present.

BLOCKING ANTIBODIES

Patients in whom the exciting allergens have been identified from the history or by skin tests are often treated by specific desensitization. This consists in a course of carefully graded injections of the suspected allergen, beginning with extremely small doses, which are gradually increased. Although this practice has been found empirically to be useful, its rationale was uncertain until the discovery that the sera of patients who had been subjected to courses of desensitization contained an antibody which was specifically able to inhibit the skin-sensitizing activity of the reaginic antibody. This was termed 'blocking' antibody, and it appears to act by combining preferentially with the antigen and so preventing its interaction with the skin-sensitizing antibody attached to the tissue. Blocking antibodies, in contrast to homocytotropic antibodies, are not destroyed by heating at 56° for 30 minutes, and, on fractionation of serum, they are found with the IgG. The occurrence of a similar phenomenon in rats and guinea-pigs has already been mentioned, and this explanation—though not fully proved—appears to be sufficient to render unnecessary alternative postulates such as that desensitization causes specific immunological tolerance or suppression of antibody formation.

Desensitization is most commonly practised for the treatment of hay fever and asthma due to pollens when the symptoms are not adequately controlled by antihistamines, but it can be used for hypersensitivities due to other specific agents when it is not possible to avoid contact with these agents (e.g. streptomycin sensitivity in nurses at tuberculosis sanatoria). The most frequently incriminated pollens in Britain are those of Timothy, Cocksfoot and Fescue grasses, which appear to share a common antigen or antigens, whereas on the North American continent ragweed pollen is the chief culprit. Practice has changed little since the treatment was first popularized in this country about 1910. The pollen is treated with acetone to remove lipids, and is then extracted with 10 parts of a weakly alkaline buffer to yield a solution containing 100,000 'Noon units' per ml. Dilutions are made from this solution, and adrenaline (1 : 2,000) is often added in order to minimize local anaphylactic reactions. Beginning some three months before the hay-fever season, the patient receives a series of about 50 subcutaneous injections, starting with 20 'units' and increasing gradually so that 20,000 to 100,000 'units' are given over the course of 80 days. Controlled trials have shown that when pollen sensitivity was the underlying cause hay fever was relieved in about 80 per cent of patients and asthma in about 90 per cent by specific desensitization, whereas 30 per cent of comparable patients were relieved to a similar extent by injections of an inactive control solution.

An alternative method is to replace the series of injections by cautious administration of pollen extracts emulsified in an oily base, which can be done within one day. There is a danger of causing violent general reactions, but good results have been claimed for this method of treatment.

THE NATURE OF SENSITIZING ANTIGENS

As already mentioned, the tendency to develop atopic sensitivity runs in families, and is probably due to their inherited capacity to make reaginic antibody. Those in whom this tendency is most pronounced will even make reaginic antibody in response to such antigens as diphtheria or tetanus toxoids, but in general it appears that certain sorts of antigens give rise to reaginic antibodies more readily than others. This might be because a particular route of entry into the body favours the production of such antibodies. Indeed, if entry by the respiratory tract were important then effective antigens would have to be available in finely particulate form of the right size (e.g. pollen, face powder, dust, dried insect scales) and would have to withstand desiccation. In the case of horse dander, it has been found that the majority of sensitive patients are sensitive only to one out of the seven or eight distinct substances which have been identified in horse-dander extract. On the other hand persons sensitive to plants may react to extracts from a variety of apparently different species. In such instances it is often the case that the species all belong to a common genus (e.g. *Euphorbia*) and they presumably share certain common antigens such as the very potent allergen chlorogenic acid. Helminths also are a very regular cause of reaginic antibody production in infected persons, as well as in infected animals, causing homocytotropic antibodies to be formed long after the infection has been eliminated.

Much work has been done on the chemical nature of the active material in pollens, etc., and it has usually been found that the most active materials are large peptides with a high carbohydrate content. This may mean either that molecules of this kind are particularly likely to give rise to reaginic antibodies, or that they are most able to withstand desiccation and exposure to light without loss of antigenic activity.

COT DEATH

A probable form of anaphylaxis, which has only recently been recognized as such, is cot death; it occurs exclusively in bottle-fed and never in breast-fed babies, and is probably responsible for some 2,000 deaths a year in this country. Characteristically, healthy infants aged between 6 and 9 months are put down in their cots after a feed, and go to sleep. When looked at later they are found to be dead, without any obvious cause. An experimental model has been put forward to support the view that death results from anaphylaxis due to inhalation of small amounts of vomited cow's milk. It was shown that breast-fed infants rarely had much antibody against cow's milk proteins, but that infants fed on cow's milk, unlike breast-fed infants, developed antibodies as early as the second week of life. This is presumably due to absorption of small amounts of the proteins of cow's milk from the gut, either intact or without being broken down sufficiently to destroy their antigenicity. Young guinea-pigs could be sensitized experimentally against cow's milk proteins by injection or feeding. They responded to inhalation of cow's milk, or of the stomach contents from bottle-fed babies, by an acute anaphylactic reaction. However, the picture in conscious animals in no way resembled the quiet and unspectacular fading out which occurs when babies die with cot death. Nevertheless, if the guinea-pigs were lightly anaesthetized so as to reproduce a condition resembling sleep, and milk was then introduced into their trachea, they died with a gradual failure of respiration but without any of the bronchospasm and violent struggling which would be manifested by the conscious guinea-pig. Post-mortem examination revealed little except histological evidence of desquamation of bronchial epithelium cells—the whole picture bearing a striking resemblance to cot death.

ARTHUS-TYPE REACTIONS: REACTIONS DUE TO ANTIGEN-ANTIBODY COMPLEXES

It may seem a far cry from an experimental reaction in the skin of a rabbit to human serum sickness or acute glomerulonephritis. Nevertheless, the connection between them is close enough to warrant consideration in some detail of a type of reaction named after Maurice Arthus, since this reaction has been the subject of much study and exemplifies a number of principles. Arthus reactions are produced when a soluble antigen is injected locally into animals which have precipitating antibodies in their circulation and in the tissue fluids. Arthus himself injected horse serum subcutaneously into rabbits which had received previous injections of the same material and were thus already actively immunized, but it is nowadays more usual to use purified serum proteins or other antigens. In this type of reaction, unlike anaphylaxis, the antibodies may come from any species, but they must be able to activate complement in the animal in which they are tested.

When a small volume of solution containing, say, a milligram or less of an otherwise harmless antigen is introduced into the skin of an immunized rabbit the initial bleb disappears, but within one or two hours a more diffuse swelling begins to show and the local skin becomes hyperaemic. Petechial haemorrhages may appear, and the area of subcutaneous oedema and erythema continues to increase for several hours, after which the reaction gradually subsides. The more antibody is present in the rabbit, the more intense the reaction and the longer it takes to disappear. Very often, especially in actively immunized animals, there is actual necrosis of the skin, but this is not seen in passively immunized animals; it may be the result of the superposition of a delayed-type hypersensitivity reaction (due to active immunization) upon the reaction due simply to the antigen–antibody interaction. In other species the picture is generally similar, except that in the guinea-pig there is always evidence of a local mild oedema within a few minutes of injecting the antigen, which is a manifestation of acute anaphylaxis at the site, and in man there may also be a rapid weal-and-flare reaction in such persons as possess reaginic antibodies to the antigen in question.

The progress of such a reaction can be followed *in vivo* in a transparent chamber implanted in a rabbit's ear and allowed to heal in place, or by placing the antigen on to a transparent vascularized tissue such as a guinea-pig's mesentery or a hamster's cheek pouch, which can be examined under a microscope in the living state. Immediately after the addition of antigen no obvious change occurs, but after about fifteen minutes the capillary circulation begins to slow down, and in the venules (which is where antigen is chiefly absorbed into the bloodstream) there appear clumps of platelets and polymorphs, which first adhere to one another and then adhere to the capillary and venule endothelium, which behaves as though it were 'sticky'. In many of the small vessels circulation ceases, and they become plugged with platelet-leucocyte thrombi, while extensive emigration of neutrophil polymorphs occurs through the vessel walls into the tissue spaces. Some of the venules in which circulation remains show rupture of their walls, and red cells stream out locally. A histological section of a fairly severe reaction site in skin after a few hours is shown in Plate 11.4, facing p. 470. It shows massive infiltration with neutrophil polymorphs, gross oedema, local segmental necrosis of venules and arterioles, and platelet-leucocyte thrombi.

At this stage mononuclear cells and eosinophils are rare. After 24 hours or so, however, the neutrophils begin to degenerate, and their nuclei become pyknotic. There are now many lymphocytes, macrophages and eosinophils, and these persist for several days. Revascularization and healing occur rapidly.

By means of the fluorescent antibody technique, or by using radioactive or fluorescent antigens, it is possible to detect in histological sections the localization of the antigen and antibody. Shortly after injection, antigen lies partly free and partly complexed with antibody in the tissue spaces. Within a few minutes, and increasingly thereafter, the walls of small blood-vessels in the neighbourhood contain antigen–antibody complexes lying in the subendothelial layer between the endothelial cells and the basement membrane. These complexes presumably result from the meeting of blood-borne antibody with antigen diffusing in from the local depot. They can be seen in histological sections by means of fluorescent labels. The antigen–antibody complexes, both free in the tissue spaces and within the vessel walls, are soon taken up by the neutrophil polymorphs which arrive in increasing numbers (Plates 11.5, 11.6, pp. 470–1). Such cells have been shown to digest ingested complexes quite rapidly, but a proportion of them are apparently killed in the process, as is evidenced by break-up of their internal structure. The contents of their granules, which include enzymes capable of digesting collagen, probably contribute considerably to the local tissue damage. Examination after 24 to 48 hours shows that most of the antigen–antibody complexes have been removed, but those remaining can still be detected, not only in neutrophil polymorphs, but also in macrophages which have apparently ingested dying neutrophils. In some species, such as the mouse, eosinophils are also engaged in very active phagocytosis of cell débris.

It is possible, by administration of nitrogen mustard or of specific antisera against neutrophil polymorphs, to deprive rabbits or guinea-pigs temporarily (for 3 to 4 days) of circulating neutrophils. If a passive Arthus reaction is performed during this period, singularly little damage results. Antigen–antibody complexes can be seen lying in the tissue spaces, and even more in the vessel walls, where they collect especially in the sub-intimal layer, but there are no platelet–leucocyte thrombi and no vascular necrosis. The complexes are gradually removed from the tissue spaces, probably by macrophages, but they remain in the vessel walls unchanged until the neutrophils return to the circulation. When this happens there occurs a brisk inflammatory reaction, in which neutrophils adhere to and invade the vessel walls in large numbers, phagocytosing the complexes and at the same time causing segmental necrosis of the vessels on a scale not much less than occurs in an ordinary Arthus reaction. Once the complexes have been removed the inflammatory reaction ends and healing ensues.

It appears, therefore, that the essential lesion in the Arthus reaction is an inflammatory invasion of blood-vessels, consequent upon the deposition of antigen–antibody complexes in their walls, and that the damage is done by the neutrophil polymorphs. We do not know how far the polymorphs act by plugging the smaller vessels and obstructing blood flow, by means of enzymes released from the granules (lysosomes) when they are damaged, by altering the local environment as a consequence of their intense lactic acid production or low redox potential, or in other ways. Neither do we know how the antigen–antibody complexes have their effect, but there are some hints that activation of C′ is involved. In the guinea-pig γ_2 antibodies, which activate C′, cause Arthus reactions, whereas γ_1 antibodies, which do not activate C′, do not. It was related in Chapter Five that activation of the C′ sequence as far as C′7 results in formation of a chemotactic factor for polymorphs. However, rabbits congenitally deficient in C′6 can exhibit Arthus reactions not much less severe than occur in normal rabbits; this suggests that activation of C′ as far as an earlier stage (e.g. C′3) can also cause polymorph accumulation, perhaps as a result of damage following phagocytosis of antigen–antibody complexes. These are much the most damaging when they are formed actually in the vessel walls (it does not matter whether antibody is in the blood and antigen introduced into the tissues or *vice versa*). Injection of preformed antigen–antibody mixtures directly into the tissues of a normal animal results in an inflammatory reaction with outpouring of polymorphs, but although vascular necrosis occurs it is much less marked. It may be noted that antigen–antibody complexes formed *in vitro* have been shown to possess quite definite biological activities. These depend greatly upon the proportions in which the antigen and antibody are present. As already discussed in Chapter Nine, complexes can be formed with IgG whose molecular ratios vary from Ag_2Ab in great antigenic excess (where there is no aggregation) through $(Ag_3Ab_2)n$, (AgAb)n, etc., to $(AgAb_4)n$, for example, in antibody excess. The complexes with greatest biological activity are those in which antigen is present in moderate (three- to tenfold) excess of the equivalence ratio. Such soluble complexes injected intravenously can produce a picture of acute anaphylaxis in a guinea-pig or mouse; they can cause isolated guinea-pig intestine to contract *in vitro*; they can bring about liberation of histamine from a rabbit's platelets suspended in normal plasma. The amounts required to produce these effects contain many times more antibody than would be required to produce corresponding effects if it were already 'fixed' on the tissues. Nevertheless, it appears that such complexes can set in train, albeit relatively ineffectively, the same series of biochemical events as underlie the changes in acute anaphylaxis, as well as activating C′ and causing polymorph immigration. There is suggestive evidence that the conjunction of these properties greatly enhances the pathogenic effects of such complexes.

SERUM SICKNESS

Serum sickness is so called because it was first described as a common sequel to the intravenous or intramuscular injection of therapeutic antiserum (usually of horse or rabbit origin) into man. Some eight days after administration, or earlier if serum had been administered on a previous occasion, the patient would feel unwell. The temperature would rise, lymph nodes all over the body, and especially those draining the injection site, would become swollen and tender, the spleen might enlarge, and soon afterwards there would often appear a generalized, usually urticarial rash and painful and swollen joints. During the course of the next few days the condition would gradually subside although it might persist for a week or more. If blood were examined at the height of the fever there would be an increase in neutrophil and eosinophil polymorphs, and if the serum complement level were measured it would be abnormally low. There would often be a transient albuminura. Even in the days when crude antiserum used to be given serum sickness did not occur always, and now that most antitoxins, etc., are prepared as 'refined' globulins (which are much less effective antigens than the material from which they are prepared, and can be used in smaller quantities) serum thickness is relatively uncommon. It only occurs when foreign serum proteins are administered, and never after human serum proteins.

Although the immunological nature of serum sickness has long been recognized, understanding of the mechanism is fairly recent. When the plasma of persons who had had an injection of foreign (e.g. horse) serum was examined at frequent intervals for the presence of the foreign serum proteins and of antibody against them, it was found that, in those persons who developed serum sickness, symptoms began while horse proteins were still circulating and shortly *before* antibody against horse serum proteins was detectable in the blood. The symptoms ended at about the time when horse proteins had disappeared, and antibodies were present in high titre. Patients who developed little or no antibody against horse serum proteins (and may have been made immunologically unresponsive by the large amounts injected) did not get serum sickness. This indicated that serum sickness was associated with the development of antibodies against the foreign serum proteins, but its onset did not coincide with the actual appearance of free antibody. For obtaining clear-cut evidence, however, the use of whole serum, or even of refined globulins, is unsatisfactory because a mixture of proteins is injected and antibodies against the various constituents appear at different times. A clearer picture is obtained when laboratory animals, rabbits, for example, are given large injections (of the order of 1 gram) of purified foreign proteins, such as bovine albumin or bovine γ-globulin. A large proportion of the animals develop serum sickness, and careful examination shows that in the course of the disease they have a severe but usually transient acute glomerulonephritis, or carditis and arteritis, or both. The onset of disease occurs when antibody begins to be produced, but, owing to the large amount of circulating antigen still present, antibody is not detectable by the usual means, being complexed with the antigen in the form of soluble complexes (see Fig. 11.2). Antigen–antibody complexes are generally swept out of the circulation quite fast and broken down in the reticulo-endothelial system, but the rate at which this occurs depends upon the nature of the complexes. Those formed in large antigen excess are quite small (Ag_2Ab), and are removed rather slowly, whereas those formed at equivalence or in antibody excess [$(AgAb)n$, $(AgAb_2)n$, etc.] are much larger and are removed rapidly. Thus the length of time during which soluble complexes exist in the circulation, and their amount, will depend upon how long the animal takes to make antibody, and how fast it makes it, as well as upon how much antigen was originally administered and upon its nature. All the evidence points to the fact that

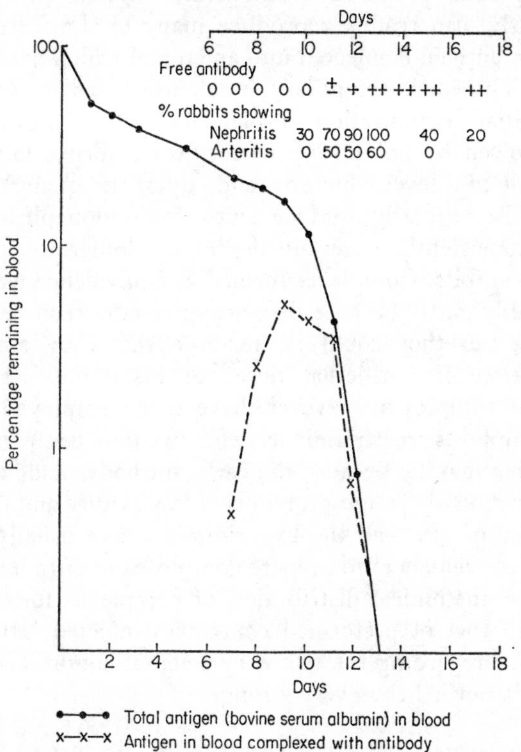

FIG. 11.2. Diagram to illustrate the time of appearance of the lesions of nephritis and arteritis in relation to the phase of rapid disappearance of injected antigen following the formation of antigen–antibody complexes. Rabbits were injected with a single dose of radioactively labelled bovine serum albumin (250 mg/kg) intravenously. [Modified from Dixon, Vasquez, Weigle and Cochrane (1958) *Arch. Path.* **65**, 18.]

serum sickness lesions are associated exclusively with the presence of circulating complexes, of the type which are formed at moderate but not extreme antigen excess.

PREFORMED ANTIGEN–ANTIBODY COMPLEXES

If circulating antigen–antibody complexes are the pathogenic agents, it should clearly be possible to produce similar effects in normal animals by injecting preformed soluble complexes prepared *in vitro*. This has in fact been done by several workers, who have shown that such complexes, prepared in moderate antigen excess injected intravenously, can readily reproduce many of the features which occur when antigen is injected into an animal which has circulating antibody. These are temporary hypotension (as in anaphylactic shock); initial sequestration of platelets and polymorphs in the lungs, followed by polymorph leucocytosis; abrupt fall in serum complement to a level which depends upon the quantity injected. They can also regularly produce acute glomerulonephritis in mice, and, less consistently, a certain degree of glomerulonephritis and arteritis in rabbits. Complexes formed at equivalence were ineffective, probably partly because they are so rapidly removed from the circulation, but they could be made effective by simultaneous administration of non-lethal doses of histamine. Rather large amounts of complexes, however, have to be employed, and preformed complexes are certainly less effective than complexes formed *in vivo*. This may be because the early antibody made after intravenous injection of foreign protein is of low avidity and forms more effective complexes than the hyperimmune sera usually used (for reasons of convenience) to prepare complexes *in vitro*, or it may be because the anatomical distribution of complexes formed *in vivo* differs from that of preformed complexes injected intravenously. The case for regarding the two experimental conditions as closely analogous is nevertheless very strong.

POLYARTERITIS

During experimental serum sickness in rabbits a necrotizing arteritis is produced which closely resembles in its histological appearance polyarteritis nodosa in man. From what has been written above it appears to be due to the presence of soluble antigen–antibody complexes in the arteries, and probably within their walls. The detailed mechanism by which the damage and invasion of the arterial walls by neutrophils and eosinophils is brought about is presumably the same as that in an Arthus reaction in the skin. How far does this resemblance imply a similar aetiology?

'Periarteritis' was originally described as a fatal disease characterized by the presence of numerous macroscopic nodules along the course of arteries throughout the body. The term 'polyarteritis' was later suggested as more appropriate since there was involvement of arterial walls as well as periarterial tissue. On microscopic examination the involved arteries, which were of the calibre of the primary branches of the coronary arteries or the hepatic arteries, showed inflammation and necrosis of the vessel wall, thrombosis and a perivascular exudate of polymorphs and eosinophils, with macrophages and lymphocytes. Frequently the cases occurred in individuals with an atopic background and asthma and eosinophilia were present. Death usually occurred from uraemia, coronary thrombosis, cerebral haemorrhage or gastro-intestinal bleeding. Cases have been described more recently in which polyarteritis is diagnosed early and arrest of the disease by treatment with cortisone has been achieved.

From 1940 'polyarteritis nodosa' has been repeatedly noted in serum sickness, and in patients who have received sulphonamides, thiourea, Dilantin, iodides, penicillin and other drugs. Following the description of similar vascular lesions in rabbits treated with large doses of serum proteins, the drug-induced human cases of polyarteritis nodosa disease were argued on this analogy to be due to Arthus-type hypersensitivity reactions to exogenous or other antigens.

The drugs in question are capable of being converted by simple chemical reactions, which could conceivably take place in the body (and in the case of penicillin actually occur *in vitro*), into derivatives which would combine with tissue or plasma proteins and thus give rise to potentially antigenic hapten–protein conjugates. However, no such antigens and/or their corresponding antibodies have actually been demonstrated in human patients, and the explanation must be regarded as purely tentative.

Some observers have distinguished such drug-induced vasculitis from 'periarteritis nodosa', pointing out the distinctly better prognosis in this group, and the difference in distribution of lesions, which were in the small intrinsic arterioles while the larger arteries were spared. The lesions were in consequence difficult to pick out at autopsy with the naked eye, and were quite different from the macroscopic nodules of periarteritis nodosa. The term 'allergic vasculitis' has been applied to this group, which is recognized to have a much better prognosis and to respond much more effectively to corticosteroid therapy.

On the assumption that true polyarteritis nodosa is originally due to antigen–antibody complexes, it would have to be postulated that some antigen was being continuously generated and introduced into the circulation both before and during the time in which lesions were occurring and that antibody against the antigen was being produced simultaneously. Presumably when renal involvement has reached the point of no return, malignant hypertension will be sufficient to maintain and increase the vascular damage until death occurs from cerebral haemorrhage, coronary thrombosis or renal failure.

EXPERIMENTAL MODELS OF GLOMERULONEPHRITIS

Before discussing possible immunological theories for human glomerulonephritis, it is important to consider the various experimental models which have been proposed as valid replicas of the human disease in one or more of its various aspects. It should be realized that it is possible to provoke the same features of the pathological lesion in more than one way. At risk of oversimplification, the following classification is based on the immunological mechanisms which are thought to be involved in each experimental group.

I. *Deposition of Antigen–Antibody Complexes in the Capillary Bed of the Glomeruli*

This form of disease is nosologically related to serum sickness, and has already been mentioned as a consequence of the interaction *in vivo* of a circulating foreign antigen and antibody. Another sphere of human pathology in which this mechanism may operate is systemic lupus erythematosus, in which circulating complexes of auto-antigen and antibody (p. 627) have been shown to be deposited in the glomerulus. A more remote possibility is that the lesion of the Kimmelstiel-Wilson kidney, a complication of long-standing treated diabetes, may result from an analogous mechanism involving complexes of exogenous insulin and insulin antibody.

Several types of experiment have shown that a single large dose or repeated small doses of soluble foreign proteins injected intravenously lead to accumulation of both antigen and antibody (also complement if the antigen–antibody interaction is one which fixes complement) as complexes within the glomerular capillaries, presumably as a consequence of the anatomical arrangement of the renal circulation. In this site they cause (in rats, mice and rabbits) an inflammatory response which resembles that seen in human acute (Type 1) nephritis, and, provided that the antigen–antibody complexes are soon removed, healing occurs without sequelae.

However, by varying the conditions under which the experimental animal is exposed to the antigen–antibody complexes resulting from repeated daily injections of foreign proteins, it has been found possible (in the rabbit) to produce a range of lesions covering the whole spectrum of human glomerulonephritis in its acute, subacute and chronic phases. A critical factor in determining the nature of the lesions was the amount of antibody produced by the animals. Animals giving a vigorous antibody response, more than sufficient to combine with the antigen, were found to develop a transient acute nephritis. Rabbits giving a rather poor antibody response, and in which the amounts of injected foreign protein were carefully adjusted so as to maintain a slight excess of antigen over antibody, were found to develop the pathological picture of subacute and chronic glomerulonephritis. This condition was presumably the result of *in vivo* formation of relatively small and soluble antigen–antibody complexes, which cross the endothelium and basement membrane of the glomerular capillaries, and accumulate mainly between the basement membrane and epithelial cytoplasm, where they become detectable by immunofluorescence as irregular lumpy masses or as electron-dense deposits under an electron microscope. At the other end of the scale, rabbits which did not develop detectable antibody had no proteinuria and no morphological signs of renal disease.

Intravenous injection of various antigen–antibody complexes, formed *in vitro*, has been shown to produce glomerulonephritis in mice, rats and rabbits. The glomerular localization occurs immediately after injection. This carries the important implication that renal damage can be caused by antigens with no special affinity for, or immunological relationship to, the kidney.

Recent work with the electron microscope has clarified the intimate details of lesions of both experimental and human nephritis. The normal glomerulus (Plate 11.8a, following p. 470) is seen to be made up of capillary endothelial cells, basement membrane and epithelial cells of Bowman's capsule, which number approximately one to every three endothelial cells. The cytoplasm of the endothelial cells away from the nucleus forms an attenuated layer which lines the capillary lumen completely except for small characteristic interruptions, interpreted by some as pores and by others as vesicles within the cytoplasm. The basement membrane forms a central layer between endothelium and epithelium, and varies from 0·5 to 1·0 μ thickness in young animals and children but becomes thicker with ageing. The epithelial cells are large with abundant cytoplasm which is organized peripherally into a profusion of branches which end as 'foot processes' implanted on the outer aspects of the basement membrane.

In experimental acute serum sickness nephritis, and in acute post-streptococcal nephritis in man, the main features are swelling and proliferation of capillary endothelial cells, swelling of mesangial (stalk) cells and the patchy presence of polymorphs. The result is that the circulation through the affected glomeruli becomes temporarily slowed. There are scattered foci of thickening or fraying of the glomerular basement membrane, but the epithelial cell foot processes are not greatly disorganized (Plate 11.8B).

In the chronic nephritis associated with prolonged circulation of antigen–antibody complexes the glomerular basement membrane shows much more marked and characteristic changes. These complexes accumulate in the zone between basement membrane and epithelial cells, where they appear to be protected from phagocytosis, for they are able to persist there for many weeks. An irregular lumpy thickening of the basement membrane on the epithelial side results, with considerable disorganization of the epithelial cell foot processes (Plate 11.8C). The endothelial side does not thicken (possibly since by phagocytic activity the endothelial cells keep this surface clear). Very comparable findings to these appearances, as seen in electron micrographs of the experimental disease, are present in kidneys from lupus nephritis (Plate 11.8D).

Immunofluorescent staining reveals that the antigen and antibody are characteristically deposited in a granular or lumpy fashion along the glomerular capillary walls. Staining for complement components shows that these also are present with the same distribution (Plates 11.9A and 11.9B).

The mechanisms leading to the localization of soluble complexes in glomeruli are not fully understood, but there is nothing to indicate any special immunological link with glomerular components. The localization may be in consequence of the filtration function of the basement membrane, which becomes overloaded, and some experiments suggest that the size of the immune complexes may be an important factor in this. Thus injected methyl cellulose particles of small size also localize to and damage the glomeruli, but with larger particles, which are more rapidly cleared by sinus-lining macrophages of the liver and spleen, no damage results. Probably the larger-sized complexes which occur in animals producing high levels of antibody are also more efficiently cleared by reticulo-endothelial cells with less resultant damage in the glomeruli.

II. *Interaction of Antibody with a Glomerular Antigen (either Integral or secondarily attached): Masugi Nephritis*

An experimental model which has stimulated a great deal of interest was first elaborated by Masugi. He prepared 'nephrotoxic' antiserum in ducks against homogenized rabbit kidney, and then injected the serum back into rabbits. After about five days the recipients began to pass protein and casts in their urine, to an extent depending on the dose of antiserum injected. Rabbits with mild proteinuria recovered, but a considerable proportion of those with heavy proteinuria went on to develop nephritis which was eventually fatal. The histological changes resembled those in acute and subacute human nephritis. Renal disease has been produced by similar means in rats and dogs, and the general mechanism is now understood in fair detail.

Although antisera prepared against kidney components generally contain antibodies to many distinct antigens, their nephrotoxic properties depend almost completely upon antibody against an antigen present in the glomerular basement membrane. A similar antigen is present in capillary basement membranes in other parts of the body such as the lung, and antisera prepared against other tissues may therefore also be nephrotoxic. When the antiserum (e.g. duck anti-rabbit, rabbit anti-rat, rabbit anti-dog kidney) is injected into the appropriate species of animal there may or may not be evidence of immediate renal damage. Thus the rabbit anti-rat kidney system causes, but the duck anti-rabbit does not cause early haematuria and proteinura. How does this difference occur? Recent experiments stress the role of complement which may conceivably damage the selective permeability of the glomerular basement membrane, much as it damages the red cell membrane in immune lysis (see Chapter Five and Plate 11.5, following p. 468). As in immune haemolysis, IgM antibody is, molecule for molecule, many times more effective than IgG. Furthermore, the initial damage produced by rabbit anti-rat kidney serum is prevented by measures which (temporarily) lower the complement level in the rat. Also a pepsin digested antibody, lacking the Fc piece (Chapter Four) and unable to bind complement, causes much more mild and transient immediate damage to the kidney than does intact antibody. Duck antiserum against rabbit kidney does not produce comparably severe acute renal damage, presumably because it fails to activate rabbit complement. Nevertheless, duck antibody can be shown by immunofluorescent staining to become rapidly attached as a thin deposit on the glomerular basement membrane. For immediate renal damage to occur large amounts of antiglomerular antibody are needed. Examination of the kidney at the height of the proteinuria shows marked infiltration of the glomeruli with polymorphs, which is closely correlated with the activation of complement. A lesser degree of acute damage can nevertheless occur in the absence of polymorph infiltration.

A few days after the injection of heterologous nephrotoxic antibodies, even in amounts far too small to cause acute renal damage, a second process sets in. The recipient has begun to make antibodies against the foreign serum proteins (including the immunoglobulin) and after five or six days enough antibodies appear to react with any circulating foreign immunoglobulin and, more importantly, with that firmly fixed by virtue of its antibody function on the basement membrane. Not only can host antibody be shown to accumulate at this site but complement components also. (Although duck antibody against rabbit tissue does not fix rabbit complement, rabbit antibody against duck proteins does so.) The result is an acute glomerulonephritis. However, because the foreign antibody remains on the glomerular basement membrane for a long time (its half life experimentally being some 4–6 weeks), and host antibodies against it continue to be made, this second process usually progresses to chronic glomerulonephritis, even though initial changes are reversible up to at least a fortnight after onset. The development of the second stage can be prevented if the recipient animal has already been made immunologically tolerant towards the foreign immunoglobulin, or arrested if sufficient doses of immunosuppressive drugs are given to stop the further production of antibody against it.

In the early stages, before secondary changes have occurred, the electron microscope shows that the glomerular basement membrane of such kidneys is thickened rather uniformly along its length on the side towards the endothelial cells. Deposits are not found between the basement membrane and the epithelial cells and there is no disorganization of their foot processes. The endothelial cells actively proliferate and polymorphs are usually present among these. Immunofluorescent staining for autologous immunoglobulin shows a rather heavy uniform linear distribution along the capillary walls (Plate 11.9C, following p. 468).

III. *Auto-immune Experimental Nephritis*

Auto-immunity should properly be included in Chapter Fifteen, but it will be discussed here because glomerulonephritis can be produced experimentally by stimulation of antibody in animals against antigens of their own kidneys. Two distinct processes appear to be involved. One is closely related to the Masugi type nephritis discussed above and involves antibodies against glomerular basement membranes. The other is the counterpart of serum sickness nephritis and involves antibodies against antigens present in the distal segment of the proximal convoluted tubule cells.

Nephritis involving auto-antibodies against glomerular basement membranes was first successfully produced by immunizing sheep with suspensions of purified dog or rat basement membranes in Freund's complete adjuvant. The sheep developed a fulminating extracapillary glomerulonephritis within one to three months. Their plasma did not at the time contain demonstrable auto-antibody against glomeruli, but if both kidneys were removed surgically antibody appeared in the circulation before the sheep died. This antibody could attach not only to the glomeruli of the species from which the immunizing antigen was derived but also to sheep glomeruli. Similar antibody could also be eluted from the glomeruli of the affected sheep. Such antibodies when passively transferred to animals of the same species as the original donors of the tissue used for immunization, or to other sheep, caused nephritis in the recipients. Further studies have been made in a number of mammalian species, and in all of them immunization with heterologous glomerular basement membranes has led to production of similar autobodies against glomerular basement antigens and a similar type of nephritis.

It is interesting that the most effective antigens are derived from species whose glomerular basement membrane antigens are closely similar to but not identical with those of the recipients. Autologous glomeruli or glomeruli from animals of an altogether different order (e.g. frogs, turtles) do not elicit autoantibodies. It seems that in order to act as immunogens at all the antigens must be in some measure different from those of the recipient, but must be sufficiently similar to evoke cross reacting antibodies (see discussion in

Chapter Fifteen, p. 604). However, similarly effective antigenic material can be obtained from concentrated urine both of homologous or heterologous species—implying that it must be continuously released by and passed out from the kidney, probably becoming altered in the process, but that it does not get back into the bloodstream so as to act as an immunogen.

The nephritis caused by autoantibody against glomerular antigen is characterized by the deposition, detectable by immunofluorescence staining, of immunoglobulin and complement in a *smooth linear layer* along the *endothelial* margins of glomerular basement membranes. This immunoglobulin can be shown to be almost entirely specific auto-antibody. The characteristic appearance is shown by Plate 11.10B, following p. 470.

The second form of auto-immune experimental nephritis was originally produced in rats by immunizing them with repeated injections intraperitoneally of rather large amounts of homologous or heterologous kidney tubule tissue in Freund's adjuvant, but was later shown also to be produced by a single injection of less than 1 mg of a partially purified tubule material. The onset of proteinuria occurs 2–3 months after immunization, and the disease is closely akin to certain forms of the nephrotic syndrome in man, with chronic proteinuria, hyperlipaemia and hypoalbuminaemia. Histologically there is a membranous glomerulonephritis, and by immunofluorescent staining immunoglobulin and C′ components are observed in a granular distribution along the glomerular basement membrane. Electron microscopy reveals *lumpy deposits* on the *epithelial* aspects of the basement membranes, characteristic of glomerular damage due to the deposition of circulating antigen–antibody complexes, in contrast to that due to antibody against the glomerular basement membrane itself. The antigen in the deposited complexes has been shown to be antigenically identical with a component normally present in the apex of the cells in the distal portion of the proximal convoluted tubules, and to be of rat origin even when the immunizing antigen is heterologous. This implies that the disease is due to circulating complexes of auto-antibodies with this tubular antigen, which must by some means be liberated into the circulation rather than excreted in the urine.

The significance of these experimental diseases to nephritis in man is discussed below.

Experimental Glomerulonephritis and Streptococcal Antigens

Because of the association between human glomerulonephritis and infection with certain 'nephritogenic' types of streptococci, many attempts have been made to induce nephritis in animals infected with, or injected with, streptococci or their antigenic products. These studies are complicated by the fact that the infections of pharyngeal lymphoid tissues can be reproduced only in primates. However, infection of the respiratory tract of monkeys with nephritogenic human strains has always failed to result in nephritis, although this lesion followed infection with group C streptococci.

In 1954 an important claim was made that rabbits, injected intravenously with filtrates of Type 12 streptococci, developed hypertension at about eight days after the first injection. Some animals showed proteinuria and microscopical haematuria, but glomerular lesions resembling those of human nephritis were not found. After precipitation and concentration of the filtrate material and its injection into monkeys in rather large doses, glomerulonephritis with crescent formation and eventual glomerular fibrosis resulted.

Various groups of workers have examined the effect of growing Type 12 streptococci in the peritoneal cavities of mice and rats inside chambers which allowed free passage of proteins, etc., but were impermeable to cells (this being the nearest practicable experimental means of mimicking human streptococcal tonsillitis in rodents). Although it is agreed that this procedure can result in necrosis of convoluted tubules, only in one experiment, in which the chambers were maintained in rats for 60 days, has it been claimed that glomerular lesions resulted and that streptococcal antigen and rat antibody were found in the lesions.

The results are compatible with the hypothesis that a streptococcal product becomes attached to the glomerulus and damages by virtue of a toxic effect, or that the damage follows a subsequent interaction with antibody against the product. The tubular necrosis which follows the use of streptococci within diffusion chambers appears to be due to streptolysin S, a diffusible exotoxin of streptococci.

Nephritis in Man

In 1836 Richard Bright developed a picture of acute haemorrhagic nephritis which is substantially identical with our present-day concept. He related how a child or an adult who has had scarlatina may suddenly find his urine greatly increased in volume or that it is tinged with blood, that his face is swollen, his ankles oedematous, or his hands puffy. This disease of the kidney, which is associated with streptococcal pharyngitis or scarlatina, does not appear during the height of the infection, when the streptococci are at their greatest abundance, but only after an interval of 10 to 14 days. The comparison of this sequence of events with those in which a dose of foreign serum leads to subsequent serum sickness was made by Bela Schick in the early years of the present century. In 1907 his famous study *Die Nachkrankheiten des Scharlach* reviewed his extensive experience of clinical cases of scarlet fever. Nephritis, endocarditis, arthritis and lymphadenitis were listed as the scarlatinal 'Nachkrankheiten', and the latent period required before their onset was declared to be that period necessary for the production of active sensitization or immunization.

Moreover, the important observation was made that acute nephritis can occur as a part of the syndrome of serum sickness, and therefore it is apparent that other antigens besides those in streptococci can call forth the hypersensitivity involved in the renal damage of acute nephritis. In a few cases, a food or other allergen has been uncovered as the precipitating factor. The case has been described of a man who developed urticaria, increase in blood urea, albuminuria, and other evidence of acute glomerulonephritis when he ate beef protein. Anaphylactoid purpura, which includes often the appearance of patches of urticaria and angioneurotic oedema, painful effusions into joints (Schönlein's disease), and severe abdominal pain (Henoch's purpura) as well as haematuria, also represents a type of immunologically provoked kidney damage. Acute glomerulonephritis, with the sudden onset of proteinuria, haematuria, cardiac failure and oedema may also form part of the clinical picture in systemic lupus erythematosus and polyarteritis nodosa. In all but the last clear evidence for the presence of circulating complexes has been given. In some cases of anaphylactoid purpura the complexes consist of autologous IgM and IgG, the former having the property (for reasons unknown) of behaving as an antibody to native, undenatured, IgG. In systemic lupus erythematosus not only may circulating complexes be present due to autoantibody to endogenous DNA or to nucleoprotein, but such complexes have been shown to be present in large amounts in the affected glomeruli, and are presumably the cause of the renal damage.

Post-streptococcal Nephritis

Obviously the clinical features of acute nephritis form a syndrome which may be associated with disease processes other than those in which hypersensitivity to streptococci occurs. However, the discussion which follows relates specifically to the 'post-streptococcal' clinical syndrome. Recent epidemiological evidence strongly links this syndrome with a pharyngitis due to a few only out of a large number of known serological types of β-haemolytic streptococci. In contrast to rheumatic fever, whose incidence following severe infections is fairly constant, the attack rate of acute glomerulonephritis varies greatly. In some follow-up studies there has been a negligible incidence of nephritis, while in others up to 33 per cent has been recorded. Nephritis may occur in epidemic form. One such epidemic occurred during the war of 1914–18, when about 1000 cases of nephritis appeared among the British troops within a period of six months. The epidemiological data suggest that whereas rheumatic fever may be due to any one of a wide range of streptococcal types, acute nephritis results from infection with a few 'nephritogenic' streptococcal types, of which the most frequently implicated is Type 12, and occasionally Types 4, 1, 49 ('Red Lake') and a few others. However, the attack rate may also vary widely among outbreaks due to the same streptococcal type. Possibly host factors determine such differences; or, alternatively, quantitative differences in nephritogenic activity occur within the single streptococcal type.

It is of considerable interest that acute nephritis appears never to recur in any patient. This contrasts with the situation in rheumatic fever where frequent relapses are usual. Although as a result of streptococcal pharyngitis antibodies are formed against both the extra-cellular (streptolysin O, streptokinase, hyaluronidase, etc.) and the intra-cellular antigens (M and T proteins), only those against the type-specific proteins are likely to be related to the causation of acute nephritis. Such type-specific antibodies to M protein are detected later in the disease than the other antibodies, but according to Lancefield's careful studies may persist in the blood for upwards of twenty years. It is probably significant, in relation to the non-recurrence of acute nephritis, that these antibodies protect against reinfection with the same type of streptococcus. The role of antigen–

antibody interaction in the pathogenesis of the glomerular lesions has been supported by the demonstration by the fluorescent antibody technique that immunoglobulin and C′ components are present at the sites of the glomerular lesions. Since the glomerulus in nephritis is the site of obvious inflammation, with an influx of inflammatory cells including polymorphs, it would of course be expected that exuded serum globulin would increase in such areas. However, the idea that the immunoglobulin at the site of the glomerular lesion is antibody has been strengthened by showing that it could be eluted from the glomerulus by the treatment with buffer at pH 3·3 of frozen sections of kidney from patients. This is a procedure which causes the dissociation of antigen–antibody complexes. Complement has also been shown, with the aid of a fluorescein-labelled antibody to a component of human complement β_{1C}, to be localized in the glomerular lesions. In a series of renal biopsies taken from cases of acute post-streptococcal glomerulonephritis evidence was obtained for the presence of Type 12 streptococcal products in at least 6 of 10 cases in which it was sought.

Levels of circulating haemolytic complement are almost always found to be low in acute glomerulonephritis. This is apparently not due to loss of complement in the urine, and could, in part at least, result from fixation of complement at such lesions. A very low initial level and the persistent depression of complement have been found to correspond to a poor prognosis, but the interpretation of serum complement levels is too uncertain to predict the outcome of the acute attack.

In recent years renal biopsy has made it possible to demonstrate both the earliest changes that occur in acute nephritis and the relation between such changes and the subsequent clinical course. In the acute phase the glomeruli contain many more cells than usual, and the capillaries appear compressed and devoid of blood. It has been shown that these changes are the result of hyperplasia and hypertrophy of the capillary endothelial cells, and cellular infiltration of the intercapillary space—presumably due to the irritant effect of antigen–antibody combination in the region of the glomerular basement membrane, which may be visibly thickened. In contrast to chronic nephritis there is little change in the glomerular epithelial cells except for some cytoplasmic swelling, and the foot process organization is mostly normal. On account of the glomerular proliferation Bowman's space is often narrowed. Biopsy studies have also emphasized that during a first attack of nephritis the lesions previously considered typical of subacute or chronic glomerular nephritis, such as epithelial crescents and adhesions, can already be present 1 to 3 weeks after onset. Nowadays a patient rarely dies in the acute phase, but when he does so it is usually the result of massive endothelial and epithelial cell proliferation, leading to anuria.

The most obvious changes to be seen in the electron microscope are dense deposits within or on the epithelial side of the basement membrane of the glomeruli. In addition there is generally a diffuse and irregular thickening of the basement membrane, with a loss of epithelial cell foot processes and the swelling of endothelial cells. Immunofluorescence staining reveals that human immunoglobulin and C′ components are present in a typically irregular and granular fashion (Plate 11.10A). This picture is highly reminiscent of experimental disease due to deposition of antigen–antibody complexes, such as that found in the kidneys of rabbits with chronic serum sickness described previously.

It is sometimes held that post-streptococcal nephritis is a self-limiting disease which does not lead to chronic nephritis, whereas perhaps a more usual view is that, after clinical subsidence of the acute attack, proteinuria may persist for 10 to 30 years before renal insufficiency and finally death in uraemia develop. Careful studies conducted 20 years ago showed that in this country renal failure occurred in 8 per cent of cases. In a large series studied in the U.S.A. no such long term consequences were noted, but the observations were mainly based on epidemics of Type 12 post-streptococcal nephritis in military recruits and schoolchildren, and it is probable that these represented a group with less severe original glomerulonephritis than any hospital series.

Subacute Nephritis

The production was described above of experimental glomerulonephritis due to auto-antibodies against glomerular basement membranes. Such antibodies would only be detectable in the serum when more were being produced than could become attached to the animal's own glomeruli, i.e. in a condition of gross over-production. The possibility obviously arises that disease could be due to such antibodies, without evidence of their presence being obtained by examination of the serum. In about one-third of cases of human chronic or subacute glomerulonephritis, of the kind in which renal transplantation is considered as a therapeutic measure, immunofluorescent staining for human immunoglobulin reveals that this is deposited in a linear (as opposed to irregular) fashion along the glomeruli, such as to suggest the presence of antibody against basement membrane (Plate 11.10B, following p. 470). One such subject has been studied who was prepared for a renal transplantation by removal of his diseased kidneys; after their removal antibody against glomerular basement membrane became demonstrable in his serum; and the normal kidney which was then transplanted ceased to function after a few days and on removal was found to contain human immunoglobulin attached to the glomeruli. From it antibody was extracted by dissociation at acid pH, and the extracted antibody was injected into a small squirrel monkey in which it caused lethal acute nephritis. This case provides a somewhat dramatic proof of the production of auto-antibody against glomerular basement membrane in man, and of the ability of such antibody to cross react with glomeruli of monkeys. It is a reasonable inference that under certain circumstances, which have not been defined, but probably involve some form of transient renal damage, human beings may—like experimental animals—form auto-antibodies against glomerular antigens and that these result in chronic subacute glomerulonephritis. If this is the case, it seems reasonable to suppose that one possible form of such transient renal damage is acute post-streptococcal nephritis.

RHEUMATIC FEVER

Rheumatic fever is another disease which occurs as a delayed complication of focal infection with Group A β-haemolytic streptococci, especially pharyngitis or tonsillitis. The story usually is that a child recovered from the acute infection and was well for one to three weeks; it then developed rheumatic fever, with fever, carditis and polyarthritis, and less commonly subcutaneous nodules, erythematous rashes or chorea. The pathological changes are destructive changes in heart and blood-vessel walls. The basic lesion is the Aschoff body, the essential components of which are still debatable. It is seen in its most typical form as a microscopical granuloma adjacent to small vessels in the myocardium. The subcutaneous nodule, which is large enough to be easily palpable, is usually considered to represent the same process, possibly an aggregate of small lesions.

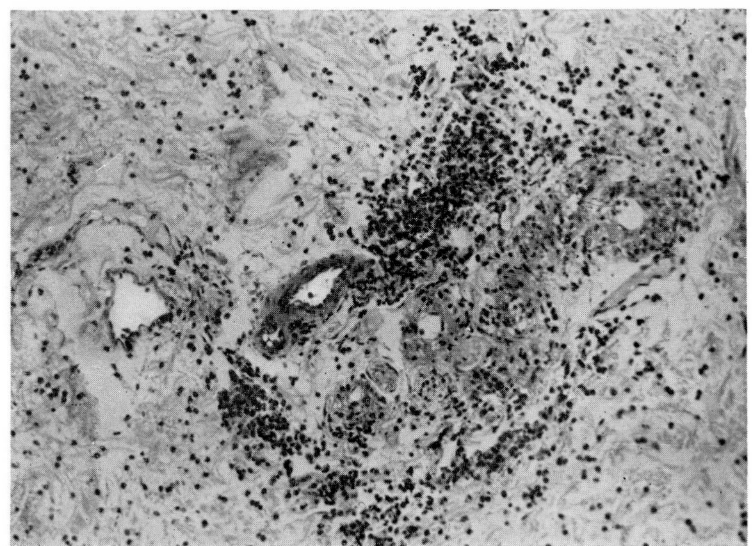

PLATE 11.4. Early mild Arthus response in rabbit, 6 hours after injection of 1 mg of bovine serum albumin into a sensitized animal. Dermal vessels surrounded by polymorphs. The cellular infiltration is greatest around venules. (× 200).

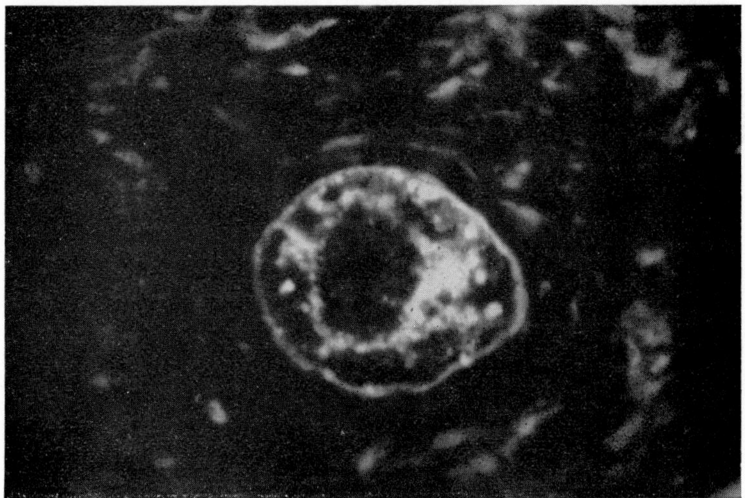

PLATE 11.5. Fluorescence micrograph. Arteriole in the skin of a guinea-pig showing the presence of antigen-antibody aggregates within the vessel wall. In this case antibody had been injected into the skin at this site 24 hours previously, and fluorescein-labelled antigen was injected intravenously, 30 minutes before death. (× 750).

[From a preparation by Dr. J. Oort.]

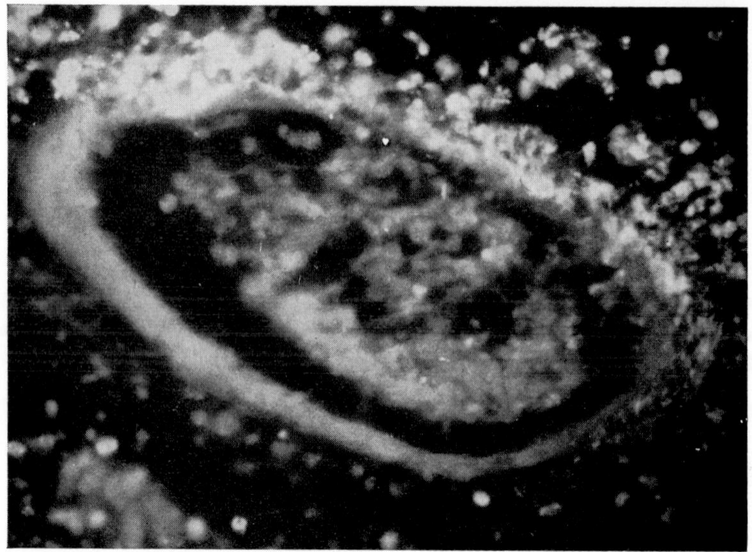

PLATE 11.6. Fluorescence micrograph. Later stage of lesion illustrated in Plate 11.5. Venule at 3 hours showing antigen-antibody complexes within lumen and within the wall. The upper segment of the vessel wall is infiltrated with polymorphs which have taken up fluorescein-labelled antigen-antibody complexes.

[From a preparation by Dr. J. Oort.] (×800).

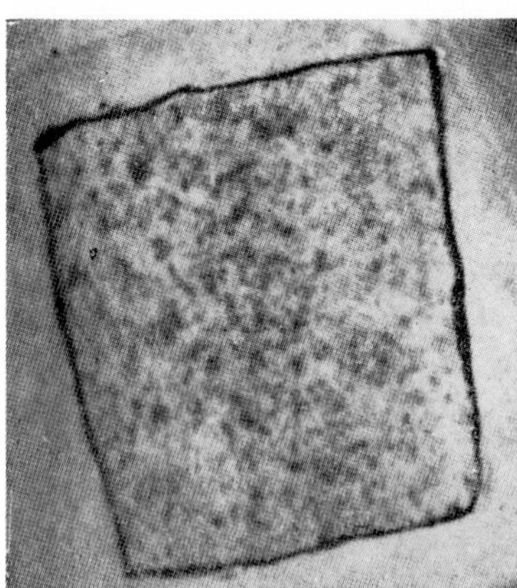

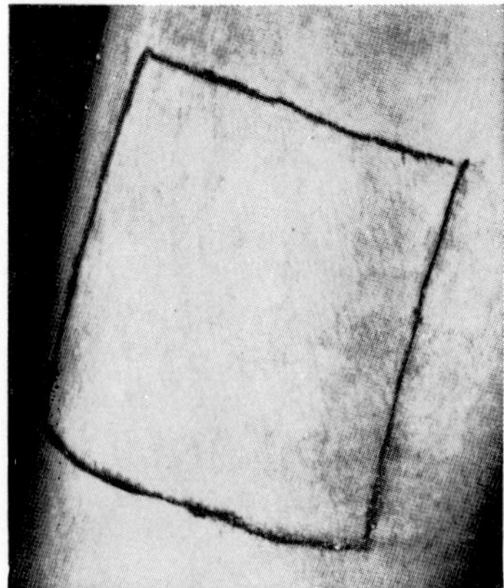

PLATE 11.7. A. Petechial haemorrhages in the skin at the site of application of a patch test with Sedormid in propylene glycol to a patient sensitized with this drug. B. Control patch test.

[From Ackroyd J. F. (1949) *Clin. Sci.* **7,** 249.]

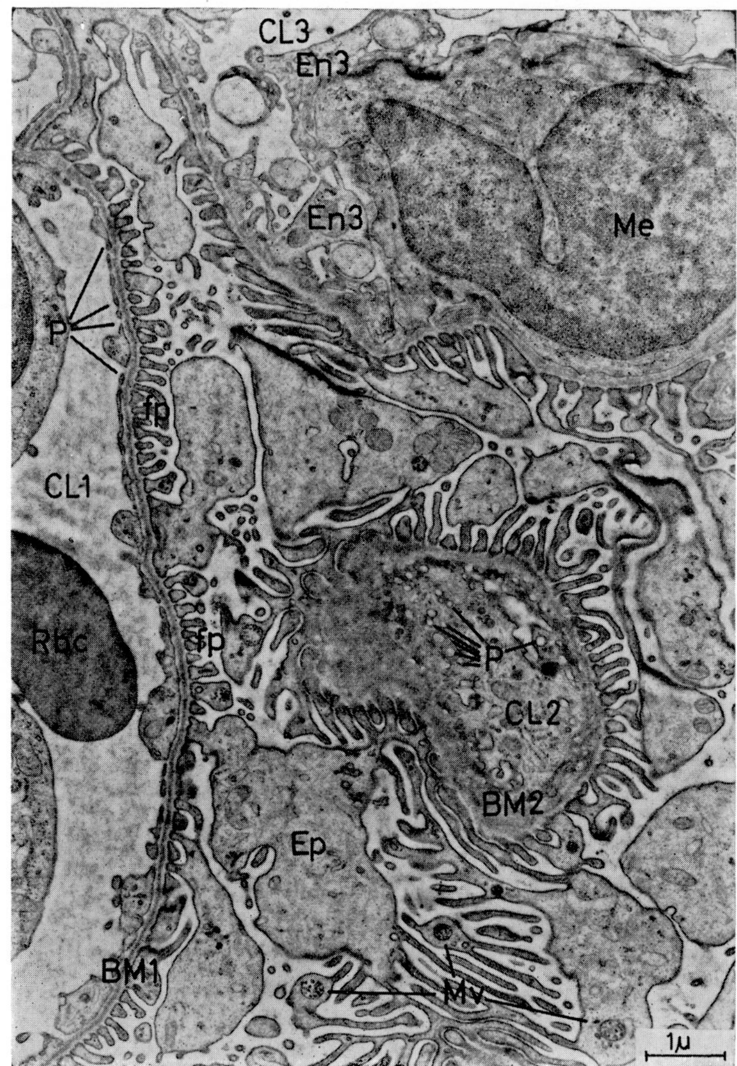

PLATE 11.8A. Portion of a glomerulus from a normal rabbit. To the lett is a patent capillary loop (CL1) with a wall composed of thin endothelium fenestrated (P), a basement membrane of constant thickness (BM), and foot processes (fp) illustrating the range of variation in size and shape within a normal glomerular loop. CL2 is another loop cut at its tip and thereby revealing the arrangement of fenestrae (P) in the endothelial lining film. The basement membrane (BM2) is variable in width because it has been cut tangentially. A third loop (CL3) shows endothelial cytoplasm (En3) covering a mesangial cell (Me). Other abbreviations: Rbc = erythrocyte; MV = multivesicular body; EP = epithelium. (×11,040).

[Electron micrograph by Dr. J. D. Feldman.]

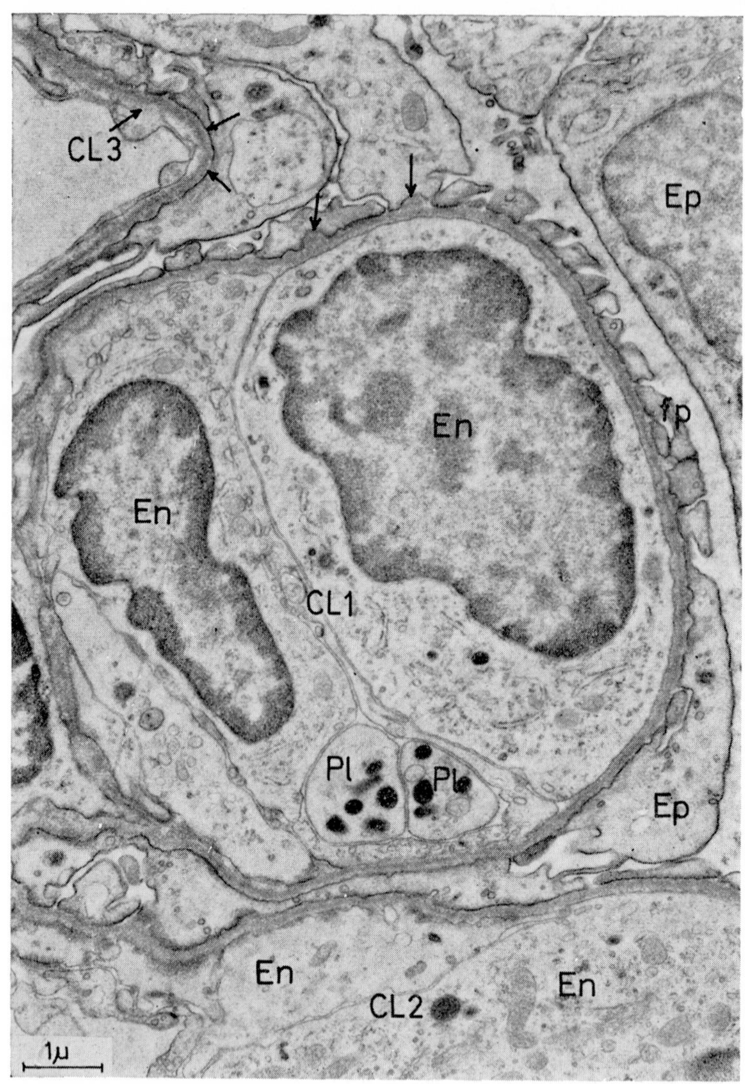

PLATE 11.8B. Parts of three glomerular loops from a rabbit with early serum sickness elicited by one large injection of BSA. The central loop (CL1) is completely occluded by two swollen endothelial cells (En) and two platelets (P1). The lower loop (CL2) also is filled with swollen endothelial cytoplasm (En). The upper loop (CL3) is here empty and patent. However, its basement membrane is frayed (arrows) and there are also alterations of the basement membrane of CL1 (arrows). Foot processes are somewhat broadened and perhaps even smeared in one or two loci. (×10,880).

[Electron micrograph by Dr. J. D. Feldman.]

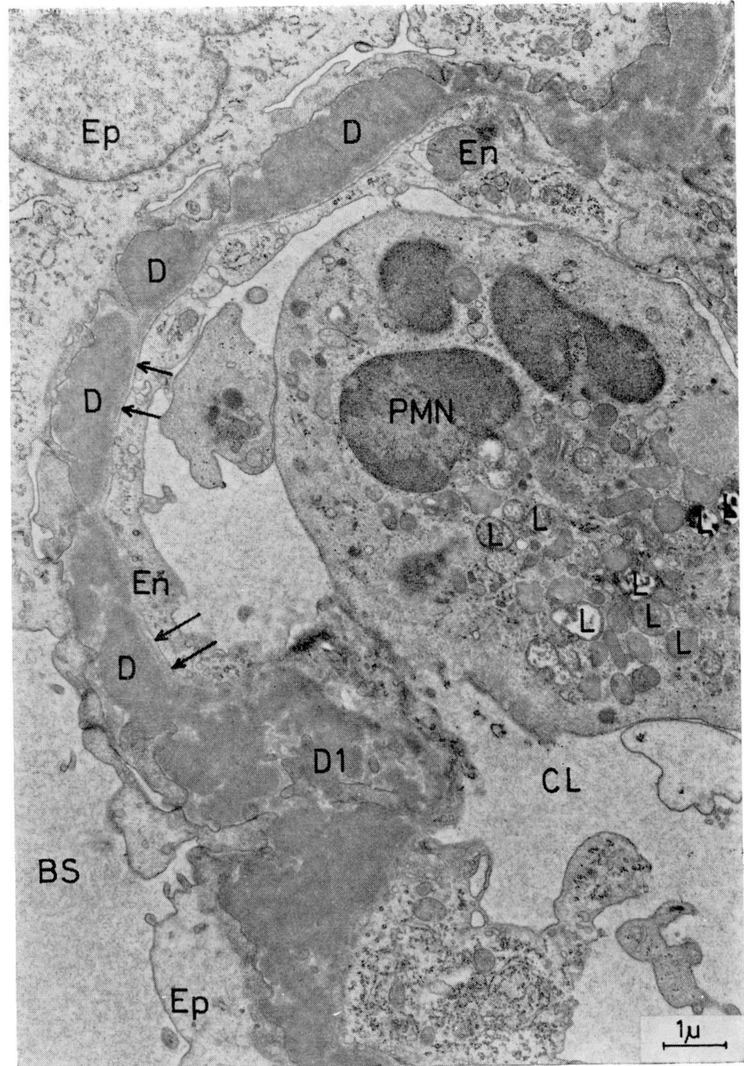

PLATE 11.8C. Part of a glomerular loop from a rabbit injected daily for several months with BSA. The most striking change is the presence of dense deposits (D) protruding from or in the basement membrane beneath epithelium (Ep). At arrows remnants of the original basement membrane are still visible. At D1 the basement membrane, with its dense deposits, is wrinkled and folded in, signifying beginning collapse of the loop. Accompanying these alterations are the loss of foot processes and the absence of fenestrae in somewhat swollen endothelium. A polymorphonuclear leukocyte (PMN) occupies the lumen (CL) of the loop. Within its cytoplasm are granules (L) in varying stages of degranulation or enlargement (i.e. lysosomes). Other abbreviations: BS = Bowman's Space. (×8,400).

[Electron micrograph by Dr. J. D. Feldman.]

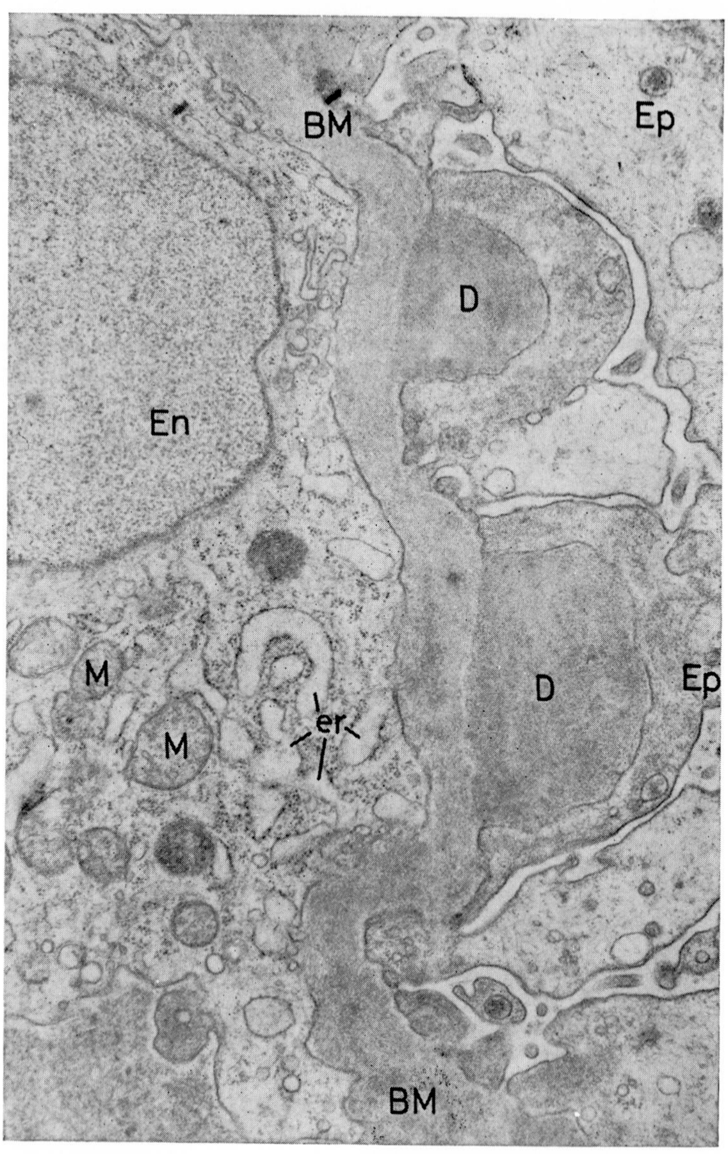

PLATE 11.8D. Part of a glomerulus from a case of human lupus nephritis, showing two large deposits on the epithelial side of the basement membrane from a small capillary loop. Around these deposits there are no epithelial foot processes but, instead, a continuous sheet of epithelial cytoplasm. Within the lumen the endothelial cytoplasm is swollen. [Abbreviations as in Plates 9.8a, 9.8b and 9.8c.] (Magnification about 17,500 times.)

[Electron micrograph from Dr Stanley M. Kurtz.]

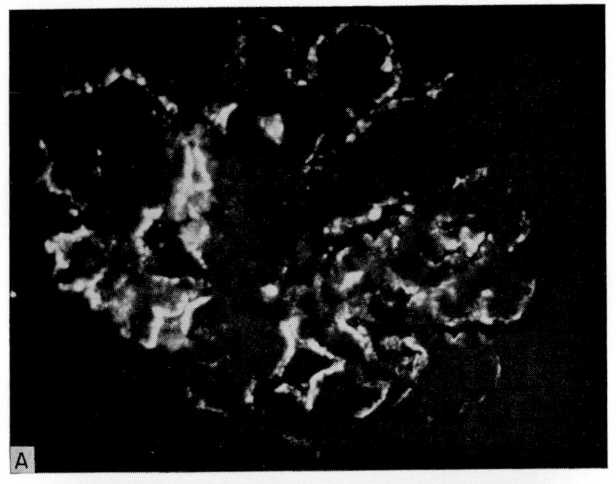

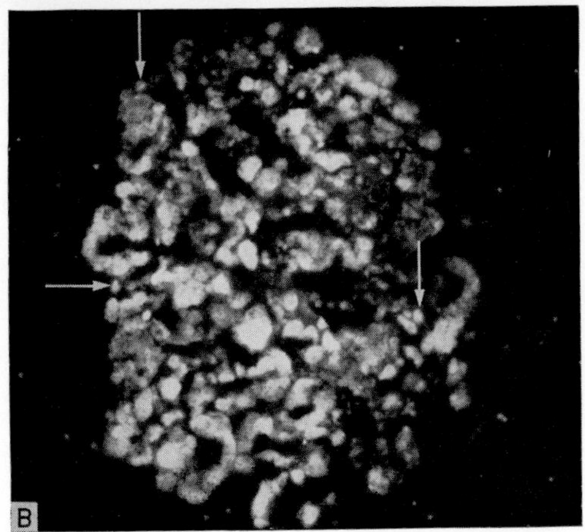

Experimental glomerulonephritis

PLATE 11.9A. Fluorescence micrograph of a glomerulus from a rabbit developing acute serum sickness nephritis after injection of bovine serum albumin. The injected antigen is distributed in a granular pattern along the capillary walls. Similar distribution was also noted when sections were stained for rabbit immunoglobulin and β_{1C} globulin (C′3).

A similar picture is seen in section from kidneys of patients with acute post-streptococcal nephritis, stained to reveal human immunoglobulin or C′.

B. Fluorescence micrograph of a glomerulus from a rabbit with chronic glomerulonephritis induced by repeated injections of bovine serum albumin. Section was stained with fluorescent antiserum to bovine serum albumin. Bovine albumin, rabbit immunoglobulin and C′3 are localized similarly as heavy granular deposits (arrows) along the capillary walls.

A similar picture is seen in sections from some cases of human chronic glomerulonephritis stained to reveal human immunoglobulin or C′. [See Plate 11.10A.]

C. (*overleaf*).

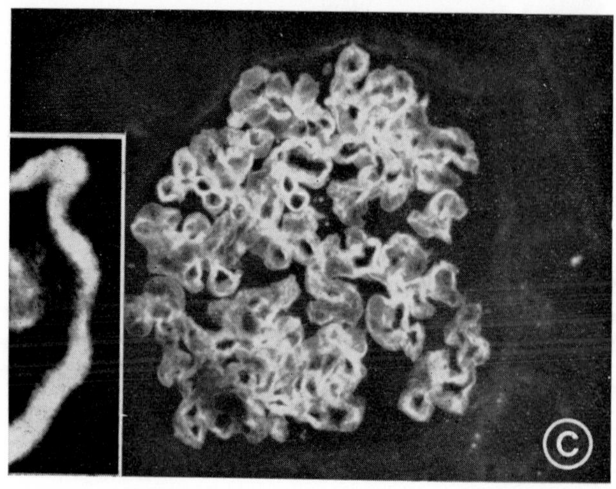

PLATE 11.9C. Fluorescence micrograph of a glomerulus from a rat with nephrotoxic (Masugi) nephritis, 30 days after injection of rabbit nephrotoxic antibody. Section was stained with fluorescent antiserum to rat immunoglobulin. Note the uniform linear distribution of autologous immunoglobulin along the capillary walls. Inset shown at higher power is from a glomerular capillary wall of similar rat but stained for rabbit immunoglobulin. A similar linear localization is seen.

An identical distribution of human immunoglobulin is found in human subacute glomerulonephritis (see Plate 11.10B).

[Illustrations for A-C from Unanue, E.R. and Dixon, F. J. *Experimental Glomerulonephritis* in Advances in Immunology, Vol. 6. 1967.]

PLATE 11.10. (*facing*). Immunofluorescence studies of human renal glomeruli from cases of nephritis. The tissue sections are stained to reveal human immunoglobulin.

A. From a case of chronic glomerulonephritis in an adult. Immunoglobulin is distributed in a granular fashion along the capillary walls, typical of antigen-antibody complexes. The eluted antibody did not attach to glomerular basement membrane.

A similar distribution of immunoglobulin is seen in cases of systemic lupus erythematosus.

From F. J. Dixon (unpublished).

B. From a case of Goodpasture's syndrome (pulmonary haemorrhage with subacute glomerulonephritis). The smooth linear distribution of immunoglobulin is due to the presence of auto-antibody against the glomerular basement membrane. (This antibody, after elution from the kidney, proved to be neophrotoxic in a monkey.)

[From F. J. Dixon., *J. exp. Med.* **126,** 989, 1967.]

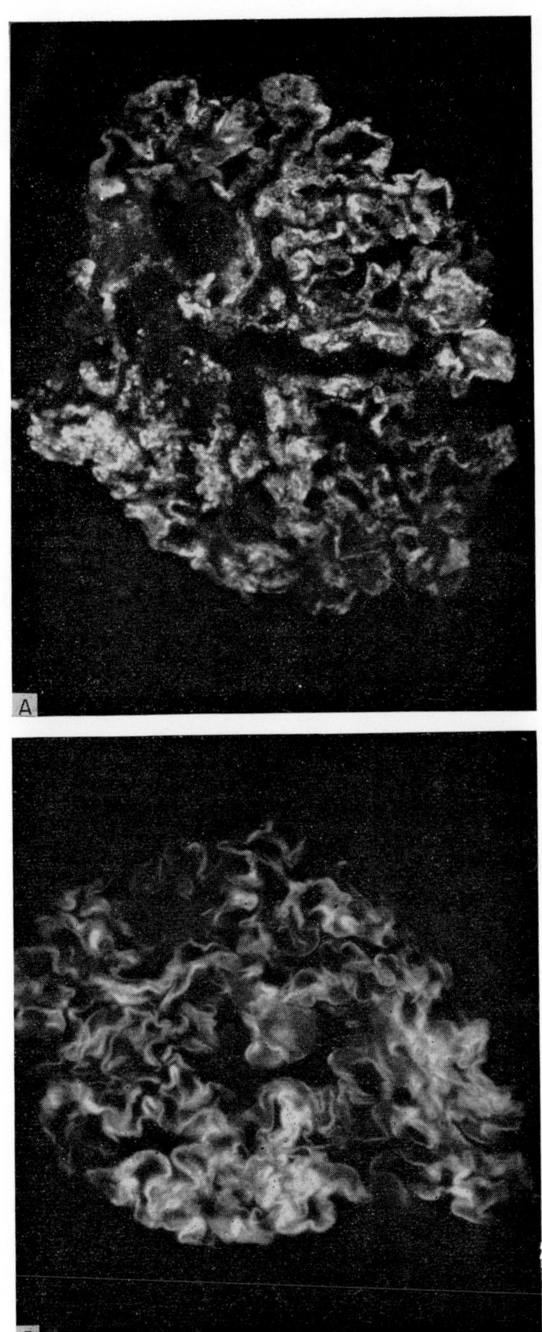

PLATE 11.10. (*Caption facing*).

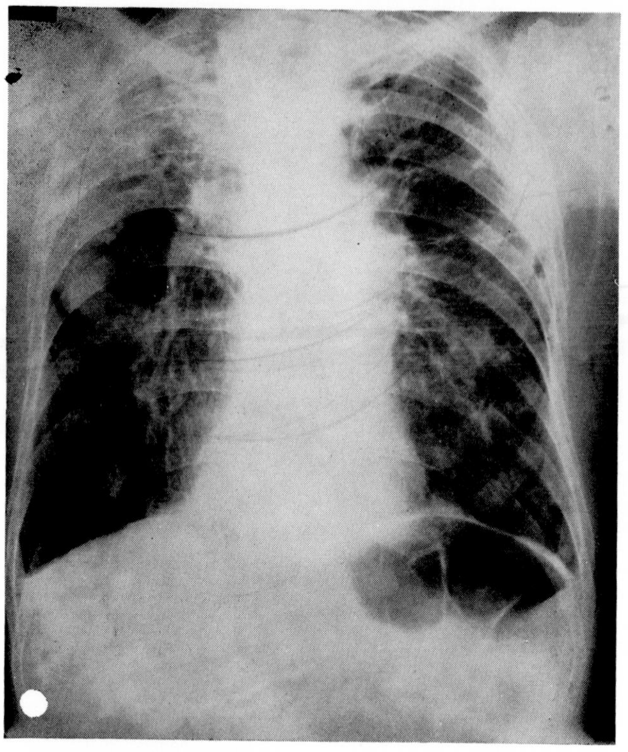

PLATE 11.11. Antero-posterior chest x-ray from acute case of farmer's lung syndrome. Diffuse fine mottling over whole of both lung fields with increase in hilar shadow.

[Photograph provided by Dr. R. M. E. Seal.]

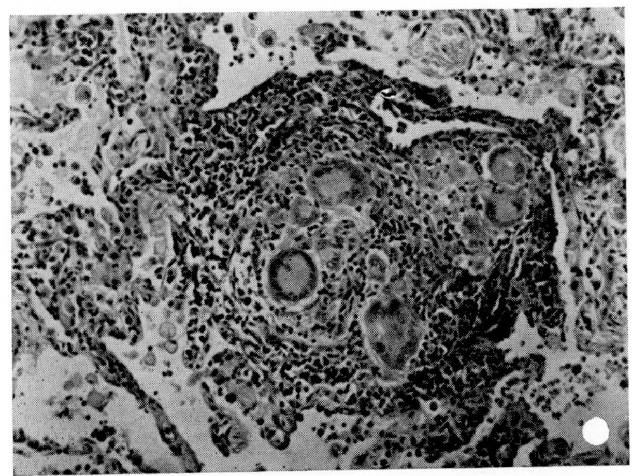

Plate 11.12. Histology from an acute case of farmer's lung syndrome. Note the epithelioid and giant cell granuloma in the wall between two alveoli (H and E stain).

[Preparation provided by Dr. R. M. E. Seal.]

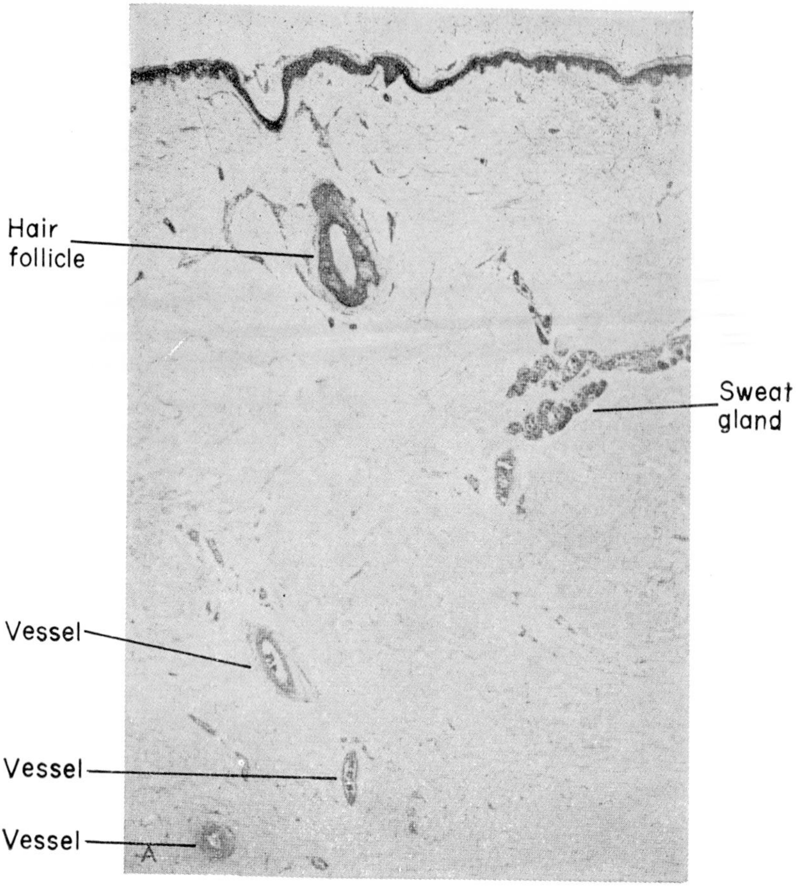

Hair follicle

Sweat gland

Vessel

Vessel

Vessel

A

Plate 12.1a.

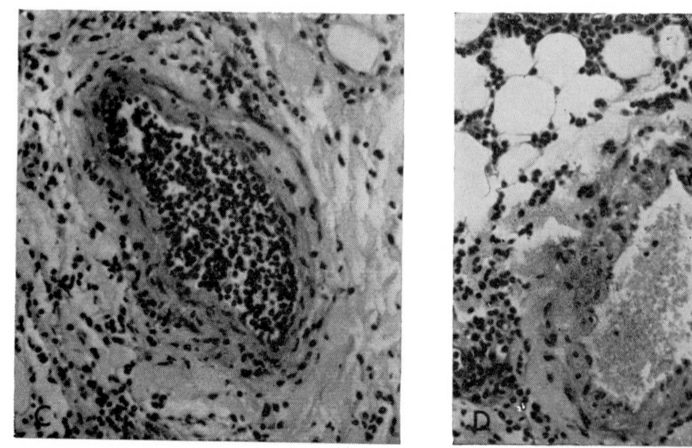

Plate 12.1c.

Plate 12.1d.

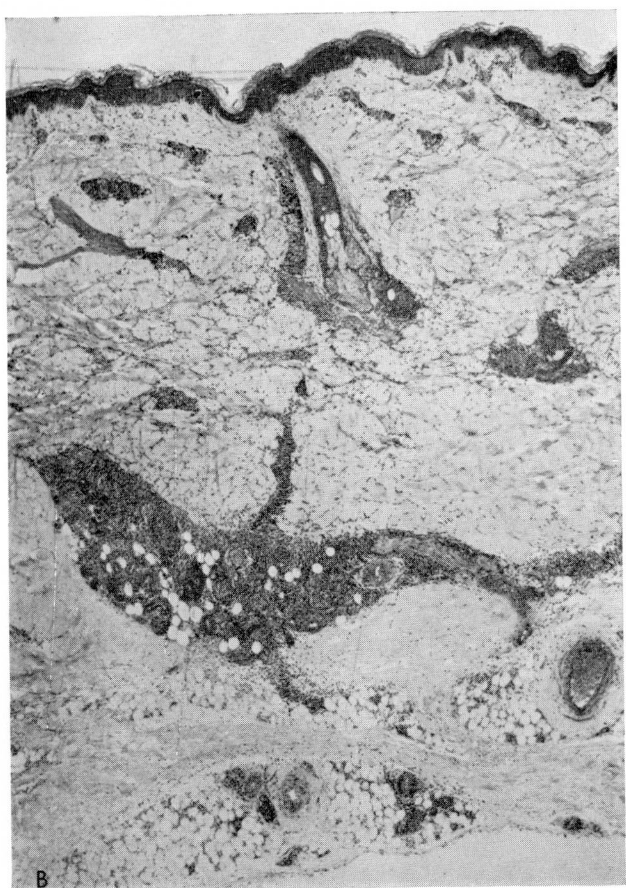

PLATE 12.1B.

A. Skin from tuberculin-negative human subject inoculated 48 hours previously with 100 units PPD. The skin is essentially normal and shows the usual distribution of hair follicles, sweat glands and blood vessels. (× 30).

B. Skin from tuberculin-sensitive human subject inoculated 48 hours previously with 10 units PPD. Hair follicles, sweat and sebaceous glands, and blood vessels are embedded in a dense infiltrate of mononuclear cells. Mononuclear cells are abundant between the collagen fibres of the hypodermis, in the fat and around the blood vessels. (× 34).

C. Venule in deep plexus packed with mononuclear cells—mainly small lymphocytes. There are also many extravascular lymphocytes. (× 163).

D. Corresponding arteriole: white cells are virtually absent from the lumen but are abundant in the neighbouring fatty tissue. (× 173).

[Preparations kindly provided by Dr. J. S. F. Niven.]

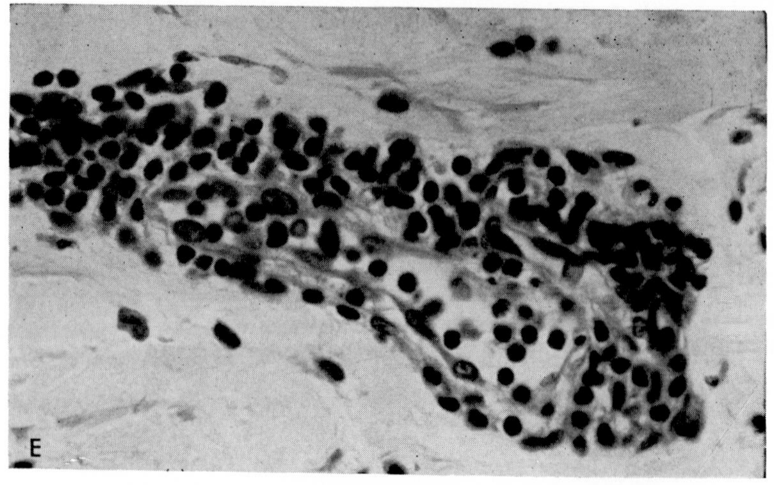

PLATE 12.1E.

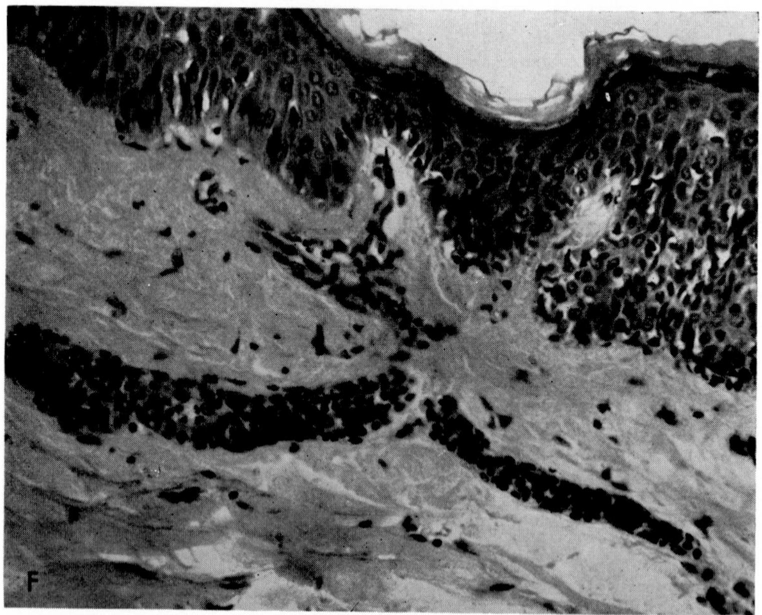

PLATE 12.1F.

E. Capillary in the dermis with swollen endothelial lining cells, and lymphocytes in the lumin, some of which are passing into the subintimal space and through the basement membrane. (×547).

F. Squamous epithelium showing oedema of the Malpighian layer and capillaries in the dermis stuffed with lymphocytes, some of which have migrated through the vessel wall. (×259).

[B, C, D, E and F are taken from the same subject.]

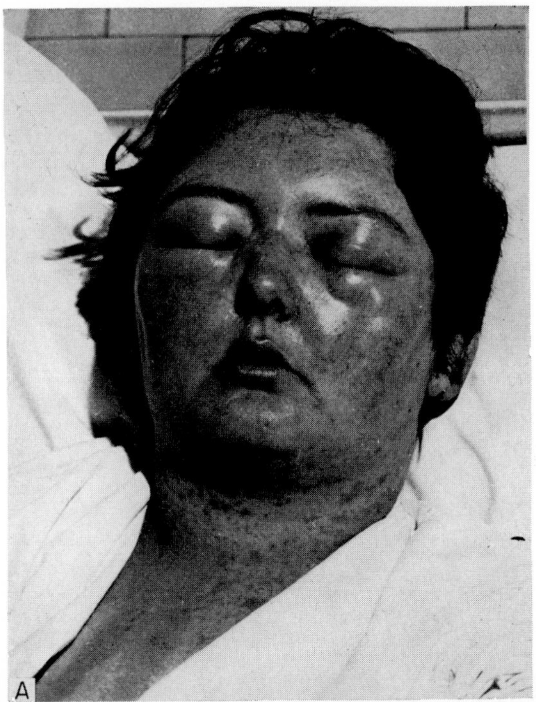

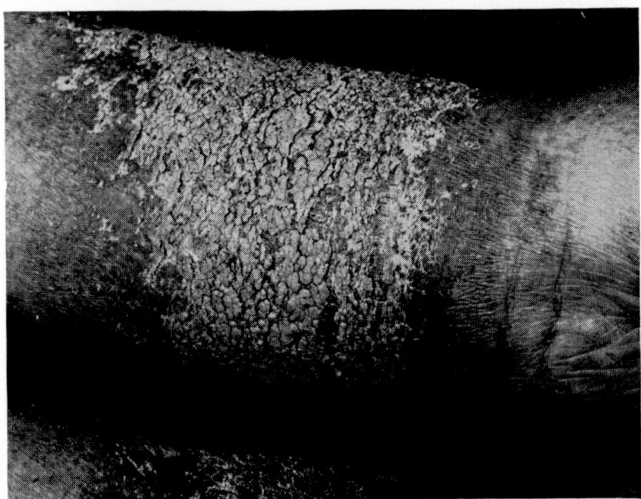

Plate 12.2 Contact dermatitis.

A. Patient in acute phase of dermatitis of face due to the use of a hair dye containing paraphenylene diamine. *Note* the confluent erythematous macular rash which follows the trickle of hair dye down the front of the upper chest. This resolved rapidly on treatment with cortisone.

B. Contact sensitivity to dye in a wrist watch strap. Chronic lesion at the stage of exfoliative keratitis.

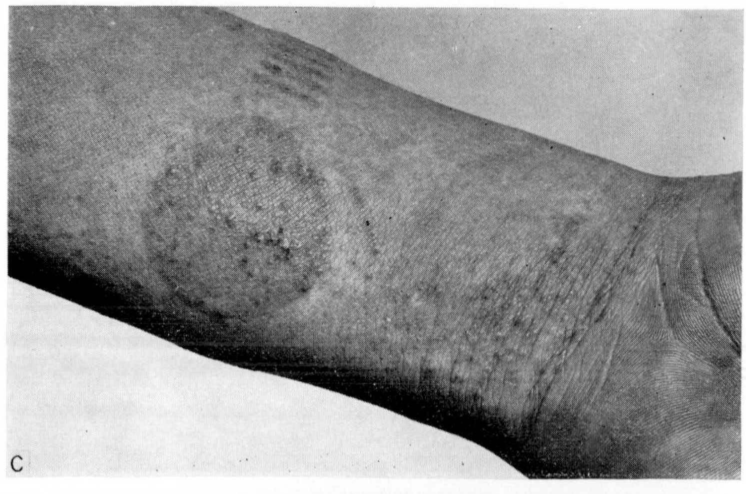

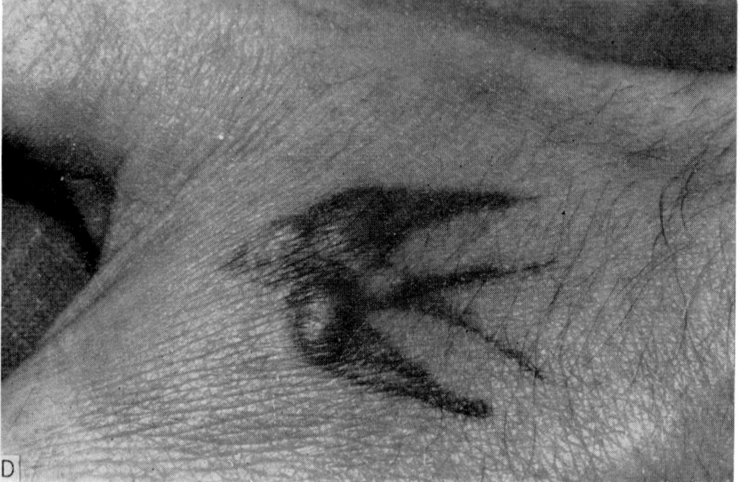

C. Nickel dermatitis. Area of papular erythema which corresponds with the contact area of the back and metal band of a wrist watch.

D. Mercury dermatitis. This person's tattoo showed no abnormality until he became sensitized to the mercury in a tooth stopping. Two months later the red area of his tattoo which contained cinnabar (mercuric sulphide) became the site of itching vesicles. The same patient on another occasion gave a local reaction after an injection of tetanus toxoid which contained thiomersalate (organic mercury derivative).

[Photographs a, b, c, were provided by Dr. J. A. Milne of Glasgow. Photograph d was provided by Dr. J. S. Comaish of Newcastle.]

A view which has prevailed widely in the past was that the Aschoff body represented a focus of collagen degeneration with surrounding cellular reaction of myocardial histiocytes. There is no evidence that β-haemolytic streptococci can ever be isolated from such lesions, which cannot, therefore, result from direct microbial action. Three alternative hypotheses are, first, that they arise from some form of hypersensitivity and thus may be analogous to the para-vascular lesions of serum sickness; secondly that they result from a direct effect of toxins (e.g. streptolysin O or S) which diffuse from the primary infective focus, and thirdly, that they are a consequence of auto-immunity.

Evidence strongly suggesting a hypersensitivity process was obtained by Murphy and Swift, who induced Aschoff-like cardiac lesions in a small proportion of rabbits injected repeatedly in their skin with a variety of *different* immunological types of Group A streptococci. Since immunity to Group A streptococci is type-specific, and depends mainly on antibodies against the M protein, repeated natural infections of man would be expected to involve a different type in each recurrence, and indeed the epidemiological evidence from human sources strongly supports this view. The myocardial lesions resulting in the experimental rabbits closely resemble Aschoff bodies, but the careful study of Murphy leaves no doubt that they are the result of focal muscle-fibre necrosis. Murphy's view is that the typical Aschoff nodule in man similarly contains injured muscle fibres. His histological studies clearly established the fact of the occurrence of focal lesions of the myofibrils in the heart in human rheumatic fever, and this fact considerably helps in the understanding of the way cardiac failure can supervene in acute rheumatic fever. However, it is difficult to see how the Aschoff nodules can occur by this process in the centres of the cusps of the mitral valve or aortic valves which are devoid of such muscle fibres.

The principal systematic studies relating acute streptococcal disease and rheumatic fever were made in the United States among the recruits at Warren Air Force Base, and established that acute rheumatism followed throat infection with Group A streptococci in 3 per cent of cases. In this respect rheumatic fever is quite unlike acute glomerulonephritis, the incidence of which relative to streptococcal infection varies markedly from one geographical region to another and is apparently dependent upon infection with a few selected streptococcal M-types of organism. Also, unlike acute glomerulonephritis, rheumatic fever often recurs with further streptococcal infections. Recurrence can follow infection with any Group A streptococcus, and hence can be provoked successively by organisms which contain differing M antigenic proteins.

An important observation which supports the relation between streptococcal infection and acute rheumatism is that chemotherapy of the infection greatly reduces the incidence of this complication. Penicillin administered early in the course of an acute streptococcal throat infection eliminates Group A streptococci from the throat and also suppresses the subsequent rise of antibody. Indeed, on the basis of these findings American observers recommended that all patients with streptococcal pharyngitis should be given a ten-day course of penicillin in order to prevent rheumatic fever. This recommendation has not, however, been widely adopted since firstly, a doubt exists whether the incidence of this complication generally is as high as 3 per cent, and secondly, the suppression of antibody response consequent upon rapid elimination of organisms from the tissues renders the patient liable to reinfection with the same type of streptococcus. However, in subjects who have already had an attack of rheumatic fever, prophylactic chemotherapy with sulphonamides or antibiotics so as to prevent further streptococcal infections is a recommended precaution.

The antigenic component of the streptococcus responsible for giving rise to the hypersensitivity is unknown. Since different types of streptococci can provoke a rheumatic fever relapse, hypersensitivity to the M- and T-type specific antigens cannot be responsible. On account of the large number of antigenic components which are described in streptococci the analysis of the antigens responsible for the hypersensitivity presents a formidable problem. Many different antibodies against streptococcal products appear in the sera of convalescent patients, but those which have been studied to date have proved to be against extra-cellular rather than cellular antigens. Of these, particular stress has been placed on streptolysin O. Antibody to this antigen is almost universally produced *in vivo* during the course of streptococcal infections, including those associated with rheumatic fever. Patients with rheumatic fever tend to have higher antistreptolysin O titres than patients with uncomplicated streptococcal disease. They also tend to reveal higher titres of some other antistreptococcal antibodies (e.g. against streptokinase and streptodornase). In response to non-streptococcal antigens, however, rheumatic patients do not produce more antibody than do non-rheumatic subjects. These data suggest that rheumatic fever does not occur from a genetically determined increase in ability to give an antibody response, but that a more intense antigenic stimulus (determined, for example, by the numbers and communicability of the streptococci in the environment) is responsible for the heightened response. Nevertheless, there is quite strong evidence for a genetic predisposition to develop rheumatic fever, and the factor controlling susceptibility appears to behave as Mendelian recessive character. Its mode of operation is not known, but it is thought probably to relate to the nature of the tissue reaction evoked by chronic streptococcal infection. Children with rheumatic fever and their immediate relatives have been found to give a history of apparently unrelated allergic symptoms (hay fever, asthma, vasomotor rhinitis, etc.) in 64 per cent, compared with 18 per cent in a comparable control group.

The hypothesis that the lesions of rheumatic fever result from auto-immunity is discussed in Chapter Fifteen. It may be summarized here by stating that auto-antibodies against heart components can certainly be produced as a consequence of damage to the heart (e.g. following coronary infarction or open heart operations), but there is no evidence that in such cases they cause significant further damage, and they may rather be regarded as the result of liberation into the circulation of antigens normally concealed in the sarcolemma and subsarcolemmal regions and unavailable to stimulate immunologically competent cells. However, it has also been shown that a number of strains of Group A streptococci contain antigenic material in their cell walls which elicits antibodies in experimental animals and man which cross react with components present in the sarcolemma and subsarcolemmal layer of heart muscle from man, rabbit, guinea-pig and possibly other species. The antigen in question is not related to the protective M antigen, though closely associated with it. Both the streptococcal and the cross-reacting antigens have general properties suggesting that they occur as complexes of lipid, protein and carbohydrate, not unlike the occurrence of blood group and transplantation antigens.

About one-quarter of patients with recent clinical streptococcal infection have been found to have demonstrable antibody to the cross reacting antigen in their serum when tested a few weeks after the infection, even though the great majority suffered no non-suppurative complications. More than half of the patients who suffered such complications, and most patients with inactive rheumatic heart disease, had demonstrable antibody levels. The presence of antibody is evidently not sufficient by itself to cause rheumatic fever. However, in heart tissue obtained from cases of acute rheumatic carditis extensive deposits of bound immunoglobulin have been found by immunofluorescence in the myofibres and vessel walls at the sites where the cross reacting antigen is characteristically located. Such deposits were associated with typical histochemical changes, shown by a purple reaction with periodic acid Schiff stain and metachromasia with toluidine blue, which were so extensive as to suggest that the physiological function of the cardiac myofibres would have been disturbed. Furthermore, bound immunoglobulin is also found in auricular appendage biopsies taken from the great majority of patients with active rheumatic heart disease. Thus there is presumptive evidence that under some additional circumstances the cross reacting antibody does cause damage.

What these circumstances are has not been clearly demonstrated. One possibility is that concomitant delayed type hypersensitivity accentuates or initiates the damage to myofibres and smooth muscle, and may also be the cause of a mononuclear cell infiltration around damaged muscle fibres leading to the formation of Aschoff bodies. Another is that the initial cardiac damage results from a direct toxic action of a streptococcal product. Thus streptolysin O exerts a marked cardiotoxic action on the intact animal, as well as bringing about the rapid lysin of many types of cells *in vitro*, including erythrocytes. Cholesterol is a potent inhibitor of streptolysin-O haemolysis and mice given cholesterol become resistant to streptolysin O. It has been claimed that patients with myxoedema, nephritis and diabetes are refractory to rheumatic fever recurrences, possibly due to their high cholesterol blood levels. Moreover, the use of a diet including egg-yolk products, which leads to increased blood levels of cholesterol, is similarly claimed to protect the subjects of rheumatic fever against recurrences following streptococcal infections. The explanation, however, may not be so simple as this. For example, egg yolk contains substances, one of which has been characterized as N(2-hydroxyethyl) palmitamide, which have a very powerful anti-inflammatory action, and in very small amounts will diminish the intensity of experimental Arthus reactions.

OTHER DISEASES DUE TO IMMEDIATE-TYPE HYPERSENSITIVITY REACTIONS

FARMER'S LUNG SYNDROME AND OTHER DISEASES DEPENDENT ON INHALED ANTIGENS WHICH PROVOKE INTRAPULMONARY ARTHUS-TYPE RESPONSES

Diseases of this group, sometimes referred to as *organic dust diseases*, are characterized by increasing respiratory distress, accompanied by fever and general malaise, brought on by inhalation of dust from mouldy hay (Farmer's lung syndrome), sugar-cane waste (bagassosis), maple bark dust (maple bark stripper's disease), paprika dust (paprika splitter's disease), cotton waste (byssinosis) and the dust of aviaries (pigeon fancier's lung syndrome).

Unlike the sudden rapid development of an asthmatic attack of wheezing and severe respiratory difficulty, the typical acute case of Farmer's lung syndrome develops gradually within 6–8 hours after exposure to dust from mouldy hay. The disease occurs typically among the hill farmers of the wetter, western parts of the British Isles and is associated with the use of hay incompletely dried on the ground and stored with a high moisture content. These storage conditions lead to a fermentative rise in temperature within the hay bales and the predominating growth of thermophilic bacteria: *Thermopolyspora* (*Micromonospora*) *polyspora*. When the farmer works with this mouldy hay during the subsequent winter feeding of animals, often indoors, he becomes exposed to enormous numbers of released bacterial spores, and their accompanying protein and polypeptide antigens.

Examination of the patient during such an acute attack reveals an increased respiratory rate, cyanosis and moist crepitations over the lung bases. These signs correspond with an extensive impairment of the peripheral gas-exchanging tissues due to the presence of disseminated interstitial small granulomata, which may show on the X-ray as a diffuse fine mottling over the lung fields (Plate 11.11). Biopsy reveals such granulomata to be composed of a central collection of epithelioid and giant cells with peripheral lymphocytes (Plate 11.12).

A succession of such attacks throughout several late winter and spring seasons may lead finally to severe chronic disability, with permanent dyspnoea and cough and severe weight loss, due to permanent areas of fibrosis and emphysema in the lungs. Otherwise, at an earlier stage, the withdrawal of patients from exposure to dust of mouldy hay is quickly followed by recovery of pulmonary function.

Unlike the situation in atopic hypersensitivity, the blood of such patients can be shown to contain copious amounts of precipitating antibody to several antigenic components of *T. polyspora* and intradermal injection of saline extracts of the latter yield after about 4 hours typical erythematous lumps corresponding with the onset of an Arthus-type reaction. A proportion (18 per cent in one series) of farmers not suffering from disease can also show precipitins. The complement-fixation test can also be used for diagnosis.

The recently recognized clinical syndrome which occurs in bird fanciers (e.g. pigeon keepers, budgerigar breeders) appears to have a similar aetiology. In these instances the causative agent is dust containing dried bird dung, and the antibodies elicited have been found to be mainly directed against serum proteins, especially albumin, of the species of bird involved.

Precipitin antibodies have also been demonstrated to the appropriate antigen in the sera of patients with bagassosis, and maple stripper's disease (in which the important provoking antigen is the fungus *Coniosporium corticale*).

An interesting iatrogenic variant of this type of disease has also been described as a reaction to inhaled dried porcine or bovine pituitary tissue used for the treatment of diabetes insipida and referred to as 'pituitary snuff-taker's disease'.

IMMEDIATE-TYPE HYPERSENSITIVITY REACTIONS DUE TO DRUGS

As has already been mentioned in Chapter Six, a number of drugs are capable, either without change or after modification in the body, of combining chemically with tissue or plasma proteins to form antigenic proteins whose serological specificity is determined by the attached group. A good example is benzylpenicillin which spontaneously breaks down under slightly acid conditions to form a number of highly reactive compounds such as *benzylpenicillenic acid*. This can react directly with the terminal amino groups of lysine on the proteins to form a conjugate of the type protein-lysyl-α-amide of benzylpenicilloic acid. It can also react after further degradation to form a mixed disulphide of penicillamine *via* the S—H groups of the amino acid cysteine present in the proteins.

Such compounds, formed with their own plasma proteins, have been shown to be quite powerful antigens in experimental animals, and to stimulate antibodies against the attached penicillin derivatives. Both anaphylactic and serum sickness type of reactions may occur on administering penicillin to persons who have previously had penicillin parenterally, and the serum of virtually all persons who exhibit such reactions has been shown to contain antibodies specific for benzylpenicilloyl determinants. The obvious explanation, though it has not been strictly proved, is that sensitization has been due to penicillin–protein conjugates. Persons who have received penicillin treatment without exhibiting allergic reactions are also liable to have antibodies against penicillin but the levels are usually lower. IgM antibodies are the most commonly detected, but IgG (and possibly IgA) as well as reaginic antibodies are also formed. It will be the patient who has reaginic antibodies who is liable to an anaphylactic reaction on repeated contact with penicillin (unless protected by the simultaneous presence of sufficient blocking antibodies—see p. 446). The patient with high levels of IgM or IgG antibodies is more liable to the serum sickness type of manifestations, such as rashes and arthralgia, when sufficient penicillin–protein conjugate is present to allow the accumulation of circulating antigen–antibody complexes.

Apart from direct tests for the presence of anti-penicilloyl antibodies in the serum—which can be made by haemagglutination of penicillin-coated erythrocytes—sensitization can be detected by injecting into the skin small amounts of penicilloic acid conjugated to synthetic polypeptides, chosen to avoid the additional complication of introducing a foreign protein. Persons sensitized to penicilloyl determinants show local immediate or delayed-type responses.

Recent observations using various semi-synthetic penicillins, all of which contain the common nucleus 6-aminopenicillanic acid though they do not all have the complete benzylpenicilloyl determinant, have indicated that traces of highly immunogenic contaminating materials are commonly present in commercial preparations of all penicillins, even though these are already highly purified. One such impurity is probably some protein derived from the *Escherichia coli* used as a source of enzyme in the preparation of 6-aminopenicillanic acid, and a second may be a complex derived from the penicillin molecule by polymerization on storage in solution. Thus not all the immunological activity of penicillins is due to the formation of penicilloylated protein. Some subjects, who showed anaphylactic reactions to the parent penicillin (but not to a skin test antigen such as the benzylpenicilloyl polypeptide conjugate mentioned above) gave no reaction to penicillin when these impurities had been specially removed. It appears, however, that in the large majority of cases sensitization is against penicilloyl proteins and is due to mechanisms of the type outlined in the previous paragraph.

This example illustrates the general principles which are thought to underlie the development of hypersensitivity to many drugs, although in most instances we do not have so clear an idea of the intermediate chemical steps involved in the formation of drug-protein conjugates. Furthermore, the clinical picture is often complicated by the co-existence of hypersensitivity to the drugs of the delayed type, described in the next chapter, and sometimes by drug-induced destruction of blood cells discussed below.

DRUG-INDUCED PURPURA, AGRANULOCYTOSIS AND ANAEMIA

Certain drugs, notably allyl*iso*propylacetylurea (Sedormid), quinidine, amidopyrine, stibophen and phenolphthalein, occasionally give rise to special types of hypersensitivity reaction, which depend upon the presence of circulating antibodies against determinant groups of the drugs but whose consequence is the destruction of one or more of the formed elements of the blood, leading to purpura, agranulocytosis or haemolytic anaemia. Despite the fact that many people take such drugs, reactions of this kind are very rare. There is no way of predicting which individuals will be susceptible, for there is no evident association with other allergies, nor of foretelling when the syndromes will occur. They never do so within the first week of first taking the drug, but otherwise may happen at any time during prolonged drug therapy or following any one dose if therapy is intermittent. Most often one type of cell is affected in sensitization to a particular drug, for example platelets with Sedormid or quinidine, red cells with stibophen, granulocytes with amidopyrine; but in another individual the same drug may affect a different cell, for example, quinidine haemolytic anaemia or stibophen purpura; very occasionally thrombocytopenia and haemolytic anaemia or leucopenia both occur in response to a single drug in the same person. The cell damage occurs only while the specific drug is present in the body, and when the drug is stopped recovery invariably occurs with no treatment—even though antibody persists. It is likely that the mechanism of cell damage is similar in each case, but since there are some special considerations for each type of cell they will be treated separately.

PURPURA

In the typical case ingestion of the drug is followed within a few hours by destruction of platelets so extensive as to lead to purpura. In such patients application of the drug to the skin also leads to local petechial haemorrhages (Plate 11.7). It was early shown that platelet lysis could be reproduced *in vitro*, and that the following phenomena were obtained:

(1) Patient's serum (fresh) + platelets from the patient *or* a normal person + a dilute solution of the drug, → platelet lysis on incubation at 37°

(2) Normal serum (fresh) + patient's platelets + drug does *not* → platelet lysis

(3) Patient's serum (fresh) + platelets but no drug does *not* → platelet lysis

(4) Patient's serum (heated at 56° for 30 minutes to destroy complement) + platelets + drug does *not* → platelet lysis.

Lysis occurs, however, if fresh normal human or guinea-pig serum is also present as a source of complement.

From these and some subsidiary observations it can be deduced that a sensitive person's serum contains antibody against the drug (not against the platelets themselves) and that antibody and drug have combined on the surface of the platelets in such a way as to activate complement and so damage the platelet membrane. There are two ways in which cell damage might occur, illustrated in Fig. 11.3. According to the pathway, originally favoured, on the left hand side of the figure, at step 1 the drug combines with some cell constituent so as to convert the drug from hapten to a complete antigen; in step 2 antibody combines with the drug-cell complex, and activates complement. This would account for the need for the drug to be present, and for the specificity for the type of cell in question because antibody is directed against a complex of the two. However, there is evidence against the validity of this mechanism. Thus, if cells treated with the drug are washed, the drug is easily removed and no effective complex can be detected. Furthermore, the occasional individual's serum may contain antibodies which will actually form a precipitate on addition of the drug (e.g. Sedormid) and yet the lytic specificity is still for platelets. The alternative mechanism illustrated on the right hand side of Fig. 11.3 is presently regarded as the more probable. In this the immunogen is regarded not as the cell-drug complex but as a complex (or

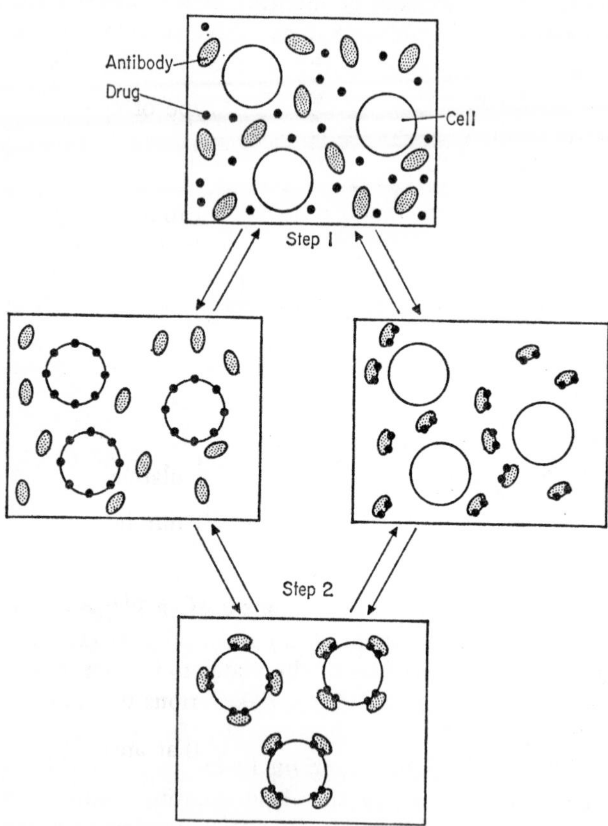

FIG. 11.3. Two possible mechanisms for the first stages of reaction leading to attachment of anti-drug antibodies to cells.

[Modified from Shulman N.R. *et al.*, *Ann. Int. Med.* 1964, **60**, 506]

conjugate) with a soluble plasma protein such as is thought to account for the immunogenicity of penicillin. In stage 1 antibodies against the drug (hapten) form complexes in solution. It is known that such antibodies have high affinities (the association constants being 10^7 to 10^8 litres per mole—see p. 403), sufficient to permit antibody–drug complexes to form despite competition by albumin and other plasma proteins which often bind such drugs in normal serum. In stage 2 the complexes become adsorbed to the cell surface. In the few instances where the affinity of the complex for platelets has been studied it has been found to be comparable to that of the antibody for hapten. The extent to which complement takes part in the adsorption process (which is in fact an example of Immune Adherence—p. 198) is uncertain, but its activation at the surface is responsible for cell lysis.

Even if this mechanism is correct, it remains to be explained why only certain persons manifest an idiosyncrasy towards the drug, and why a particular cell type is involved. Two unproved hypotheses, which are not mutually exclusive, are that some peculiarity in the metabolism of the drug causes highly immunogenic derivatives to arise, and that symptoms only occur when the subject has formed antibodies of unusually high affinity for the drug. In order to account for the involvement of a particular cell it has been suggested that this depends upon some fortuitous property of the drug and antibodies of a particular class. There is some support for this explanation in the finding that in cases of quinidine idiosyncrasy thrombocytopenia is associated with 7S antibodies whereas haemolytic anaemia is associated with 19S antibodies.

Post-transfusion Purpura

This rare disease, which resembles drug-induced purpura in its abrupt onset, fulminant course and complete spontaneous remission, is caused by isoantibody against an antigen in platelets acquired following transfusion. About one week after an otherwise uneventful transfusion acute thrombocytopenia develops and the patient's serum is found to contain antibodies against the donor's but *not* his own platelets. The sequestration and destruction of his platelets is due to the presence of complexes of antibody and the foreign platelets, and once the latter have been eliminated the condition resolves spontaneously even though the antibody may persist in the circulation.

Haemolytic Anaemia Due to Drugs

Drug-induced haemolytic anaemia has been described following stibophen, quinidine, phenacetin and other drugs. Its course is similar to the thrombocytopenia described above and its causation is thought to be similar. It can be differentiated readily, by its typical history, from most other kinds of acute red cell destruction, though confusion could arise in cases in which the subject's red cells are intrinsically sensitive to a particular drug—due for example to glucose-6-phosphate dehydrogenase deficiency—as in favism or primaquine sensitivity.

AGRANULOCYTOSIS

Temporary, or even permanent, severe depletion of polymorphonuclear leucocytes is well known to follow the taking of quite a wide variety of drugs, including not only amidopyrine, quinidine and phenolphthalein, mentioned already, but also such as sulphonamides, phenylbutazone, arsphenamine, gold, thiouracil, chloramphenicol and chlorpromazine. Granulocytopenia commonly occurs without anaemia, although they may accompany one another. The patient is liable to develop severe ulcerative and necrotic inflammation, usually in the mouth and throat, from which bacterial infection spreads rapidly and often ends fatally. Because of the tendency for the throat to be affected the condition is sometimes known as 'agranulocytic angina' (L. *angina:* a choking sensation).

Agranulocytosis is rare, and never occurs until the patient has taken the drug in moderate to large doses for several, and usually for many, days. Furthermore, it is preceded by a stage in which the number of blood granulocytes is diminished, and if the drug is withdrawn at this stage the condition nearly always returns to normal. Consequently it is a wise precaution to perform regular white blood cell counts on patients who are receiving prolonged courses of treatment with drugs known to be liable to produce agranulocytosis.

There are biochemical reasons for supposing that certain of these drugs in excessive amounts over long periods of time might prove toxic to cells by interfering with their metabolism, and even for indicating that the myelocytic cells might be more susceptible than other cells. In fact it is probable that a direct toxic effect of the drug, or of some metabolic product, underlies most cases of agranulocytosis. However, in some instances, and especially in the case of amidopyrine, the person who develops granulocytopenia or agranulocytosis manifests an undoubted *hyper*sensitivity to the drug. A dose one-tenth of that which is commonly prescribed to, and has no ill effect upon, a normal subject may cause a transient but marked fall in the circulating granulocytes during the succeeding few hours. Furthermore, it has been found that the serum from such a patient tested *in vitro* may agglutinate leucocytes (from a normal person or from the patient himself) in the presence of the drug, but not in its absence. Such findings are by no means constant, but the resemblance to drug-induced platelet lysis, already mentioned, is obvious, and the hypothesis has been put forward that the mechanism of damage involves adsorption of antibody–drug complexes such as has been discussed above. Complete proof of this has not been given.

Drug-induced agranulocytosis is essentially a clinical phenomenon, and the current uncertainty about the part played by immunological hypersensitivity, as opposed to a biochemical idiosyncrasy, in its causation illustrates the difficulties which face the investigator who has no model in experimental animals against which to check his observations. Whereas the *in vitro* demonstration of leucocyte lysis or agglutination by the patient's serum in the presence of the drug undoubtedly supports the concept of an underlying immunological hypersensitivity, failure to provide such a demonstration does not exclude it, since the drug may well have to undergo some unrecognized metabolic change in the body before it becomes active as a hapten. Furthermore, there are strong ethical objections against attempting to transfer, by serum or by lymphoid cells, a serious condition, such as granulocytopenia, from a patient to a normal subject. Even if this were attempted, the total mass and the regenerative power of granulocytes and their precursors is such as to make it probable that very large amounts of serum or of cells would need to be transferred. Finally, since the patient with granulocytopenia may be expected to recover if the drug is withdrawn, but is liable to go on to agranulocytosis if its administration is continued, it is rarely, if ever, justifiable to persist with the drug in order to determine the mechanism of granulocyte destruction. Thus a direct approach is barred, and the alternative ways require the development of an analogous experimental model and the continued search for *in vitro* evidence of immunological damage to the granulocytes. At the present time the role of hypersensitivity cannot be regarded as more than hypothetical.

DERMATOPHYTIDS

A few persons who acquire fungus infections of the skin are liable after a while (usually 3 to 8 weeks) to suffer from localized skin eruptions which are named *epidermatophytids*, *moniliids*, *trichophytids*, etc., after the causative agents. Such eruptions may be violent or mild, and are usually papulo-squamous, though sometimes pustular, or vesicular, and a condition resembling erythema nodosum may even occur. Malaise and fever may rarely accompany the eruption, and it has been repeatedly observed that at the time when '-id' reactions occur skin tests with extracts of the infecting fungus are invariably positive. Not infrequently an eruption of this type is brought on by vigorous treatment of a local fungal infection of the feet or scalp, and follows such treatment within ten days or so.

It is generally considered that '-id' reactions are the result of dissemination of fungi or their products *via* the bloodstream in persons who have become hypersensitive to these as a result of the cutaneous infection. The papules or vesicles do not contain demonstrable living fungi; *Trichophyton* has been isolated from pustular eruptions, but it is doubtful whether these belong to the same category. However, the facts that the lesions are commonly sterile, or that fungal infections are not observed in other organs, do not exclude the explanation that hypersensitivity to fungi is the underlying, and haematogenous dissemination the immediate, cause of the eruptions. Positive blood cultures have been obtained from patients with mycotic infections of the feet associated with a mycid on the hands, and fungi have been isolated in biopsies of regional lymph nodes draining localized infection. Experimental observations in guinea-pigs and rabbits showed that *Trichophyton* could be disseminated from inoculated skin sites into the bloodstream over periods of many days, but that fungi introduced into the bloodstream produced lesions only in damaged skin, and in less than half the animals. Thus it appears that fungi are greatly restricted in the sites at which they can grow in the body. However, it is difficult to explain why eruptions due to lesions on the feet tend to occur especially on the hands, and some workers have postulated that the '-id' reactions may be due to external transplantation of fungi to the skin of the hands, accompanied by loss of the usual morphology and viability of the fungi while dwelling there.

It is not certain whether immediate-type or delayed-type hypersensitivities are involved, and it seems probable that either, or more probably both, are present. This could account for the variability of the clinical manifestations. The conditions invariably clear up when the primary infection is cured, and, if this is difficult or requires prolonged treatment with antifungal agents, they can sometimes be much improved by a cautious series of desensitizing injections of fungus extract.

A point which must be borne in mind in considering '-id' reactions which appear after vigorous local medication of fungus infections is that the sensitization may actually be due to the medicament used. For example, many ointments contain salicylic acid, and a few contain mercury salts, and the application of such ointments to a weeping skin surface may occasionally produce sensitization, or a hypersensitivity reaction in a subject already sensitized.

INSECT BITES AND STINGS

Persons stung by insects receive an injection of a mixture of pharmacologically active agents, such as histamine, histamine liberators or serotonin, and enzymes such as hyaluronidase, lecithinase and proteases. Those who are bitten by a horse-fly or a midge, for example, receive an injection of saliva which often contains regurgitated crop contents as well as digestive enzymes and anticoagulants. These substances produce irritant effects of their own, but many readers will be familiar with the fact that bites and stings tend to become more irritating when repeated, and the reaction comes increasingly to resemble a local anaphylactic, or, more usually, an Arthus-type of reaction. Much remains to be investigated in this field, but such research as has been done confirms the suggestion that hypersensitivity to the injected materials underlies the severe reactions which are not infrequently seen. There is also evidence that persons may become sensitized by inhalation of dust containing dried insect bodies or excreta, so as to manifest hypersensitivity reactions even when bitten or stung apparently for the first time. It is probable that both immediate- and delayed-type hypersensitivities are involved.

PARASITIC INFECTIONS

It has long been recognized that infections with parasites, such as intestinal worms, are often accompanied by blood eosinophilia, and it has been suggested that this is due to an immunological process. Conditions in which blood eosinophilia is common include intestinal infections with hookworms, roundworms or whipworms; various forms of filariasis; guinea-worm infection (dracontiasis); mite infection of the lungs (including at least some cases of 'tropical eosinophilia'); and hydatid disease due to *Taenia echinococcus*. In all such conditions there is ample opportunity for the prolonged absorption of antigenic materials from the parasites, which can give rise to hypersensitivity reactions at the sites where they are released. The best evidence that this occurs comes from hydatid disease, in which the echinococcus forms cysts containing excretory and breakdown products of the worms. Such cysts are surrounded by inflammatory cells, with many eosinophils and also plasma cells. If cysts rupture and their contents are absorbed into the circulation, the patient is liable to undergo an acute anaphylactic attack. Furthermore, hydatid cyst fluid will often form typical antigen–antibody precipitates with serum from infected persons, and if such persons are injected intracutaneously with hydatid cyst fluid (Casoni test) they produce a local weal and flare and/or Arthus reaction. In some patients a delayed-type skin reaction occurs. The Casoni test is liable to remain positive for many years after the infection has cleared up.

A rather different parasitic infection in which hypersensitivity to the worm (or its products) is thought to underlie the damage it causes is *onchocerciasis*, an important cause of blindness in West and Central Africa and in South America. The adult worms living in the subcutaneous lymphatics give rise to a chronic inflammatory reaction, partly attributable to development of hypersensitivity on the part of the host. Acute ocular inflammation occurs when the larval form (microfilaria) enters the eye *via* a blood vessel, but the extent to which antibodies or delayed type hypersensitivity are responsible for this is not settled.

The Role of Eosinophils

As has already been mentioned, eosinophils in large numbers invade tissues in which an antigen–antibody reaction has taken place. They appear to be attracted by some product of the antigen–antibody reaction, and it has been shown that if tissues from sensitized guinea-pigs mixed with antigen *in vitro*, or tissues from guinea-pigs which have died from anaphylaxis, are transferred to the peritoneal cavity of normal guinea-pigs, the recipient develops a very marked eosinophilia within the next 24 hours. The active agent has not been identified, but it is probably not histamine. The eosinophils of rodents are very actively phagocytic, and ingest cellular débris, mast cell granules, etc., but it is not certain whether this is true of eosinophils from other species, nor is it known what function the eosinophils serve in these reactions. Nevertheless, the association of eosinophilia with the occurrence of antigen–antibody reactions is so close that the presence of the one should always suggest the presence of the other.

THE PART PLAYED BY COMPLEMENT IN HYPERSENSITIVITY REACTIONS

No one knows the detailed sequence of biochemical events by which is brought about the release of pharmacologically active agents or the damage to tissue cells resulting from antigen–antibody interaction. As regards cell lysis, a model is available in the lysis of sheep erythrocytes by antibody against antigens, either normally present or artificially attached, on the cell surface. In this system, as discussed in Chapter Five, cell lysis occurs when the membrane has become damaged as the result of the combination of the antigen and antibody followed by the ordered interaction of the components of complement, in the presence of suitable cations. Less well studied, but apparently similar, is the lysis of cells in tissue culture by the action of antibodies prepared against their surface antigens. However, in most immediate-type hypersensitivity reactions, other than those such as Sedormid and quinidine damage to platelets described above, or those due to auto-antibodies, it is the antibody which is adsorbed on to tissue cells or free in solution and antigen is added from without.

More because of experimental difficulties than from want of trying, there is as yet no final answer to the question how far haemolytic complement is involved in or responsible for anaphylactic or Arthus-type reactions. Evidence in favour of the participation of complement in anaphylaxis comes from studies of reactions *in vitro*, from which it appears that anaphylaxis requires the presence of Ca ions and that it is inhibited by various agents which are known to inhibit the haemolytic activity of some of the components of complement. The parallel between inhibition of anaphylaxis and of immune haemolysis, however, is not exact and the action of some reagents is contradictory (e.g. several amino-acid esters or peptides will inhibit haemolysis but not anaphylaxis, whereas KCN or iodoacetate inhibit anaphylaxis only). Furthermore, anaphylactic reactions can be obtained on addition of antigens to tissues or cells taken from sensitized animals, which have been washed so thoroughly that no detectable haemolytic complement is present or in living animals congenitally deficient in some of the complement components. In such circumstances, if complement plays a part in the reactions it must be required in minimal amounts and must be bound to or present within the cells, and not supplied from outside as in immune haemolysis.

As regards the role of complement in serum sickness and Arthus-type reactions the position has recently become more clear. Complement is certainly activated by the antigen–antibody complexes which are responsible, when these are tested *in vitro*, and only those complexes which activate complement appear to cause reactions of this type *in vivo*. Furthermore, in animals temporarily depleted of complement or congenitally deficient in certain components the reactions are much less severe or absent. As was discussed in Chapter Five, activation of components as far as C′3 appears to be required for immune adherence to occur, and as far as C′7 for the generation of a factor chemotactic for the polymorphs, whose local immigration is the main cause of damage. Although anaphylatoxin (see below) can be formed when complement is activated as far as C′3, its importance in the pathogenesis of such reactions remains to be proved. There is thus a strong case for regarding activation of complement through various stages as far as C′3, and perhaps as far as C′7 as being an essential ingredient of the pathogenetic effects of circulating antigen–antibody complexes.

Anaphylatoxin

About 1910, before the role of histamine in anaphylaxis had been proposed, it was considered by many workers that the interaction of antigen with antibody in plasma gave rise to a hypothetical toxin, 'anaphylatoxin', which was responsible for the visible effects of anaphylaxis. Various means were proposed whereby this might occur; e.g. proteolytic cleavage of antigen, or of the antigen–antibody complex, by a non-specific proteolytic ferment which was considered to be associated with 'complement'; or, more ingeniously, removal by the complex of the normal plasma trypsin inhibitor, so that a natural plasma protease begins to digest plasma proteins liberating toxic products of cleavage. There was experimental evidence to support this, since fresh rat or guinea-pig plasma, incubated with antigen–antibody aggregates, did in fact develop the property of producing an anaphylaxis-like picture on reinjection into a normal guinea-pig or dog. Peptone preparations, made by enzymic digestion of various proteins, were already known to do the same.

The idea that anaphylatoxins might mediate anaphylaxis was

shaken by the discovery of the important role of histamine, and even more by the discovery that they could be produced by incubating normal plasma with various agents other than antigen–antibody complexes, such as agar, kaolin, starch or inulin. Furthermore, it was observed that a piece of gut from a sensitized guinea-pig would still contract vigorously *in vitro* on adding antigen, even though it had been made unresponsive to anaphylatoxin by a few repeated applications of this agent. Finally, anaphylatoxin prepared from rat plasma is much more active than that from guinea-pig plasma when tested on guinea-pig smooth muscle, and yet neither act on rat smooth muscles (e.g. the uterus), which can nevertheless contract as a result of antigen–antibody interaction.

Interest has revived in anaphylatoxin since it was shown that in some species it is reasonably potent in releasing histamine from mast cells, which removes one of the apparent contradictions which led to its neglect. Furthermore, it has been shown that formation of anaphylatoxin (by whatever agent) requires the participation of the components of complement. Materials with anaphylatoxin activity have been shown *in vitro* to be formed when activation occurs as far as C′3 and at the stage of C′5. Thus a case can be made for considering that anaphylatoxin formation may be an intermediary step in some reactions resembling anaphylaxis—e.g. when antigen–antibody complexes cause contraction of the guinea-pig ileum or histamine release from mouse peritoneal mast cells. However, as regards 'true' anaphylaxis, mediated by homocytotropic antibodies, the weakness of the case for regarding as essential any reactions involving complement still remains.

THE SHWARTZMAN REACTION

If endotoxins (complexes containing polysaccharide, polypeptide and lipid derived from the cell-walls) of many Gram-negative bacteria are injected in a dose of a few micrograms into the skin of adult rabbits, the skin exhibits a very mild degree of local inflammation. If, some 24 hours later, an intravenous injection is given of the same or another endotoxin in similar amount, the injected areas of skin becomes sites of petechial haemorrhages, which begin after some 2 hours and by the end of 4 hours form confluent deep purple lesions. Histological examination shows extensive invasion with polymorphs, leucocyte-platelet thrombi and necrosis of the vessel walls, particularly of the venules. This reaction was first described by Shwartzman in 1928, and is named after him. If the first injection is given by vein, followed 24 hours later by a second *via* the same route, the rabbits are apparently unharmed by the first, but 12 to 24 hours after the second injection they become ill and some die. At autopsy there is regularly found bilateral cortical necrosis of the kidneys, and often patchy haemorrhagic necrosis in other organs such as the spleen or liver. Essentially this phenomenon was described in connection with experimental cholera by Sanarelli in 1924, and it has been named the Sanarelli–Shwartzman or the 'generalized Shwartzman' reaction. The histological findings in such cases consist in plugging of glomerular capillaries and spleen and liver sinusoids with acellular homogeneous material, which may consist of a complex of altered fibrinogen with acid mucopolysaccharides set free from the tissues, as a result of some effect of the endotoxin. Since endotoxin has been shown to render the lysosomes (see Glossary) of cells abnormally fragile, the release of enzymes from them may be the underlying cause of the cell damage.

It is by no means certain that the two reactions occur by similar mechanisms. They are mentioned here because they are hypersensitivity reactions in which there is at least a superficial resemblance to immunological processes and small amounts of antibody able to combine with the carbohydrate components of many endotoxins can be detected in the serum of normal animals. Such antibodies have presumably arisen by stimulation with cross reacting antigens present in the normal bacterial flora, and the reason for this will be apparent from the discussion of the structure of the 'O' antigens of Gram-negative bacteria on p. 229. Nevertheless, in the words of Prof. Lewis Thomas: 'No one has yet succeeded in fitting the Shwartzman reaction into any recognizable category of immunological events, although many efforts have been made to do so. As a result, the reaction and its relatives have wandered in and out of the finest-print sections in immunological texts, never accounted for, and usually regarded as a kind of mad cousin of proper immune reactions.' The reader who wishes to delve deeper is referred to the review article listed in suggestions for further reading at the end of this chapter.

Attempts have been made to relate to the generalized Shwartzman phenomenon the lesions found in two human situations: Waterhouse–Friderichsen syndrome (acute adrenal haemorrhagic necrosis) and bilateral cortical necrosis of the kidneys. The assumption is made that the lesions in these conditions are produced by a mechanism similar to that operating in the Shwartzman reaction, as a consequence of absorption into the circulation of large amounts of bacterial endotoxin. Although usually associated with meningococcal septicaemia, the Waterhouse–Friderichsen syndrome occasionally occurs in overwhelming infections by other bacteria such as *E. coli*, *Haemophilus influenzae* and staphylococci. In a recent analysis of 52 fatal cases of meningococcal septicaemia, of the 40 that came to autopsy all but 4 showed typical adrenal lesions.

The treatment of this condition presents the clinician with something of a dilemma since replacement therapy for the damaged adrenal gland logically makes use of cortisone or its analogues. However, cortisone has been shown strikingly to potentiate both local and general Shwartzman reactions, and human cases are described in which cortisone therapy for meningococcal septicaemia apparently led to bilateral cortical necrosis of the kidneys. Presumably replacement without overdosage is the ideal, but in the absence of any routine method for assessing adrenal function, the exact dosage required to ensure this is difficult to determine.

FURTHER READING

Ackroyd J.F. (1964) The diagnosis of disorders of the blood due to drug hypersensitivity caused by an immune mechanism. In *Immunological Methods* [Ed. Ackroyd J.F.]. Blackwell Scientific Publications, Oxford

Austen F.J. & Bloch K.J. (eds) (1968) *Biochemistry of Acute Allergic Reactions*. Blackwell Scientific Publications, Oxford

Bloch K.J. (1967) The anaphylactic antibodies of mammals including man. *Progr. Allergy*. **10**, 84

Brocklehurst W.E. (1962) Slow reacting substance and related compounds. *Progr. Allergy*. **6**, 539

Cluff L.E. & Johnston J.E. (1964) 'Drug Fever.' *Progr. Allergy*. **8**, 149

Dixon F.J. (1963) The role of antigen–antibody complexes in disease. *The Harvey Lectures* **58**, 21

Feldman J.D. (1964) Ultrastructure in immunologic processes. *Adv. Immunol.* **4**, 175

Gell P.G.H. & Coombs R.R.A. (eds) (1968) *Clinical Aspects of Immunology* Section IV. The Allergic State as Responsible for Clinical Hypersensitivity and Disease. Blackwell Scientific Publications, Oxford

Grabar P. & Miescher P. (ed.) (1959) *Immunopathology*. 1st International Symposium, Schwabe, Basel

Grabar P. & Miescher P. (ed.) (1962) *Immunopathology*. 2nd International Symposium, Schwabe, Basel

Grabar P. & Miescher P. (ed.) (1963) *Immunopathology*. 3rd International Symposium. (See especially 'Mechanisms of Immunogenic Kidney Diseases', p. 208.) Schwabe, Basel

Grabar P. & Miescher P. (ed.) (1967) *Immunopathology*. 5th International Symposium. (See especially 'Mechanisms of inflammation induced by immune reactions'.) Schwabe, Basel

Lawrence H.J. (ed.) (1959) *Cellular and Humoral Aspects of the Hypersensitive States* (including the Shwartzman phenomenon). Hoeber, New York

Mills L.C. & Moyer J.H. (ed.) (1961) *Inflammation and Diseases of Connective Tissue*. Saunders, London

Mohos S.C., Hennigar G.R. & Fogelman J.A. (1963) Insulin-induced glomerulosclerosis in the rabbit. *J. exp. Med.* **118,** 667

Murphy G.E. (1960) Nature of rheumatic heart disease. *Medicine* **39,** 289

Osler A.G., Lichtenstein L.M. & Levy D.A. (1968) '*In vitro* studies of human reaginic allergy'. *Adv. Immunol.* **8,** 183

Parish W.E. & Pepys J. (1968) The lung in allergic disease. In *Clinical Aspects of Immunology* [Ed. Gell P.G.H. and Coombs R.R.A.]. Blackwell Scientific Publications, Oxford

Riley J.F. (1959) *The Mast Cells*. Livingstone, Edinburgh

Samter M. (ed.) (1964) *Immunologic Diseases*. Little Brown, Boston

Shaffer J.H., Lo Grippo G.A. & Chase M.W. (ed.) (1959) *The Mechanisms of Hypersensitivity*. Henry Ford Symposium, Churchill, London

Shulman S. (1968) 'Insect Allergy'. *Progr. Allergy* **12,** 246

Sulzberger M.B. (1940) *Dermatologic Allergy*. C.C. Thomas. Springfield, Ill.

Unanue E.R. & Dixon F.J. (1967) Experimental Glomerulonephritis: Immunological events and pathogenetic mechanisms. *Adv. Immunol.* **6,** 1

Zweifach B.W., Grant L. & McCluskey R.T. (eds) (1965) *The Inflammatory Process*, Academic Press, New York

CHAPTER TWELVE

Delayed-type Hypersensitivity

Specific Cell-mediated Hypersensitivity

In this chapter we shall consider allergic reactions which develop many hours after the test antigen is placed in or on the tissues. The substances which excite this form of altered specific reactivity are many and various. They may be organic chemicals or simple derivatives of chemical elements such as metals which act by penetration through the mucous membranes or skin; they may be components of micro-organisms which reach the tissues along with invading living agents of disease; or they may be antibiotics or drugs injected by syringe. While certain points of distinction can be drawn between the immunogens and adjuvants which cause delayed hypersensitivity and those which provoke immediate (antibody-dependent) hypersensitivity, these two reactive states often co-exist and the stimuli which give rise to one often excite the other.

Delayed-type allergic reactions are placed in a separate category for the principal reason that they cannot be shown to relate to circulating antibody. The procedure of passive transfer by serum is uniformly unsuccessful. However, transfer by cells of lymphoid tissue, inflammatory exudates or the white cells of the blood has been successful, and similar success in transfer of the mechanism of homograft rejection has led to the concept that all these phenomena are specific allergic cell-mediated processes.

Historically, the phenomenon of delayed-type hypersensitivity received recognition first in the sphere of chronic infective disease and was early known as *bacterial allergy* or the *allergy of infection*. The classical example is the response to the proteins of the tubercle bacillus which develops in an experimental animal or man infected with tubercle bacilli and which Zinsser (1921) originally distinguished as a 'delayed' reactivity:

'. . . one in which there is no immediate effect, but within 4, 5 or more hours (after injection of tuberculoprotein), a swelling becomes apparent which in the course of 12 to 24 hours results in a swollen oedematous area of varying intensity, often with a central necrotic spot and, occasionally, haemorrhage. This reaction may not reach its highest development until about 48 hours after the injection, and is accompanied by distinct signs of inflammation and some death.'

A similar kind of relationship between various protein-containing antigens of micro-organisms and hypersensitive responses of the delayed type exists in a wide variety of chronic infectious diseases, caused by bacteria, viruses, fungi and protozoa. Often the intracutaneous test with a protein extract of the organism has gained recognition for its specific diagnostic value. Even parasitic infestations may set up this type of response although immediate-type reactions are regarded as more prominent in such helminth infestations as trichiniasis, filariasis and ascariasis. However, in, for example, echinococcus infestation the Casoni skin test which utilizes hydatid fluid as the test material results in a combined immediate and delayed-type response, of which the delayed-type response is of more consistent value for diagnostic purposes.

Another sphere in which the student of medicine will encounter the phenomenon of delayed-type hypersensitivity is dermatology. The most common route for sensitization by the natural products of the environment and the many synthetic chemicals of the modern way of life is the percutaneous one, involving direct contact with the skin. Following such contact with skin and mucous membranes the delayed type of reactivity is more common than the immediate type and results in characteristic lesions varying from macules or papules to vesicles which break to leave weeping raw areas. Such lesions in the acute stage are referred to as *eczematous dermatitis* in this country. The test for contact hypersensitivity which is used by the clinician is the so-called 'patch test'. This involves application of the allergenic material under an adherent semi-occlusive dressing in a concentration which is non-irritating to normal skin.

Inciting agents for contact hypersensitivity (contactants) are often not immunogens as such, but graduate to full immunogenic status following combination with one of the body's own proteins. This step may occur directly or only after the chemical has undergone a change outside the body. Thus benzyl penicillin acts after a conversion to products such as benzyl penicillenic acid and benzyl penicilloic acid. The metal nickel can act following the action of acidic sweat on nickel-plated objects in contact with the skin (Plate 12.2, following p. 468) although the actual chemical excitant is uncertain.

Usually sensitization results from surface contact after a latent interval of a week or so, but often longer. A later re-exposure results several hours later in local itching and, after 24 hours, in a patch of eczema.

It would appear that any area of the skin or mucous membrane can respond to develop contact hypersensitivity. However, just as adjuvants such as oily suspensions of mycobacteria are of crucial importance in causing severe delayed hypersensitivity to follow injection of an antigen, so also factors such as existing irritations of the skin are often crucial for the development of sensitization.

For many reasons it is convenient to consider separately in this chapter the phenomena of contact hypersensitivity and the delayed hypersensitivity of microbial disease. However, it must be emphasized that current work has stressed the basic similarities in the mechanisms involved. Both depend on altered reactivity of the cells (particularly lymphocytes and macrophages) of the lympho-reticular tissues. In the case of contact sensitivity there is indeed a clear demonstration in man that organs other than the skin are involved. Thus, an area of sensitized skin has been transplanted to a prepared site on a non-sensitive identical twin. This area of skin then loses its sensitivity. Conversely, non-sensitized skin transplanted to a sensitized host acquires his contact sensitivity. It is also clear that sensitization to contact hypersensitivity develops only if the draining lymphatics from the skin to the regional lymph node are intact. If these lymphatics are cut or the regional lymph nodes removed within 48 hours after the sensitizing exposure, sensitization does not develop.

Delayed-type hypersensitivity reactions in experimental animals have always been found to depend on the activity of living cells. In the transfer of this form of hypersensitivity between animals by means of suspensions of cells from lymph nodes, spleen or peripheral blood white cells the important cell is believed to be the lymphocyte. The duration of the hypersensitivity transferred in this way appears to depend on the length of time that the cells can survive and function in their new host. Because of the homograft reaction (see Chapter Thirteen) this time is likely to be short unless the transfer takes place between isogeneic individuals. With transfer between the members of stocks of ordinary outbred guinea-pigs, the passively acquired hypersensitive state lasts four or five days at the most. When isogeneic guinea-pigs are used (in which the transferred cells may be expected not only to remain alive but to multiply) the recipients may remain sensitive for several months.

MANIFESTATIONS OF A DELAYED-TYPE RESPONSE IN THE SKIN

Although clinically the prominent lesion is the vesicle in contact dermatitis and the erythematous papule in bacterial allergy, the underlying changes in the dermis are basically similar. Let us follow the details of a classical example: the local tuberculin response or *Mantoux test* reaction. When a 0·1 ml volume of 1 in 1000 dilution of old tuberculin (a culture filtrate of tubercle bacilli, grown in broth and containing some of the proteins of the bacillus) is injected into a normal person, nothing obvious happens, but when the same solution is injected into a patient with tuberculosis, although there is no obvious immediate effect, after a few hours redness appears at the injection site and gradually over the next 18–48 hours an indurated lump develops. Whereas the lump in an immediate-type hypersensitivity reaction (such as would be produced by the injection of a protein extract into a hay-fever or asthma subject) consists mainly of oedema fluid with relatively few cells, the delayed-type response on sectioning shows a dense collection of cells, consisting in the main of perivascular masses of mononuclear cells (i.e. macrophages and lymphocytes). We can therefore get near to characterizing the delayed-type response if we define it as a specifically provoked, slowly evolving mixed cellular reaction which includes especially lymphocytes and macrophages.

The histology of a fully developed local reaction to tuberculin in the skin of a sensitive subject is shown in Plate 12.1, following p. 468. The initial infiltration of the subcutis (at 2–3 hours) with polymorphonuclear leucocytes is succeeded later (5–6 hours) by characteristic local perivascular accumulations of mononuclear cells (macrophages and lymphocytes). Presumably the perivascular mononuclear cellular collections represent the cells which had early emigrated in company with the polymorphs but which had become immobilized around the vessels. Later another wave of cellular emigration occurs on a more massive scale. The cells are mixed, but the polymorphs become dispersed while the mononuclear cells build up in perivascular cuffs.

Traditionally these events are contrasted with those of an Arthus-type response. The histological picture in this case is one of acute inflammation with oedema, leucocytic infiltration of the tissues and perhaps obvious vasculitis. Early in its course large numbers of polymorphonuclears stick to and pile up on the vessel walls and then migrate in large numbers into the surrounding tissue which becomes progressively more swollen and remains oedematous for 18–24 hours. The polymorphonuclear response in the tuberculin reaction is relatively weak and the mononuclear response appears relatively strong. It is accepted by most observers that there are no absolute differences between the histological patterns in a delayed-type and an Arthus response. The same cellular ingredients are present, although their proportions differ.

An analogous sequence of cellular events occurs in the dermis at the basis of a homograft of skin in the days preceding its rejection (Chapter Fourteen).

MECHANISM OF THE DELAYED-TYPE RESPONSE

The analysis of the cellular components of the local delayed-type reaction is complex and many different views have been advanced. Since the cellular reactions which occur in the regional node at the time of induction of contact hypersensitivity appear to involve large and small lymphocytes, the local perivascular accumulations of mononuclear cells might be interpreted as the homing of specifically conditioned small lymphocytes to their homologous antigen. This hypothesis has been tested by the transfer of radioactive labelled cells from hypersensitive donor guinea-pigs to normal recipients. It is found that tritium-labelled cells appear in the local tuberculin lesion in numbers (2–8 per cent) to be expected from their proportion in the circulating cells. Over 90 per cent of the cells which infiltrate at the site of locally injected antigen are host cells. No specific attraction seems to obtain, at least for the vast bulk of the assembled cells. Thus labelled cells also accumulate at the site of immunologically unrelated delayed-type reactions in numbers comparable with those at the test site. An alternative hypothesis is that the specific direct interaction between sensitized cells and antigen involves only a few of these. The interaction then triggers off the accumulation subsequently of large numbers of host cells.

There is evidence that the cells which cause the inflammatory reaction are not limited to the actively sensitized cells which interact specifically with the local antigen. Additional cells of the same or different types, e.g. macrophages, may be rendered similarly reactive by a non-specific secondary mechanism, dependent on factors released from the primarily sensitized cells (see, below, the discussion of the *in vitro* phenomenon of antigen inhibition of migration of macrophages from plasma-clot explants of lymphoid tissue).

DEMONSTRATION OF THE HYPERSENSITIVITY OF CELLS 'IN VITRO'

Some years ago it was found that the leucocytes of tuberculous animals are subject to injury or necrosis when placed in an environment containing tuberculoprotein. Thus if a fragment of spleen or bone marrow from a tuberculous animal is grown in culture and exposed to tuberculin at concentrations greater than the normal, migration of cells from the tissue is seen gradually to stop and later some cells within the fragment disintegrate. On further analysis, the migration can be divided into three phases. Polymorphs migrate in the first 24 hours, but do not survive for more than 2 or 3 days. Macrophages migrate more slowly; but, by the fifth day, form a prominent zone outside the tissue fragment. Fibroblasts eventually succeed the macrophages and by the tenth day are dominant. Tuberculoprotein is apparently without effect on the early polymorphonuclear migration, but produces pronounced inhibition of macrophages and a definite, though lesser, inhibition of fibroblasts. Explants from guinea-pigs with Arthus reactivity to horse serum and other antigens were not affected by these antigens *in vitro*. The effect of tuberculin on the explants from tuberculous animals was confined to the tuberculoproteins, and carbohydrate or nucleic acid fractions of the tubercle bacillus were ineffective.

It is difficult to say whether the tuberculoprotein directly kills the cells. Possibly the reaction causes the cells to acquire adhesiveness so that their migration from the cell mass is stopped. The same antigen-induced adhesiveness may explain another phenomenon which has been repeatedly observed, namely that the intraperitoneal injection of quite tiny doses of antigen into the guinea-pig with delayed hypersensitivity causes the macrophages to adhere in clumps to the peritoneal lining. In this instance the antigen does not appear to kill the macrophages but induces a surface stickness and a heightened phagocytic activity.

The fact that cells from animals with immediate-type hypersensitivity are not damaged by a similar exposure to antigen has led to the concept that the observed effects *in vivo* depend primarily upon the response of blood-vessels or smooth muscle ('target organs'), whereas all cells are directly vulnerable in delayed-type hypersensitivity. The same concept is discussed below in relation to corneal hypersensitivity and, indeed, was the basis for the original use of this as a test-site to indicate hypersensitivity of the delayed type only.

Originally there was an inclination to generalize from the results of tissue cultures of spleen and bone marrow to a belief that all cells of the body can become directly sensitized to antigen. However, sensitivity to tuberculin appears not to be widespread among the cells of the tuberculous animal, as was formerly believed, and tests for effects on isolated ectoderm cells such as corneal or cutaneous epithelium, or endoderm cells such as hepatic epithelium, have proved negative even when such a delicate indicator of cell damage was used as the oxygen uptake measured by the Warburg technique. We are probably justified in limiting the types of cell which are noticeably affected by the antigen to macrophages and the fibroblasts of some tissues, although some effects on the lymphocytes have been described, such as their transformation into lysosome-rich proliferating cells, with a morphological similarity to macrophages.

Macrophage emigration from lymphoid tissue explants can be inhibited by as little as 1 μg/ml of antigen. Macrophage sensitivity is evident in explants of lung and regional lymph nodes five days after immunization, when delayed skin reactions are first obtainable; macrophages in distant lymph nodes and spleen become sensitive 2–4 weeks after immunization (see Plate 12.3, following p. 662).

Methods have been developed for studying the migration of collections of macrophages, such as oil-induced peritoneal exudate cells from sensitized guinea-pigs packed into capillary tubes. *Such preparations invariably contain a small proportion of lymphocytes.* When the cells are allowed to emigrate into fluid media a well-defined fan of migrating cells appears at the tube mouth after one or two days. In the presence of the specific antigen the migration of cells from guinea-pigs with delayed-type hypersensitivity was inhibited. Observations with this system have shown that interaction of cells from sensitized donors with antigen may affect the migration of adjacent cells from unsensitized donors. Thus antigen will inhibit migration of all the macrophages from mixtures of peritoneal exudate cells even if only 5–10 per cent of the cells came from a sensitized animal.

Such experiments appear to indicate that the macrophages are the cells primarily implicated. However, when special precautions were taken to separate macrophages from lymphocytes in the peritoneal exudates it was found that the migration of purified suspensions of macrophages, even when taken from a sensitized animal, was not inhibited by adding the antigen. For inhibition to occur it was necessary for sensitized lymphocytes also to be present. Furthermore, when lymphocytes from a tuberculin-sensitized animal were mixed with unsensitized macrophages in a ratio as low as 2 to 98, migration of the mixed cell population was strongly inhibited by exposure to tuberculin. This finding suggests that the cells *primarily* reacting with antigen are lymphocytes, and that macrophages become affected secondarily. How this occurs is not at present known, but it has been found that when lymphocytes from sensitized guinea-pigs are incubated with the specific antigen a cell-free, non-dialysable factor (or factors) is released which causes normal macrophages to adhere to one another and inhibits their migration. There is some evidence that the same factor, or another released concomitantly, can stimulate other lymphocytes to undergo differentiation and division *in vitro*, as measured by uptake of radioactive thymidine into their nuclei.

CELLULAR EVENTS INVOLVED IN THE DEVELOPMENT OF CONTACT HYPERSENSITIVITY: CHANGES IN THE REGIONAL LYMPH NODES

The most striking of the cellular events during the induction of contact hypersensitivity by application of a chemical sensitizing agents such as 2,4-dinitro-1-chlorobenzene (DNCB) to an area of skin are seen in the draining lymph nodes, which enlarge markedly during the ensuing 4 or 5 days. The changes bear a close resemblance to those occurring in the lymph nodes draining the site of a skin homograft. The first change occurs on the second day with the development of small numbers of pyroninophilic 'blast' cells in the mid and deep cortex. These gradually increase to maximum numbers on the fourth day. It can be shown (by removing the painted skin at various time intervals) that the subsequent train of events has been set in motion within 12 hours of applying the irritant. The number of small lymphocytes also appears to increase. These immature cells in general resemble the haemocytoblasts of Plate 7.4C, following p. 278, as stained with methyl-green pyronin, but the appearance in the electron microscope shows that the cytoplasm has little organized endoplasmic reticulum, nor do such cells contain demonstrable γ-globulin. This cell is therefore different from that shown in Plate 7.5C but resembles that in Plate 3.3. The cytoplasmic basophilia is accounted for by the presence of very numerous free clusters of 3–8 ribosomes. The nucleus is leptochromatic and provided with prominent RNA-containing nucleoli. There are numerous mitoses. Both immature and mature plasma cells are strikingly absent from these cell collections at the fourth day, although mature and immature plasma cells, such as would be expected to be associated with antibody formation, appear increasingly in the medulla from the fifth day onwards.

The pyroninophilic lymphocytes develop in the mid and deep layers of the cortex of the lymph node (Plate 7.1, Chapter Seven). At their outer limits, these areas adjoin the outer regions of the cortex with their organized cortical nodules containing germinal centres, and at their inner limit they adjoin the medulla. These appear to be the areas of the node where the small lymphocytes from the blood first enter the node from the post-capillary venules (see Chapter Seven) and to correspond with the so-called 'thymus dependent areas' which are maximally depleted of lymphocytes after thymectomy of the newborn mouse. By making autoradiographs of sections of lymph nodes following suitably timed injections of radioactive thymidine (which becomes incorporated almost exclusively into the DNA of cells which are preparing to divide, and once incorporated remains with the nuclear material at subsequent cell divisions) it has been found that the burst of cell division results in the production of new labelled daughter cells which are small lymphocytes. The onset of delayed-type (contact) sensitivity coincides with the appearance of these labelled lymphocytes in the circulation at the fourth and fifth days.

It is possible that the large pyroninophilic lymphocytes seen in the paracortical areas are differentiated small lymphocytes which have accumulated *via* the bloodstream at the site of the irritant chemical in the skin and have moved into the adjacent regional node. It is uncertain whether they have gained a new capacity (i.e. to interact specifically with antigen by a surface receptor perhaps analogous with antibody), or whether they have replicated a capacity pre-existing in some of their precursors. It is tempting to infer that by their active division and differentiation they provide the new population of cells (small lymphocytes) which are the 'effectors' in subsequent hypersensitivity reactions, part of them remaining in the nodes where they have been formed and part spreading to the circulating pool of cells and to other parts of the animal's lymphoid tissues.

The foregoing changes during the sensitization process to delayed hypersensitivity stand in contrast to those seen in antibody production. In the latter case (Chapter Seven) the medulla of the regional node responding to a secondary stimulus of antigen becomes populated with plasma cell precursors at the second day onwards and germinal centres appear in the cortex at about the fourth day and enlarge progressively for about a week thereafter.

Effect of Thymectomy

After neonatal thymectomy of mice, delayed-type hypersensitivity reactions and homograft rejection are severely impaired, and the proliferation of blast cells in the thymus dependent (paracortical) areas of the draining lymph nodes after the application of sensitizing chemicals is absent. However, injection of such antigens as give rise to antibody formation leads to germinal centre development and plasma-cell proliferation even in neonatally thymectomized mice.

The exact mode of control exerted by the thymus on the delayed-type response is unknown. Presumably the absence of the blast cell response after thymectomy depends on the absence of small lymphocytes from the thymus dependent areas. The simple hypothesis that the thymus directly supplies the necessary cells to these areas of the lymph node is rendered difficult by the finding that although suspensions of radioactively-labelled thymus cells injected intravenously have been found to migrate to the thymus dependent areas, such populations are less efficient on a numerical basis than other lymphoid cells in restoring the immunological competence of thymectomized mice.

INDUCTION OF DELAYED-TYPE HYPERSENSITIVITY

Induction of Contact Hypersensitivity

Contact hypersensitivity is induced chiefly by a process of percutaneous absorption following the application to the skin of substances of low molecular weight, e.g. nickel salts, urushiol from the primrose or poison ivy plant, paraphenylene diamine (hair dye). Experiments have shown that any individual can be rendered sensitive to the primrose (*Primula obconica*) providing a sufficient number of applications of a concentrated extract of the leaves is made on the skin.

Many of the chemicals that sensitize the human patient will induce sensitivity in the guinea-pig. Examples of chemicals which are often used experimentally in this way are picryl chloride, 2,4-dinitrochlorobenzene, urushiol (from the poison ivy plant) and nickel salts. For a successful sensitization to result from the repeated applications it is usually necessary to put the excitant on to a previously irritated area of skin or to use concentrations of the sensitizing agents sufficient by themselves to cause mild irritation of normal skin.

It is apparent from inspection of the list of effective sensitizing agents that they include many substances which are used specifically in industry and elsewhere for their ability to react with proteins, e.g. chrome salts which are used as tanning agents, chrome salts, formalin and picric acid which are used as tissue fixatives, and paraphenylene diamine, which is an extremely fast hair dye. Studies with penicillin have shown that the actively sensitizing derivatives penicillenic acid and penicilloyl are able to combine with protein. In the case of the various nitro- and chloro-substituted benzenes, those forms which cause sensitization are those forms which combine with proteins. Similarly, of various chemically related compounds tested for their ability to *provoke* a contact lesion in an already sensitized animal, only those which can combine with protein are successful.

Although a combination of the excitant chemical with some body protein appears to be a preliminary and necessary requirement for the action of either a sensitizing or a provoking substance, this is obviously not the whole story. The fact is that the intravenous injection of preformed complexes of excitant and protein, such as, for example, picryl chloride combined with serum albumin, gives rise to antibody production and immediate-type hypersensitivity rather than to contact reactivity. This focuses attention on the need for local factors in the sensitization process—e.g. areas of cutaneous inflammation or granulomata composed of accumulated lymphoid cells. An additional consideration is that reactivity in a skin test can only be expected from a (hapten-protein) complex which is similar or identical to the complex which caused sensitization in the first place. This follows since both induction of sensitization and the test reaction are characterized by *carrier specificity* (see p. 508).

Parenteral injection of the drug or simple chemical usually fails to give rise to contact hypersensitivity. However, Landsteiner and Chase showed in the guinea-pig that an intraperitoneal injection could give rise to contact skin reactivity providing that the injection was made of the chemical linked to an insoluble protein (picric acid linked to red cell stromata was one substance used), and this was incorporated into an oily adjuvant mixture containing dead tubercle bacilli. As in the case of the Freund-type adjuvant mixture which is used for stimulating the production of high serum antibody levels, the active constituent of the tubercle bacillus which is active in directing the immunological response towards delayed hypersensitivity is the chloroform soluble wax fraction (see p. 254).

In the case of homograft rejection, it has been shown how a population of lymphoid cells derived from the thoracic duct can be stimulated by circulation through the vessels of an isolated allogeneic kidney. The cells then home to the lymphoid tissues for subsequent development of the ability to give an accelerated reaction to a further graft of the same allogeneic specificity. When sensitization occurs from a locally applied homograft, the main development and concentration of sensitized lymphocytes occurs in the regional lymph node.

Presumably all skin sensitizing antigens must possess solubility and diffusion properties which enable them to pass through the unbroken skin. The fact that a high proportion are fat soluble may indicate that passage along sebaceous glands is one way in which this occurs. However, although a broken surface is not essential, skin already affected by dermatitis (and already well populated and traversed by lymphoid cells) is particularly liable to become sensitized. This often occurs in response to potential sensitizing agents in applied medicaments, as sufferers from eczematous dermatitis discover to their cost.

The resulting sensitization is not, of course, restricted to the area of skin which has made contact with the excitant. The whole skin, and indeed the whole individual, is sensitized, though areas remote from the site of application take a longer time to achieve their maximum sensitivity. The sensitization usually dates from the sixth to the eighteenth day after the start of the treatment. The first sign of its appearance is usually a vascular flushing of one of the skin areas used for preliminary sensitization and is attributable to persistence of traces of the sensitizing agent. The presence of sensitivity is conveniently demonstrated by a patch test on an untreated area to which the chemical excitant is applied as a solution in an oily solvent or on a small square of cloth which is held in position against the skin; it can also be shown by injecting intracutaneously either the excitant or a chemical conjugate of the excitant and some soluble protein.

General clinical experience indicates that individuals differ in the readiness with which they acquire contact hypersensitivity. For many years these allergies were regarded as innate individual idiosyncrasies and the title 'drug idiosyncrasy' was widely applied. However, to some substances everyone can apparently develop sensitivity. Although in the ordinary way of life only a few people become sensitized to the Japanese primrose plant (*Primula obconica*) it has been found that any person can be rendered sensitive by the use of a concentrated extract of Primula leaves, providing that it is applied a sufficient number of times. Some persons became sensitive after one application, others required several. Hereditary influences presumably determine these differences, the existence of which as a series of small gradations suggests that they depend on a large number of individual genes. Hereditary factors can be segregated in guinea-pigs by inbreeding, so that groups are obtained with high and low susceptibility to a given agent. Certainly, with many sensitizing agents, there exists a proportion of individuals who, in spite of frequent and universal exposure, never acquire reactivity. In the case of poison ivy, a survey using the patch test revealed that about 75 per cent of persons acquired sensitivity. In Chapter Eleven the genetic influences which determine atopy were discussed. No relationship has been shown between the predispositions to develop these two different allergic manifestations, and contact sensitization may occur in atopic or nonatopic subjects with equal frequency.

Induction of Cell-mediated Hypersensitivity in Infective Diseases

Cell-mediated hypersensitivity probably accompanies all infections, but it is more strikingly evident in some, including tuberculosis, mumps, vaccinia, brucellosis, psittacosis and lymphogranuloma venereum. Induction of tuberculin hypersensitivity can be achieved by the injection of dead as well as living, virulent or attenuated tubercle bacilli. With injection of heat-killed mycobacterial cells the resulting hypersensitivity is relatively poorly developed. Greatly increased sensitization in the guinea-pig can be achieved by suspending the dead bacilli in hydrocarbon oils such as paraffin oil. However, the immunological result of this procedure is obviously different from an actual infection with bacilli, since circulating antibody levels to various components of tuberculin are increased and immediate-type hypersensitivity is also induced.

The reasons for the existence of a highly developed state of delayed-type hypersensitivity in human or guinea-pig infective diseases has provided a subject for much experimental work. A fundamental early experiment was performed by Dienes and Schoenheit more than 40 years ago, in which they injected an unrelated antigen (ovalbumin) into a tuberculous guinea-pig, particularly into actual areas of tuberculous granulation tissue, and demonstrated that the animal developed a delayed type of cutaneous response to ovalbumin. This clearly suggested that the initial manipulation of antigen by the cells within such granulomata could be decisive for the induction of delayed-type hypersensitivity.

A follow-up of such work led to the separation of chemical components of human type *Mycobacterium tuberculosis* which were capable of replacing the whole cells in inducing the delayed type of hypersensitivity. Thus a chloroform-soluble waxy material can be isolated from human type *M. tuberculosis* which when injected with tuberculoprotein or other protein antigens in a water-in-mineral oil emulsion leads to marked delayed-type hypersensitivity. Further purification of the active material reveals it as a macromolecular lipid which hydrolyses in alkali to a mixture of mycolic acids and a glycopeptide. The former is a β-hydroxy branched chain fatty acid of unusual molecular size (C_{84}) and structure. The latter contains amino acids; D- and L-alanine, D-glutamic acid and *meso*-α, ε-diaminopimelic acid; aminosugars; galactosamine, glucosamine and muramic acid; and the sugars; arabinose galactose and mannose. This composition suggests a relationship to mucopeptide—the structural component of the bacterial cell wall and to the possession of surface-active properties.

Another approach to the same problem has regarded the intracellular persistence of phagocytosed organisms in such diseases as brucellosis, listeriosis, psittacosis, tuberculosis, etc. as the important determinant of the delayed-type sensitization. Possible support for this view may be found in the observation that tuberculin hypersensitivity can be produced in the guinea-pig by allowing a preliminary uptake of tuberculoprotein by the cells of a peritoneal exudate *in vitro* before injecting the washed cells into another animal. By this means delayed skin reactions were produced to intracutaneously injected tuberculoprotein 10 to 12 days later. These were claimed to be indistinguishable from those occurring in animals which were sensitized by injection of living BCG vaccine.

Induction of Pure Protein Hypersensitivity: Delayed Hypersensitivity Arising Without the Aid of Adjuvants or Infective Processes

A mild type of hypersensitivity to protein antigens can arise unaided by the foregoing processes of infection or oily adjuvants. This was first described as a transient occurrence during the response of guinea-pigs and man to injection of foreign proteins—a phase of delayed skin hypersensitivity before the subsequent development of Arthus-type sensitivity. The route of injection, the dose of protein antigen and rate of release of antigen have been regarded as crucial factors for the induction of delayed hypersensitivity. The classical experiments of Mote and Jones showed that repeated *small, intradermal* injections of rabbit serum proteins eventually induced in man a delayed-type skin reactivity to the antigen in question. On this view the commonly used dose of several milligrams of a soluble protein is regarded as inducing both delayed-type hypersensitivity and antibody synthesis. With such large doses, however, the sensitization process passes rapidly through the stage of delayed hypersensitivity to the production of circulating antibody, and the concurrent development of Arthus-type hypersensitivity is regarded as masking the delayed hypersensitivity. With diphtheria toxoid, for instance, 3/10th Lf. (0·05 μg) given by the intracutaneous route leads to a period of delayed hypersensitivity which is more slow to appear than when larger doses are used but which is more pronounced and lasts for a longer period. Eventually, however, circulating antibody and an Arthus hypersensitivity will develop.

Another method of sensitization is the injection of protein precipitates in the form of antigen–antibody precipitates prepared in antibody excess which can sensitize against the antigen component of the complex without stimulating detectable antibody formation. The action here may depend on slow release of antigen from the specific precipitates. Other methods depend on the use of denatured proteins and proteins linked to simple organic haptenes.

The identity between sensitization to bland proteins as described by Mote and Jones with that to bacterial products following an injection has not been universally accepted. Thus animals sensitized to proteins in the above ways and without the induction of detectable serum antibody do not respond to a skin test with subsequent necrosis, and do not develop shock on systemic challenge with antigen. Also the skin reactions have been generally found to reach maximum as much as 12 hours sooner and to die away quicker than those which follow an immunization procedure in which the same antigens are injected in oily mixture with mycobacteria. It is also curious that in humans multiple skin testing with tuberculin does not usually induce the delayed-type response unless there is pre-existing low-grade sensitization. It should be stressed that the skin reaction to tuberculin in tuberculous disease is able to persist unchanged for considerable lengths of time and is not disturbed by repeated skin tests or the presence of obvious circulating antibody to tuberculoprotein. In the present state of knowledge, it is not possible to decide whether these differences are of qualitative or merely quantitative nature, but some authors prefer to classify the weaker, pure protein reactions as 'Jones-Mote' reactions. Nevertheless, by the criterion of their transferability by lymphoid cells and not by serum, they clearly belong to the general category of 'specific cell-mediated hypersensitivity reactions'.

The common denominator of these factors for induction of delayed-type hypersensitivity (or homograft rejection) is in all probability the optimal stimulation of a particular class of immunologically competent cells which are under the influence of the thymus gland and which accumulate in distinctive compartments in the lymph nodes.

ANTIGENIC SPECIFICITY OF DELAYED HYPERSENSITIVITY

In the discussion (Chapter Six, p. 212) of the specificity of antibodies which result from immunization with hapten–protein conjugates, it was indicated that normally the resultant antibodies are found to be hapten specific. In experiments on delayed hypersensitivity this finding is quite different. Thus, guinea-pigs sensitized with small doses of hapten–protein conjugates will react to the immunogen but not to the hapten bound to an unrelated protein.

It might be inferred that these facts indicate a fundamental difference between the immunity mechanisms of antibody formation and delayed-type hypersensitivity. However, it is now also established that carrier specificity is also sometimes a property of antibody, especially the earliest produced IgG and IgM antibodies of the guinea-pig and rabbit. The elicitation of a secondary response of antibody production has also been shown to be carrier specific—even though the resultant antibodies might be hapten-specific. The induction of tolerance to haptens is also carrier dependent.

In the light of the currently available facts, it would appear justifiable to infer that the *initial* specificity of antigen recognition by the immunologically competent cell is similar in both types of response. However, in the case of continuing antibody production there appears a progressive narrowing of the molecular area involved in specific combination with antigen. As yet there is no clear evidence that the delayed-type hypersensitivity response similarly evolves with time in the direction of a narrowed specificity for smaller determinants on the antigen molecule (and increased binding energy for these).

The requirement that a close correspondence should exist between immunizing and test antigen for the demonstration of delayed hypersensitivity has prompted the interpretation that high binding energy is necessary for reactions between antigen and *cells*, and that this normally also requires a large area of interaction.

CURRENT SYNTHESIS OF EXPERIMENTALLY DERIVED CONCEPTS FOR INTERPRETATION OF THE ROLE OF CELL-MEDIATED HYPERSENSITIVITY

Cell-mediated immunity is regarded as a property of a thymus-controlled population of small lymphocytes which are able specifically to react with a relatively large antigenic determinant of the immunogen. The hypersensitivity phenomenon manifested by these cells cannot be attributed to antibodies synthesized by other cells and subsequently transferred to these lymphocytes but derives from some built-in property of the lymphocytes themselves. The prototype phenomenon of delayed hypersensitivity—the skin reaction—occurs as a response to antigen which calls forth a steadily mounting exudation of cells which progresses to local necrosis.

In the years preceding the appearance of the first edition of this book in 1963 the principal *in vitro* model which was accepted as reproducing the essential features of delayed hypersensitivity was that of Rich and Lewis (1928) in which it was shown that addition of antigen (tuberculin) to explants of spleen or buffy coat from tuberculous guinea-pigs inhibited emigration of cells from these explants, but had no effect on spleen explants from non-tuberculous animals. It was later shown by others that the sensitivity of spleen and bone marrow explants from tuberculous guinea-pigs and fowls to a range of different tuberculins ran parallel with skin or wattle reactivity.

In this model it seems clear that immobilizing effects were produced on several constituent cells (macrophages, fibroblasts and lymphocytes) of the explant. However, the macrophage is by all accounts the most visibly affected cell. By comparison the inhibition of migration of lymphocytes or fibroblasts is considerably less. Although the original authors referred to the production of cell death, this model really gave no clear indication of how this came about.

A similar but simpler model is the immobilization and clumping of macrophages which occurs when antigen is introduced into the peritoneal cavity of a sensitized animal. The macrophages stick to one another and to the wall of the peritoneum, but there is no component of necrosis in this model.

Two other models are available for homograft reactions. In one such, monolayer target cell cultures of fibroblasts are used into which lymphocytes from homograft sensitized animals are introduced and cause cytolysis of the target cells. It is stressed that initial close contact of lymphocyte and target cell is observed before onset of lysis and that relatively high ratios of lymphocytes to target cells are necessary for this effect, which, unlike the cytolysis brought about by antibody, occurs in the absence of complement. In other models, destruction of monolayer cells has been achieved by peritoneal macrophages from homograft-sensitized animals. Again, the adherence of macrophages to target cells is followed by lysis, which occurs quicker than that achieved by lymphocytes and at a lower ratio of macrophages to target cells.

It is therefore evident that, if we accept these models, effective destructive action on suitable target cells can be achieved by close contact of either *macrophages* or *lymphocytes*, but that probably the former is very much more efficient in this capacity. The superiority of the macrophage in this respect may derive from its more extensive and plastic cytoplasm, and its more liberal supply of lysosomal hydrolytic enzymes.

A recent experimental model for studying the effect of antigen on migration of macrophages makes use of purified suspensions of lymphocytes and macrophages (p. 499) and shows clearly that the reaction is controlled by the essential presence of lymphocytes in the mixture and that only a small proportion (1 in 50 cells) is necessary. Incidentally, use of the same methods for separating a peritoneal exudate into pure suspensions of lymphocytes and a pure suspension of macrophages has led to the demonstration that only the lymphocytes can act to transfer a delayed hypersensitivity response to an unsensitized guinea-pig. Pure macrophage suspensions were unable to effect either local or systemic transfer of hypersensitivity.

The lymphocyte can therefore act as the specific initiating cell in delayed hypersensitivity, tumour and homograft rejection reactions and a few sensitized lymphocytes after contact with antigen can secondarily involve a large number of *normal* macrophages to produce mutual adherence and immobilization of the whole population. Presumably the property which enables sensitized lymphocytes to react specifically with antigen is a macromolecule akin to antibody, even though antibody secreted by lymphocytes has never been detected in circumstances related to delayed hypersensitivity. In any case, this antibody-like entity would have to differ from most secreted antibody, since lymphocytes bearing these hypothetical receptors can only interact effectively with molecules which are themselves immunogenic (see discussion on specificity, p. 508) in contrast to haptens, which are able to combine with specific antibody but do not themselves cause antibody production.

It is not at present known how the material released by lymphocytes on contact with the antigen causes the macrophages to adhere to each other and become immobilized. Possibly more than one factor is involved; one, which appears to be rather smaller than albumin, is active (once formed) in the absence of antigen, but there is some evidence to indicate that a possible second factor (? antibody) acts only when antigen is also present.

A further complicating observation is that under circumstances when a suspension of labelled parenteral lymphocytes from a pure-line strain of mice are injected intravenously into the F_1 hybrid (obtained by mating this strain with a different pure-line mouse) in order to induce a graft-*versus*-host reaction (see p. 101) clear evidence of actual transformation of lymphocytes to macrophages within the liver resulted. The thesis that lymphocytes convert to macrophages during inflammation dates from Metchnikoff. However, on present evidence such transformation appears to be an exceptional occurrence, and there is no real evidence that macrophages specifically reactive for antigen can derive from specifically sensitized lymphocytes.

Further influences upon the lymphocyte–macrophage exudate population may depend on pharmacological mediators released early after the interaction of sensitized lymphocytes with antigen. Thus, during the course of a delayed-type response in the guinea-pig skin, extracts made from the lesion at increasing time intervals yield a permeability factor (LNPF) which rises and falls in amount over a time course which agrees with that of the size of the lesion. It has not been possible to show that antigen can act to release LNPF from lymphocytes derived from a sensitized animal, and since normal lymphocytes when damaged can also release LNPF an alternative explanation is possible that its local accumulation corresponds with the accumulation of lymphocytes from which LNPF may be released in consequence of the stasis and any resultant damage.

However, since LNPF itself promotes further cell accumulation the resulting process could have an auto-catalytic character and account for the fact that most of the cells in a delayed-type skin are not specifically sensitized cells.

The final act in the process of target-cell destruction in homograft or tumour rejection may relate to the phenomenon of allogeneic inhibition (which is explained in Chapter Fourteen) in which cytolysis follows close apposition of two cells of different genotype (and presumably different surface transplantation antigens). The *in vitro* experimental demonstration of such cytolysis is obtained after the aggregation together of different pairs of cell types by means of phytohaemagglutinin or heterologous antibody. Aggregation of even non-sensitized lymphocytes to allogeneic target cells will lead to the cytolysis of the latter and therefore the only requisite theoretically necessary for conferring cytolytic ability on a normal lymphocyte need be the possession of a surface located antibody-like entity which would serve to link its surface to that of the target cell. This phenomenon has so far only been shown in the mouse.

TUBERCULIN HYPERSENSITIVITY IN TUBERCULOSIS

The increased specific reactivity to a protein of the bacillus which develops in the course of tuberculous disease was apparent in the observations of Robert Koch concerning the different tissue responses to a first and second contact with virulent tubercle bacilli: namely the *Koch phenomenon*. In his words:

> 'If a normal guinea-pig is inoculated with a pure culture of tubercle bacilli, the wound, as a rule, closes and in the first few days seemingly heals. After 10 to 14 days, however, there appears a firm nodule which soon opens, forming an ulcer that persists until the animal dies. Quite different is the result if a tuberculous guinea-pig is inoculated with tubercle bacilli. For this purpose it is best to use animals that have been infected 4 to 6 weeks previously. In such an animal, also, the little inoculation wound closes at first, but in this case no nodule is formed. On the first or second day, however, a peculiar change occurs at the inoculation site. The area becomes indurated and assumes a dark colour, and these changes do not remain limited to the inoculation point, but spread to involve an area 0·5 to 1 cm in diameter. In the succeeding days it becomes evident that the altered skin is necrotic.

It finally sloughs, leaving a shallow ulcer which usually heals quickly and permanently, and the regional lymph nodes do not become infected. The action of tubercle bacilli upon the skin of a normal guinea-pig is thus entirely different from their reaction upon the skin of a tuberculous one. This striking effect is produced not only by living tubercle bacilli, but also by dead bacilli, whether killed by prolonged low temperature, by boiling or by certain chemicals.'

Since the Koch phenomenon could be elicited by killed cells, Koch proceeded to look for a bacterial extract with the same activity, and finally evolved a preparation called *old tuberculin* (OT). This consisted of a glycerine-broth culture of human type, *M. tuberculosis*, maintained for 6 to 8 weeks, concentrated by boiling to one-tenth of its volume, and finally freed from bacilli by filtration. The specific tuberculo-protein can nowadays be made by precipitation with ammonium sulphate or trichloroacetic acid from unheated culture filtrates from living bacilli in a synthetic medium. This *purified protein derivative* (PPD) is preferable to old tuberculin since it is reasonably constant in composition and its potency is standardized for diagnostic purposes.

Allergic reactivity to tuberculin is readily demonstrated in the guinea-pig. The injection into a normal guinea-pig of as much as 2 ml of Koch's old tuberculin has little effect. But the injection of 0·1 ml into a guinea-pig, in the eighth or tenth week of tuberculous infection, may kill it within a few hours. Tuberculous patients or animals respond to an injection of tuberculin or PPD in three ways:

General toxaemia. The healthy adult who has been infected, but who is not suffering from clinical tuberculosis, can withstand the injection of about 0·01 ml of neat old tuberculin intramuscularly, without complaining of more than some malaise and pain in the limbs. But, in a clinically tuberculous patient, a severe reaction may develop, characterized by malaise, cough, dyspnoea, limb pains, vomiting and a high fever with rigors and marked lymphopenia. This reaction is also delayed by comparison with, say, acute anaphylactic shock and the pyrexia does not begin until about 4 hours after injection. Furthermore, although in anaphylactic shock there is a transient fall in the blood levels of granulocytes and platelets, the lymphopenia is less marked. Febrile reactions with headache and malaise are produced in sensitized subjects by inhalation of minute amounts of tuberculo-protein and such reactions are frequently seen in pharmacists who handle the dried PPD without adequate precautions.

Focal reaction. After the systemic administration of rather larger doses of OT to tuberculous animals, at the site of pre-existing tuberculous foci there can be seen by the naked eye dark red areas of congestion ringing the tuberculous granulation tissue. Focal necrosis may result.

Local reaction. This is seen in man as the typical delayed-type cutaneous response, after the intracutaneous dose of only 0·1 ml of 1 in 1000 dilution of OT as a slowly developing granulomatous response, reaching a maximum of 48 hours and subsiding over the following 7 days. However, with large doses given subcutaneously the local site within a few hours becomes very congested, dark red or almost violet in colour. Later the area may slough.

In the case of infection of man or experimental animals with *M. tuberculosis* the cutaneous reactivity is seldom obscured by coexistent Arthus-type reactivity. This circumstance is highly convenient for the diagnostic reliability of the Mantoux and other tuberculin tests. However, when guinea-pigs or rabbits are injected with tuberculo-protein separated from the bacilli, high titres of circulating antibody can be built up following repeated doses, and injection of tuberculo-protein subcutaneously will then give rise to Arthus-type responses.

In man, a truly remarkable degree of sensitivity can occur in cases of tuberculous infection. Thus severe local swellings can result from an intracutaneous injection of 1 unit (about 0·000028 mg) of the standard preparation of PPD. By contrast, even highly sensitized guinea-pigs require 100 units before they give a clearly visible reaction. Sensitized cattle or rabbits require still more. Rats and mice do not show typical visible skin reactions at any level of antigen, although a histological response occurs.

A delayed type of *corneal reactivity* can be obtained in a highly sensitized animal when antigen is injected directly into the cornea. The response is a milky white opacity increasing up to 24 or 48 hours after injection. The corneal response is particularly valuable for indicating the presence of delayed-type allergy in the presence of antibody-determined hypersensitivity. The presence of precipitating antibody will determine an Arthus type of response on intradermal or subcutaneous injection, and this will obscure a subsequent delayed-type response. The cornea is non-reactive even in animals with high titres of circulating antibody. This has been attributed to the lack of blood vessels in the cornea since, as explained in Chapter Nine, the tissue damage in Arthus reaction is dependent upon an antigen–antibody interaction in the lumen or walls of blood vessels. This concept is supported by the finding that Arthus reactions can take place in a cornea which has become vascularized as a result of the previous application of an irritant. The recent demonstration that vascular channels do exist in a normal cornea does not apparently invalidate this argument since they normally exist in a collapsed and relatively non-functioning condition. The corneal test cannot be used, of course, in man.

THE ROLE OF DELAYED-TYPE HYPERSENSITIVITY IN TUBERCULOUS INFECTION

Two major questions arise. First, how do the hypersensitivity reactions relate to pathogenesis? Secondly, does this immunological hyper-reactivity confer on the body any real immunity or protection? Both are highly controversial issues.

As Rich has clearly pointed out in his book *The Pathogenesis of Tuberculosis*, in the hypersensitive animal a bland antigen substance behaves as though it were an acute toxin, inducing reactions varying from mild inflammation to total local necrosis, and death when given systemically.

In delayed-type hypersensitivity convincing evidence has never come forth that humoral antibody bears any causal relationship to the tissue reactivity and damage. Presumably the destructive activity of the antigen in delayed-type hypersensitivity results from a direct interaction with the sensitized cells with which it comes into contact. Further, no intermediary factors analogous to histamine and the other pharmacological agents which act in antibody-conditioned responses have been demonstrated in bacterial allergy. Nevertheless, the materials released by lymphocytes on contact with antigen, and the lymph node permeability factor (p. 511), when injected into the skin, cause increased capillary permeability and a gradual selective accumulation of mononuclear cells.

How far is tuberculin hypersensitivity responsible for the disease manifestations in man? This is a difficult and controversial problem. As in many other such complicated problems, analysis will depend upon accurate measurement of the many simultaneous and interacting processes. In tuberculous infection in man we are sadly deficient in methods for measurement of such factors, and the argument from artificial experiments, often employing relatively vast doses of bacillary products, is full of pitfalls.

The central fact which establishes the importance of hypersensitivity in tuberculous infection is that tubercle bacilli have very little power of producing necrosis of tissue in the normal body. In tissue cultures of macrophages 50 or so bacilli can be present in a single intact cell. Also, there has been a general lack of success in demonstrating a primary toxicity of any kind in any chemical fractions of mycobacteria. Tuberculoprotein can be injected into a person who has never previously had contact with tubercle bacilli in large amount without producing either local necrosis or constitutional upset. On the contrary, when hypersensitivity has become established, both tubercle bacilli and tuberculoprotein act upon the body as though they were possessed of a high degree of toxicity. As a result of this change, the tissues of the allergic body will become inflamed and undergo necrosis with amounts of tuberculoprotein which would be harmless in the normal. Admittedly, claims to have shown direct toxic activity by mycobacteria fractions have been put forward by various investigators. Examples would be the so-called cord factor (Bloch) and the Pmko lipopolysaccharide (Choucroun). Tubercle bacilli of various kinds can cause severe toxic reactions if injected in sufficient quantity. However, there is no indication that, weight for weight, the bacterial bodies of virulent strains are any more toxic than those of attenuated or avirulent strains of mycobacteria.

The idea that hypersensitivity accounts for the tissue damage in human tuberculous infection such as the caseation and cavitation, as well as the general toxaemia, lassitude and wasting, is based on analogies drawn from the guinea-pig. The experimental findings of the Koch phenomenon and the hypersensitivity to tuberculoprotein as manifest in the guinea-pig have been regarded as comparable to clinical events in man. It is notoriously difficult, of course, to transfer data from one animal species to another, but, at least in regard to his capacity to develop hypersensitivity during tuberculous infection, man is able to exceed by far even the guinea-pig. A highly hypersensitive person may react to an intracutaneous injection of 0·1 ml of a 1 in 1,000,000 dilution of old tuberculin which is a far smaller amount than is required to produce a reaction in the hypersensitive guinea-pig.

The events of the Koch phenomenon are often compared with the results of so-called primary and post-primary (or reactivation) types of disease in man. The primary complex consists of the usually small peripheral pulmonary granuloma (Ghon focus) with enlarged granulomatous draining lymph node. This may be compared with an early state of affairs in the guinea-pig. However, whereas in the latter the progressive multiplication of tubercle bacilli and their spread by lymphatic channels eventually leads to generalized miliary tuberculosis and death, in man the primary complex usually regresses to a small fibrotic and sometimes calcified pulmonary focus which may include living tubercle bacilli for long periods of time. Even though such an individual remains intimately exposed to persons with open tuberculosis it is extremely rare to find evidence at autopsy that a second primary complex has occurred. Reactivation disease takes the form of a gradually evolving caseous and fibrotic pulmonary focus without lymph-node involvement. The inference is that this altered behaviour in the reactivation stage depends upon the acquisition of hypersensitivity. The advent of such events as sudden bronchopneumonic extension or cavity formation is regarded as the more violent manifestation of such hypersensitivity.

The actual result of any local contact of tubercle bacilli with host tissue will depend on many factors, of which the dose of infecting organisms and the degree of allergy of the tissues are presumably of the highest importance. When a mass of necrotic (caseous) tuberculous granulation tissue with its contained bacilli and large amounts of tuberculoprotein is suddenly liberated into a bronchiole of a highly allergic lung, then the expected sequel would be a violent exudative pneumonia (tuberculous bronchopneumonia) and when liberated into the pleural cavity, an acute exudative pleurisy.

Tubercle bacilli vary in their ability to invade the tissues of the body progressively and eventually to cause death in a susceptible species like the guinea-pig. It might be thought that the more virulent organisms would show some difference from the less virulent or avirulent organisms in their allergenic activity. As pointed out above, the tubercle bacilli, through their wax fraction, possess the ability to enhance the immunogenicity of tuberculoproteins. On the basis of extraction studies of 6-week cultures, the content of wax D in mammalian tubercle bacilli shows a fair correlation with the various degrees of virulence of different bacillary species. However, there are difficulties in accepting that these findings mean that individual bacilli possess an amount of wax in direct proportion to their virulence, for it is not necessarily fair to compare the wax content of bacilli grow *in vitro* with that of bacilli growing in human tissues.

Apart from such claims, it is apparent that mycobacteria vary in their ability to multiply shortly after their introduction into the animal body, at a time before allergy has become established. Thus, the avirulent cultures do not multiply at all if injected in small doses, whereas the virulent organisms multiply at a rate characteristic for and proportional to the degree of virulence of the strain. Hence, the severity of the toxic damage, which depends on the amount of available antigen, must also depend on the rapidity with which multiplication occurs *in vivo*.

RELATIONSHIP OF TUBERCULOPROTEIN ALLERGY TO IMMUNITY IN TUBERCULOSIS

Bacterial immunity refers to the state of resistance of the host and may be specific or non-specific. *Bacterial allergy* refers to that state of heightened reactivity of the tissues which results in accelerated inflammation or possibly necrosis of tissue. On what basis could this cellular reactivity prove to exert a protective effect? Theoretically an allergic response on the part of any individual tissue may be either beneficial or harmful to the whole animal according to the circumstances. Thus the allergic ulceration of the skin in the Koch phenomenon may be regarded as a constructive effort to shed bacilli from the body and prevent their progress into the tissues. However, ulceration in a tissue such as the lung may lead to a disastrous bronchopneumonic extension of disease.

Is there such a thing as immunity in tuberculosis? In the guinea-pig, immunity can be shown to be induced by the use of the attenuated strain of bovine organisms known as BCG. When a vaccine of these living organisms is injected into guinea-pigs and these are challenged at, say, 4 weeks later, by the injection of a fully virulent culture, it can readily be shown that the lesions of the disease develop more slowly than in the animals of a control group which did not receive BCG. But the immunity produced in this case is only relative. The guinea-pigs always eventually succumb to tuberculosis, albeit some time after the controls. When vaccines of killed tubercle bacilli are used instead of the living BCG organisms the degree of immunity induced is even less.

In man most prophylactic efforts have also made use of attenuated living organisms. Although BCG was first used as long ago as 1925, only in recent years have really reliable results been collected to prove the efficacy of this vaccine. The notable series of reports of the trial organized by the Medical Research Council should have removed any remaining doubts. Under strictly controlled conditions in a group of 65,000 English schoolchildren, the reduction in the incidence of tuberculosis over a five-year period that could be attributed to the vaccine was 83 per cent. The same trial also included a test of another mycobacterium: the murine type of *M. tuberculosis* (the vole bacillus). This microbe is a variant of the mammalian tubercle bacillus which is naturally pathogenic for the field mouse. Since it is not an attentuated strain of a known human pathogen it was argued that it could not revert to a phase which was virulent for man. Under the same trial conditions as BCG, vole bacillus reduced the incidence by 87 per cent, although it proved more liable to produce local ulceration at the site of infection. Another important finding was that the vaccinated groups failed to show a single case of severe generalized miliary tuberculosis or of tuberculous meningitis, although these occurred in a few instances in the unprotected control group. The results also made it clear that vaccination could confer significant protection, not only against primary tuberculosis, but also against the post-primary or reinfection type of disease.

The way in which such immunity operates is far from clear. Certainly, the role of humoral antibodies has not, so far, been shown convincingly. This is in spite of the fact that various kinds of antibodies against the protein and carbohydrate constituents of the organism can readily be demonstrated in the sera of human patients or experimental animals harbouring the tubercle bacillus or after BCG vaccination. Attempts to transfer the acquired resistance produced by BCG passively to normal animals by the transfer of serum have always apparently failed. The possible relation of this immunity to an increased ability of the phagocytes to restrain intracellular growth of tubercle bacilli was discussed in Chapter Two (see the section on cellular immunity). It was shown there that evidence from tissue culture and *in vivo* experiments indicates that cells from immunized animals can inhibit intracellular growth.

Simultaneously with the development of humoral antibodies and immunity, the tuberculous animal develops hypersensitivity. So far as is known, this state of allergy is manifest only against certain proteins of the bacillus, the tuberculoproteins, although it has recently been claimed that the glycolipid of the Pmko wax fraction mentioned above will elicit such response. A similar allergic reactivity to tuberculoprotein can be induced in the guinea-pig by injecting it along with the so-called wax D fraction of these organisms. However, animals rendered allergic in this way are without resistance to subsequent challenge with virulent organisms.

When animals have been vaccinated with BCG they acquire both immunity and hypersensitivity. Repeated injections of tuberculoprotein can abolish hypersensitivity, at least as judged by a skin reaction, but such desensitized animals retain their acquired resistance. So, on the face of it, allergy can be present in the absence of demonstrable immunity and immunity can be observed in a desensitized animal. Accordingly, it has been argued that allergy exists quite independently of immunity; and, as a corollary, it is often implied that all immunity is 'good' and all allergy is 'bad'.

It is questionable whether it is possible to desensitize all the tissues of a guinea-pig so completely that it can be regarded as wholly non-allergic. So argue those who regard allergy as useful; they also point out that it has not been possible in the experimental animal to increase resistance without at the same time increasing allergy. On this view, the increased inflammatory response of the allergic individual is of survival value to the host, for example, because the macrophages will accumulate more rapidly, and prevent rapid dissemination of bacilli *via* the lymphatic vessels. The question has been put to test by studies of the ability of intense inflammation to hinder the dissemination of bacilli. It is found that the inflammation from an allergic reaction comes on too late to prevent the dissemination of bacilli through the lymphatics. Indeed, in the recent Medical Research Council trials it emerged that subjects with strongly positive skin reactions to tuberculin had a greater risk of developing clinical tuberculosis subsequently than those with only moderate skin sensitivity, and therefore very high levels of allergy may apparently be a disadvantage.

THE CLINICAL SIGNIFICANCE OF THE MANTOUX TEST

A Mantoux test is a test for delayed-type hypersensitivity using tuberculoprotein, in which 0·1 ml of a high dilution of old tuberculin (OT) or purified protein derivative (PPD) is injected intracutaneously into the skin of the forearm. The details of the procedure are further discussed in Chapter Sixteen, p. 681.

A positive reaction indicates past or present infection with the tubercle bacillus of either human or bovine type. A negative reaction, of course, usually indicates the absence of disease, but it is well recognized that during phases of a rapidly progressing infection, as in tuberculous bronchopneumonia, a negative result may occur as a result of desensitization by bacterial products. Also, the Mantoux test is negative during the early stages of infection (a period of about three weeks).

The test has been used in prognosis, since the classical observations of Heimbeck which correlated the liability to develop clinical tuberculosis in nurses with the results of Mantoux tests done at the time of entry at hospital training. Clinical tuberculosis subsequently occurred about eight times as frequently in the negative as in the positive groups. Subsequent results have borne out the prognostic implication of a negative Mantoux test when the subjects are entering a relatively highly contaminated environment. But the concept of the Mantoux test as an indicator of immunity is highly questionable. Indeed, the testing routine largely begs this question, since the finding of a positive reaction in a nurse who presents herself for training means, with the few exceptions of those who are in course of developing the disease, that these persons have already recovered from a past tuberculous infection, and therefore they must possess a degree of immunity, for otherwise they would be either ill or dead. Also, as is usual in such circumstances, Heimbeck's nurses had been carefully examined for signs of disease before they were enrolled and all those with a history of or with symptoms of tuberculosis had been excluded. The concept of the Mantoux test as an indicator of immunity is only valid, therefore, in a statistical sense. In this way it can provide the administrator with a useful aid to the selection of nurses for work in tuberculosis wards, but it could be highly misleading in the case of an individual in another occupation.

HYPERSENSITIVITY IN INFECTIVE DISEASES OTHER THAN TUBERCULOSIS

In the early part of this chapter, allergy to tuberculin was adopted as the classical example of delayed-type hypersensitivity, and the exquisite degree of the allergy which can develop in human beings to this antigen, and the important role which it plays in the pathogenesis of this disease, tended to make this example of bacterial allergy overshadow that seen in other infective diseases. Although it is not ordinary considered in relation to acute infections, delayed-type allergy can be shown present following infections with the streptococcus, the pneumococcus and the staphylococcus. The acute viral diseases also show that a similar specific allergic state exists as a result of infection with, for example, influenza, mumps, measles and herpes simplex agents. But it is in the chronic bacterial, viral and mycotic diseases that delayed-type allergy develops its most obvious and important manifestations. Among the bacterial diseases this type of allergy has been shown to be developed in typhoid fever, undulant fever, chancroid, whooping-cough, tularaemia and leprosy. Among viral diseases a classical example is provided by the response to revaccination with vaccinia virus. (This has been named, unfortunately—'the immediate response', and refers to the indurated red papule which is most obvious at about 24 hours after inoculation.) Also, a high degree of delayed-type allergy occurs in psittacosis, trachoma and lymphogranuloma inguinale. Cat-scratch fever, which is thought by some to be a virus infection, also yields a typical delayed-type skin response to the intradermal injection of a heated extract of an excised human lymph node from a case of the disease. (Some workers have postulated that the causal agent in this condition belongs to the psittacosis–lymphogranuloma group of viruses. However, no reaction is produced in these cases on testing with the group antigen of the psittacosis virus group.)

Among the fungal diseases the delayed type of allergy is consistently present; coccidioidomycosis is a dust-borne disease of the arid regions of the south-western parts of the United States. Inhabitants in these areas show a high incidence of infection as shown by a positive coccidioidin skin test. Similar skin reactivity can occur in other mycoses, such as, for example, blastomycosis, aspergillosis and the dermatomycoses. Immediate- and delayed-type responses frequently co-exist and can often be shown to be directed towards different antigenic components of these fungi. In the dermatomycoses, trichophytin, an extract of triturated cultures of a *Trichophyton* fungus, often shows a typical delayed-type reaction in the skin, but a few subjects also give immediate-type urticarial reactions.

Delayed-type allergy is prominent in syphilis, and has been shown to occur in certain protozoal diseases. In dermal leishmaniasis a tuberculin-like reaction has been obtained with an extract of cultured leishmania. In parasitic helminth infestation, such as, for example, trichiniasis, filariasis, schistosomiasis and hydatid disease, immediate-type reactions have usually dominated the picture. Skin tests with hydatid fluid (Casoni tests) often give an immediate weal and flare reaction, but the delayed-type reaction (the Casoni reaction, p. 486) is regarded as more reliable for diagnostic purposes. Table 12.1 lists some of these diagnostic tests.

Finally, the delayed-type reactions feature among the sequelae of insect bites. Very frequently both immediate weal-and-flare reactions and delayed-type indurated skin lesions may occur following the bite of the same insect in the same individual.

Generally speaking, when applied to problems of diagnosis, these reactions all resemble the tuberculin test in denoting the occurrence of infection without giving any clear indication as to its activity. The reactions are further limited in their usefulness by the fact that, once they become positive, they often remain so for many years. Hence there is a danger that current symptoms become attributed to disease which happened years before. In general there is much uncertainty about the average duration of delayed-type hypersensitivity in these conditions. It is commonly assumed in the case of tuberculosis that only in very exceptional cases will the test be negative in healthy persons who have been previously infected, providing that a sufficient strength of antigen is used for testing. Hence a negative response is taken to indicate absence of past or present infection. But this is a matter which depends upon the environment of the individual subsequent to testing. In a relatively highly infected environment, individuals who recover from infection usually incur frequent contact with tubercle bacilli and so have their hypersensitivity frequently restimulated. However, Daniels found that 8·6 per cent of young adults in the Royal Navy who reacted to 0·01 mg of OT initially became negative to 0·1 mg or 1·0 mg of OT within one year. Presumably this was related to their being exposed, subsequent to testing, to a smaller risk of chance infection than the average town-dweller.

In many of the above examples, the diagnostic use of a positive test result is obscured by the prevalence of such findings among the normal members of the community. Thus in certain geographical regions of the south-east United States skin tests with histoplasmin are positive in over 50 per cent of the population. The significance of a positive or a negative test must therefore in all cases be judged

TABLE 12.1

Delayed-type skin tests in common use for diagnostic purposes

Agent	Disease	Test substance
Bacteria	Tuberculosis	Tuberculoprotein (old tuberculin, purified protein derivative). Culture filtrate, usually modified by prolonged heating
	Leprosy	Lepromin: an extract of infected skin
	Brucellosis	Brucellin: a filtrate of a 20-day broth culture of *Br. melitensis* or *Br. abortus*. 'Brucellergen' is a nucleoprotein extract of the organisms
	Glanders	Mallein: a culture filtrate
	Johne's Disease (cattle)	Johnin: a culture filtrate
	Tularaemia	Protein extract of *Pasteurella tularensis*
Fungus	Dermatomycosis	Trichophytin: a culture filtrate
	Coccidioidomycosis	Coccidioidin: a culture filtrate
	Histoplasmosis	Histoplasmin: a culture filtrate
Metazoon	Hydatid disease	Casoni antigen: hydatid cyst fluid
Protozoon	Leishmaniasis	Extract of cultured leishmania
Virus	Mumps	Preparation of killed virus from the yolk sac of infected chick embryos
	Psittacosis	Group (heated) and specific antigens used
	Lymphogranuloma inguinale (venereum)	Formerly pus from an LGV bubo was used. Now extract of yolk sac of embryonated egg in which LGV or psittacosis virus has been grown is used
	Cat-scratch fever	Heated extract of excised lymph-node is from the disease

against the background. Similarly the occupation of the subject may need to be taken into account in judging the result. Although in this country a negative Brucellin test could be used to exclude the diagnosis of brucellosis in a veterinary worker, a positive result would contribute little information.

Few of the preparations which are listed in Table 12.1 are at present available in a purified condition. For many, such as LGV antigen, the potency is subject to considerable variation and, until a purified preparation of standardized reactivity is available, it will be difficult to assess the value of the tests.

A point of theoretical interest is that in all of the above examples in which studies have been done, the chemical nature of the component of the infective agent responsible for the delayed-type reaction has proved to be either protein or nucleoprotein.

LEPROSY

Leprosy manifests two distinct types of disease in man: tuberculoid and lepromatous. Tuberculoid leprosy involves scanty *Mycobacterium leprae* in granulomatous proliferative skin lesions; it can be interpreted as a self-limiting disease in patients who possess a high level of resistance. Lepromatous leprosy involves large numbers of bacilli in destructive lesions; it is a severe and progressive disease in patients with little resistance.

There are clear indications that cell-mediated hypersensitivity mechanisms play a role in determining the two characteristic pathogenetic mechanisms in these types of disease. The causative organism, *M. leprae*, which has not yet been cultured *in vitro*, has only recently been shown to be able to infect animals (hamster, mouse and rat). In the normal animals these infections remain localized at the site of injection (footpad or ear). However, when the immunological capacity of mice is reduced by thymectomy plus whole body X-radiation, there follows a dramatic increase in multiplication of *M. leprae* at disseminated specific sites on the skin surface. The histology of these now closely resembles the necrotic, bacillary-laden lesions of human lepromatous leprosy. This evidence therefore indicates that cell-mediated hypersensitivity mechanisms determine the granulomatous (or tuberculoid) disease, with high immunity and positive lepromin tests (see below) and the lepromatous disease, with low immunity and negative lepromin tests.

The *lepromin* reaction is included in Table 12.1 as an example of a delayed-type diagnostic test. This requires special discussion, however, since it presents many atypical features compared with the classical tuberculin test. The antigen *lepromin* is prepared from infected human tissue skin lesions rich in *Mycobacterium leprae* as found in patients with the lepromatous type of disease. The biopsied skin is first autoclaved, then ground in phenol-saline, the larger particles of tissue separated by filtration and the final suspension diluted and re-autoclaved. On injection into the skin of leprosy patients, two types of reaction may be observed. First, an erythematous papular lesion may appear at 1 and 2 days and disappear after 3 or 4 days. This is the '*early*' or *Fernandez* reaction and closely resembles a classical delayed-type reaction. Secondly, a late nodular reaction may appear which begins after 7 days and reaches a maximum in 3 or 4 weeks. With currently used lepromin which is chosen to give prominent '*late*' or *Mitsuda* reactions, the early reaction is slight and usually ignored. Histologically the late lepromin reaction is a granuloma made up of epithelioid cells and lymphocytes with prominent giant cells. It resembles in appearance the typical lesion of tuberculoid leprosy.

The lepromin test is typically positive in tuberculoid disease, yielding both an early and late reaction. A high proportion of healthy people (not necessarily selected from endemic leprosy areas) are also positive. In this respect the lepromin reaction bears analogy with the tuberculin test. In contrast, in lepromatous leprosy both early and late reactions are characteristically negative. Diagnostically a positive lepromin test is of little value except to exclude lepromatous leprosy; a negative test cannot exclude leprosy infection but would confirm a clinical diagnosis of lepromatous leprosy.

Possibly the *late* or *Mitsuda* reaction depends on the same mechanism which determines the accelerated formation of tubercle when tubercle bacilli are re-injected into tuberculous guinea-pigs. It is significant that autoclaved bacilli from many different species of mycobacteria have elicited typical granulomatous late reactions in tuberculoid leprosy subjects. It is also reported that normal healthy skin or liver, prepared in an identical manner to lepromin, will provoke the same, although weaker, pattern of response in different types of leprosy as elicited by lepromin itself.

The reason for the absent lepromin reaction in lepromatous leprosy is obscure. It is interesting that this selective reactivity applies to *M. leprae* antigens, and tests with other mycobacteria resulted in positive test results in both lepromatous and tuberculoid forms of disease.

STAPHYLOCOCCAL DISEASE

In general the application of traditional immunological procedures in the treatment of staphylococcal infections has proved disappointing in practice. The definition of the various toxins of the staphylococcus (in particular the α-toxin) and the development of antitoxic immunity in animals, at first raised hopes that this knowledge would be useful in treatment. But the fact that the lesions of staphylococcal infection arise in individuals who generally possess demonstrable circulating antitoxin and persist in spite of rising titres of antibody against this (and other staphylococcal toxins) would appear to provide good evidence against the importance of α-toxin in pathogenesis; and the use of antitoxin has also proved disappointing in the treatment of human lesions. Finally, vaccination with killed cultures of staphylococci fails to provide convincing protection against infection in either man or animals.

The possible role of hypersensitivity in staphylococcal infection was suggested by experiments performed more than thirty years ago, in which rabbits were challenged at weekly intervals with a series of 4 ten-fold dilutions of staphylococci and the lesions observed. It was found that the size of the resulting lesions which were produced by large doses became successively smaller, but the animals at the same time became liable to the production of purulent lesions by doses which were 100 times less than the minimal infective dose for the normal rabbit. With the large doses the effect is attributable to immunity, probably in the main to an ability to resist the necrotic effects of the α-toxin and leucocidin. Presumably hypersensitivity to staphylococcal protein may explain the second result. Indeed, the intracutaneous injection of formalin-killed staphylococcal vaccines in rabbits induces a state of delayed-type hypersensitivity. In such animals, minimal doses of live organisms produce abscesses which are larger and more severe than in control rabbits. Part of this effect may be attributed to the non-specific effects of inflammation which can be shown to increase the susceptibility to this particular organism. Thus it has been shown that the areas of inflammation recently produced in the skin by thermal, chemical, bacterial and immunological injury were more susceptible to staphylococcal infection than was normal skin. Presumably, in spite of the increased supply of polymorphs in such inflammation, other effects such as vasodilation, thrombosis, increased capillary permeability and increased lymph flow may be responsible for the increased susceptibility.

How far delayed-type hypersensitivity increases the severity of local staphylococcal infections in man remains to be determined.

STREPTOCOCCAL DISEASE

With α- and β-haemolytic streptococci, as well as with *Streptococcus pneumoniae*, it has been shown possible to induce a high degree of delayed-type hypersensitivity. Thus the intracutaneous inoculation of *Strep. viridans* vaccine results in a marked skin reactivity to killed organisms reinjected 8–10 days later. The reaction resembles a tuberculin skin response. With a higher degree of sensitization such as after several intracutaneous doses of vaccine, corneal reactivity can also be induced and such hypersensitive animals often react lethally to intravenous injection of streptococci. In contrast, when the preliminary injections were given intravenously the result was immunity without concomitant hypersensitivity. In other words such animals injected intracutaneously with living *Strep. viridans* gave smaller and firmer lesions.

In man, skin testing with vaccines of killed streptococcal antigens such as M-protein, and culture filtrates containing enzymes such as streptodornase and streptokinase and other products, has demonstrated very frequently delayed-type allergy towards streptococci, which in adults becomes wellnigh universal. The incidence of sensitivity increases generally with age, and superimposed on such a rise there is a sharp increase in the number of reactors at the time of epidemics of streptococcal sore throat.

The varied clinical patterns exhibited by infection with streptococci have been compared with a similar variation in the case of tubercle bacilli. Thus a common infection with Group A streptococci in the case of a 10-year-old child is a sore throat with or without the rash of scarlet fever. Here, a sharp febrile illness lasting a week may be followed by subsequent complications such as nephritis, rheumatic fever or erythema nodosum. Such patients show exquisite sensitivity following skin tests with streptococcal nucleoprotein. By contrast, the infant under 6 years shows a prolonged low-grade process of infection with frequent suppurative complications and widespread dissemination of organisms to produce such disease as streptococcal osteomyelitis. Rheumatic fever and nephritis rarely follow such illness in this age group.

This gross variation in the clinical picture with age bears comparison with the situation as it applies to tuberculosis and is interpreted to depend mainly on the development of both increased immunity and increased hypersensitivity with increasing experience of these organisms. Which, if any, of the manifestations of streptococcal disease are attributable to this hypersensitivity is not at all clear, but erythema nodosum should probably be numbered among them. Reactions to skin tests with streptococcal antigens in patients with erythema nodosum are consistently positive, and the tests frequently induce systemic reactions, including aggravation of the nodular skin lesions.

DELAYED-TYPE ALLERGY TO TOXOIDS AND VACCINES

Sensitivity to the materials which are used for prophylactic immunization occasionally occurs and may be so pronounced as to cause quite severe reactions. Such sensitivity is not uncommon in persons who have had a past infection with the same type of organisms as that from which the prophylactic is derived. A common example is provided by diphtheria toxoid (or toxin). A Schick test is intended to detect the absence or presence of circulating antitoxin. Diluted diphtheria toxin containing about 1/50 MLD of toxin (as determined in the guinea-pig) is injected intradermally. If an area of redness due to mild local damage is produced the test is positive and the subject is susceptible to diphtheria. But so-called false or *pseudo-reactions* occur due to the presence of delayed-type hypersensitivity to the protein of the toxin itself or to contaminating proteins. The pseudo-reaction has a maximum at 24–36 hours and then fades so as to have gone in 3 or 4 days. A control for the presence of a true Schick-positive reaction is provided for by the injection into another site of a mildly heated solution of the toxin, which can no longer give a reaction due to toxin but can still provoke the delayed skin reaction. Even in the presence of a pseudo-reaction, the true Schick reaction can be detected, since a positive will still be readable at 4 to 5 days and will pigment and desquamate before fading. Usually, however, a pseudo-reactor will be Schick-negative since a positive reaction would indicate that the subject must have been previously exposed to the organism (or to doses of diphtheria prophylactics) and has therefore had an opportunity for acquiring immunity.

Besides confusing the result of a Schick test, the delayed-type reaction can be the source of severe local reaction when soluble or alum-precipitated diphtheria formol toxoid is used for immunization. The pseudo-response to the Schick test therefore should act as a warning against provoking such an occurrence.

A delayed-type skin response is commonly observed at the time of smallpox vaccination and especially of revaccination. This is the so-called 'immune' or 'immediate' response, in which a red papule develops at 24 to 48 hours. Both terms are highly misleading. It has already been explained that the tuberculin response cannot be regarded as an indicator of immunity in any individual case. The presence of a positive delayed-type skin test implies that the subject has been vaccinated previously and has acquired a hypersensitivity to a protein constituent of the vaccinia vaccine (which could exist without co-existent immunity). The term 'immediate' for a delayed-type response is most unfortunate, but was originally intended to stress the fact that the hypersensitivity reaction was quicker than the papular reaction due to vaccinia virus infection, which, even in the accelerated response of the revaccinated subject, will not usually occur until the third or fourth day. Presumably the fact that a progressive reaction to develop papule, vesicle, pustule, etc. occurs sooner in a revaccination response than in a primary vaccinial response is also dependent upon delayed-type allergy, but in this case to the antigens of a living and multiplying virus.

DELAYED-TYPE REACTIVITY IN SARCOIDOSIS AND DISEASES OF RETICULAR TISSUES

The skin of patients with sarcoidosis, Hodgkin's disease, giant follicle lymphoma and other reticuloses is often less reactive in a tuberculin (Mantoux) test than would be expected when compared with unaffected persons from a similar age group. This lack of reactivity is not confined to tuberculin but appears to be part of a general deficiency of response (often termed *anergy*) to a wide variety of antigens normally producing skin reactions of the delayed type, e.g. *Candida albicans* or mumps virus. It would seem plausible to suppose that in most reticuloses these immunological changes represent a non-specific depression due to replacement of the lymphoid tissues by abnormal cells. However, the mechanism of such anergy in sarcoidosis may be different from that in other reticuloses, and this condition will be considered separately.

Sarcoidosis. Although some investigators have claimed that patients with sarcoidosis possess serum factors (anticutins) which depress activity of tuberculin and other antigens in the skin response, positive tuberculin responses in tuberculin-insensitive sarcoid patients can be induced by injecting into their skin leucocytes from tuberculin-sensitive donors and then injecting the site with tuberculin. In other words, a deficiency of the reactive *cells* is indicated. The lymphocytes in sarcoidosis show no diminution of numbers in the blood, but when peripheral blood leucocytes from such patients are maintained in tissue culture they are found to be relatively unaffected by added tuberculin. As previously explained (this chapter) the migration of tissue-cultured peripheral blood white cells from patients with pulmonary tuberculosis is decreased by tuberculin, and these *in vitro* findings confirm the lack of tuberculin reactivity in the lymphoid cells from sarcoid cases. In sarcoidosis such reactivity is deficient rather than totally absent, for injection of cortisone, systemically or into a local site, will often render a tuberculin-insensitive patient reactive to tuberculin. Also, use of a water-in-oil suspension of tuberculin instead of an aqueous solution will reveal low levels of skin sensitivity in sarcoidosis. Both these procedures are known to enhance weak tuberculin reactions in normal persons. By contrast, cortisone is not able to restore tuberculin skin reactivity in Hodgkin's disease and other reticuloses—indicating that the mechanism of the deficiency is different in these cases.

Patients with sarcoidosis given BCG immunization generally fail to develop a positive tuberculin reaction. There is evidence that contact sensitizing chemicals, e.g. dinitrochlorobenzene, also fail to sensitize patients with sarcoidosis as readily as normal subjects. Despite this deficiency in the acquisition of delayed-type hypersensitivity, various investigations have failed to reveal any diminution in the antibody response to re-immunization. Nevertheless, other reports describe a significant decrease in the response of patients with sarcoidosis to a *primary* stimulus of tetanus toxoid. These results would possibly agree with the view that antibody-forming cells are already responding to a strong antigenic stimulus so that the primary response is competitively inhibited. The pronounced hyper-γ-globulinaemia of such cases gives some support for this concept.

On the basis of their defective delayed hypersensitivity mechanisms the patients with sarcoidosis might be expected to show a decreased ability to control infections with bacteria, fungi or viruses. Whether this is so is far from clear. Tuberculosis has, indeed, been reported frequently in association with sarcoidosis and Hodgkin's disease. However, in sarcoidosis the data relate predominantly to cases in negroes of the United States, in whom tuberculosis is relatively more common. Sarcoidosis has been associated with two fungal infections in particular, histoplasmosis and cryptococcosis, but it is uncertain whether these represent instances of fungal infection complicating sarcoidosis or the fungal disease simulating sarcoidosis.

A useful diagnostic application of these immunological defects in sarcoidosis is provided by the application of skin and complement fixation tests with mumps virus antigen. Since most normal adults have already had a previous attack of mumps they will yield positive results in a delayed-type skin test and a complement fixation test with mumps virus antigen. A diagnosis of sarcoidosis is suggested when a negative skin test (read at 24 and 48 hours) is associated with a positive complement fixation test. Similar results are given in Hodgkin's reticulosis.

The Kveim Test in Sarcoidosis

This test resembles closely the 'late' or Mitsuda reaction to lepromin in cases of tuberculoid leprosy. Like this, the granulomatous reaction may depend on the same mechanism as that which determines the accelerated formation of tubercles when tubercle bacilli are injected into a tuberculous guinea-pig. However, until the nature of the antigenic component is elucidated it would be rash to conclude that the reaction is necessarily an immunological one. The test consists of the intradermal injection of a heated (pasteurized) saline suspension of sarcoid tissue obtained from a sarcoid spleen or lymph node. In patients with active sarcoidosis a dusky red nodule develops slowly over the next few weeks at the injection site. Histological examination, which forms an essential part of the complete test, reveals sarcoid tissue (scattered miliary nodules of epithelioid cells and giant cells, with close resemblance to miliary tubercles, but lacking central caseation).

The most widely held views attribute the Kveim specific stimulus either to host tissue in the test material that has been altered by sarcoidosis or to a foreign or infective agent (e.g. a mycobacterium, virus or mycoplasma or an exogenous agent such as pine pollen).

Possibly the closest analogy exists in the diseases berylliosis or zirconium granulomatosis, in which trace amounts of soluble zirconium salts or beryllium salts (without tissue components) can in sensitized persons give rise to skin granuloma of sarcoid-like appearance.

One common hypothesis of sarcoidosis attributes this disorder to many and varied antigenic stimuli. However, it seems unlikely that there are several different unrelated stimuli since the same Kveim test suspension can give similar responses in cases of sarcoidosis all over the world. Also sarcoidosis has a sharply defined geographical localization in North America and Northern Europe.

Another hypothesis regards the sarcoid process as a genetically determined immunological anomaly which manifests itself by decreased delayed-type responses and abnormal granulomatous responses to a variety of agents. However, the available evidence shows that individuals who were known to be previously tuberculin positive lost their reactivity on the development of sarcoidosis and were observed to regain sensitivity after regression of the sarcoidosis.

HODGKIN'S DISEASE

Hodgkin's disease is usually set aside from other lympho-proliferative diseases since histologically it appears as a granulomatous proliferation including many different types of cell which are not only of lymphatic origin. Thus eosinophils, mast cells and connective tissue cells are involved. Lymphoproliferative disorders such as lymphosarcoma and chronic lymphocytic leukaemia are common in most animals besides man. Hodgkin's disease is apparently restricted to man.

In some ways the immunological disorder of Hodgkin's disease can be regarded as the opposite of that of sex-linked congenital hypogammaglobulinaemia: antibody production and all immunoglobulin levels are normal, but the patients have a depression of all forms of delayed-type hypersensitivity.

The most consistent globulin alteration of Hodgkin's disease is elevation of the α_2 fraction which coincides especially with phases of activity of the disease. Hypoalbuminaemia is also commonly found, especially in patients with Hodgkin's disease of the liver. The γ-globulin fraction may be sometimes elevated but is usually within normal limits. Antibody production to a variety of antigens has usually been found to be normal but it has been claimed that the response to secondary stimuli is better than to primary immunization.

Most studies of delayed hypersensitivity have depended on chance previous exposure for immunization. Patients with Hodgkin's disease give, in general, poor or absent responses to such antigens as tuberculin, mumps virus antigen, *Candida albicans*, *Trichophyton gypseum*. These are substances to which a high proportion of a normal adult population might reasonably be expected to show positive delayed-type skin hypersensitivity. In one trial the results in comparison with controls were tuberculin 23 and 71 per cent; mumps antigen 14 and 90, *Candida albicans* 19 and 92 and *Trichophyton gypseum* 16 and 68 per cent.

Preliminary studies of the mechanism of allergy in Hodgkin's disease have been made by testing the ability of leucocytes from a sensitive donor to transfer reactivity to a Hodgkin's patient recipient. Neither local or systemic transfer of hypersensitivity could be effected. In this respect the patient with Hodgkin's disease differs from cases of sarcoidosis and lymphoproliferative disorders such as chronic lymphatic leukaemia, to whom transfer can be successfully achieved.

LYMPHOPROLIFERATIVE DISORDERS
(lymphosarcoma and lymphatic leukaemia)

In these conditions the immunological deficiency differs from that in Hodgkin's disease by more commonly involving the mechanism of antibody production, so that during the terminal months of these conditions a decrease in the level of all the immunoglobulins of the blood commonly occurs. Patients also may possess diminished delayed hypersensitivity to common allergens, although this is less constantly present than in patients with Hodgkin's disease.

An increased incidence of auto-immune disorders such as acquired haemolytic anaemia, leucopenia and thrombocytopenia has also been frequently described as accompanying lymphatic leukaemia and lymphosarcoma. (See also p. 332.)

INFECTIONS COMPLICATING THE LYMPHOPROLIFERATIVE DISEASES

Infections may frequently complicate the clinical course of cases of Hodgkin's disease or leukaemia. In leukaemia cases local factors may precipitate infection just as they do in any case of malignant neoplasm by mechanisms such as production of fistulae or destruction of protective surfaces. Other factors are, however, necessary to explain the increased sensitivity to infection of these cases, of which lack of granulocytes and deficient immunoglobulins are probably the most important. The immunological deficiency and the pattern of resulting lesions will depend on the type of leukaemia. Acute leukaemia cases constantly manifest infections, especially of the mouth and pharynx, and septicaemia commonly occurs. Chronic lymphocytic leukaemia has the next highest incidence of infections, which in many instances take the form of pneumococcal pneumonia.

The deficiency in acute leukaemia probably relates mainly to the lack of granulocytes. Infective complications occur particularly during relapse and subside during remissions of the disease. It is of great interest that patients with chronic myelocytic leukaemia remain relatively free from infections. In this form of leukaemia the blood contains an increased number of relatively mature types of granulocytes. In acute leukaemia the white cells of the blood are made up principally of immature blast forms, which have a poor phagocytic function, and deficient cytoplasmic lysosomes.

Chronic lymphatic leukaemia is frequently accompanied by hypogammaglobulinaemia. The increased incidence of recurrent pulmonary infection due to pyogenic cocci is analogous to the situation in sex-linked congenital hypogammaglobulinaemia. No correlation exists between the incidence of infection and the absolute number of blood granulocytes. As in hypogammaglobulinaemia tuberculosis is uncommon.

Hodgkin's disease is not uncommonly associated with tuberculosis. In some series as many as 20 per cent of cases are thus affected. Other diseases which have been associated with Hodgkin's disease are cryptococcosis and, in appropriate endemic geographical areas, brucellosis. In each of these three diseases, there is evidence that cellular immunity, presumably dependent on delayed hypersensitivity, is important for resistance. The same occurs in the thymus-determined immunological deficiency states (see Chapter Eight). Certain virus diseases are also seen with unusual frequency, such as herpes zoster and verruca.

DELAYED HYPERSENSITIVITY IN THE GENESIS OF RASHES

Although rashes are the most characteristic manifestations of many infections, especially those caused by viruses, there have been few studies about how they arise. As long ago as 1913 von Pirquet suggested that the rash of measles might be an allergic response to the disseminated virus. Presumably the papular and vesicular rashes of vaccinia and variola, the analogous pox virus diseases of animals, the maculo-papular rash in measles, and the lesions of zoster and herpes simplex may partly or wholly be explained in this way. Among bacterial diseases similar explanations may apply to the rash of meningococcal septicaemia or meningitis (spotted fever). However, the petechial rashes of various rickettsial diseases (endemic and epidemic typhus), and of virus diseases such as dengue and Chikungunya, are quite different in their causation.

The time course of multiplication and dissemination of the microbial antigens may be broadly inferred from the model of mouse-pox. Here it can be shown that on entering the host the virus proceeds to multiply at a primary focus. Then, after a day or two, viraemia is followed by localization and multiplication of the virus in such sites as the liver, spleen or bone marrow. These stages all occur in the incubation period, and the arrival of fever signifies that the internal replication of the virus has reached a point when a fresh entry into the blood occurs (secondary viraemia). The localization of virus in the skin and its multiplication possibly within foci of virus-bearing blood leucocytes within the dermal venules could provide sufficient antigen to elicit local delayed hypersensitivity reactions, which would contribute to the erythema and induration of the papule, and possibly to vesicle formation. The histological changes at the site of a smallpox vesicle are compatible with this explanation. The earliest change is a dilatation of the capillaries of the papillae of the dermis, with accumulation of leucocytes in the lumen and swelling of the endothelium. The venules of the dermis become cuffed with lymphocytes and macrophages, as in a delayed-type hypersensitivity skin response. Later, cells of the mid-layer of the epidermis enlarge, lyse and give rise to a vesicle cavity.

This general thesis of the role of cell-mediated hypersensitivity in rashes is supported by the following additional facts. First, demonstrable delayed-type skin responses are common in virus infections, and the time between the first exposure to virus and the appearance of the rash is adequate for sensitization to occur. Secondly, maculo-papular rashes can occur in the course of attempted desensitization of guinea-pigs with contact hypersensitivity after the injection of large intravenous doses of antigen. About 6 hours after such an injection a blotchy, raised, red, measles-like rash develops.

THE RELATIONSHIP OF HOMOGRAFT REJECTION TO HYPERSENSITIVITY REACTIONS OF THE DELAYED TYPE

The transplantation of living tissues from one individual to another belonging to the same species (homografts) usually results in the eventual destruction and rejection of the graft. The *homograft reaction,* as it is called, is an immunological response to antigens which are present in the graft but not in the recipient. Like other antigens they often stimulate antibody production, and several such antibodies have been demonstrated: haemagglutinins, haemolysins, leucocyte agglutinins and so on. For reasons which are discussed more fully in Chapter Thirteen, it is considered that serum antibodies are usually unable by themselves to effect the destruction of an established solid graft such as an orthotopic skin homograft, although they can act with complement to destroy transfused red and white cells or a graft of single cells, such as ascites tumour cells, when they are proliferating freely in the abdominal cavity of the recipient.

The homograft reaction has the following characteristics in common with delayed-type allergy:

(i) The reaction is accompanied by the infiltration into the graft of mononuclear cells (lymphocytes, macrophages and plasma cells).

(ii) While it has nearly always proved impossible to transfer the ability to reject a first homograft passively with serum alone, it can be transferred by means of living cells obtained from an animal which has already received a homograft, when these are derived from lymphoid tissues such as the spleen, the bone marrow and particularly those lymph nodes regional to the homograft.

For reasons which will become apparent in Chapter Thirteen, experiments giving clear-cut evidence for this statement can only be carried out with animals from inbred strains, and only the conclusions are given here.

The idea that homograft reactions are essentially a form of delayed-type hypersensitivity response receives support from two sets of observations made in guinea-pigs, in which species such responses are most easily observed. The first is that if an animal which has received a skin graft and rejected it is now injected intracutaneously with a tissue extract from the *same* donor, an obvious local skin reaction ensues. This skin reaction has all the characters of a typical delayed-type response. Its intensity varies with the degree of sensitivity of the recipient, showing a good inverse correlation with the survival time of the homograft from the same donor. Furthermore, the same tissue extract produces only a relatively minor and non-specific reaction when injected intracutaneously into an unsensitized animal.

A delayed-type reaction can also be produced passively and in a reverse manner. Thus grafts from a donor A are used to sensitize recipient B. Cells from the lymph nodes of B which are regional to the graft are later injected intracutaneously into A, with the result that the activated lymphoid cells are brought into contact directly with the transplantation antigens of the cells in the dermis of A *in situ*. Once again a delayed-type skin response is the result. No comparable reaction is evoked by means of killed cells or serum from B, or by living cells from a normal guinea-pig of the same inbred strain as B.

THE PASSIVE TRANSFER OF DELAYED-TYPE HYPERSENSITIVITY IN MAN

Many people have tried to extract from lymph node or spleen cells of animals showing delayed-type hypersensitivity some factor (for example, some special sort of antibody) which could passively transfer to normal animals the capacity to give a delayed-type hypersensitivity reaction to the antigen in question. As has already been stated, such a capacity can quite easily be transferred by injecting live cells from sensitized animals, and the sensitivity persists for so long as the cells remain alive in their new host—that is, for a few days if donor and recipient are genetically different so as to cause a homograft rejection (see Chapter Thirteen), and for weeks or months if they are genetically identical. However, in experimental animals such as the guinea-pig it has proved extremely difficult to obtain clear evidence that killed sensitized cells, or extracts from them, could passively transfer delayed-type hypersensitivity, and most attempts to show this have failed. Nevertheless, it has been demonstrated by several workers that in man what appears to be a transfer of this kind is achieved quite readily. It is possible that some fundamentally different mechanism exists in man, but more probable that the difference is due to the fact that man is a species in which the delayed type of hypersensitivity reaction is peculiarly well developed and easily elicited.

Leucocytes are obtained from the peripheral blood of a donor who has a moderate or marked degree of delayed-type hypersensitivity to tuberculin, or to diphtheria toxoid, and the cells are washed gently so as not to damage them. They can then be disrupted by repeated freezing and thawing, so that no intact cells remain. The material, which contains what J.S. Lawrence (who first demonstrated it) has termed 'Transfer Factor', is then treated with sufficient of an enzyme (deoxyribonuclease) to destroy the viscous nucleic acid which is released from the disrupted cells, and the extract obtained from about 0·2 ml of cells is injected into the skin of an unsensitized person, who has given no reaction to previous intracutaneous testing with the antigen in question. If the recipient is tested 24 hours later at a distant skin site (e.g. on the other arm) he will now produce a typical delayed-type reaction to the antigen. If a smaller quantity of cell extract is used, from 0·02 ml of cells for example, the recipient may not give a delayed-type reaction when tested at a distant site, but will still give one when tested at the site into which the cell extract was injected. Circulating antibody is apparently not transferred by this technique. For example, after transfer of hypersensitivity to diphtheria toxoid no neutralizing antibody to diphtheria toxoid can be demonstrated in the recipient's blood, or even at the local injection site, although tests for antitoxin are so sensitive that 0·002 unit (approximately 0·000024 mg) is detectable.

The sensitivity transferred by leucocyte extracts is quite specific, and is only elicited by those antigens to which the donor is sensitized. A point of considerable interest is that the hypersensitive state is not only present 24 hours after transfer, but in a high proportion of recipients it persists for periods as long as two years—a feature quite unlike anything which might be expected from transfer of an antibody which in man would be expected to have a half-life of little more than 20 days. Furthermore, delayed-type hypersensitivity transferred to a negative recipient in the way described has been transferred in turn by means of an extract of his now sensitized peripheral blood leucocytes to a second negative recipient.

Attempts to show that human Transfer Factor can passively transfer delayed hypersensitivity to guinea-pigs have so far failed, but the administration of guinea-pig cell extracts to humans has, for obvious reasons, not been attempted.

The nature of Transfer Factor is at present unknown, but the activity has been found to persist apparently undiminished after treatment not only with deoxyribonuclease but also with ribonuclease or with trypsin. This excludes the possibility that the factor is single stranded nucleic acid but not that it might be double stranded nucleic acid or nucleoprotein or antigen in some way associated with nucleic acid. There is some experimental evidence that antigenic materials taken up by phagocytic cells can become bound to ribonucleic acid and, in such form, are unusually potent in evoking immunological responses. If the factor proves in fact to contain modified antigen it will remain of great interest, but its activity will, of course, represent an active sensitization rather than a passive transfer of delayed-type hypersensitivity.

INHIBITION OF CELL-MEDIATED HYPERSENSITIVITY

There are many reasons why it is important for the physician or surgeon to be able to mitigate or prevent the effects of delayed-type hypersensitivity. There are good reasons to believe that much of the damage in many chronic infective diseases, in auto-immune diseases and in contact or drug eczema stems from this source. Also, for purposes of transplantation of tissue it is necessary to prevent the immunological response which brings about graft rejection and which is mainly, at least, dependent on delayed hypersensitivity mechanisms. Usually the need will be to suppress a state of established hypersensitivity but it is also important to consider how the action of antigen or adjuvants in creating such hypersensitivity may be inhibited.

PROCEDURES FOR SUPPRESSION OF DELAYED HYPERSENSITIVITY

Suppression both of the induction and of the manifestation of delayed hypersensitivity can be achieved either by specific procedures which involve use of the hapten or hapten-carrier conjugate or of non-specific measures (e.g. X-rays, drugs and anti-lymphocyte serum). Many of these procedures have specific applications. The use of X-radiation, drugs and anti-lymphocyte sera have, in the recent past, found important uses for suppression of the homograft rejection mechanism and the discussion of such non-specific procedures will be found in Chapter Thirteen. The corticosteroid drugs have a wide application, being used for the treatment of many disease states which involve cellular hypersensitivity. They will be considered in this chapter.

SPECIFIC PROCEDURES

The state of unresponsiveness may be produced by antigen administration either before or after sensitization. When it is so produced before sensitization, it falls under the general heading of *tolerance* induction and includes phenomena such as suppression of contact sensitivity by prior feeding with allergen and *split tolerance* or '*immune deviation*'. Procedures to render sensitized animals non-reactive by specific means are included under the term *desensitization*.

Sulzberger–Chase Phenomenon

When non-sensitized animals are fed with certain allergenic chemicals, a state of specifically depressed reactivity can be induced involving both the acquisition of delayed-type sensitivity and the production of antibody. The animal acquires resistance to subsequent efforts to sensitize with the same allergenic chemical. The matter is further discussed in Chapter Three, pp. 113–17 and 120–3.

Split Tolerance: Immune Deviation

It has already been pointed out that the injection of a simple protein antigen without adjuvants results in the guinea-pig in subsequent antibody production and Arthus-type (antibody-dependent) hypersensitivity. When such an injection is followed by an immunization procedure (antigen in water-in-oil emulsion plus killed mycobacteria) which would normally result in a prolonged and high level of delayed-type hypersensitivity, this process may be blocked or 'deviated' so that antibody production occurs without significant delayed hypersensitivity. This selective depression of certain immune responses to an antigen with retention of others has been called 'split tolerance' or 'immune deviation'.

The injection of antigen in complete Freund-type adjuvant has distinctive effects which do not occur in animals immunized without mycobacterial peptidoglycolipid. Besides the production of delayed hypersensitivity, in the guinea-pig γ_2-antibody production is markedly increased (see Plate 7.3, following p. 278), cytophilic antibody production is increased, and when suitable antigens such as brain are used, production of organ-specific auto-immune diseases such as allergic encephalomyelitis are facilitated. In immune deviation secured by the prior injection of soluble antigen alone, antigen adsorbed on aluminium hydroxide or antigen in incomplete Freund adjuvant, these distinctive effects are diminished, although total antibody production remains intact.

The prior exposure of a guinea-pig to antigen leads to a reduced ability to transfer the delayed hypersensitivity to normal recipients by lymphoid cells, indicating that the mechanism of immune deviation is dependent on specific alteration or elimination of some part of the population of immunologically competent cells by antigen. These observations are most readily explained by assuming that different cell types are responsible for the induction of the different forms of immune response. It has already been explained in Chapter Three that delayed hypersensitivity and antibody-producing systems differ in their response to thymectomy or bursectomy in a way which also suggests that distinct cell populations under the control of the thymus or of the bursa of Fabricius (or its analogue in mammals) subserve respectively the functions of delayed hypersensitivity or antibody biosynthesis.

Desensitization

Desensitization refers to the introduction of new antigen to suppress established hypersensitivity transiently and it acts, presumably, by combining with the cells which mediate the response rather than by blocking the induction of hypersensitivity. This phenomenon of desensitization can be demonstrated by exposure of the cells used for passive transfer to small doses of the sensitizing immunogen *in vitro*. This, in itself, is a demonstration that desensitization is a peripheral (or efferent) rather than a central (or afferent) inhibition. The sensitized cells by interaction with antigen become unable to effect a transfer of hypersensitivity to their new host, an effect which would devolve upon the small lymphocyte. In addition, antigen introduction into the peritoneal cavity of sensitized guinea-pigs causes transient disappearance of the macrophages, which clump together on the wall of the peritoneal cavity, and thus it is possible that some of the results of densensitization may depend on immobilization of macrophages.

It has previously been mentioned that the phase of manifestation of delayed-type hypersensitivity is often transient so long as no depot of antigen in sensitizing form remains. In clinically important active delayed-type allergies, however, such a depot may be impossible to remove, and although sensitized cells are probably being eliminated by interaction with antigen, new ones are continuously being generated. However, in auto-immune diseases the damage from delayed-type hypersensitivity reactions may itself create or release new immunogen for the sensitizing process and therefore it might be of value to suppress the development of new reactive cells by drugs or other means, in the hope that the supply of sensitizing immunogen and the vicious circle will be interrupted.

In simple protein hypersensitivity (p. 507) desensitization is readily attained and a single injection of antigen is able to abolish the reactivity for relatively long periods, although it returns sooner or later. Desensitization in infective processes has been successful. By daily injections of tuberculin and a killed tubercle bacillary emulsion in increasing quantities over several weeks, an impressive degree of desensitization can be achieved so that patients become unreactive to several million times the quantity which would induce a skin response. In spite of this, desensitization has failed to establish itself in the therapy of this disease. Desensitization in contact eczema has yielded highly variable results. Since the specificity of contact hypersensitivity reactions involves to a considerable degree the protein carrier, presumably successful desensitization would require the use of the hapten linked to carrier protein—but unfortunately the proteins which operate *in vivo* have not been identified.

NON-SPECIFIC PROCEDURES

Corticosteroids

It has been found empirically that the corticosteroids have a striking effect in some of those diseases which have been attributed to delayed-type allergy. Such dramatic effects as subsidence of joint swelling in rheumatoid arthritis, healing of eczema or resolution of the lesions of systemic lupus can follow the administration of cortisone or hydrocortisone, as well as the increased stimulation of the adrenal cortex by the use of pituitary adrenocorticotrophic hormone. In patients treated with large doses of cortisone of ACTH the cutaneous tuberculin reaction also becomes markedly diminished.

The reason for the beneficial effects of these corticosteroids is far from clear. In some species, such as the rabbit, rat or mouse, such drugs, in moderate to large doses, cause a rapid and extensive depletion of small lymphocytes from the lymphoid tissues and blood, which persists so long as the drugs are administered. Some workers claim indeed to have demonstrated a cytotoxic effect upon these cells in tissue culture as well as inhibition of lymphocytopoiesis. In man, the monkey and the guinea-pig given similar, or usually smaller, doses there is also an initial fall in numbers of circulating small lymphocytes, but this is only transient and the levels return to normal despite continued administration of the drugs. Nevertheless, these corticosteroids, in prolonged and relatively large dosage, are known to lower the blood lymphocyte levels in lymphatic leukaemia over many weeks, and can presumably depress lymphocytopoiesis in man.

Although, under controlled conditions of immunization, depression of antibody production by cortisone has been demonstrated in species of the first group, it has not been found in the guinea-pig or man (except perhaps in certain auto-immune diseases) nor is there evidence for more than partial suppression of delayed-type sensitization. It is therefore difficult to attribute the beneficial effects of corticosteroids in ordinary therapeutic doses on allergic reactions in man mainly to prevention of the formation of sensitized cells, although this may be a contributing factor.

A point of some importance is that these drugs can be rapidly effective when applied locally to affected areas of skin or mucous membranes whilst the inflammation in other untreated affected areas remains unchanged. This suggests that they act rather by diminishing the intensity of local delayed-type reactions by means of their known 'anti-inflammatory' properties than by lowering the underlying capacity to react with antigen. One possibility is that the threshold of resistance of cells to damage is raised, since it has clearly been shown that hydrocortisone hinders the release of lysosomal enzymes by agents which would normally cause such release. A second possibility is that the drugs prevent the sensitized cells from arriving at the local site, possibly by interfering with the establishment of lymphatic connections.

FURTHER READING*

AMOS B. & KOPROWSKI H. (eds) (1963) *Cell bound Antibodies* (includes discussions of the role of lymphocytes and macrophages in delayed type hypersensitivity reactions). Wistar Institute Press, Philadelphia

ARNASON B.G. & WAKSMAN B.H. (1964) Tuberculin sensitivity. Immunologic considerations. *Adv. Tuberc. Res.* **13,** 1–97. Karger, Basel

BLACK S., HUMPHREY J.H. & NIVEN J.S.F. (1963) Inhibition of Mantoux reaction by direct suggestion under hypnosis. *Brit. med. J.* **1,** 1649

BOYDEN S.V. (1958) The immunological response to antigens of the tubercle bacillus. *Progr. Allergy* **5,** 149

British Medical Bulletin (1967) Delayed hypersensitivity **73,** No. 1

* For general references to immunosuppression and immunopressive drugs see also Chapter Thirteen 'Suggestions'.

CHASE M.W. (1965) The allergic state. In *Bacterial and Mycotic infections of man* [Ed. Dubos R.J. and Hirsch J.G.], p. 238. Pitman, London

CUMMINGS M.M. & HAMMARSTEN J.F. (1962) Sarcoidosis. *Ann. Rev. Medicine* **13**, 19

DAVID J.R., AL-ASKARI S., LAWRENCE H.S. & THOMAS L. (1964) Delayed hypersensitivity *in vitro*. 1. The specificity of inhibition of cell migration by antigens. *J. Immunol.* **93**, 264

GELL P.G.H. & BENACERRAF B. (1961) Delayed Hypersensitivity to simple protein antigens. In *Advanc. Immunol* [Ed. Taliaferro W.H. and Humphrey J.H.] **1**, p. 319

GESNER B.M. (1965) In *The Inflammatory process* [Ed. Zweifach B.W., Grant L. and McCluskey R.T.] p. 281. Academic Press, New York

LAWRENCE H.S. (1968) *In vitro* correlates of delayed hypersensitivity. *Federation Proceedings* **27**, 3–48

LING N.R. (1968) *Lymphocyte Stimulation*. North Holland, Amsterdam

LURIE M.B. (1964) *Resistance to tuberculosis*. Harvard University Press

KARASH F. & EISEN H.N. (1962) A theory of delayed hypersensitivity. *Science* **136**, 1032

PARROTT D.M.V. (1969) The Thymus in the development of immunological responsiveness. In *Recent Adv. Clin. Pathol.* (Chapter 25) [Ed. Dykes C.]. Churchill, London

RAFFEL S. (1963) Hypersensitivity. In *Modern Trends in Immunology* [Ed. Cruickshank R.] **1**, 184. Butterworth, London

SHAFFER J.H., LO GRIPPO G.A. & CHASE M.W. (eds) (1958) *The Mechanisms of hypersensivity*. Henry Ford Symposium. Churchill, London

TURK J.L. (1967) Delayed Hypersensitivity. In *Frontiers of Biology* **4** [Eds Neuberger A. and Tatum E.L.]. North Holland, Amsterdam

CHAPTER THIRTEEN

Immunological Aspects of Tissue Transplantation

FOR many years surgeons have attempted to graft normal tissues or organs from one animal to another. In the case of particular tissues successful transplants have been recorded for a long time; the first corneal graft was made in 1852. Nevertheless, for most tissues of higher animals there has been a record of repeated failures until lines of mice were bred (by careful brother–sister mating and selection) whose genetical constitution was identical, or very nearly identical, in all members. Such pure lines were known as *isogeneic*. When skin grafts are exchanged between isogeneic individuals they become vascularized and persist and function indefinitely. The general difficulties experienced in the transplantation of tissues are therefore not due to transplantation technique. They are in fact immunological, and derive from the fact that in ordinary populations every individual is likely to differ genetically from every other—except in the case of uniovular (identical) twins. Indeed, a small number of identical twins suffering from loss of skin through burning, or from severe renal disease, have been able to benefit from grafts donated by their opposite numbers. Genetic differences are expressed ultimately by the synthesis of chemically different materials, whether these be required for the structure or the function of the cells (see, for example, the discussions on blood group substances and lipopolysaccharide antigens of bacteria in Chapter Six), and individuals with different genetic constitution—termed *heterogeneic*—are likely to differ in their chemical makeup at least in some respects. Only certain of such differences, i.e. namely those involving lipoproteins or lipoglycopeptides associated with the surface membranes of most of but not all of the nucleated cells of the body and termed 'transplantation antigens', are important in determining the fate of a graft. The problem of grafting, apart from the surgical technique, is the problem of the immunological response of the recipient against the transplantation antigens of the graft, and sometimes, as we shall see later, by cells in the graft against the transplantation antigens of the host.

THE IMMUNOLOGICAL BASIS OF GRAFT REJECTION

The foregoing bald statement of the problem neglects any attempt at an historical analysis, and assumes and oversimplifies the interpretation which has been placed upon many experiments involving the transplantation of malignant tissues and, to a lesser extent, normal tissues in various isogeneic lines of mice over the course of many years. Without the use of such inbred lines which were originally developed by pioneer workers in cancer research programmes, any such detailed interpretation would have been impossible, because of the genetic complexity of ordinary laboratory animals. For practical reasons such work has been done in mice, although some has been confirmed in birds, cattle, guinea-pigs and even in man. There is, however, no reason to suppose that the findings are not of general application—at least throughout all vertebrates higher than the cyclostomes. Indeed, the rejection process against a tissue taken from another member of the same outbred species shows a remarkable similarity of cytological and histological components and tissue relationships in all of the higher vertebrate species. Surprising as it may seem, grafts between goldfish are destroyed even more rapidly than grafts between mammals.

It is wise to begin by defining the nomenclature. 'Homograft' (or allograft) is the term used when a piece of tissue or an organ from one animal is grafted on to another animal of the same species but with a different genetic (allogeneic) constitution. If transplanted into an anatomically similar site it is called 'orthotopic'; if into a dissimilar site, 'heterotopic'. When grafts are made from one animal to another isogeneic animal they are 'isografts'; and when from one animal to another of a different species they are 'heterografts'.

The main lines of evidence for the conclusion that graft rejection depends on an immunological mechanism are as follows. First, an original homograft does not appear to be resisted by the recipient *ab initio* but for a few days continues healthy; if the graft is a tumour its cells continue proliferating freely in the new environment. This suggests that rejection depends upon an adaptive response of the host. Secondly, if at any time after a first graft has been rejected, a second graft is applied from the same (or an isogeneic) donor the sequence of events is much more rapid and the latent period of apparent acceptance is not observed. Thirdly, the graft rejection mechanism, once it has been called into existence, is systematized, so that the 'second-set' accelerated rejection described above can be displayed at any tissue site within the body which is supplied by blood vessels. Fourthly, the 'second-set' accelerated rejection response is *specific* for the animal used for the original grafting (or for any tissues derived from an isogeneic source) and is not manifest against genetically unrelated tissues. Fifthly, as would be expected from the lesser dose of transplantation antigen which is available for immunogenic stimulation, *very small* skin homografts survive somewhat longer than large ones; also, the intensity of the 'second-set' rejection depends upon the size and number of previous transplants from the same donor. Finally, in many species of animals the rejection of a homograft is attended by the appearance of antibodies in the host's serum, which can be shown to react with the graft-donor's cells (e.g. to agglutinate the donor's erythrocytes).

At this point it is necessary to stress that, in the case of a graft of solid tissue like skin, the first homograft rejection is almost certainly not due to circulating antibody alone; repeated attempts to cause some acceleration of graft rejection by passive transfer to the recipient of serum from animals of the same strain already immunized by similar grafts have consistently failed. Transfer of lymph node or spleen cells from immunized mice, however, can result in graft rejection. This was elegantly demonstrated by Medawar and his colleagues in an experiment (summarized diagrammatically in Fig. 13.1) in which they showed that a tolerated skin graft, growing in a mouse made tolerant to donor cells at birth, was rejected when the host was injected with lymphoid cells derived from a non-tolerant isogeneic animal which had been previously sensitized against donor skin. Further evidence, to be discussed later in this chapter and elsewhere (Chapter Twelve), indicates that the mechanism of skin homograft rejection is similar to that operating in delayed-type hypersensitivity reactions. Both are examples of cell-mediated specific immunity. The exact role of antibody must still be regarded as *sub judice*, and will be discussed at several points later in this chapter. In certain special circumstances (e.g. the rejection of a graft of dissociated neoplastic cells injected intraperitoneally, and the rejection of skin as a 'white graft'), antibody undoubtedly plays a crucial role in the rejection process.

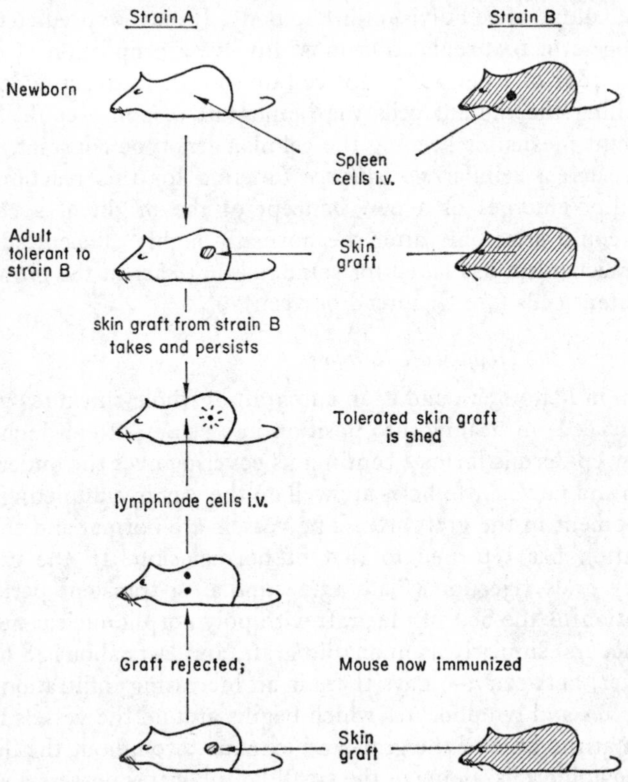

FIG. 13.1. Diagram to illustrate 'adoptive' tolerance and immunization against skin homografts.

Biological Role of the Homograft Reaction

A reaction which is as sensitive and universal as the homograft reaction is likely to have some biological significance other than representing a major obstacle to reconstructive surgery. Since it resembles the delayed-type hypersensitivity response and involves the same thymus-dependent population of lymphoid cells, it could be regarded as essentially a by-product of evolution in a world shared with micro-organisms—a plausible argument, especially if it were accepted that delayed-type hypersensitivity actually formed the basis for cellular immunity against microbes (Chapter Two). However, an even more cogent explanation for the evolution of this response would exist if occasional mutant cells arise during the normal course of cell division in the body. It may be predicted that the process of DNA replication must involve a proportion of errors (of the order of 1 per 10^6 to 10^8 cell divisions). By reacting against and killing the mutant cells the homograft response could be an important means for keeping the cellular genotype constant. If we accept such a cellular *surveillance* function for this reaction, the possibility emerges of a new concept of the origin of a cancer, which could arise only after the normally highly efficient surveillance mechanism has failed for some reason to arrest the growth of the mutant cells (see Chapter Fourteen).

Histology of the Homograft Response

As seen in Plate 13.1A and B, an autograft of whole-thickness mouse skin succeeds in healing into position in 12 days, after which time the new epidermis forms a continuous covering over the underlying dermis and new hair follicles are well on the way to completing their development in the graft area. The vessels are normal and the cell population has returned to that of normal skin. In the case of primary graft rejection (Plate 13.2A and B) a transient period of infiltration of the bed of the graft with polymorphonuclear neutrophils occurs, similarly as in an autograft, and lasts about 48 hours. However, between 3–9 days there is an increasing infiltration with monocytes and lymphocytes which begins around the vessels in the dermis at the base of the graft and extends throughout the dermis into the epidermis. Some of the small lymphocytes possess a rim of basophilic cytoplasm but mature plasma cells are uncommon, although a few usually appear after 7 days. Intracellular oedema of the epidermal cells can be seen several days before the grafts are destroyed. Histological evidence of necrosis appears on day 7/8, about 48 hours before necrosis becomes visible to the naked eye.

In the 'second-set' rejection (Plate 13.3A and B) the graft never becomes truly vascularized so that the cellular infiltration does not penetrate the graft. Intense cellular infiltration occurs in the host tissues of the graft bed along the line of the graft dermis. Histiocytes and immature plasma cells are prominent among these cells.

THE MECHANISM OF HOMOGRAFT REJECTION

The example taken in this discussion is a full-thickness skin graft—an example of a *solid tissue homograft* and one which should be clearly distinguished in kind from injected suspensions of cells such as lymphoid, bone marrow or leukaemic cells. All forms of homograft responses leading to destruction of solid organs are invariably associated with an infiltration of 'mononuclear cells', i.e. mixtures of lymphocytes and partially differentiated macrophages. Such a cellular infiltration precedes and coincides with the appearance of rejection, and these cells appear to be responsible for the pathogenesis of rejection. They may be regarded as the *effectors* of the immunological process. All forms of homograft rejection depend in addition upon an initial stimulation of the central immunological apparatus by the transplantation antigens, a part of the process which we can refer to as the *afferent arc*.

The principal sites of early response to a solid tissue homograft are in the group of regional or draining lymph nodes. At 4 days after grafting skin from one pure line of mice to the surface of another, clusters of pyroninophilic 'blast' cells can be seen in the thymus-dependent areas of the nodes, especially around the post-capillary venules of the mid-cortex. The nodes are at this time obviously enlarged. The numbers of pyroninophilic 'blast' cells reach maximum, under these circumstances at 6 days, and by 12 days, i.e. 2 days after the graft has been rejected, the number of blast cells has become considerably reduced. At this time germinal centres have appeared at the periphery of the node and developmental members of the family of plasma cells are present in the medulla. When similar experiments are done in neonatally thymectomized mice no pyroninophilic 'blast' cell reactions occur in the thymus-dependent areas, which in these animals are grossly depleted of small lymphocytes. Nevertheless, germinal centre development and plasma cell formation occur normally in the nodes of such thymectomized mice. Since suitably labelled thymocytes have been shown to migrate selectively to the thymus-dependent areas of lymph nodes, the facts as presented here suggest that the blast cell reaction occurs in a population of cells which originated from the thymus and migrated, *via* the post-capillary venules, to the thymus-dependent areas of the regional nodes draining the skin graft. Presumably the production of germinal centres in the cortex and of plasma cells in the medulla are not essential to graft rejection since, among other reasons, they occur normally in neonatally thymectomized mice which have a greatly diminished ability to reject skin homografts. They are presumably concerned with the production of humoral antibody.

The weak link in the foregoing argument is that the transformation of thymus-derived cells to pyroninophilic blast cells is as yet unproven. Moreover, the capacity to reject skin grafts can be mainly restored to thymectomized mice by grafts of thymus tissue enclosed in cell-retaining diffusion chambers. This implies that the thymus tissue can provide a hormonal factor which specifically confers on lymphocytes, irrespective of where they originated, the property of immunological competence. The exact mode of control exerted by the thymus over the cells in the thymus-dependent area, whether by stocking these areas with reactive cells or by provision of a suitable maturation-hormone, remains at present an open question. That the regional node draining a skin graft continues to be the site of production of immunologically reactive cells can be shown by the ability of cell suspensions derived from it to transfer to syngeneic immunized recipients the ability to give a second-set rejection response. This type of transfer by cells is known as *adoptive immunization* and appears to be closely analogous to the cell transfer of tuberculin hypersensitivity. The competence of the regional node cells to transfer the immunity begins at 3 to 5 days and falls off sharply at 10 to 15 days. The active immunity produced in the mice which were the donors for these cells can be shown to exist for at least 240 days. Presumably, then, the progressive loss of competence of the regional nodes is accompanied by a gradual activation of other lymphoid centres, probably by dissemination of lymphocytes from the draining nodes; it has been shown that concentrated suspensions of whole-blood leucocytes, peritoneal exudate cells and thoracic duct cells become highly effective in adoptive transfer. Since the latter cells were predominantly small lymphocytes it can be assumed that the morphology of the effector cells probably corresponded to that of a small lymphocyte. From recent studies it seems clear that activated lymphoid cells, identifiable as small lymphocytes, enter the circulation very rapidly after their formation in the regional nodes and that they persist, presumably as re-circulating cells, for hundreds of days.

We are now in a position to construct an impressive body of evidence to sustain the view that homograft sensitivity is closely related to delayed hypersensitivity as manifest in microbial infections and in contact hypersensitivity. Both types of response are removed by neonatal thymectomy and depend on similar cellular reactions in the thymus-dependent areas of the regional nodes. Both responses involve activation of lymphocytes to pyroninophilic lymphoblasts which divide to provide a population of effector cells which can transfer the reactivity to other (syngeneic) normal animals and which occur as small lymphocytes throughout the lymphoid tissues of the body.

The crucial step in establishing homograft reactivity as a delayed-type hypersensitivity phenomenon was the demonstration that guinea-pigs sensitized by skin homografts respond to an intradermal injection of living donor cells with a delayed inflammatory response just like a tuberculin response. In both guinea-pigs and rabbits, if a suspension of immunologically activated lymphoid cells from a specifically sensitized recipient is injected intradermally into the donor a similar reaction follows. This has been interpreted as the result of a local interaction between competent effector cells and the transplantation antigens of the donor.

The Influence of Humoral Antibodies on the Homograft Response

The humoral antibodies formed after rejection of a graft can be detected by a number of serological techniques such as agglutination and ability to kill (with the aid of complement) erythrocytes and leucocytes, and staining of graft cells by the fluorescent-antibody method. The ability to kill varies greatly between different target cells. Normal cells of mouse lymphoid organs are highly susceptible to cytotoxic action of antibodies directed against strong H-2 isoantigens, whereas other cells such as fibroblasts may be totally resistant. Sensitive cells appear to have a higher concentration of surface isoantigens. In general, cell suspensions of lymphoid tissues, bone marrow and leukaemic tumours are susceptible to the action of antibodies in the presence of complement *in vitro*, and resistance to cellular homografts of these tissues can be transferred passively by means of serum.

While it is by no means impossible that antibody could play a subsidiary role in accelerating the rejection of a solid tissue graft such as skin, there is no evidence that antibody ever assumes a dominant role in the rejection of tissue grafts of this type. Thus, no one has succeeded in causing the destruction of an established skin graft on a tolerant animal by means of antiserum.

One of the most significant properties of humoral antibodies is their capacity to facilitate the persistence of homografts due to the phenomenon known as *immunological enhancement*. This phenomenon of protection of the graft against cell-mediated immunity was discovered in relation to the transplantation of tumours and will be dealt with at length in Chapter Fourteen (p. 585). However, the same phenomenon seems to apply to non-neoplastic transplants. Although only slight prolongation of skin grafts has been obtained after pre-treatment of the incompatible recipient mice with antibodies or pre-immunization with lyophilized tissues, a more pronounced increase in survival times has been achived by such means when the tissues transplanted were allogeneic ovaries.

Enhancement provides in theory a method which could be of practical value for prolonging the survival of a homograft. However, attempts to suppress the homograft reaction in mice by previous intravenous injection of viable epidermal cells from the prospective graft donor have not produced very significant survival of skin grafts.

Another effect, undoubtedly mediated by serum antibodies, occurs when a skin graft is transplanted to a recipient who has been strongly immunized against the donor's tissues, for example by receiving multiple injections in Freund's adjuvant mixture. The graft bed very soon becomes the site of an Arthus-type reaction, so severe as to prevent any attempt at vascularization of the graft, which early takes on a characteristically pale appearance. Although this 'white graft' reaction is essentially a laboratory artefact it is mentioned as an instance in which sensitized cells do not play a major role in rejection.

The 'Afferent Arc' of the Rejection Mechanism

Little is known about how an orthotopic homograft of skin immunizes its host. Presumably a liaison must be arranged between the reactive cells—the small lymphocytes—and the graft antigens. The physical form in which these antigens are released from homografts of living tissue (and very probably from the tissues of intact animals as a normal physiological process) is completely unknown. They may be shed continuously by a process of wear and tear. Lipoproteins with the antigenic specificity determined by the H-2 locus are apparently released from mouse cells incubated *in vitro*. Materials with similar properties are associated with the 'membrane' fraction from homogenized lymphoid cells, and their production may well be linked with the production of the cell membranes.

No tissue specificity in transplantation immunity has been detected; all tissues appear to be able, as grafts or as injected cells, to sensitize a host in respect of all other tissues of the body.

Antigen may reach lymphocytes in the regional node by passing down the afferent lymphatics. There are several experimental demonstrations of the fact that a homograft which is not provided with lymphatic connections with the host fails to immunize for graft rejection. Thus small homografts placed in the anterior chamber of the eye do not act to sensitize the host, for at least some months. Flaps of skin have been constructed which when tested with an injection of dye gave no evidence of lymphatic connections with the host, although blood vessels adequate for the nutrition of the flap were present in the narrow pedicle. After dinitrochlorbenzene had been applied to the flap no contact sensitization was induced. Skin homografts placed in beds prepared in the flaps did not undergo rejection. However, when homografts were placed in flaps borne on presensitized animals, they were destroyed in a normal time, showing that absence of a lymphatic drainage does not prevent the expression of an existing homograft sensitivity. On this evidence the presence of lymphatics is essential for the function of the afferent arc of sensitization.

On the other hand, interaction between cell and antigen may occur in the graft and the 'sensitized' lymphocytes could then pass back to and settle in the regional node *via* the afferent lymphatic vessels or *via* the venous blood. Support for the latter view has been provided by an experiment in which lymphocytes could be 'sensitized' by being circulated through the blood vessels of an isogeneic kidney *in vitro* so as to cause rejection when transferred adoptively in a tolerant host bearing a kidney graft. Future work will be required to reconcile the apparent difference in mechanisms by which kidney and skin grafts sensitize. The kidney has a large bed of vascular endothelium where a lymphocyte might contact antigenic material and return to the host with it (or with information gained from the contact), whereas in a skin graft the earliest contact with the cells of the graft may occur mainly among lymphocytes which have migrated out of the blood vessels into the tissue spaces.

The 'Efferent Arc' of the Rejection Mechanism

The mononuclear cells which infiltrate a skin graft prior to its rejection have usually been regarded as predominantly lymphocytes, although it is admitted that they are very difficult to identify histologically. Study of tissue sections suggests that these cells, or some of them, may destroy graft epidermis by a mechanism of close-cell contact. This simple hypothesis has been given direct support by various tissue culture models. If animal A is injected with cells from animal B, then the lymphocytes of animal A after addition to a culture of fibroblasts or kidney cells from animal B will cause destruction of these visible after 24–48 hours. Within a few hours many of the lymphocytes have clustered around the target cells, a phenomenon known as *contactual agglutination*. Within about 20 hours, affected target cells have retracted their cytoplastic processes, assumed a rounded up appearance, and become detached from their glass substrate as dead cells. Effective cells can be obtained from spleen, lymph nodes or by drainage from the thoracic duct and could kill their target cells without the addition of complement to the culture. It was stated above that humoral antibodies from the serum of grafted animals can also kill cells, but only in the presence of complement. In the present model the presence of isoimmune serum does not increase cytolysis. If anything it reduces it.

Several authors have stressed the point that close contact between immune lymphoid cells and target cells always precedes demonstrable cytotoxicity in such tissue culture models. When the two cell types are separated by cell-impermeable diffusion membranes cytotoxicity is abolished. We do not know what is the detailed mechanism by which cells kill each other when plastered together. The phenomenon is not confined to homograft rejection, or to rejection of tumour cells (see Chapter Fourteen), but can occur with normal cells possessing different surface antigens. In the latter case it has been termed *allogeneic inhibition*, and an *in vitro* model for this phenomenon has been achieved by aggregating normal lymphoid cells and allogeneic target renal cells with phytohaemagglutinin, or with an heterologous cross reacting antiserum. Destruction of the target cells, and possibly of the lymphoid cells also, occurs as incubation is continued. In the homograft situation the lymphoid cells would presumably depend on cell-bound antibody to secure maintained contact with the target allogeneic graft cells.

The evidence that the small lymphocyte possesses all the properties necessary for the primary effector cell in homograft rejection is strongly supported by experiments in rats made tolerant by an intravenous injection, on the day of birth, of 80 million marrow cells, and grafted with skin from another inbred rat strain 6 weeks later. The rejection of these grafts could be accomplished by the intravenous injection of a population of virtually pure small lymphocytes derived from the thoracic duct of a normal rat.

Having presented the principal role in solid tissue rejection firmly to the small lymphocyte, it becomes essential to consider possible roles for the macrophage. The problem is made difficult by the present uncertainty concerning the frequency with which lymphocytes may convert to macrophages at the sites of skin rejections. In the special circumstances of graft *versus* host disease (see below) extensive proliferation of cells which are functionally macrophages occurs within the liver, the cells being derived from the grafted small lymphocytes. In the analysis of the basic mechanism of delayed-type hypersensitivity (see p. 510) it was shown that a few lymphocytes interacting with antigen can activate a large number of attendant macrophages to manifest increased adhesiveness. Furthermore, macrophages will ingest graft cells opsonized with isoantibody. In the present state of knowledge, therefore, it is probable that although lymphocytes may possess all that is necessary in terms of specificity and effector ability to destroy a solid-tissue homograft, in the actual *in vivo* situation their activity is supplemented by secondarily activated macrophages.

TRANSPLANTATION ANTIGENS AND THEIR GENETIC BACKGROUND

The ideal donor for a tissue graft is an identical twin, providing that the required organ in the twin is healthy. However, only about one person in three hundred and twenty possesses such a twin. Thus the future success of transplantation surgery may depend on choosing donor-recipient combinations which involve a minimum of genetic (and antigenetic) disparity between them, and it becomes essential to attempt to understand the genetic mechanisms of the inheritance of transplantation antigens. Owing to the limited availability of pure inbred strains of animals, knowledge in this field is largely limited to a few species. In all species studied the systems of antigens are complex, far more so than the blood group antigens previously worked out for the transfusion of blood. However, only a proportion of the antigens involved are *strong*; the rest are of much less consequence. The strong antigens are those which stimulate a vigorous immune response which cannot easily be overcome by immunosuppressive agents. The weak antigens induce only slow graft rejection but the effects of multiple weak antigens may be cumulative, and they may intensify those of some strong ones.

The genetic basis for histocompatibility has been well worked out in the mouse. Theoretically most interest attaches to those antigens (T-antigens) which are able to provoke transplantation immunity. However, antigens giving rise to humoral antibodies (H-antigens) are far more conveniently searched for, since serological tests can in this case be used. T- and H-antigens are not necessarily different, and the distinction is functional. Humoral antibodies may belong to several different species (haemagglutinins, leucocyte agglutinins, cytotoxins, etc.), and their exact relation to transplantation immunity must in the final analysis be made by a biological test involving actual grafting of tissue.

Fifteen genetic histocompatibility loci are known in the mouse. Four of these, H-1, H-2, H-3, H-4, have been found to exist in autosomal linkage groups of established behaviour. Of these, the antigen determined by the H-2 locus is the strongest. In man less information is available. From what we know, it is clear that the strength of the immune response to a tissue graft can often be predicted on the basis of those antigens known to be present in the donor and absent in the recipient. By selecting a donor-recipient pair with few or no strong antigen differences it becomes possible to keep the homograft reaction at bay with doses of immunosuppressive drugs below an unacceptable level of general toxicity.

TISSUE-TYPING FOR TRANSPLANTATION ANTIGENS IN MAN

The demonstration that peripheral blood leucocytes shared many tissue antigens, and that evaluation of leucocyte antigens could be used to predict skin and even kidney survival, has made the practical approach to tissue typing possible. The relation between leucocyte antigens and T-antigens is supported by two additional observations. Accelerated skin graft rejection in humans has been obtained by pre-immunization of the recipient with donor peripheral leucocytes; also, the rejection of a skin homograft is followed by demonstrable delayed-type intradermal sensitivity to the donor's white cells.

A number of techniques using human peripheral lymphocytes or leucocytes have been devised to detect tissue antigens in man.

Normal Lymphocyte Transfer

This test depends upon the assumption, verified in experimental animals, that peripheral blood lymphocytes injected subcutaneously will cause an immunological reaction against the host. The severity of this reaction would be expected to correlate with the number and strength of the antigens contained in the host tissues and absent in those of the lymphocyte donor. It was shown in the guinea-pig that the intensity of local redness and induration at 24 hours after injection correlated with the degree of histocompatibility difference between donor and recipient. In other words, when some time later skin grafts from each guinea-pig were made on to the donor of the lymphocytes, the length of time during which these grafts remained viable was inversely proportional to the intensity of the inflammatory reaction caused by the injected lymphocytes (at a later stage, about the fourth day, this first reaction is succeeded by a second, of variable intensity, which is the expected homograft reaction mounted by the host against the injected lymphocytes). The test is carried out as described, rather than by reversing the position of donor and recipient, in order to avoid sensitizing the recipient against the potential future donor.

Serotyping of Leucocytes

At the present time this method appears to be the most promising for practical purposes. Sera are obtained from certain multiparous women (i.e. immunized against paternal antigens of the foetus during pregnancy) or patients who have received repeated transfusions of blood containing leucocytes. The antibody in such sera is used against the donor and recipient leucocytes in two kinds of techniques: the ability to agglutinate the leucocytes, and the production of a cytotoxic effect on the leucocytes in the presence of rabbit complement. In the performance of the tests, donor and recipient cells are set up against as many different antisera as possible. If a similar pattern of agglutination or cytotoxicity is detected for both sets of cells, their antigenic make-up is assumed to be similar. The extent of difference between the patterns of behaviour of each set of cells with the battery of antisera reflects the degree of antigenic disparity. By cross-absorption of the antisera, it is possible in theory to obtain monospecific antisera capable of recognizing a single leucocyte antigen. Adequate cross matching can be done, however, without knowing precisely what antigens are involved.

Mixed Lymphocyte Cultures

This test depends upon the observation that when allogeneic peripheral lymphocytes are grown together in tissue culture, a proportion of them transform into large pyroninophilic 'blast' cells and undergo mitosis. The changes can be quantitated by counting the transformed cells or by measuring the uptake of radioactive thymidine. This is a 'two-way' test in which, under the usual procedure, one cannot tell whether the transformation is due to stimulation of recipient cells by donor antigen or *vice versa*. More recently, inhibition of the reactivity of one set of cells by pretreating them with mitomycin has been used to provide a 'one-way' reaction, and it has been shown that the stimulation is, in fact, mutual.

The extent of transformation depends upon the degree of antigenic difference between the two sets of cells. By means of the 'one-way' reaction it is possible in principle to decide in which direction the antigenic disparity is the less.

HOMOTRANSPLANTATION OF TISSUES OTHER THAN SKIN

The practice of grafting certain tissues is conditioned by factors which differ from those which apply in the case of skin, and surgeons have been using various homografts successfully for many years despite all that has been written above. In order to understand this a distinction must be made between *homostatic* grafts and *homovital* grafts. The former (which include bone, artery and lamellar grafts of the cornea) have cells which are not required to survive after transplantation. They provide a supporting framework into which host cells can grow. The cells of a *homovital* graft must remain alive if they are to serve their purpose.

Grafts of Bone and Blood Vessels

These are usually made with preserved tissues, and in the case of bone and artery the tissues have often been boiled or treated with formaldehyde or lyophilized before use—treatments which not only kill the cells but largely denature the proteins as well. In addition to their purely mechanical function, bone grafts and arterial grafts provide a suitable stimulus for the osteoblasts of the host bone, or the intimal and media cells of arteries, to grow out into their framework. Fresh vessel autografts may survive in part as living tissue but they too appear eventually to become replaced to a considerable extent by tissue of local origin.

Corneal Grafts

Full thickness corneal grafts are homovital grafts and occupy a different position from those of bone and vessels, since the transplant must retain its property of transparency intact and must therefore avoid those inflammatory changes which—if not too extensive—might even speed the process of vascularization and recolonization of homostatic bone grafts. Barring a mechanical displacement of the cornea or bacterial infection, the grafts always take, although about 10 per cent become opaque. A major factor in the successful survival of such grafts is the lack of blood vessels, so that the grafts remain isolated from immunologically competent cells. Such a graft is nourished by diffusion through epithelium and endothelium. Of grafts placed on vascularized corneas about half become suddenly cloudy about 2 weeks to several months afterwards. A second factor is the smallness of the amount of tissue transplanted, so that the antigenic stimulus is minimal. Indeed, clouding in a corneal graft can readily be produced experimentally by transplanting into the abdominal wall of the recipient a piece of skin from the donor of the corneal transplant. This presumably acts by providing an increased antigenic stimulus.

A full thickness corneal graft resembles a lamellar graft but in addition must provide conditions so that the delicate layer of endothelium, which separates the cornea from the aqueous humour of the anterior chamber, is preserved in a functioning condition so as to prevent the leakage of aqueous humour. That these graft cells do usually survive is partly attributable to the factors mentioned above, but an additional reason may be that even when large blood vessels grow in from the scleral margin these are separated by a thick barrier of mucopolysaccharide from the possible target cells. Thus, while the cells of the surface endothelium and epithelium of the graft are probably soon replaced *in toto*, recent studies of transplanted corneal stroma show survival of donor sex chromatin characteristics for at least 3 months with no invasion of cells from the host.

Cartilage

Grafts of cartilage must be made with living tissue, and yet orthotopic grafts take and persist with surprising readiness between randomly selected individuals. The explanation offered is that cartilage, like the cornea, is an avascular tissue and hence segregated from contact with immunologically competent cells. Probably equally important is the fact that the chondroblasts themselves are embedded in a matrix of sulphated mucopolysaccharide which does not itself act as an immunogen and into which, while it remains chemically intact, the host inflammatory cells cannot penetrate and antibodies scarcely diffuse.

Endocrines

In the case of endocrine tissues the strong general belief has existed that homografts of, for example, ovary, adrenal and testis survive considerably longer than a skin graft from the same donor to the same recipient. A powerful influence on thought has been Halsted's Law, expressed 50 years ago, that endocrine tissues can be grafted satisfactorily only when there is a physiological deficiency of their secretions in the host. All the successful grafts on which Halsted based his proposition were *autografts* of parathyroid tissue. In his work with allografts of parathyroid Halsted found that they did not survive. The same may be said of ovary and adrenal tissue homografts. Indeed, none of the recent work with ovarian allografts in genetically well-defined strains of mice or rats lends any support to the idea that such grafts are less susceptible to the allograft reaction than are skin grafts.

Since replacement therapy for endocrine deficiencies is presently so satisfactory, there appears to be little current enthusiasm for the transplantation of endocrine tissue in man, in spite of enthusiastic reports of clinical improvement following the use of grafts of parathyroid, pituitary and adrenal tissues.

Kidney Grafts

In recent years there has been an increasing number of successful transplantations of human kidneys between individuals who were not identical twins. At the present time it can be said that where the kidney donor is a sibling or parent, the patient has a 65–75 per cent chance of 1-year survival. About half the patients who survive 1 year have continued to do well for the 2 to 3 year period that they have been followed. Patients who receive kidneys from unrelated donors have not fared as well, their chances for 1-year survival being 25–40 per cent. However, when donors and recipients have been well matched (i.e. not more than one or two major antigenic differences) by tissue typing the prognosis has been about as good as if the donor was a sibling.

There is some reason to believe that the immunological response which the body can mount against a kidney is less effective than that against skin, for it is described how, when human skin has later been transplanted from the same donor, the skin has been rejected under circumstances in which the kidney has continued to function well. The argument is not conclusive, since an established graft may be partly protected by 'enhancing' antibodies, and has the advantage of already having healed in. However, the rejection response in the human has proved to be less violent and to develop more slowly than might have been expected from the behaviour of renal homografts in the experimental animal. It is difficult to analyse the reasons for this, especially since the human cases were treated with multiple drugs or irradiation procedures. It is probable that severe chronic azotaemia significantly reduces the immune response to the transplanted kidney. In this condition lymphocytes are less reactive as judged by their ability to transform *in vitro* when treated with phytohaemagglutinin.

The first successful kidney allograft was accomplished in 1959. Total body irradiation in a 'sublethal' dose of about 400 r was used to suppress the rejection response. However, attempts to use acceptable doses of whole-body irradiation for immunosuppression have generally failed. Further progress depended on the discovery and use of the more selective agents 6-mercaptopurine and its derivative azathioprine (see p. 570). Once a grafted kidney has survived in a drug-treated host for over 30 days, it is usually less vulnerable to rejection, and thereafter the rejection process may be relatively easily controlled by further drug treatment. The reason for this is uncertain, but one possibility is that 'enhancing' antibodies have been developed by this time. In controlling the rejection 'crisis' use is made of episodes of greatly increased doses of corticosteroid drugs.

The functional arrest of kidney allografts within a few days or weeks is currently assumed to depend on immunological mechanisms, but what these are is far from clear. Histological evidence suggests a reaction against the vascular endothelial cells. The failing kidney shows a progressive decrease in venous flow until oliguria ensures. The renal allograft becomes enlarged and tender. There is fever, tachycardia, proteinuria and an increase in the number of lymphocytes in the urine (up to 50,000 per hour). The level of complement (C′2) in serum falls. Histological evidence suggests that the earliest lesion is due to a reaction of infiltrating host lymphocytes against the endothelium of the cortical peritubular capillaries and venules. No changes are observed at this stage in glomeruli or arteries. Later there is disruption of the capillary walls and accumulation of fluid and cells in the interstitial tissue. The cortex becomes densely infiltrated with pyroninophilic cells. Most of these either resemble the large pyroninophilic lymphoblast cells described previously in the thymus dependent areas of local lymph nodes after skin grafting, or smaller pyroninophilic lymphocytes. In the early lesion these cells predominate over true plasma cells, which are readily distinguished from the foregoing cells by the profusion of rough endoplasmic reticulum and large Golgi apparatus within their cytoplasm. After a few days macrophages and plasma cells increase in number.

It seems likely that the pyroninophilic blast cells, which can be shown to be of host origin, when they reach the graft exert a cytotoxic effect on the endothelium of peritubular capillaries, possibly with the aid of secondarily sensitized macrophages. In this way the host blast cells indirectly bring about the gross swelling of the kidney, tubular necrosis, oliguria and the clinical syndrome of rejection.

Rejection may occur in the first few hours after transplantation. Such rapid responses could be due to two different sets of circumstances which can be avoided by careful donor selection. The first happens when there is an incompatibility between the major blood groups of the patient and donor. The afferent arterioles and glomerular capillaries become distended with masses of clumped erythrocytes. This proceeds to thrombosis of the afferent arterioles and fibrinoid necrosis of the glomerular capillary walls. These changes are an obvious consequence of the preformed isohaemagglutinins which are circulating in the plasma of the recipient. These will react with the donor's erythrocytes but more importantly with the blood group antigens which are present on the surface of the vascular endothelium cells. Secondly, rapid rejection responses may occur when the recipient has been presensitized in some way, as by previous repeated transfusions of whole blood or by multiple pregnancies. In previously nonsensitized recipients rejection of an incompatible kidney may be expected within a few days or at the end of the first week.

Later rejection 'crises' can also occur quite commonly after 11 days in human recipients of incompatible kidneys (39 of 83 patients in one series of cases). Two histological findings characterize such kidneys: fibrinoid necrosis of the walls of afferent arterioles to glomeruli and platelet thrombi within the glomerular capillaries. The platelet aggregation is such as to limit the renal flow. Fortunately platelet agglutination can be quickly reversed by corticosteroid drugs, which may explain why prompt treatment with these drugs can be so successful in inducing diuresis from a renal allograft that has suddenly and shortly before ceased to function.

Some months or even years after transplantation renal function may gradually deteriorate without any clear-cut rejection 'crises'. Proteinuria and a progressive fall in creatinine clearance are associated with the histological lesions of membranous glomerulonephritis (resembling those found in Goodpasture's syndrome and experimental nephrotoxic nephritis and experimental allergic glomerulonephritis in animals). Fluorescent microscopy reveals a linear deposit of IgM outlining the capillary walls of the glomeruli. A possible explanation is that antibody forms against antigenic components of capillary basement membranes of the graft and becomes deposited on the basement membranes in the glomeruli with added components of complement. The subsequent disruption of the basement membrane and epithelial cell foot processes would correspond with the lesions described in human kidneys (see Chapter Eleven).

Liver and Lung Transplantation

Based on the recent experience concerning kidney transplantations it would be rash to predict the nature and extent of the immunological problems which might affect the success of liver and lung transplantation. The variability of liver graft survival in an outbred population of dogs suggests that histocompatibility differences do play a substantial role and that tissue typing may be necessary to increase survival. The liver in the process of rejection undergoes striking vascular changes resulting in areas of spasm and vascular insufficiency. The liver graft, unlike the kidney, is probably capable of mounting a graft-*versus*-host reaction. Canine recipients of orthotopic liver transplants have indeed shown shortened red cell survival time and severe haemolytic anaemia. Unfortunately azathioprine and corticosteroid drugs both exert toxic effects on liver cells, and the preliminary reports of the use of antilymphocyte serum have shown it to be less effective in controlling canine liver transplants than azathioprine.

Preliminary results with lung grafts in dogs and man do not suggest that immunological rejection mechanism need pose insuperable obstacles to success. Under immunosuppression therapy a number of dogs have survived periods in excess of 2 years with functioning lung allografts and one human lung graft from a patient surviving for 18 days after operation did not show histological evidence of a rejection process.

IMMUNOSUPPRESSIVE TREATMENT

Attempts to modify the immunological response involve a consideration of the effects of these agents on the various aspects of the response including immunogenicity, cell mediated immunity, immunological memory, antibody production and tolerance. Apart from antilymphocyte serum, all the various agents to be discussed inhibit cell replication and indeed were initially developed for their anti-mitotic activities in inhibiting neoplastic growth. Many of their unwanted side effects depend on their ability to inhibit cell regeneration in the bone marrow and gut epithelium, as well as the healing of wounds.

In the case of therapy directed at securing survival of transplants the main interest is the prevention of an immunological response to the transplantation antigens in the graft. The recipient of an allograft might reasonably be expected to start by being unsensitized to these. However, as explained above, previous sensitization to blood group isoantigens as well as transplantation antigens may complicate the picture. There may therefore be an additional need to suppress an established state of hypersensitivity along the lines already discussed in Chapter Twelve.

X-RAY IRRADIATION

When *sublethal* doses of whole body radiation are used (300–600 r) the immunological response to many antigens is depressed. Obviously the results on any particular response would be expected to vary according to the nature of the antigen and the length of time that it could act as an antigenic stimulus. Most experimental studies have been made on antibody production to red cell antigens in mice and rabbits.

The main cellular changes which are seen within the first few hours after irradiation in the lymphoid tissues are inhibition of mitosis and massive disintegration of lymphocytes, followed by a period of phagocytosis of the debris which is complete within 24 hours. Next there is a period of inactivity, whose duration depends on the radiation tissue dose but may last for a week or more. Finally, there is a period of active mitosis and proliferation of lymphoblasts, so that the lymphoid tissue is completely regenerated after 3 or 4 weeks. Macrophages, reticulum cells and the epithelial elements of lymphoid tissues (such as Hassall's corpuscles) are little damaged at these levels of irradiation. Mature and immature plasma cells are relatively radio-resistant.

The immunological changes may be summarized as follows:

(i) the primary response is markedly depressed or abolished, when antigen is given 12 hours to 50 days after irradiation. Irradiation depresses antibody production more than delayed hypersensitivity. The effect on antibody production is greatest when antigen is given 24–48 hours after irradiation.

(ii) the same dose of irradiation given 3 to 4 days after the start of immunization will produce little effect.

(iii) when antigen is given 2 hours to 3 days before irradiation the antibody levels subsequently are above normal.

(iv) when large amounts of protein antigens are given during the phase of immunological depression at 1 day after irradiation with 400 or 500 r, long lasting specific unresponsiveness results to these antigens.

(v) the secondary response is relatively resistant compared with the primary.

SUPRALETHAL DOSES OF X-RAYS

In an attempt to produce a permanently tolerant recipient for a homograft, doses of X-ray have been used experimentally which totally inactivate the immunologically competent cells. However, since X-rays in such high doses destroy the capacity of most cells to divide, including not only immunologically competent cells but haemopoietic cells and the lining cells of the intestinal mucosa—producing in consequence fatal radiation sickness—it is necessary to replace the deficient marrow by a transfusion of haemopoietic tissue after irradiation in order to keep the animal alive. In practice, marrow from isogeneic or allogeneic animals can be used for such replacement, combined with the administration of antibiotics. Between 900–1200 r is a suitable supralethal dose for such purposes. At higher doses, and sometimes even at these, death occurs from radiation sickness, accompanied by pulmonary oedema and electrolyte imbalance, despite transfusion of bone marrow.

Lethal doses of X-rays of this order must destroy the host's capacity to give an immune response since long-term acceptance of grafted cells is the rule; in fact, unless these cells repopulated the host it could not survive. Proof that this occurs was achieved by the use of rat bone marrow to protect lethally irradiated mice; rat cells have a different arrangement of chromosomes from mouse cells by which they could readily be identified in the denuded bone marrow of the irradiated recipients. Such animals, which are populated by two genetically different strains of cells, are known as *chimaeras*—in this case radiation chimaeras—after the mythical monster which possessed a lion's head, a goat's body and a serpent's tail.

However, animals treated in this way are liable to be permanently impaired. The incoming bone marrow cells of rodents contain few immunologically competent cells (which is why a graft *versus* host reaction is avoided) and such chimaeras are very poor producers of antibody against potentially pathogenic micro-organisms and they remain liable to succumb to infections which would be harmless to normal animals. If spleen cells are used in addition to bone marrow, the recipients commonly suffer from a form of runt disease, called 'secondary disease', caused by an immunological reaction by the spleen cells against their new host and they eventually die—the time taken for this to occur depending upon the degree of antigenic dissimilarity between donor and host. This is also liable to happen after a transfusion of adult human bone marrow to irradiated persons, possibly because the marrow contains competent lymphocytes derived from the blood. Of course, if host and donor are genetically identical, secondary disease does not occur, but the animal is no longer a chimaera.

There is evidence that, at somewhat lower doses of radiation within the lethal range, small numbers of haemopoietic cells may survive and gradually repopulate the host. However, when this occurs in, say, a treated human leukaemia subject, leukaemic cells have been observed similarly to survive and multiply.

Supralethal doses of X-rays followed by bone marrow infusion were used at one stage to facilitate kidney transplantation in man, but no patients survived for long. Sublethal whole body irradiation, sufficient to diminish the homograft rejection process without wholly destroying the patient's bone marrow stem cells, has enabled some successful transplants to be made, but the procedure has now been abandoned in favour of the use of more selective and controllable immunosuppressive drugs.

RADIOMIMETIC DRUGS

These drugs, which act similarly to X-rays, belong in general to the class of alkylating agents. Nitrogen mustards, ethylenimines and esters of alkyl sulphonic acids are the chief biological alkylating agents. Representative drugs of each type are nitrogen mustard (bis[2-chloro ethyl] methylamine), Tri-ethylene melamine and Myleran. The mutagenic and carcinogenic activity of these agents points to the DNA as an important site of alkylation. The generally high chemical reactivity of these alkylating agents and the multiplicity of reactive centres with which they can combine, make it difficult to determine a primary reaction site but combination with the base guanine seems likely, followed by a blockage of cell division. The most promising agent at present is cyclophosphamide, which at toxic doses will suppress immunological responses more effectively than correspondingly toxic doses of X-rays. Unlike X-rays, immunosuppression lasts only while the drug is injected and responsiveness soon returns after it is stopped. The administration of cyclophosphamide during the period of application of a sensitizing contactant will completely prevent the development of large lymphocytes (blast cells) in the para-cortical areas of the draining lymph nodes. Doses which are effective in blocking cell-mediated hypersensitivity reactions also cause anaemia and leucopenia.

ANTIMETABOLITES

The antimetabolite drugs were originally tested for their ability to suppress immunological responses since they had proved effective in slowing the rate of division of tumour cells. The search led to a wide variety of substances which both interfere with the synthesis of RNA and DNA and prevent antibody formation or the development of delayed hypersensitivity.

1. *Folic Acid Antagonists*

Amethopterin or methotrexate (MTX) is the folic antagonist most in clinical use today. This drug has supplanted aminopterin, which historically was significant in being the first effective antimetabolite used in the treatment of acute leukaemia.

These drugs inhibit conversion of dihydrofolate to tetrahydrofolate by binding to the enzyme dihydrofolate reductase which is necessary for this action. Synthesis of purines and of thymine requires tetrahydrofolate, and thus folic acid antagonists may prevent new formation of nucleic acid. As is common with all antimetabolite drugs so far discovered, the effect varies from one animal species to another. Thus, while the immunological responses of guinea-pigs, mice and dogs are effectively suppressive, little effect is produced in the rabbit. Amethopterin appears to inhibit the later proliferative rather than the early inductive phase of the immunological response. In agreement with this, amethopterin, unlike cyclophosphamide, does not prevent the appearance of haemocytoblasts but stops their further rapid division to produce small sensitized lymphocytes.

2. *Purine Analogues*

(*6-mercaptopurine and derivatives*) Although their mode of action is far from being elucidated, there are a number of sites of protein biosynthesis where purine analogues could exert a blocking effect. They might, for example, interfere with the formation of template (messenger) RNA or lead to a nonsense template which would result in the synthesis of an irrelevant protein product. Doses of

6-mercaptopurine which prevent immune responses completely prevent the usual cytological changes in lymphoid tissues which follow antigenic stimulation. In sufficient doses these drugs depress the bone marrow, but in the rabbit at least they seem to have a greater inhibitory action on the haemocytoblasts which are stimulated by antigen. Moreover, rabbits to which sufficient amounts of a relatively weak immunogen (e.g. bovine serum albumin) are administered while under treatment with the drug become tolerant of that immunogen even after the drug is withdrawn. Such tolerance is specific, and the response to other immunogens administered later is unimpaired. This effect is related to the dose of the immunogen used with the drug. Thus, the proportion of rabbits which remain unresponsive increases sharply with the amount given and quite large amounts (of the order of 70 mg BSA per kilogram) were required to obtain a high incidence of specific tolerance. These experimental facts lead to the interesting hypothesis that the first injection of immunogen selects a group of cells to be stimulated to proliferate and differentiate. These cells, because of their metabolic activity, are more sensitive to the cytotoxic action of 6-MP than non-stimulated cells. It is found, in accord with this hypothesis, that single large doses of 6-MP can significantly prolong the life of a skin homograft or depress antibody production if given up to 3 or 4 days after the antigenic stimulus. This timing contrasts with that of X-rays and radiomimetic drugs, which must be given before the antigen in order to be effective. In clinical practice for the purposes of renal transplantation there is no agreed optimum dosage schedule and most surgeons start therapy with azathioprine 2–10 days prior to operation.

In the guinea-pig 6-MP can inhibit the development of delayed-type hypersensitivity even though antibody production may be little affected, and can delay the onset of experimental allergic encephalomyelitis.

A derivative of 6-mercaptopurine, azathioprine, is currently the basic immunosuppressive drug for kidney transplantation routine. It is continued at a constant or gradually decreasing level for 2 years or more after transplantation. At the time of rejection 'crises' the need for therapy to reverse the rejection process is usually met by temporary increase in corticosteroids rather than variation in azathioprine.

ANTI-LYMPHOCYTE SERUM (ALS)

A means of suppressing delayed-type hypersensitivity reactions which has considerable theoretical interest and holds some promise of practical usefulness is the use of antibodies raised in animals of another species by immunizing with purified lymphocytes or thymocytes, or cell membranes derived from them. If the course of immunization is short (e.g. two intravenous injections) the resulting antibodies are predominantly against the surface constituents of the lymphoid cells, and although they are unlikely to be exclusively directed against lymphocytes—which are rich in the 'transplantation antigens', which are common to other tissue cells also—the antisera are found to react mainly with lymphocytes. Antibodies against erythrocytes can be removed by absorption with suspensions of red cells, and the IgG fraction of the antiserum can be separated so as to remove most of the extraneous proteins. The resultant 'antilymphocytic serum (ALS)' has been found to agglutinate lymphocytes and to lyse them in the presence of suitable complement.

In moderate single doses ALS causes a transient fall in the peripheral blood lymphocyte count, which in a day or two returns to normal levels. The polymorph level is scarcely affected or may rise transiently, but some sera contain platelet antibodies which reduce the level of these cells in the peripheral blood appreciably. When repeated large doses of ALS are given severe lymphopenia may result. A point of great practical and theoretical interest is that in experimental animals (mice, guinea-pigs, dogs), even moderate doses of ALS, insufficient to cause a lasting peripheral lymphopenia, can greatly diminish or even prevent the development of delayed-type hypersensitivity reactions and can depress already established delayed-type hypersensitivity states. Thus in experimental animals ALS prevents homograft rejection, allowing prolonged retention even of heterografts of skin; greatly delays the onset of experimental allergic encephalomyelitis (p. 645); and virtually abolishes tuberculin reactions or skin reactions to chemical sensitizing agents in previously sensitized animals. In man it has been used in relatively small doses, to cause partial suppression of homograft reactions in renal transplantation so that the usual dose of immunosuppressive reagents could be diminished while the graft was still accepted and remained functional. The series in which ALS has been used have been outstandingly successful.

The mode of action of ALS has not yet been fully elucidated. Despite the fact that moderate doses do not produce a lasting peripheral lymphopenia, histological examination of the lymphoid tissues of mice and guinea-pigs treated with ALS shows that the 'thymus-dependent' areas become almost completely devoid of lymphocytes, though the lymphocytes in the cortical nodules of lymph nodes and the Malpighian bodies of the spleen are little, if at all, diminished; germinal centres are not impaired; and the thymus is unaffected (large doses of toxic preparations of ALS cause thymocyte depletion).

Since established states of delayed-type hypersensitivity can be abolished by treatment with ALS, a possible explanation appears to be that ALS destroys or inactivates (e.g. by coating their surface) lymphocytes in the peripheral circulation as well as those in the thymus-dependent areas of lymphoid tissue. Furthermore, since peripheral lymphocytes are mainly those with a long turnover time ('long-lived' lymphocytes, p. 96), it is these which become predominantly depleted and the peripheral lymphocytes come to be composed, after several injections of ALS, largely of 'short lived' lymphocytes. The long-lived cells may be those which bear the specific altered capacity to react or 'memory of contact with antigen' and indeed, after treatment with ALS, animals which had previously rejected a homograft from a given donor become immediately non-responsive to grafts from the same donor and later (as they recover from treatment) respond to further similar grafts by primary-type (rather than by a secondary-type accelerated) graft rejection.

Antibody production, as opposed to delayed-type hypersensitivity, has been studied in experimental animals and is much less affected by moderate doses of ALS. Animals are thus affected in a similar way to neonatal thymectomy, i.e. the response to some particulate antigens is depressed, but the response to soluble antigens is little impaired. Indeed, antibodies are readily made against components of the ALS itself. Furthermore, even when a homograft is being accepted under the influence of ALS, circulating antibodies against the graft are often detectable—a rather striking example of the dissociation between homograft rejection and the presence of humoral immunity referred to above.

So far as the therapeutic possibilities of ALS as an immunosuppressive agent are concerned, failure to suppress antibody production is likely to be an advantage, since it offers the prospect of avoiding the danger of increased susceptibility to bacterial infection which is inherent in the use of antimitotic or antimetabolite agents. The main drawbacks in clinical use are severe pain at the site of intramuscular injection and occasional anaphylactic reactions. Serum sickness with nephritis and arterial lesions might well be expected to occur, and has been consistently reported to follow allografting of kidneys in dogs when ALS was used. However, this complication has not been observed in man (perhaps because of the simultaneous administration of other immunosuppressive agents) and its likelihood is diminished by removal of all but the immunoglobulin fraction.

The assessment of whether a preparation of ALS is suitable for use in man at present presents great difficulty. Although ALS has several activities testable *in vitro* (e.g. agglutination or lysis of lymphocytes, transformation of lymphocytes in culture, suppression of plaque formation by antibody-producing cells in gel), none of these is sufficiently well correlated with its performance in prolonging the life of homografts to be used as an assay method. However, ALS prepared against human cells is active in primates, and by testing the ability of a preparation to prolong the life of skin homografts in chimpanzees a valid assay method appears to be available.

THE FOETUS AS A HOMOGRAFT

In mammals the one form of homograft to which they are certainly subjected is the foetus, and it is safe to state that in ordinary outbred populations the foetus never has an antigenic makeup identical with that of its mother. The fact that the foetal red blood cells may immunize the mother and that the antibodies which she forms may cause haemolytic disease in the foetus has already been discussed in Chapter Eight. This means that, in man at least, the barrier between foetal and maternal blood circulations can be broken, although in cases of rhesus incompatibility the process of immunization seems usually to relate to the larger transplacental haemorrhages which occur during the third stage of labour. Pregnancy is also the main cause, other than multiple transfusions, of the appearance of leucocyte agglutinins (which react with allogeneic but not autologous white cells) in the blood of the mothers. Furthermore, there is good evidence that fragments of trophoblasts (which are of foetal origin) enter the maternal circulation throughout a large part of the pregnancy and this certainly poses the question why a homograft response is not evoked by the mother.

The degree and type of contact between foetus and maternal tissues in different animals varies widely. The degree of union between foetal villi and the uterine mucosa may involve merely the close apposition of these two tissues or their intimate fusion. In the former case the foetal tissues of the placenta separate readily at birth. In the case of deciduate placentae, maternal tissue is shed with the placenta at birth. However, in the mole (talpa) the degree of union is such that the placenta fails to be shed and stays to be absorbed gradually by the mother. The degree of erosion of the uterine tissues and hence the number of layers of tissue involved in the foetal–maternal barrier has given rise to the following classification of O. Grosser.

(i) *epitheliochorial* in which all the maternal tissues are preserved intact. The classical example is the pig, in which maternal blood is separated from foetal blood by six tissue layers: maternal endothelium, maternal connective tissue, maternal uterine epithelium, foetal (chorionic) epithelium, foetal connective tissue and foetal endothelium. The horse and donkey have similar arrangements.

(ii) *syndesmochorial* in which the uterine epithelium disappears leaving the chorion in contact with maternal tissues. Placentae of this type are found in ruminants.

(iii) *endotheliochorial* in which the uterine mucosa is further eroded and the chorionic epithelium makes contact with the endothelium of the maternal capillaries. This type of placenta is characteristic of the carnivora: cat and dog.

(iv) *haemochorial* in which the maternal endothelium is absent and maternal blood circulates in spaces lined by trophoblast. Typical examples of this type of placenta are those of monkey and man.

(v) *haemoendothelial* in which the layer of trophoblast between the foetal vessels and maternal blood is very thin or even absent during the later stages of gestation, as in, for example, the rabbit, guinea-pig and rat.

These structural features must play an important role in determining the opportunities for maternal immunization by foetal cells. In those animals with epitheliochorial, syndesmochorial and endotheliochorial placentae the uterine fluid which bathes the surface of the chorion provides the major part of the food supply to the embryo. As explained below, a solid tissue allograft which is nourished by diffusion may enjoy permanent survival (as in the case of cartilage and cornea). Thus solid tissue skin allografts which float free in the anterior chamber of the eye or become attached to the posterior surface of the cornea survive, those which become attached to the iris and become vascularized undergo necrosis. Similar protection is afforded to solid tissue allografts enclosed in a millipore chamber which is impermeable to cells but not to tissue fluids. It can therefore be argued that only the haemochorial or haemoendothelial types of placenta run the risk of allowing homograft immunization to take place.

In the case of haemochorial and haemoendothelial types of placenta an explanation is required of why the foetal homograft fails to be rejected. The hypotheses which can be advanced to account for the survival of the foetus must fall into one of the following categories:

(i) antigenic inadequacy of the foetus.

(ii) absent or diminished immunological response of the mother.
(iii) implantation of the conceptus in a site which is immunologically privileged.

Antigenicity of Foetal Tissue

The foetus and foetal membranes together form the conceptus and although the foetal membranes form the tissue which is in direct contact with the maternal cells the immunogenicity of the foetus may also be relevant since foetal blood cells may pass into the maternal circulation during the course of pregnancy. Even if they gain access only at the time of delivery they may sensitize against future pregnancies.

In mice it has been clearly shown that F_1 hybrid placental tissue can be used to immunize the mother so as to cause accelerated rejection of a subsequent graft of paternal skin. Since the antigenic component of the placenta must come largely from the foetal trophoblast this implies that the foetal tissues of the placenta contain some potentially effective transplantation antigens. It has also been shown that mothers will reject grafts of skin from their own litters. These experiments therefore indicate that when foetal tissues interact with the mother under conditions other than those of pregnancy a homograft type of sensitization of the mother does occur.

The time of appearance of transplantation antigens during ontogeny has been extensively investigated and in general the results clearly show that foetal tissue possesses effective isoantigens from an early stage of development. Thus, about 10^7 cells from 11–12 day mouse embryos can be injected to produce accelerated graft rejection in an adult mouse. However, some experiments have suggested that embryonic tissues taken early in development are quantitatively less immunogenic than similar cells obtained during the later stages of embryonic development.

Those experiments which have directed attention specifically to the placenta and foetal membranes also reveal that transplantation antigens are present. Suspensions of placental cells from 15–17 day mouse embryos were found to be as effective as adult spleen cells in producing accelerated rejection of subsequent allografts when injected into adult recipient. Foetal blood obtained at the same stage of gestation and containing comparable numbers of nucleated cells was not immunogenic under these conditions. Thus it would seem reasonable to attribute the immunogenicity of the above cell suspensions to actual placental cells and not to blood cells which circulate through.

Immunological Response During Pregnancy

During pregnancy mammals certainly tend to be less readily immunized by many antigens—probably because of changes in corticosteroid production—though this effect is not sufficiently marked wholly to prevent antibody formation or the development of delayed-type hypersensitivity. Homografts of cattle have not been found to have significantly prolonged survival in pregnant animals of the same species. However, experiments are on record using mice and rats which show that pregnancy induces in the female some diminution of her immunological response towards the specific, paternally derived iso-antigens of her own offspring. This effect was described with allografts of skin or sarcoma tissue derived from animals syngeneic with the male parent.

The phenomena of enhancement (see Chapter Fourteen) has been invoked by some to explain these effects, although several other explanations are possible. On this hypothesis the process of pregnancy results in humoral (enhancing) antibody against the transplantation antigens of the foetus. Some recently delivered women (about 17 per cent) have been shown to produce antibody which is able to agglutinate the leucocytes of their own newborn infants or of their husband.

Syncytiotrophoblast of the human placenta has been found to throw off small groups of cells into the maternal circulation throughout the course of a normal pregnancy. Such trophoblast syncytia can be found in sections of the lungs of pregnant women and it has been calculated that the maternal tissues are bombarded with 10^5 trophoblast cells per day. These observations have led to the hypothesis that specific tolerance to paternal antigens may result, but the critical experiments necessary to prove the existence of tolerance have not been done and would be difficult to carry out in man. In animals the same phenomenon has not been reported (except recently in the chinchilla).

The Implantation of the Foetus in an Immunologically Privileged Tissue Site

The concept that the maternal uterus acts as a 'privileged site', so that the foetus although bearing foreign transplantation antigens does not act to sensitize the mother, is based on the analogy of other known sites of allograft privilege such as the anterior chamber of the eye, the brain, the substantia propria of the cornea and the cheek pouch of the Syrian hamster.

Xenografts of non-malignant human tissue when transferred to the tissue of the cheek pouch of the hamster soon gain a blood supply and survive over long periods. It is envisaged that the cheek pouch lacks an effective lymphatic drainage. In this case, sensitization of the hamster, before or at any stage after implantation of an allograft into the cheek pouch, brings about destruction of the pouch graft. The same fate occurs to grafts which have established themselves in the other privileged sites (e.g. the brain and anterior chamber of the eye) after they are sensitized by means of a skin allograft from the same donor, or if the host is given an injection of donor strain lymphoid cells. It is otherwise with the foetus: the sensitization of the mother by skin grafting with paternal or foetal skin does not appear to affect the pregnancy.

Several authors who have investigated the lymphatic drainage of the uterus have claimed that while there is a profuse plexus of lymphatic vessels in the muscular layers, even extending to the outer limits of the endometrium, the inner endometrium is devoid of lymphatics.

In addition there is the possibility of a barrier layer which would exclude effective contact between the immunologically competent cells of the mother and the foetal transplantation antigens. Thus trophoblast cells, when transplanted to beneath the renal capsule of an allogeneic host, grow without evoking a transplantation reaction. On the other hand, other tissues derived from the embryo, and the trophoblast cells after enzyme (trypsin) treatment, do evoke a cellular reaction in the surrounding kidney tissue. Presumably the possession of an immunologically inert barrier substance at the surface of such trophoblast cells might make them quite unique in their ability to invade mammalian tissues, and the same barrier substance may be invoked to explain the invasive malignancy of the cells of a chorioncarcinoma. There is a suggestion that a mucopolysaccharide rich in sialic acid could fulfil this role.

The outermost layer of the chorion is the trophoblast, which is generally accepted to be of foetal origin. In the haemochorial placentae this layer is continuously bathed by maternal blood from the time that the placenta is formed. It is therefore remarkable that small lymphocytes can be present in such maternal blood and yet do not apparently act to damage the placental tissues. Several attempts in mice, rats and rabbits have been made to influence the successful outcome of pregnancy, by presensitizing the mother with skin allografts of paternal skin. Even when the allografts were transferred at the time of egg implantation no significant effect on the pregnancy could be shown. Nevertheless, more recent work does support the possibility that the trophoblast can express an immunogenic effect during a normal pregnancy which leads to tissue changes in the placenta. Thus it is found that the placentae derived from the F_1 hybrids of two pure strains of mice are consistently heavier than those of the pure bred mice of either strain. This effect did not depend on the fact that the mother was hybrid. The same effect occurred when an inbred foetus was implanted into the uterus of a female of the other pure line strain. Such placentae of increased size do not occur when the mother is rendered tolerant of paternal antigens.

FURTHER READING

Albert F. & Medawar P.B. (ed.) (1959) *Biological problems of Grafting.* Blackwell Scientific Publications, Oxford

Amos D.B. (1962) The use of simplified systems as an aid to the interpretation of mechanisms of graft rejection. *Progr. Allergy.* **6,** 468

Amos D.B. & van Rood J.J. (eds) (1966) *Histocompatibility Testing.* Munksgaard, Copenhagen

Antilymphocytic serum (1967) Ciba Foundation Study Group No. 29. Churchill, London

Berenbaum M.C. (1967) Transplantation and immunosuppression. In *Modern Trends in Immunology,* 2 [Ed. Cruickshank R. and Weir D.M.]. Butterworth, Edinburgh

Brent L. & Medawar P.B. (1963) Tissue transplantation. A new approach to the typing problem. *Brit. Med. J.* **2,** 269

Brooks J.R. (1962) In '*La Greffe, aspects biologiques et cliniques*' [Ed. Mathé G. and Amiel J.L.]. Masson, Paris

Bussard A. (ed.) (1963) *La tolerance acquise et la tolerance naturelle a l'égard de substances antigeniques definies.* C.N.R.S., Paris

Calne R.Y. (1967) *Renal Transplantation* (2nd edition). Arnold, London

Dausset J., Hamburger J. & Mathé G. (eds) (1966) *Advances in Transplantation.* Munksgaard, Copenhagen

Gabrielsen A.E. & Good R.A. (1967) Chemical suppression of adaptive immunity. *Adv. Immunol.* **6,** 91

Hašek M., Lengerova A. & Hraba T. (1961) Transplantation immunity and tolerance. *Adv. Immunol.* **1,** 1

Iwasaki Y., Porter K.A., Amend J.R., Marchioro T.L., Zuhlke V. & Starzl T.E. (1967) *Surg. Gynecol. Obstet.* **124,** 1. (Review of use of antilymphocyte serum)

Krohn P.L. (1963) Transplantation of endocrine organs. In *Techniques in*

Endocrine Research [Ed. Eckstein P. and Knowles F.] p. 195. Academic Press, New York

LESKOWITZ S. (1967) Tolerance. *Ann. Rev. Microbiol.* **21**, 157

MEDAWAR P.B. (1958) Croonian Lecture: The homograft reaction. *Proc. Roy. Soc. 'B'* **148**, 145

MERRILL J.P. (1967) Human tissue transplantation. *Adv. Immunol.* **7**, 275

SCHWARTZ R.S. (1965) Immunosuppressive drugs. *Progr. Allergy* **9**, 246

SIMONSEN M. (1962) Graft *versus* host reaction. Their natural history and applicability as tools of research. *Progr. Allergy* **6**, 349. Karger, Basel

WILSON D.B. & BILLINGHAM R.E. (1967) Lymphocytes and transplantation immunity. *Adv. Immunol.* **7**, 189

WOLSTENHOLME G.E.W. & O'CONNOR M. (eds) (1966) *Ethics in Medical Progress with special reference to transplantation.* Little Brown, Boston

WOODRUFF M.F.A. (1960) *The Transplantation of Tissues and Organs.* Springfield, Illinois

CHAPTER FOURTEEN

Immunological Aspects of Cancer

In earlier editions we stated that it was not the task of a general book on Immunology to discuss the problem of cancer at any length, but that tumours could nevertheless be regarded as invasive grafts of tissue, which should evoke homograft reactions in so far as they possessed antigens foreign to their hosts and would be subject to the principles governing immunological tolerance. It would, in fact, not be unreasonable to regard many progressing tumours as examples of an immunological failure on the part of their hosts. Recent work, especially that related to the induction of tumours by viruses and the recognition of new antigenic determinants on such tumours, has reawoken so wide an interest in the immunological aspects of cancer that a special chapter on this subject is called for.

A great deal of our knowledge is derived from experiments employing inbred strains of mice, whose value to studies of transplantation of normal tissues has already been stressed in the previous chapter, but most of the findings have been confirmed in inbred strains of other species such as rats and hamsters. Tumours which arise spontaneously, or are induced by means of chemical carcinogens or viruses, can very often be propagated by inoculation of a sufficient quantity of tumour cells into a normal animal of the same inbred strain. However most such transplantable tumours regress, sometimes after a short period of growth, when similar numbers of cells are implanted into animals of a different strain. Some tumours are able to continue growing after transplantation to allogeneic animals provided that a large inoculum is used; and a few, which normally grow very rapidly, can be propagated in allogeneic strains even with quite small inocula.

When the recipient mice have been pre-immunized by means of

homografts of skin or other tissues of the tumour-bearing strain (whether or not the tissues come from tumour-bearing mice) they are very much more resistant. This is shown by complete failure of the tumour grafts to take or by the need for much larger inocula to achieve progressive growth. Such findings suggest that tumours share homograft antigens with normal tissues and that their growth can be inhibited more or less successfully by homograft immunity against these antigens. That this is indeed the case has been repeatedly confirmed. For example, if tumour cells (irradiated, if necessary, to prevent their rapid growth) are used to immunize mice of another strain, the recipients can be shown to have become specifically immunized against grafts of normal tissues from animals of the same strain as the tumour donor. Similarly if animals of one strain are immunized by normal tissue homografts from a second strain they show heightened resistance to implants of tumours from animals of the second strain. This can be shown by quantitative studies using implants containing graded amounts of tumour cells and observing either the minimum number of cells required to establish tumours or their rates of growth compared with unimmunized controls. Resistance may be complete or only partial, but it is specific for tumours of the second strain and is not evident against tumours from a third unrelated strain.

The finding that tumour cells and normal cells share transplantation antigens is not surprising, since neoplastic cells are unlikely to have surface structures on their membranes radically different from those of the normal cells from which they are derived.

THE RELATIVE IMPORTANCE OF CELL-MEDIATED SPECIFIC IMMUNITY AND OF HUMORAL ANTIBODIES IN PROTECTION AGAINST TUMOURS

By experiments similar in principle to those designed to evaluate the parts played by cell-mediated specific immunity and by humoral antibodies in homograft rejection, it has been found that development of cell-mediated immunity is the important factor in rejection or halting the growth of solid tumours, and of many tumour cells capable of multiplying in a single-cell (dispersed) form such as ascites tumours and leukaemias. There is also good evidence that dispersed tumour cells can be killed by the action of suitable antibodies and complement, becoming in fact lysed in the process. However, other antibodies against surface components of tumours, which do not activate complement, not only fail to kill the tumour cells but may actually protect them against the effects of cell-mediated immunity. This is the important phenomenon of 'enhancement' discussed further below (p. 585).

ANTIGENIC DIFFERENCES BETWEEN TUMOUR CELLS AND NORMAL HOST CELLS

Although, as pointed out above, the vast majority of the antigenic components of tumour cells are *qualitatively similar* to those of the normal cells of their hosts, it has become clear that many experimental and some spontaneous tumours do in fact differ antigenically from their hosts. Such differences have been sought in several ways. One has been to inject into animals of the same strain, or of the same species, or of another species, either tumour tissues (suitably killed if necessary) or normal tissues, in the hope of eliciting antibody formation against components of tumour tissues on the one hand and of normal tissues on the other. The antisera so produced have been tested (when appropriate after exhaustive absorption with normal tissue) to detect components peculiar to the tumour tissue in a variety of ways, including double diffusion in agar gels against extracts of the tissues; immunofluorescence; cytotoxicity in the presence of complement. The main difficulty in interpreting many such tests has been to be sure that what may appear to be tumour-specific antigenic components are not simply materials which are present much more abundantly in the tumorous than the normal tissues. Another approach, applicable to tumours produced by infection with oncogenic viruses, has been to test whether specific immunization with the virus in question or with tissue of tumours induced by the virus is able to protect against transplantation of other virus-induced tumours arising in the same strains of inbred animals.

The evidence at the time of writing is not entirely clear, but it may be summarized as follows:

LOSS OF ANTIGENS

1. Certain tumours and pre-cancerous tissues lack antigens characteristic of the corresponding normal tissue. For example cancers of the colon may lack the characteristic mucopolysaccharide antigens of mucus secreting cells, and thyroid carcinomata and precancerous tissues have been found to lack a characteristic thyroid 'microsomal'

antigen (see p. 636). Those antigens best studied are related to the specialized activities of the cells (e.g. secretion) and their loss is presumably a consequence of dedifferentiation. Evidence for the loss of normal transplantation antigens has been sought but, perhaps surprisingly, has not been found. The hypothesis has been advanced that loss of antigens may somehow account for the apparently uninhibited growth of tumours, but this could hardly have an immunological basis unless the growth of normal tissues were thought to be restrained by some immunological means.

NEW ANTIGENS

2. In some experimental tumours of rats and in human carcinomas of the gastrointestinal tract antigens have been detected which are absent from the corresponding normal tissue of their hosts but present in embryonic tissues of the same species. These presumably represent the products of genes which are normally repressed in adult cells.

3. Many virus-induced tumours and other tumours elicited by chemical carcinogens possess new antigens not evidently present in the normal host at any stage of development.

In the case of virus-induced tumours it is not uncommon to demonstrate by immunofluorescence the presence of an antigen in the cell nuclei which is associated with persistence of the infecting virus genome and is in fact a viral antigen. However, more importantly, it has been found that virus induced tumours also have a *new* transplantation antigen on their surface, which is characteristic of the infecting virus. This type of antigen, which appears when the infected cells undergo neoplastic transformation and is related to their changed behaviour, is probably due (in the case of DNA viruses) to incorporation of part of the viral genome into that of the host cells, so that it is reproduced at cell division. All tumours induced by the same virus, whatever their cytological characteristics, bear the same antigen. Immunization of an animal, for example by virus infection or implants of living or irradiated cells bearing the specific antigen, evokes resistance to challenge with any syngeneic tumour tissue induced by the same virus and therefore bearing the same surface antigen.

Tumours induced in mice and rats by chemical carcinogens such as methylcholanthrene have also been shown to have tumour-specific surface antigens, similarly to the virus-induced antigens, although these are often only very weak immunogens and their presence is consequently difficult to detect. A difficulty arises in interpreting such findings because potentially oncogenic viruses are so common in laboratory animals (and perhaps in all animals) that there is a very real possibility that the tumours arise as a consequence of 'lighting up' of a latent virus or that the tumour becomes super-infected with a virus. Even the use of 'germ free' mice has not got round this difficulty, since 'germ free' mice are not necessarily free from latent viruses. Thus it is possible that the antigens of tumours not knowingly induced by viruses may nevertheless unwittingly be so. However, there are reports of two sarcomas induced on opposite sides of the same animal by the same carcinogen, which had demonstrably different antigens. Such findings certainly suggest that chemically induced tumours can develop new antigens peculiar to themselves, although there is presumably not an unlimited number of possible new surface structures.

The demonstration of similar antigens in human tumours by similar methods is scarcely feasible since it would involve transplantation of tumour tissue between, for example, identical twins of whom only one had cancer. However, this difficulty could conceivably be got round by an *in vitro* test along the lines of the mixed leucocyte reaction used to detect differences in transplantation antigens between individuals described in Chapter Thirteen (p. 559). For example, if one of a pair of identical twins developed a neoplasm from which dispersed cells could be obtained (such as a leukaemia) these might be set up in mixed culture with peripheral leucocytes from the unaffected twin. If, but only if, the neoplastic cells have developed a new antigen would the normal twin's leucocytes be expected to show increased reactivity towards them. Nevertheless, it would be surprising if tumour-specific antigens were not present in at least some human tumours such as those carcinomas of the bronchus or of the bladder associated with chemical carcinogens, or those tumours for which a viral origin seem probable.

INCREASED SUSCEPTIBILITY TO TUMOURS

The fact that tumours implanted into allogeneic or heterogeneic hosts are subject to homograft reactions—even though these are not always effective—and the possession by tumour cells of a surface antigen distinct from those of their otherwise histocompatible hosts, have led to the hypothesis that the development of tumours is commonly prevented by an immunological mechanism. The suggestion has been put forward that aberrant cells possessing a foreign surface antigen may evoke a homograft reaction which arrests their growth or destroys them before an invasive tumour can develop, and the term '*immunological surveillance*' has been proposed for this mechanism. If such a mechanism exists it would be expected that depression of cell-mediated specific immunity either by general or specific means should increase susceptibility to tumours. There is considerable evidence, direct and indirect, that this is the case, although most of it is admittedly derived from experiments with oncogenic viruses.

It has long been known that tumours are more readily transplantable into very young than into older animals, unless in the latter some 'immunologically privileged' site is chosen such as the brain or the cheek pouch (see Chapter Thirteen) or the recipients are irradiated with γ-rays. This observation, however, although it indicates that depression of immunological responses permits tumour growth, does not necessarily imply that specific tumour antigens are involved. More direct evidence is provided by the apparently paradoxical phenomenon known as *enhancement* described below.

ENHANCEMENT

Although certain solid tumours are transplantable and grow readily in several strains of mice, others will normally grow only in a single strain (unless they have been 'adapted' to some closely related strain by passage through very young hosts). Tumours of the latter kind when transplanted to adult allogeneic mice grow for a while and then regress. A further transplant of the same tumour fails to grow at all—i.e. typical homograft immunity has been elicited. However, if the recipient mice are first immunized by injections of killed tumour tissue so as to make humoral antibodies against it, a subsequent transplant of live tumour cells is not rejected rapidly—as might have been expected—but actually grows better and for longer (sometimes even permanently) than it would in normal mice of the same strain. Furthermore, serum taken from mice (or even from rabbits) immunized against the killed tumour tissue, when administered to normal mice of the same strain at the time of transplantation of the tumour, causes the recipients to accept the tumour as readily as do mice actively immunized with dead tumour tissue. In other words, serum antibodies can enhance the growth of such tumours. This is not true for all tumours—for example, as already stated, malignant cells in some forms of leukaemia are killed by antibody in the presence of complement—however, the phenomenon is well established experimentally. It has also been found that, in cases when a tumour has survived permanently as a result of enhancement, it can subsequently often be transferred successfully to normal mice of the same strain without pretreatment.

A probable explanation of how enhancement works has been advanced quite recently, as follows: If antibodies against surface components, which do not *per se* kill the tumour cells, are present before any cell-mediated specific immunity can develop, and if the antibodies are sufficiently avid, they can coat the cells so as to mask their surface antigenic determinants and prevent them from coming into intimate contact with the surface of lymphocytes. Since such contact is necessary for interaction of living target cells and competent lymphocytes to result either in further sensitization or death of the target cells, these are both avoided or reduced below a critical level. Direct evidence has been given in the case of certain mouse tumours that pretreatment of tumour cells with humoral antibodies against them (a) prevents their destruction by presensitized lymphocytes both *in vivo* and *in vitro*, and (b) diminishes the capacity of the tumour cells after transplantation to evoke cell-mediated specific immunity against themselves. This last phenomenon may explain why 'enhanced' tumours are able to grow more readily even on further transplantation into normal mice.

THE ROLE OF IMMUNOLOGICAL TOLERANCE

If tumours have specific antigens absent from their hosts, and the formation of enhancing antibodies has been avoided, these might be expected to evoke at least some degree of cell-mediated immunity. The fact that tumours possessing such antigens may nevertheless grow vigorously has prompted investigations of whether and in what circumstances the expected immune response is prevented by specific immunological tolerance.

The experimental system in which answers to these questions can most readily be sought is provided by tumours arising in mice as a result of neoplastic transformation by oncogenic viruses. Such transformation occurs regularly when normal mouse cells growing in tissue culture are infected with the viruses. Tumours are also produced when mice become infected *in utero* or soon after birth.

However, with certain exceptions, such as Rous sarcoma virus of rodents and fowls (which causes very fast growing tumours), inoculation of virus into *adult* animals either does not lead to tumour formation, or leads to tumours which are local and non-malignant and commonly regress (e.g. Shope papilloma in rabbits; Yaba virus in monkeys; and—probably—molluscum contagiosum in man). Introduction of virus into adult animals, however, both elicits immunity against the virus, e.g. neutralizing antibodies, and leads to resistance to tumours induced by the same virus in the same animal or in other animals of the same species. It is when the viruses are introduced while the capacity to develop an immune response is still immature, that tumours possessing the characteristic surface antigen occur later on in a high proportion of the infected animals.

Infection early in life can come about either by congenital transmission from mothers which harbour the virus or by natural infection or experimental inoculation shortly after birth. Immunological tolerance of the viruses and of the surface antigens evoked by them might be expected to result from introduction of a sufficient dose of virus, and could then explain the subsequent unhindered growth of transformed neoplastic cells. Study of a number of different viruses has shown that this explanation is probably true—but only for certain viruses, notably those transmitted directly from the mother to her offspring and particularly those which actually infect lymphocytes (see Table 14.1). In the case of the other viruses such as mouse polyoma virus, infection by which can be acquired shortly after birth (mainly from virus excreted in the urine of cage mates), there is no evidence that true immunological tolerance occurs. In fact the mothers in a stock carrying the virus commonly have quite high levels of anti-viral antibody and passively transferred antibody is passed on to their offspring. Nevertheless, if newborn animals are inoculated with these viruses many develop tumours. The main reason why these tumours are not rejected appears to be the relatively slow maturation of cell-mediated immune responses (which are only demonstrable after about three weeks, in contrast to five days in adults). Presumably by this time the rapidly proliferating tumour cells are beyond immunological control. A contributory factor may be enhancement by humoral antibody, which appears early in these animals, as in adults.

TABLE 14.1

Comparison of oncogenic viruses in respect of induction of immunological tolerance in infected experimental animals in early life

Virus	Polyoma; adenoviruses; Simian virus 40; Rous virus	Mammary tumour agent; Gross virus; Moloney virus (some strains); avian leukosis
Mode of virus transmission to offspring	Exposure at or after birth	Transmitted *in ovo* or *in utero* and/or via milk
Immunocytes in which virus multiplication occurs	Macrophages (not lymphocytes)	Lymphocytes
Anti-viral antibody detectable in mother and offspring	+	–
Cell-mediated immunity to antigens demonstrable in mothers	+	–
Tolerance of virus	–	+
Effect of neonatal thymectomy	Increased incidence of tumours	No increased incidence of tumours; may decrease
Effect of antilympho-cyte serum	Increased incidence of of tumours	Tumours appear earlier; with different histology and in different tissues

Effects of Neonatal Thymectomy

As was described in Chapter Three, the effect of neonatal thymectomy is greatly to diminish the capacity to develop cell-mediated specific immunity. If such immunity is really the most important mechanism of immunological surveillance the result should be a notable increase in susceptibility to tumours. In the case of tumours induced by viruses in the left-hand column of Table 14.1 neonatal thymectomy decreases the latent period and greatly increases the proportion of animals in which tumours appear. However, in the case of viruses to which the animals have become truly tolerant (right-hand column) thymectomy does not assist the development of tumours—in fact their incidence may even decrease. This finding is not unexpected, since the tumours in such cases arise by neoplastic transformation of lymphocytes, the very cells whose numbers are diminished by thymectomy. So far, then, the results are in accord with the hypothesis advanced earlier.

TABLE 14.2

Failure of immunity in neoplasias involving the lymphoid system. Comparison of incidence of 'anergy' among patients in good and in poor condition. (Anergy was detected by skin testing with a variety of microbial antigens to which most normal adults gave positive reactions)

	Percent anergic	
	Good condition	Poor condition
Controls	1·4	—
Various carcinomas	0	38
Leukaemia (unspecified)	12	50
Hodgkin's disease	53	87·5
Other lymphomas	5	62

[From Lamb D., Pitney F., Kelly W.D. and Good R.A. *J. Immunol.* **89,** 555 (1962)]

Proportion of unselected skin homografts surviving in patients for 30 days or longer (i.e. substantially longer than is observed in normal persons)

Chronic lymphocytic leukaemia	7/16
Lymphosarcoma	2/6
Reticulum cell sarcoma	4/5
Multiple myeloma	3/7
Hodgkin's disease	17/20
Acute leukaemia	0/5
Chronic myeloid leukaemia	0/3

[From Miller D.G., *Ann. Intern. Med.* **57,** 703 (1962)]

However, when the effect of thymectomy was examined on the incidence of tumours induced by chemical carcinogens such as methylcholanthrene the results have been less striking. Some workers have found a suggestion of a decreased latent period and increased incidence, but others found little or no effect. This might imply that chemically-induced tumours have no specific surface antigens, but it could also imply that such antigens, if present, were only very weak immunogens.

Effect of Anti-lymphocyte Serum

By reasoning similar to that used in the preceding section anti-lymphocyte serum, which is a powerful suppressor of cell-mediated immunity (Chapter Thirteen, p. 571), should also be expected to diminish resistance to development of tumours. Some experiments to test this have been described, employing mice infected at birth with small amounts of oncogenic viruses. A few injections of ALS, administered during the first fortnight after birth, caused a marked increase in the incidence of tumours elicited by adenovirus and polyoma virus. When the effect on a leukaemia virus was tested (Table 14.1) in previously uninfected (i.e. non-tolerant) newborn mice, ALS, unlike thymectomy, resulted in the earlier appearance of tumours and these occurred in unusual forms and at unusual sites. It seems that lymphocytes are somehow conditioned by the presence of a thymus so that they can respond to virus infection by malignant growth. This conditioning is not prevented by ALS (which has much less effect on the thymus than on lymph nodes) even though cell-mediated immunity is depressed.

If it were feasible by repeated administration of ALS to suppress cell-mediated immunity throughout the major part of the life-span of inbred animals liable to spontaneous tumours, such as mice, it would be possible to test the hypothesis of 'immunological surveillance' mentioned on p. 585 by observing whether spontaneous tumours occurred, as would be predicted, earlier or more frequently in ALS-treated animals than in untreated controls.

Anergy

'*Anergy*' is a term used clinically to describe a state of general depression of immunological responsiveness without any evident cause. Investigation both of humoral antibody responses to antigens such as bacterial toxoids and of delayed-type hypersensitivity to tuberculin and other microbial antigens has shown that these are often depressed in many cancer patients. Furthermore, such patients may develop only very weak responses to chemical sensitizing agents such as dinitrofluorobenzene painted on the skin, and show a strikingly delayed rejection of skin homografts. These observations have been adduced to support the suggestion that the tumours grow because of their hosts' anergic state.

It is important in assessing them to rule out the effects of treatment with corticosteroids or antimetabolite drugs (which are often themselves immunosuppressant agents, as described below), and of general debility of the patients. Although starvation by itself does not notably diminish antibody production, as was shown by investigations on concentration camp victims at the end of World War II, the syndrome of cachexia in cancer patients is due to more than starvation and may include effects of tissue destruction, infection and possibly autoimmune reactions. Even taking these factors into account, the evidence suggests strongly that neoplasms involving lymphoid tissues (e.g. leukaemia, lymphoma and multiple myeloma) are associated with significant depression of humoral antibody production. However, in the case of other forms of cancer, such as skin carcinoma, adenocarcinoma or sarcoma of bone and muscle, antibody production has been found normal. Cell-mediated specific immunity responses are regularly depressed in patients with lymphoma, but frequently also in others with all sorts of advanced cancer (Table 14.2). Nevertheless the association between a state of anergy and progressing cancer is by no means complete, and is certainly not sufficient to justify any hypothesis that a general diminution of immunological responsiveness is of primary importance in permitting tumour growth.

The Effect of Treatment with Immunosuppressant Agents

The drugs used in treating cancer, such as alkylating agents and antimetabolites, are selected because they kill or inhibit dividing cells. Although some selectivity for the tumour is aimed at, and the schedule and route of administration is chosen so as to affect tumour cells more than others (such as bone marrow, intestinal epithelium or skin), systemic treatment inevitably inhibits to some degree the division and differentiation of lymphocytes which are essential for the multiplication of cells making a specific immunological response (see Chapter Three). Primary responses are more susceptible to such inhibition than are secondary, but the danger of a general lowering of immunological resistance is a well recognized hazard of prolonged cancer chemotherapy. Corticosteroids also (but not androgens or oestrogens), when administered in large doses over prolonged periods of time, inhibit proliferation of normal as well as neoplastic lymphocytes, even in a species such as man whose resistance to these drugs is high compared with that of rodents. Corticosteroids have been shown particularly to depress cell-mediated specific immunity (see Chapter Twelve, p. 543).

Such considerations are relevant to the question of how far the growth of tumours is checked by immunological means. Two aspects need to be regarded. On the one hand, a substantial reduction in tumour mass (achieved by local or systemic treatment) with minimal concomitant immunological depression may swing the balance in favour of rejection of the tumour—an outcome which may account, at least in part, for the complete cures by chemotherapy of, for example, chorionepithelioma and of Burkitt's lymphoma discussed below. On the other hand, incomplete killing of the tumour cells accompanied by a major depression of immunological responsiveness may swing the balance the other way. It happens not infrequently that when chemotherapy has to be stopped (e.g. because of undesirable side effects) the rate of growth and spread of a tumour is subsequently much more rapid than before chemotherapy was begun. Although neither suggestion provides a strong argument for a significant role of specific immunity in containing tumour growth, the latter especially is consistent with such a role.

Immunological Factors in the Prevention and Regression of Tumours

In the preceding sections of this chapter a case has been made out for the thesis that neoplastic cells may have specific antigens on their surface, and that when this happens the cells may elicit a homotransplant type of reaction which either destroys them before they form a detectable tumour, or, if they do so, arrests their growth. The evidence from study of tumours in experimental animals suggests that the case is well founded where virus-induced tumours are concerned, and moderately strong for tumours elicited by chemical carcinogens. In respect of spontaneously arising tumours it is at present weak, but this may be due to the fact that relatively little study has been made of them from this point of view.

The grounds for thinking that human tumours may also possess specific antigens are largely circumstantial. It is an undoubted fact that occasional tumours, with histologically proved malignant characteristics, regress spontaneously. Sometimes also when the primary site of a metastasizing tumour is destroyed (e.g. by X-irradiation) the secondaries regress without themselves being treated. Such behaviour has been observed in the case of tumours which are not thought to be hormone dependent, and it suggests that immunological rejection occurred. Furthermore, lymph nodes draining an area in which a non-metastasizing tumour is growing often show hyperplasia similar to that of nodes responding to an immunological stimulus; and one of the histological characteristics of tumours associated with a favourable prognosis is an infiltration by lymphoid cells, not unlike the picture of a mild homograft reaction. Both these features could, of course, be consequences rather than the cause of cell destruction and liberation of intracellular constituents.

Two human tumours may be mentioned concerning which the evidence is more than circumstantial, namely chorionepithelioma and Burkitt's lymphoma, and these are discussed briefly below.

Chorionepitheliomata arise as malignant proliferations of the chorionic epithelium of the placenta, including both the Langhans' cells and the syncytium, and are of foetal origin. They are thus certainly allogeneic, although their immunogenicity is likely to be masked by mechanisms similar to those preventing the foetal placenta causing a homograft reaction, which have been discussed on p. 577. It has been proposed that chorionepitheliomata grow apparently unhindered because immunological tolerance to the foetal antigens has been developed during pregnancy, but there is no evidence that such tolerance occurs to any significant extent. There is a suggestion, however, that enhancement may be involved. Some women with chorionepithelioma have been shown to possess humoral antibodies capable of agglutinating their husband's leucocytes, and these women retained grafts of their husband's skin longer than would normally be expected even in an unimmunized recipient. Other patients who had no detectable serum antibodies against their husband's leucocytes rapidly rejected grafts of their husband's skin. Only the latter eventually survived. Chorionepitheliomata are particularly susceptible to treatment with the antimetabolite drug amethopterin, complete and permanent cures being common. They also, though rarely, regress spontaneously. The factors involved in complete regression probably include unmasking of the allogeneic antigens so as to stimulate transplantation immunity (while avoiding enhancement), and sufficient inhibition of the rate of tumour growth to permit this immunity to triumph. Although amethopterin in large doses is an immunosuppressant, it is at least plausible to suppose that in the doses used successfully it performs both the above functions.

Burkitt's (*African*) *Lymphoma* is a form of tumour in which the predominant cells are primitive lymphoid cells, arising most frequently in the jaw but also in other bones or in the abdomen. It usually occurs in children below the age of fifteen years, and is rather common in a belt extending across Africa below the Sahara where the annual rainfall and minimum temperature are high. The tumour is named after D.P. Burkitt, who first drew attention to the peculiar geographical distribution of its incidence and suggested that it might be virus-induced and spread by an insect vector. Similar tumours, though much more rarely, have been found in other continents. Numerous attempts have been made to isolate a virus from the tumour tissue, and the presence of a herpes-like virus has been discovered in most samples. However, a similar virus has been found in cells of other tumours and even in normal cells, and it appears as likely to be a passenger virus as the causative agent. Lymphomas of this type grow readily in tissue culture, and there is good evidence that some, but not all, individual cells synthesize immunoglobulins under these conditions, which gives the tumour an added interest to the immunologist. The reason for considering Burkitt's lymphoma at length in this chapter is that evidence has been found, by immunofluorescence, that patients with lymphoma may have autoantibodies against their own tumour cells. Furthermore, treatment with alkylating agents such as cyclophosphamide has produced a high proportion of apparently permanent cures—suggesting, as in the case of chorionepithelioma, that immunological processes have played a part.

The most important approaches to treatment of accessible tumours are evidently surgical excision and/or local treatment by chemotherapy or irradiation, and hormone treatment when the tumours are susceptible. It is when a specific attack on the tumour is impossible, or perhaps as a support to such a specific attack, that immunological factors should be considered. Even if these are important in resisting the spread of neoplastic cells, the continued growth of a tumour implies either that the race between recruitment of specifically-sensitized lymphocytes and multiplication of the tumour cells is being lost, or that sensitized lymphocytes are unable to exert their effect because of the presence of enhancing antibodies or because, for some anatomical reason, they are excluded from close contact with their target. The aim of any treatment based on immunological principles is to increase the effectiveness of cell-mediated immunity, and possibly of specific cytolytic antibodies in the case of dispersed-cell tumours such as leukaemias, while avoiding the stimulation of enhancing antibodies. Clearly any treatment which diminishes the mass of tumour cells without at the same time excessively interfering with the immune response is likely to be beneficial, and the most hopeful situation may well be one in which only a minimal residue of tumour tissue remains to be disposed of.

Attempts have been made to achieve the aims discussed above along a number of lines, some of which are mentioned below.

Tumour cells from patients with advanced inoperable solid tumours have been chemically coupled to foreign proteins known to be powerful immunogens, and these have been injected as a water-in-oil emulsion back into their host. In a limited series of cases all the patients developed antibodies demonstrable by gel diffusion against extracts of the tumours, but not of normal tissues, and in most of them the antibodies were shown by immunofluorescence to react with the tumour cell membrane. Interestingly, the antibodies all appeared to reveal the presence of cross reacting antigens in the tumours. Whether specific cell-mediated immunity also developed was not reported. Some of the patients had previously been treated by surgery or X-rays, but received no treatment subsequent to the immunization. Of the total of fourteen, two became tumour free and remained so 4 years later, and in three the tumours were stabilized or progressed very slowly. Biopsies following the immunizing injections showed striking degeneration of the tumour cells.

This series of cases, though small, is quoted as an example of attempts to make tumour antigens more immunogenic without loss of their cancer specificity, using the 'schlepper' principle mentioned in Chapter Six (p. 210). Other methods tried on a very limited scale include incorporating tumour cells, irradiated sufficiently to prevent cell division, in powerful adjuvants such as water-in-oil emulsions containing acid-fast bacilli. The latter are liable to cause severe local lesions and discomfort to the patient. Although some results appear promising, no proper evaluation can be made until larger series, followed up for a sufficient number of years, have been reported.

An alternative approach has been to transfer passively either humoral antibodies or lymphocytes specifically sensitized against putative tumour antigens. Treatment with antisera raised in horses or rabbits against a variety of human tumours has enjoyed a temporary vogue and even a certain notoriety. Such antisera almost inevitably contain antibodies against normal cell constituents besides any specific tumour antigens, and the temporary benefit claimed following their use may well be due to stimulation of the functional activity of the reticuloendothelial system (which can result from small doses of antibody reactive with RES cells) rather than to any specific anti-tumour action. Heterologous antisera are liable to cause serum sickness and nephritis, and there is theoretically at least a risk of causing enhancement of tumour growth. Although passive immunization with heterospecific serum might prove to be useful once the relevant antigens have been identified and purified, present evidence does not indicate that the use of such sera has hitherto provided any benefit sufficient to offset the considerable risks involved. Homologous serum or immunoglobulin have also been used from patients with cancers such as Burkitt's lymphoma or melanoma during periods of remission following treatment, but significant long-term improvement has not yet been reported.

Attempts at treatment with antiserum presuppose that humoral antibodies are important in killing tumour cells. The evidence from experiments in animals suggests that even though this may be true for some leukaemias cell-mediated immunity is more important, and clinical trials of the transfer of immunity by cells have been made in various ways. Most of these meet with the difficulty that survival of transferred allogeneic cells is likely to be brief unless the recipient's power to reject them is depressed; and that if such depression is too extreme there is a danger of a severe graft *versus* host reaction. Living blood leucocytes, spleen cells or thoracic duct leucocytes have been used from donors who were either normal, or had been immunized with cancer tissue from the patient to be treated, or had been cured of a similar form of cancer to that of the recipient and were putatively immunized against their own cancer. Marked though temporary clinical improvement and histological signs of regression have been reported, but no permanent cures. The recipients in these trials may be presumed sooner or later to have rejected the donor cells. This event can be prevented by prior irradiation of the donor with a normally lethal dose (800–1000 rads) of γ-radiation to the whole body. Based on successful results in treating experimental mouse leukaemias, patients with acute lymphoblastic leukaemia have been irradiated sufficiently to destroy their capacity to reject allogeneic grafts, as well as to inhibit the leukaemic cells, and have then been given allogeneic bone marrow grafts (see Chapter Thirteen, p. 567). Although such treatment was complicated by severe graft *versus* host reactions, there was suggestive evidence that the leukaemia itself was arrested or even cured.

The examples given above illustrate not only some of the lines of thought and the gaps in our knowledge but also the practical difficulties in attempting to apply immunological methods to the treatment of cancer in man. At best they are only sufficiently encouraging to warrant continuation of such attempts. However, the recognition that specific tumour antigens exist, and the fact that when these are evoked by oncogenic viruses in experimental animals all those evoked by a given virus are similar, give grounds for hope that at some time in the future preventive immunization against at least some tumours may become a practical possibility.

Immunological Surveillance and Allogeneic Inhibition

In discussing, above, the concept of 'immunological surveillance' the assumption was made that aberrant cells are rejected because they elicit specific cell-mediated immunity in their hosts before they can multiply sufficiently to form a detectable tumour. Whether this assumption is justified depends crucially upon the question what is the minimum number of cells bearing a foreign antigen needed to elicit a perceptible degree of immunity. It has been found experimentally in mice that intraperitoneal injection of as few as 2000 spleen cells differing from their hosts in respect of one of 'strong' H-2 transplantation antigens can suffice to cause significantly accelerated rejection of a subsequent skin graft from the donor strain. Even if many times more cells were required to elicit immunity against a weaker antigen, they would probably not amount to an obvious tumour. Thus the invocation of specific cell-mediated immunity as the operative mechanism remains reasonable.

There has however, been described a phenomenon which resembles cell-mediated specific immunity in some ways, and may indeed be related to it, but which cannot strictly be regarded as immunological. This phenomenon, whose biological significance is still under discussion, has been termed *allogeneic inhibition.* It is revealed *in vitro* in the following way. Living mouse cells of two distinct kinds (e.g. lymphocytes or tumour cells) capable of growing in tissue culture are mixed together with phytohaemagglutinin which causes them to agglutinate (see Chapter Six, p. 235), and are then plated out in tissue culture dishes and incubated. Provided that the two kinds of cells are isogeneic they both grow normally, but if they are *allogeneic* plaques of inhibited growth appear, and it seems that the allogeneic cells in contact have killed one another.

Without the use of phytohaemagglutinin to glue the cells together the phenomenon occurs very weakly or not at all. The reasons for thinking that this is not an immunological phenomenon (due, for example, to the presence of pre-existing sensitized lymphocytes) are: (1) that when lymphocytes from F_1 hybrids are mixed with parental tumour cells plaques of inhibited growth nevertheless appear, although (as explained on p. 101) F_1 hybrid cells contain all the transplantation antigens of the cells of their parents and therefore should not make an immunological response against them, and (2) that two lines of allogeneic tumour cells, neither of which are immunologically competent, can also inhibit one another. Allogeneic inhibition appears to be a consequence of the close apposition of cells which differ in respect of their surface antigens. The relevant antigens are presumably the transplantation antigens, since the occurrence of allogeneic inhibition can be predicted from a knowledge of these, and the degree of the inhibition roughly parallels the immunogenic potency of their antigenic differences as revealed by transplantation.

The mechanism by which such mutual inhibition of the cells occurs is at present quite unknown, just as is the mechanism whereby pre-sensitized lymphocytes kill their target cells. It could well be that the mechanisms are the same, and that the essential property of a specifically sensitized lymphocyte is its capacity to recognize and adhere closely to the target cell without the need for phytohaemagglutinin. A similar explanation might apply to the demonstrated capacity of macrophages coated with cytophilic antibody against surface components of other cells to attack and kill the latter (see discussion in Chapter Thirteen, p. 557).

The possibility that allogeneic inhibition plays a part in maintaining immunological surveillance has been strengthened by some recently published experiments relating to the effect of allogeneic inhibition on tumour cells which were subsequently reimplanted into hosts syngeneic for the tumour cells. Carcinogen-induced mouse sarcoma cells were brought into contact *in vitro* with allogeneic lymph node and spleen cells or with allogeneic tumour cells and phytohaemagglutinin. The allogeneic cells had in each instance been irradiated with a large dose of X-rays sufficient to prevent their multiplication *in vivo*. The mixed cells were then implanted subcutaneously into their normal hosts, which had also been given a light dose of irradiation to increase their susceptibility to the tumour, and the capacity of the sarcoma cells to grow was compared with that of the sarcoma cells treated similarly but with syngeneic rather than allogeneic lymphoid cells. Marked inhibition of growth of the sarcoma *in vivo* resulted from previous admixture with allogeneic cells of both sorts. Furthermore, as predicted, F_1 hybrid lymphoid cells caused a similar inhibition. The authors of this experiment conclude that *in vivo* confrontation of tumour cells with incompatible cells leads to growth suppression. However, it remains an open question whether the development of specific cell-mediated immunity may not be required to replace the effect of phytohaemagglutinin in bringing about the needed eyeball to eyeball confrontation.

FURTHER READING

ALEXANDER P. & HAMILTON FAIRLEY G. (1968) The allergic response in malignant disease. In *Clinical Aspects of Immunology* [Ed. Gell P.G.H. and Coombs R.R.A.] p. 499. Blackwell Scientific Publications, Oxford

BRUNNER K.T., MANEL J., CEROTTINI J.C., RUDOLF H. & CHAPUIS B. (1968) *In vitro* studies of cellular and humoral immunity induced by tumor allografts. In *Immunopathology 5th International Symposium* [Ed. Grabar P. and Miescher P.) p. 342. Schwabe, Basel

BURMESTER B.R. (1962) Transmission of avian lymphomatosis. *Cold Spring Harbor Symposium on Quantitative Biology* **27**, 471

BUSCH H. (ed.) (1968) *Methods in Cancer Research.* Vol. 2. Academic Press, New York

FENNER F. (1968) *The Pathogenesis and Ecology of Viral Infections* (Chapters 16 and 17, pp. 614 and 675). Academic Press, New York

GORER P.A. (1961) The antigenic structure of tumours. In *Adv. Immunol.* [Ed. Taliaferro W.H. and Humphrey J.H.] Vol. 1, p. 345. Academic Press, New York

HABEL K. (1962) Antigenic properties of cells transformed by polyoma virus. *Cold Spring Harbor Symposium on Quantitative Biology* **27**, 433

HELLSTRÖM K.E. & MÖLLER G. (1965) Immunological and immunogenetic aspects of tumor transplantation. *Progr. Allergy.* **9**, 158

HORSFALL F.L. & TAMM I. (Eds) (1965) *Viral and Rickettsial Infections of Man.* 4th edition. Pitman, London

Immunotherapy of Cancer (1966) *Wld Hlth Orgn tech. Rep. Series 344*

KLEIN G. (1966) Tumor Antigens. *Ann Rev. Microbiol.* **20**, 223

MACPHERSON I. (1967) Advances in the study of viral oncogenesis. *Brit. Med. Bull.* **23**, 144

METCALF D. (1966) *The Thymus. Recent Results in Cancer Research,* No. 5 [Ed. Rentchnick P.]. Springer, Heidelberg

MÖLLER E. & MÖLLER G. (1967) Inhibition of tumor growth by confrontation with incompatible cells. *Cancer* **20**, 871

Viruses and Cancer (1965) *Wld Hlth Org. tech. Rep. Series 295*

CHAPTER FIFTEEN

Auto-immunity (Auto-allergy) and its Relation to Human Disease

THE immune process was originally conceived as such because of its importance in defending the body against infection. We have seen in the preceding chapters that the response can be evoked by antigenic components of micro-organisms which are not toxins or harmful in any way and by many components of animals, e.g. foreign serum proteins, which are essentially bland. In other words, the body cannot distinguish a harmful from a bland antigen and proceeds to an immune response against either. However, the body does appear to possess a built-in mechanism to prevent it making antibodies, or any other sort of immune response, against constituents of its own tissues, although it will do so readily against the tissue components of other species or even of other individuals of the same species. It might be predicted that under special circumstances the workings of this mechanism which maintains immunological tolerance to the individual's own antigens would fail, and allow the production of antibodies against, or sensitization by products of the animal's own tissues. Such events do occur and this chapter deals with some of the consequences in man and experimental animals.

In order to discuss these events, certain new terms are necessary. The process whereby an antigenic component of the body's own tissue calls forth the production of antibody or results in specific sensitization to this antigen is called *auto-immunization* or *auto-sensitization*. The result may be the production of antibody, or cell-mediated hypersensitivity which, as in allergic processes to foreign antigens, can result in tissue damage and disease—so-called *auto-allergic* disease. This term is synonymous with the commonly used term: *auto-immune* disease, the semantics of which are even more difficult to justify but which can be regarded as the consequence of and dependent upon the process of auto-immunization. The antibodies produced to a person's own antigens are called *auto-antibodies*. They are to be distinguished from *iso-antibodies*, which are produced by an individual of a species against antigens of another individual of the same species; and *hetero-antibodies* whch are produced against the antigens of a member of another species. Unfortunately the terminology used by the transplanters of tissue (see Chapter Thirteen and Glossary) is not uniform with this.

MECHANISMS OF AUTO-IMMUNITY

The following hypothetical processes might conceivably give rise to auto-immunization:

(1) Production of auto-antibody or a condition of auto-sensitization is regarded as a breakdown of the normal state of specific immunological tolerance in respect of some of the body's components. The normal state of tolerance to auto-antigens is an actively induced state created and maintained by interaction between antigenic body components and immunologically competent cells. Thus, a normal state of tolerance is not, for example, a genetically determined lack of reactivity to self components. An experiment in justification of the above assumptions has been done in the frog. Removal of the posterior pituitary during embryonic development permanently impaired pigmentation so that an albino resulted. Attempts at replacement grafting in adult life of an autologous posterior pituitary (maintained meanwhile as a graft in another tadpole) failed, i.e. the graft was rejected and the albino state was not changed, presumably since the normal state of tolerance of the frog to its own posterior pituitary depended upon continued physical contact with the developing immunological systems.

This experiment provides a model for the first process whereby auto-immunization could occur: a particular antigenic component or type of cell might not be formed until the critical period of immunological immaturity is past. Spermatozoa come into this category, appearing only after embryonic life and being sufficiently distinct from other cells to act as antigens even in the animal which made them. That they do not normally act in this way is due to the fact that they are *anatomically segregated*: they are stored and secreted away from the immunologically competent cells. Sometimes the barrier can be broken down, as in infection of the testis with mumps virus, and then the immunization of a person with his own spermatozoa can apparently occur. Another example involves one of the organ-specific antigens of the lens of the eye (see section later in this chapter) which is absent from the lenses of newborn or 26-day old rabbits, but appears later in development.

Similar reasoning suggests that the body may produce an immune response to any newly-evolved mutant cells which would presumably bear recognizably 'non-self' markers. The resultant immune response could clearly be of great benefit to the host by leading to their elimination from the body in much the same way as a tissue homograft, i.e. a normal *surveillance* role which could have great biological importance (see Chapter Fourteen).

(2) Another way in which the body might become immunized against its own components would be if some cells formed distinctive proteins or other potential antigens, even during embryonic life, which were always segregated from normal contact with the immunological apparatus so that tolerance was never developed. Possible examples of this are various constituents of the brain. It has been mentioned in Chapter Seven how the brain, possibly on account of the lack of a draining system of lymphatics, is often able to accept *homografts* or, in other words, is unable to mount the usual homograft reaction against such foreign tissue. It has been found experimentally that a suspension prepared from an animal's own brain, injected into its subcutaneous tissue, induces antibodies to it and an allergic reaction which causes inflammation in the brain (experimental allergic encephalomyelitis). An analogous process in man occurs in the encephalitis which follows the use of vaccines of rabies virus containing animal brain or spinal cord.

There is a similar example in the crystalline lens proteins of the eye. Under suitable conditions animals can be caused to make antibody against lens protein, and in later section of this chapter will be discussed the experimental production of inflammation within the eye following such artificial immunization procedures, as well as examples of human intra-ocular disease which may result from analogous processes. Thyroglobulin, a protein formed by the cells lining the acini of the thyroid gland and stored within these acini, also behaves as an excellent antigen in iso- or auto-immunization of animals. In man antibodies occur against thyroglobulin and various other thyroid components, in association with destructive lesions of the thyroid gland itself (primary myxoedema, Hashimoto's disease or lymph-adenoid goitre) and de Quervain's disease (sub-acute thyroiditis). However, although from its position in the thyroid acinus, it is tempting to regard thyroglobulin as a totally segregated antigen, direct evidence has been provided recently of the presence of thyroglobulin in the cervical lymph and serum of normal subjects. Using a method for detecting thyroglobulin by its ability to inhibit the agglutination of erythrocytes coated with thyroglobulin, 0·1 μg/ml of thyroglobulin has been found in a high proportion of serum samples from newborn human infants.

(3) Many theoretical possibilities exist whereby substances normally present within the body could be so altered by physical or chemical means (mutagenic radiations such as X-rays or ultra-violet rays, mutagenic chemicals such as 'carcinogens') or by enzyme action (e.g. during infection with pathogenic micro-organisms) as to have chemical groupings exposed on their surfaces, which are foreign to the body and potentially antigenic.

Since the surface tertiary structure of macromolecules is all-important in determining antigenic specificity it is possible that body components, especially proteins, may undergo sufficient deformation *in vivo* to create new surface determinants. For example, even the combination of antigen and antibody leads to considerable morphological change in the molecule of antibody, depending on the combining ratios involved (see Chapter Four, p. 169).

The same proposition that new antigenic configurations of protein may be revealed by biological reactions is supported by the behaviour of serum complement in relation to the entity *conglutinin* (see p. 200 and Glossary). Conglutinin is a globulin which occurs in the serum of normal ruminants, and has the ability to recognize the new configuration which complement acquires once it is adsorbed on to sensitized cells or antigen–antibody aggregates. The further entity *immunoconglutinin* (p. 197) may, indeed, be regarded as an auto-antibody. This IgG or IgM antibody occurs in the serum of man and other animals after they have been injected with bacteria sensitized with antibody. The animal's own complement will adsorb to the sensitized bacteria. The resulting immunoconglutinin is directed at the new configurations of the complement protein provided by this adsorption.

It has already been mentioned how simple organic chemical compounds (e.g. drugs such as neo-arsphenamine or penicillin) can combine within the body with a normal protein and cause it to act as an antigen. Usually the antibody formed is directed against the new antigenic determinant provided by the drug (hapten), and so has little right to be regarded as *auto*-allergic in nature. However, the immunological response may effectively involve the host protein to which the drugs have become attached. This has been suggested as the explanation of the susceptibility of a few patients following therapy with Sedormid or Quinidine. The result is a purpura which is due to an immune response against platelets which have taken up the drugs. The sera of such patients contains antibody which will react with normal platelets which have been exposed to the drug, but not to ordinary platelets. There is, however, an alternative explanation (see p. 480).

In order to account for the fact that many auto-antibodies can be recognized which react with apparently unaltered body constituents, it has been postulated that an immunogenically altered or denatured self-protein might give rise to antibody which could then cross-react with the unaltered parent substance. Some justification for this important principle has been gathered by experiments in which it was shown that a foreign thyroglobulin, when injected into a rabbit, could induce the formation of antibodies reactive with autologous thyroglobulin. Similarly the injection of various rat tissues into the rabbit has been shown to lead to formation of auto-antibodies against components of the corresponding rabbit tissues. Thus rabbits injected with homogenates of rat colonic mucosa produce antibodies which in immunofluorescent tests react specifically with the epithelial cells of rabbit colon (including the cells in the mucosa of the antibody-producing rabbits themselves).

Other striking examples which arise in the course of infectious disease also appear to represent auto-allergic responses. The well-known Wassermann reaction seems to be a clear example of such. In this serological test the positive serum reacts with an antigen obtained from beef heart, but can equally well react with similarly extracted antigen of human heart or liver. Also in the disease primary atypical pneumonia due to *Mycoplasma pneumoniae* (the Eaton agent) 'cold agglutinins', antibodies directed against antigens at the surface of the erythrocyte, occur which are demonstrable by the clumping reaction which occurs when the patient's whole blood is cooled to 0–4°C. In this instance, the presence of the antibody is indicative of infection with a defined microbe, even though the antibody in question is usually found to be specific for the I antigen of the red cells. The explanation has been advanced that mycoplasmal infection somehow modifies the I antigen so as to make it immunogenic, but definite proof of this is lacking.

A suggestive model for the possible activity of bacterial enzymes in causing antibody production against one of the body's antigens is provided by work on T-agglutinin, a naturally occurring antibody. Normal red cells of group O do not react with normal human serum. But when such cells are treated with an enzyme derived from various bacteria the cells become agglutinable by such normal sera. Experimentally, T-agglutinin titres can be caused to rise by injection of an enzyme (usually obtained from *Vibrio cholerae*), which modifies most of the animal's own red cells *in vivo* so as to reveal the T-antigen at their surface and apparently thus provides a stimulus for antibody production. At the same time the animals also produce an antibody acting as a cold agglutinin for human O cells.

(4) Finally, it is reasonable to expect that the tolerance acquired during the period of immunological immaturity may under certain circumstances be lost. The maintenance of the state of tolerance must be due to the continued action throughout normal existence of a mechanism suppressing the immune response. This appears to depend, among other things, on the continuous or repeated exposure of the immunity mechanism to the immunogenic markers of the body tissues. Thus tolerance could fail if such immunogenic markers were temporarily absent and later returned (e.g. embryonic antigens which are found in some tumours of the gastrointestinal tract), or if the suppressing mechanism were to break down for some other reason and so permit the appearance of immunologically reactive cells which Burnet termed 'forbidden clones' in his clonal selection hypothesis (1959). Indeed, in those neoplastic diseases which affect the reticular tissues, e.g. Hodgkin's disease or lymphosarcoma, it is not unusual to encounter acquired haemolytic anaemia and it is tempting to postulate that this results from the activities of autonomous immunologically potent cells arising in the affected reticular tissues.

HUMAN DISEASES IN WHICH AUTO-IMMUNITY IS POSTULATED

Below, the role of auto-immunity is considered in several spheres of human pathology. It should be realized at the outset that the demonstration of the presence of an antibody or even of sensitization to an auto-antigen does not of necessity incriminate the immunity mechanism as the *cause* of the disturbed function or manifest lesions of the disease. Just as fulfilment of Koch's postulates is required as the kind of evidence which can justify the conclusion that a particular disease is caused by a particular parasite, so the approach to the pathogenesis of auto-immune disease requires similar circumspection. The postulates for the immune aetiology of a disease might be as follows:

(1) The immune response (demonstration of antibodies that are active at body temperatures, or of cell-mediated immunity to an auto-antigen) should be found at some stage in all cases of the disease in question.

(2) The antigen, preferably isolated in purified form, should be capable of inducing the lesions of the disease following injection into an experimental animal.

(3) The disease of the experimental animal should be capable of reproduction in a normal syngeneic animal by transfer to it of antibody in serum or of immunologically potent cells in suspensions taken from sites such as lymph nodes, spleen, bone-marrow or inflammatory exudates.

CLASSIFICATION OF DISEASES INVOLVING AUTO-IMMUNITY (AUTO-ALLERGIC MANIFESTATIONS)

Diseases in which auto-antibodies or auto-sensitization of the delayed type make their appearance will be considered below together with the evidence concerning the relationship of the auto-immune manifestations and the process causing the disease. They will be dealt with on the basis of a classification which divides them into auto-immune diseases of *organ-specific* and *non-organ specific* types (Table 15.1).

A good example of an organ-specific antigen discussed originally by Uhlenhuth (1903) is the lens of the eye. Rabbits injected with bovine lens suspension produce antibodies which precipitate extracts of the ocular lens not only from cattle but also from many other mammalian species and even avian or amphibian extract. The specificity of this antibody depends far more importantly on the *organ* than the *species* of origin. Thus the lens antisera did not react with extracts of other organs. Significantly the rabbit antisera also cause precipitation of rabbit lens extract including that of the animal injected, thus acting as an auto-antibody. Similar, organ-specific immunogenic properties have been demonstrated for the brain, testis, thyroid, adrenal cortex, stomach and colon.

TABLE 15.1

Diseases manifesting non organ-specific auto-immune phenomena	Diseases manifesting organ-specific auto-immune phenomena
Characteristics	*Characteristics*
—antibodies widely reacting with different tissues of same and other animal species, e.g. anti-nuclear factors	—antibodies specified for one of a group of components from a single organ
—immune tolerance established to relevant antigens	—immune tolerance not established to relevant antigens
—antigens are accessible	—antigens segregated from contact with lymphoid cells
—experimental lesions are not readily produced Diseases arise spontaneously in later life of animals of appropriate genotype, e.g. NZB mice	—experimental lesions can be produced by injection of antigen in Freund-type complete adjuvant
—familial incidence and clinical overlap of systemic lupus, rheumatoid arthritis and other 'connective tissue disorders'	—familial incidence and coincidence of diseases within the same organ-specific group, e.g. gastritis, adrenalitis, or thyroiditis
examples systemic lupus erythematosus, some cases of acquired haemolytic anaemia, rheumatoid arthritis	*examples* lymphadenoid goitre (Hashimoto's disease) thyrotoxicosis (Graves' disease), pernicious anaemia, idiopathic Addison's Disease (primary adrenal atrophy), post-Rabies vaccination encephalomyelitis, experimental allergic encephalomyelitis

Diseases manifesting auto-immune phenomena which belong to both above categories

Diseases which involve auto-antibodies of the non-organ specific type but their inflammatory lesions are concentrated in one or a few organs, e.g. Sjögren's disease (including Mickulicz disease), ulcerative colitis, lupoid hepatitis, primary biliary cirrhosis and many cases of acquired haemolytic anaemia

The clinical and serological features of human auto-immune diseases have been envisaged to cover a spectrum of activity between clear-cut examples of organ-specific (involving antigens of the above tissues) and non-organ specific immunity. In the non-organ specific auto-immunity states auto-antibodies occur which are directed to cellular components which are commonly distributed throughout the cells or body fluids, e.g. blood group antigens or nucleoproteins. There is a strong tendency for auto-antibodies against various organ-specific antigens to occur together in individual patients, but the simultaneous occurrence of organ-specific and non-organ specific antibodies is rare. The same generalization is claimed to extend to the relatives of affected patients.

Many of the organ-specific auto-immunity states can be reproduced by the experimental procedure of injecting the relevant tissue in complete Freund-type adjuvant into a suitable animal. Thus experimental thyroiditis, adrenalitis, orchitis with azoospermia, uveitis and gastritis have been produced by these means.

This classification has been thought to be of aetiological significance; organ-specific auto-immunity is possibly due to the release of tissue components into a non-tolerant host, whereas non-organ specific auto-immunity is possibly due to a central failure of recognition of tissue antigens to which, under normal circumstances, tolerance was established.

ACQUIRED HAEMOLYTIC ANAEMIA

Haemolytic anaemia comprises a group of diseases in which the blood cells are destroyed abnormally fast, with resulting jaundice and anaemia, despite an adequate intake of all the factors necessary for haemopoiesis.

A congenital form (*congenital acholuric jaundice*) was early distinguished, in which a genetically determined defect of erythrocyte formation led to increased red-cell fragility. In this condition the cells are spherocytes, and the laboratory usually detects the increased fragility by observing the haemolysis in decreasing saline concentrations. Other cases of haemolytic anaemia occurred without a familial distribution and with an onset at any period in life, often during middle age. These cases, which appeared to lack a genetic basis, were termed *idiopathic acquired haemolytic anaemia*. An important difference between the congenital and acquired disease groups was revealed from a study of the survival of red cells transfused to normal persons and the subjects of acquired haemolytic anaemia. The congenital spherocytic cells revealed their abnormality by a diminished life-span even in healthy subjects. The cells of the acquired form showed a normal life-span in healthy recipients, whose blood groups were compatible, but normal cells were destroyed when transfused into subjects with acquired haemolytic anaemia. Indeed, it was always notoriously difficult to find suitable donors for such cases, who often reacted violently to any transfusion of blood.

The possibility that certain clinical haemolytic syndromes might be due to serum haemolysins rather than to intrinsic defects of the red cell was given a firm basis by the demonstration (in 1904, by Donath and Landsteiner) of an auto-haemolysin which was clearly able to bring about the destruction of red cells in patients with paroxysmal cold haemoglobinuria. In the course of this disease, which frequently follows syphilitic infection, patients on exposure to cold excrete haemoglobin into the urine. If mixtures of red cells and serum from such patients were cooled to temperatures below that of the body, the red cells agglutinated. In the presence of active components of complement, when the agglutinated cells were warmed to 37° they lysed. Donath and Landsteiner deduced from these results that the active agent in the patient's serum was an auto-haemolysin but that normally this antibody could not exert a pathologic effect due to an inability to combine with the erythrocyte antigen at body temperature.

It was a relatively obvious step to suggest that haemolysins which were active at body temperatures may be responsible for the commonly occurring types of haemolytic disease known as *acquired haemolytic anaemia*.

In this case some of the circulating red cells would themselves carry the antibody. The demonstration of this fact required the introduction of a new technique, which was accomplished in 1945 by Coombs, Mourant and Race and termed 'the antiglobulin sensitization test', whereby antibody-like globulins adhering to the surface of red cells could easily be detected (see Chapter Nine for an explanation of this technique).

The use of this test showed that in the acquired form of haemolytic anaemia (but not in the congenital form) the patient's red cells were coated with human globulin. The addition of antibody against human immunoglobulin caused agglutination of the cells. Red cells coated with immunoglobulin commonly occur in haemolytic disease of the newborn, and in later life following transfusion of incompatible red cells. The *iso*-antibodies, in these cases, are combined with the Rh antigens and other recognized blood group antigens of the erythrocyte surface. In acquired haemolytic anaemia the substance combined with the surface of the red cells is also an immunoglobulin and, in some cases, it can be shown to combine with an already known antigen. The first case which was defined had anti-e specificity, which is that of a rarely encountered antibody, and in general it has been shown that those antibodies which are encountered least frequently in ordinary cases of iso-sensitization are most frequently encountered in acquired haemolytic anaemia. In other words, the blood group antigens involved in the latter are those very widely distributed among the population.

Some workers have questioned whether the globulin on the red cells is a true antibody, and doubts have been expressed concerning its specificity. However, the specificity of this antibody has now been shown in various ways. Thus, when the patient was transfused with red cells having the same blood group antigens, they were rapidly destroyed, whereas when red cells were transfused from a selected donor who lacked the antigen in question they survived in the patient's circulation.

The types of antibody encountered in different patients can vary. One group acts at all temperatures up to 37°C and these are known as 'warm antibodies'. The 'warm' antibodies agglutinate albumin-suspended cells or enzyme-treated cells and give, of course, a positive agglutination test with anti-human-immunoglobulin serum. Contrariwise, the 'cold antibodies' agglutinate more strongly at low temperatures (e.g. 4°C) and act on saline-suspended cells somewhat better than on albumin-suspended cells. Cold antibodies are associated with fast moving γ-globulin that in the ultracentrifuge shows itself to be a macroglobulin (IgM) with a sedimentation constant of 19S. Red cells coated with these antibodies are not agglutinated by specific anti-human-IgG but are agglutinated, although weakly, by specific anti-human-IgM. They are much more strongly agglutinated by antisera to the β_1-globulin fraction of human plasma, presumably for the same reasons as are discussed in the paragraph below.

Coated red cells from some cases of acquired haemolytic anaemia also react better with antisera to human β_1-globulin than with antisera against the human immunoglobulins. This has been shown to be due to the fact that such cells become covered with complement components, fixed by the antigen–antibody complex, and one or more of these complement components reacts with the anti-β_1-globulin. Nevertheless, the patients' antibodies are in all likelihood true immunoglobulins.

Thus in many cases of acquired haemolytic anaemia there is excellent evidence that the patient has formed an antibody directed against an antigen present in his own red cells. Demonstrable antibody is not always present continuously, and some patients have evidence of red cell autosensitization only during periods of active haemolysis. However, many show persistently positive red-cell anti-globulin tests, even during periods of apparent remission of the haemolytic process. In such cases it might be expected that reactivation of haemolysis would be heralded by rise in antibody level but such a process is rarely demonstrable. This suggests that other physiological factors, possibly involving the activity of the phagocytes of the reticuloendothelial system, act to regulate the rate of red-cell destruction in this disease.

The mechanisms by which the auto-antibodies initiate the process of red-cell destruction are little understood. Red cells coated with incomplete antibodies may undergo auto-agglutination when suspended in human serum at 37°C. It was shown by Jandl and Castle that several macromolecular substances, including human serum proteins in concentrations only slightly exceeding physiological levels, and polyvinyl pyrrolidone (PVP) cause the agglutination of red cells previously sensitized by incomplete antibodies. It is therefore suggested that plasma proteins act on such cells *in vivo* by causing them to form unusually adherent rouleaux or small agglutinates which are trapped in their passage through the sinuses of the spleen. Agglutinated red cells are a feature of films made of blood from the spleen pulp at the time of splenectomy for acquired haemolytic anaemia, and presumably the process of destruction of such sequestrated cells is rapidly completed by erythrophagocytosis.

Besides making the red cells unstable so that they clump, incomplete antibody adsorbed to their surface may alter the metabolism of the cell. Frequently in acquired haemolytic anaemia the red cell is transformed from a disc-like cell towards a spherical form. Also, it can be shown that the rate of glycolysis of red cells to which incomplete anti-D serum has been added *in vitro* is diminished by about one-quarter, and such lowering of energy production may be a factor in determining the diminished life-span of such antibody-sensitized cells *in vivo*.

Besides the 'idiopathic' group of acquired haemolytic anaemias other cases are associated with the taking of various drugs. Those due to drugs such as quinine, Faudin and phenacetin and so forth are also probably brought about by an antibody mechanism, which resembles that which has been shown to occur in certain cases of drug-induced thrombocytopenia. In these cases, as discussed above with Sedormid purpura, the specificity of the antibody is usually directed towards the drug itself rather than one of the body's own antigens (see Chapter Eleven).

Current views on the pathogenesis of haemolytic anaemia include two main possibilities. The first is that the red cell may develop a [illegible] ponents of this idea have suggested that such [illegible] be due to the action of an infective agent. The [illegible] it is, is meagre, although virus and bacterial [illegible] hown capable of modifying the red cells so that [illegible] a new antigenicity. The experimental use of receptor-destroying enzyme to increase the T-agglutinin titre of the guinea-pig has been mentioned earlier as a possible model of auto-antigenicity. Further, in cases of primary atypical pneumonia due to *Mycoplasma pneumoniae* and infectious mononucleosis (possibly due to a virus of the herpes group) haemolytic anaemia can occur. In the group of cases of atypical pneumonia associated with *M. pneumoniae* the occurrence of cold haemagglutinins is particularly constant. In infectious mononucleosis antibodies appear which agglutinate sheep erythrocytes and will also react with ox erythrocytes (Paul-Bunnell test), and false positive serological tests for syphilis are frequently recorded. In both of these diseases, which are known to involve the lymph nodes and spleen, it is possible that the infection modifies the antibody-producing cells.

In the second hypothesis, the red cell is normal, but abnormal antibodies are produced by a malfunctioning of the antibody-producing cells. This hypothesis is particularly relevant for those cases of haemolytic anaemia associated with diseases of reticular tissues (for example, reticulum cell sarcoma, Hodgkin's disease, and giant-cell follicular lymphoma) involving the neoplastic production of abnormal lymphocytes and plasma cells, but may apply to other cases also. On this view, the antibody which reacts against the red cells results from the development of new mutant lines of antibody-forming cells which are not tolerant to the normal cell antigenic markers. The same possibility may also explain the occurrence of haemolytic anaemia in association with systemic lupus erythematosus and rheumatoid arthritis, in which, as described later in this chapter, numerous different antibodies directed against cellular antigens circulate in the blood. However, since circulating complexes of antigen and antibody may be present, a mechanism involving immune adherence (p. 198) would need to be excluded in these conditions.

It is necessary to stress that a different spectrum of disease is associated with the 'warm' as distinct from the 'cold' antibodies. In the case of the former 60 per cent of the cases are primary, the remainder being associated with reticuloses or other general disorders of the lymphoreticular tissues, or diseases such as systemic lupus erythematosus, ulcerative colitis, cirrhosis, lymphadenoid goitre, disseminated sclerosis and congenital hypogammaglobulinaemia. In the case of the 'cold antibodies' 50 per cent are primary, the remainder being associated with either cases of *M. pneumoniae* infection or generalized neoplastic disease of the lymphoreticular tissues.

Clinical cases of haemolytic anaemia which fall into the class *paroxysmal cold haemoglobulinuria* and which were mentioned in the opening paragraph of this section, are now rarely seen, since they were commoner when congenital syphilis was more frequent. Primary and secondary forms occur, many of the latter being associated with virus infections. The antibody concerned is a 7S γ-globulin with a thermal range usually below 20° and a specificity falling within the P blood group system. It sensitizes normal red cells to anti-γ-globulin but the direct anti-globulin test is only found positive during an acute attack of the disease.

Haemolytic Anaemia Due to α-Methyldopa

Patients taking α-methyldopa for the amelioration of essential hypertension occasionally develop auto-allergic haemolytic anaemia, in which their red cells give a positive direct anti-globulin test. The antibody is also often present in the plasma, and can sometimes be identified as of specificity e (Rhesus blood grouping system). Most patients with such positive serological tests have no evidence of increased red cell destruction. Several months of methyldopa treatment are essential for development of the serum auto-antibody or anaemia, which rapidly abates on withdrawal of the drug.

Recently other auto-antibodies, besides those acting on erythrocytes, have been described in the same group of methyldopa-treated hypertensives. Increased frequency of antibody to nuclear components (ANF), and of antibody to gastric parietal cells, is also found. The mechanism which works to produce this selection of auto-antibodies is at present unknown. No evidence exists for a relation to the cause of the hypertension but other drugs used in this treatment (e.g. chlorthalidone) may play a part.

Animal Models for the Pathogenesis of Auto-immune Haemolytic Anaemia

The induction of auto-antibodies against red cells by the simple procedure of injection of homologous or autologous red cells with or without adjuvant has not so far proved successful. However, two methods for inducing haemolytic anaemia have been evolved using a mouse chimaera and an aberrant mouse genotype.

In the first instance a graft-*versus*-host situation is created by injection of an F_1 hybrid mouse with lymphoid tissue of a member of one of its parental strains. A characteristic syndrome ('runt' disease) develops after a variable latent period which depends on the strain combination used for the experiment. The hybrid mice lose weight, become hunched, with ruffled fur. They typically develop an enlargement of the spleen. The disease usually progresses to death, but some mice can eventually recover. Haemolytic anaemia develops as part of this clinical syndrome as well as leukopenia and sometimes thrombocytopenia. The serum yields a positive anti-mouse-globulin test and the life-span of syngeneic ^{51}Cr-labelled red cells in affected mice is greatly shortened. The red cells circulating in the disease can be shown by a direct anti-mouse-globulin test to be carrying γ-globulin on their surface. It has been established that this is mainly directed against the H_2-histocompatibility antigens of the erythrocytes. A situation analogous to this g-v-h model could occur as a result of implantation of maternal cells during foetal life. Such a condition of genetic mosaicism would be expected to involve tolerance towards the maternal antigens. A subsequent loss of tolerance might then depend upon changes in the situation and concentration of the foreign cells in the mosaic. In proved cases of mosaicism the equilibrium between host and foreign cells is known to be unstable and to allow wide variations in the proportions of each cell type. However, no evidence for a condition of cellular mosaicism has been advanced in cases of human acquired haemolytic anaemia.

In the second model an inbred pure mouse strain NZB/Black was reported to develop haemolytic anaemia as well as certain other auto-immune manifestations. The disease is not congenital but develops rapidly in an increasing proportion of the mice after the age of 20 weeks. Anaemia, other signs of blood destruction, a positive direct anti-mouse globulin test with the affected mouse's erythrocytes and enlarged spleen are all present. By transfer of spleen cells from adult affected mice, the disease can be transmitted to young unaffected mice. At about the time when the anti-globulin tests become positive, the thymus begins to show characteristic changes with formation of germinal centres and the appearance of plasma cells and numerous mast cells.

These facts might suggest that the thymus plays a dominant role in the development of the auto-immune haemolytic anaemia, and encourage the belief that mutant, aberrant clones of lymphoid cells originate there. However when NZB mice are thymectomized immediately after birth they not only still develop auto-immune haemolytic anaemia and other auto-immune manifestations but many do so earlier than non-thymectomized animals. Thus, if 'self-reactive' clones of lymphoid cells are the basis for the auto-immunity they must be able to arise elsewhere than in the thymus, and the part played by the thymus would appear to be inhibitory rather than stimulatory.

More recently particles resembling murine leukaemia virus have been observed by electron microscopy in the spleen, thymus, lymph nodes and bone marrow of untreated NZB mice throughout their life. The same particles are also present in the lymph nodes of mice which had been reared from birth from Caesarian section in a germ-free environment and fostered by germ-free mice of a different, virus-free strain. This suggests that the virus is transmitted 'vertically' *via* the parental germ cells or the placenta.

Some of the same NZB mice which develop auto-immune haemolytic anaemia also, in ageing, develop a renal lesion resembling that of lupus nephritis, and some a positive L.E. cell test. In the F_1 hybrids obtained by crossing NZB mice with members of another pure-line NZY there is a much higher incidence of positive LE cells—although the incidence of haemolytic disease is less.

This experimental model is therefore of general interest for a study of auto-allergic manifestations (and is discussed further in a later section) since it clearly indicates the importance of genetic factors, which may, however, have to exert their influence through an infection with virus. It may be comparable with the Aleutian disease of mink, another genetically determined disease, which has widespread lesions similar to those described in human auto-immune diseases. This disease, which is transmissible by cell-free filtrates of affected tissues, depends upon a combination of virus and a susceptible host which is homozygous for the Aleutian gene. It is

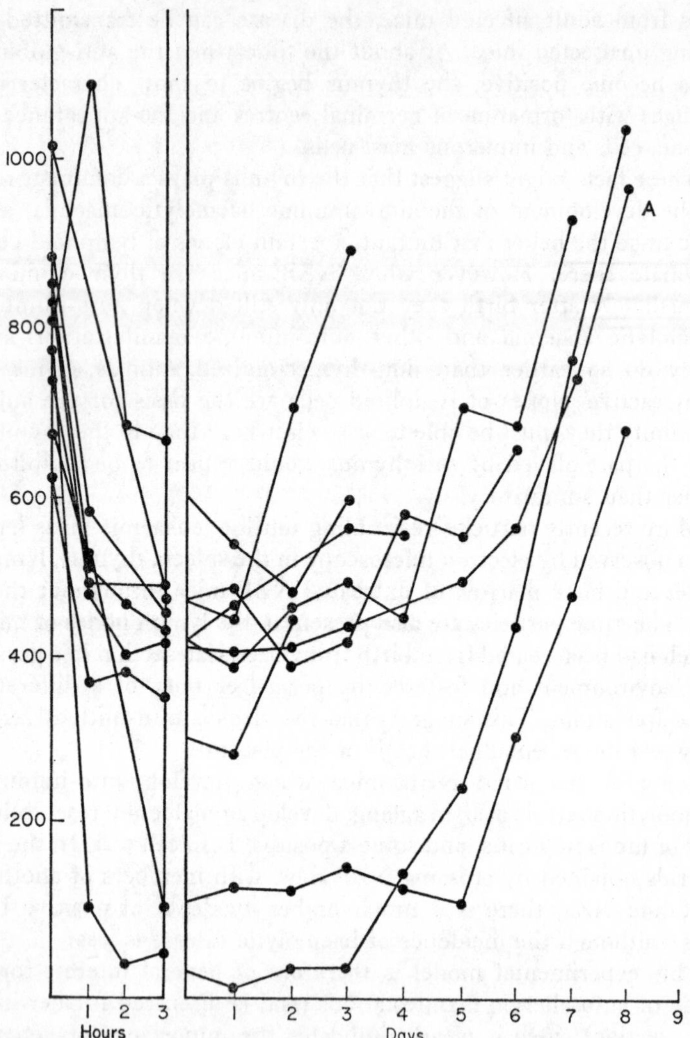

FIG. 15.1. Antiplatelet activity of sera in thrombocytopenic purpura. Platelet counts in individuals receiving transfusions of 500 ml of whole blood or 250 ml of plasma from eight patients with idiopathic thrombocytopenic purpura. [From Harrington *et al.* (1951) *J. Lab. clin Med.*]

N.B. The mean effect is represented by the line A.

characterized by the development of very elevated immunoglobulin levels in the plasma, and some of this immunoglobulin behaves as though it were aggregated. There are grounds for supposing that many of the pathological changes in Aleutian disease are attributable to aggregated IgG (see Chapter Eleven).

AUTO-IMMUNITY INVOLVING PLATELETS

It is convenient at this point to deal with states of thrombocytopenia which may be brought about by the destructive action of iso- or auto-antibodies. It was clearly shown in 1915 by Ledingham and Bedson that an antiserum prepared in rabbits against guinea-pig platelets would produce capillary damage and thrombocytopenic purpura when injected into guinea-pigs. Thrombocytopenia commonly accompanies auto-immune haemolytic anaemia and naturally leads to the presumption that it depends upon platelet auto-antibody production. However, the main need is to define the role of platelet auto-antibodies in *idiopathic thrombocytopenic purpura* (ITP). This disease affects *children* of either sex with an acute purpura and very low platelet count, usually following an infectious illness, and *adults*, particularly females, with a more chronic variable course and unrelated to previous infection.

In isolated cases of the human disease, it has been shown that the injection of their blood into normal human volunteers leads to a prompt fall in the recipient's platelets and the development of purpura (Fig. 15.1). The presence of certain antiplatelet substances in some cases of ITP is therefore established and these agents exhibit properties which suggest that they may be antibodies. Often, the *in vitro* demonstration of the agglutination or lysis of human platelets by the sera of such cases has proved possible. However, the demonstration of platelet agglutinins and lysins is technically difficult, and there is lack of agreement between the results of different laboratories regarding the existence of such serum factors.

The results of the transfusion experiments reported above and the demonstration of platelet agglutinins are both complicated by another important factor. Platelet agglutinins can be shown regularly in the blood of patients who have been previously transfused with blood or have been pregnant. Moreover, it has been found that blood from some of these transfused patients will cause thrombocytopenia when administered to normal recipients. Since most of the patients of idiopathic thrombocytopenia are treated by transfusions, the significance of the results of transfusion experiments as in Fig. 15.1 becomes questionable. Also *in vitro* agglutinin tests using the patients' own platelets are difficult to do since these are lacking. More recently the factor in the plasma of idiopathic thrombocytopenic patients which depresses the platelet levels when infused into normal individuals has been further characterized as an auto-antibody. By chromatography on DEAE cellulose an active fraction has been separated and by immunoelectrophoresis identified as an IgG immunoglobulin which is shown to be adsorbed by normal platelets (of other human beings) and appears to be species specific. One patient with ITP has been transfused with her own stored plasma during a period of disease remission when her platelet count was normal. After 2–4 days her platelet count dropped from 300,000 to 15,000: she developed a petechial eruption and prolonged bleeding time.

Further substantial evidence which supports the role of antibody in this disease is found in the occurrence of transient thrombocytopenia in the infants of mothers who have or have had idiopathic thrombocytopenic purpura.

AUTO-IMMUNITY INVOLVING LEUCOCYTES: Leucocyte Transfusion Reactions; Leucopenia

It is often possible with suitable laboratory techniques to demonstrate the presence in the serum of leuco-agglutinins, i.e. antibodies which have the ability to clump white cells. Mostly these demonstrations relate to *iso-agglutinins*. Indeed, very little is known about auto-antibodies against leucocytes and their significance in human pathology.

Patients who receive multiple transfusions of whole blood occasionally develop febrile reactions afterwards without any destruction of the red cells. Indeed, in such individuals the red cells may have a normal survival time; however, it is often possible to demonstrate the presence in the recipient's serum of antibodies directed against the white cells which are infused. If washed red cells are transfused *instead* of whole blood, the febrile reactions fail to occur. A similar sensitization with production of iso-antibodies can result from multiple pregnancies, presumably due to leakage through the placenta of foetal white cells.

Such iso-leuco-agglutinins can be of practical importance in any patient who requires repeated transfusions, as, for example, in cases of aplastic anaemia; and a case has been recorded in which the reaction against the transfused incompatible leucocytes proved fatal. In the present state of ignorance of the distribution or number of leucocyte antigens which are responsible for these phenomena, the prevention of transfusion reactions due to leucocyte incompatibility will usually be easier accomplished by preparing blood poor in leucocytes than by selecting leucocyte-compatible donors.

The occurrence of non-agglutinating white cell auto-antibodies has been described in cases of systemic lupus erythematosus, or of rheumatoid arthritis. A rather cumbersome technique (the anti-globulin consumption test, see Chapter Nine) was required for their detection. Most of these antibodies were absorbed by exposing the serum to nucleo-protein preparations and so may be identical with antibodies concerned in the LE cell phenomenon (see later in this chapter). Leucopenia is not uncommonly associated with both of these diseases. Felty's syndrome, characterized by fever, chronic arthritis, leucopenia and splenomegaly is commonly considered as an atypical form of rheumatoid arthritis. Antinuclear antibody, as demonstrated by the fluorescent-antibody technique, is constantly present in the patients with Felty's syndrome and may be responsible for, or contribute to, the production of the observed leucopenia.

Recently by means of the antiglobulin consumption test it has been shown that a γ-globulin can be eluted from the leucocytes of some (40 per cent) of the patients with *primary leucothrombocytopenia* and refixed on to normal leucocytes. This auto-antibody appeared to possess species specificity and to react with the leucocyte cytoplasm rather than nuclei.

DISEASES AFFECTING CONNECTIVE TISSUE

Systemic lupus erythematosus and rheumatoid arthritis have been highlighted as the most florid and typical examples of a group of diseases of connective tissue, members of the rheumatic disease family, and sometimes designated as 'the collagen diseases'. The group is usually taken to include, in addition, rheumatic fever, dermatomyositis, scleroderma, temporal arteritis and possibly rare entities such as thrombotic thrombocytopenic purpura. Glomerulonephritis and polyarteritis nodosa have sometimes been included, but since much of the experimental work in these two diseases has stemmed from concepts of serum sickness and antibody-determined hypersensitivity they have been considered in Chapter Eleven. Rheumatic fever (and acute nephritis) is also in a special category in view of its aetiological relationships with streptococcal infection.

The definition of the term 'collagen disease' is elusive. Disorders so designated are generally regarded as having the following features in common:

(i) Many organ systems of the body may be involved, including the skin, blood-forming tissues, kidneys, joints, muscles and serous membranes.

(ii) Conventional tissue sections often show widespread foci of hyaline (or fibrinoid) degeneration in connective tissue.

(iii) Hyper-γ-globulinaemia is a common accompaniment.

(iv) The prognosis in general is poor, but often there is a striking initial response to steroid therapy.

In the 1920's fibrinoid degeneration was described by German pathologists in the rabbit following injection of a 'foreign' protein, namely horse serum. Hence, the association of fibrinoid lesions with allergic responses was first established in relation to serum sickness. However, the use of the term 'collagen disease' dates from the morbid anatomical observations of Klemperer (1942) who regarded the apparent widespread damage to collagen as the basic feature. In the light of recent work it would appear wrong to base the definition of these diseases on the presence of presumptive damage to collagen, the existence of which is questionable. Nevertheless, the term collagenoses has found favour with clinicians for its diagnostic convenience. Certainly, mixtures of these clinical manifestations may occur frequently in the same patient, and it would be difficult to delineate a clinical boundary, for example, between rheumatoid arthritis and systemic lupus erythematosus.

RHEUMATOID ARTHRITIS

The main feature of this disease is an inflammatory reaction of the joints and peri-articular tissues. The pathological changes consist in a proliferation of the synovial membrane with the formation of granulation tissue which extends as a vascular 'pannus' layer from the margin towards the centre of the affected joint. The articular cartilage becomes gradually replaced by fibrous granulation tissue. Focal collections of macrophages and lymphocytes are found in the synovial membrane, the joint capsule, and the peri-articular tissues, or in the form of subcutaneous nodules.

The classical cases occur in women between the ages of 20 and 40. Susceptible individuals are said to be usually of an asthenic build. Sudden shock or emotional strain is often regarded as a precipitating factor.

Other features of the disease include the following:

(i) toxaemia: the patient looks pale and ill, and sometimes has fever. The sedimentation rate of the blood erythrocytes is often considerably raised.

(ii) anaemia: often clear evidence of a haemolytic process is present, without demonstrable erythrocyte abnormality.

(iii) generalized lymphadenopathy: the lymph nodes in the neighbourhood of the affected joints are often enlarged so as to be palpable, and occasionally the spleen, too, is palpable. The combination of anaemia, splenomegaly and arthritis is referred to as Felty's syndrome. A generally similar picture to rheumatoid arthritis may occur in childhood (Still's disease) in which the spleen and lymph nodes are invariably enlarged.

Rheumatoid Arthritis as a Manifestation of Hypersensitivity to Exogenous Antigen

Many theories have held the field at different times to account for the disease manifestations of rheumatoid arthritis, and twenty or thirty years ago the main causal factor was regarded to be the presence of a *septic focus* somewhere in the body. The existence of such foci was claimed to be demonstrable in a high proportion of cases. The sites claimed to be of aetiological significance were the nose and throat, the teeth and gums, the cervix, Fallopian tubes, prostate and renal tract. The surgery which was the logical outcome of belief in this hypothesis produced no constant improvement of the arthritic process, and nowadays both hypothesis and surgery have fallen into abeyance.

Rich has drawn a comparison between the granulomatous lesions occurring in this disease and the perivascular lesions of serum sickness and has stressed the high incidence of cardiac lesions similar to those of rheumatic fever. On this view the manifest inflammation is an expression of sensitivity to some foreign antigen of bacterial or other origin.

While both epidemiological and serological evidence exists that rheumatoid arthritis can be associated with haemolytic streptococcal infection, the association is certainly far less clear-cut than in the case of rheumatic fever. High streptococcal agglutinin, precipitin and anti-streptolysin O titres have been reported in about one-third of patients suffering from this disease.

The evidence derived from post-mortem sections has repeatedly stressed the importance of widespread connective tissue change. Whether damaged collagen is indeed present in such lesions is doubtful.

The histological appearance of deeply eosinophilic, opaque-looking areas is inadequate to establish actual damage to collagen. The evidence that the periodicity of the collagen fibres as demonstrated in the electron microscope was altered in such situations has not been widely substantiated. Much of the evidence relating to hypersensitivity has centred around the possibility of collagen damage brought about by antigen–antibody interaction in the tissues. A simple experiment exists which apparently provides a clear-cut demonstration that connective tissue damage can result from antigen–antibody interaction. When antigen is deposited in the cornea of a hyperimmunized animal possessing high levels of circulating antibody, a ring visible with the slit-lamp appears at the site of antibody–antigen interaction and along this line histological examination shows an intensely eosinophilic zone containing swollen and fragmented collagen fibres.

Rheumatoid Arthritis as a Manifestation of Auto-immunity

Over the past twenty years evidence has accumulated that several abnormal proteins which are possibly auto-antibodies circulate in the blood of patients with this disease. The observation was made forty years ago that the presence of some human sera enhanced the agglutination of sheep red cells which had been treated with rabbit anti-sheep cell serum. This property of some sera was not connected with rheumatoid arthritis until Waaler showed that a significant proportion of rheumatoid arthritis patients could provide such a factor, which came to be generally known as *rheumatoid factor* (RA factor).

A clue to the nature of RA factor was provided by the observation that a human serum fraction containing mostly γ-globulin would inhibit the reaction of the sensitized cell with rheumatoid arthritis serum. Subsequently, many experiments have established that RA factor can combine with normal human immunoglobulin, and this has formed the basis of several subsequent tests which all depend on the ability of rheumatoid sera to agglutinate particles which have a layer of normal immunoglobulin at their surface, e.g. sheep cells treated with tannic acid and exposed to human IgG, or particles of polystyrene latex or the volcanic clay bentonite which had adsorbed IgG. Basically, all of the different reactions are regarded as testing for the presence of antibody to immunoglobulin. But they are not identical, for sometimes human immunoglobulin and sometimes animal immunoglobulin are used as the coating for the particles. Moreover, it is clear that in certain circumstances the different tests give different results and consequently it is necessary to postulate that a number of rheumatoid factors with different specificities are involved.

Recently the recovery of purified RA factor has been accomplished from complexes with sensitized sheep cells or with mildly aggregated human IgG and has led to its characterization as a macroglobulin, or group of macroglobulins, with a sedimentation constant of 19S. Their chemical, physical and antigenic properties are very similar to the normal IgM class which is known to contain a variety of antibodies (Chapter Four). However, not all RA factor is in the form of macroglobulin; in some patients it is of the same size as IgG (7S).

These findings support the assumption that the RA factor is in the nature of an antibody. What, then, is the antigenic stimulus for its occurrence? The specific reaction in all the various tests with human or animal immunoglobulin implies that the RA factors are antibodies to immunoglobulin G or anti-antibodies. The occurrence of such antibody, an auto-antibody, would presumably lead to reactions with the antigen in the circulation. Indeed, as might be expected, the rheumatoid factors circulate in the blood as a complex. readily detected in the ultra-centrifuge, with a sedimentation coefficient of approximately 22S. This complex becomes dissociated with a change to acid pH to 19S rheumatoid factor and 7S normal immunoglobulin.

In numerous instances where this has been examined human RA factors have been found to react specifically with the H chains of immunoglobulin G, and may even be specific for H chains of a particular subclass or allotype of human IgG. RA factors generally interact more readily with immunoglobulin bound at a surface, or aggregated by gentle heating than in free solution. Furthermore, materials with the properties of RA factors can be evoked in rabbits by prolonged immunization with bacteria, and their level can subsequently be increased by injection of autologous immunoglobulin denatured by gentle heating. Considerations of this kind have led to the hypothesis that RA factors are antibodies against immunoglobulin molecules distorted in some way (e.g. by combination with antigen) so as to reveal determinants which would not normally be immunogenic in the native molecules in solution. This hypothesis may be correct, but the genetic data and the association of RA with other autoimmune diseases indicate that some abnormal immunological reactivity must also be present.

The distribution of rheumatoid factor in the tissues has been explored by the fluorescent antibody method. Human IgG can be used to detect the RA factor in sections of tissue by first labelling it with fluorescein and then by gently heating to cause molecular aggregation. In sections of the lymph nodes, subcutaneous nodules and synovial fringes from cases of rheumatoid arthritis such fluorescein-labelled heat-aggregated IgG is localized in plasma cells, in the Russell bodies within them, and in numerous cells in the germinal centres of the lymph nodes (Plate 15.1, following p. 660). The most striking histological feature of the lymph nodes in rheumatoid arthritis is the follicular hyperplasia (Plate 15.2, following p. 660) with prominent germinal centres. Plasma cells are also fairly numerous in the medullary cords. Indeed, these histological changes are similar to those produced in experimental animals which are repeatedly stimulated by antigenic materials, and the finding of RA factor in plasma cells provides additional evidence for the antibody-like nature of this entity. The presence of RA factor in the plasma cells of subcutaneous nodules and synovial fringes presumably implies that it is being formed there as a consequence of a local antigenic stimulus. The reason for the localization at these sites poses an intriguing but unsolved problem.

Even if the auto-antibody nature of RA factor is accepted it does not follow that any of the disease manifestations result from auto-immune processes. An analogy could be drawn with syphilis, in which circulating 19S antibodies against an intracellular constituent may occur and give rise to the Wassermann reaction. These may be produced in response to the tissue destruction consequent on the treponemal infection. On this analogy the RA factors could be the consequence of infection with an unrecognized agent, and without any pathogenic significance. Also, the RA factors were originally described in diseases such as liver cirrhosis before they were even associated with rheumatoid arthritis, and various conditions such as sarcoidosis which are associated with hyperglobulinaemia also may show high titres. These may be present for prolonged periods in such patients without the appearance of arthritis. Finally, rheumatoid arthritis may occur in the subjects of hypo-γ-globulinaemia. These lack detectable RA factor in their serum, as well as having very low levels of ordinary 7S γ-globulin.

The RA factor has been shown to be present in symptom-free relatives of patients with rheumatoid arthritis. If such familial clustering is genetically determined, then, in view of the preponderance of the disease in females, it would be tempting to assume that a sex-linked form of inheritance is involved, as by means of a dominant gene on the X chromosome. However, the evidence is inadequate for complete elucidation.

Many patients with rheumatoid arthritis (40 per cent in some surveys) possess antinuclear factors in their serum as shown by the fluorescent antibody technique (see next section, Systemic lupus erythematosus). Conversely, rheumatoid factors occur with high frequency in relatives of patients with lupus erythematosus. The clinical association of rheumatoid arthritis and lupus erythematosus has long been recognized. These facts, taken together with the genetic data, and the findings that several other diseases thought to be due to an autoimmune process (haemolytic anaemia, ulcerative colitis, lymph-adenoid goitre, Sjögren's disease) are often associated, have led to the view that a genetically predetermined group of persons can lose their tolerance to antigenic components of their own tissues, and develop an immunological response at these sites.

Experimental models which mimic rheumatoid arthritis

The occurrence of areas of fibrinoid degeneration in the lesions of rheumatoid arthritis might suggest that it is fibrin which is acting as an antigen in this disease, and that the rheumatoid nodule in skin or joints is an auto-immune response to local fibrin deposits. The injection of human fibrin in a Freund-type adjuvant mixture produces in rabbits a delayed-type hypersensitivity to both human and the recipient rabbit's own fibrin. When rabbits immunized in this way were injected with a suspension of human fibrin into their knee joints, the periarticular tissue became heavily infiltrated with lymphocytes and plasma cells. The lymphocytes became aggregated in typical lymphoid nodules complete with germinal centres. The articular cartilage became progressively eroded by ingrowth of inflamed synovial membrane, and the pathological picture therefore contained most of the ingredients of a human rheumatoid joint lesion. However, when direct tests of the hypothesis that autologous fibrin acts as an antigen in rheumatoid subjects were made by implanting fibrin from blood clots subcutaneously in human patients, no difference could be found between the resulting tissue responses and those of normal subjects.

A further experimental model for rheumatoid arthritis has been produced in rats by the simple injection of Freund's complete adjuvant minus any added antigen. This procedure induces, after a latent period of about 10 days, a migratory polyarthritis affecting the ankles, wrists and smaller joints of the extremities, spondylitis, skin nodules, a macular rash and, more rarely, iritis, uveitis, urethritis and diarrhoea. The syndrome is referred to as 'adjuvant disease'. The joint lesions resemble those of rheumatoid arthritis. They characteristically start with a perivenous infiltration by cells including lymphocytes and macrophages.

This disease can be produced by injection of either *Mycobacterium tuberculosis*, *M. phlei* or *Nocardia asteroides* in mineral oil. When typical complete Freund adjuvant is used (water-in-oil emulsion with added protein antigen in the water phase and killed *M. tuberculosis* in the oil phase) the incidence of disease is much reduced. This is interpreted to mean that an immunological response to the included protein interferes with the response (presumably an immunological one) to the mycobacteria.

Adjuvant disease in rats can be prevented by the injection of tubercle bacilli at birth. This interference is presumably indicative that the disease process depends on an immunological response whose specificity is determined by an antigenic component of *M. tuberculosis*. The disease can be reproduced by injection of wax D and a purified peptidoglycolipid derived from human type *M. tuberculosis*. However, the mineral oil component of the injection mixture would appear to be quite essential for the production of the disease, since saline-suspended wax D is ineffective, although an injection will serve to block the subsequent arthritogenic action of wax D in oil. Immunosuppressive drugs such as cortisone and 6-mercaptopurine and anti-lymphocyte serum will prevent the disease.

On the basis of the foregoing, the most reasonable hypothesis for the causation of adjuvant disease would depend upon an immunological response to bacterial antigenic components such as mycobacterial peptidoglycolipid which become disseminated around the body, and may indeed be carried with macrophages. A footpad inoculation of mycobacteria in oil leads to a high level of delayed-type hypersensitivity against tuberculoprotein in the rat, and formation of antibodies against protein and carbohydrate antigens of the tubercle bacillus. In the guinea-pig a delayed-type hypersensitivity to wax D also results. The dependence of the pathogenesis of this disease on delayed-type hypersensitivity is supported by the fact that suspensions of lymphoid cells from the lymph nodes of diseased animals can transmit the disease to normal recipients provided that these are also injected with tuberculoprotein.

SYSTEMIC LUPUS ERYTHEMATOSUS

The clinical dividing line between rheumatoid arthritis and systemic lupus would be difficult to draw. Indeed, the first manifestations of disease, such as loss of weight, anaemia, low-grade fever and arthritis, may resemble rheumatoid arthritis. The patient (usually a woman) with systemic lupus, however, comes to look more obviously ill, with high fever, develops a reddish 'bat's-wing' patch across her nose extending on to both cheeks, effusions into her pleural cavities and sometimes her peritoneum, while albuminuria may point to involvement of her kidneys and jaundice to involvement of her liver (lupoid hepatitis). Sometimes the history includes previous treatment of 'rheumatoid arthritis' with colloidal gold, or treatment with sulphonamide drugs, penicillin or hydrallazine.

The striking feature of this disease from an immunological point of view is the appearance in the serum of numerous globulins, with the properties of antibodies, which react with components of various cells or of the blood itself. Thus the patients with this disease may have false positive serological tests for syphilis (Wassermann reaction and Kahn flocculation tests), a haemolytic anaemia with positive antiglobulin tests for antibody to an erythrocyte antigen, a leucopenia and a thrombocytopenia.

However, in terms of pathogenesis the most relevant observation would appear to be the lupus erythematosus cell phenomenon. In 1948 Hargreaves described in the bone marrow of patients with this disease microphages (or sometimes macrophages) with cytoplasmic inclusions, which are Feulgen-positive discs of rather blurred outline and lighter colour than the nucleus (Plate 15.3, following p. 660). Such 'LE cells' are mainly polymorphs containing inclusion bodies which represent disintegrating cell nuclei. It was later shown that the phenomenon could be produced *in vitro* by adding the serum from a case of systemic lupus to normal leucocytes. The steps in the formation of an LE cell are thought to be as follows. First, some of the normal leucocytes must be slightly damaged by mechanical or other means. In this phase the cell nucleus becomes accessible to plasma factors. Secondly, reaction with the LE factor, a plasma component with the characteristics of an antibody, causes swelling of the nucleus of the white cell. The swollen nucleus is taken up by a phagocyte, usually a polymorphonuclear leucocyte. The morphological evidence that the reaction involved cell nuclei was confirmed by the observation that lupus serum could be freed of its activity by absorption with a suspension of isolated cell nuclei.

The nature of the factor in the serum can be investigated in the following way. Isolated nuclei are brought into contact with lupus serum and then gently washed in saline. Next they are heated to 56°C (a process which can disrupt many antigen–antibody complexes), and this releases a protein into solution, which is capable of inducing LE cell formation. This eluted protein has the characteristics of a pure preparation of 7S immunoglobulin.

Sometimes the factor in lupus serum reacts like an antibody to DNA. However, other sera provide antibodies to the protein component of nucleoprotein (histone) rather than to the DNA. Sera of lupus patients can also be shown to react with whole nuclei by the fluorescent antibody technique (Plate 15.4 A, B, following p. 660). By this method different sera produce different patterns of localization, sometimes resulting in a flat disc of fluorescence, sometimes as a collection of spots as in Plate 15.4A, and sometimes in a pattern corresponding to the nucleoli, suggesting that different factors occur, which are capable of reacting with different constituents of cell nuclei. It appears, therefore, that these patients develop groups of antibody-like factors which react with different chemical and morphological nuclear components, and that the nature of these may differ from patient to patient. If these factors are antibodies, they are true auto-antibodies, since they can react with nuclei from the same patient *in vitro*, and can produce LE cells *in vivo* or in blood soon after withdrawal from the body.

Do the LE factors have any relationship to the primary pathological changes which occur in the tissues of the diseased patient? At the present time, there is little evidence to support such a pathogenic role, or indeed to suggest that these factors can gain access to the nucleus of a viable cell *in vivo*. The LE factor can pass across the placenta readily in a pregnant mother whose blood contains the factor without producing any visible damage to the child. Also cases of clinical systemic lupus have been described in the subjects of hypo-γ-globulinaemia, in whom there can be little circulating antibody. Nevertheless, it is at least likely that the 'haematoxyphil bodies' found in sections from many tissues throughout the body, are due to such nuclear autoantibodies, and these antibodies may also cause nephritis. (See pp. 458 *et seq.*)

A noteworthy deficiency in the chain of evidence as compared with, say, Hashimoto's disease has been the inability to reproduce the disease in animals by immunization with nucleic acids, or nucleoproteins. Autoantibodies have been obtained experimentally against the ribonucleic acid of rabbit ribosomes, but the rabbits themselves suffered no apparent ill-effects. Antibodies against native DNA or nucleoprotein are not formed in response to injections of these materials. However, antibodies are readily formed against single stranded DNA complexed with methylated bovine serum albumin (see Chapter Six). The antibodies so formed appear to react only with single strand, denatured DNA. Again no sign of disease suggestive of SLE has been caused in the experimental animals. This failure to reproduce the disease experimentally may argue that it is not a consequence of the abnormal occurrence of autoantigens, but depends instead upon an abnormality of antibody production or of cell-mediated hypersensitivity.

A recent exploration of the disease manifestations of auto-immunity in certain pure line strains of mice has linked in a striking way the acute haemolytic anaemia (described on p. 614) as occurring spontaneously in a high proportion of adults of the NZB mouse strain) and systemic lupus. Thus by crossing this strain with a closely related one, NZW, which was not itself subject to disease, the resulting F_1 generation of hybrids were all found to die after 8–10 months with positive LE-cell tests and the characteristic renal lesions of systemic lupus, although they showed a low incidence of haemolytic anaemia.

These facts gave rise to the hypothesis that genetic factors may operate in the NZB and NZB/NZW hybrids by the development of 'forbidden clones' of abnormal immunologically active lymphocytes, which produce cellular damage eventually by either production of antibody or delayed-type hypersensitivity. A possibly relevant feature of these mice strains was the presence of germinal centres of lymphocytic proliferations in the thymic medulla of a high percentage of the more adult animals. Lymphoid nodules with germinal centres, when seen in the spleen and lymph nodes, characteristically reflect immunological reactivity, but they are not normally present in the thymus. It was therefore suggested that germinal centres may indicate the presence of the postulated abnormal clones. However, when both NZB and NZB × NZW mice were thymectomized immediately after birth, they were still found to develop auto-immune haemolytic anaemia and positive LE-cell tests, and did so earlier than the non-thymectomized controls. If therefore the disease is related to aberrant clones of lymphocytes these must arise elsewhere than in the thymus. These experiments give no support for the concept that thymectomy might have a beneficial therapeutic effect in systemic lupus. On the few occasions when this has been attempted the results failed to show any clear clinical improvement. As was mentioned on p. 615, the discovery by the electron microscope of virus-like particles in NZB and NZW/NZB mice has complicated the interpretation of the aetiological factors of the various auto-immune diseases in the mouse.

In SLE auto-antibodies to numerous tissue constituents other than nuclei occur. Antibodies occur to erythrocyte antigens c and N and other 'weak' erythrocyte antigens which fail to give rise to antibody in most individuals under circumstances in which the stronger antigens would do so. Many of the sera which give rise to *biological false-positive* reactions in routine Wassermann testing are found to be derived from patients with SLE or from the relatives of such patients. These facts suggest that such individuals possess an abnormal propensity to make antibody to a variety of tissue antigens. However, such patients show no evidence of an increased ability to make antibody to a conventional exogenous antigen such as tetanus toxoid.

DISEASES ASSOCIATED WITH SYSTEMIC LUPUS

Besides the numerous entities which have been listed as direct manifestations of SLE, several other diseases, which are themselves uncommon, may often occur in association. Examples are haemolytic anaemia, idiopathic agranulocytosis or leucopenia, thrombocytopenic purpura, polymyositis and Sjögren's disease.

Sjögren's disease or Kerato-conjunctivitis sicca is associated with the connective tissue diseases rheumatoid arthritis and systemic lupus, and consists of a chronic granulomatous replacement of the glands responsible for lacrimal and salivary secretion. Local symptoms arise from diminished secretion of the inflamed glands. Thus the patient may complain of grittiness or dryness of the eyes. Superficial erosions of the conjunctiva develop. Involvement of the major and minor salivary glands results in a dry mouth, which may be sufficient to inhibit swallowing and lead to polydipsia. Hyposecretion of tracheal and bronchial glands may also lead to recurrent respiratory infections.

The histological similarity between the nodular lymphocytic and plasma-cell granulomatous tissue in this condition and that occupying the thyroid in Hashimoto's disease, first suggested that the two diseases might arise in a similar way. However, while lymphadenoid goitre is a typical example of disease associated with organ-specific auto-antibodies (as are primary adrenal atrophy or chronic gastritis, which possess similar histological features) in Sjögren's disease there is no convincing evidence of auto-antibodies reacting specifically with salivary or lacrimal tissue. Sjögren's disease, as stated above, has a strong link with the non-organ specific auto-immune states, for in approximately 50 per cent of cases there is a co-existing connective tissue disease and there is a remarkably high incidence of non-organ specific auto-antibodies such as occur mainly in the connective tissue diseases. Thus the LE test is positive in the sera of over a third of the cases of this disease and a high proportion (over 80 per cent) give a positive test for the presence of antinuclear antibody by the fluorescent antibody technique. Complement-fixation and precipitin reactions with cellular constituents common to many internal organs, including those of lower animal species, are commonly positive in Sjögren's disease. Most cases give a positive result for rheumatoid factor. These various non-organ specific antibodies are not confined in their incidence to those cases with associated connective tissue disease. Indeed, the occurrence of these antibodies is, in some cases, distinctly higher in cases of Sjögren's disease without rheumatoid arthritis or systemic lupus.

Classification of this disease is further obscured by the association shown with cases of lymphadenoid goitre and primary hypothyroidism and by the fact there is an increased incidence of various thyroid and gastric auto-antibodies.

ORGAN-SPECIFIC EXAMPLES OF AUTO-IMMUNITY

LYMPHADENOID GOITRE (HASHIMOTO'S DISEASE)

Lymphadenoid goitre (Hashimoto's disease) is a swollen thyroid, which shows on section (Plates 15.5, 15.6, following p. 660) an almost complete replacement of the normal acinar tissue by massive collections of cells which are mainly lymphocytes and plasma cells. The thyroid epithelial cells, which in a normal gland are arranged as an even, unicellular layer around the colloid-containing acinar cavities, their outer surfaces resting on the continuous basement-membrane layer, are in this disease vastly disarranged. Some small acini unevenly lined with hypertrophied thyroid epithelial cells remain, together with solid islands of distorted cells and single isolated cells. The abnormally large epithelial cells which line these small acini, and characteristically stain dark red with eosin, have been designated Askanazy or Hürthle cells.

The patient with such a thyroid gland attracts the physician's attention on account of the myxoedema which is a consequence of the loss of the gland's endocrine function. The loss of function is, of course, due to the diminished numbers of thyroid epithelial cells in such a gland, and occurs in spite of obvious hypertrophy and hyper-reactivity of the remaining cells. The normal thyroid gland produces its metabolic effects by secreting thyroid hormones into the blood. The thyroid epithelial cells also produce thyroglobulin (a large molecule with molecular wt. 700,000) which accumulates as a constituent of the acinar colloid, and which can be broken down, apparently within the acinar cells, to the active thyroid hormone which gains access to the blood. The thyroglobulin would therefore appear to form a segregated reserve source of thyroid hormone.

The important observation was made in 1956 that the serum of patients with Hashimoto's disease contained antibodies which would react with purified thyroglobulin from human thyroid glands (including the patient's own glands, obtained at operation) in a simple precipitin test. Moreover, it had previously been shown that rabbit thyroid extracts (even the animal's own thyroid), when injected into rabbits in the form of an emulsion in mineral oil containing tubercle bacilli (Freund-type adjuvant mixture), could give rise to circulating antibodies against rabbit thyroglobulin and to the invasion of the thyroid gland by lymphocytes and plasma cells. Although this experimental model was unsatisfactory as a replica of a lymphadenoid goitre, inasmuch as the cellular invasion was relatively transient and non-progressive, the sum of these observations strongly supported the view that the cause of the disease process was closely linked with an immune response of the patient against some component(s) of this thyroid gland.

The same process in the human may lead to so-called *primary myxoedema* in which the patient appears before the physician with an atrophic thyroid gland. Lesser degrees of cellular infiltration which are local and circumscribed, instead of the diffuse involvement which is characteristic of lymphadenoid goitre, occur in Graves' disease (thyrotoxicosis). In both these cases antibodies against thyroid antigens occur in the patient's serum.

The material in the thyroid which gives rise to the precipitins found in the patient's serum is apparently normal thyroglobulin. Thus normal thyroid glands, obtained by thyroidectomy from human subjects and prepared as a frozen section on a microscope slide, will bind, in the expected sites of thyroglobulin distribution (within the acini and thyroid epithelial cells), a fluorescein conjugate of the globulin fraction of the serum from a case of Hashimoto's disease. This is shown in Plate 15.7, following p. 660. The same technical approach can be applied to sections of the patient's own thyroid gland obtained at operation. When this is done the result shows (Plate 15.8, following p. 660) a similar localization of the antibody conjugate to the thyroid colloid within the small hyper-reactive acini, but it can also be seen that the antigen is not now neatly confined within acini or acinar-lining cells but occurs as streaks which pass between the thyroid epithelial cells of the acini, out and among the cells of the surrounding granulomatous tissue. It is possible, moreover, to trace the antigen within some of the cells, presumably macrophages, of the cell infiltration. Not only do thyroid colloid and its antigens leak outwards; γ-globulin enters the acini and precipitates with the intra-acinar antigens (Plate 15.9, following p. 660).

These facts have led to the 'leak' hypothesis to explain the pathogenesis of this disease. Thyroglobulin can be regarded as an antigen which is strictly segregated throughout normal foetal and extra uterine life. As a result, the immunological mechanisms of the body have no opportunity for developing tolerance, which would normally occur by exposure to the protein at an early period during the development *in utero*.

However, the recent demonstration of material with the antigenic properties of thyroglobulin (see above) in the cervical lymph and serum of normal persons calls into question the whole concept of antigens which are regarded as sequestered within the cavity or lining cells of the acini. These difficulties with the 'leak' hypothesis have led to suggestions that alternative mechanisms are operative. Thus, it is argued that thyroglobulin (and other thyroid auto-immunogens) may be accessible antigens which do in fact succeed in inducing normal tolerance. The surgical operation of partial thyroidectomy, involving as it does much damage to the thyroid architecture, has not been shown to result regularly in a reactive rise in serum levels of anti-thyroglobulin. Similarly, when radioactive ^{131}I is used in the therapy of thyrotoxicosis, this material localizes to and damages the cells of the thyroid without inducing, in most cases, any subsequent immunological response to thyroglobulin or other thyroid immunogens. These facts argue that tolerance is normally present, in adults, to thyroid antigens.

The fact is that auto-immunization of experimental animals can be secured by the use of purified normal thyroglobulin, provided this is injected in Freund-type complete adjuvant mixture or as an alum-precipitated protein. The success of these methods has been attributed (without direct evidence) to denaturation and alteration of the thyroglobulin molecule. If the immunogenic entity in Hashimoto's disease is altered thyroglobulin which causes the formation of antibody which can cross react with native thyroglobulin the 'leak' hypothesis may still be tenable.

An alternative explanation for the pathogenesis of Hashimoto's disease invokes the appearance of 'forbidden clones' of lymphoid cells in adult life. However, Hashimoto's thyroiditis does not play a prominent part in the non-organ specific syndromes such as systemic lupus erythematosus. It is argued that the association of Hashimoto's thyroiditis and pernicious anaemia may be due to a defect of immunological tolerance to a group of antigens occurring in stomach and thyroid, but there is no evidence that the antibodies found against stomach in Hashimoto's disease are due to a common antigen in stomach and thyroid.

Any theory of pathogenesis must take into account the fact that lymphadenoid goitre occurs in families the other members of which frequently show other thyroid disorders such as Graves' disease and high levels of thyroid auto-antibodies. Typical cases of lymphadenoid goitre have been described in female (or male) identical twins. In family studies of the incidence of antibody to thyroglobulin, the distribution has been shown to conform to the inheritance of a simple Mendelian dominant trait. Possibly such genetic predisposition to the disease could work through defect of structures such as the basement membranes of the acini. Fragmentation of the basement membrane of thyroid epithelium has been described as a constant finding in cases of Hashimoto's disease, and rupture of the basement membrane has been described constantly in the early stages of experimental thyroiditis produced in guinea-pigs following a single injection of homologous thyroid in Freund-type complete adjuvant. Although this discussion has centred on thyroglobulin as the main auto-immunogen of the thyroid gland, there is no clear evidence that auto-antibody or the process of hypersensitization to thyroglobulin is able to damage the thyroid cells. However, as is explained in detail below, there are several components of the thyroid which can function as auto-immunogens.

The histological changes of lymphadenoid goitre conform closely with what might be expected from the development in adult life of a substantial leak of one or more potential thyroid organ-specific antigens. These changes are first an accumulation, in close relation to the outer limits of the acini, of masses of plasma cells and their precursors, namely immature plasma cells and plasmablasts (haemocytoblasts), and secondly, more remote nodular collections of small lymphocytes with pale-staining so-called germinal centres. The draining lymph nodes show the same type of histological change.

While these histological appearances conform with the hypothesis that in lymphadenoid goitre a series of organ-specific auto-antibodies are caused eventually to leak from the thyroid gland, the mechanism which starts such a leak remains unexplained. Also the mechanism which brings about the further damage to the acinar cells and maintains the leak is obscure. It may be that once an immunological response against some element of thyroid tissue has been produced, damage to the cells may follow and so contribute to a vicious circle by leading to further release of immunogenic material. The possible relationship of this cellular damage to cytotoxicity of antibody or to the state of delayed-type hypersensitivity is discussed below.

Classification of Thyroid Auto-antigens

1. As explained above, normal intra-acinar *thyroglobulin* is the antigen reacting in the precipitin test with antibody in the sera of patients with lymphadenoid goitre. By a quantitative precipitin test levels of up to 5 mg/ml of antibody may be present in the serum. Antibodies to this antigen can be detected by an agar-diffusion precipitin test in about 70 per cent of cases of lymphadenoid goitre. When positive the test is virtually diagnostic. By using purified thyroglobulin as an antigen, and attaching it to erythrocytes treated with dilute tannic acid, a test for this antibody has been developed which is positive (titre above 10^3) in up to 90 per cent of cases. Even the use of this

very sensitive test leaves some cases in which this particular antibody cannot be detected.

2. When complement-fixation reactions are done with thyroid gland extracts positive results are recorded in over 90 per cent of cases of lymphadenoid goitre.

In controls selected from routine blood donors aged 20–40 years, less than 1 per cent had a positive result, but about 10 per cent of a series of controls which included women over 45 years old were positive. This may be correlated with the presence of small lymphocytic foci of infiltration in the thyroids of such elderly women.

The test, as it is usually performed, appears to indicate antibody to an antigen quite distinct from thyroglobulin, and which is associated with a cell component whose behaviour on centrifuging indicates that it is a subcellular particle sedimenting with microsomes. The test is also positive in many cases of thyrotoxicosis, although the titres in these cases are on the whole lower than those in lymphadenoid goitre cases.

This antigen can be localized effectively by the fluorescent-antibody method using a double-layer method on frozen unfixed sections of normal human thyroid tissue. The first layer uses the serum of patients having a high titre of complement-fixing antibody, the second fluorescein-labelled anti-human immunoglobulin. The resulting fluorescence is localized to the cytoplasm of thyroid acinar cells (Plate 15.10). The antigen is destroyed by fixation of the section in, for example, methanol so that this 'microsomal' antigen does not interfere with the demonstration of thyroglobulin as shown in Plate 15.7, following p. 660.

3. Antibodies reacting with a further intra-acinar auto-antigen, which is distinct from thyroglobulin, have also been described and occur in 30 per cent of cases of lymphadenoid goitre.

Relationship to Virus Diseases

It has been reported that *acute thyroiditis* may occur in association with mumps. However, there is no evidence that such thyroiditis can progress to a lymphadenoid goitre, and although antibody to thyroid antigens detectable in both precipitin and complement-fixation tests may occur in the serum of such cases these do not persist following clinical recovery.

Relationship of Cellular Damage to the Immune Process

It has been suggested that a continued leak of thyroglobulin into the blood may maintain the auto-immune reaction and in this way account for the progressive nature of the thyroid lesion. However, the relationship of the various antibodies to cytopathic effects in the thyroid is at present uncertain. While thyroglobulin-precipitating antibody appears to be without cytotoxic effect, an unidentified serum agent has been found to produce cytotoxic effects in short term tissue cultures of *trypsin-treated* thyroid cells. There is fairly close relationship between the occurrence of this agent and a positive result in the complement-fixation test. However, it has not proved possible to induce thyroid lesions in the intact animal (monkey) by passive transfer of serum from cases of lymphadenoid goitre, even though the serum reacts strongly *in vitro* with an homogenate of monkey thyroid gland.

Another view is that the thyroid tissue change results from delayed-type sensitization to thyroid antigens. Thyroiditis which results in guinea-pigs injected with a saline extract of thyroid in Freund-type adjuvant mixture bears no relation to the level of circulating antibody developed against thyroglobulin, but correlates to some extent with skin sensitivity to thyroid extract. Thus all the animals with thyroiditis gave positive delayed-type skin tests, and all those which did not develop thyroiditis failed to give such skin responses. Although it is possible to show hypersensitivity reactions in patients with lymphadenoid goitre when they are skin tested with thyroid extract, the lesions which have been described are characteristic of an Arthus-type rather than of true delayed-type hypersensitivity. In view of the high titres of circulating antibody in these cases this is hardly surprising. If the thyroid damage is induced by delayed-type hypersensitivity, transfer of the disease should be possible in inbred or tolerant animals using lymphoid cells, and some claims to have achieved this have been recorded.

Relationship with Other Diseases

Examples of auto-allergic manifestations in lymphadenoid goitre, and the lesser manifestations of thyroid auto-immunity in thyrotoxicosis and focal thyroiditis are often observed in the absence of detectable auto-antibody involving many other organs or systems. Several surveys have suggested that they may fairly commonly be associated with co-existing auto-immune manifestations related to other organs, especially stomach and adrenal. Far less frequently cases occur in which specific thyroid auto-immunity accompanies more generalized auto-immune lesions in which the auto-antibodies are non-organ-specific (see Plate 15.11, following p. 660). Examples are systemic lupus erythematosus, rheumatoid arthritis, haemolytic anaemia, cirrhosis of the liver and Sjögren's disease.

AUTO-IMMUNIZATION IN THYROID DISEASES OTHER THAN HASHIMOTO'S DISEASE AND PRIMARY MYXOEDEMA

In thyroid diseases other than lymphadenoid goitre or primary myxoedema, auto-antibodies to thyroid antigens, although often present, are found in much lower titre. In *thyrotoxicosis* over half of the cases show antibodies. These are agglutinins revealed in reactions with thyroglobulin tanned red cells, and complement-fixing antibodies reactive with the microsomal antigens.

In *non-toxic colloid goitre* and *carcinoma of the thyroid* complement-fixing antibodies are rarely found and tanned-cell tests are positive, in low titre only, in about one-third of cases.

AUTO-IMMUNITY AS A CAUSE OF THYROTOXICOSIS

Thyrotoxicosis (Graves' disease) is characterized by an excessive production of a normal thyroid gland secretion, apparently due to the action of an external factor on the gland rather than by disorganization of the gland itself. In the thyroid the resultant effect is enlargement of the gland, although the acini are generally smaller than normal and lined by tall, hypertrophied epithelial cells. Like lymphadenoid goitre, thyrotoxicosis is commoner in females; both have peak incidence in middle age. A proportion of thyrotoxic patients go on to develop a condition indistinguishable from lymphadenoid goitre and may become myxoedematous over a period of several years after exhibiting the hyperthyroid condition. Both show a strikingly high incidence of auto-antibodies. One or more of the three types of thyroid-specific auto-antibodies which are found in lymphadenoid goitre are also detectable in up to 85 per cent of thyrotoxic patients.

For a long time the extrinsic factor acting on the thyroid was thought to be the thyroid stimulating hormone of the pituitary gland. More recently a thyroid-stimulating substance has been shown to occur in the serum of patients with Graves' disease. It is called *long-acting thyroid stimulator* (LATS) since it exerts a more prolonged stimulating effect on the bioassay animal's thyroid than does the thyroid-stimulating hormone from the pituitary (TSH). LATS, which is chemically and antigenically distinct from TSH, is a globulin which is associated with the IgG fraction of serum. By infusion of the IgG fraction of serum from hyperthyroid subjects into normal subjects prolonged stimulation of the thyroid occurs. In Graves' disease the patients secrete little pituitary TSH since the high blood level of thyroxine results in its suppression by negative feed-back inhibition.

LATS can be neutralized by being incubated with a thyroid gland homogenate and is therefore auto-reactive. The site of origin of the presumed auto-immunogen is not established, although the neutralizing principle in the thyroid is associated with the microsomal fraction of thyroid cells. The relationship between this auto-antibody and the complement-fixing auto-antibody in the serum of lymphadenoid goitre patients (and thyrotoxicosis), which is also reactive with a microsomal particle, is open to question. No exact correlation has been observed between serum levels of LATS and titres of thyroid cytoplasmic antibodies as determined by the complement fixation or by an immunofluorescent double layer technique on unfixed frozen sections of thyroid.

At the present stage of its investigation, thyroid hyperfunction in Graves' disease may therefore be attributed to an auto-antibody (LATS). There is, however, no clear explanation why these patients develop exophthalmos or ophthalmoplegia. These conditions result from an increase in the bulk of the retro-orbital tissues which includes the following components: increase in fat and water content; hyperplasia of the muscles, which are more or less heavily infilitrated with lymphocytes; and the accumulation of mucopolysaccharide resembling that found in pretibial myxoedema. Although high levels of LATS have been found in patients with marked exophthalmos, the general correlation between measured blood levels and the degree of exophthalmos is not good. The assay method for LATS, which involves comparing the short term and long term stimulation of radio-iodine uptake by the thyroids of mice following injection of the test material, is complicated and not entirely satisfactory, and it is possible that the observed correlation is spuriously low. For the present the most that can be stated is that LATS cannot be excluded as the cause of exophthalmos.

AUTO-ANTIBODIES IN PERNICIOUS ANAEMIA

In this disease the gastric mucosa is typically reduced in thickness and the severely reduced glandular elements are surrounded by a dense cellular infiltration consisting principally of lymphocytes and plasma cells with the formation sometimes of typical germinal centres. This histological appearance bears an obvious resemblance to that of the thyroid gland in Hashimoto's disease or primary myxoedema, and by analogy with these diseases it was feasible to postulate that pernicious anaemia involved an immune response against cellular components of the stomach glands or their secretions, particularly since nearly 10 per cent of patients with myxoedema have also pernicious anaemia and an even higher proportion are known to have impaired absorption of vitamin B_{12} (cyanocobalamin) due to lack of gastric intrinsic factor. Contrariwise, an increased lymphoid infiltration of the thyroid has been a constant finding at autopsy of patients with pernicious anaemia.

The serum of untreated pernicious anaemia patients has been found to inhibit the absorption of vitamin B_{12}, when added to a mixture of intrinsic factor plus vitamin B_{12} *in vitro* before administration to another patient. It is likely that this inhibitor has the nature of antibody. Furthermore, the immunoglobulin fraction of serum from a patient with pernicious anaemia will combine with and retard the electrophoretic mobility of a human intrinsic factor-vitamin B_{12} complex. Such antibody to intrinsic factor can be demonstrated in about 40 per cent of patients by such *in vivo* and *in vitro* tests.

In addition, complement-fixing antibodies specific for a saline extract of the body of the stomach have been found in the sera of up to 75 per cent of patients with pernicious anaemia. This antibody is specific in its reaction with gastric mucosa and does not react with other human tissue extracts. The antigenic component is present in the fundus of the stomach and sediments from saline extracts under similar conditions to the microsomal cytoplasmic particles. Pyloric mucosa lacks this antigen, which appears to correspond in distribution with the parietal cells. By the fluorescent antibody test the sera of patients can be shown to bind specifically to the cytoplasm of such cells when applied to unfixed sections of human stomach. This technique provides a more sensitive test for the same antibodies as are detected by complement fixation. Both of these are, however, distinct from those which are directed against intrinsic factor.

The relationship of such antibodies to the pathogenesis of the disease is unsolved. Gastric atrophy (atrophic gastritis) with achlorhydria is a consistent feature of pernicious anaemia, but is much more common than the anaemia itself, and the hitherto accepted concept of the disease process envisages that damage to the parietal cells, as part of the atrophic gastritis, results in decreased secretion of hydrochloric acid and later of intrinsic factor. Auto-antibodies to intrinsic factor, and to the organelles of parietal cells, could both be a result of the cellular atrophy. Since pernicious anaemia is associated with thyroid disease, and the relatives of patients with anaemia show an unusually high incidence of antibodies to both thyroid and parietal cells, there is a possibility that some genetically determined initial biochemical lesion common to thyroid and gastric mucosal cells may occur.

However, gastric atrophy has been induced experimentally in dogs by the intracutaneous injection of autologous, homologous and heterologous gastric juice in Freund's complete adjuvant. A histamine-resistant achlorhydria results and lasts for about six months. These results obtained by the workers of one laboratory therefore leave open the possibility that pernicious anaemia is a true auto-immune disease in which the gastric atrophy is induced by the response to stomach auto-immunogens. However, no evidence has been presented to suggest that in man the serum antibodies can either precede or cause the disease.

EXPERIMENTAL IMMUNE ADRENALITIS, AND IDIOPATHIC ADDISON'S DISEASE

At the present time Addison's disease is a rare condition, since the incidence of human tuberculosis has declined. Even in the days when tuberculous adrenalitis was the predominant cause of Addison's disease, cases were occasionally seen in which a tuberculous aetiology could be excluded and which gained the title *idiopathic Addison's disease.*

The main evidence that some of these cases may stem from auto-immune reactions to adrenal antigens is derived from animal experiments in which adrenalitis resulted from injection of emulsions of whole adrenal in complete Freund-type adjuvant. In the original series of experiments homologous guinea-pig tissue was used in animals in which their own adrenal tissue was left intact. Later, a more severe adrenalitis was shown to follow injection of a tissue suspension from the adrenals of the same animal (again in complete Freund adjuvant). The experimentally induced lesions consist of foci of lymphocytes, macrophages and plasma cells between and around groups of parenchymal cells. There is extensive loss of adrenal cortical cells, the remaining parenchymal cells show coagulative necrosis of the cytoplasm and nuclear pyknosis. The cellular infiltrations follow the sinusoids, radiating outwards with diminishing intensity from the cortico-medullary junction.

The evidence linking auto-immune processes to human cases of idiopathic Addison's disease is incomplete. Several reports describe the presence of serum antibodies demonstrable by the complement-fixation test both to adrenal and thyroid extracts. However, sera which were taken from cases of thyroiditis with thyroid auto-antibodies were not found to be reactive with adrenal tissue, and the adrenal antibodies cannot simply be cross-reacting anti-thyroid antibodies.

Auto-antibodies Against Antigens Shared by Adrenal Cortex and Other Tissues Making Steroid Hormones

Auto-antibodies which react with one or more constituents of cells of the human adrenal cortex have been found in the sera of one half or more of patients with idiopathic adrenal insufficiency, when tested by immunofluorescence or by complement fixation. Such antibodies have not been found in the sera of patients with adrenal disease due to tuberculosis, nor in those of patients with thyroid disease, pernicious anaemia, gonadal dysgenesis nor of women past the menopause, although they were present in one patient with Cushing's syndrome (with adrenal adenoma) out of twenty-five examined.

In between five and ten per cent of two series of cases of idiopathic adrenal cortical insufficiency antibodies were found in the serum which reacted not only with cells of the adrenal cortex, but also with cells from other tissues which are known to be involved in the synthesis of steroid hormones. These antibodies reacted with one or more of the following types of cell: theca interna, corpus luteum and interstitial cells of the ovary; interstitial cells of the testis; trophoblasts of the placenta. They reacted not only with human cells but also with corresponding rabbit cells, and one of the sera also reacted strongly with rabbit ova and weakly with rabbit sperm. Some sera reacted with antigens which were present in all the kinds of human cell listed above, whereas others reacted with antigens present in some kinds of cell only. Cross absorption experiments indicated that all the antibodies were able to react with antigens present in adrenal cortex cells, but that more than one kind of antigen must have been involved. It has been suggested that a pattern of cross reactions of this kind might be expected if the antigens involved were enzymes involved in various metabolic pathways of steroid hormone synthesis, so that some might be common to all steroid producing cells, whereas others might be confined to some kinds of cell only.

An interesting clinical observation was that the presence of antibodies of this kind was closely correlated with complete failure of menstruation or premature onset of the menopause. In one patient, whose menstruation ceased four years after menarche, ovarian biopsy showed that normal primordial follicles were present. The membrana granulosa and ova of these did not react with her own serum; however, as the follicles enlarged the follicular epithelium showed immunofluorescent staining with her own serum, and the follicles were observed to be infiltrated with lymphocytes and plasma cells and to be undergoing destruction. This observation implies that the antigen responsible only appeared in significant amounts as the follicles developed under the influence of gonadotrophin, and is consistent with the hypothesis that it was an enzyme involved in steroid synthesis.

AUTO-IMMUNITY IN RELATION TO DISEASES OF THE EYE

Two types of ocular inflammation are thought to be related to the expression of auto-immunization. The first is *phacoanaphylaxis* (hypersensitivity to lens components); the second is *sympathetic ophthalmia*, which may be due to hypersensitivity to components of the uveal tract.

Hypersensitivity to Lens Immunogens

The lens is remarkably insulated from the general immunological mechanisms of the rest of the body and its development in embryo and early life is achieved without the establishment of full tolerance to its many antigens. When rabbits are injected with saline homogenates of bovine lenses, antisera are produced which precipitate with lens extracts but do not react with other bovine tissues. These organ-specific lens antigens are not able to stimulate antibody production in their own species (rabbit) if injected without adjuvants. Several, very diverse, substances can be added to the lens extract for the purpose of rendering it immunogenic. Culture filtrates of β-haemolytic streptococci, staphylococcus α-toxin and the complete Freund-type adjuvant will act in this way. It has been shown that the organ specificity of the lens depends upon a complex array of different antigens (at least nine or ten) and the suggestion has been made that these relate to molecular structures which were acquired during successive stages of evolution. Thus the earliest vertebrate antigens, as present in the lamprey, have been transmitted unchanged throughout all the more recent phyla.

In man cataract removal is sometimes followed by intra-ocular inflammation, which may completely annul the benefits of this operation and which is thought to depend on hypersensitivity to lens protein. This complication is envisaged to stem from the escape of lens proteins during the surgical removal of a lens affected with cataract. This results in auto-immunization, followed by a hypersensitivity reaction with residual lens components. The affected patients usually show Arthus-type skin hypersensitivity reactions to lens extracts. On histological examination of the eyes removed after development of the inflammation, the lenses were found to have been invaded by polymorphonuclear leucocytes and macrophages, but no bacteria were demonstrated. It has also been noted clinically that the second eye may develop inflammation in a sensitized patient if the lens in the second eye develops cataract. Removal of the lens from affected eyes leads to prompt subsidence of the inflammatory process.

The experimental counterpart to this was induced in rabbits injected with lens protein mixed with staphylococcal toxin as adjuvant in order to sensitize the animals to this antigen. At a later date the lens was traumatized by injection of a needle. The result was a severe intra-ocular inflammation.

Hypersensitivity to Uveal Tract Components

Sympathetic ophthalmia is the much dreaded complication which occurs in an otherwise sound eye after injury to the other eye and almost always results from a perforating wound, as when a foreign body gains admission to and persists in the interior of the eye. Wounds which involve the iris or ciliary body are regarded as especially dangerous. The inflammation usually begins 4 to 8 weeks after the injury, but may occur as early as 9 days or be delayed in onset for many months or even years.

The initial changes are those of focal lymphocytic infiltration, most pronounced around the small veins of the uveal tract. Later, collections of lymphocytes, epithelioid cells and giant cells can be found in nodules in the choroid and iris. Skin reactions of delayed type appear to parallel the intensity of the disease in man, except that a negative skin reaction may be found in acute exacerbations of the disease. The presence of antibody shows little correlation with active disease. Indeed, the occurrence of antibody to uveal pigment has been shown in those patients with trauma to the eye who fail to develop ophthalmia, whereas antibodies were absent from patients who did develop the disease. These results argue that the lesions may develop from the effects of cell-mediated hypersensitivity and that antibody may sometimes exert a protective effect, possibly by the mechanism of enhancement (see Chapter Fourteen).

The experimental production of a model for this disease has been achieved by the injection of guinea-pig uveas plus Freund-type complete adjuvant into guinea-pigs. After several months, a high proportion of the animals developed lymphocyte and epithelioid cell infiltration of the choroid resembling the so-called Dalen-Fuchs nodules of sympathetic ophthalmia (Plate 15.14). Injection of other tissues with the same adjuvants failed to produce disease, as did injection of uveal antigen without mycobacteria (a constituent of the Freund-type complete adjuvant).

The exact nature of the antigen is still undetermined. An injection mixture derived from the uveas of the eyes of albino guinea-pigs was able to produce disease in the unpigmented eyes of albino animals. In cases of sympathetic ophthalmia in man, albino antigen will provoke a positive skin response. The antigen is not therefore restricted to pigment.

Uveitis can also be produced experimentally by sensitization to unrelated antigens. Inflammation of the uveal tract can occur in guinea-pigs by direct inoculation of ovalbumin or bovine serum albumin into the vitreous humour. This leads to an acute uveitis whose duration is limited. With the local exhaustion of the antigen, the inflammatory process (which is accompanied by intense local proliferation of plasma cells in the uveal tract) ceases, but it may be reactivated by either local or systemic reinjection of the original antigen. Apparently, therefore, experimental hypersensitivity reactions to extraneous immunogens can resemble closely auto-allergic processes.

DISEASES OF THE NERVOUS SYSTEM

Experimental Allergic Encephalitis

The basic immunological model which has been used to explain various human demyelinating diseases is the experimental disease entity called experimental allergic encephalomyelitis (EAE). As long ago as 1935 it was shown that oft-repeated injections of autolysed brain into monkeys would lead after six months or a year to a fatal demyelinating disease. The laborious nature of the procedure necessary for the induction of this experimental disease discouraged extensive study until it was found that the use of an injection mixture of brain and a suspension of tubercle bacilli in mineral oil produced the same disease far more rapidly. By this procedure, often by the use of a single injection, fatal encephalitis can be produced in 10 to 30 days in a wide variety of animals.

This experimental disease has been regarded as a possible laboratory prototype for multiple sclerosis, Schilder's disease, acute necrotizing haemorrhagic leuco-encephalopathy, and the various examples of encephalomyelitis which follow infectious diseases, such as measles, German measles, mumps, chicken-pox and smallpox. The closest possible analogy to the experimental disease in animals would be expected to be provided by the encephalitic disease which occasionally follows antirabies treatment. This makes use of multiple injections of a vaccine of attenuated or inactivated virus still mixed with the nervous tissue in which it grew. The histological picture of perivascularly distributed lesions in the spinal cord, brain, optic nerves, cerebral and cerebellar white matter is similar enough in man and the experimental animal to make it almost certain that the human disease is a replica of EAE.

In addition, there is widespread agreement amongst neuropathologists that the type of encephalitis which results very rarely from vaccination with vaccinia virus is indistinguishable from that which follows anti-rabies treatment and from the various other post-infection encephalomyelitides.

Those who include multiple sclerosis and Schilder's disease in the same aetiological group, while admitting their manifest differences in details, lay emphasis on the transitional cases which link these conditions with the other demyelinating diseases. The existence of such cases indicates that the differences between all these diseases may be quantitative rather than qualitative. This is stressed by the observation of Japanese workers that some forms of post-rabies inoculation encephalitis are indistinguishable from acute multiple sclerosis.

The pathological changes of EAE have not been identical in all laboratory animals. In some, such as the guinea-pig, the main lesions consist of multiple foci of cerebrospinal leptomeningitis containing histiocytes, lymphocytes, plasma cells and neutrophil leucocytes. Similar cellular clusters occur in relation to the adventitia of small veins just beneath the pia mater (Plate 15.12, following p. 660). Demyelination is inconspicuous and occurs only in the immediate vicinity of the affected vessels. In the dog and monkey, which have usually been subjected to many injections over a long period, large foci of demyelination result, and the meningeal cellular infiltrations are less pronounced (Plate 15.13, following p. 660). Thus the pattern of lesions in these larger animals is much more like that occurring in multiple sclerosis in man.

The clinical course of this disease with its characteristic remissions is difficult to reconcile with that of the acute experimental disease. However, the experimental animal after the acute attack is more vulnerable to further brain damage. Thus it is shown in guinea-pigs and rabbits that a further insult to the brain, delivered during the period of recovery from allergic encephalomyelitis, can rapidly lead to further histological changes in the brain.

The immunogen from brain or spinal cord which acts to induce EAE is organ-specific and occurs throughout all species of mammals and birds. Thus nervous tissue from any warm blooded animal (but not from fishes or amphibians) is able to produce EAE in other species. The presence of immunogen corresponds with that of myelinated white matter; foetal brain, which is deficient in myelin, is a poor immunogen. It is possible to extract from bovine spinal cord a highly basic histone-like protein which in dose of 1 μg is able to induce EAE when injected in suitable adjuvant in 50 per cent of guinea-pigs. Some have claimed that active material may be obtained as a peptide with a molecular weight as low as 4600. There may, however, be several forms of encephalitogenic protein immunogens, since by other extraction procedures an active collagen-like material has been obtained.

The evidence that the lesions of EAE themselves are the result of an auto-immune process is briefly as follows. First, all attempts to uncover an infective agent such as a virus in the injection mixture have failed, and the alternative hypothesis that the lesions result from the activation of a latent neutropic virus remains unsupported. Secondly, the fact that the mechanism is independent of iso-antibody formation or of sensitization to external agents was proved by the demonstration that the condition could be induced in monkeys by the use of antigen of a portion of the animal's own brain, removed at a previous operation.

By means of complement-fixation techniques it is possible to show that the serum in cases of EAE contains antibodies reacting with brain antigens. These antibodies might be expected to be capable of a direct cytotoxic action on nervous tissue, an action which would be comparable to the direct cellular effect of antibody in acquired haemolytic anaemia or possibly also in idiopathic thrombocytopenic purpura. However, there is no correlation between the titres of these antibodies and the presence of lesions. Also the serum does not transfer the condition to normal animals.

'*Myelotoxic factors*' have been found in the sera of animals with experimental allergic encephalomyelitis which cause dissolution of the myelin sheaths of tissue-culured explants of rat cerebellum—without any accompanying alteration in the axis cylinders. This demyelinating factor has been localized to the γ_2-globulin fraction of rabbit serum and requires complement for its activity. Similarly, demyelinating factors can be demonstrated in the sera of human patients with multiple sclerosis. The significance of these results is difficult to define since demyelinating serum factors are also present in other neurological diseases, e.g. amyotrophic lateral sclerosis, and it may well be the case that circulating myelotoxins are the result rather than the cause of demyelination in EAE (and multiple sclerosis).

An alternative view would be to attribute the damage to immunologically active cells. The morbid-anatomical appearances strongly suggest that myelin breakdown is closely associated with the foci of cellular infiltration. Injection of homologous spinal cord tissue into rabbits gives reactions which show a partial correlation, both in time and in intensity, with the neurological disease in the same animals. This skin reactivity cannot be passively transferred with serum but can be transferred to normal animals by lymph node cells. Corneal responses are also elicited using the same test material, and are found positive only in rabbits with allergic encephalomyelitis.

Finally, the role of delayed-type hypersensitivity has been strongly suggested by the demonstration of the passive transfer of EAE to normal rats and guinea-pigs, by transfused lymph node cells taken a few days before the disease was due to appear in the donors. It is essential for the success of these experiments that the transfused cells should not be promptly eliminated by a homograft reaction. Thus success in the rat followed the use of animals rendered tolerant at birth by prior injections of donor cells, and in the guinea-pig by the use of an inbred isogeneic strain. On this view, then, the damage to the nervous tissue results from the peri-venous accumulation of mononuclear cells which are homing to an auto-antigen, and which also possibly have among themselves cells (possibly the histiocytes) which can bring about direct destruction of such antigen-containing elements.

The inclusion of the bacterial products (usually mycobacteria) in the Freund adjuvant mixture greatly increases the incidence of encephalomyelitis in any group of injected animals. However, in some species the use of such bacteria is not obligatory. They apparently facilitate the production of the immune response, and the same chloroform-soluble wax fractions of various mycobacteria and related organisms which are effective in oily emulsions in increasing antibody production to protein antigens generally are also the components which allow the rapid development of encephalitis in guinea-pigs.

In conclusion, the evidence is nowadays strongly in favour of the view that the experimental lesion depends on an allergic response to auto-antigens of nervous tissue and that a delayed-type hypersensitivity is the main cause of the lesions. This does not exclude the possibility of damage by circulating auto-antibody, but those antibodies so far measured seem unrelated to the disease. Nevertheless the fact that antimyelin antibodies can cause cytopathic changes in tissue-cultures of myelin fibres leaves open the possibility that myelotoxic antibodies may act in concert with cell-mediated hypersensitivity to cause the demyelination in the experimental and human diseases.

Experimental Allergic Neuritis

The disease which results from the injection of brain or spinal cord suspensions is an encephalomyelitis without significant involvement of the nerve roots. However, it is reported that animals which are injected with suspensions of peripheral nerve develop a radiculitis with few, if any, lesions in the central nervous system. This would indicate that central nervous system tissue and peripheral nerve each contain substances not common to the other that are capable of provoking lesions predominantly in the parts of the nervous system from which they are derived.

Immunofluorescence studies similarly indicate the distinct immunogenic properties of peripheral as opposed to central nervous tissue. Thus a rabbit anti-human brain serum will attach to guinea-pig myelin sheaths both central and peripheral; a similar serum made against human peripheral nerves combines only with peripheral nerve.

Experimental allergic neuritis (EAN) like EAE has been transferred from affected to normal guinea-pigs of the same inbred strain, using sensitized lymphoid cells, and is regarded from this and other evidence as dependent on a state of delayed hypersensitivity to an immunogenic constituent of peripheral-nerve myelin. The lesions observed in rats at about 15 days after injection of rabbit peripheral nerve in Freund complete adjuvant consist of focal perivascular accumulations of lymphocytes and macrophages in association with beginning myelin breakdown in the contiguous area. The cellular sequence of events can be observed with unusual clarity in such lesions since blood vessels in nerve run parallel to the long axis so that longitudinal sections can be obtained with ease. In the early stages (8 days after inoculation) lymphocytes become attached by a cytoplasmic stalk to the endothelium of small veins, and undergo mitosis. Contiguous to such intraluminal collections of cells perivascular collections later accumulate, the cells appearing to migrate to this position by traversing the cell bodies of the endothelial cells of the small veins. The extravasated cells are larger and more heterogeneous than the intravascular small lymphocytes and appear to be identical with transformed large pyroninophilic haemocytoblasts. Subsequent damage of Schwann cells led to retraction of the myelin, beginning at the node of Ranvier.

Relationship of Experimental Allergic Encephalomyelitis to Multiple Sclerosis and Post-infection Encephalitis

If EAE is accepted to be an auto-immune disease, it becomes important to analyse how far this experimental model helps in interpreting the aetiology of the human diseases, multiple sclerosis and the various post-infection encephalitides.

All have a common basic lesion which appears as a perivenous cellular infiltration with lymphocytes and macrophages, and parenchymal destruction in the infiltrated zone ranging from demyelination with sparing of axis cylinders to total tissue necrosis, sometimes with haemorrhage and local fibrinoid deposit. Acceptance of a common basic histo-pathology has led to the *unitarian* hypothesis that the human demyelinating diseases form a spectrum ranging from the most acute cases of frank post-vaccinial or other post-infective encephalitis at one end of the scale, to the chronic, insidious, remittent and progressive form of spinal multiple sclerosis. The fact that some forms of post-rabies inoculation encephalitis are indistinguishable from the more acute forms of multiple sclerosis is the most persuasive argument that EAE could form a model for multiple sclerosis.

However, two difficulties are outstanding. First, EAE and post-rabies inoculation encephalitis are self-limiting processes whereas multiple sclerosis follows a relapsing but relentlessly chronic course. An explanation is certainly required for the fact that a proportion of animals may recover from their EAE symptoms and that these are relatively immune to further challenge. A possible explanation may depend upon the protective effect of antibodies. Such an effect can be clearly shown when complement-fixing antibodies from convalescent animals are administered to other animals challenged with spinal cord-adjuvant mixture. The serum must be started early to be effective and was ineffective when injected after onset of paralytic symptoms. The protective component was identified as a 19S macroglobulin complement-fixing antibody. These results are suggestively analogous to those obtained in the phenomenon of *enhancement* of tumour and tissue homografts (see Chapter Fourteen) and the hypothesis may be advanced that antibody may serve to inhibit those aspects of the immunological responses concerned with cell-mediated hypersensitivity. It is also possible with such 'protective' antibody to construct mechanisms whereby a demyelinating disease might wax and wane in successive cycles. Secondly, large plaques resulting from extensive reactive gliosis which occur in human cases of multiple sclerosis have never been reproduced in EAE in animals. However, it is admitted that the lesions in the larger animals, such as the dog and monkey, resemble the human lesions more closely than do the lesions of smaller animals. The histological appearances vary with different injection schedules and it is claimed that by choosing appropriate antigenic mixtures and by spacing the injections it is possible in the larger laboratory animals to reproduce lesions which are indistinguishable from those of multiple sclerosis.

An alternative and more cautious concept of the relation of EAE to human disease would, however, be as a model for the self-limiting disease states such as vaccinial and post-infectious encephalomyelitis.

Direct evidence that immunological processes are involved in multiple sclerosis would be provided by demonstrations of either serum antibody or skin test reactions to brain antigens. Antibody to bovine encephalitogenic factor has been found present in the blood of patients with multiple sclerosis. However, patients with other degenerative conditions of the nervous system (such as G.P.I.) have also shown a similar incidence of the same antibodies. Thus, antibody of this type is probably a result rather than a cause of the myelin destruction. Skin tests for the presence of delayed-type hypersensitivity have, in general, proved negative.

The cerebrospinal fluid in multiple sclerosis has an increased content of immunoglobulin (which normally only accounts for up to 3 mg per 100 ml). When injections of antigens such as tuberculoprotein are made intrathecally into Mantoux-positive patients with multiple sclerosis, the pattern of cellular response in terms of the counts of polymorphonuclear and mononuclear cells in the cerebrospinal fluid is markedly different from that in Mantoux-positive normal controls. These findings, taken with the increased immunoglobulin levels, have been used to suggest that immunity mechanisms are involved in the disease, but they do not allow any definite distinction between auto-immune or infective aetiologies.

The possibility that multiple sclerosis arises from a virus infection has long been considered and is still under active study. Cases of human disease have been reported in laboratory workers handling material from sheep suffering from the neurological disease *swayback* and, more recently, it has been reported that injection of brain tissue from cases of multiple sclerosis results in the production of the virus disease *scrapie* in sheep. Even if an underlying virus infection were to be discovered, it seems not unlikely that the pathogenic mechanism will involve an immunological response to the altered virus-infected cells.

AUTO-IMMUNE ORCHITIS AND EPIDIDYMITIS

In the introduction to this chapter it was pointed out that spermatozoa are auto-immunogenic. As long ago as 1900 Metchnikoff detected in the sera of guinea-pigs injected with their own sperm antibodies which could achieve the immobilization of fresh motile spermatozoa in the presence of complement. This finding has been confirmed repeatedly. Cross reactivity is greatest between spermatozoa of closely related species, and falls off rapidly as the relationship becomes more distant. Organ specificity is well marked and cross reactivity has been described only between brain and testis.

Of greater significance from the point of view of possible disease mechanisms is the observation that injection of guinea-pigs with their own or homologous testis in Freund-type adjuvant mixture including tubercle bacilli leads to cessation of spermatogenesis. At first a depletion and later a complete absence of mature spermatozoa is found (Plates 15.15A and B, following p. 662). The immature spermatocytes swell and become aggregated to form multinucleate giant cells lying free within the seminiferous tubules (Plate 15.14B). At 10 days after injection these changes are well established although they are patchy and leave many areas unaffected. Later, by the end of the third week, some tubules appear almost totally depleted of cells; others contain multinucleate cells. An interstitial infiltration with cells appears later (Plate 15.15C). They include lymphocytes, macrophages and mature and immature plasma cells. It has been stressed that this cellular reaction follows rather than precedes or accompanies the tubular damage and impairment of spermatogenesis.

Complement-fixing antibody, immobilizing antibody and anti-hyaluronidase were all found in the serum of injected animals. However, it is stressed that some guinea-pigs may develop aspermatogenesis under conditions where neither complement-fixing nor sperm immobilizing antibodies could be demonstrated in the serum. Antibody-containing serum could not be shown to induce aspermatogenesis or testicular damage in normal animals, even when injected intra-testicularly.

When testis in *incomplete* Freund-type adjuvant is injected into guinea-pigs, testicular damage is absent although antibody against sperm and anti-hyaluronidase appear in the serum. Addition of killed mycobacteria to the injection mixture of an antigen generally results in the induction of high degrees of delayed-type hypersensitivity, suggesting that this type of immunological response is probably of prime importance in the production of the testicular lesions. When purified preparations derived from sperm are used in skin tests, delayed-type reactions result in those animals which are injected with testis in complete Freund adjuvant and which have testicular lesions.

While it is clear from the above evidence that antibody alone cannot induce the testicular damage or azoospermia, and that delayed-type hypersensitivity must play an essential role in this, there are several difficulties for any interpretation of the lesions solely in terms of the latter process. Thus, throughout the early stages (9th–14th days) of damage to sperm production from spermatocytes interstitial mononuclear cell infiltration between the tubules is absent.

Recent investigations have successfully induced orchitis and azoospermia with refined antigens prepared from autoclaved testis homogenate extracted with phenol and subsequent digestion of the phenol phase extract with papain. Animals which were injected with this antigen in complete Freund adjuvant developed delayed-type hypersensitivity (as shown by skin tests to the refined antigen or crude testis homogenate) but no circulating antibody or testicular lesions. However, when such animals were given repeated injections of serum containing anti-testis antibody orchitis developed. By immunofluorescence antibody has been shown to make its appearance within the seminiferous tubules at the same time as delayed-type hypersensitivity first becomes demonstrable, suggesting that the later process may act to admit the damaging antibody to its target cells.

The auto-antigen which is active in the above experiments resides in the spermatozoa and spermatogenic cells. The former are as effective as whole testis in inducing aspermatogenesis. Testes of newborn guinea-pigs are immunogenically ineffective, as are the testes of guinea-pigs rendered azoospermic from previous immunization. By immunofluorescence the antigens are shown to be present in the cytoplasm of the spermatids, and in the acrosomes of the spermatozoa. The cytoplasm of giant cells appearing in the early stages of auto-immune orchitis is also brightly fluorescent.

Auto-immunization Against Spermatozoa in Relation to Sterility in Man

The ease by which azoospermia is produced experimentally in guinea-pigs raises the possibility that sterility in man could arise by the formation of auto-antibodies against spermatozoa or by the development of azoospermia following auto-allergic orchitis. Cases have been reported of sterile men with sperm agglutinins demonstrable in the blood serum and seminal plasma, and whose spermatozoa spontaneously agglutinated in the ejaculate. There are, however, only a few of such cases and in a series of 80 men with azoospermia or extreme oligospermia, sperm agglutinating antibodies were found in the sera of two cases only. Different patterns of agglutination are seen: head to head and tail to tail. By immunofluorescence it has been shown that the head to head agglutinin reacts with the acrosomal cap of the spermatozoon and in this respect it resembles the auto-antibody which is produced experimentally in the guinea-pig. It can be shown that sperm auto-agglutination interferes with the penetration of spermatozoa into the cervical mucus.

In some cases the presence of auto-antibody to sperm has been linked with occlusive lesions of the efferent ducts of the testis (vas deferens or epididymis). In such cases an opportunity for auto-immunization to sperm arises from penetration of sperm into the interstitial tissue of the testis. The resulting auto-antibodies will, of course, only be of significance when the occlusion is partial or unilateral, when they may produce sterility by causing auto-agglutination of the residual sperm output.

Although out of context in considering manifestations of auto-immunity it is interesting to note the other possibility that spermatozoa may induce immobilizing antibodies in the wife against the sperm of the husband. By the subcutaneous injection of the husbands' semen into married women it has proved easy to induce immobilizing antibody in the serum. This antibody is directed against a component of seminal plasma, rather than against spermatozoa, and the role of such antibodies in natural infertility is far from clear. Certainly it is claimed that the inoculation of female guinea-pigs with guinea-pig testis plus adjuvant renders them relatively insusceptible to pregnancy, but it is by no means certain that this would apply in man.

Very rarely, spontaneous allergic sensitization can arise in women to the contents of seminal fluid. In one extensively investigated case this sensitization was shown to be directed to a sialic-acid-containing glycoprotein of semen. A high degree of atopic hypersensitivity was shown by skin reactions to human, but not animal, semen, and coitus was followed by severe anaphylaxis with development of giant urticaria and asthma.

MUMPS ORCHITIS

Histologically the lesions of experimental allergic orchitis are not unlike those described in biopsies taken from the inflamed testes in mumps. Orchitis occurs as a sequel to about 5 per cent of cases of salivary gland infection by mumps virus. It usually follows the parotitis within 10 days. Although 80 per cent of cases of mumps occur before the age of 15, the incidence of testicular inflammation in this age group is relatively low (1·5 per cent of mumps cases). Cases occurring after puberty have a much increased incidence of orchitis (20 per cent of mumps cases). One in three of such cases of orchitis is followed by complete atrophy of the affected gland. Bilateral atrophy, which would lead to complete sterility, occurs in only 10 per cent of cases of orchitis. The fact that virus has not been found in the testis of patients with orchitis or in the testes of experimentally infected monkeys lends evidence to the view that the orchitis is a result of an auto-immunization resulting from some degree of disorganization of the gland and absorption of seminal fluid due to an initial damage by the virus. This view is also supported by the age incidence of orchitis, from which it is reasonable to infer that orchitis rarely if ever occurs in children affected before spermatogenesis has begun.

THE OCCURRENCE AND SIGNIFICANCE OF AUTO-ANTIBODIES IN VARIOUS OTHER DISEASES

RHEUMATIC HEART DISEASE AND POST-CARDIOTOMY SYNDROME

In rheumatic fever, as described in Chapter Nine, there is evidence to indicate that the development of the characteristic lesion in the heart and elsewhere may follow from a hypersensitivity developed to antigens of the streptococcus. As such, the disease does not belong in this chapter, but the possibility of auto-immunization has to be considered; firstly, since the evidence for the role of hypersensitivity is not so complete as to preclude other aetiological mechanisms, and secondly, because auto-antibody formation, even if of no aetiological significance, may prove useful for diagnosis or prognosis.

The occurrence in sera from patients with rheumatic fever of antibodies against constituents of normal or rheumatic hearts detectable by various *in vitro* techniques has often been reported. The fluorescent antibody technique has recently been applied in two different ways for detecting possible auto-immune antibodies. The first method was to apply a fluorescent rabbit anti-human-immunoglobulin serum to washed frozen sections of biopsy specimens of auricular muscle. Localized fluorescence in this case could indicate immunoglobulin fixed to tissue, and the assumption is made that this represents auto-antibody fixed by interaction with its specific antigen. The results showed such fixed immunoglobulin in numerous areas in the myocardium which by ordinary histology corresponded with areas of eosinophilic change in the muscle. In the second method, sections of human hearts are exposed to various sera. After a time the serum is washed away, and any immunoglobulin bound is then revealed by means of a fluorescent rabbit anti-human-immunoglobulin serum. By this method sera from one out of four cases of rheumatic fever revealed staining in a characteristic pattern beneath the sarcolemmae or between the muscle fibrils.

Similar antibodies were also found in a much higher proportion of rheumatic patients after cardiotomy. This suggests that the antibodies may be the result rather than the cause of myocardial damage, and this view is further supported by their appearance after cardiotomy for congenital heart defects and also in non-rheumatic patients after myocardial infarction.

There is no evidence that the immune response which they signalize can cause any of the lesions of rheumatic fever. Possibly the occurrence of such antibodies after cardiotomy may be related to the curious febrile disturbance or *post-commissurotomy syndrome* which occurs at this time. It may be significant that similar antibodies can be called forth in rabbits by injecting a vaccine of streptococci grown in a nutrient medium containing bovine or rabbit heart extracts. In this way auto-immune processes may complement the 'hypersensitivity response' to streptococci.

LIVER DISEASE

1. *Lupoid Hepatitis*

This is a condition usually seen in young women, characterized by recurring periods of jaundice, fever and sometimes joint pains. There is a prominent excess of gamma-globulin in the blood and the LE cell test may be positive (40 per cent of cases). Other auto-immune serological tests, i.e. for rheumatoid factor, or for antibody to thyroglobulin, or for complement-fixing antibody to many homologous tissue extracts (AICF tests) may also be positive. The liver is extensively infiltrated with lymphocytes, histiocytes and plasma cells, mainly in the portal tracts. Occasionally the lymphocyte aggregation amounts to formation of nodules with germinal centres.

The concept which is inferred from the name *lupoid hepatitis*, i.e. that the disease is merely a variant of systemic lupus erythematosus, is difficult to accept. Post-mortem examination of the livers of patients dying with the latter disease are usually normal or only mildly affected with fatty infiltration or congestion of the lobules. In contrast the histological features in lupoid hepatitis are similar to those of chronic hepatitis. The disease does not usually progress to overt severe systemic lupus erythematosus but to fatal hepatic failure. Many cases respond to corticosteroid or immunosuppressive therapy.

2. *Primary Biliary Cirrhosis*

This is one of the rarer varieties of *cirrhosis*, the other main types being nutritional cirrhosis (commonly associated with excessive drinking of alcohol) and post-necrotic cirrhosis. In primary biliary cirrhosis there is a distension of the organ due to stagnation of the bile in the canaliculi of the intra-hepatic biliary ducts. It must be distinguished from biliary cirrhosis secondary to obstruction of the extra-hepatic biliary channels. The strongest current evidence favours the virus of infective hepatitis as the commonest cause, but a comparable hepatic lesion develops in certain patients treated with certain drugs, notably chlorpromazine.

The following items of evidence can be advanced to support the participation of immunological events in primary biliary cirrhosis. Hypergammaglobulinaemia appears early in the course of the disease, sometimes before any clinical evidence of cirrhosis. The liver becomes infiltrated with lymphocytes and plasma cells which follow the portal tracts. By the fluorescent antibody method the plasma cells have been shown to contain immunoglobulin. Complement-fixing antibody could be demonstrated in the serum to a range of different homologous tissue extracts (AICF tests). High titres are found against liver antigen. By means of the double layer fluorescent antibody method an auto-antibody can be demonstrated in serum which binds to the cytoplasm of the epithelium of the bile ductules and sometimes to the bile within the sections of duct lumina. Over 75 per cent of the sera of cases of biliary cirrhosis contain such an autoantibody. Attachment of the antibody from serum applied to *acetone-fixed sections* of liver tissue (first layer of test) could be demonstrated by the use of fluorescein-labelled anti-human immunoglobulin in the second layer (see Chapter Nine). This auto-antibody is not restricted to cases of biliary cirrhosis but may occur in 10 per cent of normal sera, and 47 per cent of sera from cases of post-necrotic cirrhosis, and is very common in the sera of cases of acute virus hepatitis. Another auto-antibody occurring in the sera of cases of primary biliary cirrhosis has been demonstrated by application of sera to *unfixed* liver sections of human and other mammalian origin. This antibody localized to hepatic parenchymal cells and may be a non-species specific auto-antibody to a constituent of mitochondria. The same auto-antibody also occurs in a small proportion of cases of chronic hepatitis and advanced cirrhosis.

These multiple auto-antibodies which occur in the several varieties of liver disease have not as yet been shown to play a pathogenic role. Many appear to represent a reaction to the tissue damage and the possibility exists that they serve a *protective* function. Recent work has shown that antibodies which occur in some patients during the course of hepatitis and which are directed against intra-cellular lysosomes may act to protect against tissue damage induced *in vitro* by lysosomal hydrolytic enzymes.

An experimental demonstration of the secondary role of liver auto-antibodies is provided by the toxic effect of carbon tetrachloride producing liver necrosis in the rat. Within four days after the administration of CCl_4, well after the appearance of liver necrosis, an antibody appears in the serum which fixes complement specifically with rat liver antigen. The antibodies, of IgM type, were found to be reactive with microsomal and mitochondrial fractions of liver tissue. The production of auto-antibody could be prevented by splenectomy and by whole-body X-irradiation before injection. These procedures did not prevent the liver necrosis, therefore the antibodies were not considered to have any hepatotoxic effect.

ULCERATIVE COLITIS

It is characteristic of ulcerative colitis that the lower part of the colon is subject to chronic inflammation which results in diarrhoea with blood and mucus in the stools. The superficial layers of the gut wall are infiltrated with large numbers of plasma cells, lymphocytes and eosinophils. The surface is usually ulcerated and collections of polymorphs gather in the distended mucosal glands to form crypt abscesses.

With these local abnormalities of the gut wall it would be expected that such patients would be subjected to increased stimulation by immunogens contained in the gut lumen. At operation a portal bacteraemia has indeed been demonstrated. A simple hypothesis to account for ulcerative colitis may therefore involve chronic or repeated local anaphylactic responses to immunogens of the food or gut flora of bacteria, protozoa or helminths. In the rat the presence of helminth larvae has been clearly shown to lead to increased local vascular permeability and cellular infiltration in animals either actively sensitized or passively sensitized with antibody. A high incidence of raised titres of antibody to components of milk (casein and lactoglobulin) has been reported in ulcerative colitis, and since some patients improve in a significant way when placed on a milk-free diet, some cases may possibly be regarded as examples of allergy to food. It is relevant to note here that there has been similar discussion as to whether coeliac disease can be the result of an allergic response to gluten (wheat protein). However, in this case the local histological changes (atrophy and lymphocytic infiltration of the wall of the colon) are associated with the maladsorption syndrome rather than ulceration of the gut wall.

Recently the role of auto-immune responses has been explored in ulcerative colitis. Evidence of an association with other auto-immune diseases is unconvincing, in spite of occasional reference to coincidence of rheumatoid arthritis, ankylosing spondylitis or systemic lupus erythematosus. One clear association is a form of arthritis, separable from rheumatoid arthritis, in which the Rose-Waaler sheep-erythrocyte agglutination test and tests for rheumatoid factor are negative.

The presence of auto-antibodies in ulcerative colitis were shown by precipitation in agar-gel and by a haemagglutination test with sheep cells which had been coated with human colon extracts. To obtain extracts free from bacterial contamination colons were taken from infants who had died within 24 hours of birth and had never been fed. The most consistent results were obtained with a phenol-water extract at 65°C following the procedure developed for extraction of lipopolysaccharide antigens from Gram-negative bacteria. Phenol-water extracts of colons with contained bacterial flora yield antigenic extracts which react equally with normal as with the serum from cases of ulcerative colitis.

Considerable interest attaches to the nature of this antigen and to the fact that lipopolysaccharide extracts of *Escherichia coli* 014 can inhibit the agglutination of red cells coated with the colonic extract. Several different strains of *E. coli* can similarly absorb the auto-antibodies from the sera of cases of ulcerative colitis. Thus an antigen common to many strains of *E. coli* may be involved, which may correspond with the 'heterogenetic' (or Kunin) antigen.

Auto-antibodies can also be detected by immunofluorescence using a section of gut tissue, the antigen being revealed throughout the section in a distribution corresponding with mucus. The auto-antibodies can be absorbed with phenol extract of sterile human colon and are probably the same as the haemagglutinating antibodies described above.

Auto-antibodies to gut tissue can be readily induced in rabbits by injection of scrapings of *rat* gut in Freund's complete adjuvant mixture. This is an interesting example of the general rule that auto-antibodies can be more readily produced by the injection of antigens which are similar but not identical with the self-material. Rabbits injected similarly with *E. coli* have also produced auto-antibodies to gut.

However, the question still arises whether any of these auto-antibodies are responsible for the tissue damage. No cytotoxic effect has been demonstrated to follow the exposure of cultured areas of the gut *in vitro*, and in rabbits producing auto-antibodies after injection of rat colon or rat ileum no damage could be shown to result in the animal's own gut.

PANCREATITIS

Precipitins against pancreatic tissue extracts are regularly present in cases of chronic pancreatitis, carcinoma of the pancreas and cystic pancreatic fibrosis. The antibodies were both species- and organ-specific. On those occasions when the antibody could be tested against the patient's own pancreas tissue, a precipitin reaction could not usually be obtained. Thus the main part of the present evidence is sufficient to indicate iso-antibody rather than auto-antibody formation. Experiments in rabbits, which were injected with pooled pancreatic extracts from several animals, resulted in serum antibodies which would not react with extracts of the pancreas of the rabbit producing them. Their reaction pattern with individual rabbit pancreatic extracts appeared to indicate a system of pancreas iso-antigens similar to, but distinct from, erythrocyte groups.

THE ROLE OF AUTO-IMMUNITY IN DISEASE OF THE THYMUS

Myasthenia Gravis

This disease, usually seen in females, is characterized by the easy fatigability of various muscle groups such as those of the eye, the face, the larynx and the extremities. The aetiology of the disease is unknown but the presumption has been that an impairment of neuromuscular transmission was present since the muscle weakness is readily reversible by choline esterase inhibitors. The occurrence of transient myasthenia in a proportion of infants born of affected mothers suggests the presence of a humoral inhibitor which is transferred across the placenta. Since the weakness in infants lasts up to two months, this inhibitor could be maternal IgG; indeed, evidence for the presence of a neuromuscular inhibitor in the globulin fraction of serum has been recently reported.

It has been known for many years that the thymuses removed surgically from patients with this disease quite regularly (in 70 per cent of cases) show the presence of numerous germinal centres within lymphoid nodules in the medulla of the gland—appearances which are rare in thymuses derived from normal individuals. A true hypertrophy is frequently absent, as normal weight limits may not be exceeded. No change is usually seen in the cortex, which may in fact be reduced to a thin layer over the medulla, which is expanded by the presence of numerous lymphoid nodules with or without germinal centres. It should be emphasized that the normal thymus, in contrast to other lymphoid tissues (Chapter Seven) shows little evidence of hyperplasia or antibody production in response to the injection of antigens into the circulation. Germinal centres, identical with those of the thymus in myasthenia gravis, appear in the spleen of experimental animals following intravenous injection of antigens and in the lymph nodes which drain the site of locally injected antigen. The lymphoid hyperplasia of the thymus in myasthenia has been compared with the changes in the thyroid in Hashimoto's disease, where the increased numbers of plasma cells and germinal centres have been interpreted as an immunological response to increased local escape of thyroglobulin and other segregated immunogens. The changes in myasthenia gravis include far fewer plasma cells than in lymphadenoid goitre. However, both

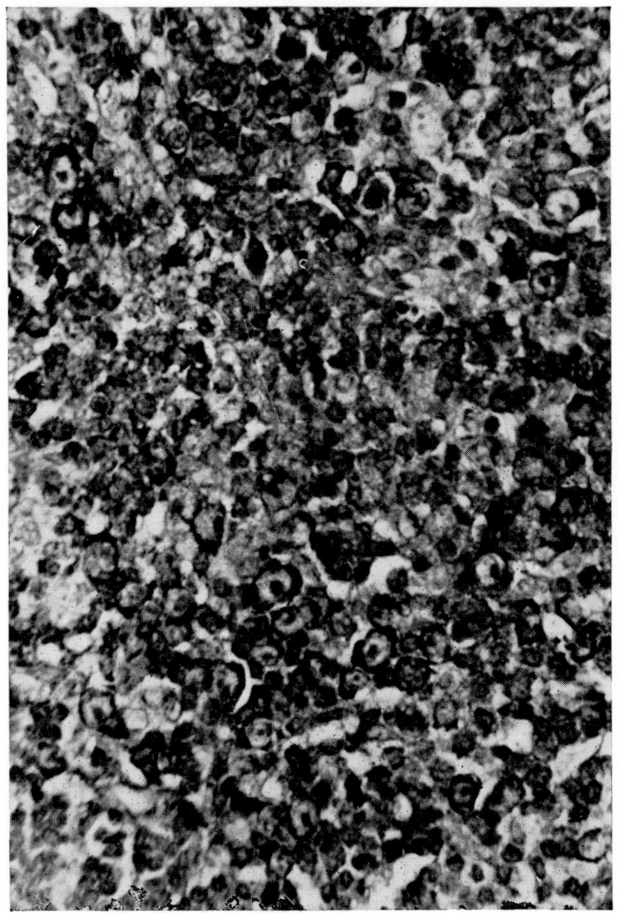

PLATE 12.3A. Reaction in thymus dependent area of a lymph node draining the skin on which the chemical sensitizing agent oxalone had been painted 4 days previously. Note the many large pyroninophilic blast cells in the paracortical area. (× 570).

[Photograph kindly supplied by Dr. D. M. V. Parrott.]

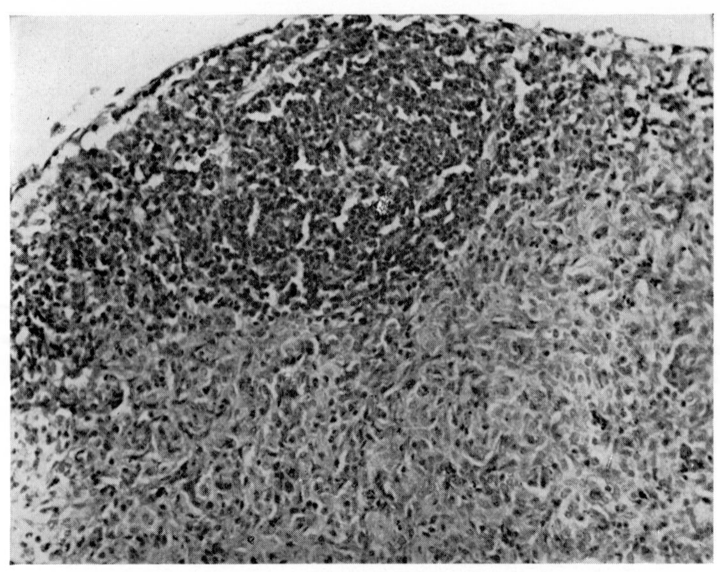

PLATE 12.3B. Low power view of draining lymph node from an animal treated in the same way but which had been thymectomized soon after birth. Note the absence of large pyroninophilic blast cells from the paracortical area. The appearance of the lymphoid follicle is normal. (× 120).

[Photograph kindly supplied by Dr. D. M. V. Parrott.]

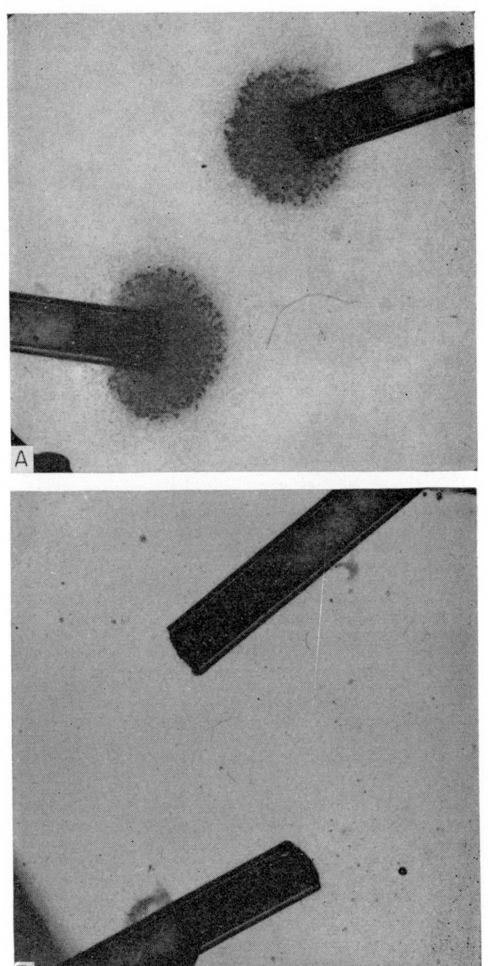

PLATE 12.4. (*opposite*). Antigen inhibition of the migration of peritoneal exudate cells from sensitized guinea-pigs. The exudate cells are packed into capillary tubes and allowed to migrate out into a fluid medium.

A. control preparation. Exposure of cells from a normal guinea-pig to antigen has not affected the migration from the mouth of the capillary.

B. positive result with cells from guinea-pig with contact hypersensitivity. The exposure to antigen has prevented the formation of the normal fan of migrating cells.

[Preparation of Dr. D. C. Dumonde.]

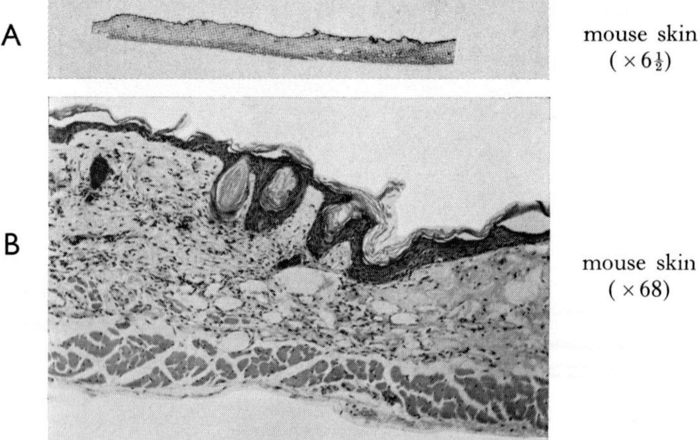

PLATE 13.1A and B. Graft acceptance. Healing of the graft into the bed is almost complete at 12 days. The epidermis of the host and graft form a continuous covering and new hair follicles are developing in the graft. Coincident with an organized blood supply, the cellularity of the dermis is restored to normal.

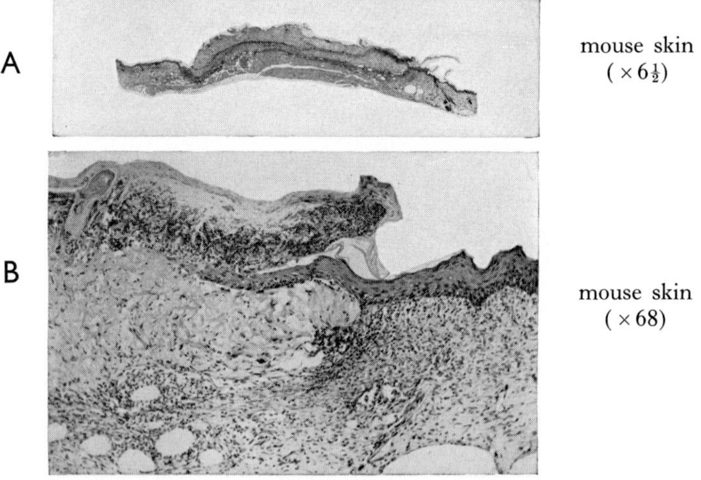

PLATE 13.2A and B. Primary graft rejection. At 12 days after grafting, the histological appearance of the graft indicates that a stasis of blood flow has occurred in the mid-dermal plane of the graft due to a breakdown of the capillaries at this level. The host epidermis has begun to undermine the dead tissues of the graft and, as frequently occurs, a portion of the graft dermis is incorporated into the tissues of the host. Note the increased cellularity of the graft and of the graft bed due mainly to an infiltration of host lymphocytes and monocytes with histiocytes and relatively few plasma cell polymorphs.

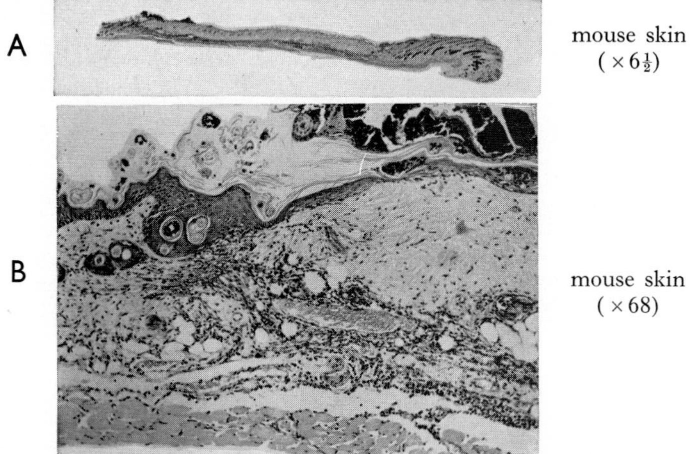

PLATE 13.3A and B. 'Second Set' rejection. The reaction bringing about the accelerated rejection of a homograft is concentrated in the graft bed, the graft itself never becoming truly vascularized. At 4½ days after grafting, the graft epidermis is already dead. Note the cellularity of the graft bed region, which is comprised chiefly of histiocytes and plasma cells with polymorphs and relatively few lymphocytes and monocytes.

[All photographs are taken from sections of mouse skin stained with H. and E., kindly provided by Dr Sheila Doak.]

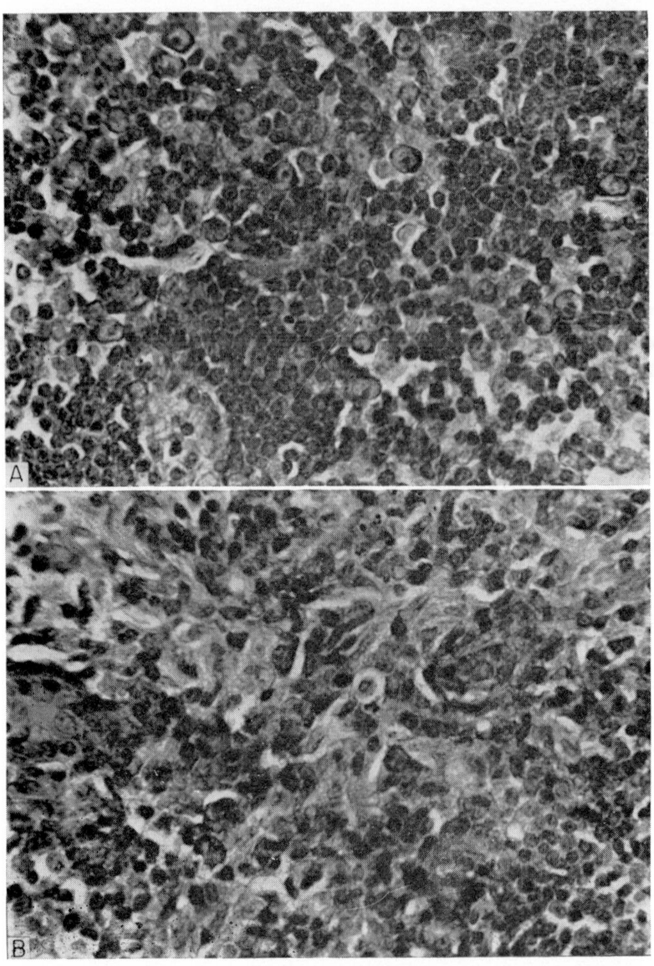

Plate 13.4A. Paraffin section of mouse lymph node showing the histological reaction to a skin graft. Methyl green-pyronin stain. The whole-thickness skin graft from a different pure-line strain of mouse was implanted in the region of the node four days previously. Note the presence of large pyroninophilic haemocytoblasts included among the closely-packed small lymphocytes of a thymus-dependent area. ($\times 760$.)

Plate 13.4B. Paraffin section of mouse lymph node showing the histological reaction in a neonatally-thymectomized mouse to a skin homograft. The conditions of the experiment were the same as those of 13.4A. Note that in this thymectomized animal the thymus-dependent area appears relatively denuded of small lymphocytes and the usual blast cell response has failed to occur.

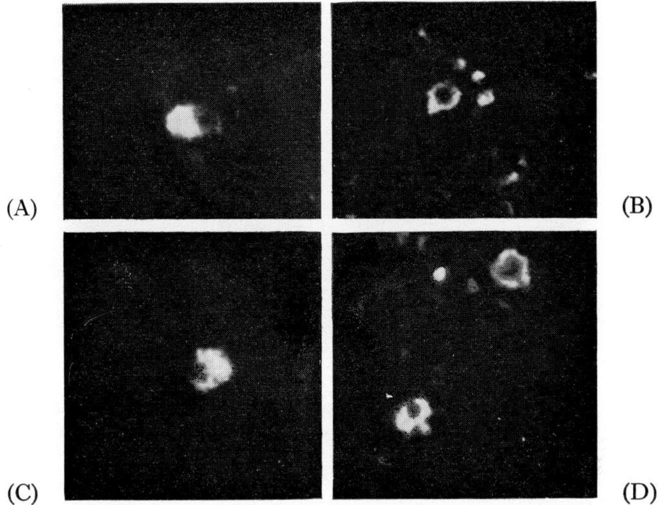

PLATE 15.1. Fluorescence micrograph. Mature and immature plasma cells in the lymph nodes of a case of rheumatoid arthritis. Frozen section treated with fluorescein-labelled heat aggregated human γ-globulin, which reacts with rheumatoid factor. The localization of this is revealed as bright fluorescence present in the cytoplasm of isolated cells and as extracellular granules. [Preparation of Drs J. McCormick and A. G. S. Hill.]

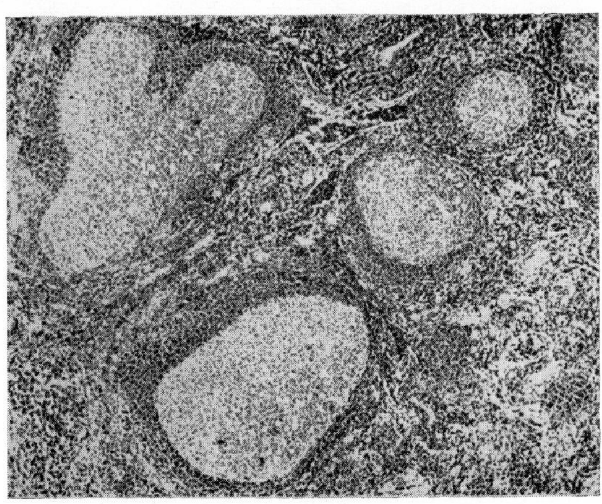

PLATE 15.2. Rheumatoid arthritis. Axillary lymph node showing typical lymphoid hyperplasia. Enlarged lymphoid nodules with very prominent pale germinal centres. Haematoxylin and eosin. [Preparation of Dr A. H. E. Marshall.] ($\times$72).

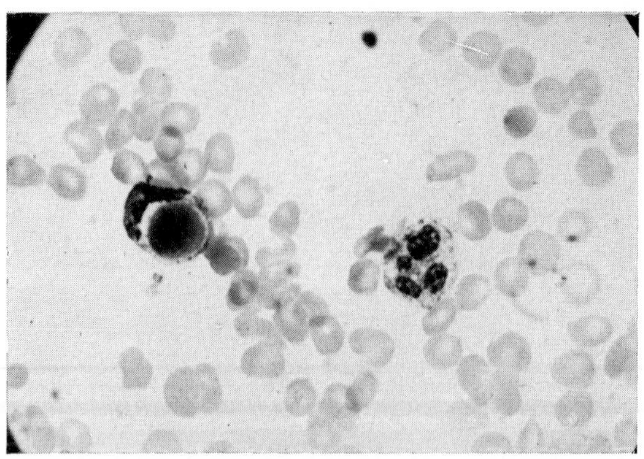

PLATE 15.3. Systemic lupus erythematosus, L.E. cell phenomenon. In the centre is a normal polymorphonuclear neutrophil leucocyte. On the left the polymorph contains a typical L.E. inclusion. (× 1100)

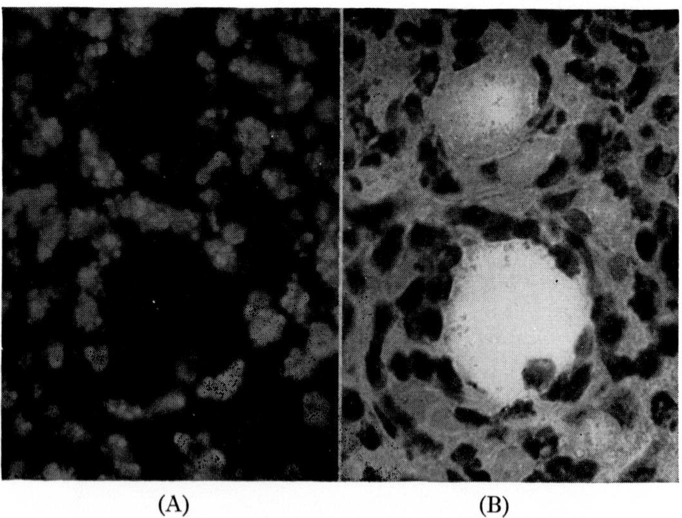

(A) (B)

PLATE 15.4A. Fluorescence micrograph. Reaction between the serum of a case of systemic lupus erythematosus and the nuclei of a frozen section of normal human lymphoid tissue. Localized anti-nuclear factor was revealed by use of second layer of fluorescein-conjugated anti-human γ-globulin. B. Same section as above stained with neutral red to show the pattern of nuclei. (× 800)

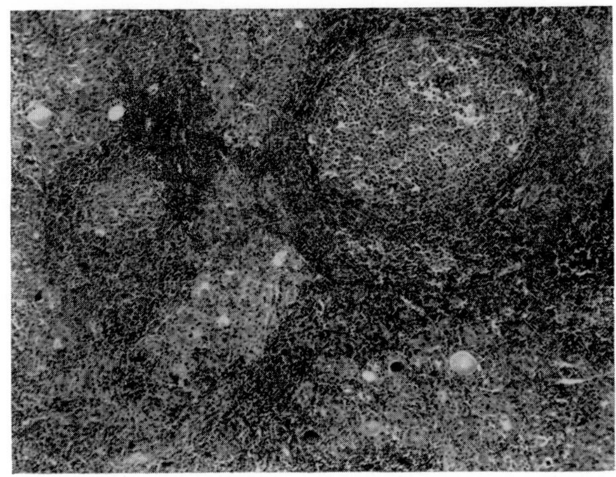

Plate 15.5. Thyroid gland from case of Hashimoto's disease (lymphadenoid goitre). The normal acinar tissue has been largely replaced by dark strands comprising the cells of the infiltrating granuloma (lymphocytes, plasma cells, macrophages). Top right is a lymphoid nodule with germinal centre. The areas of remaining small acini appear as pale islands against the darker granuloma. Haematoxylin and eosin. ($\times$ 60).

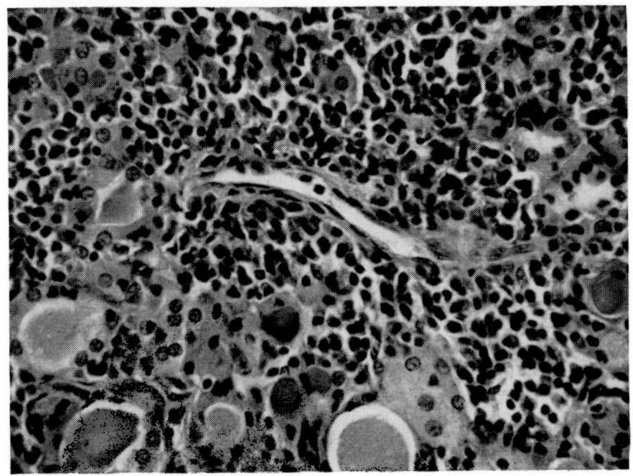

Plate 15.6. High-power view of same thyroid as Plate 15.5. The small distorted acini are surrounded by plasma cells. Centre of field is a venule, which has a broad surrounding zone of lymphocytes and plasma cells. Haematoxylin and eosin. ($\times$ 235).

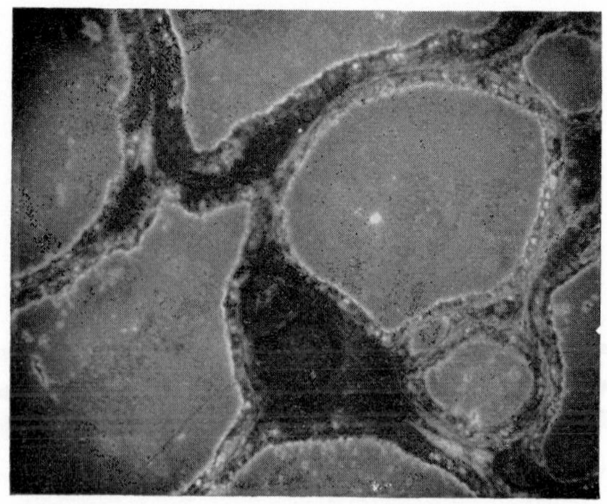

PLATE 15.7. Fluorescence micrograph. Frozen section of a thyroidectomy thyroid, which has almost normal architecture, treated with a fluorescein conjugate of the serum globulin of a patient with Hasimoto's disease. The fluorescence, which indicates the normal distribution of one of the thyroid auto-antigens (thyroglobulin), is localized to intra-follicular colloid and to discrete areas within the acinar cells. (×128). [Reproduced from *Proc. Roy. Soc. Med.* (1956) **50,** 953.]

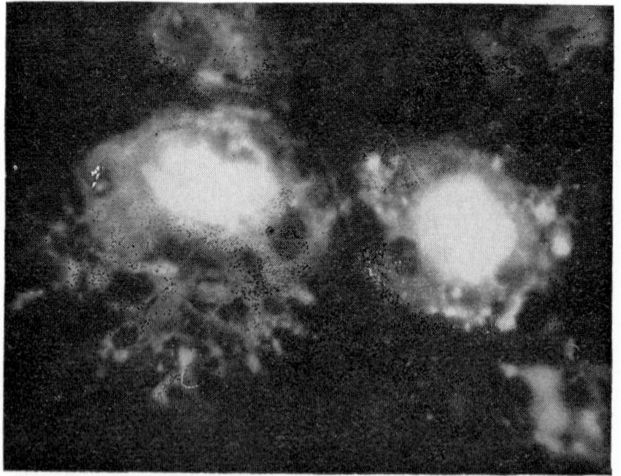

PLATE 15.8. Fluorescence micrograph. Frozen section of thyroid of a patient with Hashimoto's disease, treated with a fluorescein conjugate of the patient's own serum globulin. Two small follicles are lined by faintly fluorescent epithelial cells. Outside the follicles, bright fluorescent spots and streaks are scattered in and among the cells of the granulomatous infiltration and represent antigen which has leaked from within the acini. (×440). [Reproduced from *Proc. Roy. Soc. Med.* (1956) **50,** 953.]

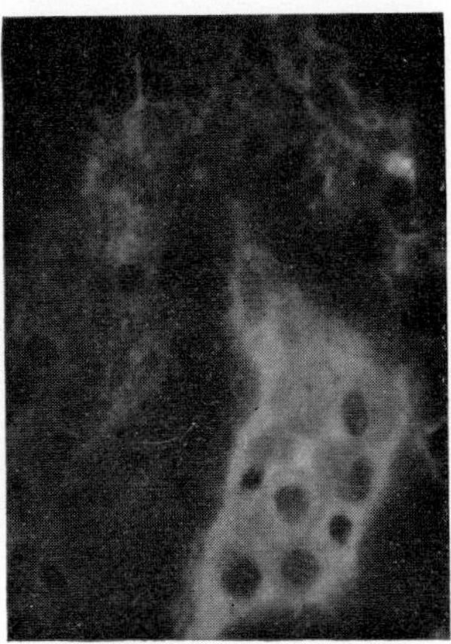

PLATE 15.9. Fluorescence micrograph. Frozen section of thyroid of patient with Hashimoto's disease, treated with a fluorescein conjugate of anti-human γ-globulin. Bright fluorescence corresponds to γ-globulin which has gained entry to the acinar lumen. Also within acinus are several macrophages: 'colloidophages'. ($\times$330).

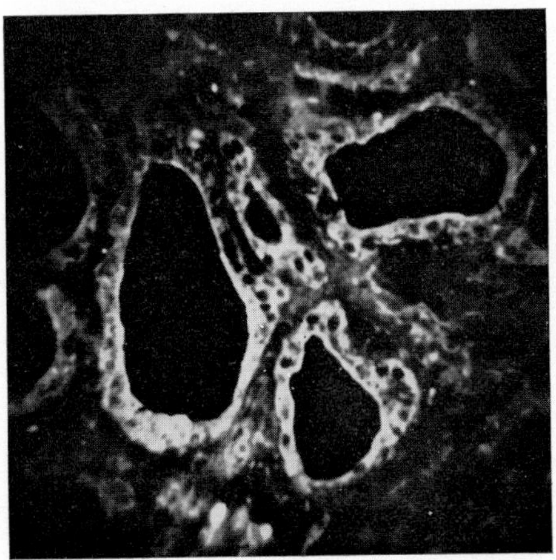

PLATE 15.10. Fluorescence micrograph: unfixed frozen section of a normal human thyroid treated first, with serum from patient with Hashimoto's disease and second, with fluorescein-labelled anti-human γ-globulin. The reaction of the patient's antibody with the epithelial cells of the thyroid acini is shown by specific fluorescence of their cytoplasm. The thyroglobulin-containing colloid, which might have been reactive with other antibodies in the patient's serum, has been washed out of the acini during the manipulation of this unfixed tissue section. ($\times$130).

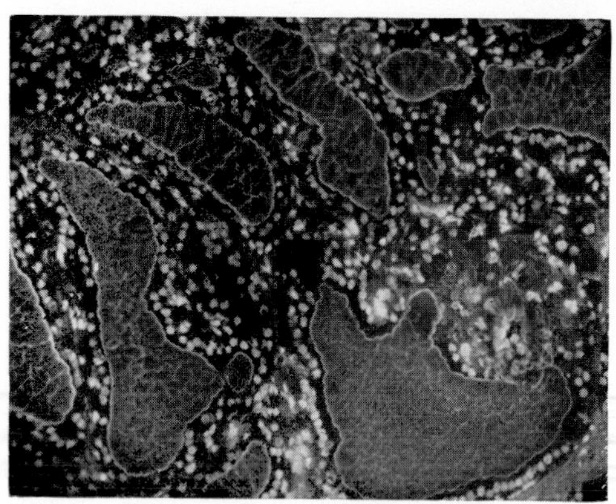

Plate 15.11. Fluorescence micrograph. Demonstration of anti-nuclear factor in serum of patient with Hashimoto's disease. Frozen section of thyroid of a thyroidectomy specimen of normal architecture, treated successively with patient's serum, and with a fluorescein conjugate of anti-human γ-globulin. Note that besides the typical localization of fluorescence to intra-acinar colloid (as in Plate 15.7), localization to the nuclei of the acinar cells has resulted also. ($\times$130).

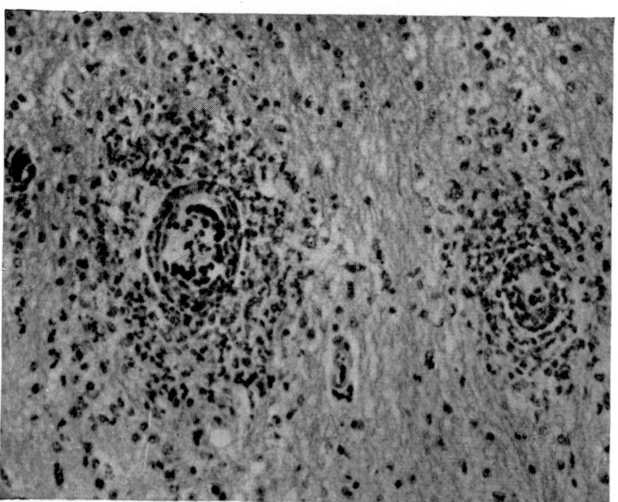

Plate 15.12. Experimental allergic encephalo-myelitis in the guinea-pig. Cuffing of vessels in medulla oblongata by mononuclear cells and occasional polymorphs. Haematoxylin and eosin. ($\times$150). [From White R. G. and Marshall A. H. E. (1958) *Immunology* **1,** 116.]

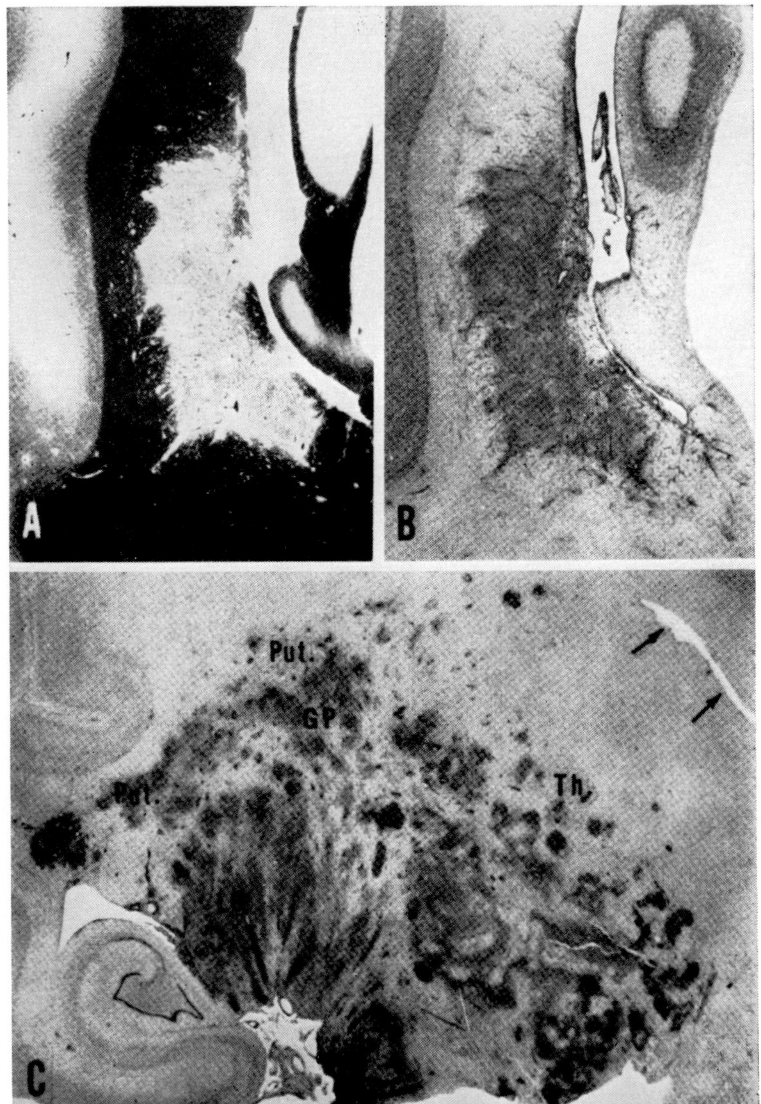

PLATE 15.13. Experimental allergic encephalo-myelitis. A and B. Monkey 25 days after the first inoculation of the brain antigen.

A. Large demyelinated focus in the white matter adjacent to the inferior horn of the lateral ventricle (Woelke myelin stain).

B. Note the orientation of the lesion to the blood vessels. (Cresyl violet stain.)

C. Haemorrhages and granulomata in the basal part of the brain. The body of the lateral ventricle is indicated by arrows. GP, Globus Pallidus; LG, Lateral geniculate body; Put, putamen; Th, thalamus. (Cresyl violet stain.) [From Shiraki H. and Otani S. (1959) in *'Allergic' Encephalo-myelitis*, ed. Kies and Alvord. Thomas, Springfield. P. 58.]

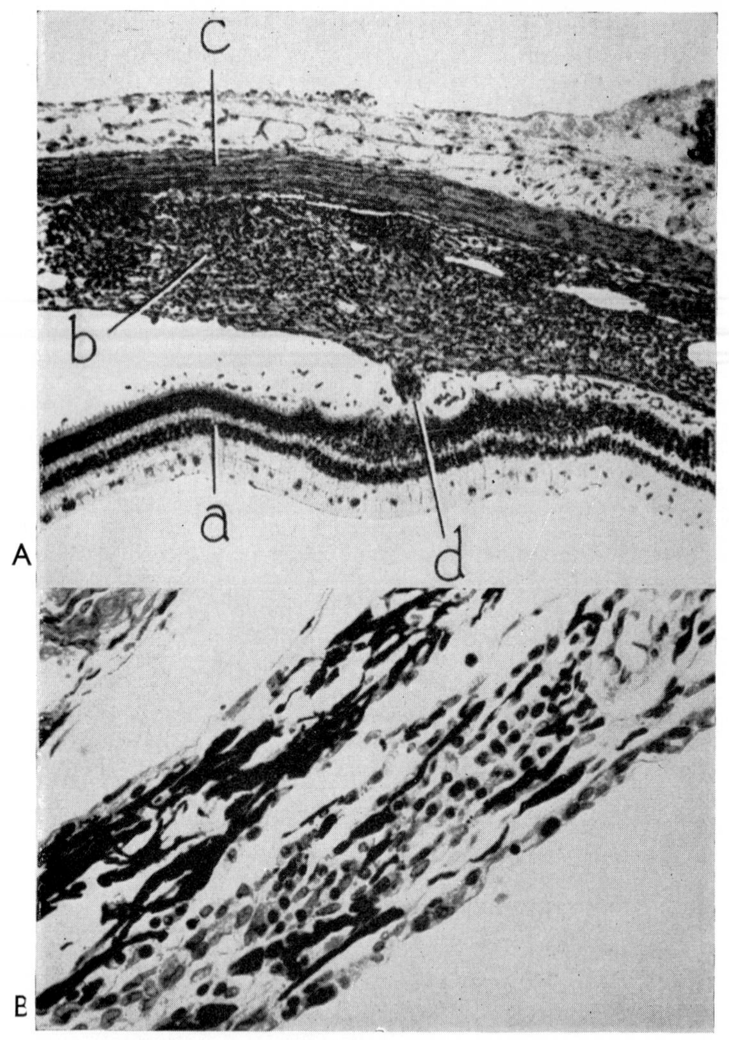

PLATE 15.14. Allergic uveitis in guinea-pig.

A. (*a*) retina, (*b*) nodule of lymphocytes, epithelioid cells and plasma cells, (*c*) sclera, (*d*) Dalen-Fuchs nodule.

B. Early lesion of the same type, also in the guinea-pig. Haematoxylin and eosin. (× 450).

[From R. C. Collins (1953) *Amer. J. Ophthal.* **36,** part II, 150.]

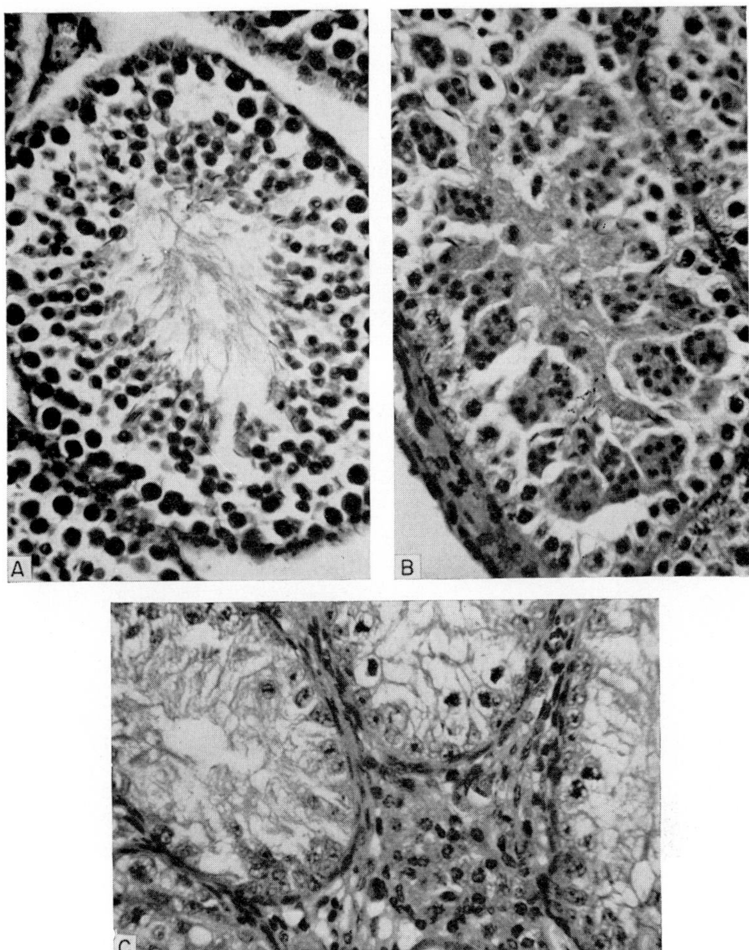

PLATE 15.15. Auto-immune orchitis. Development of histological changes in testes of guinea-pigs given injections of an extract of autoclaved guinea-pig testis with complete Freund-type adjuvant.

A. Seminiferous tubules at 9 days after injection. The histological appearance is normal. (× 200.)

B. 14-day lesion. *Note* the depletion of spermatozoa and aggregation of immature spermatocytes to form multi-nuclear giant cells. [× 200.]

Note also the absence of interstitial cellular infiltration.

C. 28 day lesion. *Note* the atrophy of tubules. At the periphery groups of cells represent the proliferation of Leydig cells.

Interstitial cellular infiltration is a prominent feature. (× 200)

[Preparation of Dr. John Holborow.]

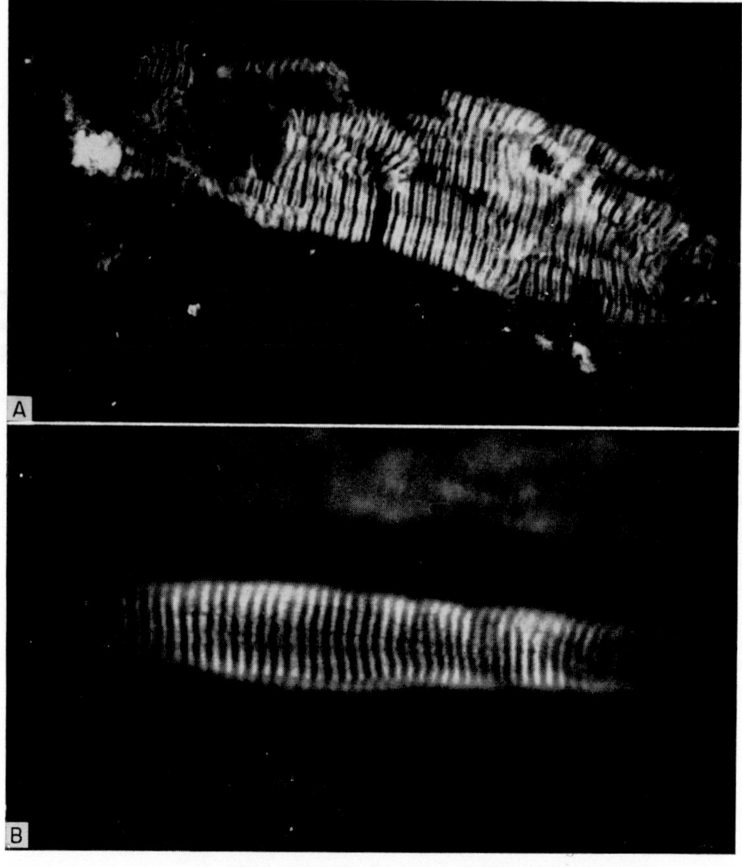

PLATE 15.16. A. Fluorescence micrograph. Section of human skeletal muscle treated with first, serum from patient with myasthenia gravis and second, fluorescein-labelled antibody to human γ-globulin. This result shows double bands of fluorescence which correspond to the A bands with a nonfluorescent dark line in the centre of each (H bands).

B. Fluorescence micrograph. Section of human skeletal muscle treated with first, serum from a *normal individual* and second, fluorescein-labelled antibody to human γ-globulin.

Note bands of fluorescence, which are single and narrower than the double bands in A, and which correspond with the I bands.

A positive result as in (A) is regarded as typical of the serum from cases of myasthenia gravis. The type of result as shown in (B) is obtainable with normal serum and is without diagnostic significance.

[Presentation by Dr. John Vetters.]

plasma cells and germinal centres can be readily induced in the thymus of guinea-pigs by direct injection of antigen into the gland. Alternatively the cellular response in myasthenia could be a spontaneous reaction of lymphoid cells, i.e. a forbidden clone of mutant cells.

The histological changes in the thymus, together with the absence of generalized lymphoid change, indicate that in myasthenia gravis an immune response has arisen in the gland itself, which, if capable of reacting with nerve endings or muscle components, could possibly produce the disease phenomena. It is, therefore, an intriguing fact that thymus contains muscle-like (myoid) cells which share antigenic determinants with skeletal muscle.

One possible target for the aberrant cells or antibodies which may thus originate in the thymus is muscle. There are three kinds of histological pictures which are found in sections from patients of myasthenia gravis: an acute necrosis of myofibres with associated inflammatory cellular reaction, commonly seen in the heart; a progressive atrophy of individual muscle fibres with the formation of local collections of cells (*lymphorrhages*), and in the later stages a simple atrophy of fibres or groups of fibres without alteration of staining reaction or cellular changes of inflammation. The lymphorrhages are collection of lymphocytes, histiocytes and occasional plasma cells. They are not situated with particular relation to the motor end plates. They are almost unique to myasthenia gravis but occasionally are seen in the muscles in rheumatoid arthritis.

The evidence for the occurrence of antibodies directed against muscle in myasthenia derives mainly from the use of the fluorescent antibody method. The more recent findings indicate that all sera (including normal sera) show some reactivity with skeletal muscle, but that the sera from cases of myasthenia gravis showed reactivity in far higher dilutions. Antibodies, reactive in these higher dilutions (>1:60) were found in about one third of cases of myasthenia gravis. All sera reactive under these conditions with muscle also reacted with thymus gland sections, which showed a localization of the resulting fluorescence to the epithelial cells in the medulla of the gland.

The antibodies to muscle have been found reactive with both skeletal and heart muscle. Using the complement-fixation variation of the fluorescent antibody technique (Chapter Nine) positive reactions occurred with skeletal muscle only. Further studies have suggested that two muscle antibodies are present in sera from cases of myasthenia gravis: one, the S antibody, reacts with skeletal muscle and is able to fix complement and the other, the SH antibody, reacts with both skeletal and heart muscle but is not able to fix complement. The constituent of muscle concerned in this reaction is far from clear, but most observers have stressed the fact that the resulting fluorescence of localized antibody occurs as striations which correspond with the A bands of the myofibrils (see Plate 15.15, following p. 660). The distribution pattern would indicate that the antigen could be the contractile protein myosin and antibodies directed specifically to myosin gave a similar pattern of A-band staining in normal skeletal muscle fibres by immunofluorescence. Normal sera (and many sera from myasthenia gravis), on the other hand, produce faint localization to I bands, which are the alternating stretches of the myofibril between the A bands.

The cross reactivity displayed by epithelial cells of the thymus medulla and skeletal muscle is probably explained by the muscle fibre-like (myoid) cells which have been a long-known histological feature of the thymus medulla of many animal species and which resemble striated muscle cells in electron micrographs.

So far it has proved difficult to see how the antibodies against muscle could relate to the defect of transmission at the neuromuscular junction, evidence for which is supported from physiological and pharmacological data. So far, the studies with fluorescent antibody have failed to detect any antibody localization at the neuromuscular junction.

The highest incidence of antibodies against muscle has been found in hospitalized patients with recent severe disease. Almost all myasthenic patients with a tumour of the thymus (thymoma) have antibodies to both muscle and thymus. However, muscle antibodies apparently bear no relation to the occurrence of neonatal myasthenia, since infants have been reported with muscle antibodies derived from the mother without myasthenia, and the latter has occurred in the absence of demonstrable muscle antibodies.

Besides the typical changes, referred to above, a particular type of thymic tumour, the *lympho-epithelioma*, is associated with myasthenia gravis in about 75 per cent of instances. This variety of tumour consists of large spheroidal cells resembling the normal epithelial reticulum of the medulla of the thymus, intermingled with varying proportions of lymphocytes. Germinal centres may be present within the tumour and also in the compressed remnant of normal medulla adjacent to it. The tumours of this type have a constant relation with immunological changes. Hypo-γ-globulinaemia is sometimes found in association with such neoplasms (and at other times with simple hyperplasia of the thymus). Removal of such tumours has occasionally precipitated the appearance of hypo-γ-globulinaemia. Lympho-epithelioma is associated occasionally with auto-immune haemolytic anaemia.

In considering the role of the thymus in the production of auto-immune diseases, including myasthenia gravis, it has already been pointed out that thymectomy at birth fails to prevent the haemolytic anaemia and positive LE tests in NZB and NZB×NZW mice. Indeed, the disease manifestations developed earlier than in the non-thymectomized controls. In man the effect of thymectomy on the myasthenic process has long been the subject of controversy. It now seems to be accepted that the operation is of value in women of less than 40 years with severe disease and in the absence of a thymoma. Possibly those clinical cases with the most fluorid hyper-plastic changes show most improvement.

It has recently been postulated that the basic lesion in the human disease is an auto-allergic '*thymitis*' such as can be induced in guinea-pigs by injecting guinea-pigs with heterologous (calf) thymus *or* muscle in complete Freund's adjuvants. The thymic changes in these animals consisted of zones of lymphocytic infiltration around Hassall's corpuscles in the thymic medulla and in addition the animals developed a myasthenic type of neuromuscular block on electromyography. The neuromuscular block failed to develop in animals which were previously thymectomized, suggesting that this occurred by the release of some inhibitor of neuromuscular trans-mission from the abnormal thymus. In the human disease it is suggested that the 'thymitis' may result from auto-sensitization by a thymoma or that the thymoma itself is symptomatic of such 'thymitis'. It is not, however, clear what would be expected to perform an analogous role to the Freund's adjuvant, and much more will require to be known before this animal model can be accepted as relevant to the problem of myasthenia gravis.

Auto-antibodies to Skin

A patient with dermatitis may be sensitized to extraneous chemicals and develop contact hypersensitivity more readily than a person with a normal skin (Chapter Twelve). The possibility of *auto-sensitization* to skin was first suggested by the dermatologist Whit-field, who concluded from clinical observation, that local skin irritation could provoke a generalized eruption two weeks later.

Auto-allergy to skin has been induced on several occasions in experimental animals, and some authors have described low levels of auto-antibody to skin as a normal occurrence in adult (as opposed to new-born) rabbits and rats and it is postulated that traumatic release of skin auto-antigen may mediate local inflammation through the agency of antigen-antibody complex formation.

Antibodies to skin antigens have been found to occur frequently and to high titre in patients with pemphigus vulgaris, by a method which detects their attachment to a skin section by means of fluorescein-labelled anti-human globulin. The basic histological lesion in all forms of pemphigus is a loss of cohesion between adjacent cells of the pickle-cell layer of the epidermis (a process called *acantholysis*). The antigen is located in the desmosomes between these cells. So far, search has failed to find similar antibodies in normal persons or patients with other diseases, except for some cases of myasthenia gravis. The antibody to *intercellular antigen* occurs in other bullous skin diseases; in a type of pemphigus foliaceus endemic to Brazil and aetiologically distinct from pemphigus vulgaris, intercellular antibody was present in high titre in 93 per cent of sera. A demonstration that the antiserum can damage normal skin to produce bullae is lacking. Similar antibodies, which were reactive *in vitro* with sections of homologous rabbit skin, producing therein a similar intercellular pattern of fluorescence, could be induced by injecting rabbits with oesophageal mucosa. These antibodies did not, however, produce lesions in the skin of the injected rabbit and could not be shown to have become attached to it *in vivo*.

TREATMENT OF AUTO-IMMUNE DISEASES

Since auto-immune diseases result (by definition) from damage to tissues by immunological process it would seem axiomatic that treatment should be directed to effective interference with some associated part of this response, presumably by the use of some kind of *immunosuppressive* drug. At the theoretical level there are many specific methods for suppressing either a humoral or a cell-mediated immunological response. They have been discussed in detail in Chapter Three (under the heading of tolerance) and Chapter Seven (under feed-back inhibition of antibody synthesis) and Chapter Twelve (under immunological deviation and desensitization). Specific immunosuppressive drugs were also discussed in Chapter Thirteen.

Briefly, therapy could make use of any of the following processes:
(i) removal of the immunogen or the adjuvant responsible for the response,
(ii) inhibition of antibody production,
(iii) inhibition of cell-mediated hypersensitivity,
(iv) blocking of chemical mediators, e.g. by anti-histamines or general anti-inflammatory drugs,
(v) removal of complement components (e.g. by snake venom).

In practice possible therapy is limited by the chronic and slowly progressive nature of most auto-immune lesions. Thus, although the corticosteroid drugs have been used predominantly in the past, the risks involved in prolonged treatment, frequently with gradually increasing dosage, come to be greater than the advantages. This will often be the case in a disease such as rheumatoid arthritis or ulcerative colitis. There is no certain and specific *immunological* reason for the success of corticosteroid drugs when they do work, and presumably they depend mainly on their anti-inflammatory activity for their efficacy.

The present expansion in the use of immunosuppressive drugs followed the demonstration (in 1963) of the effectiveness of 6-mercaptopurine in suppressing the primary antibody response and allograft rejection in experimental animals. Soon afterwards the same drug was applied to the treatment of human auto-immune diseases, limited success being reported in acquired haemolytic anaemia and chronic hepatitis. In its modified form of azothioprine and combined with corticosteroid drugs (a regime which had proved effective in maintenance of renal homografts) successful suppression of systemic lupus erythematosus and rheumatoid arthritis have been reported in about 70 per cent of cases. Table 15.2 gives a broad picture of the current experience with purine anti-metabolites in those and other possible auto-immune conditions.

It should not be assumed that the improvement shown in Table 15.2 necessarily stems from an immunosuppressive effect. Indeed, neither nephrosis nor psoriasis, which also show improvement under the same treatment, are acceptable as auto-immune diseases on other evidence. Also, patients who are under treatment with purine anti-metabolites have been simultaneously tested with injections of immunogens, such as keyhole limpet haemocyanin, and found to provoke high titres of antibody in both primary and secondary responses and typical delayed hypersensitivity responses. However

TABLE 15.2

	No. of treated cases	Percentage of improvements
Ulcerative colitis	62	77·5
Rheumatoid arthritis	128	72·2
Chronic and lupoid hepatitis	93	71·0
Auto-immune haemolytic anaemia	82	62·0
Idiopathic thrombocytopenic purpura	83	58·0
Systemic lupus erythematosus	194	56·2
Lupoid nephritis	60	55·5
Chronic glomerulonephritis	167	47·8
*Nephrosis	232	55·2
*Psoriasis	85	85

Modified from data provided by Dr G.B. Elion at WHO Conference on use of anti-metabolites in disease associated with abnormal immune responses (1967)

* Neither nephrosis nor psoriasis are acceptable as auto-immune diseases on present evidence.

(in contrast to whole-body irradiation), immunosuppressive anti-metabolite drugs do predominantly inhibit delayed-type hypersensitivity. In cases of rheumatoid arthritis treated with chlorambucil it was found that in spite of the clinical improvement the incidence of positive LE tests increased.

Two further possible therapeutic approaches need to be mentioned. With several immunosuppressive drugs (such as 6-mercaptopurine, amethopterin and cyclophosphamide) specific tolerance has resulted in animals to antigens which were injected at the same time. This leads to the possibility that use of a suitable intensive and short course of treatment might induce permanent and specific benefit. A further possibility remains that by stimulating the production of certain types of immunoglobulin (such as antibody with enhancing activity) suppression of cell-mediated hypersensitivity could result. Thus it is claimed that the rheumatoid-like arthritis which occurs in association with hypogammaglobulinaemia can be ameliorated by administration of gamma-globulin. Indeed, the use of immunosuppressive drugs may be attended with the danger that they inhibit auto-antibody responses which are themselves protective in function.

FURTHER READING

ACKROYD J.F. (1964) The diagnosis of disorders of the blood due to drug hypersensitivity caused by an immune mechanism. In *Immunological methods*, p. 453 [Ed. Ackroyd J.F.]. Blackwell Scientific Publications, Oxford

ANDERSON J.R., BUCHANAN W.W. & GOUDIE R.B. (1967) *Autoimmunity: Clinical and experimental.* Thomas, Springfield, Ill.

ASHERSON G.L. (1965) 'Auto-immune disease'. *Abstracts of World Medicine* **37,** 289

ASHERSON G.L. (1968) The role of micro-organisms in auto-immune responses. *Progr. Allerg.* **12,** 192

BALDWIN R.W. & HUMPHREY J.H. (1965) Auto-immunity. *A symposium of the 5th Congress of the International Academy of Pathology.* Blackwell Scientific Publications, Oxford

BROWN P.C., GLYNN L.E. & HOLBOROW E.J. (1967) The dual necessity for delayed hypersensitivity and circulating antibody in the pathogenesis of experimental allergic orchitis in guinea-pigs. *Immunology* **13,** 307–14

BURNET F.M. (1961) Auto-immune disease: some general principles. *Post-graduate Medicine* **30,** 91

DACIE J.V. (1962) The haemolytic anaemias, congenital and acquired: Part II, *The auto-immune haemolytic anaemias*, 2nd ed. Churchill, London

DUMONDE D.C. (1966) Tissue specific antigens in *Recent advances in immunology* **5,** p. 245. Academic Press, New York

FIELD J.B. (1962) Insulin resistance in diabetes. *Ann. Rev. Medicine* **13,** 249

GELL P.G.H. & COOMBS R.R.A. (ed.) (1968) *Clinical aspects of immunology.* Blackwell Scientific Publications, Oxford

GLYNN L.E. & HOLBOROW E.J. (1964) *Auto-immunity.* Blackwell Scientific Publications, Oxford

KIES M.W. & ALVORD E.C. (ed.) (1959) *Allergic encephalomyelitis.* Thomas, Springfield, Ill.

KUNKEL H.G. & TAN E.M. (1964) Auto-antibodies and disease in *Advances in Immunology* [Ed. Dixon F.J. and Humphrey J.H.] **4,** p. 351. Academic Press, New York

LEVINE L. & STOLLER B.D. (1968) Nucleic acid immune systems. *Progr. Allerg.* **12,** 161–91

MIESCHER P.A. & GRABAR P. (eds) (1968) Immunopathology: Vth International Symposium 1967. Schwabe, Basel

PATERSON P.Y. (1966) Experiment allergic encelphalomyelitis and auto-immune disease. In *Advances in Immunology* **5,** p. 131. Academic Press, New York

ROITT I.M. & DONIACH D. (1965) Autoimmunity and disease. In *The Scientific Basis of Medicine Reviews.* Athlone Press, London

SAMTER M. (ed.) (1965) *Immunologic diseases.* Little Brown, Boston

THOMAS L. (1964) Mechanisms of Tissue Damage in Diseases Involving Hypersensitivity in *The Streptococcus, Rheumatic Fever and Glomerulonephritis* [Ed. Uhr J.W.]. Williams & Wilkins, Baltimore

WAKSMAN B.H. (1962) Auto-immunization and the lesions of auto-immunity. *Medicine* **41,** 93

ZABRISKIE J.B. (1967) Mimetic relationships between Group A streptococci and mammalian tissues in *Advances in Immunology* **7,** p. 147. Academic Press, New York

CHAPTER SIXTEEN

Prophylactic Immunization and Serotherapy

THERE are few people in our society who would not accept that the minds and skill of children and adults should be educated so as to fit them to encounter the common ideas and the general tasks which they will meet in the community in which they develop, and that to leave this process to chance and haphazard experience alone is insufficient. For the immunologist and the physician the same applies to equipping the growing child with the immunological experience required to make a sufficiently rapid response to overcome the common diseases which he will meet as he grows up. Fortunately in the case of a number of the more important diseases the provision of an immunological education has become a relatively simple and tear-free process. The essential requirements are that active immunization with suitably potent agents should be begun early; that the administration be repeated after a suitable interval (in man usually not less than one month) so as to produce a good secondary response; and that immunity be restimulated at intervals which depend upon the nature of the immunizing antigen, and the time course of the infection which it is intended to combat. The rationale underlying these requirements has been outlined briefly in Chapter Ten.

A brief description will be given of the commoner and more useful forms of vaccine or therapeutic antiserum, together with a suggested schedule of immunization. For reasons of space the presentation must be brief and somewhat dogmatic. Nevertheless, it is important to be aware that constant efforts are being made to improve the efficacy and quality of the materials used, and that the schedules suggested often represent a compromise between what is practicable and what is most desirable. The mother must not be expected to bring her baby up for inoculation more often than is absolutely necessary, and there is a limit to the number of pricks which even army recruits will stand.

Before considering individual vaccines in detail there are three general points which require discussion, namely the rate of development of the capacity to make immunoglobulins in young infants; the effect of maternal immunity on the antibody response of the baby; and the possibility of simultaneous immunization against several disease agents.

DEVELOPMENT OF IMMUNOLOGICAL CAPACITY IN THE INFANT

It has been explained in Chapter Eight that some newborn animals, such as human babies, are born with plasma levels of immunoglobulin (IgG-, but not IgA- or IgM-) similar to those of their mothers as a result of transfer across the placenta before birth; that others, such as piglets or calves, are born without immunoglobulin but rapidly acquire IgG- and IgA-globulin after ingestion of colostrum; and that others, such as mice and rats, obtain some immunoglobulin before birth and some by suckling. In order to find out at what age and to what extent immunoglobulins begin to be made by the babies themselves, it would be necessary either to allow accurately for the pre-existing globulins (i.e. to know their rates of breakdown and dilution as the baby grows) or to study newborn animals which for some reason (e.g. by deprivation of colostrum, in the case of ungulates) are not supplied with immunoglobulins from the mother. This has been done in experimental animals. In man some information has been obtained from studies of babies born to mothers with hypogammaglobulinaemia, who begin life with very little immunoglobulin of their own. Significant amounts were not found in the babies' plasma until the fourth to twelfth week, and normal levels (600–1,100 mg/100 ml) were not reached until at least 6 months, and sometimes much later. These findings fit well with the observation that the immunoglobulin levels in infants born to normal mothers fall steadily during the first months of life (the period during which maternal globulin is catabolized and diluted by growth, and during which little new synthesis occurs). They also accord with the finding that lymph nodes of newborn infants have poorly developed lymphoid nodules, and that germinal centres and medullary foci of plasma cells are almost completely absent.

On the basis of these facts it might be expected that the capacity of infants to make antibody would be less than that of adults. In practice the truth of this prediction depends upon the potency of the antigen preparation. It has been shown, for example, that even premature infants can respond to powerful antigen stimuli, such as typhoid vaccine, by making some macroglobulin antibody. Although the response to alum precipitated diphtheria toxoid is delayed in very young infants, it becomes normal when the toxoid is given at about 2–4 months. Similarly, early studies of the response to relatively small amounts of killed poliomyelitis vaccines showed that infants aged less than two months gave weaker antibody responses than did older children. However, these differences were much less in later studies in which larger amounts of virus preparations were used. Thus it appears that in response to adequate antigenic stimuli young infants can make antibodies. The quantities of immunoglobulin represented by these antibodies, however, are small and do not raise the level of circulating immunoglobulin significantly.

EFFECT OF MATERNAL IMMUNITY

The above studies of the immunological capacity in early life were made on infants which had not received the specific antibodies in question from their mothers. What happens when maternal antibody is present? In man the levels of antibody in the maternal circulation and the cord blood at birth are about equal, and consequently a baby born to a mother who has a high level of antibody will share this level with her. Unless the baby is stimulated to make antibody of its own, the antibody level declines by about half every 21 days, and after 6–9 months no detectable antibody will remain. At present few mothers possess much antibody against tetanus toxin, for example, but a considerable proportion have been immunized against diphtheria toxin and poliomyelitis virus. Some careful research has been carried out under the auspices of the Medical Research Council to discover how an infant, already immunized by maternally transmitted antibody against these antigens, will respond to a course of immunization with them when this is begun at various times after birth. The findings may be generalized as follows: maternally transmitted antibody can inhibit the antibody response to antigens such as poliomyelitis vaccine, or to diphtheria toxoid or pertussis vaccine (even when these are mixed with an adjuvant). The degree of inhibition depends upon the level of pre-existing antibody and on the antigenic potency of the preparations. In the absence of antibody, even when a course of two- or three-monthly injections of a potent antigen is begun as early as the first week after birth, a good antibody response is usually elicited. When the amount of maternal antibody is quite small there may be little or no interference with the response, but when the amount is large (for example, more than 0·5 units/ml of diphtheria antitoxin or an agglutinin titre against pertussis of 16 or over) there may be no apparent response at all. However, even when no evident primary response was elicited, the response to a booster injection of antigen a year later is considerably greater than in a child which had no previous contact with the specific antigen. Tetanus toxoid, diphtheria toxoid and pertussis vaccine, especially when an adjuvant is added, are potent antigens in the sense used above; so are killed formalin-treated poliomyelitis vaccines of Types II and II. Potent vaccines prepared from poliomyelitis Type I are less readily prepared, but this has been achieved in recent years.

The infant during the first year of life is particularly at risk from poliomyelitis or pertussis infection. Consequently there is value in beginning immunization early in life with three spaced injections (which are much more effective than two), even though better initial responses are elicited by postponing immunization—especially with poliomyelitis vaccine—until the child is 6 or 9 months old. Although the risk of severe tetanus or diphtheria is not high in the first year of life, it is argued that a mother is more likely to bring her child for completion of an immunizing course which she knows already to have begun than she is to bring it for the first time at an older age, when the injunctions of the doctor or the clinic have begun to be forgotten and other cares have intruded themselves. Furthermore, valuable protection will have been given to many of the children by the early course. Since a booster injection at around 1 year almost invariably gives rise to an excellent immunological response in such children, this approach appears to be both logical and desirable. It is also arguable, with equal logic but with a perhaps more optimistic estimate of the willingness of mothers to bring their children for injection and a more pessimistic assessment of future improvements in poliomyelitis antigens, that immunization with diphtheria, pertussis and tetanus should be done in infancy and that poliomyelitis immunization should be postponed until after the age of 6 months.

MIXED ANTIGENS

Although it is nowadays usual to combine various immunizing agents in a single injection, it is important to realize that this can only safely be done after considerable preliminary research. Experience has shown that it is unwarranted to assume that when a mixture is made of two or more materials, each of which will produce a reasonably predictable and satisfactory degree of immunity when injected singly, the effect of the materials will be additive. The response to one may in fact diminish that to the others, or one (e.g. pertussis vaccine) may enhance antibody production to other constituents, and may also at the same time changed the nature of the response so that a greater degree of delayed-type hypersensitivity results. The ingredients of *combined prophylactics*, as such mixtures are known, have to be chosen, and their quantities adjusted with care to ensure that what is judged as an adequate response is produced to each—a process which usually involves compromise.

For the sake of simplicity each prophylactic agent is treated below separately, but the practical immunization schedules for routine immunization suggested at the end of this section are based on the use of combined prophylactics which have been proved efficacious.

IMMUNIZATION WITH SPECIFIC PROPHYLACTICS

DIPHTHERIA

Purified toxin treated with formalin (formol toxoid, FT) forms the basis of all preparations in use today. Its antigenic effect is increased, and the number of injections necessary is cut down by adsorption on to aluminium hydroxide (to give APT) or on to hydrated aluminium phosphate (to give PTAP, purified toxoid aluminium phosphate). The latter is a less variable and slightly more powerful prophylactic. The virtual disappearance of diphtheria in Britain between 1941 and 1951 was largely due to immunization of the child population with two doses of diphtheria APT.

On general grounds, the earlier the immunization the better, even though in the first three months or so the maternally transmitted antitoxin may interfere with the immune response to injected toxoid. This effect can be overcome by the use of a larger dose of toxoid. Routine immunization of infants starting at 3 months or earlier is advised. In practice, diphtheria prophylaxis is often started at 2 months, along with pertussis vaccine.

A single boosting dose (formol toxoid) is given at the time of entry to school, and another booster dose at the age of 9 to 11 years. The reason for using formol toxoid rather than APT or PTAP for the boosting doses is that statistical evidence has been collected to show that when alum-containing vaccines are given during epidemics of poliomyelitis there is a small but significantly increased risk of paralysis affecting the injected limb. Vaccines containing *H. pertussis* also appear to have a similar effect. The consensus of opinion among persons concerned with immunization programmes is that it is necessary to use an adjuvant along with formol toxoid in order to ensure adequate immunization with the two first doses, and since these should be given at an early age, when the risk of poliomyelitis is low, APT or PTAP are recommended.

Older children or adults immunized with the usual diphtheria prophylactics sometimes exhibit delayed-type reactions of varying degrees of severity. This is particularly likely to occur after actual infection by the diphtheria bacillus in earlier life. It has been found that such reactions are less common when Toxoid–Antitoxin Floccules (toxoid combined with a quantity of antitoxin slightly less than the equivalence ratio, TAF) are used, and for this reason TAF is recommended by some authorities when the first immunization is delayed.

Before immunizing adults it is usual to look for the presence of antitoxin, indicating previous prophylactic immunization or clinical or subclinical diphtheria, by means of the Schick Test (Glossary, p. 721).

TETANUS

Tetanus toxoid prepared by formaldehyde treatment of purified tetanus toxin is invariably used. It is a fairly potent antigen, even without added adjuvants, and its administration is singularly free from any unpleasant reactions. Immunization may be begun at any age, but since the risk of tetanus is present at all ages it is advisable in infancy. In man immunity dependent on the presence of antitoxin in the blood rarely occurs naturally and does not follow recovery from the natural disease, presumably since paralytic doses of tetanus toxin are nevertheless below the threshold for immunization. The usual course consists of two injections separated by an interval of 6 to 12 weeks, followed by a third injection 6 to 18 months later. Further boosting doses at five-yearly intervals will ensure that a high level of immunity is retained, but persons likely to be exposed to a special risk of tetanus (such as soldiers on active service or stablemen) should receive boosting doses more often.

When a wound, such as may carry a risk of tetanus, occurs in a person who is immune to tetanus (i.e. within 6 months of a second injection or within 5 years of a third injection of tetanus vaccine, spaced as described above) the treatment consists simply in administering a single further dose of toxoid intramuscularly. This is because the antibody response is so rapid in the immune person that it will occur before there is time for any *Cl. tetani* in the wound to elaborate significant amounts of toxin. The efficacy of such treatment was amply demonstrated by the extraordinarily low incidence of tetanus in those armies in the Second World War which relied solely on active immunization.

Otherwise the prevention of tetanus in persons already wounded depends upon the following principles:

(i) Prompt and thorough wound toilet should aim to convert a possible 'anaerobic' wound into a clean, well-drained area which is free from foreign bodies and necrotic tissue. In clean superficial wounds which are treated soon after their infliction it may be unreasonable to insist on specific protective measures.

(ii) Reliance may be placed on proper wound débridement plus treatment with an antibiotic which would normally be a long-acting preparation of penicillin (Ministry of Health Memo., 1964). This would be the recommended treatment in cases with history of severe reaction to injections of antitoxin. However, difficulties may arise in practice since strains of *Clostridium tetani* vary in their sensitivity to penicillin and the infection may include bacteria which destroy penicillin by penicillinase production. Also, with certain types of wound the antibiotic may penetrate inadequately to the site of infection.

The antibiotic should be given at the time of injury and the dosage maintained until healing is virtually complete. When treatment of the wound has been delayed for more than six hours, or the wound is such that adequate concentration of antibiotic may not reach the site of infection, or the wound is heavily contaminated, antitoxin should be given in addition to antibiotic. In experiments designed to test this point, infected animals were submitted to delayed treatment with either antibiotics or horse antitoxin and the superiority of the latter was clear.

(iii) When a person is not known to be immune, or is incompletely immunized, 1500 units of tetanus antitoxin must be given intramuscularly to confer temporary passive immunity. The dose is not reduced for a child. The injection should be repeated at weekly intervals as long as the risk of tetanus persists. In certain countries homologous (human) tetanus antitoxin is available and can be used for such prophylaxis, especially in cases in which hypersensitivity reactions to horse serum proteins is probable. In the same circumstances, and when human serum is not available, hypersensitivity reactions may be avoided by a switch to bovine tetanus antitoxin, which is reported to give only rarely reactions in those who have previously reacted to horse serum.

(iv) It is desirable that patients who receive passive immunization should also be actively immunized against tetanus with toxoid at the first opportunity. Theoretically this is best done 6–8 weeks afterwards, by which time no passive immunity due to the antitoxin is likely to remain. Second or repeated prophylactic treatments with horse antitoxin are to be avoided since, apart from the increased risk of anaphylaxis, the second dose will be promptly destroyed by an immunological response against the foreign protein (see p. 701). It is therefore dangerous to rely for protection on repeated doses of antitoxin.

(v) *Concurrent active and passive immunization.* Since the above recommendation that active immunization shall be given at some time after the use of passive protection may prove to be inconvenient or impracticable the use of aluminium phosphate precipitated tetanus toxoid (PAPT) or aluminium hydroxide precipitated toxoid (APT) as a more powerful stimulus than soluble toxoid has been recommended for use at the same time as passive protection with antitoxin. Thus, 1500 units of tetanus antitoxin may be injected into one arm intramuscularly and followed immediately with an injection into the other arm of 0·5 ml of PAPT. This procedure would normally be followed 6–12 weeks later by a booster dose of 0·5 ml of PAPT.

(vi) *Combined antibiotic and active immunization.* Evidence has been provided recently that the combination of antibiotic protection with a long-acting penicillin preparation and active immunization with PAPT or APT at the time of injury may act in the previously non-immune subject to prevent tetanus spores from germinating until adequate active immunity has developed.

Reasons for Advocating Active Immunization Against Tetanus

Many fatal cases of tetanus result from wounds in non-immune persons which are not regarded as serious enough for propylactic antitoxin, e.g. stab wounds from thorns or insect bites, and may not even have brought the patient to see a doctor. Active immunization is of especial value in the case of patients with atopy since the necessity for serum prophylaxis in the event of wounding is avoided and the chance of hypersensitivity reactions is avoided. In any case, a person who has received prophylactic antitoxin should be subsequently given active immunization with a course of tetanus toxoid. This is best done 6 to 8 weeks afterwards, by which time no passive immunity due to the antitoxin is likely to remain.

WHOOPING-COUGH (PERTUSSIS)

There is little doubt that when vaccines are used which are properly prepared from a mixture of freshly isolated, fully virulent phase I strains which are carefully killed by formalin or merthiolate, immunity can be obtained. However, there is reason to believe that many of the vaccines used in the past were useless. The Medical Research Council's (1959) report has shown that vaccination caused a reduction of 80 per cent in the incidence of the disease and that the cases occurring in the vaccinated group were on the average less severe and of shorter duration than in the control group.

In view of the severity and the prevalence of whooping-cough in infants early protection is obviously desirable. Many authorities now recommend that the first injection of the course should be given at 2 or 3 months of age, followed by two further injections at monthly intervals.

The question of booster doses is debatable. One may be required at school entry age, but from the available figures it is clear that pertussis is a killing disease only in the first year of life, and at 5 years the average child should be in a position to cope with an attack of pertussis unaided.

Alum-precipitated vaccines have not been used by the Medical Research Council as yet, but as the alum may have an adjuvant effect they have been preferred in some American trials. However, when such vaccines are used at the time of poliomyelitis epidemics occasional cases of paralysis occur, particularly in the injected limb, and there is statistical evidence relating this to the injections.

Besides a possible risk of aggravation of poliomyelitis, pertussis vaccination is complicated very rarely by encephalitis attended by convulsions. Also minor systemic reactions involving the nervous system have been reported 6 to 12 hours after an injection.

TUBERCULOSIS

In Britain BCG ('Bacille Calmette-Guérin') vaccine is commonly used, although vole-bacillus vaccine has also been employed, BCG vaccine consists of living bacteria derived from an attenuated bovine strain, which is of such low virulence that when injected into the highly susceptible guinea-pig it multiplies at the injection site and in the draining lymph node for some weeks, but produces neither generalized tuberculosis nor death of the animal, and the bacilli are eventually killed by the host.

The original route of administration used by Calmette was by mouth, but the vaccine is nowadays given intracutaneously (if given subcutaneously an abscess is more likely to develop). The dose is 0·05 to 0·1 mg in 0·1 ml volume, which is injected into the skin over the deltoid region, using a 'tuberculin' syringe with a fine short-bevelled needle. Normally, a bluish-red papule develops at the injection site after about 3 weeks, increases slowly up to about 5 weeks and then subsides. Occasionally the skin may ulcerate.

In recent years, vaccination by a percutaneous method has been practised, and it is claimed to be simpler and less likely to cause troublesome local lesions. The original Birkhaug apparatus is a spring-activated instrument making forty simultaneous punctures. A small filter paper impregnated with BCG vaccine is placed on the arm, and the punctures are then made through it. The needles are set to penetrate to a depth of 2–3 mm. Heaf's modification, now used in this country, has only six needles and is simpler to use.

Although in some countries infants are routinely given BCG soon after birth, vaccination is usually offered in this country to hospital nursing and medical staff, to medical students, and to contacts of known cases of tuberculosis. Controlled trials organized by the

Medical Research Council have shown that in such groups (which include the young adult age group which is most susceptible to tuberculosis), BCG vaccination confers substantial protection against clinical infection for at least six and a half years. There is also evidence that such vaccination gives a measure of protection against infection by other acid-fast organisms such as the leprosy bacillus. Before BCG is administered to a child or an adult it is essential to find out whether the individual is sensitive to tuberculoprotein, since an already sensitive person may have a severe reaction. For this purpose the Mantoux test described below is generally used.

BCG vaccine has been issued in liquid form, but this has the minor disadvantage that the vaccine must be stored in a refrigerator and the major disadvantage that it deteriorates rapidly and must be used within 14 days of manufacture. For these reasons freeze-dried BCG vaccine is likely to become more popular, since this can be kept for a week or so (before being reconstituted) at room temperature, and retains its potency adequately for at least a year in the refrigerator.

The Mantoux Test

This test gives a measure of the degree of delayed-type hypersensitivity of an individual towards tuberculoprotein, and is an indication that he or she has had a past or has a present infection with tubercle bacilli. The underlying histological changes which occur in a positive test are discussed in Chapter Twelve. The test is performed by injecting intracutaneously 0·1 ml of a standardized solution of tuberculoproteins, which is prepared either from Old Tuberculin (OT; a concentrated filtrate from cultures of human or bovine strains) or from Tuberculin Purified Protein Derivative (Tuberculin PPD; a preparation of partially purified protein from the culture filtrate from human strains). The amount injected is defined in terms of Tuberculin Units, which are related to the activities of the International Standard Preparations. One tuberculin unit is the activity contained in 1/100,000 ml of the standard OT, or in 0·000028 mg of the Standard Tuberculin PPD. A feature of tuberculo-protein is that it adsorbs rather readily on to glass, and consequently not only must extra careful precautions be taken in cleaning glassware which has contained tuberculoprotein, but also when dilutions are used containing less than 1000 units per ml these must be freshly prepared from a concentrated stock solution.

It is advisable to use a very small dose, 10 tuberculin units or even less, for a first test, since tuberculin-sensitive patients may develop severe reactions with higher doses. A positive reaction consists in the development at the injection site (forearm) of induration and surrounding erythema which becomes apparent after 12 hours and reaches its maximum size at 48 to 72 hours. The usually accepted criterion is that the area of induration should measure at least 6 mm in diameter when examined at 48 hours. If the subject does not react to so small a dose, one or more further tests should be done with larger doses, until no reaction is obtained to 100 units. Only then may an individual be regarded as tuberculin negative.

In children's clinics it is sometimes more convenient to employ the 'patch' test. The skin is carefully cleaned with acetone, and gauze impregnated with a solution of OT in a jelly is applied under plaster and left in contact for 48 hours. When the gauze is removed a tuberculin-sensitive child will show a red, slightly raised area at the site of contact with the gauze. A positive reaction is reliable, but negative reactors require confirmation by an intracutaneous test.

Occasionally in medical practice, but more commonly in veterinary practice, a question arises whether a positive tuberculin test indicates infection with a particular type of mycobacterium (e.g. *M. tuberculosis* of human, bovine or avian strains, or *Mycobacterium balnei* or *ulcerans*, or, in cattle, *Mycobacterium johnei*), and tuberculin preparations have been made from these different organisms in the hope that the intensity of the skin response to the particular tuberculin from the infecting organism will be greater than those to other tuberculins. In practice it is found that there are extensive cross-reactions between the different preparations. Until it has proved possible to standardize one preparation in terms of another, in animals which are infected with each separate organism, it will remain unjustifiable (except possibly in very practised hands) to interpret such skin tests as indicating infection with any particular strain of mycobacterium.

It has recently been called in question whether weak reactions to 100 TU indicate in all cases that the subject has been infected with human or bovine tubercle bacilli, or whether contact with saprophytic acid-fast bacilli could be responsible. The evidence indicates that, at least in this country, such weak positive reactions should be regarded as due to *Mycobacterium tuberculosis*.*

* It should be remembered that the tuberculin test may be negative in severe cachexia or in cases of rapidly advancing tuberculosis.

SMALLPOX

Vaccination involves the introduction of vaccinia (cowpox) virus into the epidermal cells. Prior to the work of Jenner (end of eighteenth century) 'variolation' was practised. This involved the introduction into the skin of live variola virus obtained from the vesicles of a mild case of smallpox. (See page 2.)

Smallpox vaccine is nowadays commonly prepared from vaccinia virus which has been maintained alternately on the skin of a rabbit and the skin of a sheep or a calf (the purpose of such alternation being to prevent simultaneous selection of other organisms peculiar to the sheep or calf from which the final vaccine is prepared). The virus is scarified into a wide area of cleaned and shaved skin and material from the mature vesicular eruption is collected by means of a sharp spoon and is ground up and suspended in 1 per cent phenol (to kill any bacteria). Glycerol is added and the vaccine stored at $-10°C$. When kept at this temperature the lymph retains its potency for months but if stored at temperatures over $-10°C$ must be used within 7 days. Smallpox vaccine in this form is often known as glycerinated lymph.

Smallpox vaccine is also prepared by growing vaccinia virus in embryonated eggs or in tissue culture of suitable cells such as bovine amnion. The virus obtained in this way is free from bacteria, and can be purified so as to be relatively free from other materials. Such purified material may be freeze-dried, and in this form it may be kept for long periods at a temperature below 10°. Suitable material contains in each ml not less than 100 million infective units for the chick embryo chorio-allantoic membrane.

Vaccination is carried out by first preparing a clean area of skin, usually at the posterior border of the deltoid, with soap and water or an ether-soaked swab. A small drop of vaccine is placed on the skin and inoculated into the epidermis by a single scratch about 1 cm long or by the multiple pressure method. After a couple of minutes the excess lymph can be wiped away with a sterile gauze swab. No dressing need be applied.

The primary vaccination will be followed by the appearance at the third or fourth day of a red elevated papule with surrounding hyperaemia which progresses within a day or so to form a vesicle. This enlarges, becomes umbilicated and increases gradually to the ninth day, when the lesion becomes pustular (see Fig. 16.1). There may be

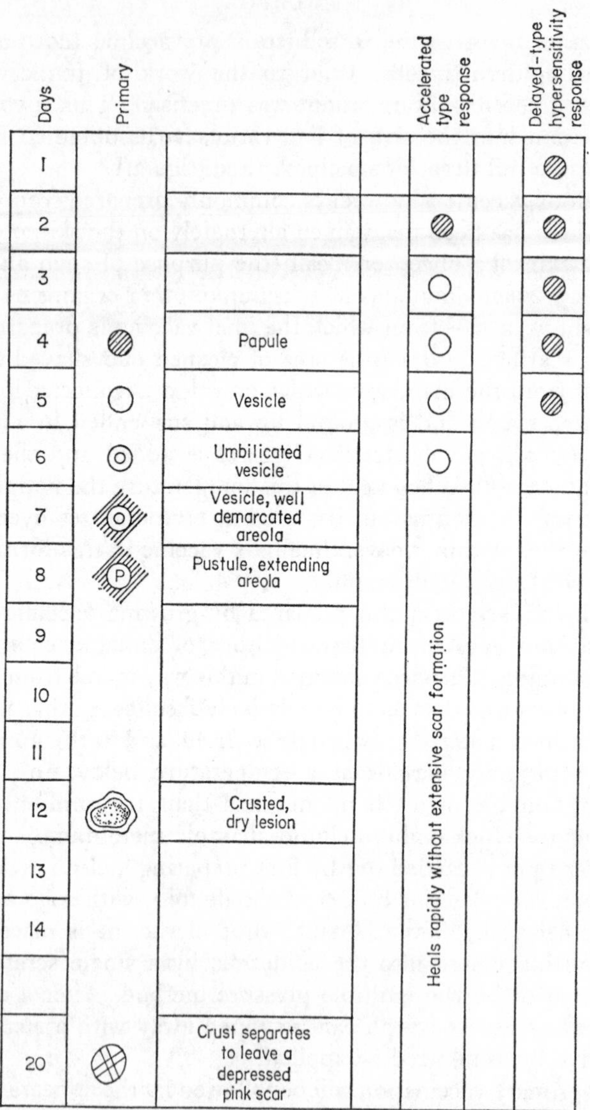

FIG. 16.1 Diagram to illustrate the time course of different reactions to smallpox vaccination.

some pyrexia and tender lymph nodes may be palpable in the axilla.

Revaccination after a successful primary 'take' in early life may result in events which are indistinguishable from those given above, especially if more than 10 years separate the two vaccinations. More commonly a 'vaccinoid' or accelerated response results in which the same events evolve more quickly and are lessened at each stage. A third type of reaction occurs, particularly in those who have been often and quite recently vaccinated. It has been called the 'early', the 'immediate' or 'immune' reaction. The term immediate is very unfortunate since the reaction would appear to be fundamentally a 'delayed-type hypersensitivity response' to the proteins of the vaccine. The term 'immune' is also misleading and it is unwise to accept this type of reaction as indicating the possession of immunity to vaccinia virus. Only vaccination which results in vesiculation should be accepted as successful.

The altered reactions seen in previously vaccinated persons were noted and carefully described by Jenner (Figs. 16.2(a) and 16.2(b)). They depend upon the resultant of two processes: (1) a decreased ability of the virus to infect and destroy the epidermal cells, and (2) an increased ability to give a delayed-type response to the proteins in the infected glycerinated calf lymph. To Jenner may perhaps be ascribed the first description of a delayed-type hypersensitivity reaction.

After successful vaccination immunity to variola major is probably complete for three years, although individuals vary. Thereafter the risk of infection on exposure increases with each year until there is virtually no protection 20 years after primary vaccination. The risk of death from smallpox, however, is greatly diminished even very many years after successful vaccination.

Complications of Vaccination

Sometimes bacterial infection of the site of vaccination may occur. The common invaders are staphylococci and streptococci but rarely tetanus has followed vaccination. In persons of negro ancestry there may be a tendency to keloid formation.

Generalized Vaccinia: Although the virus is believed to reach the bloodstream in most individuals either at the time of vaccination or later during the period of the primary response, it is only very rarely that a generalized eruption results. However, generalized vaccinial lesions may occur during the second week after vaccination,

AN

INQUIRY

INTO

THE CAUSES AND EFFECTS

OF

THE VARIOLÆ VACCINÆ,

A DISEASE

DISCOVERED IN SOME OF THE WESTERN COUNTIES OF ENGLAND,

PARTICULARLY

GLOUCESTERSHIRE,

AND KNOWN BY THE NAME OF

THE COW POX.

BY EDWARD JENNER, M.D. F.R.S. &c.

——— QUID NOBIS CERTIUS IPSIS
SENSIBUS ESSE POTEST, QUO VERA AC FALSA NOTEMUS.

LUCRETIUS.

London:

PRINTED, FOR THE AUTHOR,

BY SAMPSON LOW, N°. 7, BERWICK STREET, SOHO:

AND SOLD BY LAW, AVE-MARIA LANE; AND MURRAY AND HIGHLEY, FLEET STREET.

1798.

FIG. 16.2(a)

[13]

CASE IV.

MARY BARGE, of Woodford, in this pariſh, was inoculated with variolous matter in the year 1791. An efflorefcence of a paliſh red colour ſoon appeared about the parts where the matter was inſerted, and ſpread itſelf rather extenſively, but died away in a few days without producing any variolous ſymptoms *. She has ſince been repeatedly employed as a nurſe to Small-pox patients, without experiencing any ill conſequences. This woman had the Cow Pox when ſhe lived in the ſervice of a Farmer in this pariſh thirty-one years before.

* It is remarkable that variolous matter, when the ſyſtem is diſpoſed to reject it, ſhould excite inflammation on the part to which it is applied more ſpeedily than when it produces the Small Pox. Indeed it becomes almoſt a criterion by which we can determine whether the infection will be received or not. It ſeems as if a change, which endures through life, had been produced in the action, or diſpoſition to action, in the veſſels of the ſkin; and it is remarkable too, that whether this change has been effected by the Small Pox, or the Cow Pox, that the diſpoſition to ſudden cuticular inflammation is the ſame on the application of variolous matter.

CASE.

Fig. 16.2(b)

especially in children suffering from chronic eczematous conditions of the skin. The course is often severe and a mortality of 30–40 per cent is recorded, although the prognosis is much improved if human hyper-immune serum is administered. *Kaposi's varicelliform eruption* is the clinical name given to the lesion which appears in eczematous subjects, consisting of numerous large umbilicated vesicles filled with clear serum. The vesicles continue to appear in successive crops which are mostly confined to the already eczematous skin. The patients may have been themselves vaccinated or can acquire the infection from other vaccinated subjects. A similar clinical condition can result from infection by herpes simplex virus. Eczematous subjects should therefore not be vaccinated except when there is a high risk of exposure. They should also not be put at risk by the vaccination of other members of the household. This condition should be distinguished from that in which a recently vaccinated child (or the vaccinator) develops odd vesicles on the face or elsewhere due to transfer of live vaccinia virus to these sites. Several fatal cases of generalized vaccinia have been reported in infants with immunological deficiency diseases. These have typically involved cases with a defficiency (aplasia or absence) of the thymus (see Chapter Eight). Since these cases have a well-known tendency to develop intercurrent infection there is a natural anxiety on the part of the clinician to vaccinate them thoroughly, but when the vaccines consist of living attenuated virus (such as vaccinia) or bacteria (as in BCG) a fatal generalized infection may result.

Post-vaccinial encephalitis is the most serious complication and carries a mortality of 50 per cent. Though there is much variation in the figures from different regions, they uniformly indicate an increasing liability to post-vaccinial encephalomyelitis with advancing age. The disease has its highest incidence between 6 and 12 years of age. According to the Netherlands figures the disease is 10 to 30 times as common after primary vaccination at school age as in infancy. There is a general consensus of opinion that encephalitis is much less common after revaccination than after primary vaccination. However, really satisfactory figures to support this are not available.

Symptoms appear first during the second week after vaccination. There is no doubt that the disease is often diagnosed wrongly, since diagnosis depends upon a process of exclusion of known virological causes of encephalitis. Numerous cases have been reported that failed to show on histological examination of the central nervous system the typical lesions of perivenous demyelinating microglial encephalitis. Numerous attempts to isolate vaccinia virus from the central nervous system have failed. One possibility is that the encephalitis is caused by the activation of a latent neurotropic virus. Another suggestion is that the disease is analogous to experimental allergic encephalomyelitis (see p. 645).

Two specific measures have been used for the prevention of post-vaccinial encephalomyelitis. A controlled study on Dutch recruits has been carried out in which one group received 2 ml of a 16 per cent solution of immunoglobulin made from recently vaccinated subjects and the other group a placebo of gelatin glucose solution. In the first group of 53,630 recruits 3 cases of post-vaccinial encephalitis were reported: in the control group of 53,044 recruits thirteen cases were reported. The present incidence after introduction of the prophylactic vaccinial immunoglobulin is 1 case among 30,000 subjects receiving primary vaccination.

An alternative method is that of preliminary vaccination with a killed, preferably formalized vaccine. Later vaccination with live vaccine would then be done in persons already possessing serum neutralizing antibody. This procedure has been followed by an incidence of 2 cases of encephalitis in 91,000 primary vaccinations.

Finally, some authorities strongly recommend that primary vaccination should be restricted to the first 2 years of life.

Protection following Vaccination

Vaccination is best performed during the first three months of life. The available evidence indicates clearly that successful vaccination produces immunity to smallpox. The degree and duration of immunity varies in different individuals but complete protection may be expected for 5 to 7 years. Revaccination may be required when adult life is reached and again before a journey to an area of infection.

POLIOMYELITIS

INACTIVATED POLIOMYELITIS VACCINE

Extensive trials were carried out in the United States during 1954 of a vaccine (Salk-type) consisting of strains of virus derived from each of the three main antigenic groups which were grown in monkey kidney cells maintained in tissue culture and then inactivated with formalin. The trial results indicated that vaccination engendered a marked (about 80 per cent), but not complete, protection against paralytic disease. Three injections of the vaccine have usually been given, but present indications are that a fourth dose results in a higher and much better maintained antibody response.

During the extensive use of the vaccine in 1955, a group of the vaccinated contracted poliomyelitis under circumstances which suggested that virus in the vaccine had survived the formalin treatment. The safety margin in formalin inactivation is slight, but by overtreatment it is easy to destroy the antigenicity. With the benefit of the American experience a modified vaccine was introduced in Britain in 1956 using less virulent but still highly antigenic strains. The present vaccine is produced by infecting monkey kidney cell cultures separately with each of the three types of poliovirus (Brunenders type 1, MEF-1, type 2, Sankett, type 3). At the same time there were introduced improved and more stringent methods of testing for possible residual living virus after the formalin treatment. Such testing is now done by injecting test samples of the treated virus suspension intracerebrally into cynomolgus monkeys rendered highly susceptible by cortisone treatment.

Poliomyelitis vaccine is normally prepared in monkey kidney cells which have not been propagated in series (so as to avoid possible activation of other latent viruses), and the culture medium must contain less than one part in a million of animal serum and the smallest effective concentration of antibiotics. The last precautions are taken to guard against reactions in sensitive subjects. Recent improvements in techniques for concentrating and purifying virus from the culture medium have made it possible virtually to eliminate extraneous materials and to produce a considerably more potent vaccine.

Three subcutaneous injections are given, with intervals of 4 to 6 weeks between the first and second dose and 7 to 12 months between the second and third. It is recommended that vaccination be begun at the age of 7 to 10 months, or even earlier (see introduction to this chapter), and that a fourth injection be given on entering school.

ORAL POLIOMYELITIS VACCINE

Infection with poliovirus, even when subclinical, is followed by long lasting immunity, and subclinical infection (if this could be guaranteed) would therefore appear to be the ideal form of prophylaxis. To achieve this end Sabin developed attenuated strains of poliomyelitis virus which can multiply in the cells of the human intestinal tract, and stimulate antibody, but have lost the ability to invade cells of the central nervous system. Sabin's strains of virus can be grown in monkey kidney tissue culture under conditions similar to those used for growing virus for inactivated vaccine, but additional precautions must be taken to ensure that no extraneous viruses are also present. After preliminary trials in small groups of children, in which great attention was paid to the possibility of the virus reverting to a more virulent form, live vaccine composed of a mixture of attenuated strains of the three main types of poliomyelitis virus has been administered orally to many millions of children in several countries of the world. The virus has been found not only to grow in the intestinal tract of the children who were consciously infected but to spread to other children or adults in contact with them. Satisfactory antibody responses have nearly always been recorded, but experience is too short at present to allow the long term protective effect to be assessed and compared with that elicited by inactivated virus vaccines. Oral vaccines have the great advantage that they are relatively cheap, since much smaller quantities of virus can be used to establish infection, and they are easy to administer on a large scale, being simply placed on a lump of sugar or actually incorporated into sweets. Such vaccines can be preserved frozen for long periods, but they have not yet been successfully freeze-dried.

In this country three doses of trivalent vaccine are given at 6 to 8 week intervals and a reinforcing dose is given at school entry. A single administration of trivalent oral poliomyelitis vaccine may not result in simultaneous development of immunity against all three antigenic types of poliovirus. Second and third feedings are necessary in order to give each of the three types an opportunity of colonizing the intestines.

Intervals of 4 to 6 weeks should also elapse between successive feedings of oral virus, the reason being that one type of poliovirus may be prevented from establishing itself in the intestines while one or both of the other types are still multiplying, a process which may last 4 to 6 weeks after the initial infection was produced.

Oral poliovirus vaccine has the advantage that it can be used in the face of an epidemic: large numbers of persons can be immunized by feeding the vaccine during a very short space of time. Field trials have shown that such procedures can effectively halt the course of an epidemic. On the other hand injection of killed vaccine does not prevent the vaccinated subject from being locally infected and shedding the virus. Thus the normal cycle of transmission of the virus in the community is not broken and the vaccinated subject may even become a carrier.

The relative merits of inactivated and attenuated vaccines has led to considerable controversy. Both are clearly highly effective in producing immunization. It has been maintained that live vaccines are ideal for maintaining immunity in a population which has a basal immunity engendered by inactivated vaccine, since the risk (even though this is apparently very small) of reversion to more virulent forms can then be virtually discounted. There seems little doubt that a small number of cases of paralytic poliomyelitis which occurred in the United States of America were associated with the use of living vaccine. The risk to children is probably no greater than 1 in 2·5 million vaccine doses, but in adults the risk is greater and a significant proportion of the *small* number of paralytic cases arising in a community using the live vaccine may follow administration of the vaccine virus.

Routine Immunization Schedules

All the foregoing prophylactic agents are suitable for use in infants or children, and some of them can be satisfactorily combined as mixed prophylactics. On the basis of experience gained from trials in Britain and other countries the Ministry of Health issued a memorandum to general practitioners in September, 1961 (modified reprint, 1965), in which were put forward two suggested alternative schedules for routine immunization. The main considerations are: (1) to provide the greatest possible measure of immunity against each particular disease; (2) to reduce to a minimum harmful reactions or complications, including provocation poliomyelitis; (3) to keep as low as possible the number of injections given and the number of visits necessary. Since no single schedule can fully meet all these considerations, the two schedules P and Q represent different attempts to reach a compromise (Table 16.1).

TABLE 16.1

SCHEDULE P (as modified by Ministry of Health, 1961)

Age	Visit	Vaccine	Injection	Interval (weeks)
1 to 6 months	1	Diphtheria, Tetanus, Pertussis	1	4–6
	2	Diphtheria, Tetanus, Pertussis	2	4–6
	3	Diphtheria, Tetanus, Pertussis	3	
7 to 11 months	4	Poliomyelitis (oral)	—	4–8
	5	Poliomyelitis (oral)	—	4–8
	6	Poliomyelitis (oral)	—	
18 to 21 months	7	Diphtheria, Tetanus, Pertussis	4	
Smallpox during the first 2 years, preferably in the second year (see Note a)				
School entry		Diphtheria, Tetanus and Poliomyelitis (oral)		
8 to 12 years		Diphtheria and Tetanus Smallpox re-vaccination		
Over 12 years		BCG (see Note c)		

SCHEDULE Q (as modified by Ministry of Health, 1961)

Age	Visit	Vaccine	Injection	Interval (weeks)
6 to 10 months	1	Poliomyelitis (oral)	—	4–8
	2	Poliomyelitis (oral)	—	4–8
	3	Poliomyelitis (oral)	—	
11 to 13 months	4	Diphtheria, Tetanus, Pertussis	1	
	5	Diphtheria, Tetanus, Pertussis	2	4–6
18 to 21 months	6	Diphtheria, Tetanus, Pertussis	3	
Smallpox during the first 2 years, preferably in the second year (see Note a)				
School entry		Diphtheria, Tetanus and Poliomyelitis (oral)		
8 to 12 years		Diphtheria and Tetanus Smallpox re-vaccination		
Over 12 years		BCG (see Note c)		

Notes

(a) An interval of at least two weeks should normally be allowed to elapse after an injection of Diphtheria/Tetanus/Pertussis vaccine before undertaking vaccination against smallpox. When vaccination against smallpox precedes an injection of one of the other vaccines it is desirable to allow at least three weeks to elapse.

(b) It is advisable to allow an interval of three weeks after any dose of oral poliomyelitis vaccine before any other immunizing procedure is undertaken.

(c) BCG vaccine may be given to schoolchildren aged 10 years or more at the discretion of the Medical Officer of Health.

(d) Children who have already started, but not completed, a course of immunization with Salk vaccine may, at the doctor's discretion, be given oral vaccine as follows:

(i) If a child has had only *one* injection of Salk vaccine, a full course of three doses of oral vaccine should be administered.

(ii) If a child has had *two* injections of Salk vaccine, the second one of which was given not more than one year previously, two doses of oral vaccine, at an interval between doses of not less than four weeks, may be given starting not earlier than ten months after the second injection, in place of a third injection of Salk vaccine. If the second injection of Salk vaccine was given more than one year previously, a full new course of three doses of oral vaccine should be administered.

(iii) If a child aged 5–12 years has had *three* injections of Salk vaccine, the fourth injection may be replaced by one dose of oral vaccine.

ENTERIC FEVER

A vaccine of killed typhoid bacilli was first employed by Almroth Wright in 1897. In animals it has been shown that vaccines containing the 'O' somatic antigen can protect against intraperitoneal challenge or even against infection by mouth in epidemics caused by naturally occurring virulent strains; the H or flagellar antigens apparently give no protection. The usual vaccine has been prepared from smooth virulent organisms killed by heat and preserved with 0·5 per cent phenol. Statistics derived from the First World War and the African campaigns of 1940–3 indicate that such a vaccine was highly effective in reducing morbidity (of the order of tenfold) and mortality due to typhoid. More recently Felix showed that another antigen of *S. typhi*, named Vi because it was characteristically associated with virulent strains, could also be important in protecting mice. The Vi antigen is preserved in antigenic form much more effectively when the vaccine is killed with 70 per cent alcohol and the vaccine subsequently stored in 25 per cent alcohol.

Current vaccines against enteric organisms are prepared from single or from several strains of *S. typhi*, *S. paratyphi A*, *S. paratyphi B* and *S. paratyphi C* that are smooth and have the full complement of 'O' somatic antigens and, in the case of *S. typhi* and *S. paratyphi C*, also contain the Vi antigen. They are killed by heat or by a bactericide chosen to retain maximum antigenicity. The number of organisms per ml is 1,000 million *S. typhi* and 500–750 million *S. paratyphi A*, *B* and *C*. The vaccine is given in two subcutaneous doses, usually with an interval of a month between them, and the second dose contains twice as many organisms as the first (recommended doses are 0·5 and 1·0 ml of phenolized vaccine or 0·25 and 0·5 ml of alcoholized vaccine). It is not uncommon for enteric vaccines to cause temporary general malaise, mild fever and local tenderness. This is probably due to their content of endotoxin, and is less with alcoholized vaccines. In recent field trials carried out in Guyana both an acetone-killed and a phenolized typhoid vaccine were shown to confer a high degree of protection.

CHOLERA AND PLAGUE

Cholera vaccines are prepared so as to contain equal numbers of organisms from smooth strains of the two main types of *V. cholerae* Inaba and Ogawa, which are killed by heat or by a bactericidal agent. One ml contains at least 8,000 million vibrios. The dosage schedule is similar to that of enteric vaccines, and indeed the two are sometimes combined. Experience in the Middle and Far East suggests that cholera vaccines have some measure of success in prophylaxis (though not in treatment) of cholera.*

Plague vaccine is prepared from cultures of the capsulated form of *Past. pestis* in such a manner that the final vaccine contains the greatest possible amount of capsular material. The organisms are commonly killed with formaldehyde, and the vaccine made up to contain 3,000 million bacteria per ml, in a medium containing 0·5 per cent phenol and not more than 0·025 per cent formaldehyde. The dosage schedule is similar to that of enteric vaccines. Plague vaccine is of value as a prophylactic where plague is endemic, or in epidemics.

YELLOW FEVER

Yellow Fever vaccine is another live vaccine. The way for its development was paved by the demonstration that a certain strain (17D) would multiply in chick embryo tissue cultures and retain its virulence for mice, but after about 100 passages the virus became attenuated and quite avirulent for man. The results with earlier vaccines prepared from this strain were confused by the fact that human serum was included in the medium used for culturing the chick embryos, and the vaccines were subsequently liable to give rise to homologous serum hepatitis. Serum is now not used, and this

* Since the biotype El Tor is becoming increasingly a cause of cholera, vaccines may include this also.

complication does not occur, but it must be borne in mind that the vaccines still contain a considerable amount of egg protein which can cause a severe reaction in persons with atopic hypersensitivity to eggs. The vaccine is usually prepared in a freeze-dried form and is reconstituted in saline solution immediately before use. It retains its potency, when dried, for at least a year at 0°, but loses potency within a few days at room temperature. All reconstituted vaccine not used within 30 minutes should be discarded because of the instability of the virus.

A single subcutaneous dose (usually 0·5 ml) gives immunity within 10 to 12 days which endures for at least 6 years. If both smallpox and yellow fever immunization are required, yellow fever inoculation should always precede smallpox vaccination by at least 4 days. If smallpox vaccination has been carried out first there should be an interval of 21 days before yellow fever inoculation. The reason is to avoid interference of the one virus with the other, whether by interferon production or by other means. Recently a mouse brain 17D vaccine has been introduced. Two scratch vaccinations separated by an interval of 14 days have been shown to give 98 per cent protection.

RABIES

In 1885 Pasteur vaccinated, apparently successfully, a boy who had been bitten by a rabid dog with a suspension of dried spinal cord from a rabbit which had been infected with virulent rabies virus. Drying the infected nervous tissue had successfully attenuated the virus in it. Rabies in man is a disease with a variable, but generally long, incubation period, and Pasteur considered that sufficient time might be available to immunize the patient in the interval between the bite and the onset of the disease. The Pasteurian method, using dried infected rabbit spinal cord, is still used in some countries, but most health authorities now favour a vaccine (Semple type) prepared from the ground-up brains of infected sheep or rabbits in which the virus is killed with phenol or β-propiolactone. The presence of nervous tissue in the vaccine makes it potentially dangerous since it may cause demyelination in the patient, by a process presumably analogous to the experimental allergic encephalomyelitis which can readily be produced in several different species of animals by injecting either homologous or heterologous brain tissue (Chapter Fifteen). The reported incidence of this complication following rabies vaccination varies between countries but is probably 1 : 4,000 to 1 : 10,000 of patients treated.

Bites and other wounds should be given local treatment by thorough washing with soap and water. Severe bite wounds on the face or finger bites call for immediate application of anti-rabies serum, some of which should be infiltrated beneath the wound if possible. The serum is prepared in horses and 'refined' by pepsin digestion. The recommended dose of serum is 40 I.U./kg body weight. At least 14 daily doses of vaccine should be given, and in high risk cases, in which serum is also given, further doses of vaccine should be given 10 and 20 days after the conclusion of this treatment. These later injections of vaccine are liable to produce extremely painful local lesions; they should use, if possible, non-encephalitogenic vaccine (see below).

In recent years vaccine free from encephalitogenic nervous tissue have been prepared from a virus grown in duck embryos and inactivated with β-propiolactone. This is already finding extensive use for propylactic vaccination of veterinary and other workers whose occupations involve contact with possibly rabid animals. A different approach to the preparation of safe rabies vaccine is to grow the virus in the brains of very young animals. Infected brains of rats and mice harvested *before the start of myelination* are a rich source of fixed rabies virus, yet are non-encephalitogenic when tested in guinea-pigs. Human subjects injected with them have developed very satisfactory high concentrations of neutralizing antibody.

TYPHUS

Vaccination against scrub typhus has not proved effective because there exists a large number of different strains of the causative agent, *Rickettsia nipponica*. A more effective prophylactic vaccine can, however, be prepared against epidemic (louse-borne and murine) typhus, by growing the rickettsiae in the yolk sacs of embryonated eggs (or in the lungs of small rodents or the peritoneal cavities of gerbils) and killing them with formaldehyde. The killed rickettsiae are concentrated and purified by shaking an aqueous suspension with ether or fluorohydrocarbons.

The vaccine is administered by subcutaneous injections, repeated at frequent intervals (e.g. six-monthly) while exposure to infection continues. It does not prevent infection, but renders the illness milder and very markedly reduces the mortality. Treatment with suitable antibiotics is the method of choice.

INFLUENZA VACCINE

Successful prophylactic vaccination against influenza is difficult to achieve both because antibody immunity is short-lived (for reasons discussed in Chapter Ten) and because of the tendency for influenza virus to vary in its antigenic constitution from one epidemic to another. The first influenza A strain was isolated in 1933 and antigenic variation within this strain was recognized when viruses recovered from different epidemics were not antigenically the same. In 1946 an antigenic variant A′ appeared in Australia and spread so that all epidemics for the next few years were caused by this virus. In 1956 another new A variant appeared (A^2 or Asian virus) which was responsible for the pandemic of 1957. In 1940 in New York a virus markedly different in its antigenic make-up appeared and was called type B. Antigenic variants of this have been found since 1940. Another variant (type C) is known but does not cause epidemics.

When there is evidence that an epidemic is imminent, and a vaccine can be prepared so as to include the epidemic strain, there is evidence that vaccination will confer a useful degree of protection. For example, during the 1957 epidemic caused by the 'Asian' variety of influenza A, a vaccine was prepared which contained this strain and in a controlled trial the incidence of clinical infection in vaccinated persons was cut to about one third of that in the unvaccinated group.

Influenza vaccine is prepared by growing strains of virus, currently recommended by the World Influenza Centre of the World Health Organization, in the allantoic cavity of chick embryos. The allantoic fluids are inactivated with 0·01 per cent formaldehyde in the cold, and the virus is purified (e.g. by centrifugation) and resuspended in buffered saline. Such treatment destroys infectivity, but retains the haemagglutinating activity for fowl red cells and the antigenicity of the virus. The vaccine is stable at 2–10° for at least 18 months, and for about one week at room temperature. Two adequately spaced doses of killed vaccine are recommended for primary immunization, although one dose may be given when an epidemic is imminent.

Given as a single deep subcutaneous injection, not less than 10 days before exposure to infection, it may be expected to confer protection for a few months. In some vaccines a mineral carrier or oily adjuvant is incorporated and although higher antibody titres have been obtained they have not received general acceptance. A living attenuated virus has been developed in Russia as a nasal spray. Unlike the killed vaccine, this live prophylactic is said to be effective even when used in the face of an influenza epidemic.

MEASLES (MORBILLI) VACCINES

In this country, measles is nowadays a relatively harmless childhood disease. However, in certain of the developing countries measles has a high mortality and an effective prophylactic vaccine is needed. Unfortunately none of those available present are completely satisfactory. Attenuated live measles virus vaccines have been developed by passage repeatedly through human, monkey and chick embryo cells, which produce long-lasting immunity, but which have sometimes provoked severe pyrexial reactions and more rarely, convulsions. Inactivated virus vaccines have so far failed to provide long-lasting immunity and are therefore unlikely to be of value, except perhaps for prophylaxis against any severe reactions which might otherwise be encountered with live virus vaccines.

It is debatable how far it is worth while attempting in this country to achieve prophylaxis against measles or other endemic diseases (e.g. those due to the commoner types of adenovirus) which are usually mild, and the time of whose appearance is unpredictable. Consideration of this difficult question is beyond the scope of this book.

GERMAN MEASLES (RUBELLA) VACCINES

The reason for attemping immunization against rubella is not to stop children from developing the disease, which is usually mild, but to protect the foetus *in utero* from the serious damage which this virus can cause in the first three months of pregnancy. Natural infection with rubella in childhood protects against foetal and maternal virus infection, and some doctors have advocated the deliberate exposure of young girls to active infection in order to promote natural immunity. However, this procedure has the danger that the virus may be further spread in an uncontrolled way to other young women who are pregnant. What is wanted is a rubella virus which is modified so as to immunize the recipient without further spread. A standard method for achieving such a result is to propagate the virus serially in a foreign host. After seventy-four passages in kidney cells of the African green monkey, a virus emerged which infected monkeys but gave no evidence of spread to contact controls. A trial with this type of virus in young girls has shown that a subcutaneous injection can lead to the development of neutralizing antibodies without development of overt disease (fever, rash or lymphadenopathy). It is hoped that these encouraging experimental results may lead to a generally available prophylactic vaccine, but the practical objections to the use of monkey-kidney cells as a source of virus remain to be overcome.

PASSIVE IMMUNIZATION WITH ANTIBODIES

Passive immunization by means of antiserum is used either prophylactically, when active immunization is not feasible, or therapeutically to reinforce the body's own antibody, or to tide over a period before antibody production has got under way. For therapeutic purposes such large amounts of antibody are required that it is rarely feasible to obtain them from human beings, and therefore they must nearly always be made from the serum of hyperimmunized animals. In order to diminish the amount of foreign protein which must be injected along with foreign antibodies, it is usual to concentrate the antibodies by means of salting them out together with the γ-globulin fraction at high salt concentrations or by treatment with organic solvents. In many instances the product is still further 'refined' by treatment with an enzyme (pepsin), which partly breaks down antibody resulting in loss of the Fc piece (see Chapter Four), followed by gentle heating, by means of which unwanted constituents of the antiserum are still further diminished.

Passive immunization, whether with human or with foreign antibodies, has the disadvantages of being short-lived. If a given amount of human antibody is administered intramuscularly or intravenously into a patient, the antibody becomes diluted in the recipient's plasma and lymph. When this has occurred the initial concentration corresponds to dilution with a volume of plasma equal to approximately 8 per cent of the body weight. After this, human antibody (at least the principal IgG component) is gradually broken down with a half-life of around 24 days (i.e. the concentration drops by half every 24 days), and thus some protection may endure for several weeks or even months. When foreign antibody is used another factor comes into play, namely the immunological response of the recipient against the foreign protein injected. Thus after an interval of 10 to 14 days (or even earlier if foreign serum or antitoxin has been administered previously), it is quite usual for a person who has received antiserum himself to develop antibodies against the constituents of the antiserum, with the result that these are rapidly eliminated from his circulation. The process is often accompanied

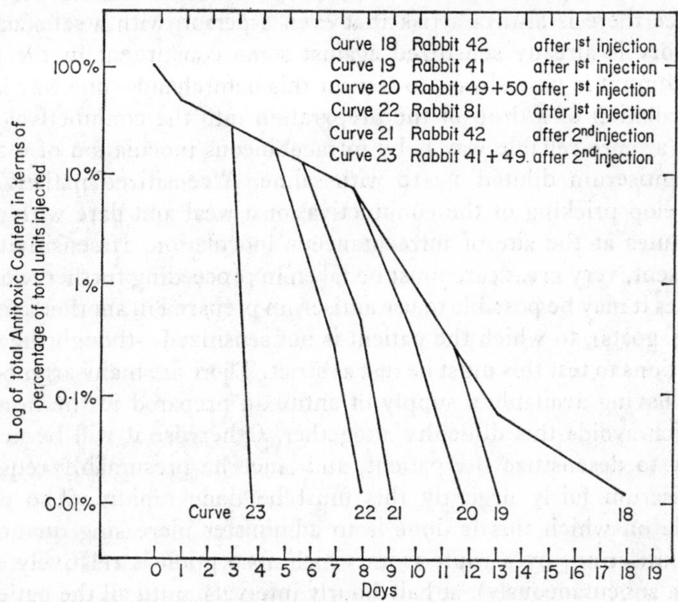

FIG. 16.3. Elimination of diphtheria antitoxin (made in a horse) from the blood of rabbits. Curves 21 and 23 relate to rabbits which had received an earlier injection of similar material, whereas curves 18, 19, 20, 22 relate to rabbits injected for the first time. Note the accelerated elimination when the rabbits begin to make antibody against the horse antitoxin. Those animals receiving second injections tend to eliminate antitoxin sooner. [After Glenny and Hopkins (1923) *J. Hyg. Camb.* **22**, 12.]

by serum sickness (see Chapter Eleven), which occurs most commonly when crude antiserum or unrefined globulins are used. A very important point is that from this time onwards no antibody remains in the recipient, and furthermore if he receives a further dose of antibody he will not only eliminate it very rapidly, but runs a considerable risk of serious reactions such as anaphylaxis (see

Chapter Nine). These facts have long been known in animals, and are illustrated in Fig. 16.3, but they have been less well appreciated as regards the use of antiserum in man.

PRECAUTIONS TO BE TAKEN

Before administering antiserum or refined antitoxins it is important to enquire whether there is a record of previous administration and whether the patient has a history of asthma or of infantile eczema. Since there is always a risk that even a person with a satisfactory history is already sensitized against some constituent in the preparation it is wise always to test for this beforehand—one way is by installation of a drop of the preparation into the conjunctival sac, but a more reliable way is by intracutaneous inoculation of 0·2 ml of antiserum diluted 1 : 10 with saline. A sensitized patient will develop pricking of the conjunctiva, or a weal and flare within 10 minutes at the site of intracutaneous inoculation. If sensitivity is present, very great care must be taken in proceeding further. Sometimes it may be possible to use antiserum prepared in another species (e.g. goats), to which the patient is not sensitized—though the precautions to test this must be just as strict. There are many arguments for having available a supply of antitoxin prepared in the human, which avoids this difficulty altogether. Otherwise it will be necessary to desensitize the patient, and since he presumably requires antiserum fairly urgently this must be done rapidly. The principle on which this is done is to administer increasing quantities of antiserum, by a route from which absorption is relatively slow (e.g. subcutaneously), at half-hourly intervals, until all the patient's antibody has combined with the foreign protein, and the rest of the antiserum can then be given intramuscularly without immediate harm. It is usual to begin with 0·2 ml of a 1 : 10 dilution, and to increase the dose tenfold each time (provided that no general symptoms develop) until 2 ml of undiluted material can be given without ill effect. After this the residue is administered intramuscularly. Adrenaline (1 : 1000 solution) must *always* be at hand when giving foreign antiserum, even to an apparently unsensitized person, since it may be required as a life-saving measure to counteract acute anaphylaxis. The dose for adults is 0·5 ml intramuscularly immediately and 0·5 ml every 20 minutes if the systolic blood pressure remains below 100 mm of mercury. Antihistamine drugs are also useful to minimize the after effects such as urticaria or oedema. *All* patients should be kept under observation and warm for 30 minutes after receiving an injection.

It should be borne in mind that a sensitized person is likely to respond to the antiserum by making antibody against it even more rapidly than usual, and that the beneficial effects of the antiserum will consequently be short-lived. Other measures, such as antibiotics or surgery, should be instituted at the same time.

The use of refined antitoxins, owing to their diminished antigenicity, has markedly diminished the incidence of complications of the kind described above, but they are nevertheless sufficiently common to permit no relaxation of precautions.

TETANUS ANTITOXIN

Tetanus antitoxin is prepared from the serum of horses immunized against tetanus toxin, and is invariably issued as refined globulins. For prophylaxis against tetanus in a non-immunized person who has a deep or penetrating fresh wound, a fresh wound with contused or devitalized tissue, a fresh wound which cannot be completely closed, or a wound already more than 4 hours old before it is cleaned and repaired, the dose is 1500 units given as soon as possible, and repeated within a week if the risk continues. In some countries human tetanus antitoxin is available and can be used for prophylaxis or therapy, especially in cases in which hypersensitivity reactions to horse serum proteins is probable. At the present time such human antiserum is available only in certain localities of Great Britain. In some countries use is made of bovine antitoxin, which when refined by ethanol fractionation is reported to be unlikely to provoke reactions in patients hypersensitive to horse serum. For therapeutic purposes, when infection with *Cl. tetani* is established, the dose is not less than 50,000 units, given by the intramuscular route.

Prophylactic use of tetanus antitoxin should be followed by active immunization. In certain circumstances this can be done at the same time as passive immunization (see p. 678).

DIPHTHERIA ANTITOXIN

Diphtheria antitoxin is prepared from the serum of horses immunized against diphtheria, and is always issued as refined globulins. It is nowadays rarely used for prophylaxis, except in exceptional circumstances (e.g. when a mother has diphtheria at the time of childbirth), since *Corynebacterium diphtheriae* is susceptible to antibiotics and active immunization is widespread. The prophylactic dose is 500 to 2000 units. For therapeutic use a dose of not less than 10,000 units should be given.

GAS-GANGRENE ANTITOXIN

Separate antitoxins (in the form of refined globulins prepared from horse antiserum) are available which neutralize the alpha toxins formed by *Clostridium oedematiens*, *septicum* and *welchii* respectively, but they are commonly combined together. Their use is nowadays largely confined to treatment of established gas-gangrene, since antibiotics and surgical débridement constitute a far better form of prophylaxis. The therapeutic dose is not less than 30,000 units of antitoxin against oedematiens and perfringens, and 15,000 units against septicum.

BOTULINUM ANTITOXIN

A mixed antitoxin prepared against the toxins of *Cl. botulinum* types A, B and E is available in the form of refined globulins prepared from the serum of immunized horses. Botulism is nowadays practically unknown in Britain, but occurs elsewhere. The prophylactic dose is 10,000 units and the therapeutic dose (by intravenous injection) not less than 50,000 units.

OTHER ANTISERA

Antisera are made against various other bacteria and toxins, and also against snake venoms. The latter especially are used widely in countries where poisonous snakes occur. The essential point to remember is that the toxins in snake venoms are highly specific for the species and may even vary markedly within a species according to the locality. Hence the therapeutic administration of antivenom is only likely to be useful if the species of snake is known and antiserum prepared against this species is used.

HUMAN γ-GLOBULIN

The serum of normal adults contains smaller or greater amounts of antibody against a wide variety of infective agents to which the population is exposed more or less continuously. When adult serum in this country is pooled, the chances are very high that the pool will contain significant amounts of antibody against such viruses as measles, rubella, poliomyelitis and infectious hepatitis. Since the levels of antibody required to give clinical protection against such viruses (which have a long incubation period) are very low, it is possible to use pooled human serum as a source of protective antibodies. It is usual to prepare concentrated γ-globulin from the serum, both because the total amount of protein is thereby reduced to one-fifth without loss of antibody activity, and because there is evidence that administration of purified γ-globulins (unlike whole serum) rarely, if ever, gives rise to homologous serum hepatitis. Human γ-globulin must be given by intramuscular and *not* by intravenous injection, since by the latter route it may give rise to severe, and even fatal, systemic reactions which may perhaps be due to the effects of small amounts of aggregated γ-globulin resulting from the process of manufacture. Aggregated γ-globulin can fix complement and cause increased capillary permeability (see Chapter Eleven). There is, however, no danger of anaphylactic reactions, nor of unduly rapid elimination of the antibody, as is the case when foreign serum is used. Although iso-agglutinins may be present in the preparation, their concentration is too low to give rise to any difficulty.

Human γ-globulin is used mainly for prophylaxis or attenuation of measles in children who are more than 6 months old (up to which age they are likely to be immune because of persisting maternal antibody) and less than 3 years, or who for other reasons must avoid a full-blown attack of measles. If sufficient γ-globulin is administered shortly after contact with infection complete protection results; if γ-globulin administration is delayed for some days the child will get measles but the attack is likely to be very mild or mild; whereas if γ-globulin is given late in the incubation period the usual doses will have only a negligible effect. A rough guide to the doses needed for protection and attenuation is given in Table 16.2. If an attenuated attack is desired, which will have the advantage of giving lifelong active immunity, it is necessary for contact with an infectious patient to be sufficiently close and prolonged to ensure that infection takes place.

Another use is prevention of rubella in pregnant women who have not already had the disease, if they are exposed to infection during the first three months of pregnancy, since infection at this stage carries a real risk of producing congenital deformities in the foetus. For this purpose a dose of 0·5. g of γ-globulin with a high antiviral titre should be given as soon as possible after exposure.

Temporary but not always certain protection may also be given by means of γ-globulin to persons who are about to be, or have very recently been, exposed to infectious hepatitis or poliomyelitis. Before the introduction of an effective poliomyelitis vaccine prophylaxis by human γ-globulin was tried extensively in the U.S.A., and the attack rate was reduced by about 60 per cent. The dose used for this purpose is 0·5 g for infants, 1 g for children 1–6 years and 1·5 g for children 7 years and above.

TABLE 16.2
Gamma-globulin treatment in measles at different ages

	Under 1 year	1 to 3 years	Over 3 years
Prevention	3 ml	6 ml	9 ml
Attenuation	—	3 ml	3 ml

The quantities refer to a solution of pooled human γ-globulin containing 250 mg in 3 ml fluid, administered within a week of exposure to infection. When attenuation is desired the γ-globulin should be withheld until about 7 days after exposure.

When a paralytic case occurs in a family it is more than probable that the family contacts were exposed to the disease simultaneously or are so far into the incubation period that γ-globulin is likely to be ineffective. There are special indications for the use of γ-globulin in the case of exposed children who have recently undergone tonsillectomy or nurses or medical personnel entering an infectious area.

Specific Hyperimmune Human Globulin

In circumstances in which human γ-globulin is used, convalescent serum from a person who has had the specific infection could clearly also be used with greater effect. Such serum, however, is usually less readily available, and its use carries a risk of transmitting homologous serum hepatitis. This risk can be avoided by fractionating and concentrating the γ-globulins from the serum. In Holland extensive use is made of concentrates prepared from the serum of recently vaccinated persons for the prophylaxis of smallpox in contacts and for the prevention of serious sequelae of smallpox vaccination such as generalized vaccinia and encephalomyelitis. In this country 'immune' gammaglobulin in doses of 1·5 gram has been used apparently successfully in a few outbreaks of smallpox infection to prevent the spread of infection to close contacts or to modify the resulting disease.

There is much to be said for preparing human tetanus antitoxin in a similar way from volunteers who have received repeated tetanus toxoid injections. This could be reserved for prophylaxis and treatment of persons who are already sensitized to horse antitoxin.

CONTROL OF VACCINES AND SERA

All vaccines and sera for use in man are controlled in Great Britain under the Therapeutic Substances Act, and each is covered by a separate schedule. The requirements laid down under the regulations have the force of law and all manufacturers must obey them. Most vaccines and antisera of established value are also included in the British or U.S. *Pharmacopoeias* and the *International Pharmacopoeia*, which contain separate monographs relating to each particular preparation. The aim of the Therapeutic Substances Regulations is to ensure that the material is potent (in so far as it is possible to assess the potency quantitatively), that it is safe, and that it will not give rise to unpleasant or undesirable reactions when used. The monographs in the British Pharmacopoeia also lay down standards of potency, toxicity etc., and give some details about properties whereby the preparations can be recognized, and about the method of manufacture. Most of these aspects do not require further consideration here. However, some consideration must be given to the question of making quantitative assessments of potency. The great difficulty in assessing a vaccine, or even an antiserum, is that we are very often not sure precisely what factors control its efficacy —nor, even when we think we are dealing with some relatively simple toxin, can we be certain that we know what factors will influence its antigenicity in the host, or, in the case of an antitoxin, its biological efficiency. The only really certain way of being sure that a vaccine or a serum is clinically effective is to subject it to a large-scale controlled clinical trial. Such trials require the cooperation of a large number of physicians and patients, and a very elaborate organization. Furthermore, they will only give the answers in respect of the particular materials which were tested in the trial.

USE OF BIOLOGICAL STANDARDS

A practical solution to the problem of giving a quantitative value to the potency of biological materials of this kind was found in the setting up of biological standards. These consist of actual physical samples of a typical lot of the material which is to be standardized, stored in such a way as to maintain its properties stable. A test or tests are devised, such as can be carried out in laboratory animals or in a test tube, whereby the particular biological activity which one hopes to be associated with the therapeutic effectiveness can be measured, and the performances of the unknown and of the standard materials are compared. Such tests might comprise injecting one or two doses of a vaccine, or of a preparation of a toxoid, into groups of animals under standardized conditions (usually using more than one dose level, so as to permit a dose-response relationship to be worked out), and taking blood samples and estimating the amount of a particular antibody which their plasma contains after a standard interval of time; or they might consist in finding the dose of vaccine required to ensure 50 per cent survival of the vaccinated animals when challenged later with, say, 100 or 1000 times the dose of toxin or living micro-organisms required to kill normal animals; or, in the case of an antiserum, in measuring the amount which will just give 50 per cent protection of groups of animals against the lethal effects of a standard dose of toxin. It is often possible to devise several tests, using different end-points, or different varieties of animal, which purport to measure the same property of the material being investigated. If two samples are then compared in each of the different forms of test, and if they both contain the same active constituents, and the tests measure the same biological activities, the ratio of the potencies of the two samples should turn out to be about the same in each of the different assays. Furthermore, if these two samples are compared in properly controlled clinical trials in man it is to be hoped that their relative potencies will be the same as those shown by at least some of the laboratory tests. Sometimes this turns out to be the case and sometimes not. For example, in an extended clinical trial of whooping-cough vaccines in this country, it was found that the relative therapeutic efficiency (i.e. diminution produced in the incidence of pertussis infection) of the five vaccines used correlated reasonably well with their ability to protect against pertussis-vaccinated mice, of a suitable strain, challenged intracerebrally but that there was no correlation with the ability of the mice to withstand intranasal challenge. Thus the intracerebral challenge route, artificial though it seems, probably provides a technique which can justifiably be used for comparing the potencies of pertussis vaccine with those of the standard. Another vaccine which has been very extensively tried in man is poliomyelitis vaccine, and in this case the antigenic efficiency in man has been found to correlate reasonably well with the ability to stimulate the production of antibodies in chicks or guinea-pigs. On the other hand, extensive trials carried out by the World Health Organization in Yugoslavia and later in Guyana showed that the effectiveness of typhoid vaccines correlated very poorly with the ability of the vaccines under test to protect mice against intraperitoneal challenge. This might have been expected for reasons discussed in Chapter Ten, but since no better test of typhoid vaccines has been devised, and the mouse protection test at least shows that the vaccine has some immunizing capacity, this particular test continues to be used.

Once standard preparations have been set aside, and suitable tests have been devised, any unknown preparation can be assayed against the standard preparation, and its relative biological potency can be found. The international standards (which are kept by the World Health Organization) or the National Standards have already been assigned arbitrary potencies in terms of some convenient number of 'biological units' per unit weight of the material. Hence it is possible for any country to lay down, for a substance for which a standard exists, that it shall have particular potency in terms of national or international units. The first biological standards were for hormones and for vitamins and were set up by the League of Nations. Antisera were standardized soon afterwards, there being a standard antiserum for each particular kind of antitoxin. The reason for choosing antisera rather than toxins as the standard materials was that antisera are remarkably stable, whereas toxins are not only difficult to prepared pure, but tend to 'toxoid', i.e. to become altered so as to lose their toxicity without losing their ability to combine with antibody. Since the Second World War the biological standards have been maintained by the World Health Organization. The development of standards for vaccines is quite recent—partly because the methods of assay were not adequately developed, and partly because prophylactic immunization has recently come into greater prominence. There are still relatively few standard preparations of vaccine, and most of these are national rather than international standards. However, we may expect that in the future more and more satisfactory vaccines will have been assayed in terms of accepted standard preparations, using techniques of assay which correlate with their desired therapeutic properties in man.

FURTHER READING

Anti-measles vaccination (1963) *Wld Hlth Org. tech. Rep. Series, 263*

Attenuated poliomyelitis vaccine (1963) *Lancet* (leading article) **i,** 149

The *British Pharmacopoeia* (1968) General Medical Council, London

CANNON D.A. (ed.) (1959) *Symposium on Immunization in Childhood.* Livingstone, Edinburgh

COHEN S. (1963) Gamma globulin metabolism. *Brit. Med. Bull.* **19,** 202

DICK G.W. (1963) Symposium on immunization. *Brit. J. clin. Pract.* **17,** 619

EVANS D.G. & SMITH J.W.G. (1963) Response of young infants to active immunization. *Brit. Med. Bull.* **19,** 225

GELL P.G.H. & COOMBS R.R.A. (eds) (1968) *Clinical Aspects of Immunology* Section V. Immunoprophylaxis and Immunotherapy. Blackwell Scientific Publications, Oxford

Human Viral and Rickettsial Vaccines (1966) *Wld Hlth Org. tech. Rep. Series 327*

MEDICAL RESEARCH COUNCIL (1959) Vaccination against whooping cough (final report). *Brit. med. J.* **i,** 994

MEDICAL RESEARCH COUNCIL (1959) Tuberculosis vaccines. Clinical Trials Committee Report. *Brit. med. J.* **ii,** 379

MEDICAL RESEARCH COUNCIL (1968) Vaccination against measles: clinical trial of live measles vaccine given alone and live vaccine preceded by killed vaccine. *Brit. med. J.* **ii,** 449

PARISH H.J. (1965) *A History of Immunization.* Livingstone, Edinburgh

PARISH H.J. (1968) *Victory with Vaccines. The Story of Immunization.* Livingstone, Edinburgh

PARISH H.J. & CANNON D.A. (1962) Prevention of Tetanus. *Brit. med. J.* **i,** 868

PRESTON N.W. (1965) Effectiveness of pertussis vaccines. *Brit. med. J.* **ii,** 11

SMITH J.W.G. *et al.* (1963) Simultaneous active and passive immunization against tetanus. *Brit. med. J.* **i,** 237

UHR J.W. & MÖLLER G. (1968) Regulatory effect of antibody on the immune response. *Adv. Immunol.* **8,** 81

The use of human immunoglobulin (1963) *Wld Hlth Org. tech. Rep. Series 263*

WILSON G.S. (1967) *Hazards of Immunization.* Athlone Press, London

Glossary

ADJUVANT 1. In pharmacology generally, a remedy or drug which assists or modifies the action of other remedies or ingredients.
2. A substance which can increase the specific antibody production to, or degree of sensitization against, an antigen.
See also Freund's adjuvant.
(L.: *ad, juvare*, to help.)

ADJUVANTICITY Property of an antigen, irrespective of its determinant groups, which makes it a good immunogen. Adjuvanticity is often increased by aggregation of the antigen, and may be an expression of its interaction with macrophages.

ALLELE When there exist alternative genes acting at the same locus on the chromosome these are termed alleles.
(Gk.: *allelon*, mutual.)

ALLERGEN Term applied to immunogens (q.v.) which have a marked tendency to elicit the formation of skin sensitizing (homocytotropic) antibodies or reagins.

ALLOGENEIC (allogenic) Of different genetic constitution (embraces the term *heterogenic* and the term *homologous* when misused in this sense).
(Gk.: *allos*, other; *genos*, race.)

ALLOGRAFT See *homograft*.

ALLOTYPES Name first used by J. Oudin to describe antigenically distinct forms of gamma-globulin occurring in rabbits which could be recognized by their ability to elicit specific antibodies in some other members of the same species. The different allotypes of gamma-globulin were shown to be under genetic control.

The term is now used to include genetically controlled polymorphic variants of plasma proteins in general. Thus the existence is known in various species not only of gamma-globulin allotypes but also of beta-globulin and alpha-globulin allotypes (e.g. haptoglobins, β-lipoproteins).

AMINO TERMINAL Applied to that end of a polypeptide chain at which the amino acid has a free amino group. This is the end released last from the polyribosome during synthesis.

ANERGY Absence of a hypersensitivity reaction such as would be expected in other similarly sensitized individuals.

ANGSTROM (Å) A unit of length convenient for the description of molecular dimensions. 10^{-8} cm or 10^{-1} mμ.

ATOPY Term first used by Coca to describe a tendency to immediate-type hypersensitiveness to allergens which is present in some human individuals, but not in others; atopy is associated with a hereditary predisposition to acquire hypersensitiveness on contact with such allergens. The tissue sensitizing antibodies responsible are termed '*atopic*' (or *reaginic*). (Gk.: *a*, out of; *topos*, place.)

AUTO- Derived from self, e.g.

auto-antibody: antibody reacting with constituents of the subject's own tissues.

auto-graft: graft of the subject's own tissues.

auto-immunization: immunization against constituents of the subject's own tissues.

autologous (often used incorrectly for *autochthonous*): derived from the subject itself.

BENCE-JONES PROTEIN Proteins first described by H. Bence-Jones in 1847 as occurring in the urine—typically of cases of multiple myelomatosis—which coagulates on heating the urine to 60°. See Chapter Four.

BETA-2A-GLOBULINS See Immunoglobulin A.

BETA-2M-GLOBULINS See Immunoglobulin M.

BIOLOGICAL FALSE POSITIVE REACTION (B.F.P.R.) Positive reaction given by sera of certain individuals in Wassermann reaction or flocculation tests, such as the Kahn test, and not attributable to infection by *Treponema pallidum* or related spirochaetes. Such reactions are common in certain types of presumed auto-immune disease.

BLAST = haemocytoblast.

CARBOXY TERMINAL (see amino terminal) The end of a polypeptide chain possessing an amino acid with a free carboxyl group. This end is released from the polyribosome first during synthesis.

CISTRON The region of a chromosome which controls the synthesis of a single complete polypeptide chain. The term is often used loosely as a synonym for 'gene', but it should strictly be used only when the size of the region has been determined by means of genetic complementation tests.

(See, for example, *Gene Action* by Hartman P.E. and Suskind S.R., Prentice-Hall, 1965 or *The Genetics of Bacteria and their Viruses* by Hayes W., Blackwell Scientific Publications, 1968).

CLONE A group of cells or organisms of like hereditary constitution which have been reproduced asexually from a single individual cell or organism. (Gk.: *Klon*, a twig.)

COMPLEMENT (synonym: alexin) Term used to describe co-factors present in fresh normal blood serum which are necessary for the full activity of antibody on cells, e.g. for haemolytic or bactericidal activity—but which are by themselves inactive. See Chapter Five.

COOMBS TEST (synonym: anti-globulin test) Cells (e.g. Rh+ human erythrocytes) which have been treated with non-agglutinating antibody (e.g. 'warm incomplete' Rh antibody) have antibody bound on their surface, even though they are not agglutinated. Such cells are agglutinated, and the bound antibody thereby demonstrated, on addition of antibody against the bound globulin (e.g. rabbit anti-human globulin).

The Direct Coombs Test in clinical medicine usually refers to detection of incomplete antibody on washed erythrocytes by the use of a small amount of anti-human γ-globulin.

COPRO-ANTIBODY Antibody released into the intestinal tract and appearing in the faeces. Such antibody is probably formed by plasma cells in the intestinal mucosa and submucosa, and contains a high proportion of IgA.

CROSSING-OVER Term used in genetics to describe the process whereby homologous segments of genetic material are exchanged during the first division of meiosis, or, less commonly, at mitosis; the effect is as if homologous chromatids broke symmetrically and rejoined cross-wise.

One hypothesis for the origin of variable amino acid sequences in the L and H chains of immunoglobulins postulates somatic recombination occurring between two similar but not identical genes coding for the same polypeptide.

CRYOGLOBULIN Globulin which precipitates from serum at 0–4°C.

DENATURATION Loss of the native configuration of a macromolecule, usually with resulting loss of solubility in physiological salt solution. It is the result of extreme pH changes, heat treatment or treatment with chemical agents. Often involves rearrangement of disulphide bonds.

DETERMINANT GROUP That part of the structure of an antigen molecule which is responsible for specific interaction with antibody molecules evoked by the same or a similar antigen. When antibody is formed in response to a protein to which distinctive chemical groups (hapten) have been conjugated artificially, the structure of the determinant groups is very often identical or closely similar to that of the hapten.

DISULPHIDE BOND Covalently linked sulphide groups –S–S–. They are important in cross-linking of polypeptide chains in proteins, in which two molecules of cysteine become linked *via* their –SH groups to form –S–S– bridges. On reduction the bond may be split to yield two –SH (sulphydryl) groups.

ENDOCYTOPLASMIC RETICULUM System of paired parallel membranes of approximately 80 Å thickness which occur in the cytoplasm of protein secreting cells. Ribosomal particles are attached at regular intervals along the outer surfaces of a pair of membranes. Current ideas favour the view that the space (cisterna) between the paired membranes is in communication throughout the whole extent of the E.R. and probably communicates with the surface of the cell.

ENDOTOXIN (synonyms: Boivin antigen, bacterial pyrogen) By contrast with Exotoxin, a toxin closely associated with the body of the bacterial cell, and which does not readily diffuse into the culture medium during active growth.

Chemical structures: macromolecules composed of protein, polysaccharide and lipid components. In the case of Gram-negative bacteria the endotoxin appears to be derived from the bacterial cell walls and closely related to the 'O' somatic antigen. See Chapter Six.

EOSINOPHILIA An increase in the number of eosinophil granular leucocytes in blood (or tissue). Commonly occurs when reaginic antibodies and the specific antigen are simultaneously present in the body.

EPITOPE Specific antigenic determinant site or area on a molecule.

EUGLOBULIN That fraction of plasma proteins which is insoluble in distilled water or in dilute salt solution at a slightly acid pH. The fraction contains part of the IgG and IgM, as well as some enzymes such as plasminogen. Such proteins are also precipitated by 33 per cent saturated ammonium sulphate (see also pseudoglobulin).

FEEDBACK INHIBITION Inhibition of activity in a metabolic pathway by the end product of that pathway.

FEULGEN REACTION A chemical reaction based upon the release of aldehyde groups from the deoxypentose sugar of DNA by mild acid hydrolysis. The aldehydes released are detected by the use of Schiff's reagent (leucofuchsin) which gives a reddish purple colour in their presence; i.e. those structures in a tissue section which contain DNA are stained red by this technique.

F_1-HYBRID The first generation offspring of a mating between the members of two pure inbred strains. Their cells possess antigens characteristic of both parents.

FIBRINOID A material having many of the staining properties of fibrin; found in thrombi or degenerate parts of chronic inflammatory lesions.

FLUOROCHROME Fluorescent group attached to a larger molecule, thereby conferring capacity to fluoresce on the whole molecule.
('Fluorene', a fluorescent hydrocarbon from coal tar; Gk.: *chroma*, colour.)

FREUND'S ADJUVANT *Complete Freund's adjuvant:* a water-in-oil emulsion of an antigen (which usually distributes itself in the aqueous phase); to the oily phase killed *Mycobacterium tuberculosis* or a related organism is added. The emulsion commonly contains mineral oil mixed with an emulsifying agent.

Incomplete Freund's adjuvant: As above but without *Mycobacterium tuberculosis* or other bacillary addition.

GERMINAL CENTRE (synonyms: lymphocytopoietic nodules, secondary nodules of Ehrich). A reactive change in the cortex of a lymph node, thymus, Malpighian body of the spleen or any accumulated mass of lymphocytes consisting of a loosely packed, roughly spherical collection of cells which are larger and have paler more open nuclei than the surrounding cortex of closely packed small lymphocytes. They usually include many cells with mitotic figures.

GOLGI ELEMENT or apparatus Intracellular organoid first defined by means of the silver method of Golgi (1898) in nerve cells and later found in almost all differentiated cells of vertebrates, but being particularly prominent in protein-secreting cells.

In electron micrographs of osmium-fixed material the Golgi element consists of a collection of round or oval bodies outlined by a smooth surfaced membrane. In the majority of exocrine glands it forms a localized dense mass, situated between the nuclear and the excreting poles. In leucocytes it is a dense mass located in the concavity of the nucleus. In the plasma cell it usually appears as a juxta-nuclear mass or (in Giemsa, or haematoxylin and eosin stained material) a colourless zone outlined by the surrounding basophilia and abutting on and overlapping the nucleus.

HAEMOCYTOBLAST Round cell (diameter = 15–20 μ in frozen sections) with central or slightly eccentric nucleus; the cytoplasm is deeply basophilic (due to high content of RNA) and frequently shows a clearer zone shaped as a crescent at one side of the nucleus (this being the negative image of Golgi element and perinuclear mitochondria); no granules are visible in the cytoplasm. The nucleus is round with chromatin loosely arranged as tenuous strands bounding relatively large spaces; basophilic nucleoli (due to high content of RNA) are prominent and vary in number from one to five.

HALF-LIFE Time taken to decrease to half. When the rate of decrease is exponential (i.e. the rate of disappearance at any given time is proportional to the amount present at that time) the half-life is a constant quantity.

HAPTEN A specific protein-free substance whose chemical configuration is such that it can interact with the specific antibody combining groups on an antibody molecule, but which fails by itself to elicit the formation of a detectable amount of antibody.
(Gk.: *haptein*, to grasp.)

HETERO- Other (implication, from another species).
hetero-antibody: antibody which reacts with an antigen from another species of animal.
hetereocytotropic: term applied to antibodies which attach to certain kinds of cell in animals of a different species from that in which they were made (cf. homocytotropic).
heterogeneic: with a different genetic constitution (in transplantation), synonym: *allogeneic.*
heterogenetic, *heterophile:* terms applied to antigens which occur in more than one species of animal, and may be immunologically related to antigens also found in plants or microbes (e.g. Forssman antigens).
heterograft: graft taken from an animal of a different species.
heterologous (synonym: heterospecific): derived from another species (very general—includes animal species or chemical d fferences).
heterotopic: applied to tissue grafts, in which the tissue is grafted into a site anatomically different from that in which it was present in the donor.

HOMO- Derived from like (used in contrast to iso = identical) e.g.
homocytotropic: term applied to antibodies which attach specifically to certain kinds of cell in the same species as that in which they are made (e.g. mast cell homocytotropic; macrophage homocytotropic).
homograft: graft derived from one animal to an animal of the same species but differing in genetic constitution.
homologous: derived from an animal of the same species (but different genetic constitution). When difference in genetic constitution is to be emphasized, the term *allogeneic* should be used.

HOMOLOGOUS DISEASE Wasting disease in animals which have been lethally irradiated and have recovered following the transfusion of lymphoid cells derived from normal animals of the same species, but of a different strain. Regarded as a manifestation of graft *versus* host interaction.
(The term is based on the use of 'homologous' for 'allogeneic'.)

HYALINE (in connective tissue) An alteration in sections of fibrous connective tissue and the walls of blood vessels whereby the fibres assume a homogeneous glassy or refractile appearance. This change in refractive index is dependent upon an increase in local protein concentration. The affected area of tissue is acidophil (or stains well with acid dyes like eosin). 'Hyaline' is also usually used in descriptive pathology for:

(i) fused blood platelets
(ii) condensed fibrin } 'hyaline thrombi'
(iii) droplets of refractile appearance within cells.
(iv) transparent refractile urinary casts.

HYDROGEN BOND A weak attraction between one electronegative atom and a hydrogen atom that is covalently linked to a second electronegative atom.

IMMUNOGEN, IMMUNOGENIC Able to elicit antibody formation or sensitization.

IMMUNOGLOBULIN (Ig.) This general term has been introduced to describe all proteins which have antibody activity, together with those proteins without known antibody activity but which share a common antigenic specificity with them and are produced by similar cells. Thus such proteins are included as myeloma proteins, Bence-Jones proteins and subunits of antibodies.

Within the immunoglobulins different classes are recognized as follows:

IgG (γG) — corresponding to γ-globulin
IgA (γA) — ,, ,, γ_{1A} or β_{2A} globulin
IgM (γM) — ,, ,, γ_{1M} or β_{2M} globulin
IgD (γD) —
IgE (γE) —

(See Chapter Four.) The use of these terms has the advantage that they do not imply any statement about electrophoretic mobilities, unlike the terms at present in common use, whose implications in this respect are only broadly true.

IMMUNOLOGICAL PARALYSIS Absence of normal specific immunological response to an antigen, resulting from previous contact with the same antigen, administered in a quantity greatly exceeding that required to elicit an immunological response. The normal capacity to respond to other unrelated antigens is retained.

The term immunological paralysis is usually employed when specific unresponsiveness is induced in adult life, while 'tolerance' has been used when unresponsiveness is induced before the immunological apparatus is fully developed. It is not clear that there is any essential distinction between the mechanisms involved in each case.

IMMUNOLOGICAL TOLERANCE Absence of the normal immunological response to an antigen; especially failure to give a homograft response, so that an allogeneic tissue graft may be retained for an indefinite period.

Specific immunological tolerance may be induced under certain circumstances by contact with relatively large amounts of antigen(s)—e.g. during embryonic or early post-natal life. Animals so treated subsequently fail to respond to the antigens in question but respond normally to unrelated antigens.

IMMUNOLOGICALLY COMPETENT CELLS Term introduced by P.B. Medawar to indicate cells which are able to respond to contact with any particular immunogen by manifesting or developing a specific immunological capacity. Such responsiveness would include the formation of specific antibody, or the ability to react in delayed-type hypersensitivity reactions or in homograft rejection. See Chapter Three.

INTERFERON A soluble protein, whose nature is not yet known, which is produced by many animal cells within a few hours after uptake of living or suitably killed virus. Interferon suppresses the growth of the same or many different viruses in other cells by interfering with the synthesis of new virus nucleic acid. See Chapter Two.

ISO- Derived from an animal of identical genetic constitution. (Gk.: *isos*, equal.) (In general applicable to inbred pure lines or homozygotic twins.)
isogenic: of the same genetic constitution.
isograft: graft between animals of the same species and the same genetic constitution.

isologous: derived from animals of the same genetic constitution (often used synonymously with isogenic).

ISO-ANTIBODY Term used to indicate antibody which reacts with an antigen present in the tissues or fluids of another member of the same species of animal, but not in the animal itself.

(This use of the term iso- does not correspond with the other uses in transplantation and genetics, where iso- implies that the genetical constitution is identical. Iso-antibody is widely used by workers on blood group serology and transfusion.) In this sense also *iso-immunization*, *iso-antigen*.

ISO-ANTIGEN Constituent of cells or body fluids of an animal which can elicit specific antibody formation in some other (genetically different) animals of the same species but not in the animal itself.

ISOPHILE ANTIBODY Term applied to antibody formed in response to immunization with red cells which reacts with constituents of the red cells which are peculiar to the red cells used, and do not cross-react with antigens present in red cells of other species. (In contrast to 'heterophile'.)

KURLOFF CELL Cell containing a single spherical eosinophilic and metachromatic cytoplasmic inclusion, which contains a sulphated mucopolysaccharide and protein. Occurs in the circulation and lymphoid tissues (including thymus and spleen) of guinea-pigs, attaining highest numbers in females especially during late pregnancy and after treatment with oestrogenic hormones. Variously described as a modified lymphocyte or reticular cell.

LECTIN Agents derived from plants which display specific antibody-like activity towards cells or materials derived from animals. Generally used to describe agents which specifically agglutinate human blood cells. Lectins commonly behave as anti-A or anti-H. (W.C. Boyd also suggested that *lectin* could apply to those normal antibodies thought not to result from antigen stimuli.) ('Legere', to pick or choose—W.C. Boyd.)

LEPTOCHROMATIC Type of chromatin network of the nuclei of cells in the sections of fixed and embedded tissues, the strands of which are tenuous and separated from each other by open spaces.

LYMPHOCYTE Round cell with scanty cytoplasm, diameter 7–12 μ. In stained preparations cytoplasm is transparent, lacking basophilia, but at times containing azurophilic granules. The nucleus is round, sometimes indented, with chromatin arranged in coarse masses and without visible nucleoli. Lymphocytes may be actively motile.

LYMPHORRHAGES Collections of small round cells (mainly lymphocytes and macrophages) occurring in the muscles in cases of myasthenia gravis and more rarely of rheumatoid arthritis. (The related muscle fibres usually show slight degenerative changes and there may be actual muscle atrophy.)

LYON HYPOTHESIS States that only one of the X chromosomes in a female (XX) somatic cell nucleus is active. This predicts that in a female heterozygous for an X-linked dominant gene only half her somatic cells will manifest the effect of the gene.

LYSOSOME A term introduced by de Duve to describe a class of intracellular vesicles which can be separated by high-speed centrifugation of many disrupted cells, and which contain a number of hydrolytic enzymes (e.g. acid phosphatase, glucuronidase, lipase, cathepsins) which are set free when the vesicles are disrupted. The granules of neutrophil and eosinophil polymorphonuclear leucocytes contain similar enzymes. Their function is regarded as to digest materials taken into the cell by pinocytosis or phagocytosis. Such materials are at first contained in small vesicles or 'phagosomes', which fuse with the lysosomes to form 'phagolysosomes'.

MAST CELL There are two types of mast cell, the common *tissue mast cell* which arises in loose, well-vascularized connective tissue, and the blood mast cell (mast leucocyte or *basophil*) whose origin is the bone marrow and whose habitat is the peripheral blood. The nucleus of the tissue mast cell is round or oval; that of the basophil is more polymorphous. Mast cells can be recognized by the presence in their cytoplasm of basophilic and usually metachromatic granules. These were regarded by Ehrlich, the discoverer of the mast cell, as stored nutriment (*mastung* =feeding). The basophilic metachromatic component is an acid mucopolysaccharide, heparin. Mast cells also manufacture and store histamine and, in mouse and rat, 5-hydroxytryptamine.

MUCOPEPTIDES Molecules containing amino sugars (including muramic acid) and amino acids. The amino acids are commonly linked to the carboxyl group of muramic acid by a peptide bond with the amino group of alanine. Common constituents of bacterial cell walls.

MUCOPOLYSACCHARIDES Polysaccharides containing a minor proportion of chemically linked protein or polypeptide (e.g. blood group substances).

MUCOPROTEINS (synonym:glycoproteins) Proteins containing a minor proportion of chemically linked carbohydrate.

Many plasma proteins contain two per cent or more of carbohydrate, e.g. γ-globulin, orosomucoid, α_1-glycoprotein, transferrin, caeruloplasmin.

MYOCYTE Cell morphologically resembling a muscle fibre cell which occurs in the medulla of the thymus in certain species including man.

OLIGOSACCHARIDE Compound composed of a small number of pentose, hexose or heptose (5, 6 or 7 carbon sugar) units joined by glycosidic linkages. The sugars may have nitrogenous or other substituents.

E.g. di-, tri- tetra-saccharides, in contradistinction to polysaccharides. (Gk.: *oligos*, few; *sackar*, sugar (from Sanskrit).)

ONCOGENIC Capable of causing normal cells to acquire neoplastic characteristics. Usually applied to viruses, such as adenoviruses. (See Chapter Fourteen.)

OPERON Genetic unit consisting of adjacent genes functioning together under the joint control of an operator and a repressor.

OPSONIC INDEX Ratio of phagocytic activity of patient's blood for a given microbe to the phagocytic activity of blood from a normal subject. The phagocytic activity is measured by incubating equal volumes of a bacterial suspension (of appropriate density) and of fresh citrated blood for 15 minutes. A stained film is then prepared and the average number of bacteria contained in each polymorphonuclear leucocyte is measured.

The opsonic index was introduced by A.E. Wright as a means of studying the progress of resistance during the course of a disease.

OPSONIN A substance, usually also an antibody, occurring in blood serum which attaches to bacteria and other particles and facilitates their phagocytosis.
(Gk.: *opson*, dressing or relish.)

ORGAN SPECIFICITY Descriptive of antigens which are restricted to a particular organ or tissue, e.g. lens protein, thyroglobulin, some antigens in brain or testis.

It is not uncommon for immunologically similar antigens to occur in corresponding tissues in individuals from a wide range of different species.

ORTHOTOPIC Grafts transferred to positions formerly occupied by tissue of the same kind.

PARAPROTEIN Term used to describe myeloma proteins or the macroglobulins of Waldenström's macroglobulinaemia, introduced at a time when such proteins were considered to be essentially abnormal globulins. (Gk.: *para*, beside, except.)

PARATOPE Site or area on an antibody molecule complementary to the epitope.

PAUL-BUNNELL TEST Test for ability of serum to agglutinate sheep erythrocytes due to presence of heterophile antibody in cases of infectious mononucleosis (glandular fever). The antibody also acts on ox erythrocytes.

PERIODIC ACID-SCHIFF TECHNIQUE Various non-diffusible tissue structures which contain the 1:2 glycol grouping –CHOH–CHOH– or amino-glycol grouping $-CHNH_2-CHOH-$ or the oxidation product –CHOH–CO– may be oxidized by periodic acid to aldehyde derivatives, which are detected by the use of Schiff's reagent (leucofuchsin) which gives a reddish-purple colour in their presence. Typical PAS-positive substances, appearing red by this technique, are glycogen and polysaccharides generally, phospholipids, cerebrosides, mucoproteins, glycoproteins, cellulose and amyloid.

PHACO-ANAPHYLACTIC ENDOPHTHALMITIS A generalized inflammation of the uveal tract produced by the liberation of lens proteins in persons who are hypersensitive to this substance (usually as a result of auto-immunization).

PHAGOCYTIN A basic protein lethal for Gram-negative bacilli derived from leucocytes; and considered to play a role in the intracellular destruction of phagocytosed bacteria.

PINOCYTOSIS Drinking by cells, as opposed to phagocytosis, eating by cells. Microscopical term to indicate the engulfing of globules of fluid at the surface of the cell and the passage of these into the depths of the cytoplasm. (Gk.: *pinein*, to drink; *kytos*, cell.)

POLYSOME Cluster of ribosomes held together by a strand of messenger RNA. The messenger RNA moves out from the nucleus and attaches itself to a ribosome which moves along its length. The attachment subsequently of other ribosomes in sequence produces the appearance of the polysome cluster.

PREMUNITION A postulated type of immunity in protozoal infections, dependent upon the mutual tolerance of host and parasite, whereby a subsequent infection is modified so long as parasites persist in the host but which disappears after parasite elimination.

PSEUDOGLOBULIN In contrast to euglobulin, the fraction of plasma globulins which is soluble in distilled water. The term is sometimes used to mean the fraction of plasma proteins precipitated between 33 per cent and 46 per cent saturation with ammonium sulphate. It contains part of the γ-globulin, and many β- and some α-globulins.

REAGINIC ANTIBODY Term used to describe skin-sensitizing antibodies in human atopic subjects. ('Reaginic' is sometimes used by venereologists for antibody responsible for positive Wassermann or TPI tests.)

RECEPTOR-DESTROYING ENZYME (synonyms: RDE, Neuraminidase). Enzyme derived from filtrates of *Vibrio cholerae* cultures, which acts to break a glycosidic linkage by which the acetyl neuraminic acid is bound to an adjacent sugar residue.

H
C
HCH O H C—NH—Ac
H
—O—C—C
α O
COOH
Site of action
CHOH
CHOH
CH_2OH

This destroys the cell receptor sites for certain viruses (e.g. myxoviruses), and thus the name is derived. Myxoviruses themselves may possess neuraminidase activity.

PRIMARY STRUCTURE (of a protein) The number of polypeptide chains, the member and sequence of amino acids in the peptide chains and the situation of inter- and intrachain disulphide bridges.

RIBOSOME Cytoplasmic particle (usually about 150 Å diameter) composed of ribonucleic acid and protein, which are considered to be the sites at which protein synthesis takes place. In fully differentiated cells of the pancreas or liver most of these particles are attached to membrane surfaces within the cytoplasm, but in embryonic tissues and many tumour cells the particles appear free in the cytoplasm.

RUNT DISEASE Condition of dwarfing which follows the injection of mature allogeneic immunologically competent cells into immunologically immature recipients. Characterized by failure to thrive, lymph node atrophy, hepato- and spleno-megaly, anaemia and diarrhoea.

SCHICK TEST An *in vivo* test for the presence of diphtheria antitoxin, introduced by Bela Schick in 1913. A small quantity of diphtheria toxin (1/50 of the minimum lethal dose for a guinea-pig, in 0·2 ml) is injected intracutaneously into the skin of one forearm, and an equal quantity of heat-inactivated toxin into the other. In a subject who *lacks* immunity (very little or no antitoxin being present) the active toxin produces a *positive* reaction, i.e. a local inflammatory reaction, which is present at 48 hr., maximal at 4 to 5 days, and gradually fades. In an *immune* subject no such reaction is produced, and the test is *negative*.

Some persons give a delayed-type hypersensitivity reaction to the proteins in diphtheria toxoid, as a result of previous infection or prophylactic immunization. This '*pseudoreaction*' is manifested by an inflammatory response at the sites of injection both of the active and of the inactivated toxin, which may mask the true reaction. However, pseudoreactions are maximal at about 36 hr. and fade before a true positive reaction has reached its peak. By reading the test after 48 hr. and again after 5 to 7 days the true reactions may be determined at the second reading. Caution should be exercised in immunizing a subject who gives a pseudoreaction, since he is liable to have a severe delayed-type reaction to the diphtheria prophylactic employed.

SCHLEPPER A substance which when mixed with another substance which by itself is not immunogenic, or only very weakly so, converts the second substance into a good immunogen. Pig serum was often used for this purpose, but nowadays methylated bovine serum albumin is used more commonly. The 'schlepper' is thought to form an immunogenic complex, and acts as a carrier.

(German: *schleppen*, to drag.)

SECONDARY DISEASE Disease resulting from the attempt to restore a lethally irradiated animal with bone marrow from an allogeneic source.

SEDIMENTATION COEFFICIENT AND CONSTANT The sedimentation coefficient represents the rate of sedimentation of a solute in cm per sec., per unit centrifugal field of force (dynes/gram). The sedimentation coefficient is expressed in sec. The absolute sediment constant is derived from an observed sedimentation coefficient by correction to conditions in water at a temperature of (usually) 20°C. Sedimentation constants are expressed in Svedberg (S) units where one Svedberg (S) = 10^{-13} times the absolute sedimentation constant.

SESSILE ANTIBODY Antibody which is attached to tissues sufficiently firmly to resist removal by, for example, washing or perfusion.

SIMONSEN PHENOMENON Simonsen (1957) produced splenomegaly in young chickens by injecting 18-day embryos intravenously with adult fowl leucocytes. The effect is characterized as a *graft-versus-host* reaction; and the term has been extended to include other probable graft-*versus*-host reactions such as the production of inflammatory foci on the chorio-allantoic membrane of the embryonated hen's egg by adult fowl cells. The increased cellularity of the spleen or in other foci is mainly due to host cells, although the reaction is evoked by the donor cells.

SPECIES SPECIFICITY Antigens occurring in the members of a species and restricted to this species are termed species specific.

SULPHYDRYL Name given to the univalent radical –SH, usually attached to carbon, which occurs in proteins as a result of the presence of the amino acid cysteine. The presence of –SH groups is important for the activity of many enzymes, which are inactivated when the –SH is combined with heavy metals or is oxidized. –SH groups may become joined to form –S–S– (disulphide) bonds, thereby attaching polypeptide chains to one another and profoundly affecting the shape of the molecules.

SVEDBERG (See SEDIMENTATION COEFFICIENT).

SYNGENEIC Synonym for *isogeneic*.

TERTIARY STRUCTURE (of a protein) The three-dimensional folding of the polypeptide chain(s) which characterizes a protein in its native states.

TERTIARY NODULE (PARACORTICAL NODULE) Area of aggregation of cells in a lymph node at the inner limit of cortex and projecting inwards to encroach on the medulla. The area occupied corresponds with the 'thymus dependent area'.

TRANSPLANTATION IMMUNITY Term applied to accelerated graft rejection, due to a state of immunization of the recipient by previous contact with antigens present in the graft.

VACCINATION 1. Originally: the inoculation into the skin of living vaccinia virus to produce a state of immunity against smallpox.

2. Current usage: the injection or ingestion of an antigen with the intention of producing a state of immunity in the recipient.

VACCINE 1. A suspension of dead or living organisms which is injected (or ingested) with the intention of producing a state of immunity in the recipient animal.

2. Originally: a suspension of cowpox vaccine used for inoculation to produce immunity against smallpox.

3. Current usage extends term to solutions of bacterial and viral antigens (e.g. toxoids of *Cl. tetani*) and pollens (pollen vaccines).

VAN DER WAALS FORCE Weak attraction, acting over only a very short distance, which operates between all types of molecules, polar as well as non-polar.

XENOGENEIC Of the genetical difference of a different species of animal.

XENOGRAFT Graft taken from a different species of animal (synonym: heterograft).

(Gk.: *xenos*, foreign.)

Index

Acquired haemolytic anaemia 608–613
  in neoplastic diseases of reticular tissues 605
  pathogenesis of 612
Actinaria 14
Adaptive enzymes, relation to antibody synthesis 140
Addison's disease (*see also* Idiopathic adrenal insufficiency)
  relation of 'idiopathic' disease to auto-immunization 641
  relationship to experimental adrenalitis 641
  susceptibility to infection in 41
Adenovirus
  persistence of in host cells 416
  possibility of vaccination against 19
Adjuvant arthritis 626
Adjuvanticity (*see* Glossary for definition)
Adjuvants 18, 250–6 (*see also* Glossary for definition)
  cellular effects of 302–4
  endotoxin from Gram-negative bacteria 255
  Freund complete and incomplete 253–5, 303–4
  mineral carriers 303
  mycobacterial peptidoglycolipid 254
Adoptive immunization 549, 552
Adoptive tolerance 549
Adrenalectomy, effect on infection due to pneumococci 43
Adrenalitis, experimental production in guinea-pig 641
Affinity of antibody, changes during immunization 134
Agammaglobulinaemia (*see also* Immunoglobulin deficiency)
  congenital sex-linked 328
  primary acquired 328
Age, relation to immunity 39–41
Agglutination reactions 6, 370–83 (*see also* Haemagglutination)
  definition 350
  passive agglutination tests 374
  range of sensitivity of 371
  role of electrolytes in 370
  sensitivity of 357, 370–83
  slide test for blood-grouping 372
Agglutinins, to Streptococcus M.G. 379
Agranulocytic angina 482
Agranulocytosis 323
  drug-induced 478, 482
Alexander H.J. 30
Alexine 7 (*see* Complement)
Allele (*see* Glossary for definition)
Allergen (*see* Glossary for definition)
Allergic encephalomyelitis 644–51 (*see also* Encephalomyelitis)
Allergic vasculitis 457
Allogeneic (*see* Glossary for definition)
Allogeneic inhibition 143, 556, 597
Allograft (*see* Glossary for definition)
Allotypes 159 (*see also* Glossary for definition)
  association of antibodies with 249
  Gm 162
  immunization of child against maternal IgG 322
  InV 162

Alum as adjuvant 19
Aluminium hydroxide, as adjuvant 250
Aluminium phosphate
  as adjuvant 252
  granuloma formation by 252
Amethopterin (MTX) 668 (*see also* Methotrexate)
Amino-terminal (*see* Glossary for definition)
Anaemia, acquired haemolytic 24
Anaesthesia, effect on resistance 80
Anaphylactoid purpura 466
Anaphylatoxin
  as mediators of anaphylaxis 489
  formation of 488
  participation of complement 488–489
Anaphylaxis 14, 16, 428
  bradykinin in 438
  following coitus 655
  in the dog 14
  in man 442
  in the rabbit 434, 442
  local 443
  mechanisms of 438
  reversed 439
  species variation in 441
  SRS-A in 440
Anergy 530, 590 (*see* Glossary for definition)
  as cause of tumour growth 590
Angström (*see* Glossary for definition)
Anthrax, species variation in resistance to 36
Antibiotics 24
  effect in gastro-intestinal flora 47
Antibodies
  absorption from gut 315, 317
  affinity of 252
  antibacterial effect in pneumococcal pneumonia 419–20
  antiviral, neutralizing 235, 394–6, 412–18
  as adjuvant 252
  bactericidal effect of 418
  biosynthetic mechanisms for 238
  blocking 367, 375
  carbohydrate content 153
  cold 610
  cytophilic 176, 381–2, 436, 541
  effect on clearance of bacteria from blood 76
  effect on streptococcal infections 420
  effect on dispersed tumour cells 581
  equilibrium constants of 179
  immunogenic properties of 153
  in brucellosis 378, 424
  incomplete 367, 375
  incomplete in erythroblastosis foetalis 378
  in gonorrhoea 424
  in graft rejection 548
  in milk 315
  interaction with antigen 178, 179
  in tuberculosis 424
  molecular weight 153
  non-agglutinating 375
  non-precipitable 367
  opsonic effect of 419
  persistence of in virus infections 234
  protective effects of 408
  regulating effect on immunological response 259–62
  role in enteric infections 421–4
  saline 375
  sedimentation coefficients 153
  univalent 375
  warm 610
Antibody fragments, transmission *in utero* 315
Antibody production 85, 268
  at local site of injection 262–6
  by foetus 312
  by the central nervous system 270–1
  by the liver 266–8
  by localized haemolysis in gel 397
  by lymph nodes 263
  by lymphoid tissues 262
  by single cells 397, 396, 142
  by the spleen 263
  by the thymus 269

cellular changes in relation to adjuvants 302–4
cells involved in 282
development of in infant 672
effect of ascorbic acid deficiency 258
effect of nutrition on 258
in appendix 257
in germ-free animals 257
in relation to salivary glands and gut 266
in udder 317
microdroplet technique 397
relation to germinal centre formation 295–302
role of central and peripheral lymphoid tissues in 262
suppression by pre-existing antibody 261
Anticutins 531
Antigen-antibody combination
in varying proportions 349
reversibility of 356
Antigen-antibody complexes
activity *in vitro* 453
biological activity 453
effects following injection of preformed complexes 456
Antigenic competition 143
Antigens 84
absence from antibody 141
carbohydrate 21
cross reactions between 215
distinction from immunogen 210
H 558, 694
I 604
interaction with immunologically competent cells 110
molecules, valency of 350
'O' 231, 694
of Gram-negative bacilli 22
of haemophilus 22
of human erythrocytes 23
of plants 233, 235
of proteins 235
of streptococcus 22, 558
of viruses 233
Rhesus 23
size of site involved in combination with antibody 215
specificity of 212
T 558
V 694
Antiglobulin
consumption test 379, 381, 618
fluorescent, uses of 389
in diagnosis of Rh. disease 375
test in haemolytic anaemia 609
Anti-histamine drugs 16
Anti-immunoglobulin test 609
Antilymphocyte serum (ALS) 571
mode of action of 572
'Antiseptic paint' 307, 334
Antiseptics 11
Antitoxins (*see also* individual agents)
diphtheria 5
flocculation reaction 367
Aplastic anaemia 323
Appendix 93, 282
Arrhenius S. 13
Arthus M. 15, 429
Arthus phenomenon 16
Arthus reactions 449
activation of complement components in 452
histology 451
Aschoff L. 70
Aschoff body 470
Askonas B.A. 267, 268
Aspermatogenesis 18
Aspergillus fumigatus
immunity in infections with, 426
Asthma 16, 443
hereditary basis for 443
Asúa, de 71
Atopy 444 (*see also* Glossary for definition)
nature of sensitizing antigens in 448
Auto-allergic disease, definition 600, 606
Auto-antibody (Definition, *see* Glossary)
cold 605
consequences of transfer across placenta 321

Auto-antibody—*contd.*
mechanisms for stimulation of 601–5
to the eye-lens 602
to nuclear constituents 628
to steroid hormones 642
Auto-antigens, in thyroid tissue 635
Autograft (*see* Glossary for definition)
Auto-immune complement fixation test (AICF) 658
Auto-immune disease
criteria for definition of 606
definition 601
in association with lymphoproliferative disorders 534
treatment by corticosteroid drugs 667
treatment by means of immunosuppressive drugs 667
Auto-immunity 10, 17, 18
after carbon tetrachloride damage to liver 659
against muscle 663
in diseases of the thymus 662
in liver diseases 657–9
in pancreatitis 661
in post-cardiotomy syndrome 656
in primary biliary cirrhosis 658
in rheumatic heart disease 656
in ulcerative colitis 659
to myosin 663
Auto-immunization (*see also* Glossary for definition)
by loss of tolerance to self components 605
relation to diseases of the eye 643
Autologous (*see* Glossary)
Autosomal recessive alymphocytic agammaglobulinaemia 325
Auto-vaccines 10
Avery O.T. 21, 22, 214
Avian leukosis 589
Avidity 125
definition 356
in toxin-neutralization 394
methods for study of antigen-antibody binding 401–4
Azathioprine 563, 570, 667
Bacille Calmette-Guérin 20
miliary tuberculosis following 334
results of MRC trials with 519, 681
use in immunization 680
Bacillus anthracis 63, 75
Bacteraemia 78
factors involved 79
Bacterial allergy (*see also* Hypersensitivity, delayed type) 29, 493
Bacterial capsules 76
effect of antibody on phagocytosis 76
Bacterial endocarditis 77
Bacterial genetics 22
Bacterial toxins, neutralization of, by antibody 408
Bactericidal activity
activity against Gram-negative species of bacteria 50
of blood 50
sensitivity of method for determining 357
Bacteriocines 47
Bacteriophage 22, 394
cell wall receptors for 230
typing by means of 230
Bagassosis 475
Barber, Mary 18
Basement membrane, antibody to, in nephritis 462
Beard J. 92
Behring L. von 5, 30
Bence-Jones protein 158, 159, 163, 338
antigenic type of 338
nature of 338
relation to Ig sub-units 338
(*see also* Glossary for definition)
Benign chronic granulocytopenia 323
Bentonite
effect on immunogenicity 251
effect on biosynthesis of IgM 251
Benzol poisoning 323
Berylliosis 533
Beryllium sulphate, as adjuvant 302

Besredka A. 171
Beta-2A-globulin (*see* Immunoglobulin A)
Beta-2M globulin (*see* IgM, Macroglobulin)
Billingham R. 31
Bing-Neel syndrome 342
Biological standards, use of 708
Biological False Positive Reaction (*see also* Glossary for definition) 388
  for syphilis 627, 630
Birkhaug apparatus 680
Blackley 16
Blockade of reticulo-endothelial system 242
Blocking antibodies, in atopy 444, 446–8
Blood
  bactericidal mechanism of 48
  transfusion 23
Blood-brain barrier 71
Blood group antigens 172, 220
  A substance 218, 221
  B substance 221
  cross-reactions with bacteria 218, 225
  e-antigen 610
  end groups of 222
  H substance 221
  I-antigen 172
  Le[a] substance 221
  Rh-antigen 610
Blood groups 11, 23
  relation to heterophile antigens 225
  relation to *E. coli* 225
Boivin A. 226
Boivin antigens 227
Bone, homografts of 560
Bone marrow
  antibody formation in 267–9
  origin of lymphocytes bound for thymus 280
Bonington, Sir Ralph Bloomfield 10
Boorman K.E. 18
Booster Response 87 (*see* Secondary response)
Bordet J. 7, 13, 30, 189, 200
Bordetella pertussis 302
  action in increasing formation of rat mast cell sensitizing antibody 256
  as adjuvant 255–6
  histamine sensitizing activity of 256
Botulism
  passive immunization against 704
Bovine gamma globulin, elimination from blood of rabbit 244
Boyden S.V. 381
Bradykinin, in anaphylaxis 432, 435
Brain
  antibody formation in 270
  as an immunologically privileged site 577
Brambell F.W.R. 314
Brent L.E. 31
Bright R. 465
Brucellosis
  cell-mediated hypersensitivity in 522, 524
  cellular immunity in 65
  Brucella abortus 20, 65
  Brucella tularense 20
Buchner H. 7, 12
Bufo marinus 93
Burkitt's lymphoma 593
  role of insect vector in 594
  treatment by cyclophosphamide 594
Burnet F.M. 31, 32, 89, 113, 141
Bursa of Fabricius 105, 110, 325
  anatomy of 280
  equivalent organ in man 106
Bursectomy plus irradiation
  effect on germinal-centre development 105
  effect on immunoglobulin biosynthesis 105
  immunoglobulin production after 106
Byssinosis 475

Calcium alginate, as adjuvant 250
Calf scours 317
Calmette A. 12
Cancer, immunology of 580
Candida albicans 334
Capsular polysaccharides (*see also* Pneumococcal capsular polysaccharides)
of *B. anthracis* 232
of *H. influenzae* 232
of *Str. pneumoniae* 232
role in phagocytosis 60
Capsule swelling 21
Carboxy-terminal (*see* Glossary for definition)
Cardiolipin 387
as immunogenic determinant 208
Cartilage, homografts of 501
Casoni test 486, 523
Caspersson T. 288
Catabolism
of antigen inside macrophages 287
of foreign immunogens 244
of heterologous antiserum 701
Catheter fever 79
Cat-scratch fever, delayed-type hypersensitivity in 524
Cellular immunity 8, 64, 67
in invertebrates 90
relation of degree of immunity to number of organisms present 67
role of delayed-type hypersensitivity in 66–7
Cellular reaction, to immunogens 282
Central arteriole of the white pulp 276
Central nervous system, antibody production in 270–1
Cerebrospinal fluid, immunoglobulin levels in multiple sclerosis 652
Cerumen, bactericidal activity of 46
Charrin A. 6
Chase M.W. 29
Chediak-Higashi syndrome 324
Chemicals, sensitization by 494–5
Chemotaxis 60, 61
of macrophages 200
of neutrophil polymorphs 199
Chimaeras 88
production after supra-lethal X-irradiation 567
Chlorambucil 668
Cholera 20
immunization against 695
of chickens 3
vibrio of 6
Cholesterol, in relation to rheumatic fever 474
Chorionepithelioma, amethopterin in treatment of 593
Chorionic gonadotrophin, immunochemical estimation 399
Choucroun N. 516
Chromium (^{51} Cr), as a cell label 404
Chromosome marker techniques, for study of cell migration 404
Cirrhosis, primary biliary 658
Cistron (*see* Glossary for definition)
Clasmatocytes 242
Clearance of bacteria from blood 75
role of liver and spleen 77
role of lungs 78
role of polymorphs 78
Clinical trials, of vaccines 707
Clonal selection, hypothesis 141
Clone 32 (*see also* Glossary for definition)
Clostridium tetani, persistence of spores in tissues 51
Clostridium welchii, persistence of spores in tissues 51
Coca A.F. 444
Coeliac disease, as manifestation of allergy to gluten 660
Colchicine, as adjuvant 302
Cold agglutinins 379
in auto-immune disease 613
in blackwater fever 379
in primary atypical pneumonia 379, 612
in trypanosomiasis 379

relationship to T-agglutinin 605
Cold auto-antibody 605, 610, 613
Colicines, definition of 47
Collagen, damage to, in auto-immune diseases 622
Collagen disorders 619–31
Colon, antibodies to 659–60
Colostrum 171
- antibody in 256
- IgA transport into 316
- of calf 36
- of piglet 36
- relation to haemolytic disease of pig 321

Combined prophylactics 675
'Committed (immunologically competent) cells' 89
Common cold 20
Complement 7, 30, 188 *et seq.* (*see also* Glossary for definition)
- action
  - stages of mechanisms 192
  - morphology of cell lysis in electron microscope 191
- antibodies against 197
- biological significance of 202, 203
- components of 190
- deficiencies of 196
  - in inbred mice 197
  - in inbred rabbits 197
  - in man 197
- in Arthus-type responses 488
- in glomerulonephritis 468
- in hypersensitivity reactions 487
- species differences in 197

Complement fixation test 383–8
- advantages of 386
- applications of 386
- in detection of incomplete antibody 386
- in diagnosis of gonococcal arthritis 385

Compound granular corpuscles 71
Congenital acholuric jaundice (*see* acquired haemolytic anaemia)
Congenital neutropenia 323
Congenital splenic hypoplasia 324
Conglutinin 200, 603 (*see also* Immunoconglutinin)
Coniosporium corticale, in maple-stripper's disease 476
Connective tissue diseases 619–31
Contact sensitivity
- evidence for peripheral sensitization of lymphocytes in 504
- induction of 503
- patch test for 505
- relation of sensitizing agents to their ability to combine with protein 503
- to nickel salts 503
- to plant products 503

Cooke R.A. 16, 17
Coombs R.R.A. 18
Coombs test (antiglobulin test) (*see* Glossary for definition)
Coons A. H. 28, 242, 389
Co-operation, between thymus and marrow-derived cells 103
Copro-antibody 171, 422 (*see also* Glossary for definition)
Cord factor 516
Cornea, grafts of 500
Corneal test
- in allergic encephalomyelitis 648
- in delayed-type hypersensitivity 514–15

Corticosteroids (*see* Glucocorticoid drugs and Cortisone)
Corticotrophin, immunochemical estimation of 399
Cortisone (*see also* Glucocorticoid drugs)
- effect in sarcoidosis 531
- effect on antibody production 258
- effect on inflammation 42
- effect on latent infection of rats with *C. pseudo-tuberculosis* 42
- effect on lymphocytes 259
- effect on phagocytosis 42
- effect on tuberculous disease 42
- resemblance of immunological effects to X-irradiation 258

'Cot death' 322, 448–9
- allergy to cow's milk in 448–9

Cowpox 686
C-reactive protein 201
Crossing-over (*see* Glossary for definition)
Cross-reacting antigens, role in stimulating auto-antibody 604
Cross-reactions between antigens 11, 12
Cryoglobulin 342 (*see also* Glossary for definition)
Cryoglobulinaemia 346
Cryoprecipitation, after intravenous injection of bacterial endotoxin 346–7
Cumley 24
Cushing's disease, increased susceptibility to infection in 41
C_X-reactive protein 201
Cyclophosphamide 568, 668
Cytophilic antibodies 176, 436, 541
  macrophage, in mouse 174
  to particulate antigens, test for 381–2
  to soluble antigens, test for 382–383

Dale H.H. 16, 431
Dalen-Fuchs nodule 645
Dander
  antigens of 448
  hypersensitivity to in man 443
Danysz phenomenon 355
Daphnia 9, 90
Dean H.W. 353
Delaunay A. 18
Delayed-type hypersensitivity (*see* Hypersensitivity, delayed-type and Immunity, cell mediated)
Denaturation (*see also* Glossary for definition)
  of proteins, effect on antigenic specificity 220
Dendritic cells 274, 287, 298
Denys J. 8
DNA, production of antibodies against 629
'depot effect', of adjuvants 252
Dermatitis
  contact 494
  (*see also* Contact sensitivity)
Dermatophyte fungi, resistance of skin to 45
Dermatophytids 483
Desensitization 542
  in contact hypersensitivity 543
  in simple protein hypersensitivity 543
  in tuberculosis 543
  use in atopic subjects 446–7
Determinant groups 85, 216, 248 (*see also* Glossary for definition
  definition 204
  size involved in secondary response 121
Dextran 67, 178
  relation of immunogenicity to molecular size 206
  size of antigenic determinant of 216
Diabetes mellitus
  increased susceptibility to infection in 51
  tuberculous infection in 41
Dienes L. 29
Di George syndrome 297
Dinitrophenyl (DNP) in fluorescence quenching 403
Diphtheria antitoxin 15, 150
  as a 'normal' antibody 49
  elimination from blood of rabbit 243
  of horse 243
Diphtheria immunization 18, 676, 693
  effect of maternal antibody 674
  passive 15, 703
Diphtheria toxin
  conversion to toxoid for practical immunization 675–6
  demonstration by gel diffusion 363

failure of young children to respond to 40
natural antibody to 49
neutralization of 84, 355–6, 367–368
species difference in resistance to 36
Disulphide bond (*see* Glossary for definition)
Dochez A.I. 21
'Doctor's dilemma' 10
Dodd, Barbara E. 18
Donath-Landsteiner phenomenon 609
Dracontiasis 485
Drug allergy (*see* Contact sensitivity)
Drug-induced purpura 478
Drug sensitivity 476
and agranulocytosis 482–3
and haemolytic anaemia 481
and polyarteritis 456–7
as cause of purpura 478–9
penicillin hypersensitivity 476
Dubos R.J. 39
Dungern, Von 351
Dust cells 73
Dys-γ-globulinaemia 330, 332 (*see also* Immunoglobulin deficiency)

Early-killing period, after local injection of bacteria 62
Eaton agent (*see Mycoplasma pneumoniae*)
Echidna 93
Eczema 332
Eczematous dermatitis 494
Edelman M. 155
Egg 313
passage of antibody from hen into 313
Egg yolk, anti-inflammatory agent in 474
Ehrich W.E. 273
Ehrlich P. 6, 12, 25, 18, 30, 113, 200, 139, 349
Electron microscope, studies in glomerulonephritis 459–60, 462–3, 464, 468–9
Electrophoresis 90, 149 (*see also* Immuno-electrophoresis)
of antibodies in starch gel 151
Elek S.D. 26, 363
Ellipsoids of spleen 276
Eltor *Vibrio cholerae* 695
Encephalomyelitis
complement fixing antibody of brain in 648
demyelination in 647
encephalitogenic immunogen of brain 647
experimental allergic (EAE) 602, 645–52
in relation to pathogenesis of multiple sclerosis 651
in relation to pathogenesis of vaccinial or post-infectious encephalomyelitis 651
myelotoxic factors in 648
necessity of Freund's complete adjuvant for production of 645
post-vaccinial 646
prevention by prior injection of brain immunogen 541
role of cell-mediated hypersensitivity in 648
Endocrines, homografts of 562
Endocytoplasmic reticulum 289, 290 (*see also* Glossary for definition)
Endocytosis 307
Endophthalmitis phacoanaphylactica
experimental 643
following cataract extraction 644
Endotoxin (*see also* Lipopolysaccharides and Glossary for definition)
adjuvant effect of 226–7, 250, 255
effect on germinal centres 227
effect on Shwartzmann reaction 227, 489
molecular structure of 228
shock due to 80

'Enhancement' 241, 582, 585–6
of growth of chorionepithelioma 593
Enteric fever 372
immunization against 421, 694
role of antibodies in 421–4
Enzymes, neutralization by antibody 409
Eosinophilia (*see also* Glossary for definition and Tropical eosinophilia)
associated with Ag/Ab reactions 486
associated with Arthus reactions 451
associated with helminth infestation 485
Eosinophil leucocytes 451
of rodents 486
role of 486
Epidermatophytids 483
Epidermophyton 46
Epididymitis 655
Epithelioid cells, in adjuvant granuloma 304
Epitope (*see* Glossary for definition)
Eptatretus stoutii 91, 92
Equilibrium dialysis 401–2
Erythrocytes
agglutination of 372–3
enzyme treatment of 375, 377, 378
tannic acid treatment of 374
Erythrophagocytosis, in spleen 611
Escherichia coli 102
antigenic overlap between O14 and colonic extracts 661
Euglobulin (*see* Glossary for definition)
Exanthems (*see* Rashes)
Exhaustion hypothesis for immunity (Pasteur) 5
Exophthalmic ophthalmoplegia, in Graves' disease 639
Exotoxin 5, 6

Fagraeus, Astrid 28, 288
Farmer's lung syndrome 475
Farr's method 368, 369
Fatty acids, bactericidal activity at surface of body 45
Feedback inhibition (*see* Glossary for definition)
Felty's syndrome 619
Fenner F. 31
Fernandez reaction 526
Ferritin, use in localization of antibody in electron micrographs 291
Feulgen reaction (*see* Glossary for definition)
Fever (*see also* Pyrexia)
effect on phagocytosis 82
F_1 hybrids 102, 614 (*see also* Glossary for definition)
Fibrin barrier 62
Fibrinoid 620 (*see also* Glossary for definition)
Flagellin, presence in plasma cells 285
Flame cells 295
Fleming A. 273
Flemming's tingible corpuscles 273
Flocculation reactions 367
Fluorescence quenching 402
Fluorescent antibody method
for detection of antibody by 'sandwich' method 291
for detection of antibody in syphilis 388
for localization of hormones 401
in rheumatoid arthritis 624
in study of fate of antigen 242
techniques for using 389
use in lymphadenoid goitre 636
Fluorescent treponemal antibody test 388
Fluorochrome (*see* Glossary for definition)
Foetus
antigenicity of foetal tissue 574–6
as a homograft 573
onset of antibody production in 257, 312

transmission of antibody to 312–315
Folic acid antagonists 569
'Follicles', of lymphoid tissue 273
Formaldehyde 18, 19
action on toxins 219
sensitization to 211
Forssman antigens, occurrence of 189, 225
Freeman J.E. 16, 17
Freemartin cattle 88
Freund J. 18
Freund's adjuvant 303–4 (*see also* Water-in-oil emulsions) (*see also* Glossary for definition)
mode of action 253–5
Friend virus 332
Fucose, in blood group substance 223
Fungus infections
delayed-type hypersensitivity in 484
id-reaction in 484
immunity to 426

Galactose as hapten 215
Gamma-1A-globulin (*see* Glossary for definition) (*see also* Immunoglobulin A)
Gamma-globulin (*see* Glossary) (*see also* Immunoglobulin)
Gas-gangrene 18
passive immunization against 704
Gastric parietal cell antigen 640
Gastrin, immunochemical estimation 399
Gastro-intestinal tract (*see also* Gut)
bacterial content of 47
invasion by micro-organisms after X-irradiation 47
Gelatin, immunogenicity of 207
Gel-diffusion techniques 360–5
Generation of diversity of antibody specificity, relation to thymus 328
Genetic control
of antibody production
role of carrier in 249
role of determinant group in 248
of antibody variation 144
of biosynthesis of antibodies 140
of blood groups 223
of lipopolysaccharide antigens of Gram-negative bacteria 229
of transplantation antigens 557–8
Genetic factors
in Aleutian mink disease 615
in asthma and hay fever 443–4
in auto-immune disease 625
in contact sensitization 505
in diseases involving polymorphs 324
in haemolytic anaemia 612
in non-specific immunity 36
in NZB and NZB/NZW mice 615, 629
in rheumatic fever 473
in rheumatoid arthritis 625
in systemic lupus erythematosus 630
in tissue transplantation 557–8
Germ-free animals
bacillary dysentery in 47
lymph nodes in 272
'Germ line' hypothesis 145
Germinal centres (*see also* Glossary for definition) 273, 274, 329
cellular reaction in, after immunogen injection 136
death of cells in 297
dendritic cells in 298
distribution of immunogens in 298
effect of bursectomy in chickens on 93
in germ-free animals 297
in the thymus 662
role in immunological memory 300
role in provision of Y-cells 300
role in selection of proliferation of high avidity cells 302

Ghon focus 517
Giant follicular lymphoblastoma 329
Glenny A.T. 18, 19, 28, 411
Globulins 24 (*see* Glossary for definition)
α 24, 27, 149
β 24, 27, 149
γ 24, 27, 92, 149
γ-globulin in *Petromyzon* 92
T 149
Glomerulonephritis 17
appearances of glomeruli in E.M. 460
experimental, auto-immune 463
experimental, from localized Ag/Ab complexes 458
experimental Masugi nephritis 458
experimental, streptococcal 465
in man 465–75
in systemic lupus erythematosus 458
relation of chronic renal failure to acute streptococcal nephritis 469
streptococcal, in man 467
Glucagon
immunochemical estimation of 399
immunogenicity of 206
Glucocorticoid drugs 43
activity against endotoxins 43
effect in cell-mediated hypersensitivity 43
effect in pneumococcal infections 43
effect of neonatal administration to mice 103
effect on antibody production 43
effect on lysosomes 43, 543
effect on protein absorption from the gut 318
effect on Shwartzman reaction 43
mode of action of 543
species variation in effectiveness of 543
Glucose, as hapten 215
Gluten, allergy to 660
Gm groups 162–3
Goebel W.F. 22, 214
Golgi element (*see also* Glossary for definition)
of plasma cells 289, 290
Gonococcal infections, role of fever in 81
Gonococcus
as a cause of vaginitis in young girls 40
complement fixation test 386
Grabar P. 26
Grafts (*see* Homograft)
Graft *v* host reaction 101, 143, 614
Gram-negative bacteria 231
as adjuvants 255
Granulocytopenia 482–3 (*see also* Leucopenia)
Granulomatous disease (*see* Chronic granulomatous disease)
Griffith F. 20
Group antigens of streptococci 20
Growth hormone, immunochemical estimation of 399
Guinea-pig
anaphylaxis in 438, 439, 441
complement 190–1, 195, 197
homocytotropic antibodies resembling IgE in 438
passage on antibody from mother to foetus in 315
two types of homocytotropic antibody in 438
Gut
absorption of antibody from 314, 317–18
antibodies present in 422
immunization by protein from 322
Gut-associated lymphoid tissue, anatomy of 281–2

Haemadsorption, of viruses 378
Haemagglutination
by viruses 46

inhibition technique 374, 398
serum inhibitors of 378
Haematoxyphil bodies 629
Haemocyanin 206
Haemocytoblast (*see also* Glossary for definition) 97, 288
Haemolysis, mechanism of 191 (*see also* Haemolytic disease and Haemolytic anaemia)
Haemolytic anaemia (*see also* Acquired haemolytic anaemia)
drug-induced 478, 481
in NZB mice 614
in runt disease 614
Haemolytic disease of newborn
in horses 321
in man 318
in mules 321
in pigs 321
prophylaxis of 320
relation to ABO blood group system 319
Haemophilus influenzae 63
capsule and resistance to phagocytosis 60
Hageman factor 435
Hagfish (*see Eptatretus stoutii*)
Half-life (*see also* Glossary for definition)
of antibodies 700
of IgA 170
of IgD 174
of IgG 167
of IgM 172
Haller A. von 57
Hamster cheek pouch 577
Haptens (*see also* Glossary for definition) 22, 85, 110, 177, 204, 205
Haptophore groups 13, 30, 139
Hargreaves M.M. 627
Hashimoto's disease (*see* Lymphadenoid goitre)
Haurowitz F. 30
Hay-fever 443–5
desensitization in 447–8
historical 16
H-chains 155, 165
classification of 159
myelomas producing in mice 344
Heaf multipuncture apparatus 680
Heart
antibodies following commissurotomy 657
antibodies in rheumatic fever 656
antigen cross-reactive with streptococci 473
Heat-aggregated serum albumin, clearance from blood 74
Heavy chain (*see* H-chain)
'Heavy Chain disease' 165
immunological deficiency in 344
Heidelberger M. 20, 21, 25, 27, 366
Heimbeck J. 521
Helminth infections, hypersensitivity in 485, 524
Henoch's purpura 466
Hepatitis
in wasting syndrome after neonatal thymectomy 104
prophylaxis by human gammaglobulin 706 (*see also* cirrhosis)
Hereditary angioneurotic oedema 196
Heredity (*see* Genetic control and Genetic factors)
Herpes virus
antibody to 416
persistence of in cells 416
Hetero-antibody (*see also* Glossary for definition) 23
Heterocytotropic antibody 177, 346 (*see also* Glossary for definition)
Heterogeneic (*see* Glossary for definition)
Heterogenetic (*see* Glossary for definition)
Heterografts 24, 547 (*see also* Glossary for definition)
effect of anti-lymphocyte serum on 571
Heterologous (*see* Glossary for definition)
Heterophile antigens (*see also* Glossary for definition) 224

Heterotopic (*see* Glossary for definition)
Hexose monophosphate shunt 324
High-zone paralysis 115
Hinton flocculation test 387
Hirst J.C. 46
Histamine 16
  in mast cells 433
  relation to anaphylaxis in guinea-pig 431
  release of, from mast cells 441
Histiocytes, occurrence and function of 72–3
Histocompatibility antigens
  in men 230
  in mice 230
Histology of lympho-reticular tissues (*see* individual tissues)
Histoplasmin test 524
Hodgkin's disease
  brucellosis in 535
  cryptococcosis in 535
  delayed-type hypersensitivity in 533, 588
  serum protein levels in 533
  tuberculosis in 535
  virus diseases in 535
Homocytotropic antibody 175, 436 (*see also* Glossary for definition)
  in man 445
Homograft (*see also* Glossary for definition) 25, 29
  foetus as 573–8
  of blood vessels 560
  of bone 560
  of cartilage 561
  of cornea 560
  of endocrines 562
  of kidney 562
  of liver 565
  of lung 566
Homograft rejection
  afferent arc of 551, 554
  biological significance of 549
  cells responsible for destruction of the graft 556
  dependence on lymphatic connections 555
  efferent arc of 551, 556
  evidence for rejection as an immunological mechanism 548
  histology of 550
  influence of antibody on 553–4
  peripheral sensitization in 555
  pyroninophilic blast cells in 551
  relation to delayed-type hypersensitivity 537
  role of macrophages in 557
  surveillance function of 550
Homologous (*see* Glossary for definition)
Homologous disease (*see* Glossary for definition)
Homostatic grafts 560
Homovital grafts 560
Hopkins B.E. 411
Hormones, immunochemical assay of 398–401
Horror autotoxicus 18, 114
Horse
  haemolytic disease in 321
  serum from 15
Horse dander, immunogenicity of 207
Hortega, Del Rio 71
Hudack S. 263
Human γ-globulin
  specific hyperimmune
    use in smallpox prophylaxis 706
    use in tetanus prophylaxis 707
  therapeutic use of 704–7
Humoral hypothesis of immunity 8
Hunter J. 57
Hyaline (*see* Glossary for definition)
Hyaluronidase 63
Hydatid cyst fluid, relation to P_1 blood group specificity 224
Hydatid disease, hypersensitivity in 485
Hydrallazine, relation to S.L.E. 627
Hydrocortisone (*see* Glucocorticoids)
Hydrogen bonds (*see also* Glossary for definition) 178

Hydrophobia (*see* Rabies)
β-Hydroxybutyric acid, bactericidal effect in tissues of 51
Hyper-gamma-globulinaemia 620
Hypersensitivity
antibody mediated (*see* chapter 9 428 *et seq.*)
delayed-type (*see* chapter 12 493 *et seq.*)
historical 14
pure protein type of 507
to dermatophyte fungi 483–4
to insects and parasites 485–6
Hypersensitivity, delayed type (*see also* Contact sensitivity) 28, 29, 85, 205 (*see* chapter 12 493–545)
after smallpox vaccination 530
antigenic specificity in 508
cellular changes in regional node 500
cellular immunity and 65–7
correlation with *in vitro* inhibition of macrophage migration test 499
determinant groups involved 508
effect of thymectomy on 502
homing of specifically sensitized cells to test site in 497
in chronic bacterial disease 522
induction of 120
in helminth disease 523
in mycotic diseases 522
in protozoal disease 523
in reticuloses 530
in sarcoidosis 530
in staphylococcal disease 527
in streptococcal disease 528
in syphilis 523
in virus diseases 522
manifestations in the skin 496
passive transfer in man 538
procedures for suppression of 540
rashes due to 536
relation to bacterial allergy 493
role of mycobacteria in induction of 120
role of lymphatics in 495
tests for
in vitro inhibition of macrophage migration 498
peritoneal clearance of macrophages after antigen injection 498
corneal test 514
to vaccines and toxoids 529
transfer of, between isogeneic or allogeneic animals 496
Hypo-γ-globulinaemia 329 (*see also* Immunoglobulin deficiency)
combined or Swiss type 262
secondary acquired 332
transient 329
Hypothyroidism
increased tendency to infection in 41
in lymphadenoid goitre 632

Idiopathic adrenal insufficiency, auto-antibodies to steroid hormones in 642
Idiotype specificity 159
'Id' reactions 483
'Immediate response', to smallpox vaccination 522
Immune-adherence reaction 198, 613, 388
role in phagocytosis 389
Immune deviation 541
Immunity
acquired 35
cell-mediated 29, 121
duration of 413
effect of anaesthetics 804
effect of irradiation 80–1
induction of 120
innate 35, 36
maternal, effect on immunization 673–4
natural 35
non-specific 8, 36
potential 239

Immunity—*contd.*
racial differences in 37
specific cell-mediated 85
to bacteria 76, 418–24, 493
to viruses 234, 412–18
variation with age 39–41
Immunization
against cholera 695
against diphtheria 675
against enteric fever 694
against influenza 698
against measles 699
against pertussis (whooping cough) 679
against plague 695
against pneumococcal pneumonia 441
against poliomyelitis 689–92
against rabies 696
against rubella (German measles) 699
against smallpox 683–9
against streptococci 420–1
against tetanus 676–7
against tuberculosis 680–2
against typhus 697
against yellow fever 695
effect of maternal immunity on 673–5
historical 18–21
of infants 673
passive with γ-globulin 704–7
passive with specific antibody 700–4
routine schedules 692–4
use of mixed immunogens 675
Immunochemistry, historical 12
Immunoconglutinin 197, 603
Immuno-electrophoresis 26, 149, 151
identification of component lines in 364
technique 363–4
Immunoferritin technique 392–3
Immunofluorescence 389–92
Immunogenic (*see also* Glossary for definition)
stimulation of lymphoid tissue 122
Immunogenicity
effect of adjuvants on 251
effect of adsorption to particles 251
effect of molecular aggregation on 251
effect of surface configurations on 110
genetic factors in 210
influence of hapten/carrier ratio 251
influence of non-specific factors on 251
of foetal tissue 575
of insulin 211
of proteins, relation to primary amino acid sequence 205
role of genotype of injected animal 211
threshold effect 115
Immunogens 84, 85, 204 (*see also* Glossary for definition)
distinction from antigen 210
interaction with antibody precursor cells 135
labelling of, for kinetic studies 240
localization to germinal centre cells 136
persistence in tissues 243
polysaccharide 6, 242
'weak and powerful' 115
Immunoglobulins 27, 85 (*see also* Glossary for definition)
action of papain and pepsin on 157
antibody-combining sites of 177
biological characteristics of 167
catabolism 307–8, 167
classification of 150, 154
concentration in body fluids 167
definition 153
levels in immunological deficiency diseases 329
loss from body 311
normal 27
presence at surface of immunologically competent cell 112

presence in exocrine secretions 307
production, cells involved in 295
S-S bonds of 157
structure of 156 *et seq.*
values in extravascular pool 306–307
presence in C.S.F. 307
IgA
catabolism of 310
molecular structure of 170
presence in secretions 170
secretory form of 170
IgD 174
IgE 174, 445–6
IgG 124, 308
biological properties of 167–8
catabolism of 309, 310, 311, 332
control by feedback mechanism 259
half-life of 305
pinocytosis of 310
γ_2 in guinea pig 541
IgM 124, 171
catabolism of 310
Immunoglobulin deficiency
acquired 329
clinical manifestations of 333
congenital sex linked 329
secondary acquired 332
selective 330
transient in infancy 333
Immunoglobulin terminology (*see* Glossary for definition)
Immunological deficiency diseases 323–37
deficiency of IgA in 333
deficiency of parathyroid function in 333
infection with fungi in 333
injection with pyogenic cocci in 333
interferon production in 334
investigation of 335
meningitis in 333
pneumonia in 333
treatment 335
Immunologically competent cells 88, 94, 205 (*see also* Glossary for definition)
life cycle of 106
Immunological memory 239
Immunological paralysis 87, 211 (*see also* Glossary for definition)
induced by small doses of immunogen 115, 212
induced by undegradable materials 212
Immunological surveillance 585
Immunological tolerance (*see also* Tolerance, Immunological paralysis, Sulzberger-Chase phenomenon) 31, 87–8, 113–114, 541
Immuno-suppression 138, 565–73 (*see also* Tolerance)
non-specific
by anti-metabolites 138
by bursectomy 138
by corticosteroid hormones 138
by immuno-globulin 138
by reticulo-endothelial blockade 138
by thoracic-duct drainage 138
by thymectomy 138
by X-rays 138
specific
by antibody 138
Immunosuppressive treatment 565–573
by anti-lymphocyte serum 571–572
for kidney homografts 563
with whole-body X-irradiation 566
Imuran (*see* Azathioprine)
Incomplete antibody 367, 375
Incubation period, relation to subsequent immunity 417
Indian ink 73
Infantile agranulocytosis 323
Infantile eczema 322
Infantile sex-linked recessive agammaglobulinanaemia 325

Infection
in agranulocytosis 323–4
in Chediak-Higashi syndrome 324
in chronic granulomatous disease 324
in heavy-chain disease 344
in Hodgkin's disease 534
in immunological deficiency diseases 333–5
in leukaemia 534
in myelomatosis 311
in sarcoidosis 532
Infectious mononucleosis, heterophile antibody in 226, 612
Inflammation
caused by *Mycobacterium tuberculosis* 58
caused by *Staphylococcus aureus* 8
effect of liquoid on 63
local immunity dependent on 63
relation to defence 57
role in immunity 62
role in localizing infection 63
Influenza 19
immunization against 698
role of antibody in preventing disease 415
role of antibody in recovery from 415
role of interferon in recovery from 415
Insect bites 485
Insulin
immunochemical estimation 399
immunogenicity of 206
interstrain differences, of antibody response to, in mice 248
Interbreeding 37
Interferon 54–8, 334, 408 (*see also* Glossary for definition)
effect in embryo 39, 56
mode of action 56
molecular weight of 55
role in resistance to virus disease 55
stimulus for causing release from cells 55
Intrinsic factor, antibody to 640
Invertebrates
adaptive responses in 90
phagocytosis in 90
response to homografts 90
Inv groups 162
Iodine (^{131}I), as radio-active label 244, 308–9
Irradiation (*see* X-irradiation)
Irwin M.R. 24
Isaacs A. 54
Iso-agglutinins 332
Iso-antibody 23 (*see also* Glossary for definition)
Iso-antigen (*see* Glossary for definition)
Isogen(e)ic (*see* Glossary for definition)
Isograft (*see* Glossary for definition)
Isologous (*see* Glossary for definition)
Isophile antibody (*see* Glossary for definition)
Isotypic specificity 159

Jacobs J. 29
Jandl J.H. 611
Jenner E. 2, 3, 686
Jesty B. 2
Jones-Mote reaction 507

Kabat E.A. 27
Kahn flocculation test 387
Kallidin (*see also* Bradykinin) 435
Kappa L chains 158
Kass E.H. 44
Kauffmann F. 17, 22
α-ketoglutaric acid, bactericidal effect in tissues 51
Kimmelstiel-Wilson kidney 458
Kitasato S. 5
Klebsiella pneumoniae 63, 75
Klemperer P. 619
Koch R. 29, 512
Koch phenomenon 512

Kraus R. 6
Kunin antigen 661
Kupffer cells 70, 72, 77, 287
Kurloff cell (*see* Glossary for definition)
Küstner H. 446
Kveim test 532

Lachrymal glands, auto-antibodies to 630
Lactic acid
  bactericidal activity at surface of body 45
  bactericidal activity in tissues 51
Lambda-type light chains 158
Lamprey (*see* Petromyzon)
Lancefield R. 20, 467
Landsteiner K. 11, 21, 23, 29, 204, 214
Latency or Latent phase of infection 48
Latex particle agglutination 374
  in rheumatoid arthritis 623
Lattice
  hypothesis 25, 351
  relation to complement fixation 192
Laudable pus 11
Lawrence J. 539
L.E. cell
  in myasthenia gravis 662
  in systemic lupus erythematosus 627
  in Sjögren's disease 631
Lectin 235 (*see also* Glossary for definition)
Lederberg J. 31, 32, 141
Leishmaniasis
  delayed-type hypersensitivity in 524
  half-life of IgG in 167
Lens, auto-antigens of 643
Leprosy 525
  cell-mediated hypersensitivity in 525
  effect of fever on resistance to 81
  localization of lesions in 81
Leptochromatic (*see* Glossary for definition)
Leuco-agglutinins 618
Leucocyte-platelet thrombi, in Arthus reactions 451
Leucocytes
  agglutinins for 321
  auto-antibodies in rheumatoid arthritis 618
  in normal lymphocyte transfer reaction 559
  in S.L.E. 637
  in transfer of delayed-type hypersensitivity 539
  pavementing of 60
  source of transfer factor 539
  typing of histocompatibility antigens in 231, 559
Leucopenia 381 (*see also* Agranulocytosis)
  due to auto-antibody 618
  following X-rays 80
  in lymphatic leukaemia 534
  of newborn children 321
Leukaemia
  acquired haemolytic anaemia in 332, 534
  chronic lymphatic 332
  effect of anti-lymphocyte serum on incidence of 589
  effect of neonatal thymectomy on 588
  in agammaglobulinaemia 329
  viruses causing 589
Levine P. 23
Lewis substance or antigen 223
Lichen myxoedematosus (*see* Papular mucinosis) 345
Light chain of immunoglobulin molecule 155
Lipids, antigens 208
Lipopolysaccharides
  enhancement of resistance by 68
  in Gram-negative bacteria 226
  of *Mycobacterium tuberculosis* 516

Listeria monocytogenes, cellular immunity in 66–7
Liver
  antibody synthesis in 266–8
  as part of the reticulo-endothelial system 70–7
  lupoid hepatitis 657
  primary biliary cirrhosis 658
Lobar penumonia 21
Loutit J.F. 18
Low zone paralysis 115
Lupoid hepatitis 657
Lurie M.B. 37, 66
Lymphadenoid goitre 603, 607, 631
  auto-antigens involved in 635
  cytopathogenic effects in tissue culture by auto-antibody from 637
  experimental production of 634
  in families 634
  in twins 634
  histology of 632
  myxoedema in 632
  relationship to other diseases 637
  relationship to virus disease 636
  thyroid auto-antibodies in 636
Lymphatic nodules 277
Lymphatics
  relation to auto-immunogenicity of brain 602
  role in immunity 68–9
  role in immunization to skin grafts 555
Lymphatic sinuses 71
Lymph node permeability factor 511
Lymph nodes
  antibody synthesis in 263–4
  cellular reactions involved in antibody production in 282
  filtering action of 69
  germinal centres of 273–4, 292 *et seq.*
  histological changes in during sensitization 500–2
  histology of 271–5
  in rheumatoid arthritis 621, 624
  phylogenetic development of 92
Lymphocyte reaction, mixed 123, 559
Lymphocytes, large (*see also* Glossary for definition) 98
  in blood smears 99
  in lymph and tissues 99
Lymphocytes, small (*see also* Glossary for definition)
  as immunologically competent cells 100
  description 94
  differential rate of labelling with thymidine in various tissues 95
  in graft *v* host reaction 101
  in relation to tolerance 101
  long and short-lived 95–6
  motility of 95
  preparation of pure suspensions of 100
  separation by density 95
  short-lived 98
  transformation of 97
Lymphocyte transformation reaction, relation to delayed-type hypersensitivity 123
Lymphocytophthisis (*see* Thymic aplasia or Swiss-type agammaglobulinaemia)
Lymphoepithelioma 664
Lymphorrhage 663 (*see also* Glossary for definition)
Lyon hypothesis 324
Lysosomal granules 299, 324
  damage by endotoxin 43
  protection by corticosteroids 42
Lysosome (*see* Glossary for definition)
Lysozyme 52
  co-operation with IgA in bacteriolysis 52
  presence in phagocytes 52

Macleod C.M. 413
McMaster P.D. 242, 263

Macroglobulin α 153
identity of β, β_{2m} and γ_1 153
γ_1 153
biosynthesis in foetus 257
Macroglobulinaemia 164, 172, 295, 341
appearance of Ig-producing cells in 295
auto-antibodies in 343
clinical features of 342
rheumatoid factor in 343
Sia test in 342
treatment of 342
Macrophages 58–63, 64–7, 70–5, 78, 284
activation by endotoxin 67
activation by high molecular weight dextrans 67
blockade of 138
immunological role of 283–7
inhibition factor 498
intra-cellular digestion processes in 67
phylogeny of 89–90
role in immunogenicity 136–7
role in inflammation 58
Madsen T. 13
Magic bullet, the ideal chemotherapeutic agent (Ehrlich) 19
Malaria 38, 167, 311
immunity in 425–6
sickle-cell trait in 38
Malpighian bodies 71, 277
Mammary gland, concentration of antibody in colostrum 316
Mancini technique 361
Mantle zone 277
Mantoux skin test 496, 681
clinical significance of 520–1
reversion of a positive to a negative reaction 523
Maple bark stripper's disease 475
Marking ink 218
Marrack J.R. 25, 351, 354
Marschalkó type plasma cell 289
Marx C.F.H. 28
Mast cells (*see also* Glossary for definition)
distribution of, in body 433
heparin in 433
histamine in 433
role in anaphylaxis 438–41
serotonin in 433
Mastitis, local antibody synthesis in 316–17
Masugi M. 17
Masugi-type nephritis (*see also* Nephritis) 17, 461
Maternal immunity 671–2
Mayer M.M. 190
Measles 19
immunization against 699
incubation period and duration of immunity against 413, 416
prophylaxis and attenuation of by γ-globulin injection 705
role of antibody in protection 412–14
Medawar P.B. 24, 31, 89
Medical Research Council 673, 679–81
trials of vole bacillus and BCG 519
Meinicke flocculation test 387
Meister J. 4
Melanin granules 324
Memory (*see also* Secondary response) 86–7, 132, 239
in amphibians and primitive mammals 93
memory cells 87, 102, 132, 136–137, 143
Meningococcal septicaemia 324
Menkin V. 62
6-Mercaptopurine 563–9, 668
Messenger RNA 141
Metalophil cells 71
Metchnikoff E. 7, 8, 30, 65, 89
Methotrexate 569, 666
α-Methyldopa, haemolytic anaemia due to 613
Mice
auto-immune haemolytic anaemia 614
myeloma induction in 341
systemic lupus in 629

Mickulicz disease (*see* Sjögren's disease)
Microphage (*see also* Polymorphs)
immunological role of 283
role in inflammation 58
Microsporum audouini, ringworm due to 46
Migration studies of cells 293
by chromosome marker techniques 404
by ^{3}H-thymidine 404
Miles A.A. 45
Milk
allergy to cow's milk in cot death 448–9
allergy to, in ulcerative colitis 660
transfer of antibody to 315
Milk spots 72
Mitogens
from pokeweed 97
from red-kidney bean 97
Mitsuda reactions 526
Mixed agglutination 379
Molecular weight
of antibodies 154
role in immunogenicity 206
Moniliasis, after antibiotic therapy 47
Moniliids 483
Monoclonal gammopathy 344–7
in association with papular mucinosis 345
in association with xanthomatosis 345
Mononuclear cells 551
Monospora bicuspidata 9
Montague, Lady Wortley 1
Morgan I.M. 18
Mourant R.A. 18
Mouse-pox, as a model of virus infection with rash production 536
Mucopeptide (*see* Glossary for definition)
Mucopolysaccharides (*see* Glossary for definition)
Mucoproteins (*see* Glossary for definition)
Mudd S. 30
Multiple myeloma 337 (*see* Myelomatosis)
Multiple sclerosis
as a virus disease 652
EAE as an experimental model for 650
relation to scrapie and swayback 652
Mummies, persistence of blood-group substances in 224
Mumps, in pregnancy 41
Murphy G. 471
Mutation, somatic 30, 145
Myasthenia gravis 662–5
congenital 662
effect of thymectomy on 665
Mycobacterium balnei 81
Mycobacterium tuberculosis
as adjuvant 250
effect on biosynthesis of individual Igs 254
multiplication within macrophages 65
Mycobacterium ulcerans 81
Mycoplasma pneumoniae 379
Mycotic disease, immunity in 426
Myelin
antibody against 647
nature of immunogens in 647
Myelomatosis 32, 164, 311, 332
amyloidosis in 339
antibody production in 339
Bence-Jones protein in 338
in man 337–40
in mice 341
morphology of cells in 340–1
morphology of myeloma cells 340
nature of protein produced in 154
relation of myeloma proteins to antibody 339–40
virus particles in tissues from 341
Myelotoxic factors 648
Myleran 568
Myocyte (*see* Glossary for definition)
Myoid cells 664
Myxoedema
in lymphadenoid goitre 632
pretibial 639

Nasal polyps 445
Negative phase of resistance 68
Nephritis (*see also* Glomerulonephritis) 17
  in man 465–7
  Masugi 17
  subacute 469
Nephrosis 311
Nephrotoxic serum 461
Nervous system, diseases of immunopathology 645–52
Neufeld F. 21
Neuraminidase 46
Neuritis
  damage by lymphocytes in 650
  experimental allergic E.A.N. 649–650
  role of cell-mediated hypersensitivity in 649
Neutralization tests
  of toxins 393–4
  of viruses 394–6
Neutropenia 323 (*see also* Agranulocytosis)
  due to aplastic anaemia 323
  due to benzol 323
  due to radiomimetic drugs 324
  due to X rays 324
N.Z.B. mice 614, 629
Nitrogen mustard 568
Noon L. 16
Noon units 447
Normal antibodies 49
  origin of 49
  restricted specificity of 49
Normal lymphocyte transfer reaction (NLTR) 559
Nuclear factors (ANF), in systemic lupus erythematosus 628
Nucleic acids
  antibodies against 628
  immunogenicity of 209
  role in interferon production 56
Nuttall G.R. 11, 12, 259

Oakley C.L. 265
Oakley-Fulthorpe technique 360
O-antigens, of Gram-negative bacteria 226
Old tuberculin 513
Oligoribonucleotides, role in stimulation of antibody production 302
Oligosaccharide (*see* Glossary for definition)
Omentum, antibody synthesis in 264
Onchocerciasis 486
Oncogenic (*see* Glossary for definition)
Operon (*see* Glossary for definition)
Opsonic index (*see also* Glossary for definition) 10
Opsonin (*see also* Glossary for definition) 9, 63
Optimal proportions 353, 365–6
Orchitis
  due to mumps 656–7
  experimental 253
    auto-antibody in 652–4
    cell-mediated hypersensitivity in 653
    nature of immunogen 654
    synergistic role of antibody and delayed hypersensitivity in 654
Organic dust diseases 475
Organ-specific antigens 17
Organ specificity (*see also* Glossary for definition)
  as basis for classification of auto-immune diseases 606
Orthotopic (*see* Glossary for definition)
Osserman E.F. 164
Ouchterlony O. 26
Ouchterlony technique 360, 362
Oudin J. 26, 159, 360–1
Oudin technique 360–1
Ovary Z. 396
Ovum, antibodies in, in birds 313

Pancreatitis, iso-antibodies in 660

Papain, treatment of antibody 27
Paprika splitter's disease 475
Papular mucinosis 345
Para-cortical zone 96, 502
Paralysis, immunological (*see also* Tolerance) 87
Paraproteins (*see also* Glossary for definition) 32
Parasitic infections
  eosinophilia in 485
  hypersensitivity in 485
Parathyroid hormone, immunochemical estimation of 399
Paratope (*see* Glossary for definition)
Paronychia 46
Paroxysmal cold haemoglobinuria 609, 613
Partial identity, reaction of 363
Passive anaphylaxis 396
Passive cutaneous anaphylaxis(PCA) 396, 437
Passive immunization 18
  against botulism 704
    diphtheria 703
    gas-gangrene 704
    measles 705
    rubella 705
    snake venoms 704
    tetanus 703
  by means of pooled human gamma globulin 700
  duration of 700–1
  in pregnancy of various animals 314
  precautions required 702–3
Pasteur J.L. 3, 4, 5, 30, 696
Pasteurian treatment, of rabies 18
Pasteur Institute 4, 5
Patch test 494
Paul-Bunnell test 226, 612 (*see also* Glossary for definition)
Pauling L.A. 353
Penicillary arterioles of spleen 276
Penicillin 19
  sensitization by 218, 476–7
Penicillinase, neutralization by antibody 409
Peptidoglycolipids
  adjuvant activity of 304
  of mycobacteria 254
Peri-arteritis 457
Perifollicular envelope 277
Periodic acid-Schiff technique (*see* Glossary for definition)
Peripheral sensitization 122
Pernicious anaemia
  auto-antibody against intrinsic factor in 640
  auto-antibody against organelles of parietal cells in 641
  complement-fixing antibody in 640
  experimental models for 641
  fluorescent antibody test for auto-antibody in 640
  relation to gastric atopy 641
Pertussis immunization against 20, 679
  encephalitis as a complication 680
Petromyzon 91, 92
Peyer's patches 93
  anatomy of 281
Pfeiffer R. 6, 7, 28, 418
Pfeiffer phenomenon 418
Phaco-anaphylactic endophthalmitis 643 (*see also* Glossary for definition)
Phage-neutralization tests 395
Phagocyte 8
  migration from blood vessels 61
  organization at different stages of ontogeny 59
  strategic disposition of 68
Phagocytin (*see* Glossary for definition)
Phagocytosis
  by amoebae 89
  effect of adrenaline on 61
  effect on antibiotic therapy 65
  historical 7
  in the sponges 90
  relation to adherence 198
Phipps J. 2
Phylogeny of immunological response 89

Physalia 14
Phytohaemagglutinin 597
Picryl proteins 218
Pig, haemolytic disease of newborn in 321
Pigeon fancier's lung syndrome 475
Pillemer L. 190
Pine pollen, sensitivity to, in sarcoidosis 532
Pinocytosis (*see also* Glossary for definition) 307, 310
Pirquet C. von 15, 536
Pituitary snuff-taker's disease 476
Placenta
  as an immunological barrier 577
  immunogenicity of 575–6
  passage of antibody across 312
  structure of 313, 573–5
Placentation, types of 573–4
Plague 20
  immunization against 695
Plasmablast 291
Plasma cells 28, 343
  antibody synthesis by 287–93
  cytology 288–9
  definition 287
  in hypo-γ-globulinaemia 329
  in myeloma 340
  life span 293
  presence in foetus 256
  Russell bodies in 292
  studies on single cells 142, 366–7
  ultrastructure 289–91
  with flaming cytoplasm 295
Plasmacytoid lymphocytes 295
Plasmacytoma 337
  (*see also* Myelomatosis)
Plasma proteins (*see* Immuno-electrophoresis)
Plasma volume of man
  in anaemia 310
  in pregnancy 310
  in surgical shock 310
  in water retention 310
Platelets, antibodies to
  after transfusion 617
  in pregnancy 617
  in thrombocytopenic purpura 617
Pleurisy, as manifestation of tuberculous allergy 517
Pneumococcal capsular polysaccharides 60, 218
  immunogenicity of 207–8
  immunological paralysis due to 233
Pneumococcal polysaccharide Type III, as antigen in quantitative precipitin test 351
Pneumococci 20, 64
  antibody to 150
  type III 218, 351
  type XIV, cross reactions of 218, 222–3
Pneumocystis carinii 335
Pneumonia
  due to *Pneumocystis carinii* 335
  due to *Streptococcus pneumoniae* 20
  primary atypical, auto-antibody production in 604
Poison ivy, hypersensitivity to 503
Poliomyelitis 19
  immunization against 689
  paralysis following use of 680
  prophylaxis by human-γ-globulin 706
  prophylaxis by pooled human Ig 416
  protection in hypo-gamma-globulinaemia 416
  role of antibody in preventing infection and disease 415
Poliomyelitis vaccine
  formalin-treated (Salk) 690
  oral (Sabin) 691
Pollen hypersensitivity 443
  antigens in 448
  desensitization to 447
Polyarteritis
  in experimental serum sickness 456
  nodosa 456–7
Polymerization 25
Polymorphonuclear leucocytes (*see also* Agranulocytosis), digestion of micro-organisms in 78

Polyoma virus 589
Polypeptide antigens, synthetic 248
Polysaccharides, as immunogens 243
Polysome (*see* Glossary for definition)
Porter R.R. 27, 155
Portier P. 429
Post-capillary venules 96
Post-commissurotomy syndrome 657
Pouilly-le-fort 4
Poulik M.D. 155
Prausnitz C. 446
Prausnitz-Küstner test 446
Precipitin reaction 350–70
(*see also* Antigen-antibody reaction)
Danysz phenomenon 355
definition 349
historical 6
influence of electrolytes 355
Mancini technique 361
procedure for decreasing cross reactions 359
reaction of identity 362
reaction of partial identity 363
quantitative procedures 365
reversibility of 355
specificity of 359
Precipitin tests
immuno-electrophoresis 363
optimal proportions 353, 366
qualitative tests 359
quantitative test 351, 365
radio-immuno-electrophoresis 365
ring test 359
Pregnancy
diagnosis of, by haemagglutination inhibition test 398
immunological response during 576
Premunition (*see* Glossary for definition)
Prick tests, in atopy 444
Primary atypical pneumonia (*see* Pneumonia)
Primary myxoedema 632
Primary response 124–5
Primary structure (*see* Glossary for definition)
Primula obconica, contact hypersensitivity to 503
Prince Albert of Monaco 14
Properdin 50, 201
relation to specific IgM antibodies
Prophylactic immunization 671 *et seq.* (*see also* under individual antigens)
Prophylaxis 6, 14, 428
Protein-losing enteropathy 311
Proteins, immunogenicity of 206
Proteo-anaphylaxis (*see also* Arthus phenomenon and reactions) 15
Proteus organisms, killing within phagocytes 64
Protozoal diseases, immunity in 424–6
Pseudoglobulin (*see* Glossary for definition)
Pseudomonas pyocyanea 6
Pseudo-Schick test reaction 529
Pure-lines of animals, definition 546
Purified protein derivative (PPD) 513
Purine analogues 569
Purpura 479
antiglobulin consumption test in 381
due to sedormid 478
idiopathic thrombocytopenic 617
Pyrexia, influence in resistance 81
Pyrogen (*see also* Lipopolysaccharides and Endotoxin) of Gram-negative bacteria 227
Pyroninophilic 'blast' cells 120–1, 551

Quaternary ammonium compounds, as adjuvants 255
Quellung phenomenon 21
de Quervain disease (*see* Subacute thyroiditis)

Quinidine 218
as cause of purpura 478–81

Rabbit, Arthus reaction in 449–50
Rabies 4, 18, 19
vaccination 696
encephalomyelitis due to 602, 697
Race R.R. 18, 609
Radiation chimaeras 567
secondary disease in 567–8
Radiculitis (*see* Experimental allergic neuritis)
Radio-immunoelectrophoresis 365
Radio-immuno-assay 368–70, 398–401
Radio-iodine, as label for IgG 309
Radiomimetic drugs 259, 568
Ramon G. 18
Rashes, relation to delayed-type hypersensitivity 536
Reaginic antibodies (*see* Glossary for definition) 444–5
Receptor-destroying enzyme (RDE) (*see* Glossary for definition) in virus haemagglutination 378
Receptor theory 13
Red cells (*see also* Haemagglutination, Cold and Warm autoantibody) 609
antibodies to, after medication with methyldopa or chlorthalidone 613
antibodies to, in infectious mononucleosis 612
antibodies to, in NZB mice 614–615, 630
antibodies to, in runt disease 614
antibodies to, in SLE 630
blood group antigens in 172, 220–2, 225, 610
damage by complement and antibody 189–91
fate of, in haemolytic anaemia 61
modification by micro-organisms 605
T-antigen 558
Renal biopsy, in glomerulonephritis 468
Renal cortical necrosis 490
Reticular cells 272
Reticulo-endothelial system 70, 89, 323
blockade of 73
stimulation by cortisone 75
stimulation by lipids 75
stimulation by oestrogens 75
Reticuloses 324
Reversed anaphylaxis (*see* Anaphylaxis)
Rhesus antibody (*see also* Haemolytic disease of newborn) 18
association with alpha-methyldopa treatment 613
association with haemolytic disease of newborn 609–10
following transfusion of incompatible red cells 609
Rhesus antigen (*see also* Haemolytic disease of newborn) 224, 260
immunization by 318
iso-immunization by, in pregnancy 319
prevention of iso-immunization 319
Rhesus iso-immunization 319
in animal species other than man 321
prevention by natural ABO incompatibility 319
prevention by passive immunization with Rh-antibody 320
Rhesus monkey 23
Rheumatic fever 470–4
activity of cholesterol in 474
activity of palmitamide in 474
genetically determined susceptibility to 473
role of streptococci in causation 470–1
Rheumatoid arthritis 620–7
experimental models for 625
role of septic foci in causation of 621

Rheumatoid factors 161, 622
experimental production by injection of bacteria 623
immunoglobulin form of 622
sedimentation coefficients of 623
sites of biosynthesis 624
Rhodamine antibody conjugates 391
Ribbert H. 70
Ribonuclease, immunogenicity of 206
RNA-extracts of macrophages, role in antibody production by lymphoid cells 285
Ribosome (*see also* Glossary for definition)
role in antibody biosynthesis 289
role in biosynthesis of interferon 56
Rich A.R. 29, 509
Richet C. 14, 429
Ricin 6, 13
Ridgeon, Sir Colenso 10
Ring test (*see also* Precipitin reaction and tests) 359
Ringworm (*see also* Dermatophytids)
age incidence 46
Rittenberg D. 27
Roger C.A. 6
Rous P. 24
Roux E. 5–6
Rubella
congenital defects due to 39–40
immunization against 699
prophylactic use of γ-globulin in pregnancy 203
Runt disease (*see also* Glossary for definition) 614
Russell bodies 292

Sabin A. 691
Sabin F.R. 241
Sabin vaccine 689, 691
Saliva, antibody content of 170
Salmon D.E. 5
Salmonella (*see also* Enteric fever) 17, 22
destruction of, *in vivo* 422
titration of antibody against 371
Vi antigen of 371, 421
Salmonella typhi, destruction on skin 45
Salt concentration, effect on bacterial agglutination, 355
Sanarelli G. 490
Sanarelli-Shwartzman reaction 490–1
potentation by cortisone 491
relationship to Waterhouse-Friderichsen syndrome 490
renal cortical necrosis in 490
Sandwich technique (immunofluorescence method for antibody) 291, 391
Saponin, as adjuvant 250
Sarcoidosis 530–3
effect of cortisone in 531
energy in 530
Kveim test in 532
mumps virus skin test in 530
relationship to tuberculosis 531
Scarlet fever 466
Schick, Bela 15, 466
Schick test 529 (*see also* Glossary for definition)
in young children 40
Schilder's disease 645
Schlepper 210 (*see also* Glossary for definition)
Schoenheimer R. 27
Schönlein's disease 466
Schultz E.A. 431
Schultz-Dale reaction 431
Schulze, venules of 274
Schütze 11
Schweigger-Seidel sheath 276, 300
Scrambler gene 146
Sea sickness, remedies for 16
Sebum 46
bactericidal activity of 46
'Secondary' disease 568 (*see also* Glossary for definition)
Secondary infection, due to surgical operations 29

Secondary response 86–7 124
'Second Set', accelerated graft reaction 548
Secretory IgA 171
Sedimentation coefficient 124 (*see also* Glossary for definition)
Sedimentation constant (*see* Glossary for definition)
Sedormid 218
  as cause of purpura 478
'Selective' hypothesis 111
  for antibody biosynthesis 141
'Self-marker' hypothesis 88
Semen, allergic sensitization against 655
Sensitization 431
  passive, with serum containing antibody 446
  Prausnitz-Küstner test 446
Septic focus 621
Serotherapy 6, 7, 20, 42, 569 *et seq.*
  precautions necessary 702
Serotonin 432
  in platelets 433
  in mast cells 433
Serum sickness 15–16
  after antiserum therapy 453
Serum treatment (*see* Serotherapy)
Sessile antibody (*see* Glossary for definition) 16
Shaw G.B. 10
Shigella, natural antibody to 49
Shock 74 (*see also* Anaphylaxis)
  due to haemorrhage 79
  due to trauma 79
Shwartzman G. 489
Shwartzman reaction 227, 489–91 (*see also* Sanarelli-Shwartzman reaction)
Sialic acid, as constituent of immunological barrier 577
Sia test 342
Sickle cell trait 38
Side-chain theory 13
Simonsen phenomenon (*see* Glossary for definition)
Sinuses
  of blood 71
  of lymph 71
Sinus-lining cells 71
Sjogren's disease 630
  association with S.L.E. 630
Skin, resistance mechanisms of 45
Skin sensitization, mechanism of 504
Skin tests
  in leprosy 525
  in sarcoidosis and reticulosis 530
  involving delayed-type hypersensitivity 524
Slow-reacting substance (SRS-A) 432, 434
  release from mast cells 441
Smallpox 1, 2, 18, 19, 681 (*see also* Vaccination)
Smegma, bactericidal activity of 46
Smith T. 5
Snake venom, antiserum against 704
Solitary follicles 282
Somatic antigens (*see* Lipopolysaccharide antigens)
Somatic mutation, role in diversification of antibodies 145
Species specificity (*see* Glossary for definition)
Species variation, in anaphylaxis 441
Specificity 1
  carrier 121, 133, 216
    of memory cells 217
  of antibodies
    effect of duration of immunization 182
  of antigens 212
Spermatozoa
  auto-antibody against 652
  auto-immunization against 655
  immobilizing antibody to 655
Spermine 53
  oxidase 53
Spleen, anatomy of 225
Splenectomy, effect on antibody production 263

Sponges, organization of phagocytes in 9
Staphylococcal disease, delayed-type hypersensitivity in 527–8
Starfish 7
Starry-sky appearance in germinal centres 296
Skin cells 96, 106
Sterility, role of auto-immunization against spermatozoa in 654
Steroids
auto-antibodies to 642
immunogenicity of 208
Streng O. 198, 200
Streptococcal antigens
in glomerulo-nephritis 467, 469
in rheumatic fever 470–4
Streptococcal infection 17
delayed-type hypersensitivity in 528–9
Streptococcus MG, agglutinins to, in primary atypical pneumonia 379
Streptococcus pneumoniae 63, 75
Stroptococcus pyogenes, disease manifestations at different ages 39
Streptolysin 'O' (*see* Streptococcal antigens)
Subacute thyroiditis 603
Sulphonamides 19
Sulphydryl group (*see* Glossary for definition)
Sulzberger-Chase phenomenon 541
'Super' antigen 286
Suppression of antibody formation, in bursectomized chick 297
Suppression of immunological responses
by pre-existing antibody 261
influence of antibody avidity on 261
Surface active agents, adjuvant effect of 255
Surveillance 30, 550, 585, 597, 602
Suter E. 66
Swan C. 40
Swift H.T. 471
Swine fever 321
Swiss-type agammaglobulinaemia 325
Sympathetic ophthalmia 643–4
experimental production in the guinea-pig 645
Syngeneic (*see* Glossary for definition)
Syphilis
cold haemagglutinins in 609
Donath-Landsteiner phenomenon in 609
false positive tests for 388
flocculation test 388
fluorescent treponemal antibody test 388
immune-adherence test 388–9
treponema immobilization (T.P.I.) test 388
Wassermann test 387
Systemic lupus erythematosus (S.L.E.) 209, 381, 626
association with monoclonal gammopathy 345
diseases associated with 630

Tâches laiteuses 72
T-agglutinin 605
Takatsuki K. 164
Talmage D.W. 141
Tanned-cell agglutination 374
Tapioca, as adjuvant 250
Tartaric acid, as hapten 214
Tears, antibody and IgA in 170
Temperature, effect on immunological responses 91
Template hypothesis 30
Tertiary nodules 274 (*see also* Glossary for definition)
Tertiary structure (*see* Glossary for definition)
Testis (*see also* Orchitis)
auto-immunization against 653
immunogenicity of 601, 652

Tetanus 6, 18, 19, 675 *et seq.*
combined antibiotic and active immunization 679
concurrent active and passive immunization 678–9
passive immunization 678, 702
prophylaxis after wounding 677
reasons for active immunization 679
Tetryl, sensitization by 218
Theories of antibody formation 136–46
Thesaurocytes 295
Thomas L.S. 490
Thoracic duct drainage 100
effect on ability to give a primary response 100, 283
effect on ability to give a secondary response 103
Thorium dioxide 73
Thorotrast 73
Thrombocytopenia 332 (*see also* Platelets)
caused by auto-antibody 617–18
Thycydides 1
Thymocytes 96
Thymectomy 121, 144
effect in adult animal 107
in adult life 108
in the bird 105
neonatal 103, 328
restoration by spleen cells 107
restoration of immunological function following pregnancy 108
wasting disease following 103
Thymic aplasia 325
Thymoma (lympho-epithelioma) 330
Thymus 328
anatomy of 277
and long-lived lymphocytes 107
dependent cells 325
epithelial cells of 228
hormonal factor in 552
hormone 107
myoid cells 279
phylogeny of 92
production of lymphocytes in 279
Thymus-dependent areas 122, 274, 283, 501
Thymus grafts, restorative effect after thymectomy 108
Thyroglobulin
activity as an auto-immunogen 634
existence of tolerance to 634
Thyroid
auto-antibodies to 635
auto-immune disease 631–8
Thyroiditis
acute, in relation to mumps 636
experimental 253
focal 637
Thyrotoxicosis
auto-immunization in 638
LATS in 638
Thyrotrophin, immunochemical estimation of 399
Tingible corpuscles 296
Tiselius A. 27, 149
Tissue cultures
for virus neutralization tests 395
of macrophages 65
Titre, definition of 357
Titration methods, disadvantages of 358
Tobacco mosaic virus 200
Tolerance (*see* Immunological tolerance)
breaking by cross-reactive immunogen 118
by indigestible immunogens 115
effect of cortisone on 114
induction 113–14, 137
after cortisone 114
after thymectomy 114
after X-irradiation 114
effect of age on 114
effect of macrophages on 115
effect of rate of catabolism of immunogen 115
effect of size and physical state of immunogen on 113, 117
partial 118

Tolerance—*contd.*
 persistence in presence of immunogen 114
 production by oral administration of chemicals 117, 541
 recovery from 118
 split 541
 to virus-induced tumours 587
Tolerant cells 116
Tonsils, anatomy of 281
Toxin-antitoxin mixture 19
Toxin-antitoxin neutralization 12, 367
 method of test 394
 role in protection 408-10
 sensitivity of method for detecting antibody 357
Toxins
 of bacteria, potencies of 410–11
Toxoids 219
Toxophore groups 13, 30
'Transfer factor' 539
Transformation, of lymphocytes 97
Transfusion reactions, due to autoantibody to leucocytes 618
Transitional cell 288
Transplantation
 antigens 557
 of blood vessels 560
 of bone 560
 of cartilage 561
 of cornea 560–1
 of endocrines 562
 of kidneys 562
 of liver 565
 of lung 565
 of skin 24, 548–57
Transplantation antigens 547
 genetic control of 557–8
 methods of tissue typing for 558–559
 strong and weak 558
 T- and H-antigens 558
Transplantation immunity (*see also* Glossary for definition) (*see also* Chapter 13 and Homograft rejection)
Transport piece 316
 synthesis by glandular epithelium 266
Treponema pallidum 256
 immobilization test (T.P.I.) 388
Trichinella infestation, homocytotropic antibody in 438
Trichomonas, local antibody synthesis 265
Trichophytids 483–4
Trichophyton 46
Tri-ethylene melamine 568
Tritiated adenosine, as a cell label 405
Tritiated thymidine, as label for DNA 404
Tritiated uridine, as a cell label 405
Trophoblast, syncytia in lungs 376
Tropical eosinophilia 485
Trypanosomiasis, immunity in 425
Tubercle bacilli
 cord factor in 516
 peptidoglycolipids in 254, 304
 pmko wax 516, 520
 virulence of 517, 518
 wax D in 254, 304, 520
Tuberculin
 effect on sensitized leucocytes 509
 old 513
 purified protein derivative 513
Tuberculin hypersensitivity 28
 general 513
 focal 513
 local 513
 relation to immunity 518–20
Tuberculin tests 28, 682
 clinical significance of 520–1
 Mantoux test 520–1
 patch test 682
Tuberculosis
 cortisone in 42
 effect of recumbency on disease 52
 immunization against 680
 in mitral stenosis 52
 in negro and white races 38
 in pulmonary stenosis 52
 in twins 38

localization of disease at lung apices 52
miliary, prevention by BCG vaccination 519
relation of immunity to allergy in 518–20
resistance to disease in golden years 40
role of delayed-type hypersensitivity in 515–18

Tuberculous bronchopneumonia 517

Tumour antigens
- loss during transformation from normal to cancerous state 582
- sharing of antigens of normal tissue 581
- tumour specific antigens 583

Tumours
- adjuvants for increasing immunogenicity of 595
- antigenic difference from normal cells 582
- antigenic overlap with normal tissue 581
- Burkitt's lymphoma
- chemotherapy of chorion-epithelioma and Burkitt's lymphoma 592, 594
- chorionepitheliomata 593
- induced by chemicals 583
- induced by viruses 583, 594
- regression and prevention of by immunological factors 592
- transplantation of 24
- treatment by allogeneic lymphocytes 596
- treatment by immunological means 594–7
- treatment with antiserum 596

Tumour immunity 580 *et seq.*
- effect of age of host 587
- effect of ALS 589
- effect of immunosuppressive agents 591
- effect of neonatal thymectomy 588
- influence of specific tolerance 580

Twins
- exchange of skin grafts in 546
- incidence of tuberculosis in 38

Typhoid (*see* Enteric fever)

Typhus 19
- immunization against 697

Tyrosine, in immunogenicity of proteins 207

Uhlenhuth P. 11–12

Ulcerative colitis
- association with rheumatoid arthritis 625
- auto-antibody in 659–61

Unitarian theory of antibodies 349

Unna-Pappenheim stain 288

Unresponsiveness, immunological (*see* Tolerance)

Urticaria 443

Urushiol 503

Uterus, as an immunologically privileged site 576

Uveal pigment, sensitization by 644–5

Vaccination 3, 10, 18 (*see also* Glossary for definition)

Vaccination (*see also* Immunization) against
- abortus fever 20
- adenovirus infection 19
- bacterial diseases 19
- cholera 20, 695
- common cold 20
- helminthic diseases 20
- influenza 19
- measles 19, 699
- pertussis 20, 679
- plague 20, 695
- poliomyelitis 19, 687–92
- smallpox 19, 683–9
- tetanus 19, 676–77
- tuberculosis 20, 680–2
- tularaemia 20

Vaccination against—*contd.*
typhus 19, 697
virus diseases 19
yellow fever 19, 695
Vaccines
control of 707–10
TAB 694
Vaccinia
delayed-type hypersensitivity to 685
encephalitis due to 685
gangrenosa 334
generalized 334, 685
virus 683
Vaccinoid response 685
Van der Vaal's forces 178 (*see also* Glossary for definition)
Variola 2
Variolation 2, 3, 683
Viricidal activity, of normal tissue fluids 53
Virus
immunogenicity of 234
neutralization test for 394
street 4
transformation of cells 583
Virus antibodies
measurement of 378
protection by 412–18
Virus diseases
duration of immunity in 413
incubation periods 413
portal of entry of viruses 413
protection by antibody against 412
Virus neutralization tests
sensitivity of 235
Vital dyes 70
Vitamin A, as adjuvant 255, 302
Voisin G. 18
Vole bacillus, results of MRC trials with 519
Voltaire F.M.A. de 1, 2

Waldenström J. 172, 342
Waldenström's disease (*see* Macroglobulinaemia)
Wassermann reaction 387
as example of auto-antibody production 604
nature of antigen 208
Wasting syndrome (*see also* Runt disease)
following neonatal thymectomy 103
in mice, virus infections in 104
Waterhouse-Friderichsen syndrome 496
Water-in-oil emulsions, of immunogens 253
Wax D 254, 304
correlation of virulence with bacillary content of 517
White P.B. 17, 22
White graft reaction 554
Whooping cough (*see* Pertussis)
Widal reaction 6, 371
Williams C.A. 26
Wiskott-Aldrich syndrome 332
Witebsky E. 17
Wood W.B. 69, 275
World Health Organization 709
Wright A.E. 8, 9, 10, 694

X-cells 130
Xenogeneic (*see* Glossary for definition)
Xenograft (*see* Glossary for definition)
X-irradiation 259
bacteraemia due to 80
cellular changes after 566
effect on antibody production 259
effect on catabolism of foreign immunogens 244
effects of administration of supralethal doses 567
immunological results of 566

in treatment of recipients of kidney homografts 563
recovery with bone marrow or foetal liver cells 109
therapeutic effects of antibodies 80
use of sublethal doses for immunosuppression 508
vaccine 19
as a cause of hepatitis 696
hypersensitivity to egg protein after use of 696
Yolk sac, route of transmission for antibody 315

Y cells (*see* Memory cells) 130, 137, 252, 294
Yellow fever
immunization against 695
Z-cells 130, 137
Zinsser H. 29, 349, 493
Zirconium granulomatosis 533
Zymosan 190